P9-DEH-571

Natural History

Reinhold Books in the Biological Sciences

The Encyclopedia of the Biological Sciences, edited by Peter Gray

Biophysics: Concepts and Mechanisms, by E. J. Casey
Cell Function, by L. L. Langley
Chordate Morphology, by Malcolm Jollie
Concepts of Forest Entomology, by Kenneth Graham
Cytology, by G. B. Wilson and John H. Morrison
Ecology of Inland Waters and Estuaries, by George K. Reid
Evolution: Process and Product, Revised Edition, by Edward O. Dodson
Management of Artificial Lakes and Ponds, by George W. Bennett
Manual of Insect Morphology, by E. Melville DuPorte
Paramedical Microbiology, by Stanley E. Wedberg
The Plant Community, by Herbert C. Hanson and Ethan D. Churchill
Principles in Mammalogy, by David E. Davis and Frank B. Golley

Consulting Editor's Statement

There is nowadays a refreshing tendency, well exemplified by Professor Pimentel's book, to regard "nature" as a whole rather than as the sum of its parts. The origin of the earth itself and the development of its physical features are just as much a part of Nature Study as are observations made on the living things which inhabit the planet. Moreover, all these things are, as Professor Pimentel so clearly indicates, part of a logical train of events which started in the remote past and is even now continuing. This is not to say that the book is strung on the familiar thread of evolution. Evolution becomes apparent to the student as the events themselves unfold.

The wide sweep of this approach does not in any way obscure the details that are given. The student who seeks, as he should, a clear understanding of the classification and interrelationship of living organisms will find them both explained and outlined in taxonomic summaries. Indeed, this new addition to the REINHOLD BOOKS IN THE BIOLOGICAL SCIENCES welds theoretical background and practical detail into an unusually coherent whole.

PETER GRAY

NATURAL HISTORY

RICHARD A. PIMENTEL

Biological Sciences Department
California State Polytechnic College
San Luis Obispo, California

New York
REINHOLD PUBLISHING CORPORATION
Chapman & Hall, Ltd., London

Library of Congress Catalog Card Number: 63-21379
Printed in the United States of America

Preface

Natural history is the study of a single thing, nature. Whether it is normally a science or an art is a matter of debate, but there is no doubt about its tremendous scope: all living and nonliving things, their activities, and interrelationships. For practical purposes, the things and their activities are often separated into individual studies, field geology for the nonliving and field biology for the living. In addition, the interrelationships constitute the field of ecology. However, these separate studies have a serious drawback—like an organism, nature as a whole is much more than the sum of its parts.

This book is written with the firm conviction that field geology, field biology, and ecology can be integrated into a single meaningful study. Such an approach serves to unify previously disconnected subject matter falling within courses designated as natural history, natural science, nature study, general science, field biology, and even ecology.

Despite the number of textbooks, none really explores all areas of natural history. Yet, biologists, elementary and secondary teachers, naturalists, and interested laymen have expressed a need for a book which is a unified treatment of the basic principles of nature. The content and approach of this book stem from my discussions with these individuals and my own teaching experience. There was unanimous agreement on the need to know how to identify living and nonliving things and to determine their interrelations and significance. Therefore this book integrates the earth's physical features with life on earth by emphasizing the interrelations of the two. The subject matter proceeds from gross identification and natural history of nonliving and then living things to ecology. It is an exposition of nature based on principles, rather than an exploration of theories and the relative merits of each. There is coverage of much material in depth, but the book is not intended to replace publications which treat regional environments, floras, or faunas, or special natural history of particular groups.

A brief introduction to astronomy stressing the earth's orientation within the solar system precedes the study of the earth's physical features. The laboratory work on this section leads from identification of nonliving things to student exploration of the physical environment, especially climatic factors, land forms, rocks, and soils of local areas.

The next group of chapters treats living organisms, and stresses the broadest aspects of structure and function, mostly in relation to distinctive features and gross appearance; nutrition and, where appropriate, food and feeding mechanisms; reproduction in reference to life cycle; and habitat and occurrence. Much of this information is provided in synoptic form. Laboratory work on organisms starts with identification and leads to field examination of the kinds and natural history of life. The remainder of the book examines the interrelations among organisms and between organisms and their environment and is supplemented by field studies.

Evolution or its counterpart is the basic unifying principle or the central theme of the book. The concept of evolution of life is developed after many similar phenomena in nonliving things have been illustrated. Each major group of living things is introduced through its role in the general scheme of evolution, and even when evolution is discussed as a separate topic, it continues as the unifying concept. Ecology, also, is examined within this framework, and a large part of community discussion is of the origin and evolution of communities. In addition, ecology serves to integrate further the field geology and field biology sections.

The book is suitable for a full year course which has no prerequisite. However, the contents are adaptable to shorter courses for beginning students or for advanced students. The beginning students might be required to master only generalizations, while advanced students might be held responsible for details and outside readings. With these alternatives in mind, each chapter was conceived as a self-contained, yet related unit, thus requiring some repetition of material. Should it prove necessary, an instructor can change the order of chapters or omit entire chapters.

Selected readings are provided with each chapter. These references are books or review articles that are considered primary sources of additional information. They range from popular to technical, and many of them contain excellent bibliographies.

Terms are placed in italic type and defined in context where first used in a chapter and a glossary provides their precise definition. In general, only terms commonly used by laymen were omitted from the glossary.

Most illustrations are original or redrawn and modified from existing figures. Some illustrations were supplied through the courtesy of other authors, and publishers and sources are credited in the figure captions. Dr. Malcolm Jollie was especially helpful in allowing the use of many excellent illustrations from his book *Chordate Morphology*.

Many individuals contributed to the preparation of this book. To Dr. Mathew F. Vessel, San Jose State College, who read the entire manuscript, I am indebted for especially detailed criticisms and suggestions, particularly for a reduction in terminology and details. Dr. Robert G. Colodny, University of Pittsburgh, provided a great deal of special information, criticisms, and suggestions for the first five chapters. Drs. Jay Savage, University of Southern California, and Richard A. Boolootian, University of California at Los Angeles, reviewed the entire manuscript and provided suggestions, criticisms, and encouragement. Dr. S. Conrade Head, University of the Pacific, submitted periodic detailed criticisms and suggestions, especially on the ecology chapters, while using a mimeographed edition of this book in his course. Dr. Kenneth L. Gordon, Oregon State University, through his course, Natural History of Oregon, was the source of many ideas, including some relating to the scope of the book.

Special thanks are accorded the many teachers, nature councilors, naturalists, and students for help in all aspects of the book.

Dr. Peter Gray, University of Pittsburgh, Consulting Editor to the Publisher, reviewed the original manuscript and was most helpful and encouraging in various aspects of final manuscript preparation. Mr. James B. Ross, Mr. R. Murray Chastain, and Mrs. Elisabeth H. Belfer, all of Reinhold Publishing Corporation, went well beyond their duties in facilitating publication.

To these individuals I extend my appreciation and thanks. Their criticisms and suggestions were most helpful in the preparation of the final material for my text. However, the final content of the book is the sole responsibility of the author.

San Luis Obispo, California RICHARD A. PIMENTEL
August, 1963

Contents

1 INTRODUCTION

Earth and Natural History Orientation

The study of nature can begin almost anywhere. One can start either with some small, even microscopic, organism or with anything of larger size, even the entire universe. Here, the start is with the universe, the most complex aspect of nature because the universe is all inclusive, but the features of the universe will be barely mentioned. The purpose of this introduction is to set the scene for study of one planet, Earth—its air, sea, land, life, and the interrelations among living organisms and their living and nonliving surroundings. Even the discussion of the earth's features will fall far short of what is known. However, this presentation will provide some understanding of nature as a single, integrated phenomenon, rather than as separate units of air, sea, land, and life. In other words, nature is *synergistic*.

This chapter provides certain details that emphasize the organization and possible origin of living and nonliving things upon our planet. Moreover, it seems justified to stress both organization and origin because both are keys to examining the nature of natural history. Organization is basic for studying nature, and origin for seeing nature as a single evolving process.

THE ORGANIZATION OF THE UNIVERSE

The extremely complex universe can be studied because it displays order in the form of units of ever-increasing size, each smaller unit being a part of every larger one. In our discussion the smallest unit of the universe is arbitrarily considered to be a *star system*. The star system that contains our earth is called the *solar system;* it consists of a *star* (the sun) and a number of bodies, such as *planets*, *asteroids*, *comets*, and others, that revolve about it. Individual planets, in turn, may have orbiting bodies, or *satellites*. Earth, for example, has a single natural satellite, the moon. Other planets in the solar system may have none or as many as twelve satellites (also sometimes called "moons"). The asteroids (asteroid belt) are a group of over 1600 very small planetlike bodies, the largest being Ceres (approximately 480 miles in diameter). The asteroids follow variable paths about the sun, but the orbits of most of them are between the planets Mars and Jupiter. Comets are generally smaller than asteroids and travel in the broadest oval paths about the sun. A star system, then, is composed of a star and various objects that orbit about the star.

The unit of universe organization next larger in size is the *galaxy*. Our galaxy encompasses the solar system plus millions of other star systems. The significant feature of galaxy organization is that the star systems are relatively close together. The most widely separated star systems within a galaxy usually are much closer together than is any star in one galaxy to its nearest neighbor in another. This relatively close relationship is related to the physical organization within a galaxy, an organization involving a myriad of stars revolving about a particular "spot," the *galactic center.*

Our galaxy is lens-shaped, consisting of stars concentrated in a central nucleus and in "arms" that spiral outward from the nucleus (Figure 1.1). These arms are composed of millions of individual stars, of star systems, and of gas and dust clouds. The parts of our galaxy's arms visible from the earth (about two-thirds of the way out from the center of the galaxy) are called the Milky Way. Individual parts of the arms and nucleus revolve rapidly about the center; our sun takes about 200 million years for a single revolution about the galactic center, which means that it travels about 600,000 miles per hour. In addition to the galactic nucleus and the "arms," our galaxy also contains *globular clusters.* These groups of stars occur just beyond the margin of the "lens" and orbit in random paths about the galactic center.

Figure 1.1 Our galaxy, an example of the spiral nebula type, and some surrounding star clusters.

The next larger unit of astronomical organization—the largest unit known—is the *galactic system* or *local group.* In it, individual galaxies are grouped into a unit by being relatively close together and distinct from other such units. Our galactic system is composed of twenty-two, or perhaps more, galaxies.

DISTANCES

If one attempts to visualize the vast distances involved in all these units of universe organization, it becomes obvious that the universe is mostly space. Measurement in miles is rarely used, except within our solar system. The common measurements are *light years* and *parsecs.* A light year is the distance light will travel during one earth year. Light travels at a speed of 186,326 miles per second, so a light year is approximately 6 trillion miles. The parsec, 3.26 light years, is used by astronomers more frequently than the light year because it is based upon astronomical relationships.

These measurements can be used to show how "empty" space really is. The earth is approximately 93 million miles from the sun. The next nearest star (actually three very close stars), Alpha Centauri, is 4.4 light years from the sun. The sun is 30,000 light years from our galactic center. Our galaxy, larger than most, has a diameter of about 100,000 light years; it is near the center of our galactic system, whose diameter is about 4 million light years. One end of our galactic system is marked by our sister galaxy, the very similar Andromeda. Beyond the limits of our galactic system other galaxies, the so-called *island universes,* are also organized into galactic systems. The distance between adjacent galaxies in other galactic systems may exceed 4 million light years, but those in our galactic system do not reach 2 million light years apart. However, only 50,000 light years from our galaxy are two galaxies; the greater and lesser Magellanic Clouds.

GALAXY ORGANIZATION

Not all galaxies are organized in the same way. The basic galactic structures are of three types: spiral, elliptical, and irregular. These variations in structure are generally explained on the basis of their different speeds of revolution. Spiral galaxies, whose components have the fastest revolution velocities about their galactic center, are most common; they comprise about 80 per cent of all galaxies, including our own. The elliptical galaxies, spheres to saucer-like discs, have slower revolution speeds than those of the spiral galaxies; they encompass about 17 per cent of all galaxies. The irregular galaxies are formless clouds of stars without either concentration into a galactic nucleus or systematic orbiting of individual stars. This group, the slowest moving, constitutes the remaining 3 per cent of the galaxies.

There is no general agreement among astronomers as to why galaxies have different revolution speeds and, hence, spiral, elliptical, and irregular structures. Some believe the three types represent the evolutionary sequence along the path from galaxy birth to death; others believe that the types are no more than a direct reflection of individual speeds at the time of galaxy formation.

STAR AND PLANET LIFE HISTORY

There are many theories about how a star or star system is formed and is destroyed. Some of these propose that the earth, for example, was once a fiery ball; others do not. The theory treated here is not necessarily the best one, but it is employed because it is relatively simple and provides an easy framework for considering the origin of the land (*lithosphere*), water (*hydrosphere*), air (*atmosphere*), and the living world (*biosphere*). The formations of stars and planets are here considered part of a single process. However, there are two possible courses in this process, one leading to multiple stars like Alpha Centauri and the other to a star (or perhaps a few stars) and planets.

Figure 1.2 One hypothesis of star and planet formation. Gravitational attraction of gaseous particles has formed a star, planets, and a satellite of the third planet.

STAR AND PLANET FORMATION

The first step in the formation of a star involves gravitational attraction, contraction, and rotation of sparse gases and cosmic dust particles to form a single cloud. As contraction occurs, internal pressures and temperatures rise; finally, a collapse of matter toward the center of the cloud results in the birth of a new star.

According to the theory employed here, a new star can be involved in three possible developments. Most new stars split, forming two stars. Other new stars will split into three, four, five, or even more stars. However, in 1 per cent or less of the cases, another series of events occur. Around the new star, there are also rings of matter, each ring generally in the position of the future orbit of a planet or belt of asteroids (Figure 1.2). Within one of these rings of matter a concentration representing the earliest stage of planet formation may in turn possess rings that will develop into moons. At this time, there is probably no real distinction between future planet and future satellites, but later the innermost whorl or whorls form the planet and outer whorls its moons. In the case of the earth, a primary inner whorl may have formed the earth and a primary outer whorl the moon.

Further discussion of planet and satellite formation is limited to our planet and moon.

EARLY EARTH DEVELOPMENT

According to the hypothesis being followed, the early earth and moon were fiery balls without hard outer crusts. While molten, the earth materials and, to a lesser extent, those of the moon were layered so that the heaviest materials formed the cores and the lightest the crusts. In the case of the earth, this resulted in three divisions: an inner and heaviest *core* about 4300 miles in diameter, possibly solid inside and liquid on the outside, both parts composed primarily of nickel and iron; a middle layer about 2000 miles thick, the rigid yet plastic *mantle;* and the *crust,* 10 to 30 miles thick (Figure 1.3). Although the mantle is probably rich in the mineral olivine (a magnesium silicate containing iron and oxygen), evidence indicates that it, like the core, contains two subunits, an innermost transition layer composed chiefly of silicates impregnated with iron and an outer layer composed largely of silicon and magnesium. The crust also consists of two parts, the basement of 10 to 20 miles of basalt, a heavy rock, and the top of about 10 miles of the lighter granite. The basalt tends to reach the surface of the crust in ocean bottoms and the granite to form the foundations of the continents.

At the time of a molten earth, gases (mostly water vapor and carbon dioxide) because of extreme heat

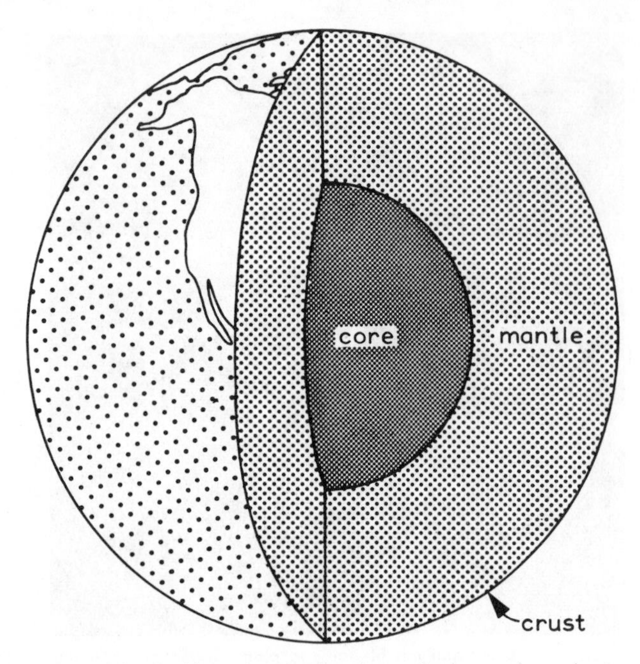

Figure 1.3 Earth's interior, showing three major layers of our planet.

exploded from the molten interior to form the earliest atmosphere. Finally, the crust solidified, a process that resulted in the additional release of carbon dioxide and water. These vapors formed an extremely dense covering of clouds over the earth—so dense that the crust was then in perpetual darkness. Although rain fell from these clouds, upon contacting the crust the water immediately boiled and returned to the clouds. Finally, as the crust cooled to the boiling point of water, 212° F., the water no longer boiled away. Shortly thereafter, the sunlight first broke through the cloud cover. However, there was still a long period of almost constant rains which resulted in the first oceans reaching their present level.

With this stage of development it is possible to consider the early conditions of the land, waters, and air, and the origin of life itself.

After the crust formed, cooling of the mantle, and perhaps the crust, may have continued for some time. The consequence of such coolings would be a gradual contraction of the deeper layers of the earth, so that wrinkles (the first mountains) appeared on the surface. However, these mountains were flattened relatively quickly by erosion caused by runoff from the torrential rains. Up to now about ten periods of major mountain building have occurred, each period being separated by a cycle of erosion and flattening of the land before the start of the next.

Although the earliest oceans contained much less salt than do the present ones, today's seas probably are much the same as those of one-half billion (or even more) years ago. It is generally believed that oceans became salty because waters from the land carried salts to the ocean; however, for some time a state of equilibrium has existed in that ocean salt loss has equalled salt gain.

During the geological phase of our history called the *Preactualistic Phase* the atmosphere most likely contained much helium and oxygen, plus early additions of hydrogen sulfide, ammonia, methane, chlorine, water, and carbon dioxide (Table 7.1, pp. 109–113). Little or no oxygen was present. Gradually the hydrogen and helium escaped to outer space, because the earth's gravitational field was too weak to contain the tremendous energy of the hydrogen and helium molecules. Loss of other materials was probably due to their being used by early life.

The Preactualistic Phase was followed by the *Actualistic Phase*. The Actualistic Phase still exists but its atmosphere always had a gaseous composition similar to the one that now exists. The source of most modern atmospheric gases was volcanic activity in the broadest sense. For millions of years, volcanoes, hot springs, and related phenomena supplied gases to the area about the earth. The lightest gases, such as helium and hydrogen, were mostly lost to space; however, heavier nitrogen, carbon dioxide, water vapor, and trace gases tended to remain.

Note that oxygen was not included among the products of vulcanism. Free oxygen, so necessary for most of earth's life, did not originate from gases released from the earth's interior. Rather, most of the first oxygen was a "waste product" of photosynthesis, the process whereby plants and certain microscopic life use their chlorophyll in the presence of sunlight to combine carbon dioxide and water to form simple sugar. However, for certain life processes most organisms require some oxygen. If one thinks about early life *forming* oxygen, but also *needing* some oxygen, he has a classic analogy to "which came first, the chicken or the egg?" However, there is really no problem in regard to early life's source of oxygen. The relatively minute amounts required by ancient organisms could easily have been supplied by either the sun or lightning separating individual water vapor molecules into basic hydrogen and oxygen.

Although this hypothetical evolution of the present atmosphere would have taken some time, the atmosphere probably has been much the same for over two billion years, and perhaps only moderate changes in the percentages of existing gases have occurred.

STAR DEATH

The life expectancy of a star is partly related to its size. The smaller the star, the longer its life expectancy! Giant stars may last only ten million years, but some small stars may last for fifty billion years.

According to many astronomers the life cycle of a star assumes the following general pattern, which is directly related to the burning of hydrogen:

For the first half of its life, a star burns steadily until 15 per cent of its hydrogen is consumed. The star then starts to change. In addition to cooling, the star in time grows in size, its diameter increasing 50 to 100 times that of the original, to form a red giant or supergiant star. (Our average size star, the sun, will probably not reach its half-life for another ten billion years, and will reach the red giant stage five billion years beyond that.) When approximately 60 per cent of the hydrogen has been burned, internal pressure decreases and the giant starts a cycle of contraction. Such stars are unstable and take one of two possible paths of development. Some alternately expand and contract, the *pulsating stars*. Others, the *novas*, undergo a series of explosions, while in still others, the *supernovas*, the explosion may be a single gigantic blast (or very few). No matter which of these alternatives occurs, if sufficient matter remains, the end product is a feebly glowing, white dwarf star.

THE SOLAR SYSTEM

Data about the solar system are summarized in Table 1.1. Included in the table are distances of each planet from the sun, plus the diameter, mass, escape velocity, surface gravity, inclination of orbit and planet axis, revolution period, maximum surface temperature, atmospheric composition, and number of satellites, where applicable, for solar system bodies. In general, these are approximate figures.

Some of the terms and/or data need clarification. None of the planets maintains a constant *distance* from the sun. The closest distance of a plant in its orbit, or path around the sun is called *perihelion* and the greatest, *aphelion*. The *escape velocity* is that velocity at which a moving body can escape from its gravitational field. The ability of a celestial body to retain an atmosphere around it depends on the escape velocity from its surface. *Surface gravity* is the intensity of the force of gravity at the surface of a planet, and is a function of mass, radius, and rotation speed. The scale for surface gravity is given in relation to the earth; and (as you can see from Table 1.1) contrary to what you might have heard, a human might suffer much discomfort but probably could "walk" upon the surfaces of all of the planets. *Inclination* is the angle formed between the orbital plane of a planet and the ecliptic. An *orbital plane* is that imaginary flat surface defined by the orbit of a given planet. The *ecliptic* is the plane containing the center of the sun and the orbit of the earth. In short, the ecliptic is the orbital plane of the earth. Thus, the ecliptic serves as a reference point in the calculation of the *inclination of orbit* and the *inclination of equator* of the planets in the solar system. *Revolution period* is the time necessary for a planet to complete its orbit around the sun (i.e., a planetary year); it is given in earth years. *Rotation period* is the time required for a planet to complete a turn upon its central axis (i.e., a planetary day). In the cases of Jupiter and Saturn, each planetary day is for the equator. This is because different latitudes of these two planets rotate at different speeds!

LIFE ON OTHER PLANETS

The data in Table 1.1 must be used in any speculation about "advanced" life on other planets. In our conjectures we can, on the basis of our present knowledge, eliminate planets beyond Mars. These outer planets not only have methane–ammonia atmospheres (some on Mars?), but also low surface temperatures; they could not support life as we know it. Mercury has extreme temperature changes and no atmosphere; the asteroids are too cold and have little, if any, atmosphere. Venus and Mars are the only planets deserving serious consideration as supporters of life. Venus apparently cannot support our "complex" life forms; high carbon dioxide and other contents cause the atmosphere to be poisonous and temperatures (because the atmosphere traps heat that otherwise would escape from the surface) too severe. There is evidence of simple plant life, with what appear to be seasonal expansions and contractions of vegetation, on Mars. However, the thin atmosphere on that planet would prevent complex living forms from existing for long. Man might be

TABLE 1.1 PHYSICAL CHARACTERISTICS OF THE SOLAR SYSTEM

	Sun	Mercury	Venus	Earth	Mars	Jupiter	Saturn	Uranus	Neptune	Pluto
Distance (million miles)										
Perihelion	—	25.6	66.8	91.4	128.5	460.5	837.7	1,700.6	2,772.7	2,757.7
Aphelion		43.4	67.7	94.6	154.9	507.3	936.6	1,869.0	2,820.6	4,581.7
Diameter (miles)	865,400	3,100	7,700	7,927	4,220	89,300	75,000	32,400	31,000	3,600
Mass (earth = 1)	333,420	0.04	0.82	1.00	0.11	318.35	95.30	14.58	17.26	0.03
Escape Velocity (miles/sec.)	384	2.2	6.3	7.0	3.1	37.3	22.4	13.1	14.3	1.9
Surface Gravity (earth = 1)	27.90	0.33	0.86	1.00	0.38	2.65	1.18	0.90	1.12	0.16
Inclination of Orbit	—	7° 0′	3° 24′	0°	1° 51′	1° 18′	2° 29′	0° 46′	1° 46′	17° 9′
Inclination of Equator	—	?	32° 0′	23°27′	23° 59′	3° 4′	26° 48′	98° 0′	29° 36′	?
Revolution Period (earth years)	—	0.2	0.6	1.0	1.9	11.9	29.5	84.0	164.8	248.4
Rotation Period (days, hrs., mins.)	—	88d	264.7d?	23h 46m	24h 37m	9h 50m	10h 14m	10h 14m	15h 48m	6d 9h 22m
Surface Temperature* (degrees F.)	11,000	770	800	140	86	−216	−243	−300	−330	−338
Atmosphere†	H, He	—	‡, CO_2, H_2O	air	CO_2, H_2O	CH_4, NH_3	CH_4, NH_3	CH_4, NH_3	CH_4, NH_3	CH_4, NH_3
Satellites	—	none	none	1	2	12	9**	5	2	none

*These are maximum approximations, except for the sun.
†H = hydrogen; He = helium; CO_2 = carbon dioxide; H_2O = water; CH_4 = methane; NH_3 = ammonia.
‡ Mostly dust and/or hydrocarbons (smog).
**Also rings.

able to breathe the Martian atmosphere for very brief periods of time; with warm clothing and a simple breathing apparatus he could probably live on Mars.

THE MOON

Although it cannot sustain complex life, some of the moon's physical properties are of interest. Its distance from the earth varies between 222,000 and 253,000 miles during a single revolution about the earth. This revolution requires 27 days, 7 hours, 43 minutes, and 11.5 seconds. Because the same surface of the moon always faces the earth, the rotation speed is equal to the revolution speed. The moon has a diameter of 2162 miles and a mass that is 1/100 that of the earth; its surface gravity is 16/100 that of the earth. There is essentially no atmosphere on the moon, so the surface temperature fluctuates greatly; in sunlight it is about 214°F. and in shade about −243°F. The escape velocity is 1.5 miles per second —considerably less than that at the earth's surface (see Table 1.1). The phases of the moon result from our view of sunlight striking the surface of the moon.

EARTH AND SUN

Most of the physical aspects of our planet, considered on a planetary scale, are influenced by the sun. Primary influences of the sun on the earth include the seasons, solar radiation, earth's magnetism, and radiation belts.

EARTH'S SEASONS

Our seasons are due to a simple association between the sun and the earth (Figure 1.4). Specifically, there are seasons because the axis of the earth is tilted. This constant direction of tilt causes the sun's rays in our latitude to be more direct and more effective in warming the earth during the summer, and oblique to our part of the earth at other seasons of the year (see Figure 2.2, p. 12). Solar rays in our latitude are least direct during the winter.

SOLAR RADIATION

The sun is a gaseous body whose surface has a temperature of about 11,000°F. Above the surface, two

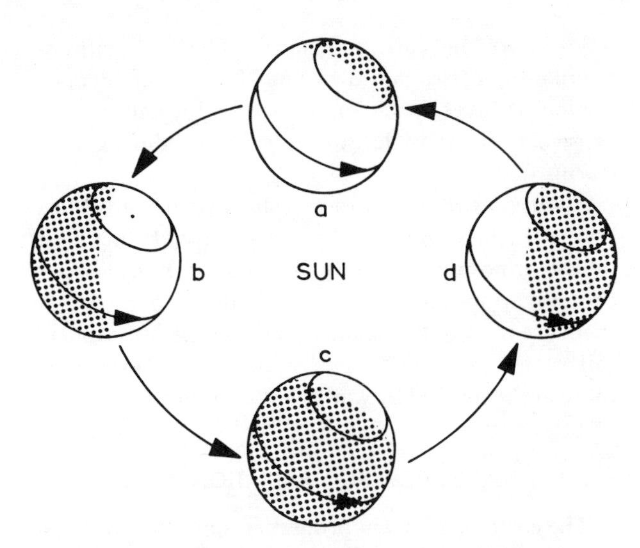

Figure 1.4 Earth's seasons. The constant orientation of Earth's axis in space during its movement about the sun causes an annual cycle of change in the angle of solar rays striking the planet. *a*, vernal equinox, March 21; *b*, summer solstice, June 21; *c*, autumnal equinox, September 23; *d*, winter solstice, December 22.

layers compose the solar atmosphere. It is the atmosphere of the sun that produces solar radiations.

Although severe solar storms are unusual, periodically (about every eleven years) especially wild storms occur. At such times, so-called fiery prominences of 30,000° F. leap from the surface in the form of arches, hedges, jets, or loops. Concurrently, relatively low-temperatured (7000°F.) sunspots appear. The sunspots are surrounded by masses of flaming hydrogen (the 18,000°F. *plages*), other violent disturbances (the 30,000° F *flares*), and certain localized areas with temperatures of one million degrees. The chief significance of these solar storms to earth life is that they release X rays and various charged particles in the form of solar radiation.

Normal solar radiation from the surface and atmosphere of the sun has various effects upon the earth. The sun's surface gives rise to *visible light*, *infrared rays*, and a complex of *ultraviolet rays*. When visible light is intercepted by water droplets, rainbows appear in the sky. Infrared rays produce earth heat and storm clouds. Ultraviolet rays create the upper two layers of our three-layered ionosphere. (The ionosphere is 40 to 220 miles up and is the last completely atmospheric zone in the atmosphere; see Chapter 2). Ultraviolet light, which causes sunburn, would be fatal to man and many other animals if most rays were not absorbed by the atmospheric ozone (a particular combination of three oxygen atoms) about 16 miles above the earth's surface. The sun's atmosphere produces radio waves and X rays which create the lowest layer of the ionosphere and which are the cause of radio and television interference during solar storms.

About 65 per cent of these solar rays are absorbed by the earth, 47 per cent by the surface, 15 per cent by the atmospheric clouds and moisture, and 3 per cent by atmospheric ozone. About 35 per cent of them are reflected back into space by the atmosphere (air, clouds, and dust) and by the surface, especially those areas covered by water, ice, and snow.

EARTH'S MAGNETISM AND RADIATION BELTS

The earth has certain properties similar to those of a magnet. Our planet creates lines of magnetic force that arch away from and back to the earth. This complex of lines of force is called the earth's *magnetic field*. The arches occur in a series of increasing size that center near the equator, the largest arches passing from one magnetic pole to the other.

Formation of the magnetic field appears to be associated with the earth's two-layered core—an inner, mostly solid, one and an outer liquid layer. It is believed that the liquid portion of the core created the magnetic field as the liquid was churned during the earth's formation. This churning movement may have produced a small magnetic field that further caused the liquid part of the core to move, thus increasing the original field and forming the general pattern of the present one. The present magnetic field pattern also exists because of tidal pull, or gravitational attraction, of the sun and the moon. Finally, our field is modified periodically by solar storms.

Earth's magnetic field produces an envelope of radiation, the *magnetosphere* (Figure 1.5). This envelope exists because the magnetic field acts as a magnetic trap, catching radioactive particles from the sun and interstellar space and holding them in a layer of radiation that surrounds the earth except at the magnetic poles.

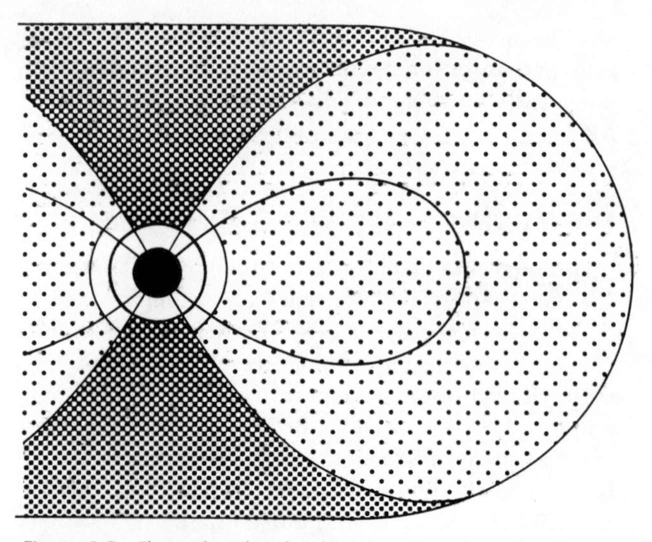

Figure 1.5 The earth and its doughnut-shaped envelope of radiation, the magnetosphere. The diagram is a cross-section through the center of the earth (from pole to pole, the earth's core being in black) and the magnetosphere (cuts are the two large areas of open stippling). Two arcing lines shown to originate and terminate on each side of the earth's core represent lines of force in the earth's magnetic field. The magnetic field traps solar and other radiation, thereby holding the radiation that typifies the magnetosphere.

EARTH FEATURES

If one were to select the best single word to indicate the characteristics of the earth, "organization" might be chosen. Whether one considers physical or biological aspects, organization applies. Moreover, the word is very descriptive of actual conditions, despite the great complexity and apparent chaos among the myriad of things upon this planet.

In future discussions, an attempt will be made to use this basic organization of features to facilitate our understanding of the natural history of earth. At the present time we will consider *form and divisions* and *affecting forces*.

FORM AND DIVISIONS

Our planet is not a perfect sphere; its polar diameter is approximately 7900 miles and its equatorial diameter about 7926.7 miles. Actually its form is pearlike, certain southern latitudes having greater diameters than comparable northern latitudes.

The division (zonation) of the earth is most fundamental in the case of global subdivision into core, mantle, and crust. In addition, as we have noted, the surface is zoned into land (lithosphere), air (atmosphere), water (hydrosphere), and life (biosphere). Each of the surface zones is composed of further units that are easily identified by unique conditions and/or structures. The lithosphere displays inner and outer crust zones plus a distinctive pattern of structural features, such as mountain and valley systems. Also, it is affected by various levels, or orders, of geological characteristics. The first-order features are the oceans and the continents; the second-order features are the processes of erosion; and the third-order features include the processes of mountain formation and uplift. The atmosphere and ocean waters both contain five main layers. Even the complexity of life displays an organization, the life spectrum.

Furthermore, order is displayed by the horizontal and vertical zonation of climate and the effects of climate as shown in soil and vegetation. Climatically, zonation features tropical, dry, warm-temperate, cool-temperate, and arctic conditions. With each kind of climate there is a definite association of living creatures (especially plants) and soils.

This discussion provides only a brief glimpse into the characteristic orderliness of earth and its phenomena. However, it does indicate a general framework for the more detailed consideration that will follow.

AFFECTING FORCES

The forces affecting us can be considered in two groups: the internal and the external ones.

Internal forces already mentioned (actually, the producers of these forces) are the physical phenomena that cause movements and modifications of the earth's crust, the magnetic field, and the radiation belts. Another internal force is *gravity*. Gravity, which from our point of view is the attraction of all objects toward the center of the earth's core, is the great leveler of our planet. It also has a bearing on previously considered processes. Gravitation maintains a constant strain upon all elevations. It causes movable objects to proceed down slope. It maintains ocean waters in a nearly spherical form that is disturbed only by winds, which cause waves, and by the gravitational attractions of sun and moon, which cause the tides.

Gravity is not merely a function of the earth's mass. It is true that mass is the main force of attraction among objects, but mass is counteracted by the earth's rotation. In fact, rotational differences affect the weight of an object at different latitudes upon this planet. However, this difference is only great enough to increase by one pound at the poles the weight of an object that is two hundred pounds at the equator.

The primary sources of external forces are the sun and moon. Other planets, moons, and stars produce minor effects. Already treated were the effects of solar radiation and sun-moon gravitation effects. In addition, solar heat reacts upon our atmosphere and lithosphere to produce weathering and other types of erosion. Erosion is related to a constant circulation of the earth's air and water reacting with solar rays and gravity. That part of the circulation that includes water alone is called the *hydrologic cycle* (Figure 17.4, p. 308). It consists of the evaporation of water from the oceans into the air to be formed into clouds, the precipitation of this water in the form of snow or rain, and the eventual return of most of the water to the ocean by runoff.

Later, we will consider the work of air and water in the reduction of landscape profiles. If the effects of these factors and that of gravity were not counteracted by uplift, vulcanism, and mountain building, the land would soon be entirely flat.

SELECTED READINGS

Gamow, George, 1948. *Biography of the Earth.* New American Library, New York.

———, 1960. *The Creation of the Universe.* New American Library, New York.

Hoyle, Fred, 1960. *The Nature of the Universe.* Harper, New York.

Kuiper, Gerald P., ed., 1953, 1954, 1961. *The Solar System.* 3 vols., The University of Chicago Press, Chicago, Ill.

Life Editorial Staff and Lincoln Barnett, 1955. *The World We Live In.* Time Inc., New York.

Life Editorial Staff and Arthur Beiser, 1962. *The Earth.* Time Inc., New York.

Life Editorial Staff and David Bergamini, 1962. *The Universe.* Time Inc., New York.

Mayall, N., M. Mayall and J. Wychoff, 1961. *The Sky Observers Guide.* Golden Press, New York.

Ross, Herbert H., 1962. *A Synthesis of Evolutionary Theory.* Prentice-Hall, Inc., Englewood Cliffs, N. J.

Strahler, Arthur N., 1960. *Physical Geography.* 2nd ed. John Wiley & Sons, New York.

Sullivan, Walter, 1961. *Assault on the Unknown: The International Geophysical Year.* McGraw-Hill Book Co., New York.

Whitrow, G. J., 1959. *Structure and Evolution of the Universe.* Hillary House Ltd., London.

Wilson, J. Tuzp, 1961. IGY: *The Year of the New Moons.* Alfred A. Knopf, Inc., New York.

Zim, Herbert S., 1956. *Stars.* Golden Press, New York.

2 METEOROLOGY AND CLIMATOLOGY

The Atmosphere, Weather, and Climate

In Chapter 1 we discussed the organization of the earth's surface into four zones: atmosphere, hydrosphere, lithosphere, and biosphere. The next several chapters will discuss in some detail the composition and characteristics of each of these major zones. In the present chapter we will examine the equilibrium, zonation, and phenomena of the atmosphere.

The characteristics and phenomena of the atmosphere are intimately related to those of the land, water, and living organisms. Two atmospheric phenomena, *weather* and *climate*, have a profound effect on living organisms and are therefore discussed at length in this chapter.

THE ATMOSPHERE

THE ATMOSPHERIC CYCLE

Although the composition of atmosphere is much the same now as it has been for the past 2 billion years, this "sameness" is, paradoxically, the result of constant change. Many factors, especially living organisms, work independently to produce the atmosphere's dynamic equilibrium (Figure 2.1).

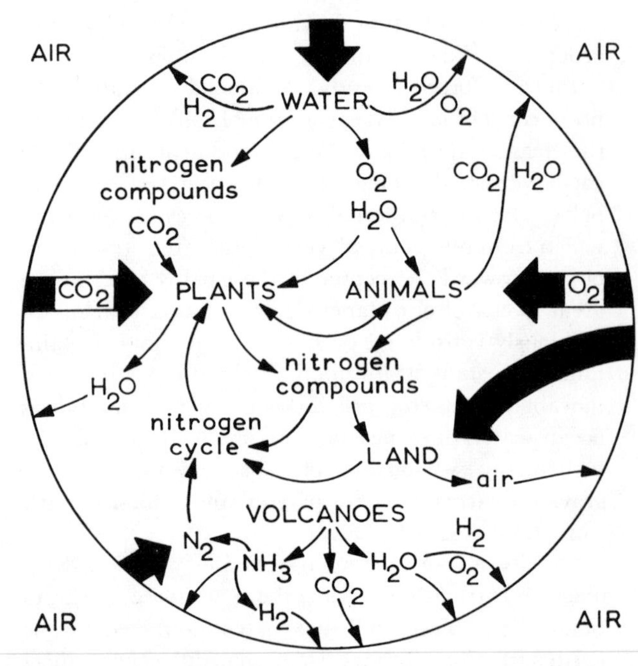

Figure 2.1 The Atmospheric Cycle, a summary of chemical interchanges between organisms and their environment. H_2 (hydrogen), O_2 (oxygen), N_2 (nitrogen), CO_2 (carbon dioxide), H_2O (water), NH_3 (ammonia).

Most life uses oxygen to burn food for energy; in this life process of oxidation, carbon dioxide is released as a waste product. During the day plants, as a part of photosynthetic activity, use carbon dioxide to produce basic foodstuffs and give off oxygen as a waste product. Night and day plants use oxygen for respiration. Both plants and animals at various times contribute some water vapor from their bodies to the atmosphere. Furthermore, organisms, in eliminating wastes and in decomposing after death, release some form of nitrogen to the ground and, secondarily, to the air.

Contribution to the atmosphere by nonliving things is a more complex procedure. Volcanoes emit water vapor, carbon dioxide, and nitrogen, chiefly in the form of ammonia. Lightning causes water vapor to be broken down into its basic components, hydrogen and oxygen, and ammonia to be broken down into nitrogen and hydrogen. Atmospheric storms also activate some of the free ammonia so that it can enter into the so-called *nitrogen cycle*. In this cycle, certain bacteria cause chemical changes (involving the addition of oxygen to the nitrogen) to produce compounds plants can use. These nitrogen compounds are used in the complex food-producing activities of plants beyond the simple sugar production of photosynthesis.

The land is a reservoir for atmospheric components or products of these components. However, rocks and soils contain free air as well as nitrogen compounds that can be assimilated by plants. Another major air reservoir is water. The various atmospheric gases are in water. So are the products of the basic air components, especially nitrogen compounds. Of course, water also provides the air with water vapor. In fact, evaporation from bodies of water is now the primary source of atmospheric water vapor.

The atmospheric cycle is only one of the many phenomena that are collectively called *biogeochemical cycles*. Each of the single cycles emphasizes the close interrelationship that exists between biological and physical phenomena. Moreover, each cycle is dynamic because it is dependent upon the interaction of many separate factors that bring about a condition of equilibrium. Because so many factors are involved, the equilibrium of none of the cycles is definitely fixed; if individual factors change, the condition of equilibrium will also change. Such an equilibrium change might occur in the atmosphere, because man is affecting certain of the separate factors. For example, man is releasing more carbon dioxide, impurities (smog), and radiation than normal. If these additions become sufficient, they can lead to a new equilibrium, one that will modify conditions for life on earth. Therefore, the atmospheric cycle and all other biogeochemical cycles constitute natural resources that man must conserve.

ATMOSPHERIC GASES

Many different gases are found in the atmosphere, but only a few are found in significant concentrations. The main gases and their approximate concentrations at sea level are: nitrogen, 78 per cent; oxygen, 21 per cent; argon, 1 per cent; water vapor, 0.01 to 4 per cent; and carbon dioxide, 0.03 per cent.

Atmospheric gases are extremely important. If it were not for them, our planet's life, with the exception of a few kinds of bacteria, would not exist. However, the individual air components are not as important as is the insulating action of the entire atmosphere. If there were no gaseous envelope, the earth's surface temperature would range from $-230°$ F. in the shade to $300°$ F. in the sunlight. In addition, our planet would have no fire, sound, weather changes, sunsets, blue skies, or auroras.

ATMOSPHERIC ZONATION

The atmosphere has five zones, each characterized by certain features. The *troposphere* (0 to 10 miles up) contains 75 per cent of the air. It is about 5 miles thick at the poles and $11\frac{1}{2}$ miles thick at the equator. Within the troposphere are clouds, as well as air movement and weather changes. The *tropopause* is a narrow transition area (not a zone) between the troposphere and the stratosphere. The tropopause has breaks that give it an overlapping, leaflike structure. The breaks give rise to the jet streams where cold northern air meets warm southern air. The three North American jet streams (the Canadian, American, and Subtropical) generally blow from the west and are about 4 miles high and 300 miles wide. They occur at altitudes of 20,000 to 40,000 feet and move at speeds of 50 to 300 miles per hour. Their names imply the general areas through which each moves.

The *stratosphere* (10 to 20 miles at our latitude) is also an area of air movement. Furthermore, it is in the stratosphere that solar ultraviolet light changes oxygen to ozone. Although ozone is a poisonous, gaseous combination of three oxygen atoms, it does filter lethal ultraviolet light so that only enough reaches the earth's surface to cause sunburn, to produce vitamin D, and to kill many bacteria.

The *chemosphere* (20 to 40 miles) is the area where airglow (a faint glow of air particles visible on clear moonless nights) begins.

The *ionosphere* (40 to 220 miles) is actually three

layers characterized by the breaking down of molecules into positively and negatively charged fragments called ions.

The final zone, the *exosphere* (beyond 220 miles), is an almost airless area that grades into interplanetary space. This outer zone does not stop abruptly; rather, the boundary is a "spray zone," where atmospheric particles spray out into space and then return immediately, assume temporary orbits before returning, or escape into space.

AURORAS

In the vicinity of the magnetic north and south poles, and 50 to 600 miles above the earth's surface, are the northern and southern lights, the *auroras*. Both lights are produced as a result of the following series of events: Explosive activities in the sun's atmosphere cause electrified particles to escape in all directions from the sun and into space. Some of these particles enter the earth's magnetic field and are deflected toward the magnetic poles. When the particles strike upper air molecules and atoms, the energy transferred to the latter causes them to glow, the different air components glowing in different colors. This glowing is observed as an aurora from the surface of the earth.

SKY COLORS

The color of the sky at any particular time and place is the result of visible sunlight being scattered by atmospheric particles. The actual color of the sky depends on the amount of atmosphere traversed by the light. As sunlight enters the atmosphere, the first wavelengths of light to be scattered are the violet waves. Therefore, when the sun is directly overhead, the black of space found within 20 miles of the earth gradually changes to a definite violet at about 12 miles altitude. Other colors are due to sunlight traveling farther. When the sun is directly overhead, the last wavelengths to be scattered are blue, which is the reason the sky is blue during most of the day. However, when sunlight strikes a place upon the earth at an angle, at dawn or sunset, the light passes through a greater distance of air, a distance sufficient for the red wavelengths to be scattered by air molecules. Therefore, sky colors have a direct relationship to the density of air particles, the differential scattering of the sun's visible wavelengths, and the distance traveled by sunlight through the atmosphere.

Rainbows and related phenomena such as halos about the sun and moon (the rings are upon clouds) are produced by much the same process. However, these latter phenomena are due to light's being scattered by rain droplets, ice crystals, and other cloud particles.

ATMOSPHERIC TEMPERATURE

The primary source of air temperature is solar radiation; therefore, surface temperatures increase during the day and decrease at night. Solar radiation is most effective when solar rays are from directly overhead, when the air is cleanest and driest, and when radiation acts upon the land rather than upon the water.

Solar rays that are direct, or perpendicular, to a part of the earth's surface are most effective in increasing air temperature because such radiation is most concentrated per unit area of the surface. This is true because any given amount of solar radiation that strikes the earth at an angle, no matter how slight, is spread over more of the earth's surface than is the same amount of radiation when the rays are perpendicular (Figure 2.2). In addition, indirect rays must pass through more atmosphere, hence be scattered by more air particles and be less effective in producing heat. Therefore, anything less than direct solar rays results in some dissipation of the full effect of sunlight striking the earth.

The full importance of perpendicular solar rays and their more efficient production of heat have already been mentioned in connection with the earth's seasons (Chapter 1, p. 7). If many people were asked

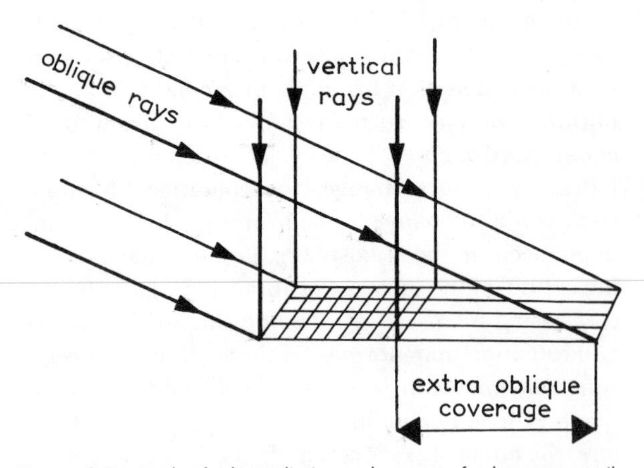

Figure 2.2 Angle of solar radiation and amount of solar energy striking the earth's surface. Maximum energy is received from directly overhead rays that strike the earth at a 90° angle.

whether they believed the sun was closer to earth in the winter or in the summer, some might assume that "summer" was the answer. However, the exact opposite is true. The essentially perpendicular rays produce the summer when the earth is farther away from the sun than it is in the winter.

Clean, dry air provides less obstruction to sunlight than does dustier, moister air. The former has fewer particles to act as obstructions to the rays, hence the maximum radiation reaches the lower atmosphere and the earth's surface. However, the conditions for maximum daytime heating are also those of maximum nighttime cooling. The night is cooler because a minimum amount of water vapor and dust provide a minimum amount of heat insulation for the surface. This is why areas characterized by clean, dry air (e.g., deserts) are noted for their relatively great fluctuation in temperature.

The land is subject to faster and greater temperature changes than is water. This difference stems from a particular property of water—it retains heat longer and acquires heat more slowly than most other substances (see Figure 3.1, p. 28). This characteristic helps to explain why most of the world's ocean area has annual temperature extremes no greater than 8° F. and why atmospheric water vapor is the most important factor in preventing great air temperature extremes. In daytime it inhibits rapid increases and at night, rapid losses.

EFFECTS OF TEMPERATURE VARIATIONS

In the lowest zone of the atmosphere (troposphere) there are changes in temperature at different altitudes. Because the greatest air density is at the surface of the earth and hence most particles are there, the highest and most uniform air temperature is also at the surface. However, there are modifications within this pattern. If a localized surface area is warmed, this air expands and its pressure decreases. Any pressure reduction also means lighter air so it is forced upward by the pressure of the denser air around it. As it rises, it reaches surrounding air of still lower pressure. Therefore, rising air expands, and with expansion, it cools. Conversely, if higher, heavier air descends, the surrounding air progressively compresses the descending air, increasing its air pressure and temperature. For these reasons, atmospheric temperature is frequently related to atmospheric pressure.

Also associated with temperature, and hence the upward and downward movements of air masses, is the capacity of air to hold moisture. As air rises, cooling reduces its capacity to hold moisture, so the water vapor condenses into water droplets, thus forming clouds. The point at which condensation takes place is just beyond the maximum amount of water vapor the air can hold at a given time and is termed the *saturation* or *dew point*. (Dew is produced on the ground through the same process.) On the other hand, as air descends, warming increases its moisture-carrying capacity (Figure 2.3).

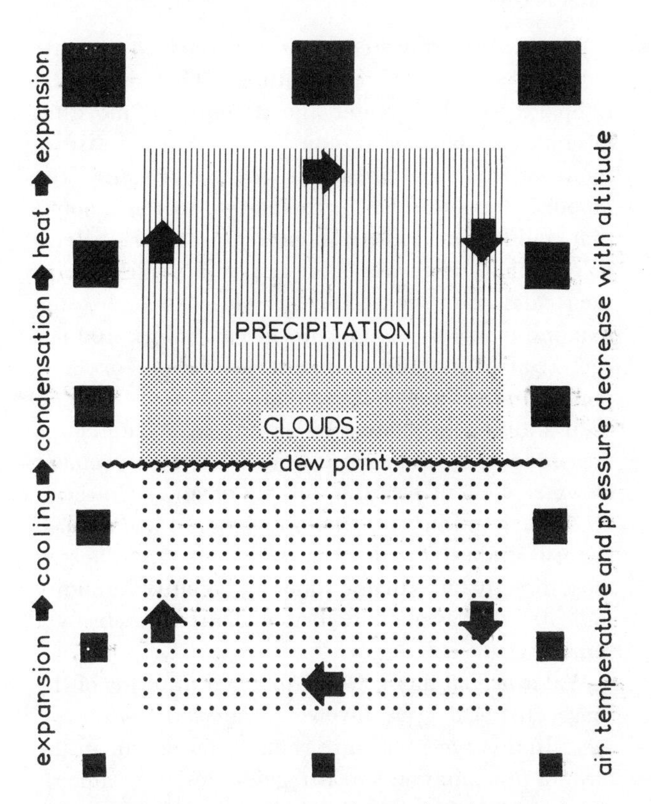

Figure 2.3 Temperature, pressure, volume, and condensation relationships in ascending and descending air. As air rises its temperature and pressure decrease but its volume increases. Related to decreasing temperature is the onset of water vapor condensation, the dew point, which causes air to rise even more and furthers the above relationships. Progressive condensation causes clouds, then precipitation. As air descends, the opposite conditions prevail.

Water condensation adds further complexity to air-temperature relations. Any water condensation involves a so-called *heat of condensation*. This heat is produced by the process of condensation and is released into the surrounding air. For this reason, the phenomenon in which air rises and cools results in heat production when water vapor condenses. Moreover, this heat is released into the surrounding air. Naturally, this warms the air, thereby causing further air expansion, rising, cooling, and condensation which if carried far enough results in precipitation. Therefore, differences in rates of air heating and cooling cause the water vapor, temperature, and pressure of adjacent areas of air to differ. These differences cause local variations in winds and general climatic conditions.

MOISTURE

The amount of water vapor necessary to saturate air is determined by temperature. The higher the temperature, the greater the amount of moisture necessary to saturate the air. A standard measurement of this relationship is *relative humidity* (the amount of moisture in air in relation to the amount that could be held at the same temperature). Relative humidity is always expressed as a percentage of the total amount that could be held. Therefore, the maximum amount of moisture air can hold is 100 per cent relative humidity and the saturation, or dew, point is immediately beyond that.

In addition to relative humidity, water content is measured by *absolute humidity*. This is a measurement of water content per unit volume of air. However, absolute humidity is generally ignored in natural history studies, because environments are affected most directly by available water and relative humidity indicates this availability better than does absolute humidity.

Water availability is best explained in terms of the biogeochemical cycle involving water, the *hydrologic cycle*. In this cycle moisture is lost from the air in the form of precipitation and is regained by the evaporation of water from the land, living organisms, and bodies of water (see Figure 17.4, p. 308). The conditions already considered indicate why and how precipitation is formed. Moreover, the process whereby increased temperature can change liquid water to vapor (evaporation) can be readily appreciated. However, three aspects of moisture replenishment deserve further consideration. First, the main source of water vapor is standing bodies of water, especially the oceans. Second, conditions that result in a continuous supply of dry air will produce maximum evaporation from the earth's surface into the air. Therefore, lower relative humidity, higher temperature, and greater wind velocity each contribute to greater evaporation of surface moisture. Third, and perhaps obviously, the moisture-holding capacity of the air is increased with any rise in temperature. Actually, for every 18°F. increase in temperature, the moisture-holding capacity of air is doubled.

Air moisture is transported by winds, along the surface of the land or upward into the higher levels of air. The movement of water vapor, causing it to mix with air, is the direct consequence of air mass movements, our next topic.

WIND

Consideration of air mass movements, or winds, must be on both a local and a worldwide scale. Locally, four major factors characterize winds. First, winds move from higher pressure areas into lower pressure areas. This is the effect of a tendency toward equalization of air pressure density, or toward homogeneity of the number of air molecules per unit volume in different places. Therefore, any lower pressure area has fewer air molecules per unit volume than does any higher pressure area.

Second (actually another way of considering the first characteristic), cold air is usually of higher pressure and weight than is warm air. This is the case because cold air (in contrast to warm) has less energy (heat) for molecular activity, and less molecular movement enables individual air particles to be closer to one another. As a result, cold air has greater particle density, weight, and pressure. Therefore, cold air, when it has the above features, penetrates through and forces its way under warm air. Following this penetration down and under warm air, the cold air often continues as a wind over the land. Before considering the next local wind feature, it must be emphasized that these temperature and pressure relationships are general tendencies. There are exceptions in which warm air has greater pressure than does cool air. For example, under local conditions warm air may be compressed until it has greater pressure than cooler air.

Third, differential surface temperatures contribute to local wind patterns. Any condition causing nearby areas to have different temperatures usually causes differences in air pressures. The role of such air pressure variation in producing winds already was mentioned.

Finally, surface features alter wind direction or

pathways. Any object, natural or man-made, causes a barrier that in various degrees modifies wind pathways.

Winds are controlled on a planetary scale by the heat of the sun and the rotation of the earth. Solar heat causes pressure differences and winds to equalize the differences. The rotation of the earth steers the major patterns of winds over the globe. Although these patterns show various modifications, winds of the northern hemisphere generally move clockwise and winds of the southern hemisphere counterclockwise.

As one might expect, world winds have a pronounced effect upon the environment of our planet. However, it amounts to no more than the mixing of warm tropical air and cool temperate air, a condition that prevents violent temperature extremes between the poles and the equator.

Examination of the pattern of world air circulation indicates how temperature and rotation bring about this pattern (Figure 2.4). Warm air of low pressure rises at the equator and moves poleward. These equatorial *doldrums*, winds with little lateral movement, are influenced by the earth's rotation. When rotation moves high levels of these winds eastward, they are piled up, creating a high-pressure area near latitude 30° Some of the air is immediately forced downward, reaches the surface, and is modified by the earth's rotation. In the northern hemisphere, the earth's rotation produces a continuous air movement to the right, in clockwise motion, resulting in the *northeastern trades* south of the high-pressure area and the *prevailing westerlies* to the north. South of the equator, counterclockwise motion results in the *southeast trades* and another band of prevailing westerlies. In both hemispheres some of the upper air continues poleward, cools, and sinks in the vicinity of the pole. The prevailing northern clockwise and southern counterclockwise motions result in the polar *northeasterlies* and the *southeasterlies*, respectively.

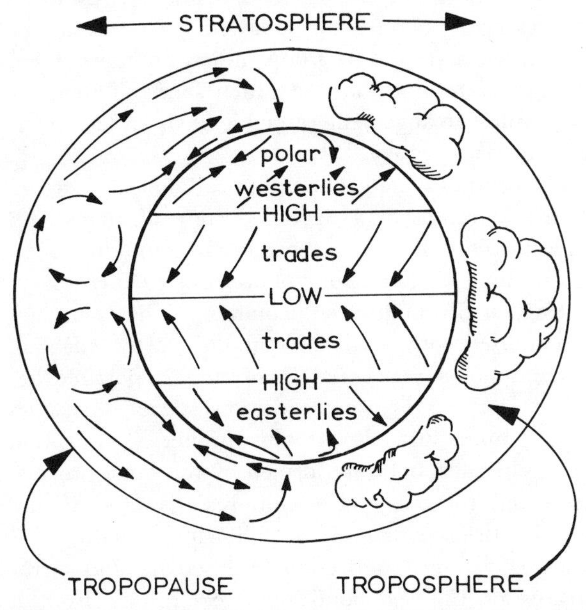

Figure 2.4 Lower atmosphere layers and world winds. Arrows give the directions and interrelationships of surface and above-surface winds in the troposphere.

CLOUDS

A cloud is visible water vapor, occurring at various heights regulated by winds, temperature, and the sun. However, clouds contain little water by weight, owing to the vapor form of the water. In other words, there is potentially little liquid water in clouds. If all the clouds covering the earth were to shed their moisture simultaneously, the resulting rainfall would add only about an inch of water to the entire surface. In spite of the insignificance of their size and moisture content, clouds are so distributed that they prevent dust storms and temperature extremes from killing us, allow no more than a 15 per cent loss of solar radiation to space, and announce future weather with some degree of accuracy. Weather forecasting is possible because clouds are often found in weather phenomena called *fronts* (see below).

There are two general methods of cloud formation: condensation and convection. Condensation of water fairly close to the ground produces the so-called "bathroom type" of clouds. The word "bathroom" alludes to the fact that water vapor condenses in the same general manner in both situations. These clouds form when warm air is blown over a cool surface or up a mountain slope, when precipitation falls through warm air, or when heat is lost rapidly from the land (e.g., the blowing of warm air from the land over cool water or ice, and the cooling of air over the land after sunset). Clouds formed by condensation usually are found below 20,000 feet and most clouds below 20,000 feet are formed in this manner.

Cloud formation by convection involves the rising and cooling of air masses. Convection clouds are usually over 20,000 feet in altitude, and frequently their water vapor has frozen to ice crystals.

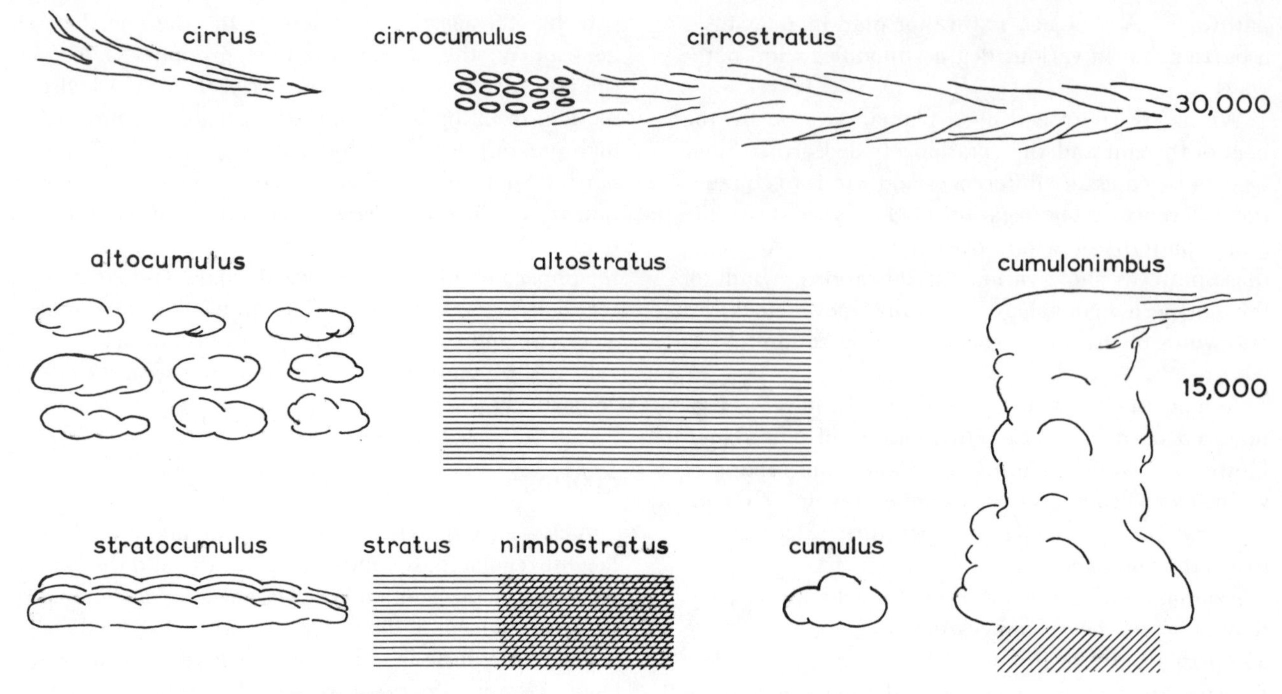

Figure 2.5 Average altitudes (in feet) and suggested forms of the ten main cloud types.

The two methods of cloud formation produce clouds with a variety of appearances. However, this confusing array of forms is classified by the United States Weather Bureau into ten genera within four families. Although these cloud genera have a number of variations called species, only the genera are emphasized here (Figure 2.5).

FAMILY A: HIGH CLOUDS (averaging 30,000 feet; mean lower level 20,000 feet)

Cirrus are detached clouds of delicate and fibrous appearance. They are without shading (except those extending from and composed of the debris of the upper frozen parts of cumulonimbus clouds), generally white in color, often of a silky or feathery appearance, and with ragged and indefinite edges. These are the clouds that are frequently brightly colored at sunset or sunrise.

Cirrus appear in such forms as isolated tufts, lines drawn across a blue sky, branched featherlike plumes, and curved lines ending in tufts. They are often arranged in bands which cross the sky like meridian lines and, owing to the effect of perspective, converge either to a point on the horizon or to two opposite points on opposite horizons. Cirrocumulus and cirrostratus often take part in the formation of these bands.

Cirrocumulus form either a cirruslike layer or patches. The patches may be either small, unshaded, white flakes, or very small globular masses. Even the masses are generally unshadowed. The flakes or masses are arranged in groups, lines, or, more often, ripples resembling those of beach sand. Often cirrocumulus arrangement resembles fish scales and is called "mackerel sky."

Cirrocumulus clouds never appear alone. They are with and represent a degraded state of cirrus and cirrostratus. For this reason, cirrocumulus often retain some scattered point of fibrous structure.

Real cirrocumulus are uncommon. They must not be confused with small altocumulus on the edges of altocumulus sheets. This confusion is possible because all states of transition occur between cirrocumulus and altocumulus proper. Transition occurs because both are formed by the same process. However, the term "cirrocumulus" is used if any cloud satisfies either of the following criteria: (1) there is definite connection with cirrus and cirrostratus or (2) the cloud observed results from a change in cirrus or cirrostratus.

To interpret weather from cirrocumulus clouds,

one must note what happens to them. If they change into cumulus, the weather is likely to be fair. If they change into cirrostratus, which in turn change to lower, thicker, clouds, it is likely to rain.

Cirrostratus form a thin, whitish veil which does not blur the outlines of the sun or moon, but the light of these objects usually gives rise to rings or halos. Sometimes the cloud is quite diffuse and only gives the sky a milky look; sometimes it more or less distinctly shows a fibrous structure with disordered threads. This latter characteristic resembles altostratus; however, cirrostratus do not prevent sunlight from casting shadows upon the ground.

Weather forecasting necessitates observing the fate of cirrostratus. If they are followed by lower clouds, rain and higher temperature are likely. If they degenerate into cirrocumulus, fair weather is most probable. Cirrostratus in the early evening is supposed to indicate clearing by morning.

FAMILY B: MIDDLE CLOUDS (mostly 13,000 to 22,000 feet; mean upper level, 20,000 feet; lowest level to 6500 feet)

Altocumulus occur either as advancing, small, isolated patches, parallel bands, or a layer of flattened globular masses. In a regularly arranged layer, the smallest masses are fairly small and thin, shaded or not, and are often at different levels. Also, the globular masses are arranged in groups, lines, or waves that in turn are organized in one or two directions and are sometimes so close together that their edges join. When they interrupt moonlight or sunlight, a corona of small, colored, rainbowlike rings (red outside and blue inside) is formed. Cirrostratus also can have a halo, but the ring is blue outside and red inside. Altocumulus frequently change into altostratus and forecast storm conditions.

Altostratus form a lined to fibrous sheet or veil that is more or less gray or bluish in color. Such a cloud resembles thick cirrostratus, but it displays no halo phenomenon; rather, the sun or moon shows vaguely, with a faint gleam, as though through ground glass. When an altostratus sheet is thin, it is most like cirrostratus; when very thick and dark, it sometimes completely hides the sun or moon. Also, when it is thick, differences in thickness may cause relatively light patches between very dark parts, but the surface never shows real relief and the lined or fibrous structure is always seen in parts of the cloud.

Rain or snow may fall from altostratus, but when the rain is heavy, the cloud layer will have grown thicker and lower, becoming nimbostratus. On the other hand, heavy snow may fall from a layer that is definitely altostratus.

FAMILY C: LOW CLOUDS (generally under 10,000 feet; mean upper level, 6500 feet; mean lower level, close to the surface)

Stratocumulus form a layer (or patches) composed of rounded patches, globular masses, or rolls. The smallest of the regularly arranged individual parts are fairly large, soft, and gray, but have darker areas. Arrangement of parts is in groups, lines, or waves that are aligned in one or two directions. Very often the parts are so close together that their edges join. When these clouds cover the sky they have a wavy appearance.

Stratocumulus may indicate changing weather. They are frequently found near thunderheads and before and behind storms.

Stratus is a low, uniform layer of cloud. The layer may be partly broken up into irregular shreds, a variety called *fractostratus*. *Fog* is a variation that reaches the ground. Stratus clouds often indicate fair weather.

Nimbostratus is much like stratus, but is darker and much thicker. This low cloud type is usually of homogeneous but formless structure. Also, the cloud has a dark gray color and appears to be feebly lighted from within.

Nimbostratus are called rain clouds and frequently have a rainy or snowy lower layer; however, they may occur without rain or snow. Even if precipitation is released, rain or snow might not reach the ground. In this case, the base of the cloud is usually diffuse and looks wet on account of the trailing precipitation. When this occurs, it is not possible to determine the cloud's lower surface.

These clouds frequently have ragged fragments that are detached but closely associated with the main cloud mass. Such fragments are generally quite dark and are called *scuds*. Scuds are also produced by cumulonimbus clouds.

FAMILY D: CLOUDS WITH VERTICAL DEVELOPMENT

Cumulus is a dense, low-altitude cloud with vertical development; however, its height is insignificant in comparison to that of cumulonimbus. The upper surface is dome-shaped and exhibits rounded protuberances, but the base is nearly flat. In general, each cloud resembles a puff of cotton.

When the cloud is viewed against the sun, it looks dark except for a bright edge. When light comes from the side, it shows strong contrasts of light and shade. When opposite the sun, the side appears brighter than the edges of the protuberances.

One variety results from wind "tearing." It has the same general appearance as cumulus but is ragged looking and constantly changing its form. Such clouds are called *fractocumulus*. Over the land, typical cumulus clouds develop on days of clear skies.

Cumulonimbus is a heavy mass of cloud with extreme vertical development. The tops are cumuluslike, resembling mountains or towers. The uppermost parts often have a cirrus cloud, spreading out in the shape of an anvil. The base is frequently torn (like nimbostratus) and gives rise to a layer of very low, ragged clouds (*scuds*) below it.

Cumulonimbus clouds are generally associated with rain or snow and sometimes hail. They are often associated with thunderstorms.

WEATHER AND CLIMATE

Weather and climate are two aspects of the same thing. *Weather* refers to the local atmospheric conditions at a given time and *climate* to the sum total of these conditions over a period of time. Both are a direct reflection of the waves of air masses which produce both "High" and "Low" pressure areas, as well as fronts. An examination of these phenomena will provide some understanding of what produces weather and climate.

PRESSURE AREAS

Pressure areas are constantly forming and changing because of ever-varying winds. The world winds are produced by the heat of the sun and are directed by the rotation of the earth and position of oceans and continents. These winds, in turn, produce pressure areas.

Pressure areas are either "Highs" or "Lows." "Highs," also called anticyclones, are characterized by winds that spiral outward in a clockwise direction in the northern hemisphere. "Lows," collectively called cyclones, feature winds that spiral inward in a counterclockwise movement in the northern hemisphere. Directions of wind spirals are just the opposite in the southern hemisphere (Figure 2.6); "Highs" are counterclockwise and "Lows" are clockwise.

"Highs" can form anywhere that air cools, sinks, and compresses. As a result of winds spiraling outward from a "High," upper air sinks to replace the lost air, the replacing air warming as it sinks and compresses. Under these circumstances, the skies are clear. "Highs" usually occur in polar and horse latitude areas (see Figure 2.4, p. 15).

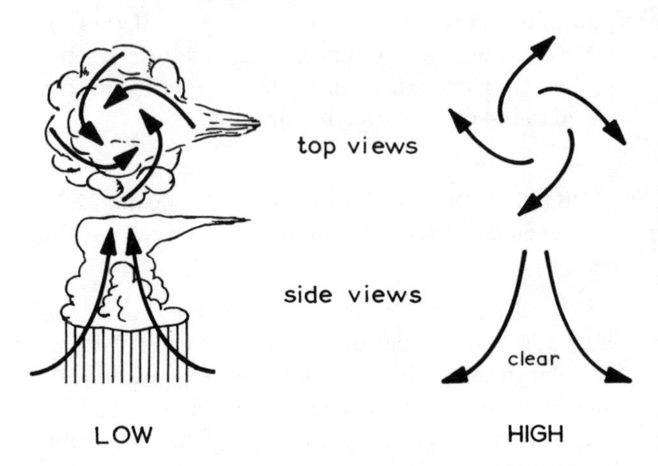

Figure 2.6 "High" and "Low" pressure areas. Arrows suggest the direction of air movement and the vertical lines imply the precipitation often occuring in a "low."

"Lows" can result from a horizontal, wavelike action between "Highs" of unlike temperatures. The winds spiraling into these "Lows" rise to colder elevations, cool, and contract. Under such conditions, the atmospheric water vapor usually condenses into clouds, and snow or rain may result. "Lows" are characteristic of the doldrums.

"Lows" of the tropics may develop into severe storms, the tropical cyclones. These cyclones are of less diameter but greater energy than are the extratropical cyclones. In fact, the energy of the tropical cyclones is so great that these storms draw considerable attention from man. Peoples in various parts of the world have special names for them; for example, Americans have *hurricanes* and peoples of the Far East have *typhoons*.

AIR MASSES

A large area with essentially homogeneous topography generally has characteristic climatic features, especially pressure, temperature, and humidity. These conditions are said to characterize a *climatic rhythm.* A single climatic rhythm is the result of a single air mass or definite seasonal changes in air masses. Therefore, an air mass is any extensive portion of the atmosphere characterized by predictable climatic features.

There are various levels of air mass classification. The two primary categories, *polar* and *tropical*, are based upon the source of the air masses. The secondary subdivisions are *maritime* and *continental* and are based on known differences in temperature, moisture, pressure, and other atmospheric conditions. Further subdivision is on the basis of geographic locations having further unique aspects of climate. The most important air masses in North America are classified below (Figure 2.7).

NORTH AMERICAN AIR MASSES

Polar Continental, or *Polar Canadian*, originates in Alaska, northern Canada, and the Arctic Region. It consists of cold, dry air that comes down through Canada to affect the midwestern and eastern United States. In the winter, it brings cold and snow; in the summer, fair weather.

Polar Maritime is of two types. *Polar Pacific* originates in the North Pacific Ocean. It brings cool, fairly moist air from the northern Pacific to cause frequent fog and winter rains along the Pacific Coast. After passing over the western mountain ranges, this air mass warms and dries, becoming the Chinook winds of the continental interior. *Polar Atlantic* origi-

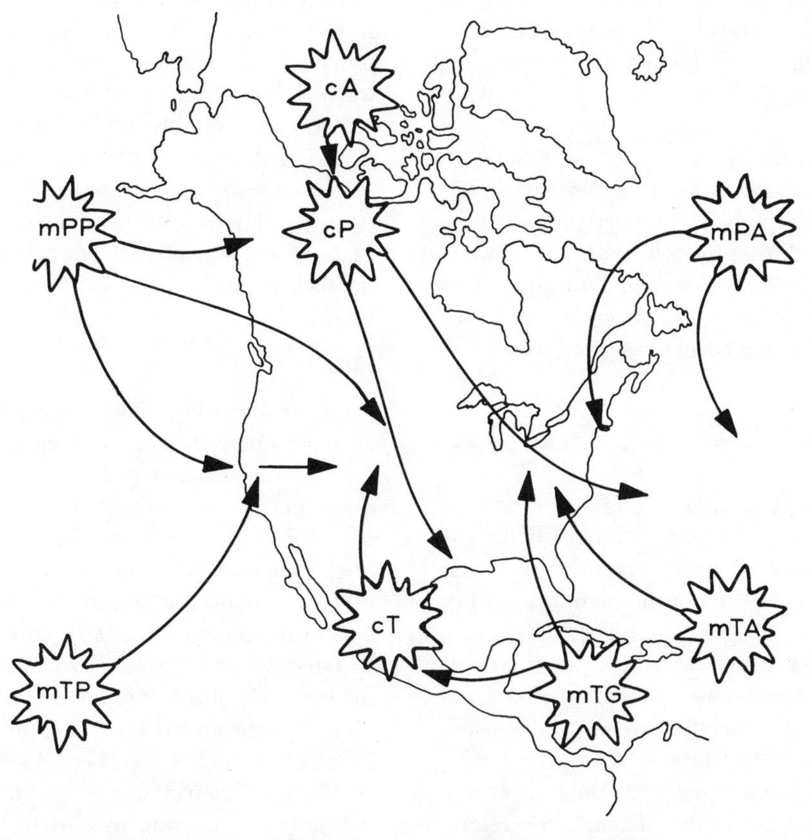

Figure 2.7 Air masses: *cA*, Continental Arctic; *cP* Continental Polar, a source of very cold winters; *mPP*, Maritime Polar Pacific, a source of cool moist winds; *mTP*, Maritime Tropical Pacific, a winter source of warm moist winds; *cT*, Continental Tropical, a source of dry hot winds; *mTG*, Maritime Tropical Gulf, a source of warm moist winds; *mTA*, Maritime Tropical Atlantic, a source of warm moist winds; *mPA*, Maritime Polar Atlantic, a source of cool moist winds.

nates from colder regions of the North Atlantic Ocean. In spring to summer it brings cold to cool conditions to the area east of the Appalachians, conditions often counteracted by the Tropical Atlantic Air Mass. In winter, Polar Atlantic brings moist cold air, leading to severe, snowy weather.

Tropical Continental consists of hot, dry air that originates from interior Mexico. It produces the deserts of southwestern North America.

Tropical Maritime is composed of three air masses. *Tropical Gulf* and *Tropical Atlantic* are much the same. Both originate in the Gulf–Caribbean–Sargasso Sea region and are warm, moist, air masses. In the summer, they bring heat, precipitation, and thunderstorms to the Midwest and East. In winter, they still bring moisture. When active, they curb the effects of Polar Continental and Polar Atlantic air masses. *Tropical Pacific* originates in the southeast Pacific subtropics. In winter, it brings cool to warm, somewhat moist air to the Pacific Coast, especially California, and to the Great Basin. During the summer, its influence is south of the United States, and the Pacific Coast is most often influenced by the Polar Pacific.

Tropical Superior is mostly an upper-air mass. In summer, it generally causes hot and dry conditions in the southwestern deserts and western plains. On occasion, especially during the winter, it moves westward, across the desert and over the mountains. This brings the rare, very hot and dry, strong winds called Santannas to coastal California, especially the Los Angeles area.

FOEHN WINDS

Santanna and Chinook winds are of a general type called *foehns*. They occur when a "High" is on one side of a mountain and "Low" on the other side. As the "High" moves up its side of the mountain, water vapor condenses, releasing heat into the air mass. Moreover, when the wind travels down the other side of the mountain water vaporization and air compression further heat it. Therefore, a warm, dry wind, or foehn, descends into the "Low."

Santannas are especially severe because they are already quite dry and hot in the "High." Therefore, condensation and compression further intensify the conditions. In the case of a Santanna, the difference in pressures between the "Low" and the "High" must be great for this foehn to develop. This pressure differential causes a wind of extremely high velocity. For example, a Santanna is a high-velocity, searing wind and may carry small pebbles which break windows and damage plants.

AIR MASS TEMPERATURE

Air masses are called cold or warm in reference to the surface area over which they are flowing. Also, they are often related to "Highs" and "Lows." Cold air masses are frequently "Highs" and have clear skies except for scattered cumulus clouds. But if a cold air mass moves over water, the "High" acquires more moisture, the mass becomes warmer and is carried upward, and cumulonimbus clouds may form and produce showers. On the other hand, warm air masses are often "Lows." This implies possible rising and, therefore, precipitation. However, if they are not affected by the inrush of air from "Highs," warm "Lows" remain fairly stable and quite moist. In fact, stability is intensified when such masses approach colder masses, because the lower layer of the warm mass becomes cooler and heavier. Within such cooled areas, clouds are of the stratus type; stratus clouds in the form of fog may extend to the ground. Although this description represents usual conditions, a "High" need not start from cold air or a "Low" from warm. An example of a warm "High" is a foehn.

FRONTS

Fronts affect local conditions because a front is an air mass phenomenon. A front is formed when cold and warm air masses from widely separated places of origin make contact. At first, the two air masses do not mix freely; rather, they retain their identities. Such a boundary often occurs near 40° north latitude. Actually the boundary is a shifting, undulating, three-dimensional structure and is often associated with a jet stream. During the latter stages of the life cycle of a front, the air masses mix and lose their separate identities. This life cycle is characterized by very active weather processes, especially the creation of various kinds of local fronts.

Fronts are not rare aspects of weather. They occur frequently as a direct result of the movement of air masses. If one considers the poleward movement of air and the fact that the easterlies blow away from the prevailing westerlies, people below latitude

60° would be mighty short of air unless something happened. Fortunately, there is a way that polar air can get to us, a way that involves fronts.

In our hemisphere, polar air gets south by forming a Polar Front. This front forms when a "High" polar air mass meets a "Low" tropical air mass. Because of the pile-up of air in the opposing masses, the pressure in the "High" increases until the front cannot be maintained. Therefore, polar air breaks through. In this breakthrough cycle four kinds of local fronts—cold, warm, occluded, and stationary—are formed (Figure 2.8). A cold front is formed when cool, swift-moving air overtakes and upthrusts warm air. This usually results in violent winds and precipitation, often a cloudburst, but of short duration. A warm front forms from a slowly moving, warm air mass overtaking and overriding a cold air mass and often leads to many days of rainfall over a wide area. An occluded front is a combination of the first two fronts, and forms when a warm front is overtaken and pushed above by a cold front. An occluded front has the weather characteristics of both a cold and a warm front. The final type, the stationary front, is no more than one of the above fronts that remains within a locality. Under these stationary conditions, the weather is unchanged until the front either moves on or completes its cycle.

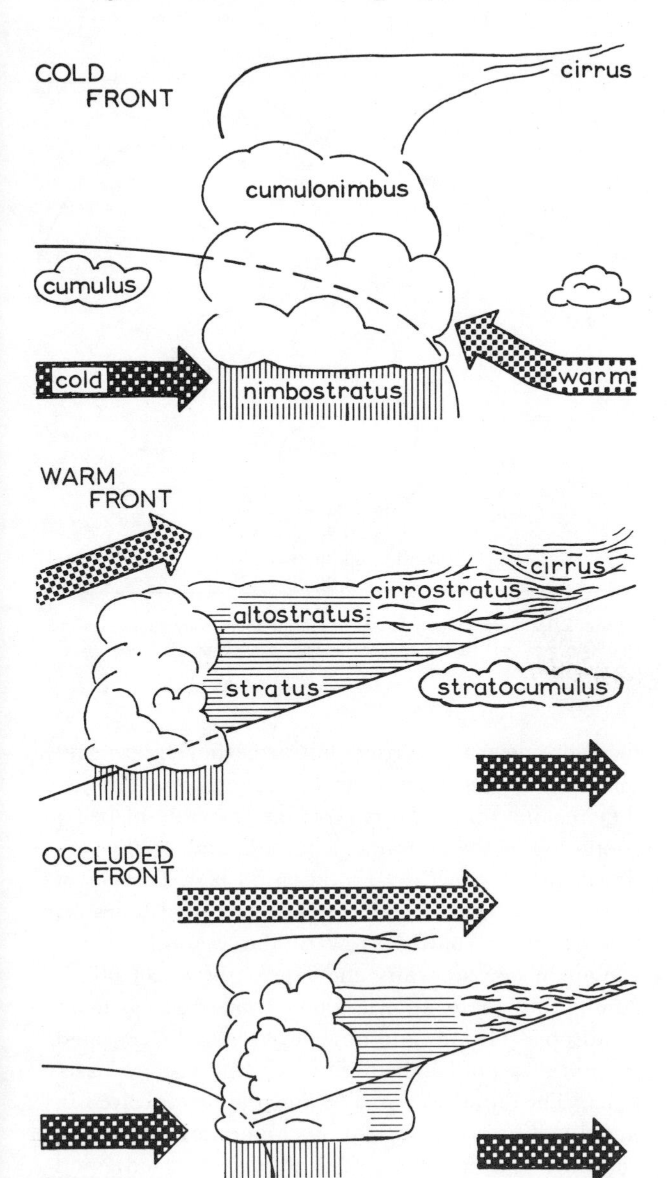

Figure 2.8 Kinds of fronts. The diagram shows the associated clouds, direction of associated cold and warm air masses, and site of precipitation (vertical lines).

An *extratropical cyclone* starts from the mixing of polar and tropical air. The life history of such a cyclone shows how cold and warm fronts combine to become an occluded front and summarizes the development and fate of a Polar Front. The life history is as follows:

First, a warm and a cold air mass come into contact. Second, a disturbance in the form of a "Low" develops in the boundary between the air masses. Third, a cyclone with its counterclockwise winds develops and sweeps into the "Low." This inward and circular movement of both polar and tropical air creates a warm front in part of the "Low" and a cold front in another part. With further development of the cyclone, the two fronts approach one another. Fourth, the cold front overtakes and thrusts the warm front upward, forming an occluded front. Finally, the cyclone uses up its energy and dissipates (Figure 2.9).

PRECIPITATION

Atmospheric moisture can be lost in many ways (Figure 2.10). *Rain* is the loss of excess moisture in the form of water droplets. It is the form of precipitation when the dew point is above freezing and droplets fall immediately to the ground. When the dew point is below freezing, excess water vapor particles are transformed into crystals in the form of *snow*.

Rain can be changed into sleet or glaze. *Sleet* is the term applied to raindrops that freeze on their way to the ground; *glaze*, or icing, to rain that freezes upon

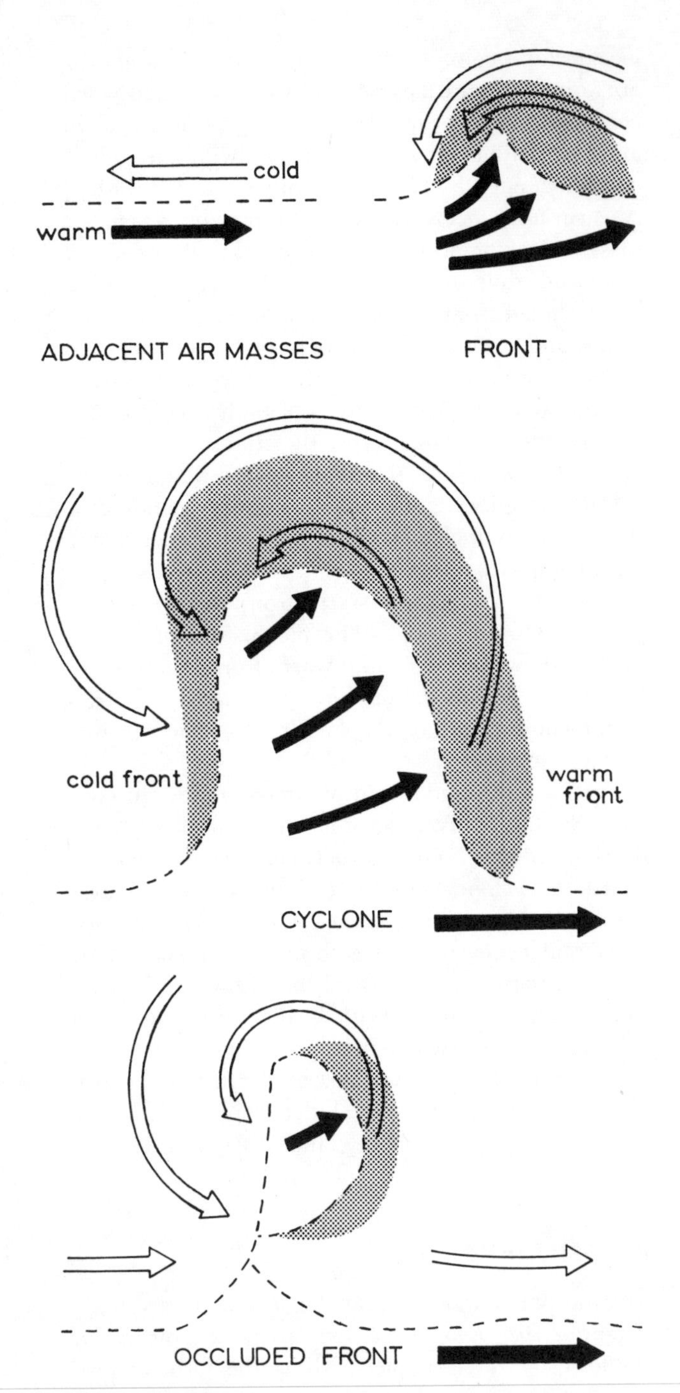

Figure 2.9 Life history of a polar front. Involved in such fronts, or mid-latitude cyclones, is the development and dissipation of distinct cold and warm fronts.

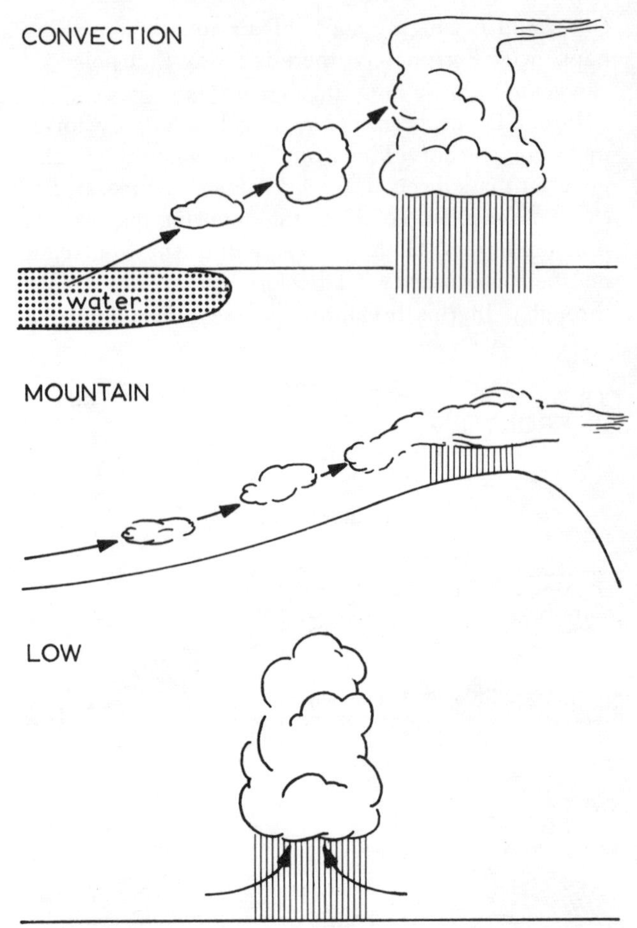

Figure 2.10 The primary causes of precipitation. Any cause involves air rising and cooling, the cooling leading to atmospheric water vapor condensing.

contacting the ground or some frozen object upon the ground.

Hail, although it resembles sleet, is formed quite differently. Hailstone formation involves water droplets being carried upward by rising air currents. As these droplets are carried upward, they freeze and may acquire an outer layer of snowflakes. Finally, they reach a mass that is no longer capable of being supported by the updrafts. They fall, and, on the way down, may "grow" by the addition of a coating of water vapor and/or raindrops. The hailstones so formed either continue toward the ground, or are caught in new updrafts and repeat the cycle of accumulating more snow, falling, and adding more raindrops. This up and down cycle may be repeated many times until hailstones reach the size of baseballs. The number of up and down cycles involved in individual hailstone formation can be determined by counting the number of clear (rain-formed) and snowy layers.

Two other forms of precipitation are *dew* and *frost*. Dew is water vapor that has condensed upon cool surface objects. It does not fall as does rain, but is the ground-level counterpart of rain. Frost is the ground-level counterpart of snow. It forms when atmospheric water vapor crystalizes directly upon the ground or when dew is frozen.

STORMS

The three major storms are *tropical cyclones*, *thunderstorms*, and *tornadoes*. The tropical cyclone influences a large geographic area, but the other two are local storms.

Tropical cyclones of North America, called hurricanes, are formed either near the southwest coast of Mexico, or east and slightly south of the West Indies. They are found in the Pacific and Atlantic areas, respectively.

A generalized hurricane life history is as follows: Hurricanes originate in the northeast trade winds when a local irregularity develops in the winds or when the southeast trades break through into the northeast trades. In either case, there is an interruption in the normal northeast flow of air, resulting in a "Low." Winds then enter the "Low" in a counterclockwise swirl, forming a cyclone; warm air rises within the "Low"; and the rising air condenses. The heat released by condensation causes adjacent air to become warmer and lighter, which, in turn, causes the cyclone to rotate faster and the air to rise higher in the "Low." This entire process leads to a progressive increase in momentum and winds up to 150 mph (occasionally, up to 200 mph) develop. Ultimately, if it is of average size, the hurricane is about 400 miles in diameter and causes widespread damage in its path. However, the central 20 miles, the "eye" of the hurricane, does not possess these damaging winds; rather, it is a zone of calm or little wind activity. During its formation, a hurricane is moving, usually at speeds of 10 to 15 mph; as it matures and travels northward, it often picks up speed, sometimes moving over the sea or land at speeds above 60 mph.

A tornado (whirlwind) is the most destructive weather phenomenon. It is fortunate that tornadoes are local storms of restricted width and length. The diameter of destruction is limited to about 1000 feet. Tornadoes follow a sinuous path, rarely more than 300 miles, before the life cycle is completed. Most of those in the United States form from late spring to early summer and affect the Mississippi and Missouri valleys. They originate from tremendous air instability that is associated with thunderstorms on hot, humid days. When conditions are right for tornado formation, suddenly from a blanket of deeply rounded cumulus clouds there appears a twisting funnel which grows to the ground. During this process, the terrifying roar of the tornado already has started. A waterspout is a tornado over water. The whirling funnel of air carries water instead of dust.

A full-grown tornado travels at speeds of 20 to 40 mph, but the traveling speed does not cause the damage. Most damage is the product of the whirling and rising winds and very low pressure. The wind speed, which may exceed 300 mph near the center, flattens things in its path. The low air pressure of the center causes closed dwellings to explode because the normal air pressure within the building is much greater than the pressure of the tornado.

Thunderstorms are somewhat rare along the Pacific Coast, but they occur throughout the United States. A thunderstorm develops after updrafts first form cumulus clouds; the cumulus then grow into cumulonimbus; and, finally, the cumulonimbus develop anvil-like tops, or thunderheads. Owing to activity within a cumulonimbus, there are concentrations of positive and negative charges within the cloud. Thus, there is an attraction of unlike electrical charges, either within the cloud, or between the cloud and objects on the ground. Contact of these charges produces violent electrical discharges, lightning. The flashes of lightning partly involve the burning of atmospheric oxygen which, in turn, leads to a partial air vacuum. The partial vacuum is almost immediately replaced by an inrush of air. It is the striking of inrushing air that causes thunder. In addition, this entire disturbance is associated with rain. Therefore, a thunderstorm consists of lightning, thunder, and frequently rain.

Squalls, *blizzards*, and *monsoons* are terms generally associated with storms. A squall is any sudden and violent burst of wind that is accompanied by rain or snow. A blizzard is a high, cold wind containing snow. Monsoons are steady trade winds along the western coast of the Pacific Ocean. The summer wet monsoons are winds from the southwest; the winter dry monsoons are from the northeast.

CLIMATE AND GEOGRAPHY

World climate is largely a reflection of conditions over the oceans. Moreover, ocean climate chiefly stems from the physical aspects of the oceans and characteristics of the winds of our planet. For example, in the winter ocean storms associated with the very low pressure of subpolar areas occur in the middle and high latitudes. In the summer, ocean midlatitudes are dominated by the very high pressure of subtropical areas and the weather is usually mild. Also, in the summer, tropical hurricanes may form and move into temperate seas. As a consequence of all these ocean conditions, the west coasts of continents have rainy winters and dry summers. However, topographic features reduce the amount of precipitation inland (Figure 2.11). In California during the winter the outer Coast Ranges cause coastal precipitation by forcing moisture-laden air from the Pacific Ocean to rise and cool. Then air travels downward into valleys between the outer and inner Coast Ranges, warms, and is less likely to lose much water vapor. Such interior, more arid valleys are said to be in a *rain shadow*. From these valleys air rises over the inner Coast Ranges, but usually not enough to cause marked precipitation. The air then drops into the severe rain shadow of the Great Valley, a true semidesert, or *steppe*. However, the marked rise and cooling of air over the Sierras once again causes significant precipitation. Finally, the 2-mile drop of air (a foehn wind) into the Great Basin again produces great aridity.

West Coast winter climate is further modified by ocean conditions. The prevailing westerlies bring the moist air that is released in association with the pattern of coastal and interior mountains and plains. However, the westerlies are relatively warmer and moister in the north than in the south. Hence, there is a progressive reduction in precipitation from the Canadian to the Mexican borders. This moisture differential is a consequence of the fact that the waters of the southern-moving California Current are colder than their surroundings in the south as compared with conditions in the north. Because the water is relatively colder, the southern air obtains less water vapor from the sea, so less moisture is available for precipitation upon the land.

CLIMATIC FACTORS AND DESERTS

The operation of climatic factors (pressure, latitude, ocean currents, topography, and continental distribution) is seen readily in the formation of deserts. Pressure is difficult to separate from the other factors. Perhaps the purest consequence of pressure alone is related to latitude. Recall that on a world basis, four "Highs" and three "Lows" exist. The "Highs" are the two polars and two subtropicals (the latter near latitude 30°, above the Tropic of Cancer and below the Tropic of Capricorn). The three "Lows" are the equatorial and two subpolars (just beyond latitude 60° in the vicinity of the Arctic and Antarctic circles). Also, recall that air rises in "Lows" and often leads to precipitation and that air descends in "Highs" and often leads to clear skies. Therefore, in the vicinity of the world "Highs" deserts are likely to be found.

Cold ocean currents or upwelling of deep, cold sea water may result in dry winds over adjacent land masses. Because ocean currents are related to air currents, cold waters generally intensify the effects of pressure and latitude.

Topography can influence climate through a variety of its features. Distance alone is sufficient to remove most moisture from winds. However, moun-

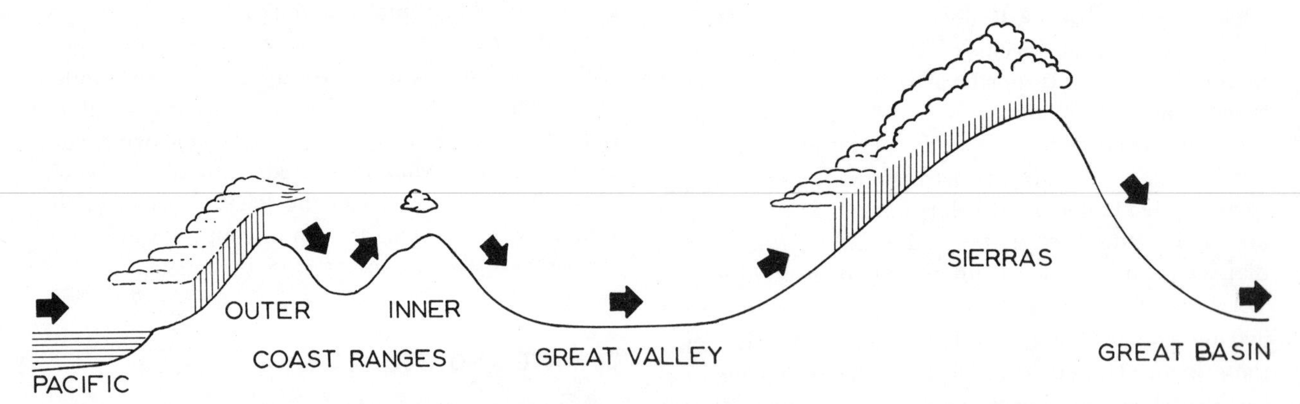

Figure 2.11 Climate and geography. The general consequences of oceanic air's rising and descending over the variable topography across central California.

tains can be much more influential. Especially when mountains are high, foehn winds can develop and cause severe aridity in the area of rain shadow.

The consequences of continental distribution are not easily seen. Land masses display an annual cycle (related to the changes in angles of solar rays) of modifying air masses. Because air masses are instrumental in climate, the continental modification of air masses can and does contribute to aridity.

CLIMATE PRODUCTION

Climates are mainly the result of solar heat reaching the earth in variable quantities that are distributed according to latitude and season. The latitudinal gradation of heat was already shown to be caused by poleward increase in the angle of solar rays striking the earth. The seasonal differences are mostly due to the annual cycle of local change in the angle of solar rays. In general, throughout the year the rays striking the equator are more direct than those striking the more poleward latitudes. Therefore, the equator receives the greatest amount of heat and there is progressive heat reduction toward the poles.

On the other hand, because air movement and ocean currents mix the heat from different areas, the poles are not as cold as they might be, nor is the equator as warm as it might be. Further curbing of possible temperature extremes comes from the variable composition of air. For example, a greater concentration of water and carbon dioxide in the atmosphere results in increased heat retention. Also, any increase in clouds or dust in the air will tend to shade the underlying land and, therefore, lessen the amount of heat received at the surface. (In this respect, overcast or volcanic dust can seriously restrict heat reaching a particular locality.) Therefore, there is a tendency for restriction of heat in potentially hotter places and transportation of heat to potentially colder areas. In spite of these local variations and tendencies to reduce pole–equator temperature extremes, about two and one-half times as much heat reaches the equator each year as reaches either pole. These extremes and the latitudinal zonation between the extremes largely account for climatic differences.

The effects of air and water currents are influenced by topography. This is best appreciated by comparison of the effects of ocean currents upon coastal and interior climates. Because of the properties of water, coastal areas are less subject to climatic extremes than are interior areas. This differential effect is further influenced by the distribution of elevations and depressions, that is, the relief of the land.

The local reception of heat is affected by many things. Forty-two per cent of solar heat is lost to space. About 43 per cent reaches the surface of the earth, and 15 per cent is absorbed by the atmosphere. However, none of the 58 per cent trapped by the earth really remains. If it did, the earth would constantly increase in temperature. Because temperature is relatively constant from year to year, the 58 per cent is lost to space just as fast as new solar heat is absorbed. During the warm season, there is (for a while at least) greater heat retention than loss; but with the coming of winter, loss is greater than retention. The general exception to this seasonal heat variation is found at the equator, where temperature is fairly constant. However, as one progresses toward the poles, seasonal differences in temperature increase.

The loss of the 58 per cent of solar heat that briefly remains at the surface of the earth and in the atmosphere does not necessarily involve a direct loss to space. The 43 per cent usually reaching the surface is never completely absorbed. In most cases, 15 per cent to 20 per cent of the solar heat is immediately lost to the air, but a greater or lesser percentage can be lost at once. Large heat loss results from such things as ice reflection; small loss results from the absorption of heat by water, black soil, and dry vegetation. However, absorption need not be related to retention. For example, the ocean does not lose its heat readily, but black soil does. Eventually, however, surface heat is lost to the atmosphere and atmospheric heat to outer space. Again, this loss need not be direct. Original air heat can be transported to the surface and surface heat to the air, to be cycled back again to the surface. Still, as stated before, on a worldwide basis, there is (except for seasonal variation) a balance between solar heat input to atmosphere and surface, and heat output to space by atmosphere and surface. Because of air and ocean currents, input in one area often causes heat to be moved to another site prior to its output.

CLIMATIC DISTRIBUTION

The fact that climate is graded geographically and tends to display regular changes with latitude and altitude cannot be denied. However, latitudinal and altitudinal changes are only a part of the total climatic picture. Each climate is not merely an arbitrary geographic subdivision of continuous trends in the various climatic factors; rather, a climatic type is somewhat uniform throughout its area of occurrence. For this reason, areas of transition between adjacent climatic types are often subject to relatively abrupt changes in temperature, precipitation, and other factors.

PAST CLIMATES

Perhaps the greatest climatic mystery is that involving climatic change through the ages. The factors causing such fluctuations through eons of time can hardly be guessed. Why are climates always migrating geographically? Only the most tentative hypotheses—probably no more than wild guesses—as to the processes involved can be made. Some of the causes might involve solar system cycles. For example, the sun might produce variable amounts of heat through time. To some extent such a variation could follow an irregular cycle of heat increase and decrease. Although each cycle might be of different duration, increase and decrease would probably be regular, with long periods of alternate warming and cooling. This would account for the regular aspects and different durations of past cycles of earth climate. A second possibility is a cyclic change in tilt of the earth's axis. This would definitely affect climate, because tilt is of major importance in influencing the angle of solar rays reaching different parts of the earth's surface. A third possibility is a change of earth's orbit from nearly circular to fairly elliptical. If earth had a circular orbit, seasonal differences in solar radiation that result from earth's varying distance from the sun would be eliminated. The maximum ellipse (ignoring axis tile) would cause a 30 per cent seasonal differential. However, at the present time the seasonal difference is 7 per cent, with the greatest heat being received during the December solstice—recall that our winter is the time when the sun is closest, but the solar rays are least direct. This present condition causes relatively mild winters and summers. In spite of these possibilities, actually no more than intelligent guesses, the poor state of knowledge about the cause of climatic changes is indicated by the lack of good explanation for the warmest recent times having been 6000 years ago.

SELECTED READINGS

Bates, D. R., ed. 1957. *The Earth and its Atmosphere.* Basic Books, New York.

Battan, Louis J., 1961. *The Nature of Violent Storms.* Doubleday & Co., Garden City, N. Y.

Byers, Horace R., 1959. *General Meteorology.* 3d ed. McGraw-Hill Book Co., New York.

Clausse, Roger, and Leopold Faey, trans. by J. Ferrante, 1961. *The Clouds.* Grove Press, New York.

Haynes, B. C., 1947. *Techniques of Observing the Weather.* John Wiley & Sons, New York.

Fisher, Robert M., 1960. *How to Know and Predict the Weather.* New American Library, New York.

Lehr, Paul E., R. Will Burnett, and Herbert S. Zim, 1957. *Weather.* Golden Press, New York.

Life Editorial Staff and Lincoln Barnett, 1955. *The World We Live In.* Time Inc., New York.

Loebsack, Theodore, 1959. *Our Atmosphere.* Pantheon, New York.

Orr, Clyde, Jr., 1959. *Between Earth and Son.* The Macmillan Co., New York.

Petterssen, Sverre, 1958. *Introductory Meteorology.* 2d ed. McGraw-Hill Book Co., New York.

Shapley, Harlow, ed., 1954. *Climatic Change: Evidence, Causes and Effects.* Harvard University Press, Cambridge, Mass.

Trewartha, Glenn T., 1954. *An Introduction to Weather and Climate.* 3d ed. McGraw-Hill Book Co., New York.

United States Weather Bureau. 1949. *Cloud Code Chart.* U. S. Government Printing Office, Washington, D. C.

———, 1949. *Manual of Cloud Forms and Codes for States of the Sky.* U. S. Government Printing Office, Washington, D. C.

———, 1952. *Weather Forecasting.* U. S. Government Printing Office, Washington, D. C.

Yearbook of Agriculture, 1941. *Climate and Man.* U. S. Government Printing Office, Washington, D. C.

3 OCEANOGRAPHY

The Oceans, Their Structures and Features

One of the rarest things in our solar system is water. As far as we know, only the planet Earth has free water, and on earth there is an abundance of this compound. In fact, if it were not for the irregularities of the continents and ocean floor, our globe would be covered by 12,000 feet of ocean. Yet, man generally ignores this fact. He emphasizes the 29 per cent of the surface that is land—an emphasis indicated by the name of our planet.

Man should not overlook the fact that the ocean, like each of the other physical aspects of our planet, is "essential to life as we know it." Before treating the properties of water, the landscape of the ocean floor, and hydrologic movements in the form of currents, tides, and waves, we should consider those qualities that make water essential to life on earth.

A planet provides, among other things, an environment that is an either-or condition for any form of life. Either the life can live within the provided environment, or it cannot. Earth provides, among other things, carbon, water, and air. The element carbon has the necessary chemical properties to allow life processes. The importance of air was already mentioned, and that of water soon will be mentioned. Moreover, it is logical that the chemical processes of life involve materials that are both available and suitable. In other words, if organisms occur, they must be intimately associated with their environment.

A logical question is, "Would all life require a carbon basis like that upon earth?" The answer probably is No! Because life is a chemical process and other chemical elements have a number of the essential properties of carbon, it is possible that other bases for life—even intelligent, generally humanoid life—could exist. However, they probably could not exist on any of the other planets in our solar system.

OCEAN WATERS

Life must have started in the ocean. This hypothesis is generally accepted for various reasons, some of which will be considered later. Here it is enough to mention that the body fluids of living creatures are similar in composition to ocean water. At least, the materials in body fluids are generally found within the sea.

PROPERTIES OF WATER

Water has properties that are essential to earth life. This liquid is necessary to mix and disperse chemicals in processes of growth and repair. In man and other mammals, and in birds, a fairly constant body temperature is possible, partly because water neither gains nor loses heat rapidly. Water also dissolves more substances than does any other liquid, a characteristic that makes it the nearest thing to a universal solvent. This solvent action allows much of the chemically complex activity of protoplasm, living substance. In addition, any material in solution will enter into chemical reactions faster than will those not in solution.

Certain properties of water cause the earth to be an environment where particular kinds of organisms can survive. First, water contracts as it cools to 4° C.; further cooling from 4° C. to freezing expands it 9 per cent. This expansion causes ice to be lighter than water per unit volume; hence, ice is able to float in the liquid phase of water. If ice were to sink, the oceans would be frozen solid, in which case earth would be a frozen planet, devoid of most of its present life.

Second, water has the capacity to absorb and store large amounts of heat. This causes seasonal climatic changes to be relatively insignificant as compared to what they would be otherwise, because large bodies of water moderate air temperature by first storing and later releasing heat.

The third property of water that contributes to the maintenance of life is its quality of neither gaining nor losing heat rapidly. Because of this and the second mentioned property, water reduces the temperature extremes of air, keeping the atmospheric temperature range within limits suitable for life.

Finally, the freezing and boiling points of water are much above those of most chemicals. This means that under normal earth conditions water is a liquid —the rarest state of matter—and is able to provide an essential medium for life processes. Therefore, earth's life is dependent upon the sea, the source of the earth's water.

TEMPERATURE

Most of the ocean has a uniformly cold temperature. Below one mile, the temperature is about 35° F. Above one mile, there is a gradual temperature rise to about 39° F. at the 600-foot level. From 600 feet upward, there usually is a rapid change to the surface. The surface temperature of ocean water ranges from about 28° F. in the polar regions to about 80° F. at the equator.

Below 600 feet the ocean's temperature tends to remain constant throughout the year. However, surface waters regularly display some seasonal variation. In about three-fourths of the surface the range between annual minimum and maximum is 8° F. Near latitudes 40° north and south, the range is about 12° F., and close to the equator it is only a couple of degrees. In certain localized, midlatitude situations, climatic conditions can produce seasonal variations of 25° to 35° F. On the other hand, daily surface temperatures vary insignificantly, generally no more than 2° to 4° F. Greater variations are extremely rare.

Ocean temperatures are much more stable than those upon the land (Figure 3.1). This stability is

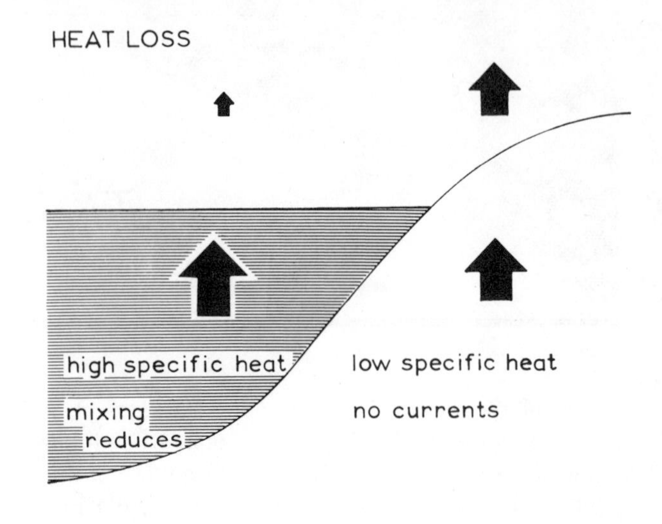

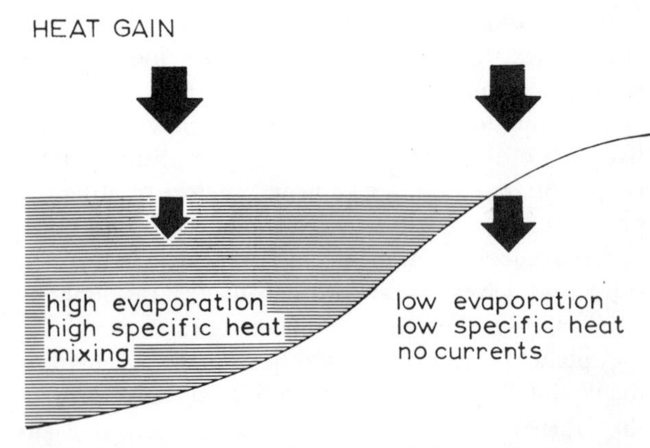

Figure 3.1 Differential heat losses and gains between land and water.

due to the physical property of water which causes neither significant gain nor loss of heat. In contrast, the properties of rocks and soils are such that great temperature fluctuations are possible, but the greatest possible extremes are not realized. Even within continents, the ocean is effective in reducing the potential ranges of temperature.

SALINITY

The salt content of the seas is fairly constant at about 34.4 parts in 1000 parts of water. The most important physical effect of this salt is to depress the freezing point about four degrees below that of fresh water. This 28° F. freezing point bears an interesting relationship to the deep-water temperature of 35°F. The difference of 7°F. (about 4°C.) from freezing means that deep water is at its greatest possible density. Any water that might become colder than 35°F. becomes lighter, hence rises and mixes with warmer water. Naturally, this serves to prevent deep water from freezing.

PRESSURE

The pressure in sea water increases approximately one atmosphere for every 33 feet of depth. Therefore, at 99 feet the four atmospheres pressure is due to the weight of water above that particular depth.

OCEAN-FLOOR TOPOGRAPHY

The bottom of the ocean is more rugged than the surface of the land. Under the waters are valleys, gorges, cliffs, plateaus, volcanoes, and mountain ranges. Moreover, all of these physical features occur on a gigantic scale, perhaps because there is less erosion within the sea than upon the land. Except for the mild sculpturing of deep ocean currents and the more abrasive undersea landslides, no major erosion factor is known to affect the ocean floor.

DEEP-SEA FLOOR

The differences between land and ocean-floor topography are emphasized when consideration is limited to that half of the earth comprising the deep-sea floor (Figure 3.2). Such a comparison emphasizes the error in calling the deep-sea area a "floor." Rather, it is ribbed, corrugated, and grooved by pronounced ridges and trenches. Superimposed upon this pattern are mountain ranges. A relief map of the ocean floor would show that it would be impossible to walk very far in a straight line—in fact, travel of any kind would be virtually impossible.

Covering the bottoms of ocean basins are sediments, the marine oozes, that are sometimes streaked with sand of unknown origin. The oozes are sometimes white, but some are yellow, green, pink, red, or brown. They are composed of remains of shells and skeletons of plants and animals, of volcanic rocks, and of some meteorite fragments.

Closer to the land at the base of the continental slopes are sediments of land origin. Erosion of the

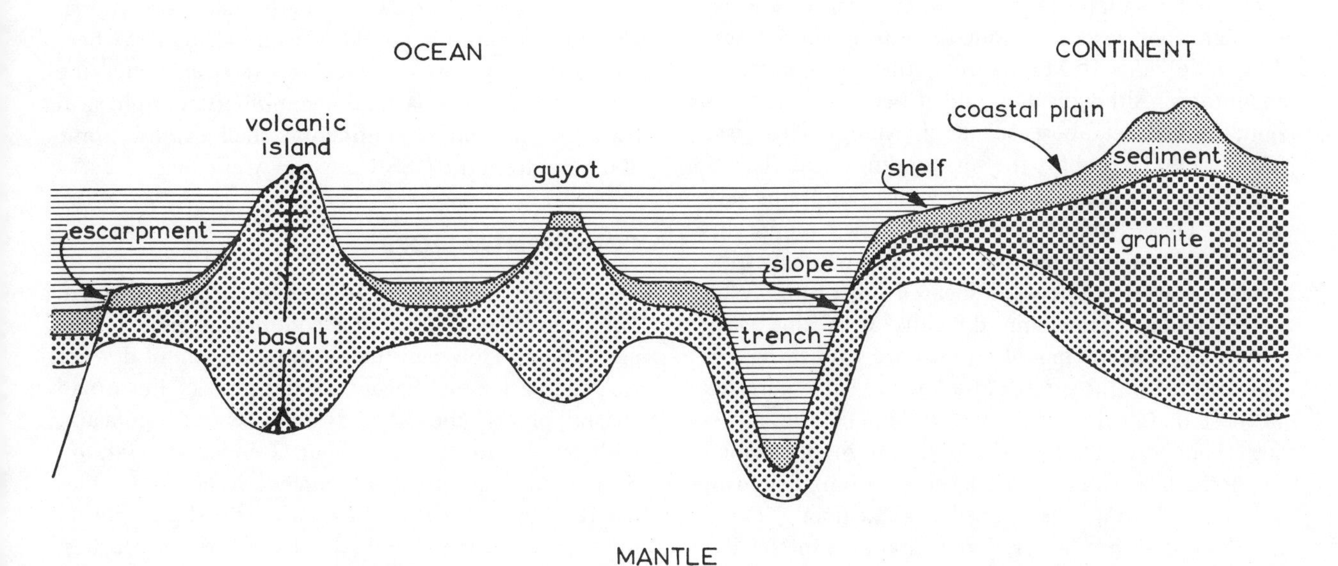

Figure 3.2 Major crustal features of continents, and especially ocean basins, as portrayed above the earth's mantle. Differential thickness in the crust and its component parts are suggested in relation to various land forms.

land causes this area to accumulate muds that may be white, red, green, blue, or black; these muds later may compress to sedimentary rock. The organic remains are also different. In contrast to pressure in deep areas, water pressure here is sufficiently low to permit more kinds of skeletons and shells to accumulate rather than to dissolve; hence, fossils are more likely to be preserved.

Ocean mountains possess many truly remarkable features. Nothing on land really compares with the great volcanic ranges like the Mid-Atlantic Ridge, a range that extends roughly from Iceland to Antarctica and is some 10,000 miles long and 500 miles wide. Most of the range is 3 miles high but also 1 mile below the surface of the sea. However, in some places the ridge is closer to the surface, and in certain areas its summits rise above the sea. Such islands as Ascension Island, the Rocks of St. Paul, and the Azores are peaks of the Mid-Atlantic Ridge. The highest peak in the range, Pico Island, is in the Azores. Pico is 7613 feet above sea level, but its base on the ocean floor is about 20,000 feet below the surface.

Other remarkable topographic features are the volcanic, oceanic islands. These islands are termed "oceanic" because they originate from vulcanism that is not directly involved in continent formation. Also, such islands are usually outgrowths of deep-sea ridges. This means that the highest peaks of the Mid-Atlantic Ridge are true oceanic islands. However, the Hawaiian Islands are an even more conspicuous group of peaks. Among these peaks of a single 1600-mile ridge is Mauna Kea, the world's tallest mountain. Although unheralded because it reaches only 13,823 feet above sea level, Mauna Kea rises about 31,000 feet above the surrounding ocean floor.

Perhaps strangest of all ocean mountains are *guyots*. These look like once cone-shaped mountains that have lost their pointed tops, a form suggesting volcanoes whose tops were sheared off, probably by wave action. The main difficulty with this wave premise is that the mountain tops are from a half to one mile below the surface and known water currents at those depths are insufficient to explain the shearing. Therefore, it is hypothesized that guyots formed at the surface and then sank, either from their own weight, or from a collapse of the ocean floor. There are more than five hundred guyots known in the Pacific Ocean and a few in the Atlantic Ocean.

The greatest mystery of the deep-sea floor is the "deeps," or trenches. These take the form of long incisions in the ocean bottom near continents and islands. As their names imply, the deepest areas known in the ocean are in such places. The greatest measured depth, 35,640 feet, is in the Mariana Trench, but bottoms of the Mariana, Philippine, and Japanese trenches all appear to be about 7 miles below the surface and 3 miles below the surrounding sea floor.

There is much speculation but little actual knowledge about how these trenches formed. Because they are near continents, there is a hypothesis that deeps are a reciprocal reaction to mountain formation on land next to the sea. A second hypothesis suggests that they form when sediments produce sufficient weight to cause a collapse in the ocean floor. Another hypothesis results from there being many earthquakes in trenches. Earthquakes are movements of the earth's crust along lines of weakness (faults) in the crust itself. Although many trenches are more curving than fault lines on land, there are theories relating deeps to fault lines.

CONTINENTAL SHELF

A continental shelf is an area of transition between a continent and an ocean floor. It also is a deposition basin for sediments from the land. Most of these transition zones are from 10 to 200 miles wide and extend from land to depths of 200 to 600 feet. They are narrowest where there are young, rugged mountains along the coast and broadest where coastal relief is low or where great rivers enter the ocean. Owing to a particular combination of physical features, the widest continental shelf extends some 800 miles from the USSR into the Arctic Sea.

CONTINENTAL SLOPE

Continental slopes are areas of remarkably uniform but steep descent from the continental shelf to the ocean floor. However, the rate and amount of descent vary in relation to adjacent coastal plains. For broad coastal plains, the slope is relatively insignificant, with a descent rate of about 2 miles in 100; off narrow coastal plains, the descent is about 4 miles per 100. In some cases, the continental slope appears to continue into the 7-mile depths of certain trenches. The land has no feature that rises or falls at so continuous a rate or for so great an amount.

Various other features characterize continental

slopes. They are believed to contain rocks intermediate between the lighter continental and heavier deep-sea floor types, and they contain sediments that are thinner (because of the steep slope) but otherwise similar to those of the continental shelfs. Their upper limit generally represents the zone of maximum sunlight penetration. Therefore, both the continental slopes and ocean deeps are often areas of perpetual darkness.

CURRENTS

In a previous consideration of layering of the earth, it was mentioned that ocean waters have five layers. The top layer, often consisting of about 100 feet of surface waters, is most directly influenced by localized wind action but is still dominated by the general pattern of world winds and earth rotation. The second layer is one in which a number of swift underwater currents are found. In general, these currents act to replace waters removed by surface currents. For example, in the Pacific Ocean there is the Cromwell Current, about 200 miles wide, between 100 and 1000 feet below the surface, and about 7000 miles long. It moves at a rate of approximately 2½ knots eastward along the equator, and terminates at the Galapagos Islands. Below this zone of swift underwater currents is a third zone of slow-moving waters that, in turn, caps at least two zones of deep-sea waters.

The swift second-layer currents generally move in a direction opposite to, but in a path related to, a surface current. For this reason, these underwater currents act to replace waters removed by surface flow. This phenomenon is best indicated by the northward-moving Gulf Stream at the surface and the associated, underwater, southward-flowing Gulf Stream Countercurrent. These two currents also serve as examples of the fact that the relationship of depths in the two surface layers can be much different from that involving the Cromwell Current. In the case of the Gulf Stream, the current is large, 3000 feet deep and 40 miles wide. Obviously, therefore, the underlying current cannot start at the 100-foot level. In fact, the Countercurrent does not even start immediately below the Gulf Stream at the 3000-foot level. Actually, the upper layer of the Countercurrent's dense, cold Arctic waters is about 6000 feet below the surface. Therefore, layering of ocean waters does occur, but it is not a precise depth zonation. Rather, there is great local variation in the depth, thickness, and width of currents that characterize individual layers.

The general movements of ocean currents are governed by factors somewhat related to those producing the winds over the world (Figure 3.3). In fact, winds are one of the forces contributing to major water movements. However, in addition to winds, the primary factors causing ocean currents are earth rotation, solar heat, and changing water density. Secondarily, currents are affected by the distribution of land masses, by climate, and by gravity.

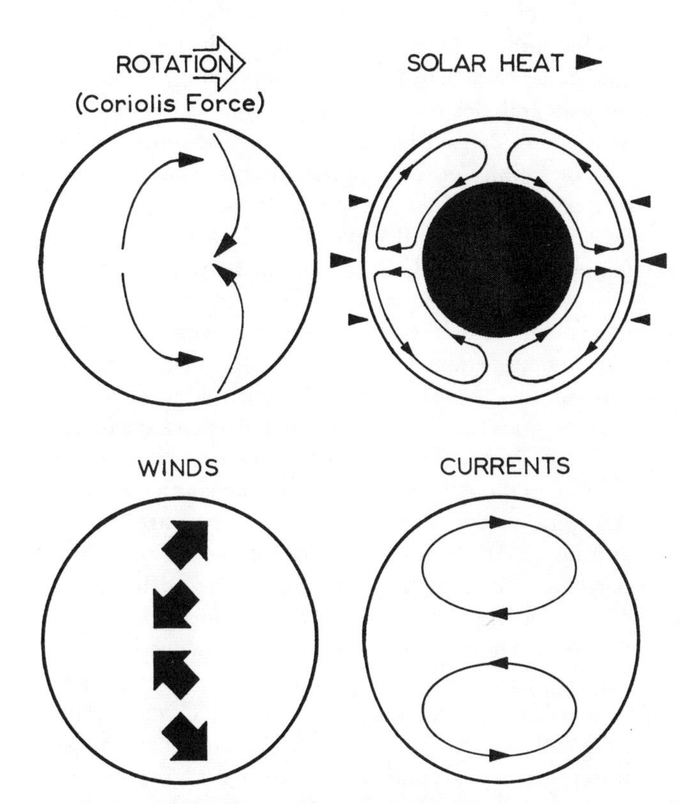

Figure 3.3 Three major factors forming the over-all pattern of ocean currents in the northern and southern hemispheres.

When the atmosphere was discussed, it was stated that the rotation of the earth partially controls the winds. The same rotation and winds work together to produce ocean currents of a pattern similar to that of the air currents. The trade winds push the equatorial currents westward and, with the earth's rotation, bend this current north in the Northern Hemisphere and south in the Southern Hemisphere. Continental barriers further serve this bending into a clockwise northern and counterclockwise southern rotation of waters, or current patterns that match those of the winds. Various modifications of the primary ocean-current pattern occur as secondary currents. The modifications are caused by any combination of the secondary current-producing factors.

The other primary current-producing factor, changing water density, is most important in creating vertical and deep-sea currents. These changes in density are caused by variations in the temperature and/or salinity of water; either decrease in temperature or increase in salinity causes water to become denser or heavier. Because there is a tendency for temperature and salinity variations between adjacent waters to be made homogeneous by water movements, currents are the means by which the differences are equalized. In general, such temperature–salinity variations also contribute to local currents as well as to the pattern of deep-sea currents.

The main pattern of the deep-sea currents is easiest to trace in the Atlantic Ocean. To the south, the cold Antarctic waters are deep because they are denser and heavier than the overlying waters. They move northward at a rate approaching 1 mile an hour. A pattern of like, but southward, movement occurs in the deep Arctic waters. However, the deepest and coldest Arctic waters are interrupted by an east–west submarine ridge near the Arctic Circle. This ridge allows the warmer, but cool, higher Arctic water layers to continue southward. Eventually, these southward-moving, cool Arctic waters meet northward-moving, warmer waters off Greenland and Laborador. The meeting of the two currents, because of their temperature and salinity differences results in a definite pattern of underwater currents. The northward-moving warmer waters are dense, mostly from a high salt content; the Arctic waters, from low temperature. When the two masses contact, they produce a mixture that is saltier than the Arctic and cooler than the warmer waters. This mixture is denser than either of its components, so it sinks to form the North Atlantic Deep Water, a current that moves southward. North of the equator, the North Atlantic meets the colder and denser Antarctic Deep Water. Finally, the Antarctic waters force their way beneath the North Atlantic.

DEEP-WATER UPWELLING

There is a general belief that ocean winds affect deep-water upwelling, and that this phenomenon, in turn, is responsible for surface temperatures and coastal fogs along the Pacific Coast of North America and elsewhere. The hypothesis is as follows: The action of wind parts the ocean surface waters, creating an area that must be filled by other waters. However, the filling is not from the surface. Rather, it is by the upwelling of deep, cold water; which mixes with warmer water at the surface (Figure 3.4).

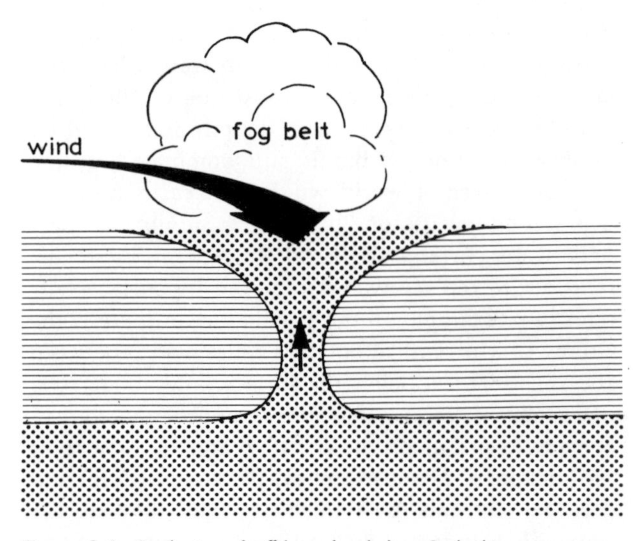

Figure 3.4 Production of offshore fog belts. Such things as ocean winds can part ocean surface waters and lead to upwelling of the deep cold waters which cool and condense surface winds.

This upwelling is thought to be of rather regular seasonal occurrence near the shore. During part of the year winds pass over areas of colder water. The cold water cools the air, causing water vapor condensation in the form of offshore or coastal fog. This cycle contributes to the Fog Belt climate of the Pacific Coast States and causes coastal temperature differences in locales fairly close to one another.

In the last few years waters of the eastern Pacific Ocean have gradually become warmer. This phenomenon could be explained on the basis of a reduction of ocean winds, hence, of deep-water upwelling. In other words, the quieting of winds could reduce the amount of cold water upwelling, and the resultant cooling of surface waters.

Another cause of deep-water upwelling is surface

water currents. Upwelling in this case occurs on the inside of arcing segments of a current. On the inside of such bends, there is created an area of low water pressure, a place that is "refilled" by upwelling. Such upwelling has very important effects upon surface water temperature and coastal fog—perhaps just as much as or even more than winds. However, the ocean currents are not generally believed to have been important in causing recent water temperature changes.

TIDES

The cyclical rise and fall of the sea once or twice a day varies in different parts of the world. Some areas, primarily oceanic islands, have a tide differential of only about a foot, whereas the Bay of Fundy in Nova Scotia has tides approaching 50 feet. The forces creating a high tide also cause the air above the tide to be extended many miles into space; even the land is affected, although insignificantly, by the agents producing the tides. Therefore, any consideration of tides has some bearing upon the air and land as well as upon the ocean.

Tides are produced by the gravitational attraction of the sun and the moon upon the earth. Since gravitational attraction is in direct proportion to mass, it may be surprising to learn that the moon exerts more influence than the sun. This is so because gravitational attraction is affected by the distance between objects as well as by their masses. For this reason, the closer, although much smaller and lighter, moon exerts more pull upon ocean waters than does the sun. However, the position of sun and moon are important in the character of the tides. When the sun, moon, and earth are in a direct line, waters of the earth on the line have the highest high tides possible and waters most remote from the line experience the lowest low tides possible (Figure 3.5). (*Note*: It makes no difference whether the straight-line order is sun, moon, earth or sun, earth, moon.) This condition of highest rising of high tides and lowest receding of low tides is called a *spring tide*. The opposite situation, called a *neap tide*, with the lowest high tides and highest low tides, is produced when a line from sun to earth and another from earth to moon form a right angle (Figure 3.5). Because this relationship causes the gravitational attraction of sun and moon to pull

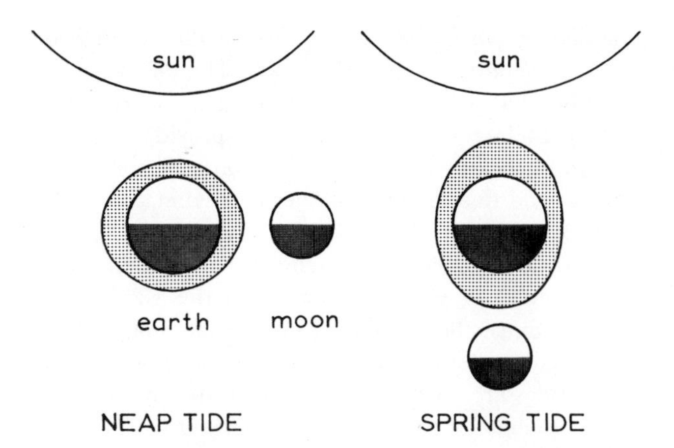

Figure 3.5 Relationships of sun, earth, and moon in producing maximum (spring) and minimum (neap) tides. Note the greater effect of the moon as indicated for neap tides.

against one another, with the moon "winning," the result is the least pronounced high and low tides. During neap tides, the highest waters are on the line passing through the center of the moon and the center of the earth, and the lowest waters on the line perpendicular to the earth-moon line and passing from the center of the earth to the center of the sun.

It is easy to understand the high tide on the side of the earth nearest the moon, because the water is facing the moon. However, to understand the high tide on the *opposite* side of the earth, one must examine differential attraction of gravity upon land and water. In the case of the land, the rocks act as if they were all at the earth's center. In other words, the moon's gravitational effect is upon the center of the globe. Therefore, the attraction of the moon upon waters on the earth's opposite side is less than upon the land; the waters are, in effect, 4000 miles farther from the moon (and, of course, waters facing the moon are 4000 miles closer than land, for the same reason). Because there is less pull upon opposite waters than upon the earth's center, a high tide is the consequence of less attraction. One might think of this as being the result of the earth's center being pulled more than is the opposite water. This opposite-side high tide is almost as high as that on the side nearest the moon.

Although the pull of gravity explains a great deal, tides are influenced by more than solar and lunar attraction. There is still the problem of why different parts of the world have variations in tide height. To understand these variations, one must first consider oscillatory basins, which are areas of the ocean floor extending outward from the land. The effects of individual basins can be likened to those on water in any container. Contained water provided with a constant rocking force will move from side to side or end to end in a definite manner that is related to the length, width, depth, and general shape of the container. The amount of movement is dependent upon the amount of energy applied and the size of the basin. Since the amount of energy, or tidal pull, is essentially constant upon different parts of our planet, local tides are most dependent upon the character of their oscillatory basins. The important feature of a given basin is how long it takes water to move outward and inward (oscillate). If the natural features of the basin are such that normal outward movement of water coincides with the period of low tide development and inward movement with high tide development, the tides will range from very low to very high. Therefore, the closer the association between tidal and oscillatory basin cycles, the greater the vertical displacement of waters; the more remote the association, the less the vertical displacement. For this reason, one can appreciate the fact that the Bay of Fundy shows a close correlation between tide and oscillatory basin cycles, and many oceanic islands show direct antagonism between these two factors.

Oscillatory basins also explain why the number of daily tidal cycles varies in different parts of the world. Some places never have more than one cycle, others generally have two, and still others may have one or two. This can be understood in terms of oscillatory basins. Basins having cycles closely related to the tidal cycle will have two tidal cycles per day. However, the more remote the oscillatory basin cycle from that normally producing a tidal cycle, the greater is the tendency for one potential tidal cycle to be cancelled out by the oscillatory basin cycle.

WAVES

Ocean waters respond readily to air movements, but it is the wave form and not the water that moves (Figure 3.6). Only a 2 mph wind is needed to produce a wave, and about one-fourth that speed to produce ripples on water. However, three factors are required to produce waves of much size: wind velocity, wind duration, and length of fetch (the distance water travels without being obstructed by land, shoals, reefs, or other obstacles). Working together, the factors produce an average maximum wave 40 feet high. To form this wave takes the equivalent of a 60 mph gale lasting two days over an uninterrupted 900 miles of ocean. When this is considered, it is not surprising that any wave over 80 feet high is considered abnormal, and the very tallest waves are about 125 feet high.

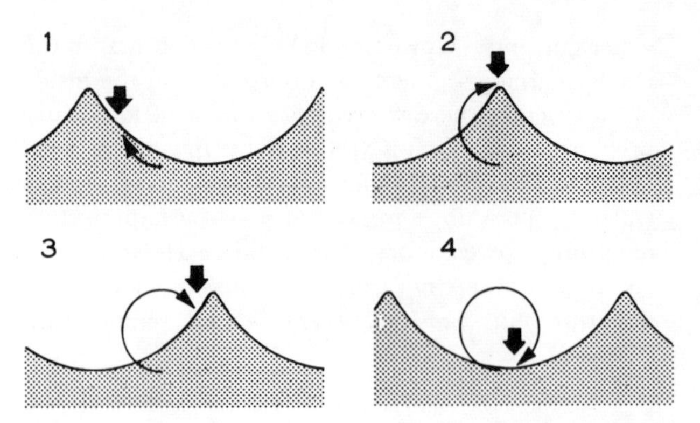

Figure 3.6 Movement of a drop of water (at arrow point) illustrates why wave form moves over the ocean but water does not move.

If one wishes to be precise, three names should be applied to waves. When a wave first forms in open water and remains in wind-blown water, it is called a *sea.* When a sea continues into relatively wind-free and otherwise calm waters, it is called a *swell.* Finally, when any wave reaches the land and breaks, it is called *surf.*

Surf visually emphasizes the tremendous energy that can be stored within waves. When large waves break, they may completely destroy man-made objects. Such things as jetties and sea walls, although constructed to withstand the full ravages of surf, are never permanent. In a few years, most are damaged or destroyed. Destruction of this kind is possible because the force of a surf is known to reach 3 tons per square foot, a force that will easily move 40-ton blocks of cement.

TIDAL WAVES

Although tidal waves are waves in every sense, they are not formed by wind and gravity, the factors producing other waves or tides. These sometimes gigantic waves are caused by submarine volcanic and earthquake activity. However, they are large only as they approach the shore. At sea, they are low and extremely fast moving, averaging about 450 miles per hour, and not likely to be noticed at all. As they approach land the friction of the shallow sea bottom causes the waves to pile up on a titanic scale, with marked depressions of the waters to their front and back. The two depressions account for the peculiar recession of shore waters during the cycle when a tidal wave strikes the land. The first indication of this cycle is the marked withdrawal of shore waters, because the forward depression causes recession, generally so great that the ocean floor is uncovered way beyond the normal lowest tide level. Next, the receding waters appear to hesitate. Then, there is a landward surge and the tidal wave carries water for some distance beyond the normal highest high tide level. In some cases, elevations of more than 50 feet may be flooded. Naturally, this is the phase that causes so much death and destruction. The third phase of the cycle is another marked recession of waters and is associated with the depression behind the wave. However, the retreat is never as great as was the first withdrawal. The final phase consists of many, ever-decreasing oscillations and eventual return to normal conditions.

Frequently, many tidal waves follow one another. In any single series, individual waves generally are spaced more than 15 minutes apart. In such cases the first tidal wave typically is neither the largest nor the most destructive.

Tidal wave destruction is not due to the force of the wave alone. Of considerable importance is the nature of the shoreline. If the shoreline is flat and straight, the most destructive waves rise about 60 feet; but if the shoreline is a V-shaped inlet, the waves may rise over 100 feet.

WAVES AND SHORE

Waves near the shore produce characteristic features at the point of junction between sea and land. The general features are a straight shoreline and an underwater profile that curves downward, first rather steeply from the shoreline, but progressively flattens out and finally merges into the gradual slope characteristic of the continental shelf. However, this mature stage of shoreline is not the only type of seascape, because crustal movements are constantly causing shores to rise and fall. This vertical mobility of most coastal areas provides landscapes that are being eroded by wave action.

EROSION MECHANISMS

Waves erode the shoreline mainly by forcing, quarrying, abrading, undermining, and dissolving. Wave impact is sufficient to break parts of the shore and quarrying can remove masses of rock to deeper water. Because both quarrying and impact are the result of wave force, the term "hydraulicking" is sometimes used for a single erosion mechanism. Abrading is the wearing effect of sand and other particles carried by the waves. The process of undermining causes areas of the shore to collapse into the ocean waves, thereby supplying more materials for hydraulicking.

SHORE CURRENTS

Water movements along the shore carry materials eroded by waves from the erosion site to a new area. Along the Pacific Coast of North America these movements cause a constant southward progression of sand and other sediments. These so-called longshore currents operate as follows:

After waves become surf, water recedes into the sea under the incoming waves. This undertow, the gravitational attraction upon surf, carries particles of solid materials a short distance out to sea. The important thing about undertow is that it is directly downslope. Because waves usually approach the shore from an angle, water brought in by waves has traveled down the shore when it completes an undertow movement. The downshore travel contributes to the offshore, or longshore, current (Figure 3.7).

It should be emphasized that waves do not follow a straight line from sea to shore. Near the shore the ocean bottom deflects them from a straight path and produces a final arcing one that more closely approximates a perpendicular to the shore. This reduces the speed of the longshore current. This reduced speed means that the arcing of an incoming wave and its undertow create a less rapid downshore movement of sediments. However, sand and other materials are carried by these currents.

SHORE DEPOSITS

Shore deposits come primarily from two sources. First, when waves destroy shore features in one area, the eroded materials are transported by the undertow into the offshore current. Then the erosion products

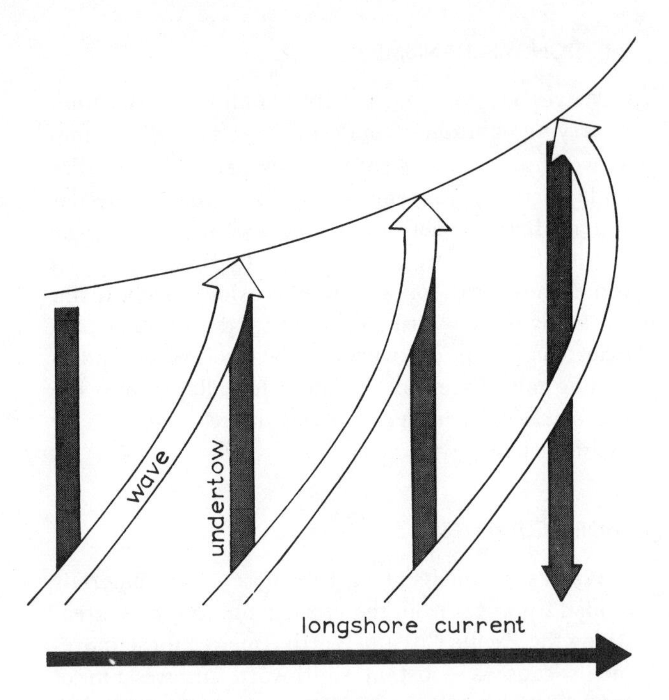

Figure 3.7 Shore currents. Oblique movements of waves toward the shore and downslope movements of undertow water contribute to a longshore current and movement of water-carried particles with the longshore current.

are partly deposited along portions of the coast that are in a cycle of shore deposition. Some of the deposits end as ocean sediments. The second source of deposits is storm waves. These waves have more energy than the normal ones striking a given area. Therefore, storm waves frequently remove finer materials already on the shore, but deposit coarser rocks and boulders.

Any shore deposit tends to be sorted according to size. The largest rocks are found farthest above the water and there is a gradation of rock size downward to ever smaller particles into the ocean. Any incoming phase of surf has more energy, hence more carrying capacity, than any phase of undertow. Therefore, receding waters progressively lose load-carrying capacity and deposit ever finer particles as they return into the sea. However, local characteristics of oceans and shores cause individual beaches to be essentially sandy, pebbly, or rocky.

The subject of waves and wave action has barely been outlined here. Later, the discussion in this chapter will be used as a basis for further consideration of the effects of waves upon the land.

RIP CURRENTS

Rip currents are formed off open coasts with sandy beaches. An open coast is one having no offshore reefs, islands, kelp, or other features to interrupt the full force of incoming waves. Therefore, on open coasts strong waves strike the shore and strong undertows move seaward through the incoming surf.

Rip currents are "the dangerous undertows" found along certain sandy beaches. However, they are not true undertows. They are related phenomena that also involve the outward movement of water. For analogy, one might consider a rip current as being a collection of individual undertows that are organized into feeder currents, a neck channel, and a head region (Figure 3.8). The rip current is formed and maintained by the feeder currents that converge from up and down the shore into a narrow neck channel and then spread into the head via eddy currents. In the head, currents move straight seaward, counterclockwise to the left, and clockwise to the right.

These fast currents (up to 2 miles per hour) produce marked effects upon the shore. The most obvious effects are due to the amount of force they produce. For example, the force develops the neck channel by easily removing the loose sand of the beach.

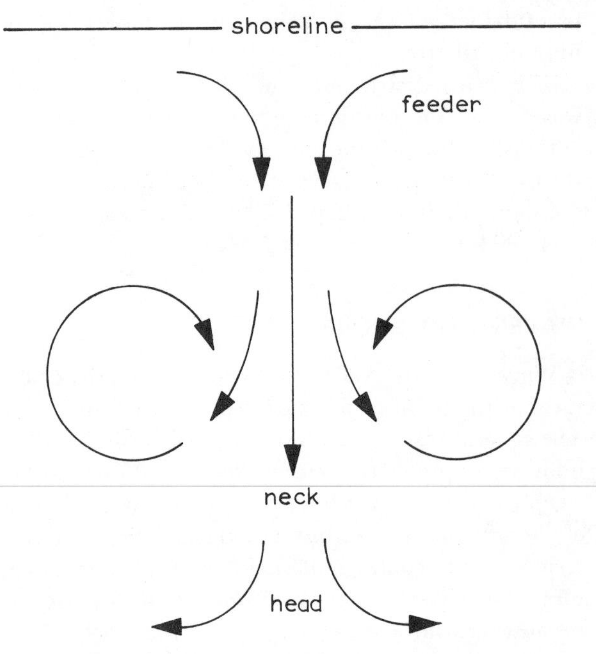

Figure 3.8 Rip current. Diagram of the structure of concentrated water retreating from a shoreline as a rip current.

Also, it causes sediments to be carried, the particles sometimes coloring the water and allowing one to see the feeder and neck channels dissipate into the head.

However, the most important effect of rip tides is the danger they create to swimmers. Probably no human can swim against the fully developed rip of a neck channel. On the other hand, even a fair swimmer need not drown if caught in a neck channel. To escape, the correct procedure is to ride the current until one is beyond its influence. From such a place, one can swim to the shore through an area not affected by a rip current.

SELECTED READINGS

Barnes, H., 1959. *Oceanography and the Sea.* The Macmillan Co., New York.

Bascom, Willard, 1961. *A Hole at the Bottom of the Sea.* Doubleday & Co., Garden City, N. Y.

Bates, Marston, 1960. *The Forest and the Sea.* Random House, New York.

Carrington, Richard A., 1960. *A Biography of the Sea.* Rinehart & Co., New York.

Carson, Rachel L., 1961. *The Sea Around Us.* rev. ed. Oxford University Press, New York.

Coker, R. E., 1947. *The Great and Wide Sea.* University of North Carolina Press, Chapel Hill, N. C.

Cowen, Robert C., 1960. *Frontiers of the Sea.* Doubleday & Co., Garden City, N. Y.

Defant, Albert, 1958. *Ebb and Flow: The Tides of Earth, Air and Water.* University of Michigan Press, Ann Arbor, Mich.

Douglas, John S., 1952. *The Story of the Oceans.* Dodd, Mead & Co., New York.

Life Editorial Staff and Lincoln Barnett, 1955. *The World We Live In.* Time Inc., New York.

Life Editorial Staff and Leonard Engel, 1961. *The Sea.* Time Inc., New York.

Petersson, Hans, 1954. *The Ocean Floor.* Yale University Press, New Haven, Conn.

Sears, Mary, ed., 1961. *Oceanography.* American Association for the Advancement of Science, Washington, D. C.

Shepard, Francis P., 1959. *The Earth Beneath the Sea.* Johns Hopkins Press, Baltimore, Md.

Sverdrup, H. V., Martin W. Johnson and Richard H. Fleming, 1942. *The Oceans: Their Physics, Chemistry and General Biology.* Prentice-Hall, Englewood Cliffs, N. J.

4 GEOMORPHOLOGY

Land Forms, Their Deformation and Formation

The surface of our planet is constantly affected by two antagonistic forces, one destructive and the other constructive. Erosion, produced mainly by weathering, underground water, streams, glaciers, waves, and the activities of organisms, tears down or reduces the landscape. Uplift and mountain building, primarily the products of volcanoes, folds, and faults, build up the land. Together, these antagonistic forces produce the features of the earth's crust and appear to follow a sequence of events known as a *geomorphic cycle* (Figure 4.1).

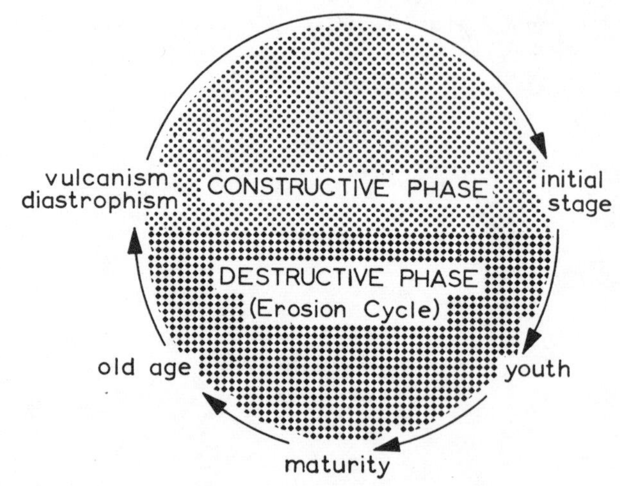

Figure 4.1 The geomorphic cycle, showing relationships of included cycles, phases, and stages.

EROSION

EROSION CYCLE

The erosion cycle, the destructive phase of a geomorphic cycle, involves the history of a land mass from the time of its uplift to its final flattening to a *peneplain* (Figure 4.1). The greatest amount of erosion normally is produced by streams; however, in certain situations other factors may be very effective. Wind is important in arid regions, and waves are most important along coasts. Erosion by underground water produces the prominent features of limestone landscapes, and coral deposits form the reefs that are so characteristic of tropical coastal seas. Weathering influences most landscapes, but usually leaves less dramatic evidence of its eroding action. For convenience, any erosion cycle is said to start from an initial, mostly constructional stage, and is further subdivided into youth, maturity, and old age.

Two main conditions affect the erosion cycle in a particular locality: amount of moisture, usually from precipitation, and amount of uplift or other constructive process. In a region in which land formation is rapid, the erosion cycle stages of youth, maturity, and old age are quite distinctive. Youth is characterized by clear definition of the origin of elevations and often by sharp, V-shaped valleys and by somewhat sharp mountain crests. In the stage of maturity, mountain slopes are often gentler and their crests are rounded or dissected. The valleys among the gently sloping mountains often are more rounded and U-shaped. In the final stage of erosion the landscape becomes a flattened peneplain with scattered, low, and much-rounded hills.

In an area of slow land formation, the same stages and general tendencies prevail; however, the characteristic landscapes are obscured. Youth is almost absent; it is very difficult to find either sharp ridges or V-shaped valleys. Maturity is like that in areas of rapid land formation, but the hills are much lower and almost immediately reach the relief just preceding old age. The landscape of old age is the same as that produced by rapid constructive processes.

The erosion cycle, modified by rapid or slow processes of uplift and mountain building, is basically the same in humid and arid climates (Figure 4.2). Modifications due to climatic differences are fairly obvious. In moist climates, the streams are joined and there is more erosion than deposition because sediments are generally transported elsewhere by the streams. Elevations are rapidly removed and the final stage, formation of a peneplain, is arrived at sooner. Only the early stage of the cycle

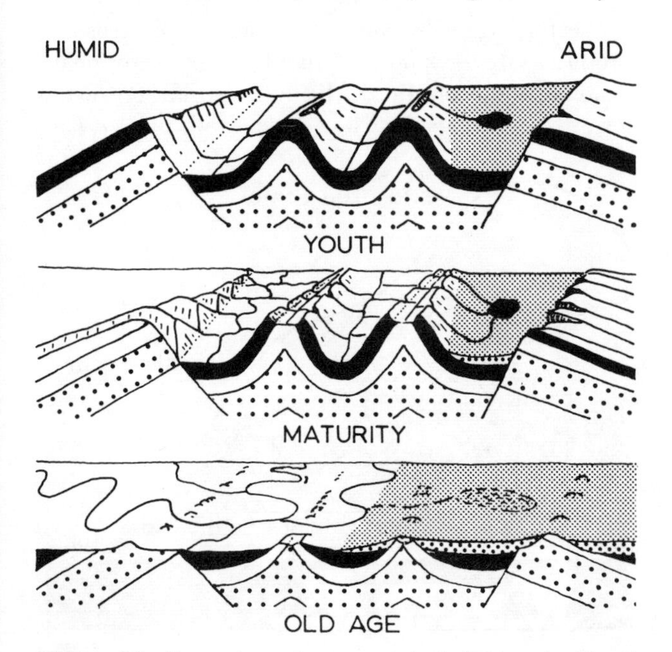

Figure 4.2 The erosion cycle; some contrasts between humid and arid regions.

contains the clear features of constructive processes. In maturity, the mountain types lose much of their bold outline; erosion produces sharp cuts in the constructional relief. Although this cycle terminates in peneplaination as a result of erosion by streams, the stages of landscape and streams do not tend to coincide. For example, although young streams may occur in young landscapes, the independence of stream and erosion cycles is more likely.

In arid climates, the modified landscape results from streams not being able to remove erosional debris. Also, the streams are independent of one another and are often temporary, each often flowing into a basin and forming a shallow, often seasonal lake. These independent streams are probably the main factor of erosion; however, in arid climates wind is of great importance. Wind scours the landscape and transports materials within the area and to other areas. Youth lasts relatively longer than in humid climates, and the outlines of constructive processes last into late youth. During this early stage, the land forms emphasize the erosion of higher elevations and deposition of the products at lower elevations within the area. This process continues into and through maturity. In maturity, the streams join into a united network and the landscape assumes the general appearance of maturity in a moist locality. Finally, after more erosion and deposition within the area, the landscape becomes a peneplain of old age.

A complete erosion cycle, including the final stage in the form of a peneplain, is no more than a very strong hypothesis because erosion might never proceed to completion before new constructive processes occur. The discussion of a complete erosion cycle is a device for understanding, rather than a description of, what may have happened in any one area, where destruction and construction of the land may work simultaneously.

A peneplain is mostly a surface of gently rolling plains, often a gentle slope from sea level to higher, interior elevations. However, these land forms are far from being monotonous terrains with no relief. It is true that their general landscape is rolling, consisting mostly of poorly defined divides between the erosion and flood plains of old streams, but there are often isolated elevations. These elevations are composed of exceptionally resistant rock, either bedrock not yet weathered or rocks more durable than most in the area.

Although the ultimate effect of erosion is creation of a peneplain, along the way to flattening a terrain, erosion is said to produce three types of destructional land forms; erosional, residual, and depositional. *Erosional forms* are empty spaces produced by the removal of materials, and include gullies, canyons, and caves. *Residual forms* are remnants of eroded topography, such as rounded peaks or ridges, sharp ridges, needlelike peaks, and arches. *Depositional forms* consist of materials that were transported from their original sites and that accumulated in a new location, e.g., deltas, beaches, and dunes. These depositional land forms are often considered constructional rather than destructional because they are elevations.

One should keep the general pattern of erosion and the erosion cycle in mind while considering the individual erosion factors. Throughout the discussions of individual agents of erosion it should be remembered that no factor is ever the only one operating in a given locality.

WEATHERING

The consequences of weathering are much the same as those of streams; however, weathering is not nearly as important a factor of degradation as is water.

EROSION MECHANISMS

The causes of weathering are the atmosphere, plants, and animals, working mechanically or chemically. The mechanical processes are those which use force to erode. Rocks are broken by being expanded and contracted by temperature; by being wedged by crystals forming, by plant roots growing, or by ice expanding from the liquid state of water; and by being undermined by burrowing animals. These mechanical processes are most effective in arid areas and on exposed mountains (i.e., places having climatic extremes.)

The chemical processes of weathering often cause the weakening of rocks by adding particular chemicals to the rocks. Such processes include the addition of oxygen, carbon dioxide, and water. Also there are processes in which liquids (mostly water) dissolve and transport particles and in which acids of plant or animal origin break up rocks into smaller particles.

MASS MOVEMENTS

The products of weathering are transported by gravity in mass movements. The movements are of four main types: slow flowage, rapid flowage, landslides, and subsidence. Slow flowage consists of imperceptible transportation of fine to large rock particles; rapid flowage, of barely visible travel of fine rock particles. Landslides are very rapid movements of fine to large rock particles, and subsidence is the slow collapse or settling of a small to large land mass.

SLOPE LIFE HISTORY

The various mass movements are associated in a sequence of changes, or life cycle, of slopes (see the many geomorphic cycle figures in this chapter). This cycle shows some, but not complete, relationship to the life history of the surrounding landscape. In youth, slopes are steep, and both erosion and mass movements are rapid. In maturity, slopes are reduced to a point where erosion and downhill movement of particles are minimized. As always, old age is a peneplain with no more than scattered remnants of past slopes and elevations.

LAND FORMS

Weathering, like any other agent of erosion, produces three kinds of land forms: erosional, residual, and depositional (Figure 4.3). The erosional forms are various kinds of holes and pits. The

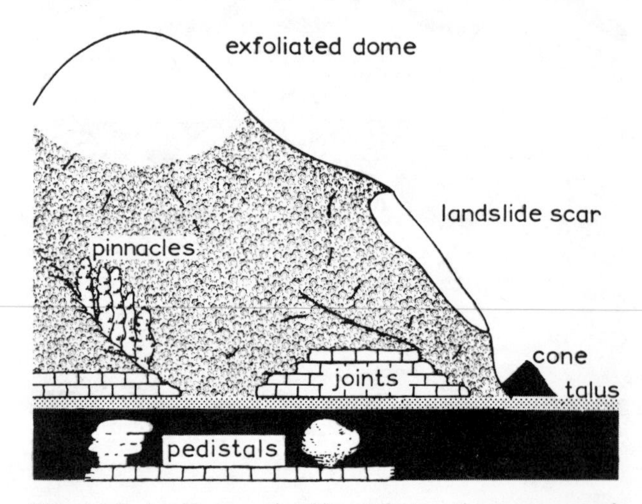

Figure 4.3 Land forms produced by weathering. The consequences of weathering often are clearest in arid climates.

residual forms are domes, mushroom or pedestal rocks, pinnacles, jointed rocks, and land scars. The weathered domes form by the "peeling off" of rock in flat but curved or rounded slabs, resulting in rounded summits on mountains. Such summits are called *exfoliated domes*. The umbrella-shaped mushroom or pedestal rocks grade into tall, slender, and pointed pinnacles. Jointed rocks have the general appearance of boxes or other flat-sided geometric figures. Landslide scars are the depressions remaining after landslides. Finally, the depositional forms are regular to irregular structures of variable composition, such as cones.

WATER

Although not as destructive locally as glaciation, water on a worldwide basis is the greatest factor of erosion. This is the consequence of a global average annual precipitation of 28.5 inches. However, the average is based on extremes of about 450 inches on the slopes of the Himalayas and less than 2 inches in a number of very arid places in the world. In spite of such variation, the world is molded by rainfall. Rainfall striking the surface of the earth has one of three possible fates in the hydrologic cycle. It may evaporate and return to the atmosphere, it may run off in streams that eventually reach the ocean, or it may seep into the ground and join the so-called underground water. The history of water in the atmosphere was already discussed. Its history as underground water and as streams is deeply involved with the eroding of landscapes.

UNDERGROUND WATER

The amount of underground water often varies according to the annual cycle of precipitation and drought and the structure of underlying rocks. During the wet season, the upper surface, or water table, is high or near the ground surface; during the dry season, especially after a long period of drought, the water table is low. Over long periods of time, however, there exists a point below which the water table does not drop. This is the level of the permanent water table. Structurally, the occurrence of this water is related to the porosity of subsurface rock layers, primarily the distribution of porous and impervious layers. For example, below the ground surface there are, first a porous layer and then an impervious layer. The impervious layer acts as a basin or container for the water which is in the porous layer. Actually, only the lower part of the porous layer contains the water and for this reason is called the zone of saturation. Above the zone of saturation but still in the porous layer there is air in the zone of aeration.

The distribution of surface water is related to that of underground water (Figure 4.4). Any surface area that is depressed below the level of the water table will contain water. Moreover, seasonal fluctuations in water-table level will be accompanied by seasonal fluctuations in associated surface waters. These con-

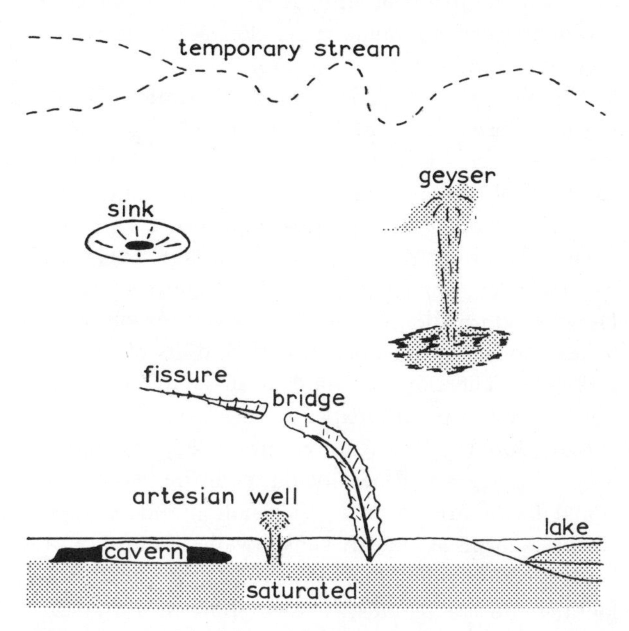

Figure 4.4 Some land forms related to underground water. Full development of features molded by such waters occurs in limestone areas.

ditions explain the seasonal variations and occurrence of many lakes. In addition, water-table changes may determine why temporary streams are dry part of the year and flow at other times. Also, the relationship between subsurface waters and a small opening at the impervious surface explains the pipe-like flow of water from artesian wells. Finally, if there is an association between underground water and the escape of hot gases from beneath the surface, the land form produced is a hot spring or geyser.

Erosion Mechanisms. Circulation of underground water leaves its mark upon a landscape. Its effects are most pronounced where the surrounding rocks are limestone, because limestone is especially soluble and is affected by the slight acidity ground water often obtains from humus, the organic matter in soil. When rainfall strikes limestone topography, water moves downward through the more porous portions of these rocks. This downward movement is associated with water dissolving the limestone and causing surface cracks, deeper fissures, and finally caves and caverns. Other geomorphic features form from water seeping through cave roofs and into caves. Because such water tends to collect on the roofs and dehydrate there, calcium carbonate accumulates into icicle-shaped rocks (stalactites) hanging from the ceiling. In addition, some calcium carbonate water may drip to the floor and dehydrate; the calcium carbonate then accumulates as elongate and conical rocks (stalagmites).

The presence of underground excavations leads to subsidence and a low but very rough topography on the surface. Due to erosion of underground features, local sinking leaves surface sink holes and natural bridges. In this topography there are few streams and most that do exist are large. There are few lakes or smaller bodies of permanent water. However, during brief periods of the wet season, rainfall can collect in small depressions and dissolve small sink holes. Therefore, the total effect is a much pitted, but generally flat, landscape.

Land Forms. The features produced by underground water are generally quite distinctive. Erosional forms are caverns, sink holes, and fissures. Residual forms are mostly sunken valleys and natural bridges. Depositional forms include cave rocks (stalactites and stalagmites), fossils (those produced by limestone replacing or casting organic remains), alkali flats, mineral deposits, cemented rocks, and geyser deposits.

STREAMS

Any movement of water over the surface of the land leads to wearing down of the land. Erosion by streams most closely approximates the activities of weathering.

Stream erosion is related to the amount of rainfall, soil porosity, and vegetation in the area; and the factors determining the erosion power are water volume and stream slope. Rainfall is directly associated with water volume; the greater the rainfall, naturally, the greater the water volume in an individual stream. Soil porosity and vegetation, however, reduce stream water volume because an increase in either soil porosity or vegetation causes less runoff into streams.

Erosion power is directly allied to water volume and steepness of stream slope. Increase in either volume or steepness of slope increases water velocity. Also, the greater the water velocity, the greater the erosion rate and sediment-carrying capacity of a stream. Actually, doubling of a stream's velocity may increase its erosion power four times and its rock-carrying capacity even more. This relationship helps explain the devastating effects of large flooding streams, because at such times water velocities increase ten to twenty times above normal..

Erosion Mechanisms. Actual removal of materials involves four processes: corrasion, impact, quarrying, and dissolution. Corrasion is similar to the work of a file and is the scraping and scratching action of particles suspended in the moving water. The ultimate product of corrasion is fine, water-worn materials. Impact is the striking (and breaking) of large rocks against one another. It, too, produces fine materials. Quarrying is downstream movement of materials by the lifting and carrying force of water. It transports the larger, at first less worn rocks downstream. Dissolution reduces rocks to the fine particles usually found suspended only in mature and old streams. All of the four processes work together in such a way that it is difficult to segregate the actions of any single factor.

Life History. Youth is the period of greatest erosion rate of streams. Young streams (Figure 4.5) are usually straight and have a steep, uneven slope which includes rapids, rock channels, pot holes, plunging pools, falls, and lakes, the uneven slope being the consequence of erosion acting upon rock

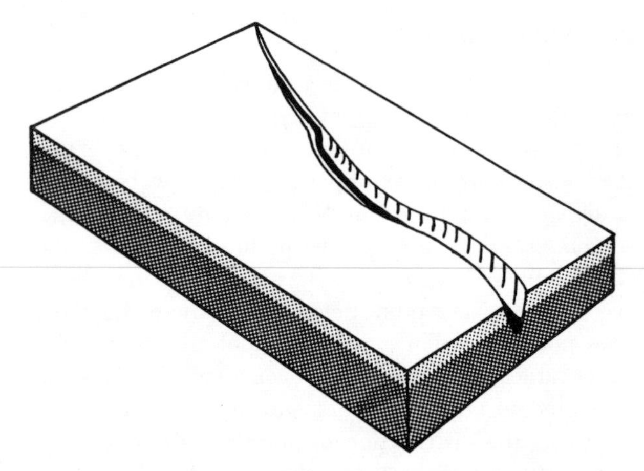

Figure 4.5 Young stream. Note the straight path, waterfall, and V-shaped valley. (After a Ward's Geomorphic model).

layers of unlike hardness. These streams have so much energy that they cut young, V-shaped valleys. The stream covers the entire bottom of these valleys. Valley walls are steep because streams are more effective in cutting a slope than weathering is in reducing the slope. Waters are generally clear because stream energy is so great and inefficient that proportionally few materials are carried per unit volume of water. In addition, young streams are most effective in stream capture, a phenomonon in which a captor stream at a lower elevation erodes into and "robs" water from a captive stream at a higher elevation (Figure 4.6).

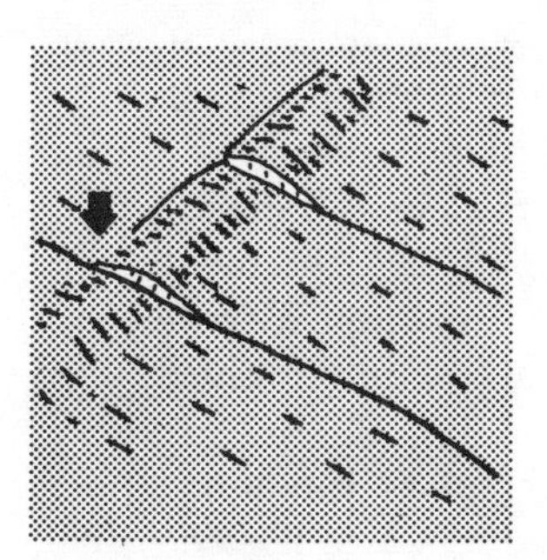
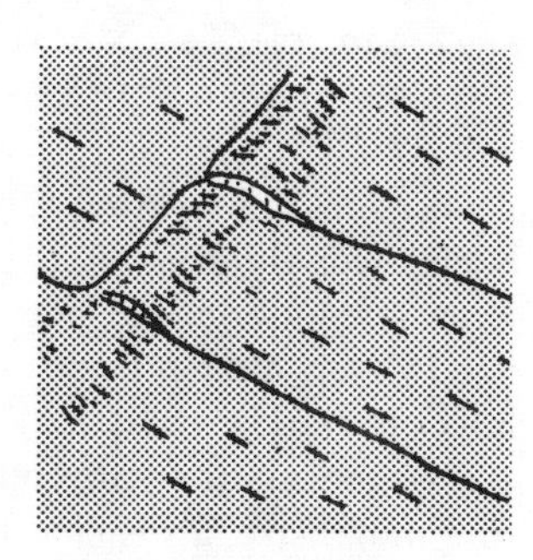

Figure 4.6 Stream capture of one young stream by another. The arrow indicates the site of capture that is completed in the illustration to the right. (After a Ward's Geomorphic model.)

The filelike action of a young stream cuts the stream bed throughout the stream's length, but cuts the bank only on curves. These bank and stream bed cutting actions are the agents for a moving of curves downstream and widening of the valley floor. However, individual curves feature both cutting and depositing of materials. Cutting in the upstream part of a single curve is on the inside bank of the arc and in the downstream portion on the outside bank. Depositing in the upstream segment is on the outside; downstream it is on the inside. Therefore, cutting is always on the straight downstream bank of any arc and depositing in the upstream bank.

Maturity is reached when the stream's slope is uniform and downward cutting of the stream bed no longer occurs. There is no stream bed cutting, because the waters carry a maximum particle load. While no deeper cutting is taking place, weathering reduces the slope of the valley walls. Then weathering plus increased lateral meandering (Figure 4.7) of the stream cause progressive development of a broad valley that is outlined by gentle slopes.

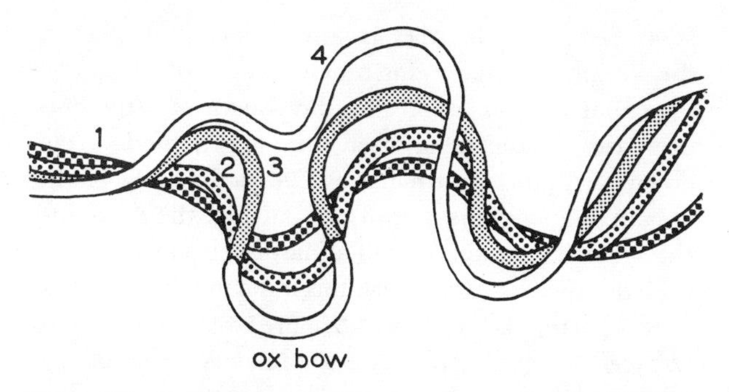

Figure 4.7 Development of stream meanders. Progressive stages (1 to 4) and retention of part of stage three as an ox-bow with the current stream (4) are shown.

Within this landscape, the meandering, mature stream occupies only a small part of the valley floor; however, during floods, the overflow deposits sediments upon and levels the adjacent land, creating a flood plain (Figure 4.8). Another characteristic of meandering mature streams is the presence of "ox-bows," curving lakes adjacent to the stream beds. These ox-bows are formed when a mature or old stream changes its path of flow. A path is changed by the normal process of cutting on the outer bank of a curve and depositing on the inner bank. The cuts and deposits cause curves to approach circles and, finally, circles to be isolated from the stream bed as ox-bows.

Further aging of a stream is dependent upon the headwaters, where the character of youth remains for some time. Eventually, the youthful headwaters erode the surrounding land and the land provides

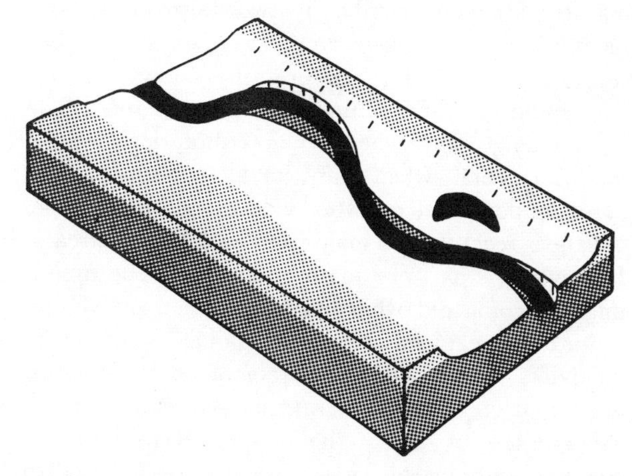

Figure 4.8 Mature stream. Note the flood plain (white), ox-bow, and stream cutting, but no natural levees as in an old stream. (After a Ward's Geomorphic model.)

fewer sediments for the stream to carry. However, the stream still maintains much of its particle-carrying capacity. Therefore, as the source of sediments decreases at the headwater, the stream bed is cut downward more and more by the main body of the stream. During this stream bed cutting, the even and slight slope characteristic of a mature stream is maintained; however, the lowering is indicated by the presence of steplike terraces (Figure 4.9). In these terraces, each "step" was a previous level of the mature stream that was stable for some time. The different steps occur because the stream is slowly but constantly changing its path.

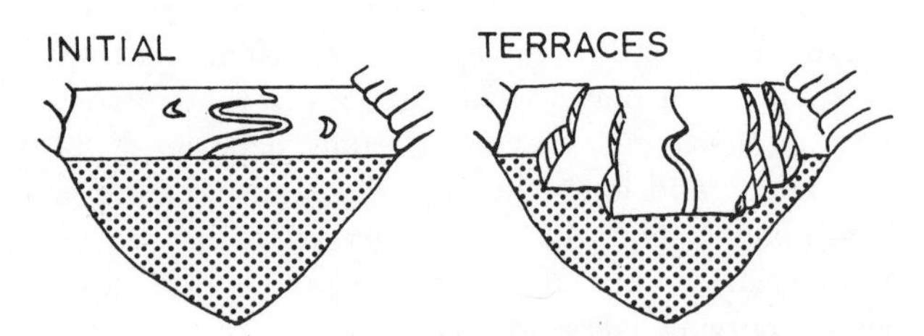

Figure 4.9 Development of stream terraces. A meandering mature stream cuts through various layers of alluvium or other materials.

The developing of meanders involves removing materials which have further effects downstream. At the stream's mouth, accumulating deposits plus the local increase of meanders since youth contribute to delta growth. As a stream ages, the delta increases in size and becomes interlaced with branched and interconnected meanders. By the stream's maturity, the delta is well formed.

To summarize, the most significant features of maturity are emphasized by its two stages of development. In the first stage, only the main stream has constant slope and is mature; the tributaries are young and have the features of young streams. The second stage is reached when tributaries become mature. Then, when many to all tributaries, and even temporary stream beds, have constant slope, old age is reached by a major part of the main stream. However, the part of a main stream near the mouth might become old while its headwaters are young.

An old stream has very little slope. Because its meanders become wider, its rate of flow decreases. With a decrease in flow rate its sediment-carrying capacity lessens, and it deposits materials upon its own bed and edges. This causes the stream bed to rise above the level of the surrounding flood plain. The sides of the stream are contained by stream bed deposits in the form of natural levees (Figure 4.10). Such a condition is often found near the mouths of large streams and in the Mississippi River where flood waters often break through natural (or artificial) levees to cause great damage.

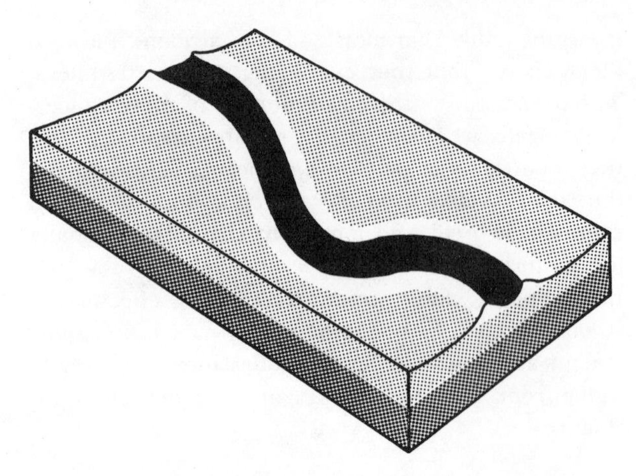

Figure 4.10 Old stream. Note the natural levees and lack of cutting as in a mature stream. (After a Ward's Geomorphic model.)

If a peneplain or any other plain containing mature to old streams is elevated, the area is said to be rejuvenated. Then the streams again start cutting the landscape and a new stream life cycle is started.

Stream Deposits and Deltas. The site and rate of deposition affect the kind of land forms produced. The primary sites for streams to accumulate fine particles, or alluvium, are on the flood plains, at the mouth, in channels, in depressions, and at the base of slopes of streams. These alluvia naturally accumulate in direct proportion to the deposition rate. The rate is greater as the stream cross-sectional area increases and both water volume and velocity decreases.

Deltas are usually deposited wherever the velocity of a river is checked by the mouth entering a large body of water such as a lake or the ocean. Due to decreased velocity of stream flow, alluvium accumulates at the river's mouth. This deposition is graded; first coarse materials and then finer materials are lost by the stream. In an ocean situation, grading produces beaches at the mouth of the stream and sand bars just off the shoreline. The bars further retard stream flow and eventually further deposition and stream development produce a delta of braided streams, oxbows, and lakes all upon the flat, muddy substrate of a salt marsh. These features are also approached in lakes, especially the larger ones, but there a fresh-water marsh forms.

Drainage Patterns. Various stream, or drainage, patterns are recognized (Figure 4.11). Dendritic drainage systems have tributaries going in all directions in a pattern resembling the branching of a tree. Rectangular drainage follows the rectangular surface pattern of rock jointing which is sometimes produced by weathering. Trellis drainage resembles rectangular, but the rectangular pattern of trellis stems from straight tributaries to main streams. For this reason only, trellis drainage displays many rectangles, each having one side upon a continuous line. Trellis drainage is so named because it resembles the pattern of vines on a trellis. More important, this drainage is characteristic of landscapes having strongly folded or dipped rock layers. Finally, radial streams, resembling the radii from the center of a circle, drain an elevation with a circular base, e.g., a dome mountain or a volcano.

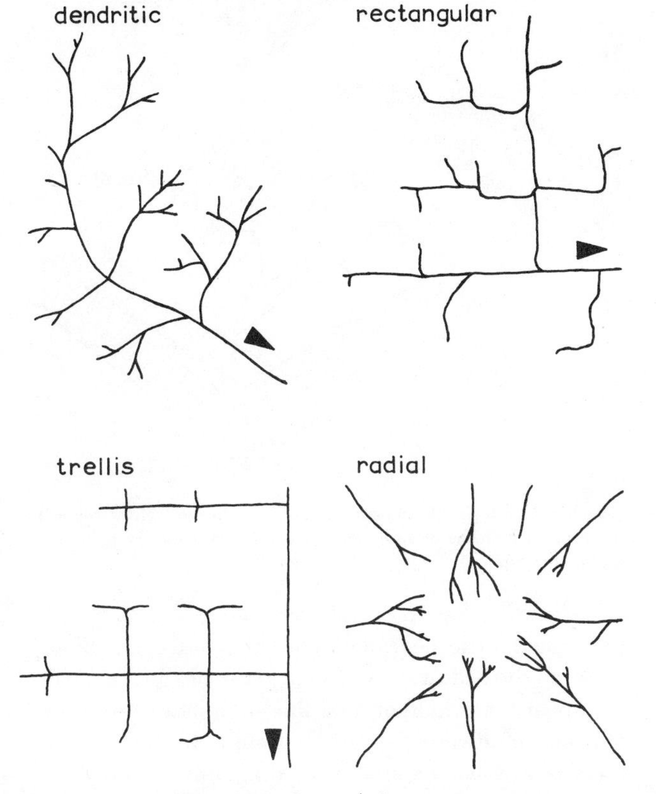

Figure 4.11 Stream drainage patterns.

Land Forms. Streams produce many land forms. Only the commoner ones are summarized here. Erosional forms include gullies, valleys, gorges, canyons, terraces, pot holes, plunging pools, and waterfalls. Residual forms include mountain divides, peaks, summits, natural bridges, and rocky valley walls. Depositional forms include alluvial fans, flood plains, and deltas.

LAKES

Lakes are usually closely associated with streams and serve to regulate stream flow. This regulation is important in preventing both flooding and drying of streams. For example, when potential flood waters enter a lake, the broad lake basin allows only a slight rise above normal lake level and, therefore, only a slight rise in streams exiting from the lake. On the other hand, during drought or periods when little or no water enters the lake, the broadness of the lake again reduces the possible effect. Lake level is hardly reduced and exit streams show little reduction in normal water volume.

The relationship between a lake and its streams does not remove the possibility that a lake may show marked fluctuations in height. However, whenever there are great changes in lake water level, they must come as a result of truly great changes in water relationships.

Life Cycle. Lakes are destroyed by processes that drain and fill them. Drainage is accomplished by evaporation and/or downcutting of exit streams. Deposition comes from such things as delta building, plant and animal remains, glacial deposits, and shoreline cycles.

Much of the shoreline cycle of lakes is like that along the ocean. Erosion undercuts and removes shore cliffs, leaving a rock terrace. The eroded material is further degraded to fine particles and the particles are deposited as a wave-built terrace which is a continuation of the rock terrace. Also, currents within the lake may cause sediments to accumulate either in offshore bars or in connections of land with islands.

Gradually, the process of deposition fills the lake. As shallows form, certain areas assume the depth and vegetation characteristic of swamps. Finally, further deposition produces a transition from swamp to land and, ultimately, the end of the lake's life cycle.

PLAINS AND ELEVATIONS

Discussion now turns from general destructive activities of water to constructional or destructional land forms whose features are often sculptured by stream erosion. Whether a particular form is destructional or constructional is dependent upon how it originally came into being, not upon its later erosion.

COASTAL PLAINS

A coastal plain is any portion of the land that was once ocean floor. Included are recently emerged shorelines and areas further removed from shores. Here, only the more remote parts of coastal plains will be discussed; shorelines of emergence are treated elsewhere.

The profiles of coastal plains range from land gently sloping into the sea to rather rough shoreline features, primarily vertical cliffs and horizontal benches but also old stacks, clefts, and caves. In further discussion, rough features will be ignored. Such land forms erode so rapidly that they barely modify the generalized life history of a coastal plain.

Life History. Coastal plains actually start in the sea. There, sediments in the form of muds, sands, and gravels accumulate; they then compress as a result of overlying sediment pressure; finally, they consolidate into various sedimentary rocks. When such areas emerge and form a coastal plain, the less resistant rocks immediately start to erode. Also, preexisting streams extend their path to reach the sea, and new streams may form. In this initial stage, such things as old islands, stacks, and shorelines are least modified.

In the youth of coastal plains, streams running into the ocean gradually wear away the layers of sedimentary rocks, the less resistant rocks eroding faster than the harder ones. In areas of less resistant rocks, tributary streams form perpendicular to the streams running into the ocean (Figure 4.12).

Maturity occurs when the tributary streams develop lowlands in softer rocks. Lowlands near the site of the shoreline before elevation are called inner lowlands; those now closest to the sea (but not including the shore) are called outer lowlands. Ridges or elevations between the two lowlands are formed by the tributary streams and are called *cuestas*. Each cuesta has a steep slope facing inland and toward the old shoreline and a gradual backfacing slope toward the present shoreline. The ridge of the cuesta is parallel to the present shoreline (Figure 4.12).

In the early maturity of coastal plains, adjacent headwaters of two opposite-running tributary streams

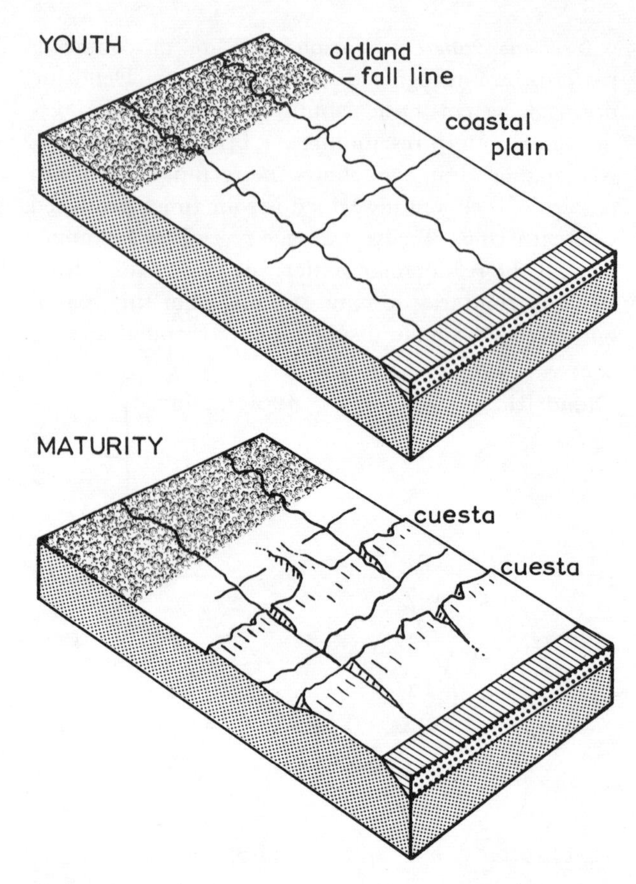

Figure 4.12 Cuesta formation. Erosion of a coastal plain elevated as part of a shoreline of emergence. Note the development of streams and stream capture.

may cause little degradation of the old ocean floor between the headwaters. Later, these headwaters will cut toward one another on a line parallel to the shore and just landward from the cuesta. If this occurs, there is a finger of land extending inland from the infacing slope of the cuesta toward the old shoreline. This extension, a cuesta bridge, gives the appearance of a mesa joined to the cuesta and is of about the same altitude as the cuesta summit.

Full maturity occurs when one seaward flowing stream, via its tributaries, captures many others and becomes the local source of drainage into the ocean. Therefore, the lower parts of captured seaward flowing streams no longer exit as streams. However, the dried paths of the captured streams may be indicated for some time; the last remaining indication is a notch, or *wind gap*, through the cuesta. It should not be assumed that the presence of a wind gap is always indicative of coastal plains and cuestas. Wind gaps occur anywhere that a stream once cut through an elevation as a *water gap*.

Although cuestas are common along old coastal plains, they also can occur inland. There, cuestas develop when sedimentary rocks of differential resistance are tilted at a low angle. This low angle of tilt distinguishes a cuesta from a related and similar-appearing land form, a hogback. In addition, cuestas have the general appearance of block mountains (see below).

INTERIOR PLAINS

Inland level terrain may be the result of erosion to a peneplain, elevation of an arm of the sea, drying of a lake, flow of lava, or deposition of glacial till or stream deposits at the base of a mountain. These plains are called young if they have not developed their stream patterns, and mature when a drainage system has been established. Usually, the drainage pattern is treelike. If the life cycle is typical, full maturity is characterized by rolling low hills and mature streams.

PLATEAUS

The life history of plateaus is in part a function of climate (Figure 4.13). However, in either dry or wet environments it starts from an essentially flat but elevated plain that has permanent or temporary streams.

During the early stages of the plateau, erosion, especially by streams, forms valleys in the old plain, leaving plateaus as highlands above the valleys. In moist climates, the valleys are V-shaped. The gentler sloping walls are usually covered by soil, talus, or other rock debris, so that the various rock strata are obscured. This slope debris remains through most of the life of the plateau, because greater moisture is allied to denser vegetation, and the vegetation helps to hold the debris over the bedrock. Also, the vegetation and slope debris provide protection from erosion for the underlying strata. In arid regions, the greatly reduced plant cover allows faster removal of erosion products, hence more activity of weathering and reduction of land features by jointing. Plateaus in dry areas are characterized by sheer walls having exposed layers from which blocks of rock are removed by jointing.

Maturity occurs when only the peaks of mountains, erosion mountains, represent the old plain surface. The peaks are a consequence of valleys forming a network and leaving only mountain-shaped remnants of the old landscape. Because the stream network is constantly growing, both young and mature streams must occur in a mature plateau.

Mature plateaus in humid and arid climates display the same basic differences as young plateaus in the same environments. In arid areas, erosion is mainly by jointing and causes steep, steplike, valley walls and small, flat, mountain summits. The much restricted summit platforms represent the level of the previous plain. In humid areas, the valley walls are covered by debris and vegetation, but the summits are usually distinct exfoliated domes. The domes may or may not be covered by vegetation.

Old age, a peneplain, occurs when there are only remnants of the old plateau but never its original surface. These remnants are most prominent in arid areas where they form mesas, buttes, pinnacles, and needle rocks scattered on the flat peneplain. Any flat-surfaced elevations that might exist represent layers that were far below the original plateau surface.

During old age, or even before, a new cycle of plateau life history can start from uplift or other causes. When such rejuvenation occurs, a later stage of life history may be seen superimposed upon an earlier stage.

DOME MOUNTAINS

Circular, oval, or elongate isolated mountains can form in many ways. For example, masses of salt can gather and produce small, inconspicuous mounds; liquid magma from beneath the earth's crust may rise through a line of crustal weakness and accumulate beneath the earth's surface in a small (laccolith) to large (batholith) pool; and erosion can isolate rounded masses from the surrounding terrain.

When first formed, domes, if of sufficient size and in a moist enough environment, develop a radial drainage system. In youth, the headwaters of these streams form a pocket in the summit of the dome. This entire headwaters system produces a circle or oval of infacing cliffs that is cut by the radiating streams. In maturity, rings of such infacing cliffs, called hogbacks, continue to develop within existing, expanding rings. Also within individual rings, the radiating streams give rise to tributaries that later join in a closed ring. With the peneplain of old age,

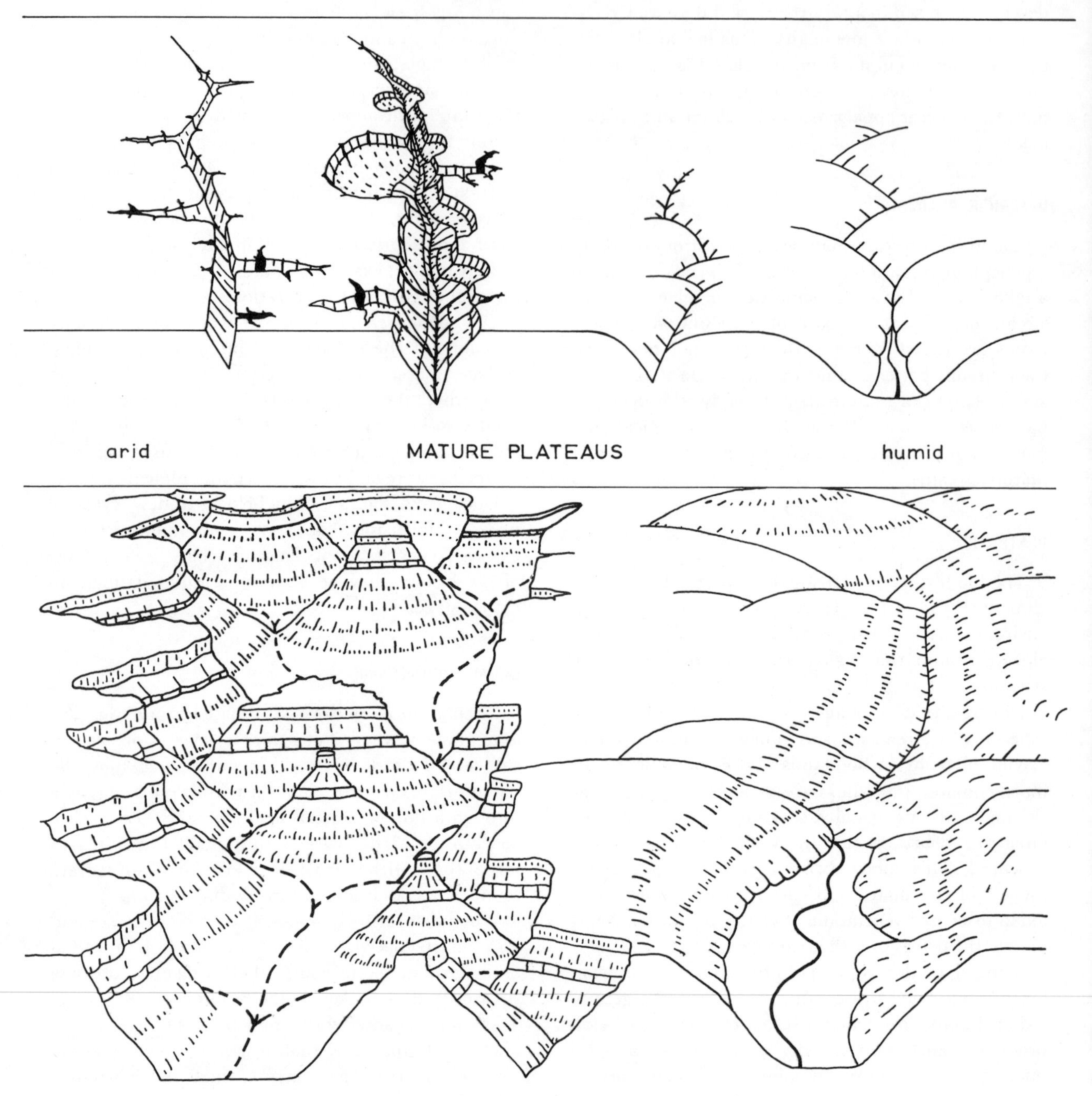

Figure 4.13 Plateau life history. Youth and maturity as found in arid and humid areas.

little more than a remnant of the closed-ring drainage may indicate the past existence of a dome mountain.

HOGBACKS

In addition to those produced by dome mountain erosion, hogbacks can form from the erosion of other land forms. Hogbacks can develop whenever strata that slope at high angles have rocks of unlike hardness, and, therefore, differential erosion occurs. They can form on the slopes of folded mountains, on a fault line where strata edges are upturned as a result of adjacent uplift, on a batholith, or on overturned strata.

The steep slope of most hogbacks faces toward, or rests upon, an elevation (see Figure 4.25). The general exception is found when overturned beds occur. Overturned beds are formed when layers are first turned upward and then arc backward in relation to a rise in land. Therefore, the steep hogback face is turned away from the elevation.

Hogbacks are actually overgrown cuestas. As a rule-of-thumb differentiation, cuestas have their strata angled up to 12° from the horizontal and hogbacks have theirs at an angle of more than 12°.

GLACIATION

During the last million years at least parts of North America, Europe, and Asia experienced four advances and four retreats of glaciers. Due to these ice movements, much of the northern and northeastern parts of our continent contain land forms molded by past glaciation. This is the case because no other erosion force is as powerful as glaciation.

Glacier Formation. Glacier formation can be summarized in a few steps. First, more snow must fall than melts each year, so obviously some snow is present throughout the year and accumulates from year to year. Such a mass of snow is called a snow field and the lowest elevation at which it occurs is called a snow line. Snow falling upon a snow field is usually dry and flaky, but as more snow falls on top the lower parts of the snow field are compressed. Compression causes the snow to melt, but the cold refreezes it into granular snow. Further precipitation upon the snow field surface causes greater compression and the granular snow is transformed to ice. While these processes are taking place, there is a transition from snow field to glacier. A snow field becomes a glacier when either granular snow or ice starts flowing.

Glaciers are not solid masses of ice. In addition to snow and granular snow in the upper layers, debris, especially rocks, is scattered throughout the mass. Also, there are cracks—small fissures and large crevasses. Associated features include ice caves, ice bridges, and once dislocated but refrozen blocks of ice. All of these structures, like those already mentioned, are irregularly distributed, but their locations generally reveal areas of stress upon the ice mass. The cracks develop when ice is stretched, as when it moves over some surface elevation.

Erosion Action. In moving rocks and other debris from a landscape, a glacier acts in a manner that can be likened to a plow, a file, and a sled. Its plowlike action is provided by the tremendous force exerted at the moving front. The filelike action, which produces grooves, or glacial scratch, on rocks beneath the ice, is due to rock fragments. These fragments originate either from material that falls upon the glacier and then "falls" through the ice, or from debris that is overridden and accumulated. The sled action comes from the mass of ice flattening the land and rounding elevations.

Glacier Types. Glaciers are classified into three types: local, piedmont, and continental. The local type consists of any single, tongue-shaped ice mass that is confined to a valley and represents the site of a former stream. Actual naming of local glaciers is based upon the surrounding environs. There are alpine, mountain, and valley glaciers. Piedmont glaciers are the product of several local glaciers that have come together. Continental glaciers cover vast expanses and are the only glacier type that moves forward without regard for terrain.

LOCAL GLACIATION

Most high mountains of the world have some snow the year round. Owing to climatic zonation, the various snow lines are lowest at the poles and become progressively higher as they approach the equator. At the poles the snow line approaches sea level; near the equator only the truly high mountains have permanent snow.

Many high mountains with snow fields obtain sufficient snowfall for glaciers to form. Even now some of these glaciers become over 1000 feet thick and extend some distance before the ice melts and the melt water collects in glacial lakes and/or runs off in glacial streams. In polar areas, glaciers may reach the sea and there be dissipated in the form of large ice chunks or icebergs. Currents move these icebergs toward the equator, but the ice normally is melted in cool temperate waters.

The features of local glaciation are best seen by considering an area before, during, and after the formation of ice. The alpine type will be used as an example.

Preglacial Landscape. Most mountain topography is modified primarily by streams and some weathering. Typical preglacial land forms are dome mountains, smooth slopes, V-shaped river valleys, and fairly deep soil. The V-shaped valleys tend to unite into a winding, irregular pattern; waterfalls are generally not present (Figure 4.14A).

Glacial Landscape. During glaciation, the valleys are filled with ice, and the summits of the lower peaks may be entirely covered by ice. However, most of the glaciers are confined to the valleys, and there is a glacial field that forks and flows in many directions. When considered as a whole, the field is a piedmont glacier (Figure 4.14B).

These glaciers display their greatest erosion power at their heads. There, at the tops of exposed peaks, the effect of accumulating snow and ice is a freezing–thawing cycle that loosens the peaks' rocks. The loosened rocks are then carried downward by the moving glacier. At the head of a single glacier, the consequence of this continuous erosion is an amphitheater-like excavation called a *cirque*.

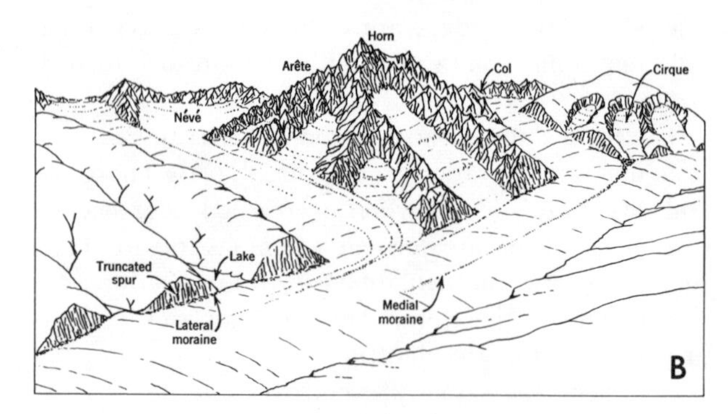

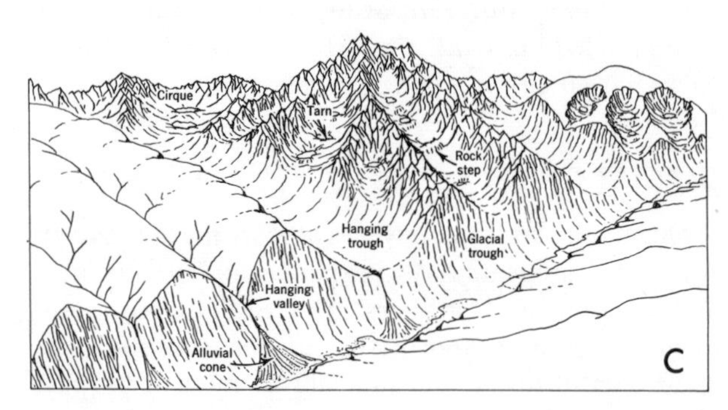

Figure 4.14 Land forms produced by local glaciation.
A. Before glaciation sets in, the region has smoothly rounded divides and narrow, V-shaped stream valleys.
B. After glaciation has been in progress for thousands of years, new erosional forms are developed.
C. With the disappearance of the ice, a system of glacial troughs is exposed. (Used, by permission, from A. N. Strahler, *Physical Geography*, John Wiley & Sons, Inc., New York 1961. After W. M. Davis and A. K. Lobeck.)

Along the bottom and sides of the path of downward movement, the freezing–thawing, filelike, plowlike, and sledlike forces produce somewhat different terrain. In relation to the mass of glacial ice, there is a downward and lateral cutting by the glacier that produces a distinct U-shaped valley profile. These valleys, called *glacial troughs*, follow the path of previous streams but do not always join at the same altitude. There is a tendency for much wider and deeper cutting in the area of the previous stream's main trunk and less U-shaped erosion in the previous tributaries, with resultant steep cliffs at old points of junction between tributaries and the main trunk. The U-shaped valleys above such cliffs are called *hanging valleys*.

The processes of glacial erosion cause rocks and other materials to fall upon the tops of the flowing glacier. Owing to the addition of debris upon moving ice, fragments on the ice are organized in lines parallel to the direction of glacial flow. These lines, called *moraines*, accumulate along the sides of a glacier as lateral moraines and at any distance nearer to the middle as medial moraines. A medial moraine forms from two lateral moraines when two forks of a glacier are joined; hence, lateral moraines on the inside of each joining fork unite to produce one or, perhaps, two lines of debris that flow down the interior top of the ice.

Moraine material is constantly being added, but large rock piles do not accumulate on top of the ice. Because of debris weight and the characteristics of ice, moraine fragments gradually sink from the top of the glacier to the bottom. This sinking of materials provides constant renewal of the particles at the glacier bottom which are responsible for the filelike action of a glacier.

Postglacial Landscape. The retreat and final disappearance of a glacier reveals a landscape that has been altered markedly (Figure 4.14C). Valleys are distinctly U-shaped and their bottoms have lateral, medial, and terminal moraines. Terminal moraines are collections of glacial debris that form at points of greatest extent of the glacier and at places where the glacial front was located for some time during the cycle of retreat. In addition to glacial erosion, the U-shaped valleys display the effects of weathering and stream erosion. For example, landslides are common and may act to dam a stream, fashioning a landslide lake. In addition, the site of a hanging valley entrance is usually emphasized by a waterfall that is cutting a notch into the mouth of the hanging valley.

The old mountain summits may be completely ringed by cirques that are now lakes. Also, the ring of cirques may leave a sharp, almost needle-like, central matterhorn peak. In addition, adjacent cirques and valleys often are separated by knifelike ridges (*aretes*) that have occasional passes (*cols*). Finally, down the mountain from the cirques, may be rock steps. These steps are the final cirque-producing activities of a contracting glacier. The steps are produced at each place where the glacial head remains for a while as it moves downhill during the general contraction cycle.

CONTINENTAL GLACIATION

Piedmont glaciers are not considered separately because their features are those of a miniature continental glacier or of interrelated local glaciers.

At the present time, only one-eleventh of the land is glaciated and the only true continental glaciers are found on the continent of Antarctica and on the island of Greenland. Now there are about 6,000,000 cubic miles of ice, enough to raise the sea level about 200 feet. However, during the last one million years, the Pleistocene Epoc, glaciers covered nearly a third of the land. The ice involved was perhaps four times the amount present today. In North America, most of Canada, the higher western mountains, and the eastern United States south to Louisville, Kentucky, were covered during one or more of the four advances of continental glaciers (See Figure 19.18, p. 381). This ice rounded the New York and New England mountains, expanded and deepened the Great Lakes, created many other lakes and rivers, diverted the Ohio and Missouri Rivers, shaped the Mississippi and Missouri valleys, and stripped eastern Canadian soil to form the rich Midwest farmlands. The tremendous forces involved were due to the action of ice that was as much as 2 miles thick.

Preglacial Landscape. Consideration of the landscape prior to continental glaciation is not as important as is the topography preceding local glaciation. Before continental glaciation, almost any type of land form can exist. In general, the postglacial consequences are lowering and leveling of the previous topography.

Glacial Landscape. If there were now a mean annual temperature decrease of less than 10 degrees, perhaps as few as 5, there would be great accumulations of snow and, as a result, continental glaciation. Any continental glacier is so large that there is little, if any, downhill slope to provide gravity flow. However, the ice creates its own kind of movement by causing a "High" pressure area to form upon the glacier. The movement of winds out of the "High" carriers snow to an ever-widening margin. This growing margin, and perhaps pressure of the thick ice mass, cause much of the movement and serve to provide and maintain the filling, plowing, and sled erosion of glaciation.

Continental glacial movement flattens the country by removing soil and rock masses. These erosion products are deposited at the front and under the glacier. If the glacier continues forward, much of the front debris is pushed ahead of the ice, but eventually the ice no longer advances and a cycle of retreat starts. The point of maximum advance is marked by a large collection of debris, a terminal moraine, which after glacial retreat is recognized as a pile of debris that has a glacially eroded landscape to one side and no such landscape on the other side. In addition, as any continental glacier shrinks, many other terminal (more accurately, "recessional") moraines may be deposited at each site where the contracting front stays for some time.

Postglacial Landscape. When a glacier disappears, the past is disclosed by the landscape (Figure 4.15). The ground shows that much of the surface soil and rock was removed. The terrain is much flattened, with topographic features similar to those of a peneplain produced by other erosion mechanisms. Such a terrain often has an abundance of mature to old streams and lakes.

Perhaps the most distinctive things in postglacial landscapes are the various kinds of glacial deposits. These deposits are called *erratics*, *till*, or *drift* and consist of assorted clay, sand, gravel, and boulders. When a glacier advances, some till is dropped as a fairly even layer of ground moraine. In certain areas, larger till masses are relased (probably under the glacier) and formed into inverted spoon-shaped or canoe-shaped hills (*drumlins*) that "point" toward the direction of past glacial movement.

Glacial streams produce other deposits. Streams are created where melt-water flows through the terminal moraine that dams a temporary glacial lake. Each of the melt-water streams, upon cutting through the moraine, leaves a low alluvial fan. Where the alluvial fans join, an outwash plain that gently slopes away from the moraine is accumulated. A second stream feature is a ridge (*esker*) that once was the rock- and debris-covered bottom of a stream flowing within the ice mass. Such ridges can extend for miles in a sinuous pattern that also contains the forks of former tributaries to the stream. Another stream product is a rounded, conical heap of gravel and boulders (called a *kame*), deposited by a stream entering a moraine lake. The conical heaps are composed of larger materials because finer particles are not immediately dropped by the stream.

A final glaciation feature is fairly common, because blocks of ice often are buried under glacial deposits. After the buried ice melts, the covering of till slumps, leaving a somewhat rounded depression, called a *kettle hole*, in the landscape.

In summary, the more conspicuous land forms after glaciation are erosional cirques, rock steps, and glacial troughs; residual matterhorns, aretes, cols, and ridges; and depositional moraines, outwash plains, eskers, kames, and kettle holes.

WAVES

We have already considered the creation of certain features of a coastal landscape by wave action. In

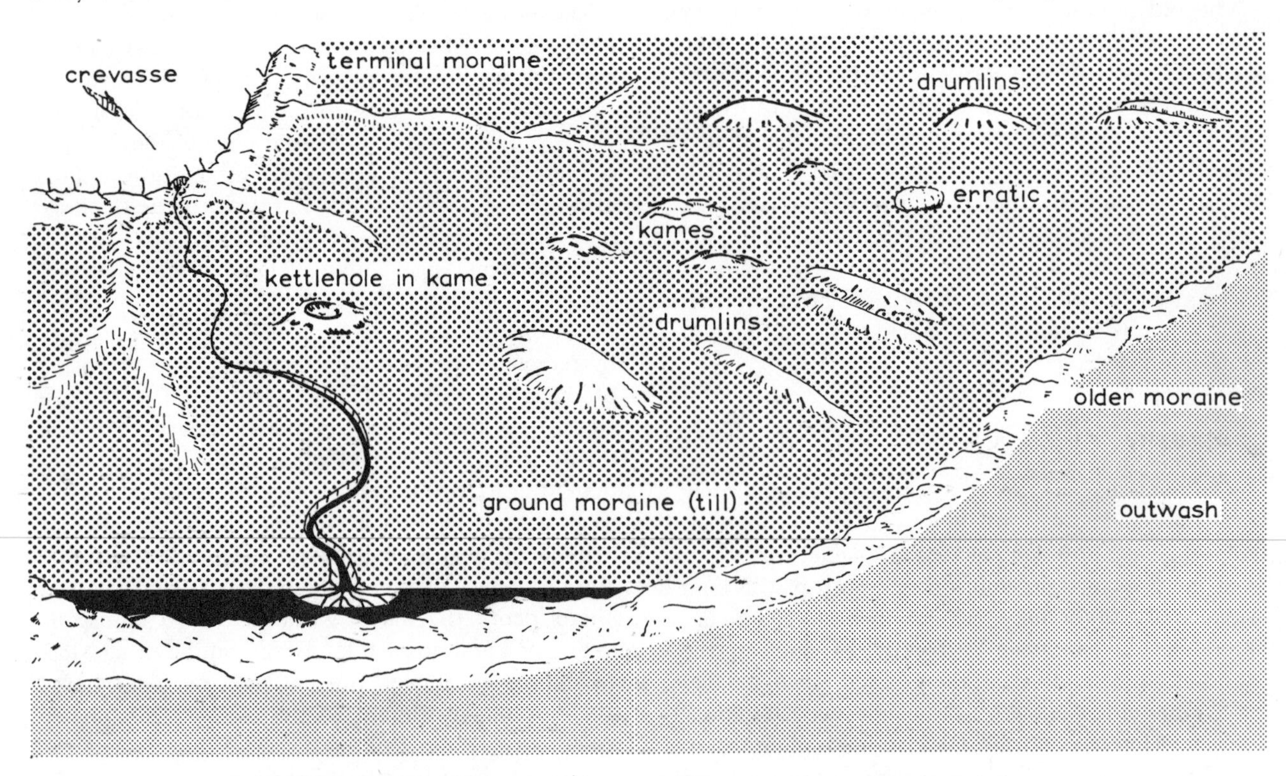

Figure 4.15 Continental glaciation, showing a retreating glacier, its terminal moraine (a recessional moraine) and features on both sides of the true terminal moraine of maximum glacial extent.

the present discussion, the effects of waves on certain shorelines and some of the land forms produced will be discussed.

SHORELINE OF EMERGENCE

Initial Stage. When land first rises above the sea, there is revealed a relatively straight, new shoreline and a gently sloping shore profile of unconsolidated sediments. The gradual slope of the land continues for some distance out into the sea.

This picture soon is altered by wave action. Waves and undertow pick up unconsolidated sediments, and the sediments are deposited offshore where the waters lose much of their energy. Because waters at that offshore point have less energy, sediments are deposited and accumulate as a ridge, or offshore bar, that eventually extends above sea level. Between the bar and the ridge, the waters are contained in a lagoon (Figure 4.16).

Youth. Along the shoreline, the lagoon starts to fill with stream sediments and salt marsh vegetation. At the same time, wave action continues to deposit materials on the outside of the bar and winds carry sand on over the bar into the lagoon. These two conditions cause the tidal marsh to grow seaward and the bar to grow landward. At the up-and-down shore margins that enclose the area of emergence, the bar merges with the land. Here, the activities of tidal marsh and bar growing toward one another soon constrict to the point of producing a tidal creek. Further growing together of marsh and bar progresses toward the center of the area of emergence, constricts the tidal creek, and finally fuses the marsh and bar. Ultimately, this

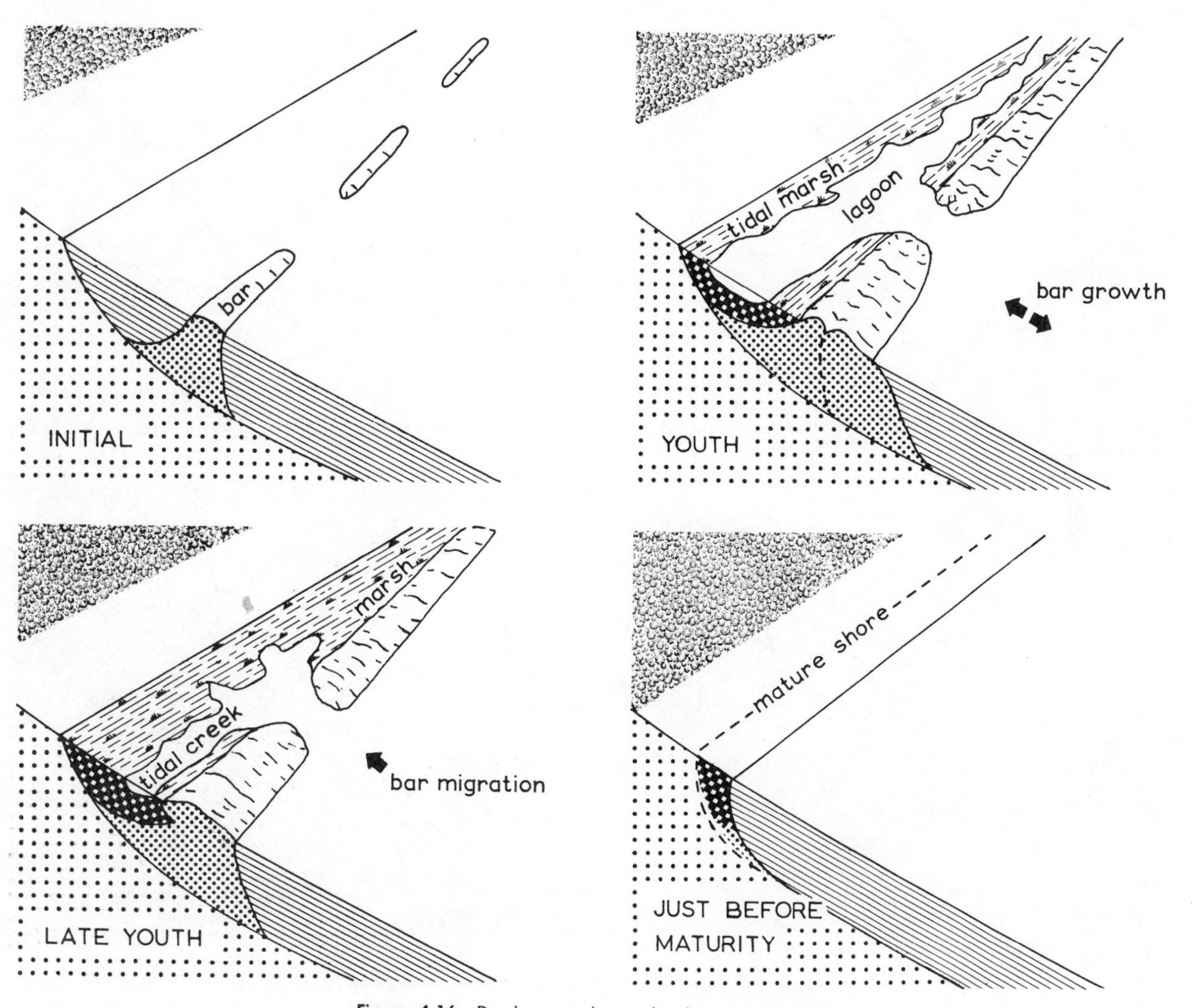

Figure 4.16 Development along a shoreline of emergence.

process extends the land out to the seaward margin of the bar. While these lagoon activities are taking place, the sea on the other side of the bar is constantly excavating its bottom near the bar, producing an ever-increasing ocean floor slope.

Maturity. When geomorphic processes completely fill in the lagoon, a new straight shoreline and deep underwater shore profile result. The underwater shore starts with an abrupt slope, but continues with an ever-decreasing one until the shore slope merges into the continental slope. This is the final condition of shore stability. Unless shore features change, the shoreline will not change. Such a stable shoreline is said to be mature rather than old.

SHORELINE OF SUBMERGENCE

Shorelines of submergence are of two types, *ria* and *fiord.* Ria shorelines develop from partial submergence of land that is interlaced with rivers. As a consequence, there is a network of bays within an otherwise plain or mountain area. Fiord shorelines are partly to completely submerged glacial troughs. The life histories of the two types of shorelines of submergence are so similar that they need not be treated separately (Figure 4.17).

Initial Stage. Submergence causes an irregular shoreline that reflects past elevations and depressions. Such shorelines may include drowned valleys (bays

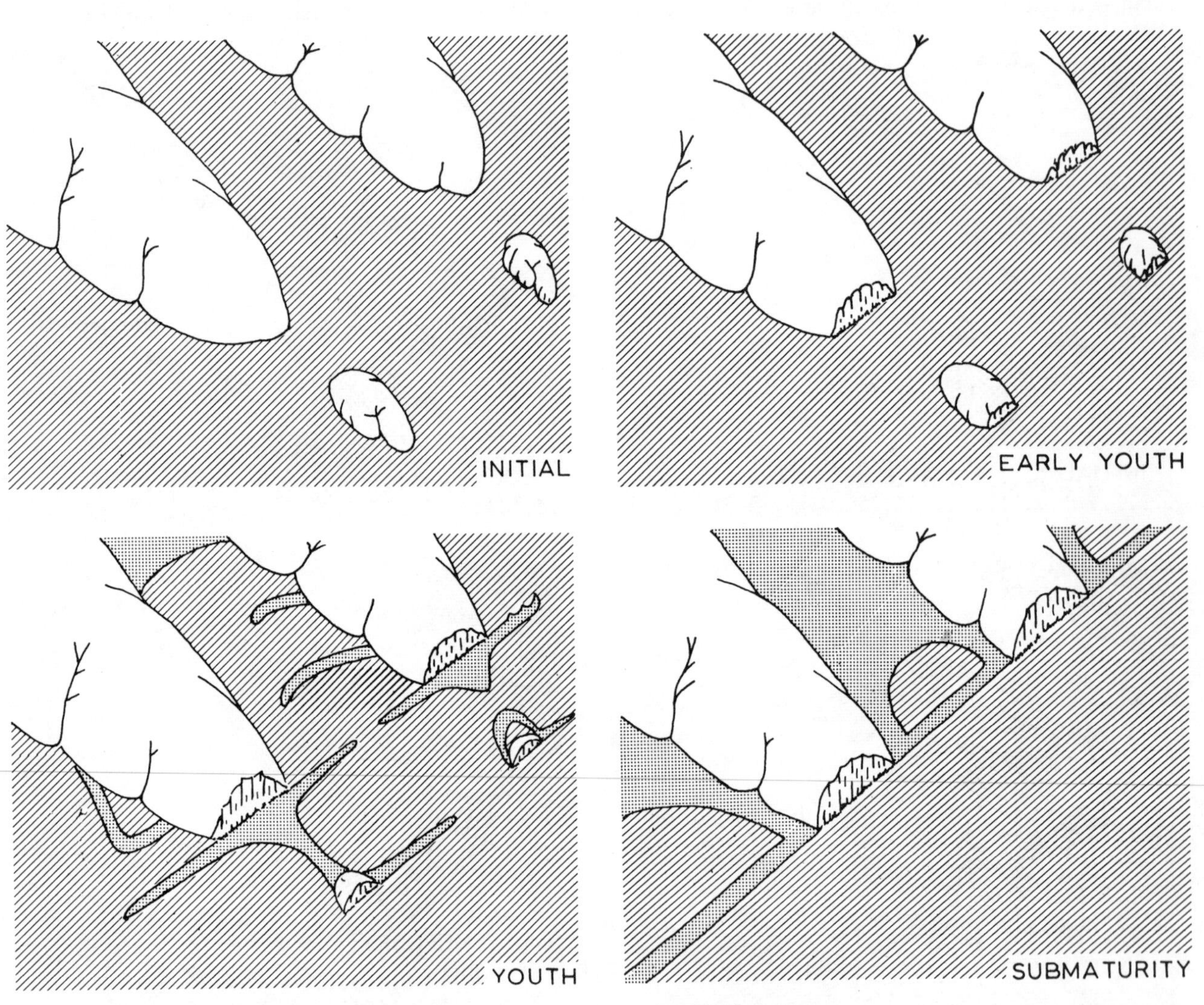

Figure 4.17 Development along a shoreline of submergence.

and estuaries), glacial troughs (fiords), and elevations (islands, peninsulas, and headlands). Underwater topography is irregular, and shoals and banks are usually present.

Initial wave action works to straighten this shoreline. Waves start cutting off the points of land and depositing detached materials in more sheltered bays or similar areas.

Youth. The points of land are subject to some irregular cutting which often leaves isolated elevations (chimneys or stacks) in front of the wave-cut cliffs. The cliffs may be excavated to form clefts, sea caves, and arches. However, the general tendency of erosion is continually to wear away the projecting land in a direction parallel to the over-all straight trend of the shoreline.

The products of erosion are deposited in the bays and any other indentations of the shoreline. These deposits frequently accumulate near the mouths of these bays. Here, they grow from the shore, forming first spits, and then bars as the sediments almost close a bay.

Submaturity. This additional stage is recognized when headlands are cut back and the bars almost completely close off the bays. However, many bays may already be blocked by bars and isolated from the sea; others may even be filled with land and bar sediments, and so actually be part of the land.

Maturity. A mature shoreline, after submergence, is no different from one after emergence. The mature shoreline after submergence fills out to the bars and the typical underwater profile develops.

COMPOUND SHORELINES

Most shorelines are not as simple as previous considerations would imply. In most areas, both submergence and emergence are superimposed on a single coastline. Such complexes are called compound shorelines. As one might suspect, their life history is dependent upon the particular sequence of past emergence and submergence.

WIND

The wind was considered as a phenomenon of the atmosphere. Its erosive action is mainly from sand and any other carried particles that mold the land forms typical of arid landscapes. Wind deposits soil and sand in heaps called *dunes* and finer dust in widespread, more or less evenly distributed deposits. Wind also excavates the landscape and forms caves, arches, blow holes, broad plains, and wind-scoured valleys. This excavation action also leaves residual "pockmarked" rocks, pedestals, mushroom rocks, table rocks, arches, and undercut cliffs. Wind even affects the particles it carries or moves. For example, sand grains are cracked, pitted, and chipped to the point of having a frosted appearance, and rocks tend to become beveled. Therefore, wind erosion is from the blowing away of materials, and from the sandblasting action of windblown particles.

Wind can cause extensive economic damage. For example, it can cut telephone wires, pit glass, and remove paint. Also, a violent, heavily laden dust storm can ruin agricultural and other lands and even be a hazard to human life.

DUNE FORMATION

Wind blowing over level sand will cause an oval sand pile to accumulate. As a symmetrical oval is formed, there is a progressive decrease in velocity on the pile side away from the wind, the leeward side. This leeward velocity decrease soon stops sand from being carried beyond the crest of the dune, and eventually the dune has a gradual windward slope and steep leeward slope. The process of dune formation also causes dune migration inland, because formation and further activity consist of sand being blown up the windward slope and depositing at the summit or just beyond on the leeward slope.

Wind direction and velocity are responsible for the variety of dunes (Figure 4.18). Parallel ridges that may or may not be interconnected are oriented either across or with the direction of prevailing winds. A second type, individual, arc-shaped or crescent-shaped *barchanes* form in many arid areas. They occur where prevailing winds are from one direction and are oriented so that the arc is centered on the wind direction and the open ends of the arc are pointed leeward. A third type, *seifs*, are half arcs that form where two prevailing wind directions exist.

DESERTS

In dry climates, wind erosion is sometimes a prominent factor in the sculpturing of the landscape (Figure 4.19). This is so in spite of the fact that rainfall usually comes as cloudbursts and leaves its mark in

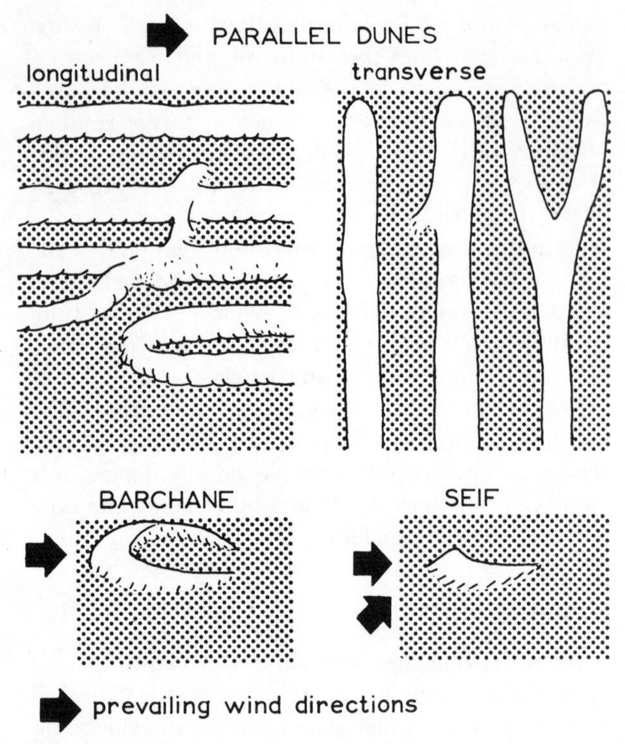

Figure 4.18 The kinds of dunes as produced by different prevailing winds.

the form of alluvial plains, gullies, canyons, deep ravines (called waddies), and temporary alkali lakes. Although flood waters sculpture such features, the features are modified by wind action. In the greatest modification, wind removes fine particles, usually leaving only the coarsest sand and rocks. This accumulation of rocks forms the characteristic substrate of arid areas and is called *desert pavement.* (Contrary to popular impressions, sandy areas and dunes do not constitute the predominant land forms of deserts.) The desert pavement frequently is stained shiny brownish to blackish by iron-manganese compounds (and perhaps polished by the winds), forming *desert varnish.* In addition to desert pavement, deserts also have the various features already mentioned as being typical of wind erosion.

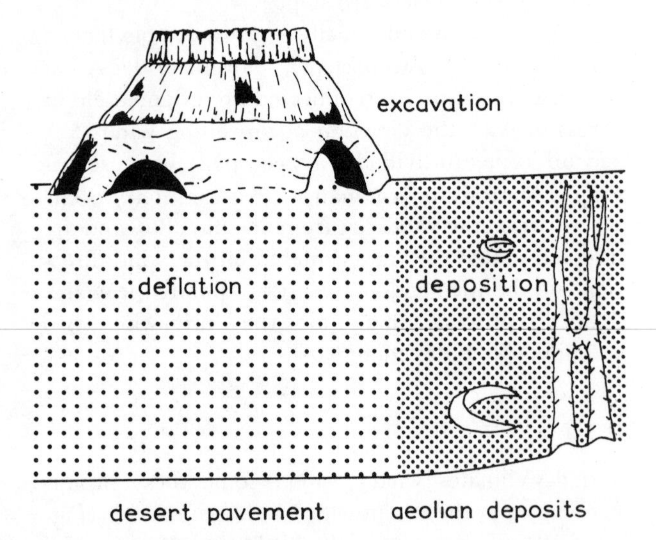

Figure 4.19 Features caused by wind erosion. Such land forms usually are best developed in arid climates.

ORGANISM ACTIVITIES

Organisms using products within their environment may construct land forms that may or may not be considered destructional. The most pronounced landscape effects are accomplished by corals, animals that produce reefs in certain parts of the world; however, certain other organisms, plant and animal, also modify landscapes.

PLANTS

Vegetation is a primary agent in the process of filling in lakes. This organism activity occurs in a very orderly sequence of plant growth forms, including submerged, floating, and emergent plants. Further details of the phenomenon of plant succession in water are left for later discussions of ecology. All that need be mentioned here is that each successive growth form accomplishes greater filling of a body of water, and succession ends with an essentially flat area of land having the characteristic vegetation for the locality.

Trees and shrubs sometimes accumulate in a stream to form a conspicuous raft or dam. A raft is a semi-floating structure that is only moderately effective in hampering stream flow. A dam is more an integral part of the landscape and is effective in creating an upstream body of water.

ANIMALS

The most prominent land forms produced by animals other than corals are those formed by beavers and other rodents, termites, ants, and earthworms. Beavers cut woody vegetation and use it to build dams that trap streams, thereby causing deeper and quieter waters where alluvium collects and successive growth of different plants occurs. Eventually, the continued activities of beavers, alluvial deposition, and plants produce a very thick layer of soil so rich that streams are sometimes diverted by man in order that he can use the land.

Burrowing rodents cause subsoil to be aerated either in place or after it is moved to the surface. The aeration favors more rapid soil formation and, in situations of slow to moderate runoff, causes more water to move underground; in conditions of rapid runoff, burrows may lead to even greater erosion than normal. Similar effects are accomplished by earthworms, but their activity is not likely to contribute greatly to erosion. Finally, termites and ants in tropical areas construct mounds or hills, sometimes about 25 feet high.

Certain extremely important, but not easily observed, geomorphic changes are brought about by microorganisms. For example, certain sulfur bacteria are responsible for the presence of sulfuric acid in many waters. This sulfuric acid is a primary agent in the leaching effects of many streams.

Coral and other rock deposits are formed by monerans and algae. Red algae are more important reef formers than are corals.

Coral Deposits. Corals, animals related to sea anemones and jellyfishes, have the ability to extract calcium carbonate and various other calcium compounds from sea water and deposit this material as coral around their bodies. Because these coral deposits remain after individual animals die, and living animals build upon the remains of the dead, large masses, called coral reefs, may accumulate. However, corals have definite temperature and salt water requirements which prevent their being found throughout the oceans. Because conditions below 18°C. are unfavorable, the reef-builders live from the surface to depths near 125 feet between latitudes near 28° north and 28° south of the equator. Their salt water requirements allow them to occur adjacent to land, but they may be killed by excess sediments or fresh water. Although these general requirements are often reflected by the shape of reefs, the three kinds of coral reefs are classified on the basis of their relation to other land masses (Figure 4.20). A *fringing reef* is adjacent to, or on the fringe of, a land mass. A *barrier reef* occurs some distance from the mainland, generally parallel to the shore but separated by an expanse of ocean. For example, the Great Barrier Reef, the world's largest, which is from a few

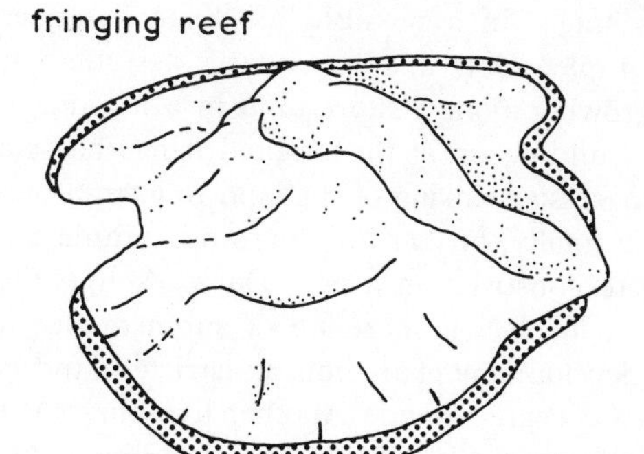

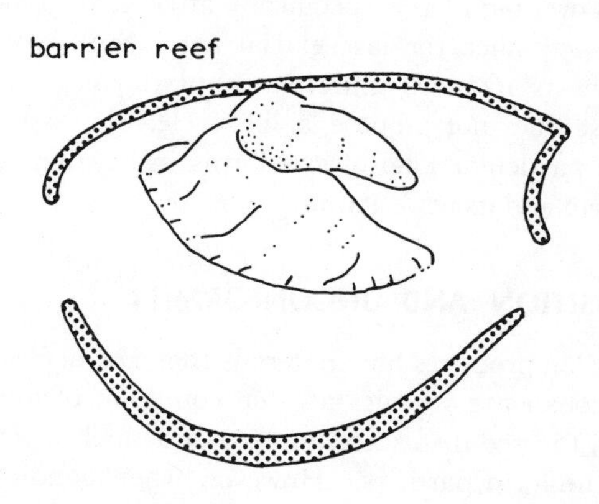

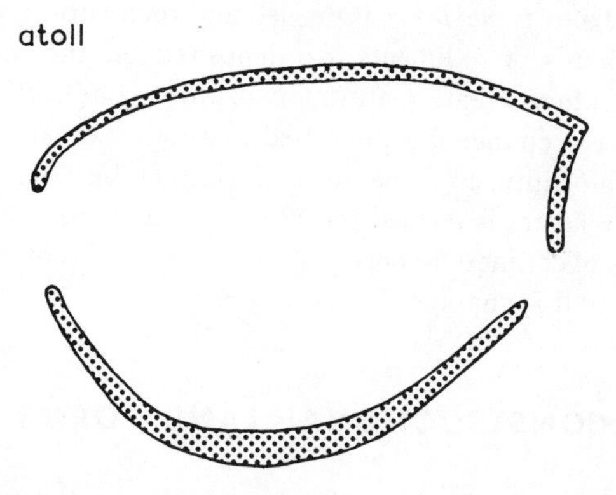

Figure 4.20 Coral island development. Subsidence of a volcanic island causes reefs to proceed from a fringing reef to a barrier reef and, finally, to a coral atoll containing a lagoon. (After a set of Ward's Geomorphic models.)

to about 90 miles offshore, begins at the northeast coast of Australia and extends about 1200 miles. An *atoll* is an essentially circular reef containing an interior lagoon. Atolls are generally remote from other land masses.

Many hypotheses exist as to how these reefs form. However, most of the hypotheses present the three reefs as stages in a possible life history sequence. For example, Darwin's hypothesis assumes: first, corals growing along a shore to form a fringing reef; second, building up of the original fringe associated with progressive sinking of the land to form a barrier reef; and finally, further building and complete land sinking to construct an atoll. Darwin's hypothesis, therefore, involves a shoreline of submergence and, for full development of an atoll, a restricted land mass such as an oceanic island. Another hypothesis is that of glacial control. It presumes the same sequence of reef formation as did Darwin; however, the rise of waters over old reefs is specifically attributed to melting of ice since the last glacial age. Still another hypothesis involves underwater platforms. This premise does not propose a life cycle, but assumes that a particular kind of reef forms in relation to a platform and its wave action.

DEPOSITION AND UNCONFORMITY

Erosion produces fine materials that are deposited in various ways. Under a given condition of topography, the sediments accumulate in a thick layer of fairly uniform particles. However, when conditions are such that the essentially homogeneous material, called a *conformable bed*, is eroded and then submerged, new kinds of sediments are deposited on the older, eroded bed, creating an unconformity. The fact that there is a change from one bed to another creates the unconformity, and the zone of contact between the unlike layers is termed the *plane of unconformity*. Such zones of contact are portrayed in many of the illustrations in this chapter.

CONSTRUCTIONAL LAND FORMS

Discussions to this point have been mostly of destructive geological processes and destructional land forms. Exceptions occur when land is elevated, because the elevation processes and their consequences are constructive. In the remainder of this chapter, the primary constructive processes, the constructional land forms produced by the processes, and the destructive results of erosion on these land forms will be considered.

There are two groups of constructive processes. The first, *vulcanism*, produces land forms from substances originating beneath the earth's crust. Vulcanism is also called igneous activity. The second, *diastrophism*, consists of various kinds of movements that mold the earth's crust.

VULCANISM

Vulcanism, or igneous activity, encompasses all aspects of the formation and movement of molten material, *magma*, within and upon the earth's crust. Magma moves toward the surface through zones of crustal weakness, because this molten material is under extreme pressure. Magma movement, depending upon whether or not it reaches the surface, is used to categorize two classes of vulcanism, intrusive and extrusive. Intrusive flows are those in which the magma is trapped within the crust; extrusive flows, those in which the magma reaches the surface.

INTRUSIVE VULCANISM

Intrusive flows also differ from extrusive in the general nature of the rocks and land forms that are produced. In general, intrusive igneous rocks have larger crystals than do extrusive, and intrusive land forms are always constructed below the surface whereas extrusive are upon the surface. Finally, the nature of the land forms differs in the two kinds of flows. The main land forms resulting from intrusive flows are volcanic necks, dikes, sills, laccoliths, stocks, and batholiths (Figure 4.21). *Volcanic necks*, also called volcanic plugs, are igneous rock masses that fill the opening, or vent, through which magma moves out of a volcano. These plugs form from the last flow of magma as a volcano becomes inactive. *Dikes* occur wherever magma solidifies in cracks or fractures in the crust; they may form in the cracks of volcano walls or in any other fissure. Dikes range in size from less than an inch wide and a few yards long to many feet wide and many miles long. The largest, in Rhodesia, is over 5 miles wide and 300 miles long.

Sills resemble certain dikes, but sills form between and are oriented parallel to the layers of rock strata. This orientation occurs because the magma forces its way between two layers (i.e., it spreads throughout a zone of unconformity). Sills also resemble stocks and batholiths, but are distinguished from them by being formed near the surface, having their top and bottom margins somewhat parallel to one another, and being smaller. The average sill covers only a few acres or square miles and is less than 100 feet thick. However,

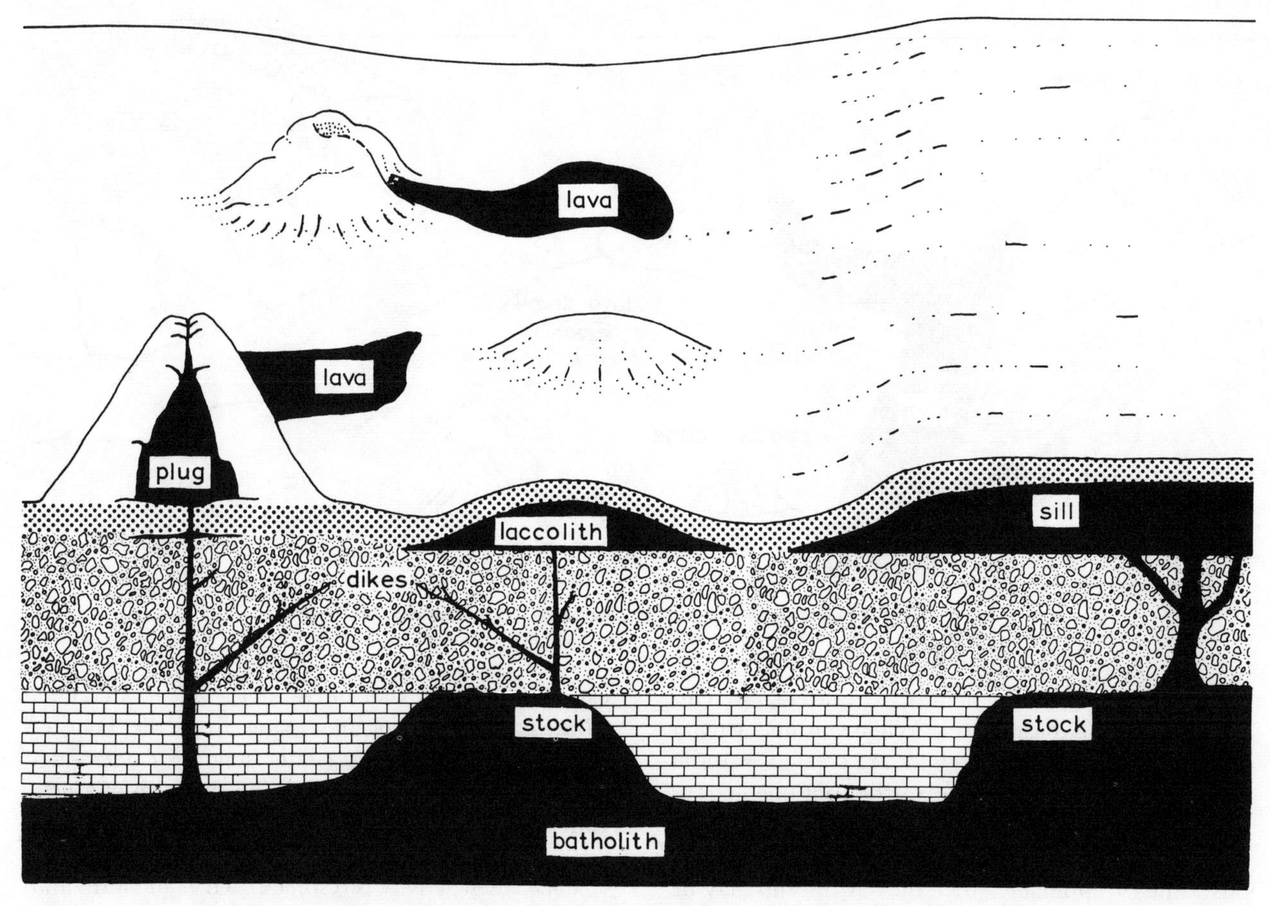

Figure 4.21 Subterranean and surface features associated with vulcanism.

they range from masses a few inches thick and covering less than an acre to those many thousands of feet thick and covering large areas.

Laccoliths, a kind of dome mountain, are formed in much the same way as sills. In both cases, magma comes up through a zone of weakness and is trapped between rock layers; however, in a laccolith the magma collects in a lens-shaped pool.

Stocks and *batholiths* form from the deepest and most extensive accumulations of magma; their top and bottom margins normally are not parallel. Segregation of these two land forms is rather arbitrary. Stocks have an area of less than 40 square miles; batholiths cover a greater area, some of them being over 100 miles wide and 1000 miles long. One of the largest provides the substance of California's Sierra Nevada Mountains. Both batholiths and sills, prior to solidification, may give rise to any of the overlying kinds of vulcanism land forms. Therefore, the deepest intrusive igneous activity is often a reservoir for more superficial intrusive and extrusive flows.

EXTRUSIVE VULCANISM

In contrast to the rock and land form features of intrusive flows, extrusive rocks either have crystals so small that few, if any, can be seen, or they are noncrystalline. This difference is due to the fact that extrusive rocks cool much faster than intrusive ones, and the faster a rock cools and hardens, the smaller are its crystals. The associated land forms are always surface features, namely volcanoes and related structures (Figure 4.22).

The types of volcanoes and allied land forms are related to the nature of the igneous activity. When activity is explosive, volcanoes are in the form of *cinder cones*, and fragmental materials are hurled from the volcano. This fragmental debris consists of ovoid

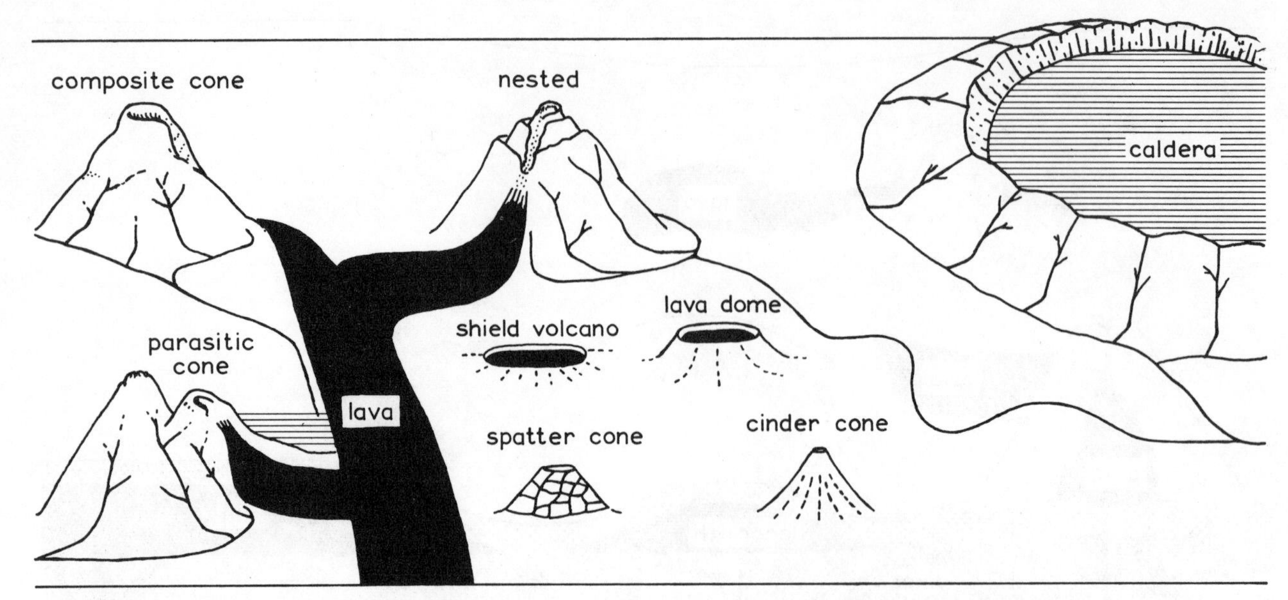

Figure 4.22 Some types of land forms created by volcanoes and their activity.

masses, called volcanic bombs; of gravel-sized cinders; and of fine volcanic ash. When volcanic activity is quieter, nearly flat lava domes are created, with no debris. These flat cones have a wide vent opening, or crater, a feature in distinct contrast to the small crater of the high cinder cones. When activity is continuously and exceptionally quiet, the flat volcano may be little more than a lava pool, or *shield volcano*, on a plain. Any nonexplosive activity results in lava flows and/or mud flows.

Most volcanoes are *composite cones*. The word "composite" is applied because the cones are formed by a combination of quiet and explosive cycles of activity. For this reason, most volcanoes are cone-shaped and are associated with a surrounding terrain that reflects both quiet and violent activity in the history of the cone.

Various features may be found in a volcanic landscape. In addition to the already mentioned land forms, including intrusive ones, there are such things as calderas, parasitic cones, spatter (or driblet) cones, nested craters, and lava bridges (or tunnels). *Calderas* are created by the explosive rejuvenation of an inactive volcano. In this rejuvenation, the top of the old volcano is freed and then collapses within the molten magma. Because the top is melted, it disappears. When the caldera becomes inactive, it possesses the broad opening of collapse and an extensive flat plain at the bottom of the opening. Crater Lake, Oregon, is one of the famous calderas. (It is misnamed, because its opening is a caldera, not a volcanic crater.) Wizard Island, a volcano rising from the floor of Crater Lake, represents a later stage of caldera development, namely rejuvenation in the form of a new cone upon the flat plain.

Parasitic cones can form on the side of an inactive volcano when activity is resumed. This land form and the caldera indicate the very resistant nature of previously formed igneous rocks. Because rocks fill old vents, renewed activity often is not from the exact site of the previous vent, so the new activity often creates a parasitic cone or, rarely, a caldera.

Spatter cones are formed if gases and lava sputter out of a crack in the side of a cone. *Nested craters* are produced when each new member of a series of rejuvenated cones is formed within the last inactive cone. In other words, nested craters are the consequence of a progressive process of cone-within-cone formation. *Lava bridges*, or *lava tunnels*, are remnants of lava passage under a pre-existing lava field. The new lava is so hot that it melts the old lava and "cuts" a path down and through the field. The tunnel forms because the final downhill flows, those that solidify upon the tunnel bottom, are less extensive and the "freezing" of the final flow involves contraction.

DISTRIBUTION OF VOLCANOES

Much of the world is affected by current and past vulcanism. At the present time there are about 430 active volcanoes, an insignificant figure as compared with the number of inactive ones. Of the active presumed 430, 80 are submarine and 350 are on land; 336 are associated with the Pacific Ocean and 94 with the Indio-Atlantic region; 275 are in the Northern Hemisphere, and 155 are in the Southern.

Volcanoes are distributed fairly evenly in a so-called "circle of fire" around the Pacific Ocean. In western North America, the only volcanoes classified as active are in Alaska, California (Mount Lassen) and Mexico (Paricutin). The most common pattern of volcanic distribution is straight to arcing or curving because they are found along lines of weakness (faults) in the earth's crust. For example, the Cascade Range of California, Oregon, Washington, and British Columbia constitutes a single set of volcanoes on a fault line. Also, this range shows that the western North American exception to the "circle of fire" condition is mostly due to inactivity of existing volcanic peaks. Actually, the Cascades contain many volcanoes that were active within the last few thousand years.

LIFE HISTORY OF VULCANISM

Any possible history of vulcanism must consider what happens to young composite cones, lava domes, cinder cones, lava beds, laccoliths, dikes, sills, stocks, and batholiths. Fortunately, vulcanism products and their destructional cycles are generally so distinctive that only the barest mention of their erosion is needed. This is especially true when the characteristic rocks of each land form are known.

At maturity, composite cones have walls with gullies and tops without craters. Also, lava domes are dissected and cinder cones degraded. Lava beds are indicated by a plain and plateau (capped by the old lava bed) topography; laccoliths are identified by the stage of a mature dome mountain. In addition, dikes and sills may be exposed on the surface. Some dikes have the general appearance of volcanic plugs; however, dike base outlines tend to be somewhat oval, whereas plug base outlines are much more rounded. Finally, stocks and batholiths are uncovered and supply mountainous terrain.

The peneplain of old age may have remnants of the composite cone in the form of necks and dikes surrounding a plug; remnants of both cinder cones and lava domes in the form of degraded plugs; perhaps some elevation indicating past lava fields; perhaps the much eroded remnants of laccoliths, or only a semblance of radial drainage; and some indication of dikes, stocks, and batholiths.

DIASTROPHISM

Deformations in the earth's crust are of two types: those in which mountains are formed, and those in which continental masses are raised or lowered with little folding of the crust. Both types of diastrophism tend to occur very slowly, usually about 2 feet per hundred years; however, individual earthquakes might cause 50-foot vertical or horizontal displacement of rock layers.

Diastrophism can be thought of as processes that warp, tilt, uplift, and depress the crust. Moreover, when these processes work together, they cause local tension, compression, torsion, or shear. For this reason, diastrophism may be considered as many distinct phenomena—uplifting, depressing, warping, folding, jointing, and faulting.

PROCESSES

In studying the features produced by diastrophism, the attitude, or position, of rock layers in reference to compass directions and to the horizontal are important. To appreciate these relationships, the terms *strike* and *dip* must be understood (Figure 4.23). Strike is applied to any continuous layer of rock seen on the surface and is no more than the compass direction of this rock layer. Dip is the number of degrees that a rock layer angles downward into the crust. Dip might best be visualized in terms of sediment deposition and later tilting. When a layer is deposited it is horizontal to the surface and has zero degrees dip; as the layer is tilted from the horizontal, its angle of dip increases.

Uplifting and Depressing. These two already mentioned processes appear as simple vertical movements of fairly large expanses of land, with no displacement of strike or dip. All large-scale movements of continents are of this type.

Frequently, these vertical displacements involve shorelines. For example, shallow ocean floors may be uplifted into a shoreline of emergence, or shores depressed into ones of submergence.

Warping. Warping provides a gently tilted, rolling countryside in which neither elevations nor depressions are obvious. The primary elevations are individual domes and the main depressions are basins.

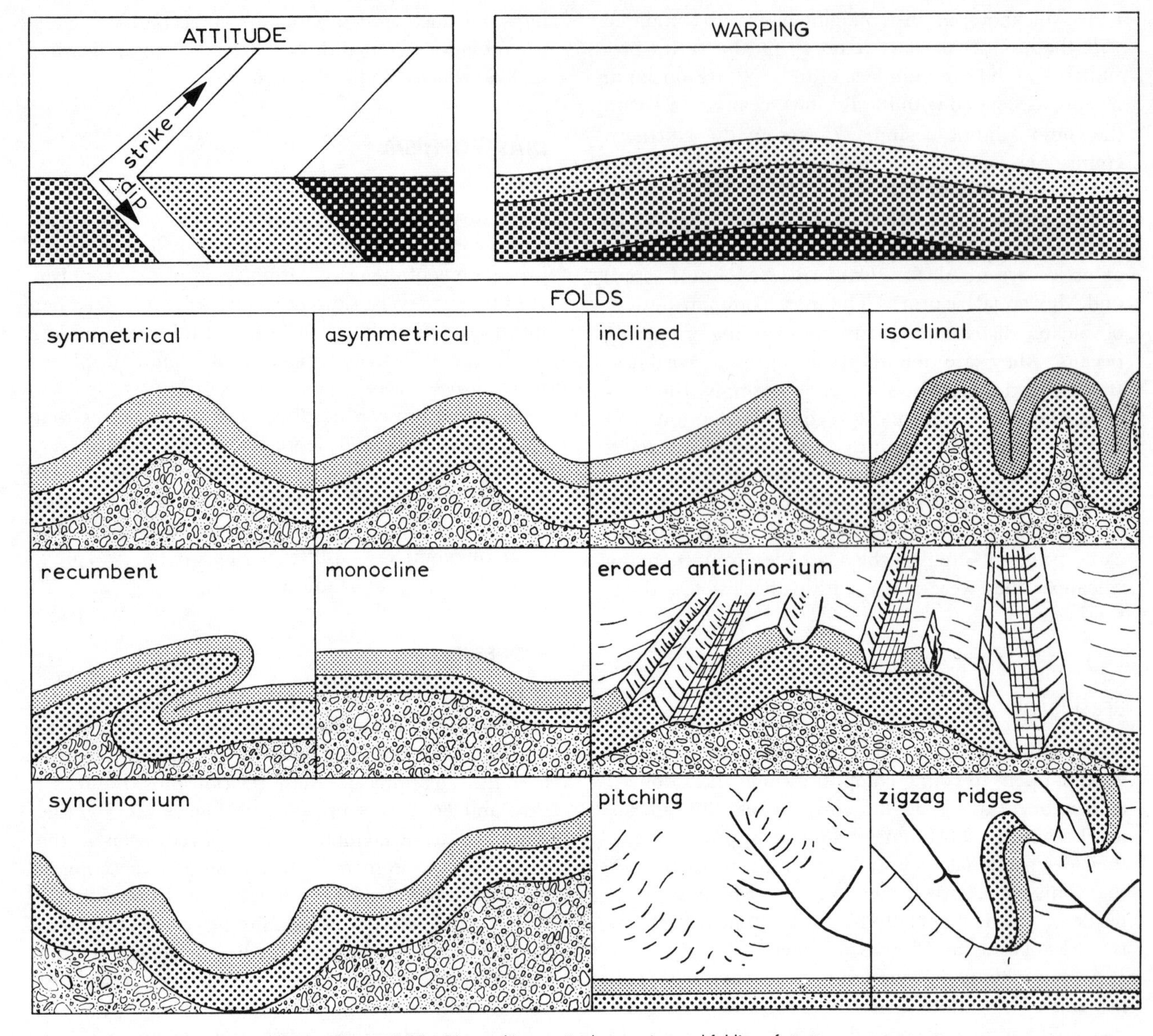

Figure 4.23 Diastrophism: attitude, warping and folding of strata.

In both domes and basins, many square miles of landscape are involved.

Folding. Widespread surface compressing and some settling movements may form a washboard-like topography of more or less symmetrical folds. The elevations so formed are called *anticlines* and the depressions, *synclines.* However, some folding creates less symmetrical land forms. Some of these less symmetrical forms are illustrated and named in Figure 4.23. If folds are somewhat tilted from the vertical, inclined or overturned folds results. If folds are pushed together, the product is an isoclinal fold. When folds are tilted over so far that their peaks almost point to the horizon, the land form is called a recumbent fold (or folds). If additional pressure is applied to recumbent folds, they may break and have part thrust toward and over the rest, creating complicated mountain structures called nappes. In addition to producing folds, folding may raise the rock layers on one side of a line and lower them on other side, creating a monocline.

Folding produces various other types of land forms.

It can elevate a circular, oval, or elongate dome mountain or depress an isolated basin. Also, it can end in individual, long, folded mountains (anticlines) or troughs (synclines), or in alternating anticlines and synclines, forming a system of folded mountains. Finally, there is folding in which the dominant movement compresses an arch of folds (i.e., small folds superimposed upon a single, large, upward fold or anticlinorium) or in a basin of folds (a synclinorium).

Anticlines and synclines at their ends merge into the surrounding flat terrain. This condition of merging in both cases involves abrupt changes in the dip of strata from the fold to the flatland and the strike of surface rocks assumes a U-pattern. Where such anticlines and synclines come together and are eroded, the resulting surface topography is a pattern of zigzag ridges (Figure 4.23).

Jointing. Joints are caused by various forces, especially tension, compression, torsion, and shear, acting upon any kind of rock. For this reason, joints are a common feature of many landscapes.

Perhaps the rocks most frequently jointed are the igneous types. Even cooling of igneous rocks leads to stresses that cause jointing. However, most other rocks also joint from the application of any or all forces of diastrophism and from the creation of like forces by weathering. Therefore, joints are features of any rocks subjected to irregular forces, especially the forces produced by cooling, weathering, and diastrophism.

Faulting. Faulting consists of very minor to extensive displacements of the earth's crust (Figure 4.24). The abrupt movements are felt as moderate to severe earthquakes. Pronounced elevation occurred in the 50-foot uplift of a portion of the Alaskan coast in 1899, and great lateral movement in the up to 21-foot offsets along part of the San Andreas Fault during the San Francisco earthquake in 1906.

Faults are zones of weakness in the earth's crust. They often are linear features, called *fault lines*, along which rock strata move as a result of diastrophism. (Terms in the discussion that follows refer to Figure 4.24. Only those in italics are generally used.) The plane of movement is called a fault plane, or fault surface; and because individual planes are rarely perpendicular to the surface, a hanging wall and a foot wall are defined. In relation to the plane of the fault into the crust, the hanging wall lies above and the foot wall below the fault plane. When the hanging wall is elevated, it forms an overhanging cliff; when the foot wall is uplifted, it never forms an overhanging cliff. Either of the cliffs so elevated is called a *fault scarp*.

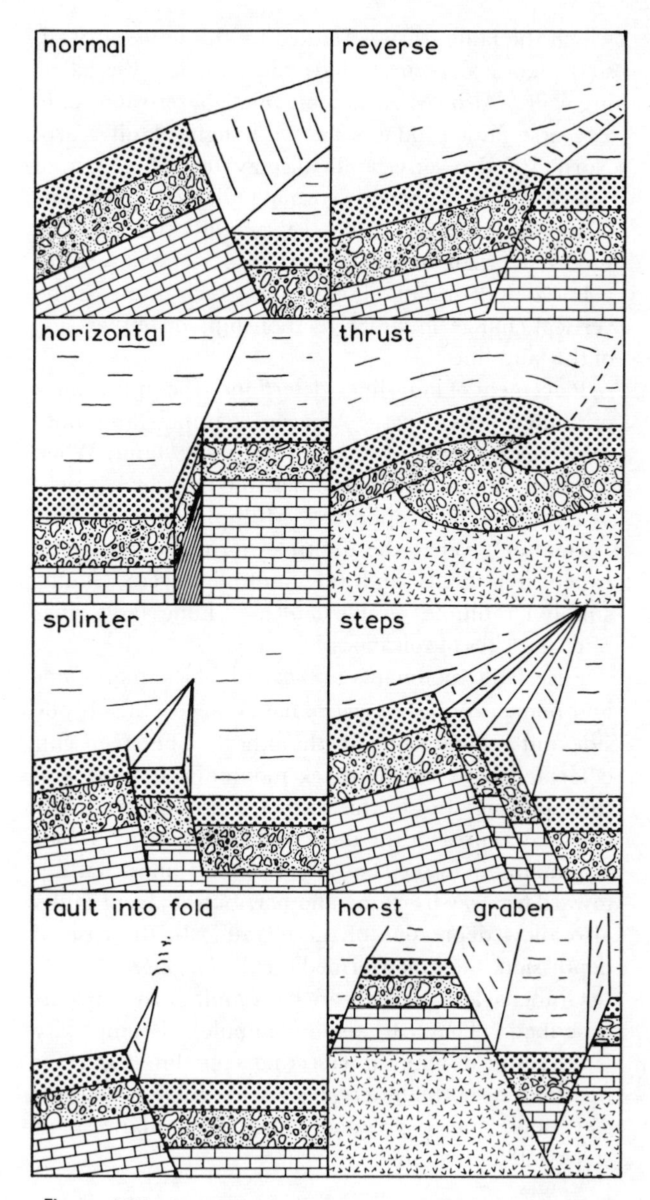

Figure 4.24 Diastrophism: faulting and land forms due to faulting.

The various kinds of faults are associated with vertical and horizontal displacements of the strata on either side of the fault line. Vertical movements produce normal and reverse faults. Lateral movements produce horizontal faults. A normal fault is one in which the fault scarp is formed by the foot wall and the hanging wall appears to have moved below the foot wall. A reverse, or thrust, fault is one in which the fault scarp is formed by the hanging wall, so the foot wall seems to have moved below the hanging wall. Also, when not modified by erosion, only a reverse fault produces an overhanging fault scarp. Normal and reverse faults display one of a pair of contrasting movements. Normal faults are extensions of the earth's crust, and reverse faults are contractions. Horizontal, or lateral, displacement creates a horizontal or lateral, fault in which there is no vertical change in strata relationships on either side of the fault line.

Placement of fault lines determines the appearance of faulted landscapes. Adjacent parallel fault lines may create a series of steps, called a step fault. When one fault line runs into another, the interior segment of land is a fault splinter. Multiple faults can be normal or reverse, the multiple normal faults being called step faults and the multiple reverse faults, simply "multiple reverse faults." Long fault lines often are sites of volcanoes.

Pure fault mountains are called block mountains and horsts. A *block mountain* has a steep cliff on one side and a slight slope on the other. The steep cliff is located between the block mountain summit and the fault line; and in the case of a normal fault, the cliff may represent the unaltered fault scarp. A *horst* is a mountain formed between two fault lines that dip toward or away from one another, but adjacent faults also allow depression of the terrain. In the case of depression, the valley formed is called a *graben.*

Grabens and horsts can be simple structures as described. They can also be complex. Complexity is the result of many intersecting fault lines and, for this reason, normally creates an irregular pattern of elevations and depressions, including many fault steps and fault splinters.

DIASTROPHISM MOUNTAIN TYPES

Folded Mountains. If formed rapidly and with little erosion, folded mountains consist of sedimentary beds that are bent into isolated domes or into a parallel series of arches and troughs. This landscape is reshaped by the forces of erosion (Figure 4.25); in most cases streams are the greatest erosion factor. Further stages of the life cycle are as presented (but oversimplified) in the discussion of erosion. The simplified picture occurs only if valley streams are the sole effective agent of erosion, so that youth consists of V-shaped valleys and sharp ridges. However, in most cases both isolated folds and series of folds follow the dome mountain type of erosion pattern; main streams drain the folds, proceed to the summit, cut into the summit, and eventually give rise to tributary streams running the length of the summit. Therefore, maturity features reduced elevations that are characterized by hogbacks. In old age, the landscape is a peneplain.

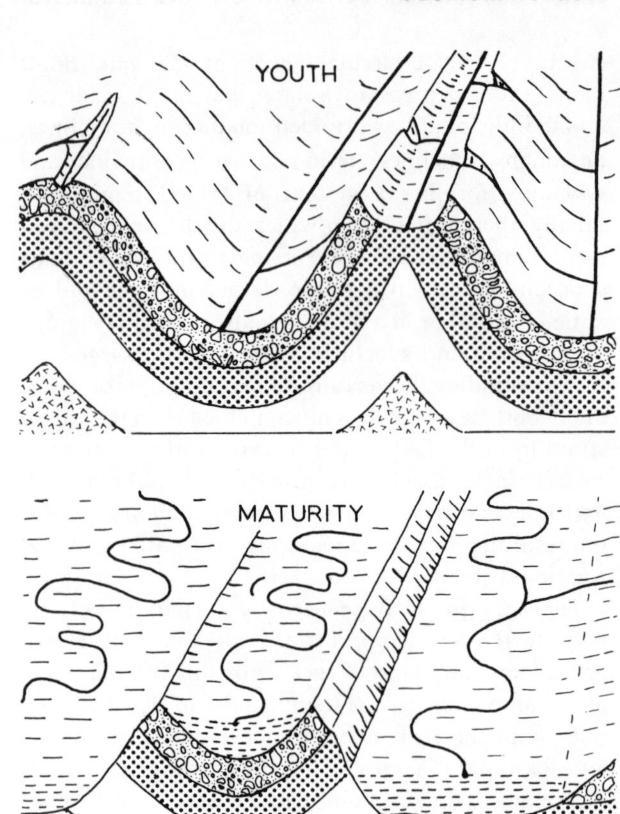

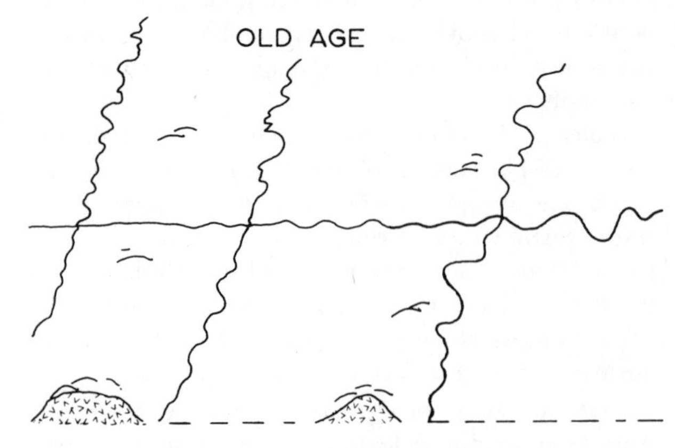

Figure 4.25 The life cycle of folded mountains.

Folding or uplift may take place after or before peneplain formation and may cause rejuvenation. If rejuvenation involves new folding, arches and troughs form, but, because the land was eroded prior to new folding, the rock strata no longer follow the folds. Erosion leads to this confusing picture because differential removal of the once continuous rock layers causes new folding to result in complexly overturned and contorted layers. On the other hand, if rejuvenation involves uplift, the landscape still emphasizes the old pattern of erosion, but is modified by the differential hardness of the various strata. Therefore, many cases of rejuvenation produce land forms that cannot be distinguished from complex mountains. In fact, rejuvenation is sufficient to characterize the new elevations as complex mountains.

Block Mountains. Initially, block mountains present a steep cliff that rises above the fault line and a gentle back slope that retreats from the summit and away from the fault line. During the youth of block mountains, erosion slightly modifies the cliff and back slope, but the original outline of the block is not greatly changed (Figure 4.26). Maturity occurs when both cliff and back slope are dissected by V-shaped valleys. The streams that excavate these valleys also form alluvial fans in front of the cliff, and those streams that drain the back slope may form a lake, especially in situations between the back slope of one block mountain and the cliff of another. In spite of this erosion, mature block mountains still maintain their general outline and the position of the fault line is not obliterated. In the early stages of old age, the once continuous block mountain becomes a row of rolling hills. This is the final picture before complete peneplaination.

Grabens and Horsts. Grabens and horsts are features of complexly faulted areas, so both tend to be complex rectangular blocks displaced between parallel fault lines. For example, grabens and horsts may occur among a confusion of fault lines or be irregular because fault lines are not linear or parallel to one another.

In many respects, horsts are complex block mountains. For this reason, the life cycle of horsts and blocks follow the same general pattern of initial clarity of features, mature modification but with the same general outline, and the old peneplain. The erosion of horsts and blocks usually produces residual forms that are characteristic of these elevations. The forms are trapezoidal and triangular facets (Figure 4.26) upon the cliffs, and each facet is produced between adjacent streams coursing down the cliff. The streams, by progressive erosion, leave, first, a trapezoidal, residual land form and, later, a triangular one. These residues are different from those of folded mountains, and the two fault mountain types often can be distinguished by observation of both sides of a fault mountain. The block has only a single fault line, hence one faceted cliff; the horst has both sides faceted.

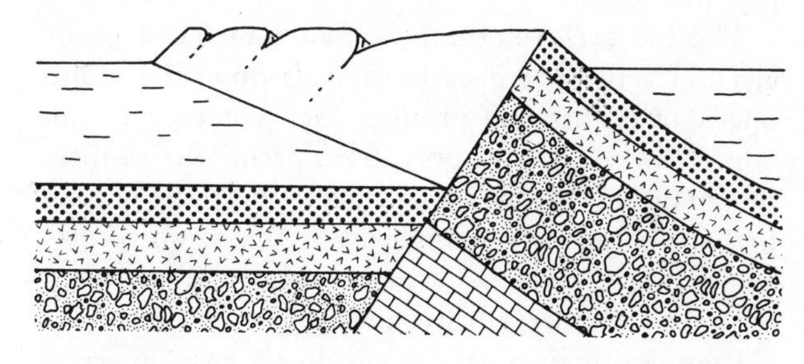

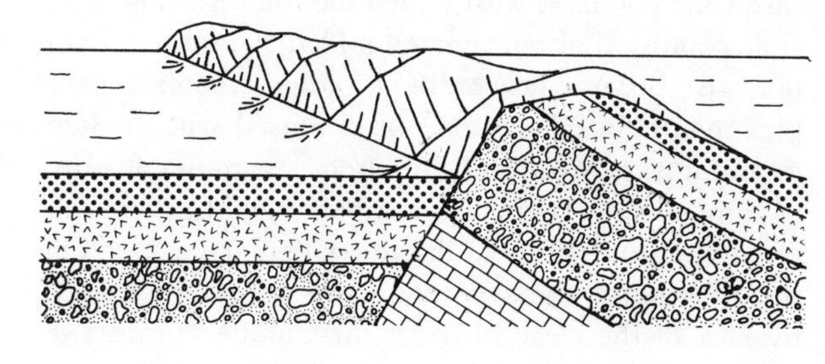

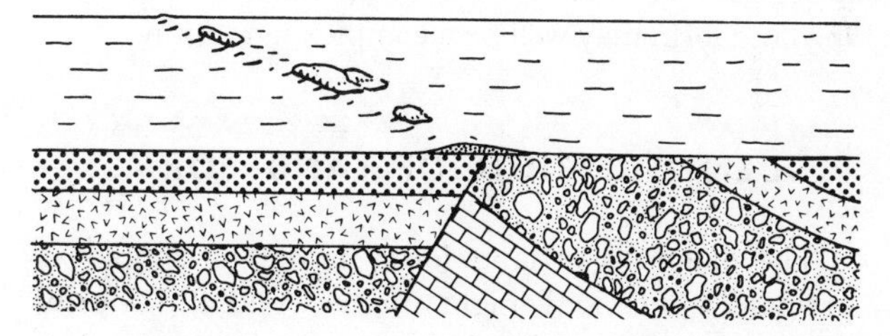

Figure 4.26 The life cycle of fault block mountains.

Complex Mountains. Complex mountains can form from any kind of rock. One might call them combination mountains because, by definition, each consists of any single mountain or group of mountains elevated as a result of more than one major process. For example, the processes of folding, faulting, and vulcanism may all contribute to formation of a single complex mountain.

The life cycle of complex mountains cannot be given in general terms. It depends upon the multiplicity of factors that produce each complex mountain. However, the factors cause a peculiarity of these mountains in that the initial stages tend to be absent, perhaps because the complexity is the result of progressive development. Otherwise, the cycle is characterized by youth, maturity, and old age.

Complex mountains are not always easy to segregate from blocks or horsts. On the other hand, they rarely are confused with folded mountains. The possible confusion of rejuvenated folded mountains does not exist, because new uplift or folding creates a complex mountain. They may be confused with faulted mountains, because faulting often is a major feature of complexity. Therefore, complex mountain erosion often sculptures trapezoidal to triangular facets. On the other hand, complex mountains are characterized by lack of the clear, distinct, or unique features of vulcanism, folding, or faulting. Rather, land forms have the perplexing characteristics of two or more processes. Therefore, when lack of clarity is observed, the land form may well be a complex mountain.

IDENTIFICATION OF LAND FORMS

The diagnosis of land forms is not as simple as previous discussions might imply. Often, basically uncomplicated land forms are not completely typical end products of the processes that created them. To be sure of what occurred, detailed study by a geologist often is required. However, many other land forms are fairly distinctive; one of the major constructive processes appears clear, especially during youth, and one or even more of the destructive processes may be apparent. In such cases, if the features discussed in this chapter are understood, they can be applied to a local situation and should lead to a fairly accurate picture of the general land forms of a locality. However, any help that can be obtained should be used. Such help is often available in detailed studies by geologists.

The more detailed geological reports are of two types, local and statewide. Both types have maps and sometimes detailed descriptions of the particular places. They emphasize the distribution of such things as fault lines, rock types, and other information that allows more precise identification of land forms. To obtain such reports, one can either consult the library of a nearby college or university, or write to the appropriate state agency. State agencies such as Departments of Natural Resources or Divisions of Mines know if such publications are available. For example, the California State Division of Mines sells individual sheets of a colored geological map of California. Like many other publications, the California map is subdivided into segments that consider local areas.

Less detailed sources of information are provided for much larger geographic areas. This information is generally summarized in a hierarchy of land form classification on a geographic basis. As in the classification of plants and animals, these land form summaries have all-inclusive categories containing a series of progressively smaller subdivisions. Such publications are of some local interest. Each places a given area into its general pattern of gross past geological history. Sometimes local land forms are described in detail.

MORPHOGENIC REGIONS

Additional help in characterizing areas is gained from the concept of morphogenic regions. Such regions are diagnosed on the basis of the predominant agents of erosion. Because agents of erosion reflect climate, morphogenic regions are associated with climate, vegetation, and soils. Table 4.1 displays these associations. In the table agents of erosion are rated as to their relative effects: maximum (1), moderate (2), and minimum (3). In the case of soil formation an "x" is used to indicate which processes are of most importance in each region. The processes of soil formation are explained in more detail in the next chapter. Gleization is a soil-forming process characteristic of arctic areas, podsolization of cool moist climates, laterization of warm and moist climates, and calcification of arid areas.

IMPORTANCE OF IDENTIFICATION

Although correct identification of land forms is not always possible, this is not as unfortunate as it might appear. Insofar as natural history relationships between organisms and their environment are concerned, precise designation of land forms is unnecessary. Usually, the only requirement is the nature of

TABLE 4.1 MORPHOGENIC REGIONS: THEIR CLIMATE, VEGETATION, EROSION AGENTS, AND SOIL FORMATION

Morphogenic Region	Climate	Vegetation	Agents of Erosion						Soil Formation			
			Glacial	Mass movement	Wind	Running water	Mechanical	Chemical	Gleization	Podsolization	Laterization	Calcification
Glacial	Perpetual frost	None	1	2	3	3	3	1–3				
Periglacial	Arctic or tundra	Tundra		1	1–2	3	3	2	x	x		
Boreal	Semiarctic	Coniferous forest		2	2–3	2	2–3	2–3		x		
Maritime	Wet, humid	Middle latitude forest		1	2–3	1–2	1–2	3		x	x	
Selva	Wet	Tropical rain forest				3	1	3		x	x	
Moderate	Humid, sub-humid	Nonconiferous forest, savanna, grassland		2	2–3	1	1–3	3		x	x	
Savanna	Subhumid, semiarid	Savanna, grass-land		2–3	2	1–3	2–3	3		x	x	x
Semiarid	Semiarid	Steppe		3	1	1–2	2–3	3			x	x
Arid	Arid	Desert		3	1	3	3	3				x

the topography, the purely geographic relationships and form of such things as elevations, depressions, and streams. This will be appreciated after the discussion of ecological factors in subsequent chapters.

SELECTED READINGS

Atwood, Wallace W., 1940. *The Physiographic Provinces of North America.* Ginn and Co., Boston.

Dury, G. N., 1959. *The Face of the Earth.* Penguin Books, Harmondsworth, Middlesex, England.

Eardley, A. J., 1951. *Structural Geology of North America.* Harper & Brothers, New York.

Emmons, William H., et al., 1960. *Geology Principles and Processes.* 5th ed. McGraw-Hill Book Co., New York.

Fenneman, Nevin M., 1931. *Physiography of Western United States.* McGraw-Hill Book Co., New York.

———, 1938. *Physiography of Eastern United States.* McGraw-Hill Book Co., New York.

Hinds, Norman E. A., 1952. *Evolution of the California Landscape.* Calif. Division of Mines, San Francisco.

Larousse Encyclopedia of the Earth. 1961. G. P. Putnam's Sons, New York.

Life Editorial Staff and Lincoln Barnett, 1955. *The World We Live In.* Time Inc., New York.

Life Editorial Staff and Arthur Beiser, 1962. *The Earth.* Time Inc., New York.

Lobeck, A. K., 1939. *Geomorphology, an Introduction to the Study of Landscapes.* McGraw-Hill Book Co., New York.

Longwell, Chester R., and Richard F. Flint, 1962. *Introduction to Physical Geology.* 2d ed. John Wiley & Sons, New York.

Namowitz, Samuel N., and Donald B. Stone, 1960. *Earth Sciences.* D. Van Nostrand Co., Princeton, N. J.

Scientific American Books. 1957. *The Planet Earth.* Simon & Schuster, New York.

Shimer, John A., 1959. *This Sculptured Earth.* Columbia University Press, New York.

Strahler, Arthur N., 1960. *Physical Geography.* 2d ed. John Wiley & Sons, New York.

Thornbury, William D., 1960. *Principles of Geomorphology.* John Wiley & Sons, New York.

Von Engeln, O. D., 1942. *Geomorphology.* The Macmillan Co., New York.

Wyckoff, Jerome, 1960. *The Story of Geology.* Golden Press, New York.

5 PETROLOGY AND PEDOLOGY

Rocks and Soils

Although their importance is often overlooked, rocks are essential to life. The solidification of igneous rock involves the release of oxygen and water into the atmosphere. The physical properties of rocks, especially those properties associated with surface temperature, have a bearing on local climatic conditions. Further, climatic associations relate to the topographic features that are really rock accumulations. Rocks and climate are important contributors to soil formation. Soil, partly rock, is extremely important in providing a substrate for plants and animals. Because rocks are composed of minerals, they supply certain nutritional needs of living creatures. For example, various salts and water are essential foods. Water, the most essential food, is in its pure form a mineral; however, in nature, because of extent and impurities, it often is a rock!

This chapter will examine the kinds of rocks in the physical environment and the effects of rocks upon local land forms. The types of rocks—their structure as affected by constructive and destructive geological processes—impart the features of a landscape.

MINERALS AND ROCKS

There are certain criteria for distinguishing between minerals and rocks. Minerals are pure or homogeneous substances of definite chemical composition and are shaped by natural inorganic processes. For example, a molecule of pure table salt is a combination of one atom of sodium and one of chlorine; so is the mineral, halite. Halite is a mineral because it is always pure sodium chloride, a compound of definite chemical composition united by processes not involving living creatures. Therefore, the criteria for a mineral would exclude any compound that is chemically variable, is a plant or animal product, or is man made. For this reason, man-made synthetic gems and manufactured products, even though they are exact replicas of minerals, are not minerals. There are about 1500 kinds of minerals in nature.

Rocks are mostly combinations of two or more minerals; however, certain pure substances can be rocks. A true mineral is also considered a rock if it forms a large feature of the landscape, as, for example, a body of pure water or a hill of serpentine, hematite, or gypsum. Any homogeneous material with variable chemical composition is a rock rather than a mineral (e.g., obsidian whose composition varies irregularly from place to place). Organic products, even pure substances, are rocks (e.g., petroleum, coal, and organic limestone). In this respect, it is of interest to note that pure but organically derived calcium carbonate is limestone, whereas the physical product is a mineral called calcite. Meteorites are also rocks.

Two additional terms, *gem* and *stone*, are frequently applied to rocks and minerals. Gems are precious and semiprecious minerals or rocks; their chemical composition is not considered. Stones can be almost any kind of rock or mineral; there is no precise definition of the term.

ROCK-FORMING MINERALS

All minerals are found either within or closely associated with rocks. However, only eight minerals are frequently encountered. These are the common rock-forming minerals. In the following account, consideration is limited to the eight common types and their diagnostic features. The purpose is not to provide any real discussion of minerals, but rather to identify them as an aid to rock identification.

QUARTZ

Quartz is the hardest of the common minerals. Its appearance is glassy but it can be clear, milky white, or any light to dark color. Structurally, it can be massive (like a chunk of glass), granular (like sand grains), or crystalline (in six-sided, geometrically organized crystals). When quartz is struck, curved chips are broken off, leaving a clamshell-like depression. Light rays sparkle and scatter in all directions from its surface. The optical properties do not include a deep or mirrorlike reflection of light.

FELDSPARS

Feldspars, a group of similar minerals, can be scratched by quartz but not by a knife. They are glassy like quartz, but have a satiny sheen not found in that mineral. Common feldspars are usually white, cream, gray, or tan, but light to dark feldspars of other colors are also found. They can be massive or crystalline. When struck, a feldspar may fracture into curved chips like quartz, but it also cleaves into slightly slanted blocks whose surfaces have a satiny sheen. The latter kind of breaking is related to the structure of the mineral and is called *cleavage*. Minerals that cleave have cleavage surfaces that, when properly oriented to light, give a deep, mirrorlike shine. The satiny sheen of feldspars is a very conspicuous mirrorlike shine.

OLIVINE

Unweathered olivine is too hard to be scratched by quartz; however, in nature it is usually weathered to the point where even feldspars might scratch it. Olivine is a glassy, green mineral. It is usually found as embedded grains in igneous rocks. Commonly, it has been altered to serpentine. When it occurs as large, pure masses, it is also dunnite, a rock. It rarely occurs as crystals. Olivine fractures like quartz and feldspars, but unlike either, it usually appears in the form of glassy, green grains. Cleavage is poor.

PYROXENES

Minerals in the pyroxene group may or may not be scratched by a knife. The commonest mineral in this group is dark greenish to black, glassy augite, which commonly occurs as grains or as a few scattered, small, short and blocky crystals in igneous rocks. Like all pyroxenes, augite is brittle, fractures unevenly, and cleaves in two directions almost at right angles to one another. Augite's crystals and cleavage distinguish it from hornblende.

HORNBLENDE

Hornblende, the commonest mineral of the amphibole group, may or may not be scratched by a knife. It is usually green or black and generally occurs as grains in igneous rocks, as parallel layers of long, thin crystals in schist, or as pure solid masses of hornblendite. It breaks, fracturing somewhat like the other common minerals, but cleaving in two directions at angles of either 56 or 124 degrees. Therefore, cleavage angles alone distinguish hornblende from augite.

DOLOMITE

Dolomite, common in sedimentary rocks and rare in metamorphic rocks, can easily be scratched with a knife but cannot be scratched by a penny. It is colorless, white, pinkish, or has light tints of color. Like calcite, it fractures into chips and cleaves into the form of a rhombus (resembling a cube, but with the corner angles not right angles). However, dolomite is harder than calcite and will fizz in acid only after being scratched or powdered.

CALCITE

Calcite is of common occurrence and barely can be scratched by a penny. It is colorless, white, or has pale tints of color. It is similar in appearance to dolomite, but can be distinguished from it in that it fizzes readily in acid without being scratched.

MICA

Micas are the softest of the common rock-forming minerals. They often can be scratched with a fingernail. This group of minerals is of common occurrence in igneous and metamorphic rocks. They are glassy or pearly minerals that are clear, white, black, or colorful. Micas readily cleave by splitting into paper-thin, transparent, flexible plates. Their cleavage causes an extreme mirrorlike shine.

ROCK TYPES

There are three major groups of rocks, *igneous*, *sedimentary*, and *metamorphic*. Igneous rocks are made by solidification of magma when it penetrates the earth's crust. Magma may solidify within the crust, shaping intrusive igneous rocks, or upon the surface, forming extrusive igneous rocks.

Sedimentary rocks are the erosion products of any kind of rock. They are composed of fine particles (marl, soil, loess, clay, sand, etc.), large particles (gravel, talus, till, etc.), fine to large cemented particles (shale, sandstone, conglomerate, breccia, etc.), organic products (amber, coal, limestone, petroleum, etc.), and chemical deposition (limestone, chert, etc.).

Metamorphic rocks are wrought from the alteration of other rocks. The different appearances of these rocks are dependent, at least in part, upon the parent material. Metamorphism produces soapy, noncrystalline rocks (soapstone and serpentine); crystal masses (marble and dolomitic marble); hard, glassy masses (quartzite); separable sheets (slate); thin, often separable, crystalline layers (schist); and distorted, crystal masses (gneiss).

IGNEOUS ROCKS

The various types of igneous rock can be recognized by their texture and composition. Texturally they range from glassy to fine grained to mixed fine and coarse grained to coarse grained to coarse and large grained to large grained. Also, any of the rocks can occur as large masses or as fragments. Insofar as composition is concerned, the chemicals found in the molten magma determine the minerals present in the solidified product, the igneous rock. If the rock has a large amount of acid-forming silica, it is called acidic or silicic; if it is low in silica and higher in sodium, calcium, magnesium, and carbonate, it is basic. There are also intermediate types.

TEXTURE

The texture of igneous rocks is determined by their rate of cooling. When cooling is very rapid, a glassy texture results. Progressively longer periods of cooling allow larger and larger crystals, the fine-grained to large-grained rocks, to be formed. This rate of cooling is associated with the kind of magma flows. For example, lavas cool very rapidly and form glassy or fine-grained rocks. On the other hand, deep batholith magma is insulated, so it loses heat very slowly and grows to coarse or large-grained rocks.

Between the extremes of glassy and large-grained rocks are many texture classes. However, it should be realized that there is actually a continuous gradation of texture from one extreme to the other; the texture classes are a matter of convenience for the purpose of identification and study, and one should not expect always to be able to assign any igneous rock to a definite texture class.

Glassy Igneous Rocks. Glassy igneous rocks are most likely to harden from magma that explodes into the air, lies upon the surface of a lava flow, or remains on a volcano. In such places, cooling is so rapid that chemical compounds do not segregate and, therefore, minerals do not form. The rock is thus a glass, or slag.

Texture subtypes are dependent upon the physical structure of the rocks. If the glass is massive (i.e., has no holes), the rock is obsidian; if it has fine, closely spaced holes, the rock is pumice (which often floats in water); if it has larger and fewer, irregularly spaced holes, the rock is scoria. The holes result when lava containing gas bubbles is solidified.

Fine-grained Igneous Rocks. Fine-grained igneous rocks have individual minerals in the shape of crystals, but the crystals are so small that the rocks usually appear noncrystalline. On occasion, fine crystal specks may be discernible. Such rocks are called *felsite*, or felsitic rocks, and are usually found in lava flows.

Felsite Porphyry. Any porphyry represents two phases of rock formation: first, the early development of larger crystals in magma; then the development of smaller crystals and/or glass. Porphyries might be confused with scoria or pumice whose holes are filled with other rock. However, porphyries have angular crystals rather than the oval or tubelike materials in some scoria or pumice.

Most igneous rocks have some scattered, larger crystals. However, a porphyry generally is not recognized unless the larger crystals constitute about 25 per cent or more of the igneous rock.

Felsite porphyry consists of visible crystals within a matrix of fine-grained, invisible or almost invisible crystals. This rock is found in dikes, laccoliths, and sills.

Coarse-grained Igneous Rocks. In coarse-grained igneous rocks, also called *granitoid rocks*, the crystals are large enough to be seen with the unaided eye and are more or less uniform in size. Although crystals reach the size of a large pea, most grains are 3 to 5 millimeters in diameter. Such rocks are in laccoliths, stocks, and batholiths.

Granitoid Porphyry. Like any other porphyry, granitoid porphyry consists of larger crystals in a matrix of finer crystals. In this instance, the finer crystals are granitoid. This porphyry also tends to differ from the felsite type by having more of the larger crystals—actually, many larger crystals rather than a few. These granitoid porphyries are found in the same places as felsite porphyries and coarse-grained igneous rocks.

Large-grained Igneous Rocks. Any igneous rock with crystals larger than a pea is called *pegmatite*. Some pegmatite crystals are more than 40 feet long. Therefore, these rocks must cool more slowly than any other texture class. Pegmatites form in deep, well-insulated places—primarily in batholiths, but also in stocks.

Fragmental Igneous Rocks. Fragmental igneous rock is produced by vulcanism. It consists of assorted, cemented, "fire-broken" fragments, so-called *pyroclastic rocks*. If such rocks are mostly volcanic dust or ash, they are called tuff; if mostly larger fragments, they are called breccia or agglomerate. The term "breccia" is applied to any kind of cemented fragments, including sedimentary and metamorphic fragments. "Agglomerate" is the specific term applied to volcanic breccia.

COMPOSITION

Within each of the texture classes, igneous rocks are further segregated on the basis of chemical composition. They are classified as acidic, intermediate, or basic. Chemical composition is indicated by color. Acidic rocks usually have 25 per cent or less dark minerals; intermediate rocks have approximately 50 per cent dark minerals; and basic rocks have 75 per cent or more dark minerals. This color criterion is used in the attempts presented below to identify the kinds of igneous rocks. Also of help in identification is the fact that intermediate rocks are rich in hornblende and acidic rocks are rich in pyroxene.

Both acidic and intermediate rocks are further subdivided on the basis of the presence or absence of quartz in the rock.

IGNEOUS ROCK TYPES

The above criteria are used to segregate the igneous rocks into the main types. Although further differentiation can be made, the classification indicated in Table 5.1 is adequate for our purposes.

TABLE 5.1 CLASSIFICATION OF IGNEOUS ROCKS

Texture	Acidic (light)	Intermediate	Basic (dark)
Glassy	Pumice, Obsidian		Scoria, Obsidian
Fine-grained (dense or felsitic)	Rhyolite	Andesite	Basalt
Fine-grained with larger crystals	Individual kinds of felsite prophyry		
Visible crystals (granitoid)	Granite	Diorite	Gabbro
Granitoid with some larger crystals	Individual kinds of granitoid porphyry		
Very large crystals	Pegmatite		
Fragmental	Tuff, Agglomerate		

SEDIMENTARY ROCKS

The different kinds of sedimentary rocks are separated on the basis of particle size, composition, origin, and whether or not the individual particles are cemented together. On the basis of origin these rocks are termed *clastic rocks* if they are the products of weathering. If the individual particles are over 10 inches in diameter, the rocks are called *boulders*; if between 2½ and 10 inches, *cobbles*; if between 1/6 and 2½, *pebbles;* if 1/6 to 1/25 inch, *granules;* if 1/500 to 1/25 inch, *sand*; if 1/5000 to 1/500 inch, *silt;* and if smaller, *clay*. However, cobbles, pebbles, and granules are usually grouped as gravel, and silt and clay as clay.

Clastic rocks are also differentiated on the basis of their primary agent of erosion. Unassorted angular, polished or scratched boulders, pebbles, and finer particles left by glaciers are called *till*. Coarse fragmentary rocks produced by weathering are called *talus*. Coarse rocks rounded by water are called *gravel*. Finer rocks, rounded and deposited by water or wind are called *sand*. The finest materials, if deposited by water, are called *clay*; if deposited by wind, they are called *loess*. Further types of clastic rocks are formed when the above types are cemented. Cemented till is *tillite;* cemented gravel is *conglomerate;* cemented talus is *breccia*; and cemented clay or loess is *shale*.

The other sedimentary rocks, according to origin, are called *nonclastic*. They are formed by decomposition, dissolution, and redeposition of other rocks and organic matter. Limestone is composed mostly of calcium carbonate remains of plants and animals. Small, soft and porous; cemented particles are called *chalk* and cemented combinations of chalk and clay are called *marl*. Also, the spongy, porous, or earthy limestones accumulated at the mouths of springs are called *tufa*, and the solid, often layered, limestone deposited in caves is called *travertine*. The different travertine layers may or may not be of different colors.

Other nonclastic rocks are common. Deposited silica is called *chert*. The mass of siliceous skeletons of diatoms (microscopic algae) is called *diatomite*, or diatomaceous earth. Carbon from plants, by processes of decomposition and progressive compaction, occurs as *peat*, *lignite*, or *coal*. Phosphate from animals or igneous rocks gathers as phosphate rock; however, phosphate often is deposited with carbonates and is incorporated within limestone. Compounds, mainly from animals, provide petroleum and asphalt. Various salts are also collected, the most common being *gypsum* and *halite*, a hydrous calcium sulfate and common table salt. The accumulation of excrement and skeletal remains of certain animals, especially birds and bats, is *guano*. Finally, iron in solution may dehydrate to form *yellow ochre*, or *limonite*, and *red ochre*, or *hematite*.

SEDIMENT STRUCTURE

Sediments usually are layered into beds that are separable from one another. In other words, each stratum normally possesses unique structure. The exact character of individual layers is dependent upon many environmental factors (e.g., current variations, seasonal and long range climatic changes, sea level fluctuations, and organism number and type changes). Due to these factors, stratification can be (1) cross-bedded, sediments laid down in one or more angles to the horizontal; (2) graded, consist of strata of mud, sand, and gravel that grade into one another; or (3) lens-shaped.

In addition, sediments and therefore layers can show the influence of other environmental features. For example, mud cracks occur where mud shrank and dried; ripple marks where waves traveled over a shallow bottom, or where wind traveled over sand; rill marks where ocean waters returned to the sea, or rain ran downhill; raindrop impressions where rain fell; and wave marks where coasts were located. Finally, fossils are frequently found in strata. These remains naturally indicate the kinds and numbers of plants and animals present during the period of deposition.

After sedimentation, the deposits may be altered secondarily. The commoner secondary alteration products are concretions, geodes, and stylolites. *Concretions* are variably shaped, seemingly foreign rock, within a stratum. They probably develop by dissolution of rather uncommon materials from the parent stratum and concentration of these materials about some object. Some concretions are cracked by jointing and then the cracks are filled by other substances. The resulting products are called *septaria*, or *septarian concretions*.

Geodes are cavities filled with crystals. The crystals grow from the edge toward the center of the cavity and probably as a result of chemicals in solution entering a cavity. *Veins* are very firm bindings between partings, or cracks, in any kind of rock, especially limestones. The binding material usually is

TABLE 5.2 CLASSIFICATION OF SEDIMENTARY ROCKS

Rock	Origin	Remarks
Talus	Rock weathering	Coarse angular fragments
Breccia	Talus	Cemented
Soil	Rock weathering	Unsorted material plus humus
Gravel	Rock weathering	Coarse fragments rounded by wind and water
Conglomerate	Gravel	Cemented
Sand	Rock weathering	Finer wind or water deposits
Sandstone	Sand	Cemented
Clay	Rock weathering	Finest material deposited by water
Loess	Rock weathering	Finest material deposited by wind
Shale	Clay or loess	Cemented
Chalk	Calcium carbonate	Soft, generally porous and fossiliferous
Marl	Calcium carbonate and clay	Soft, generally porous and fossiliferous
Limestone	Chalk or marl	Further compacted and cemented
Dolomitic limestone	Dolomite plus impurities	Compacted and cemented
Till	Glaciation	Unsorted material
Tillite	Till	Cemented
Diatomite	Diatoms	Compacted silica shells of microscopic algae
Chert or cherty rocks	Silica deposits	Impurities affect silica color and glassiness
Peat	Plants, usually sphagnum moss	Decay and compaction
Lignite to coal	Peat	Progressive compaction
Amber	Conifer gum	Fossilized resins
Petroleum	Organisms	Hydrocarbon remains
Asphalt	Organisms	Hydrocarbon remains
Tuff	Volcanic ash	Weathered and cemented
Phosphate rock	Animals or igneous rocks	Deposited, compacted, and cemented
Guano	Animals	Wastes and remains
Gypsum	Calcium sulfate	Dehydration; a mineral
Halite	Sodium chloride	Dehydration; table salt; a mineral
Limonite	Iron solution	Dehydration; yellow ochre
Hematite	Iron solution	Dehydration; red ochre
Fossils	Organism remains	Preserved, cast, etc.; often in limestone
Concretions	Altered material	Solid, variable foreign rocks in a stratum
Geodes	Growth in a cavity	Crystals within a hollow rock
Veins	Deposition	Materials filling cracks in strata

so strong that any further breaks will not occur along the original partings.

SEDIMENTARY ROCKS

Table 5.2 summarizes the common types of sedimentary rocks and their diagnostic features.

METAMORPHIC ROCKS

Metamorphic rocks are formed when any kind of rock is altered by pressure, temperature, and/or chemical changes associated with commonly occurring geological processes. These geological processes can be grouped into four types of metamorphism: contact, regional, replacement, and geothermal. *Contact metamorphism*, also called *igneous*, is caused by the extreme temperature and pressure of magma. In such metamorphism the greatest change in rocks occurs at the point of contact between the magma and adjacent rocks. *Regional* (*dynamic* or *kinetic*) *metamorphism*, like contact, is also brought about by temperature and pressure, but as a result of folding of the outer portion of the earth's crust. *Replacement* or *hydrothermal metamorphism* is caused by chemical changes triggered by superheated waters and their chemicals. *Geothermal metamorphism* is another temperature–pressure process, but the metamorphic conditions are from deep within the earth's crust. The temperature is derived from the one degree Farenheit increase of temperature for every 60 feet of depth and the pressure from the mass of materials above the site of metamorphism.

There are definite grades of metamorphism, and a graded series of metamorphic rocks can stem from a single kind of rock. Such a series is in direct relationship to the intensity of metamorphism. For example, progressive metamorphism will alter shale to slate, slate to phyllite, phyllite to schist, and perhaps schist to gneiss. This tends to be an oversimplification, because one type of schist may give rise to another schist. Another example of progressive metamorphism would be peat to lignite, lignite to bituminous coal, bituminous to anthracite coal, and anthracite to graphite. Therefore, metamorphism is a continuous process and in naming metamorphic rocks—or any other rocks, for that matter—man is indicating "landmarks" in a continuous series.

CLASSIFICATION

Metamorphic rock classification is based upon structure and texture, factors used to designate foliate and nonfoliate categories. The foliate, or leaflike, group consists mainly of thin, flat minerals, usually mica or chlorite, that cleave (separate along structural lines of the mineral) parallel to the flat dimension. Therefore, these rocks have a tendency to split into flat sheets along the plane of leaflike mineral orientation which also is the plane of cleavage. The nonfoliate types are neither leaflike minerals nor do they separate easily into flat sheets. Rather, they usually occur as crystalline masses similar to the coarse-grained igneous rocks, or as microcrystalline masses (although some crystals may be visible) similar to fine-grained igneous rocks.

Foliate Metamorphic Rocks. In the discussion of progressive metamorphism the main kinds of foliate rocks, slate, phyllite, schist, and gneiss, were named. Although there are many variations of each kind, only the main types are mentioned. *Slate* can be of almost any color. It originates and grades upward from shale and merges into phyllite. However, slate usually is a fine-grained, homogeneous rock that separates into relatively smooth, thin to thick sheets. Well-formed, thin slate is used as blackboards. Slate might be confused with cherty shale; however, the latter is much harder (cherty shale cannot be scratched with a knife; slate can).

Phyllite is very much like slate, but phyllite texture is coarser and its composition is higher in leaflike, lustrous minerals. Although phyllite may be distinguishable from other rocks, the more slate-like examples often are grouped with slate and the more schist-like examples with schist.

The many kinds of *schist* are recognized on the basis of leaflike minerals being arranged in parallel lines or bands that can be separated. Large crystals are uncommon; if they occur, they are scattered within the primary mass of leaflike and layered minerals.

Gneisses resemble schists in that both are banded and show foliation. However, only gneisses are masses of coarse-grained, although often warped and flattened, minerals. Moreover, gneisses are rarely separable into flat slabs. They are often characterized by the presence of feldspars.

Nonfoliate Metamorphic Rocks. The main nonfoliate types are quartzite, marble, soapstone, and serpentine. *Quartzite* is metamorphosed sandstone and consists of quartz sand grains fused in quartz. Therefore, when these rocks are broken and splinters or curved chips are removed, breaks are through, not around, the individual sand grains. *Marble* is metamorphosed limestone. It consists of a mass of coarse crystals that will fizz in acid. Another type of marble, *dolomitic marble*, is the metamorphic product of the mineral dolomite. Although both marbles assume the same colors and general form, dolomitic marble will fizz in acid only after being powdered. *Soapstone*, or *steatite*, is a hydrothermal alteration product composed mainly of the mineral, talc. *Serpentine* is formed in much the same manner as soapstone and is quite similar to that rock. Both soapstone and serpentine feel soapy or greasy and often are of greenish tint; soapstone can be scratched with a fingernail and serpentine cannot.

METAMORPHIIC ROCK TYPES

Table 5.3 summarizes the common metamorphic rocks and their origin.

ROCK FORMS AND STRUCTURES

The physical characteristics of each of the three major rock types are such that different kinds of

TABLE 5.3 CLASSIFICATION OF METAMORPHIC ROCKS

Original Composition	Metamorphic Process	Metamorphic Rock
Variable	Hydrothermal	Steatite (soapstone)
Variable	Hydrothermal	Serpentine
Conglomerate	Pressure and heat	Gneiss or schist
Sandstone	Hydrothermal and/or pressure and heat	Quartzite
Shale	Pressure and heat	Slate to phyllite to schist
Fine-grained igneous rocks	Pressure and heat	Schist
Coarse-grained igneous rocks	Pressure and heat	Gneiss
Limestone	Pressure and heat	Marble
Dolomitic limestone	Pressure and heat	Dolomitic marble
Diatomite	Pressure and heat	Chert

rocks are associated with certain land forms. In some respects the following treatment of forms and structures of rocks is review.

IGNEOUS ROCKS

The physical features of igneous rocks are related to whether the rocks are intrusive or extrusive.

Forms. Extrusive igneous rocks are shaped into volcanoes and allied surface forms. Intrusive igneous rocks are wedged into dikes, sills, laccoliths, stocks, and batholiths.

Structures. Igneous rocks are irregular in structure and have great resistance to erosion and pressure. The outcome of these outside forces acting upon igneous rocks is usually some kind of jointing or faulting along lines or planes of weakness. Joints assume a rectangular, columnar, circular, or angular pattern; faults occur along an essentially flat plane of weakness.

SEDIMENTARY ROCKS

Forms. Sedimentary rocks include both unconsolidated and consolidated remains of past life or of any kind of rock. In general, sedimentary rocks are products of erosion of other rocks and of deposition of the erosion fragments in horizontal layers. The layers may or may not be compacted or cemented.

Structures. Although sedimentary rocks joint and fault as do igneous rocks, the lesser resistance of sedimentary rocks to pressure allows them to fold. However, jointing, faulting, and folding are all common. Typically, joints open at right angles to the plane of deposition and in a manner to separate rectangular blocks from the main mass. Extreme pressures tend to cause faulting and block mountains. Even greater pressures may develop grabens, horsts, or complex faults. If jointing and faulting do not occur, folding is common. In fact, some type of folding is generally present—horizontal strata are rare. The folding leads to both simple and complex folds, some of which as a result of intense pressure may be overturned, asymetrical, or faulted. In many cases, sediments are affected by more than one of these forces and complex mountains result.

METAMORPHIC ROCKS

Metamorphic rock structure resembles that of its parent material. However, some differences between the parent material and the metamorphic product generally occur; the metamorphic rock tends to be harder, more crystalline, and deeper in color.

SOILS

Soil is a complex mixture of minerals and organic compounds. Because it is a decomposition product of rocks and organisms, soil is a sedimentary material and sometimes is considered a sedimentary rock.

FACTORS OF SOIL FORMATION

Five factors contribute to the formation of soil. The first two, type of parent and organic materials, provide the substance that eventually develops into soil. Parent materials are the rocks that erode to fine inorganic particles and organic materials are the plant and animal remains that decompose to soil humus. These sources of soil may display a seemingly conflicting relationship with mature soils. For example, the sources may differ in two localities but the same mature soil may form in both areas. Also, identical parent and organic sources can become different mature soils in remote locations. Although this might be perplexing, it does not belie the importance of the first two factors. Rather, it implies the possible importance of the other three factors.

These three factors are climate, topography, and time, three physical features of the environment. Their contribution is to decompose the source materials into soil. In the decomposition process, climate works mainly through weathering, water, and wind; topography, through slope. As for the final factor, time, several hundred years often are needed for an inch of soil to form. Of these environmental factors, climate often is most important in determining the mature soil type. In fact, the two most important factors in the kind of soil formation normally are climate and vegetation.

SOIL PROFILE AND HORIZONS

When a mature soil is formed, it shows vertical layering of materials. The layering constitutes a soil profile which is a cross-section of the substrate from the surface to bedrock. Each individual layer, or zone, is called a soil horizon. The four major soil horizons are *A*, the topsoil; *B*, the subsoil; *C*, weathered parent material; and *D*, unweathered parent material. These major horizons display a progression of soil formation from *D* to *A*. The major soil horizons and their subdivisions are shown in Figure 5.1. Note that the organic layers, although designated A_{00} and A_0, are not really part of the *A* horizon.

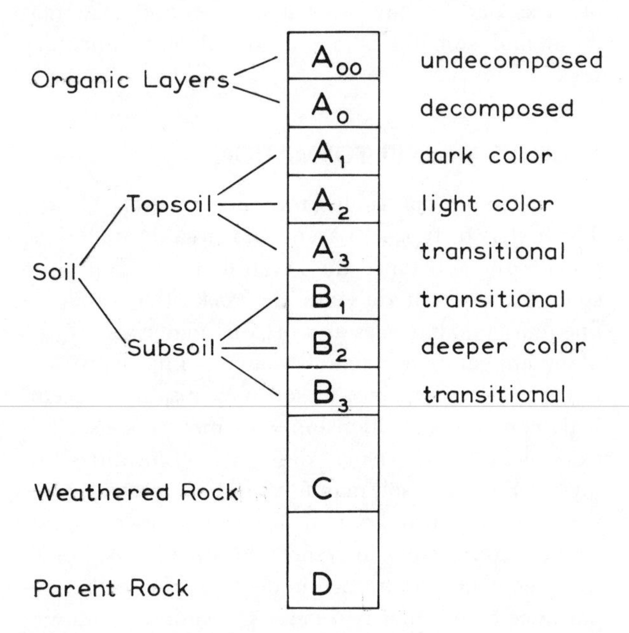

Figure 5.1 The soil profile.

Some confusion may exist because the term "horizon" is not limited to the four major subdivisions. The term is not precise. One could speak of the soil horizon and imply both *A* and *B*. Those layers constitute "the soil"; the underlying materials are weathered and unweathered rock. Also, "horizon" can be applied to finer subdivisions of any of the four major zones. Therefore, more detailed consideration of the soil profile treats the subdivided horizons.

Above the topsoil there may be two organic horizons, *01* and *02*. Although these organic horizons are not a part of the *A* horizon, *01* and *02* often are designated respectively as A_{00} and A_0, *01* consists of loose leaves and other organic debris in which the original form of most vegetative matter is discernible. *02* consists of partially decomposed or matted organic debris in which the original nature of most plant and animal matter cannot be recognized.

The true topsoil, *A*, has three subdivisions. A_1 is a dark horizon containing mostly humus, but some minerals. In the A_1 horizon the most characteristic feature is the intimate association of humus and fine rock particles. This layer when present and mixed with humus is granular, porous, and crumbly. When a distinct humus layer (A_0) occurs, the A_1 horizon is absent and there is an abrupt transition from matted and compacted humus to mineral soil. A_2 is a light horizon, representing the region of maximum leaching. The unique aspect of A_2 is the loss of clay, iron, and aluminum, with resultant concentration of quartz or other resistant minerals of silt to sand size. A_3 is a transitional horizon to *B*, but is more like *A*. Although they constitute the possible horizons within the *A* major horizon, not all of these subunits need be present in a given soil profile.

Subsoil, *B*, also may have three layers. B_1, like A_3, is a transitional horizon to *B* but is more like *B*. B_2 is usually a deeper-colored horizon, representing the maximum accumulation of leached minerals and clay; it has low humus content. B_3 is a transitional zone between *B* and *C*.

Weathered parent material, *C*, may be absent if soil formation closely follows weathering. In some grassland soils, calcium carbonate accumulates here.

The unaltered parent material, *D*, is any layer beneath *A*, *B*, and *C* horizons. Therefore, in addition to bedrock, *D* can be a zone of boulders, gravel, sand, or clay above the true bedrock. However, the *D* layer is always unaltered parent material.

SOIL EROSION

The general topic of erosion was treated previously. All that need be added is the usual cycle of soil erosion and the specific erosion factors.

The soil erosion cycle encompasses the removal of soil from an area. Therefore, it is associated with depressions, or erosional land forms; remnants, or residual forms; and transported sediments, or depositional forms. In the usual cycle, water is the most important erosion factor. If water flows over a relatively large surface area, there is a fairly even removal of surface soil by a process called *sheet erosion*. Moreover, progressive restriction of the area affected by a given amount of water causes *rill*, *gully*, and *stream erosion*. The terms "rill," "gully," and "stream" refer also to the land forms associated with each erosion type. The entire soil erosion phenomenon shows two definite associations. First, there is a correlation between the amount of water and the size of area it erodes, because any particular amount -size relationship determines whether the erosion process is rill, gully, or stream. Second, erosion processes often follow a three-step cycle of rill, gully, and stream erosion in a given area.

Although water is most important, the environmental factors of slope, wind, ice, and plant cover also modify soil erosion. Some of these contributing factors, stated in terms of how erosion rate is minimized, are as follows: greater soil permeability, lesser angle of slope, slower melting of snow, an even distribution of light rains, vegetation with a dense root system and surface cover, lack of overgrazing, neither clearing nor burning lands, and cultivating on contours rather than down slopes.

CLASSIFICATION

Soils can be classified on the basis of site of origin, texture, and so-called natural means. On the basis of site of origin, sedentary and transported soils are recognized. A *sedentary* soil is one that develops from all factors of formation operating at the site of the mature soil. A *transported* soil has its materials brought to the site of soil formation. The other criteria of classification are considered in greater detail below.

TEXTURAL CLASSIFICATION

Soils are classified according to textural composition, the proportions of its various-sized particles. In textural composition, the important soil particles are *gravel*, over 1/25 inch; *sand*, 1/500 to 1/25 inch; *silt*, 1/5000 to 1/500 inch; and *clay*, below 1/5000 inch.

If a substrate is *90 per cent or more gravel*, the substrate is not soil. No matter what the textural composition of such rocky areas, all are called *rubble*. The term "soil" is reserved for surfaces having less than 90 per cent gravel.

Textural Basis of Classification. In the textural classification of soil, gravel is analyzed separately from sand, silt, and clay and is used to provide a descriptive adjective for the soil texture name which is based upon the proportions of sand, silt, and clay. Therefore, to classify and name soils according to texture, one first determines the gravel content and, then, the finer particle content.

An adjective describing the gravel of a soil is used *only if the soil contains more than 15 per cent gravel* and is derived from one of eight gravelly-nature classes. These classes are diagnosed on the basis of shape, size, parent rock, and amount of fragments (Table 5.4).

TABLE 5.4 DIAGNOSES OF THE GRAVELLY-NATURE CLASSES OF SOIL

Classes	Per Cent in Soil	Shape[a]				Rock Sizes (inches)
		Thin	Flat	Angular	Rounded	
Shaly	75+	?	*	*		0–6[b]
Slaty	75+	?	*	*		0–6[c]
Cherty	75+			*		0–10[d]
Channery	15+	*	*	*		0–6
Gravelly	15+			*		0–3
Flaggy	15+	*	*	*		6–15
Stony	15+		*	*		15+
Gravelly	15+				*	0–3
Cobbly	15+				*	3–10
Stony	15+				*	10+

[a] ? indicates possible; * indicates characteristic.
[b] Must be slate.
[c] Must be shale.
[d] Must be chert.

Textural Classes. These soil classes designate the percentages of sand, silt, and clay content, but each possesses certain physical characteristics that aids in its identification (Table 5.5).

NATURAL CLASSIFICATION

Soil scientists still seek a better system of soil classification. Among other things, a satisfactory

TABLE 5.5 CHARACTERISTICS OF SOIL BY TEXTURAL CLASSES

Classes	Composition (%)			Physical Characteristics[a]																	
				Dry Sample					Moist Ball												
				Form		Texture			Handling			Consistency				Ribbon					
	Sand	Silt	Clay	Loose	Clods	Gritty	Intermediate	Smooth	Crumbles	Barely balls	Easily balls	Fingerprints	Stains fingers	Sticky	Excellent	Good	Poor	None			
Sand	85–100	0–15	0–10	*		*			*									*			
Loamy sand	70–90	0–30	0–15	*	+	*		*	*				+					*			
Sandy loam	43–85	0–50	0–20	*	+	*				*			*					*			
Loam	23–52	28–50	7–27		*			*			*		*				+	*			
Silty loam	0–50	50–88	0–27		*			*b			*	*	*				*	*			
Clay loam	20–45	15–53	0–27		*		*				*	*	*			*	+				
Silty clay loam	0–20	40–73	27–40		*		+	*			*	*	*			*					
Sandy clay loam	45–80	0–28	20–35		*	*					*	*	*				+	*			
Clay	0–45	0–40	40–100		*		*				*	*	*	*	*						
Sandy clay	45–65	0–20	35–55		*	*					*	*	*	?		*					
Silty clay	0–20	40–60	40–60		*		*				*	*	*	?	*						
Silt	0–12	88–100	0–12		*			*			*	*	*					*			

[a] * indicates usual; +, secondary; ?, questionable.
[b] With slick, buttery, or velvety feel.

system must be natural in the sense that it depicts the factors of soil formation. This means that any acceptable classification scheme must emphasize climate and vegetation. Therefore, any map of the distribution of natural soil categories is a generalized presentation of climate and vegetation (Figures 5.2, 5.3, 5.4, and 5.5). Although a natural classification of soils, and therefore a soil map, might seem easy to accomplish, in actual practice even the natural system is hard to produce.

The natural system presented here is discussed in some detail in the 1938 *Yearbook of Agriculture, Soils and Men.* It is a natural system because it stresses the factors of soil formation, especially climate, vegetation, parent material, and topography.

Categories. The largest category of soil classification is the order. Further subdivisions are suborders, soil groups, families, series, and types. Here, our purposes are satisfied by considering the three orders (zonal, intrazonal, and azonal) and subunits that approximate the suborders. The subunits under their respective orders are indicated in Table 5.6.

TABLE 5.6 CLIMATE AND SOIL CLASSIFICATION

Azonal Soils	Intrazonal Soils	Zonal Soils		
		Climate Controlled		
Climate Independent	Climate Influenced	Arid through Subhumid		Humid Climates
Lithosols (mountains)	Halomorphic (saline and alkali)	Red desert		Lateritic
Regosols (alluvium, sand, or alkali)	Calomorphic (calcareous)	Sierozem		Red-yellow podsolic
	Hydromorphic (water-logged)	Brown		Gray-brown podsolic
		Chestnut	Prairie	Podsols
		Chernozem		Tundra

(Vertical arrow between Azonal and Intrazonal columns: lower temperature ↓ greater moisture; arrows: Chernozem → Prairie → Gray-brown podsolic)

CLIMATE
dry cold
wet cold
ice cap
tundra
subarctic
arid
semiarid
subhumid
humid
wet
dry hot
wet hot

VEGETATION
perpetual snow and ice
tundra
boreal forest
desert grasses and shrubs
steppe
grassland
forests
rainforest

MAJOR SOIL GROUPS

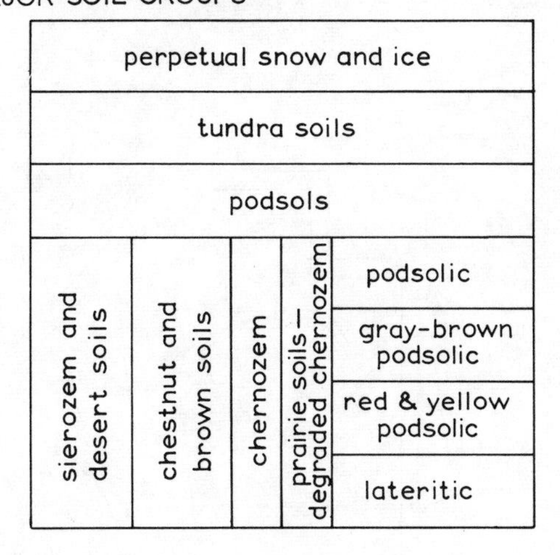

Figure 5.2 Distribution of climatic types; vegetation and major soil groups on a climatic basis.

The soil orders have a definite relationship with the factors of soil formation. Only zonal soils are fully mature and reflect climate and vegetation (Figures 5.2, 5.3, 5.4, 5.5). Because vegetation must also be mature (stable or climax) and reflect climate, mature soils can be said to reflect climate alone. However, the soil in many localities is not mature. It might be hardly differentiated, or very young. Such a soil has little or no layering and is termed *azonal*. In addition, there are substrates intermediate between azonal and zonal. These are the *intrazonal* soils, which are held back from full maturity by local land forms, parent material, and/or insufficient time for complete formation. Therefore, only *zonal* soils show close relationship to climate and vegetation, intrazonal soils show much less association, and azonal soils have very little if any direct association.

ZONAL SOILS

The four processes of zonal soil formation disclose the importance of climate and vegetation. The processes are gleization which forms Tundra soil, podsolization which forms Podsols, laterization which forms Lateritic soil, and calcification which forms Chernozem, Chestnut, Brown, Sierozem, and Red Desert soils.

Gleization includes the physical, chemical, and biological processes in arctic regions and other places where soils are always wet but have few salts. Under these conditions, a structureless but compact and sticky layer develops beneath the subsoil and characterizes a blue-gray Tundra soil. Full development of this soil normally requires tundra vegetation.

Podsolization occurs in cool, moist climates and is the process of slow organic decay in forests. It involves the production of certain acids and results in a variety of Podsols in northern and temperate forests. True Podsol is generally associated with northern coniferous forests, Gray-Brown Podsols with true deciduous forest, and Red-Yellow Podsols with mixed deciduous-coniferous forest or with southern coniferous forest.

Laterization is a distinctive process in warm, moist climates. The process leads to Lateritic soils that usually have rainforest vegetation. Also, the process includes certain peculiarities and selectivity in leaching.

Calcification is found in arid areas and, for this reason, features less leaching, especially of calcium and magnesium. The most typical calcification soil type is Chernozem, or grassland, soil. This soil has a

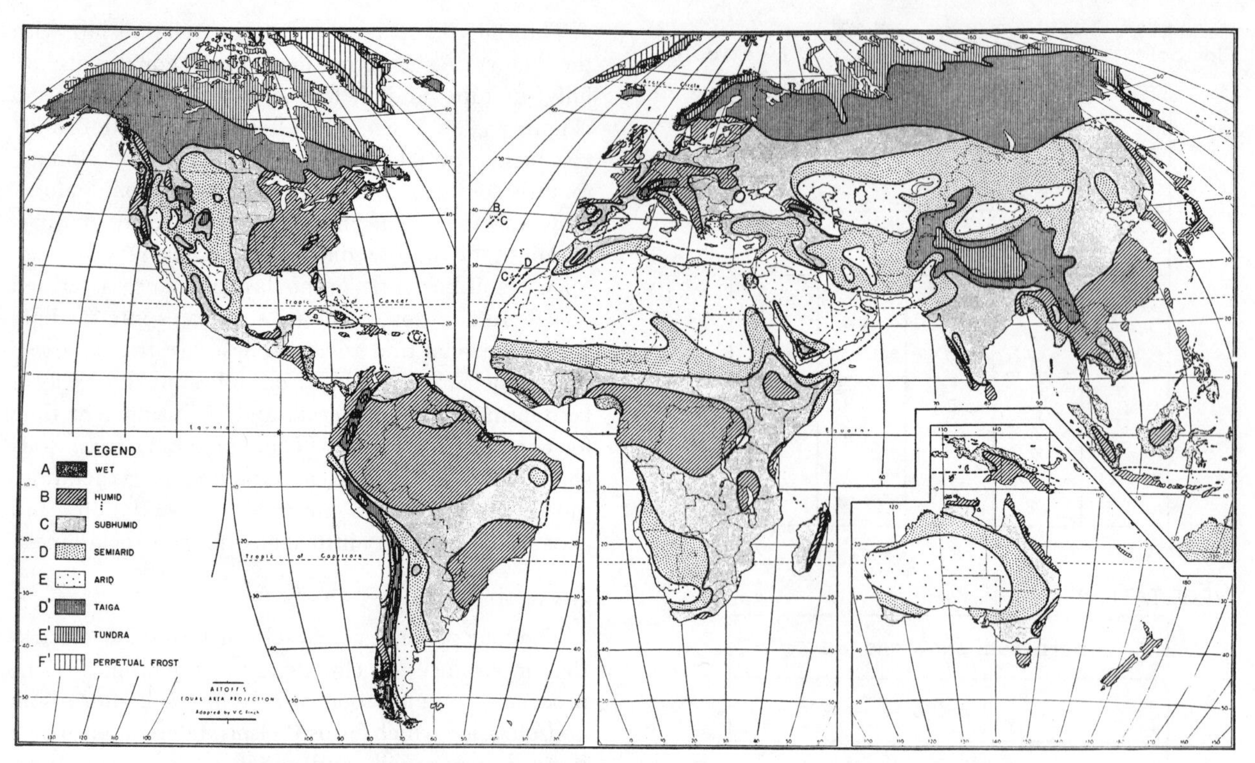

Figure 5.3 World distribution of principal climate types. (From *Yearbook of Agriculture,* 1941.)

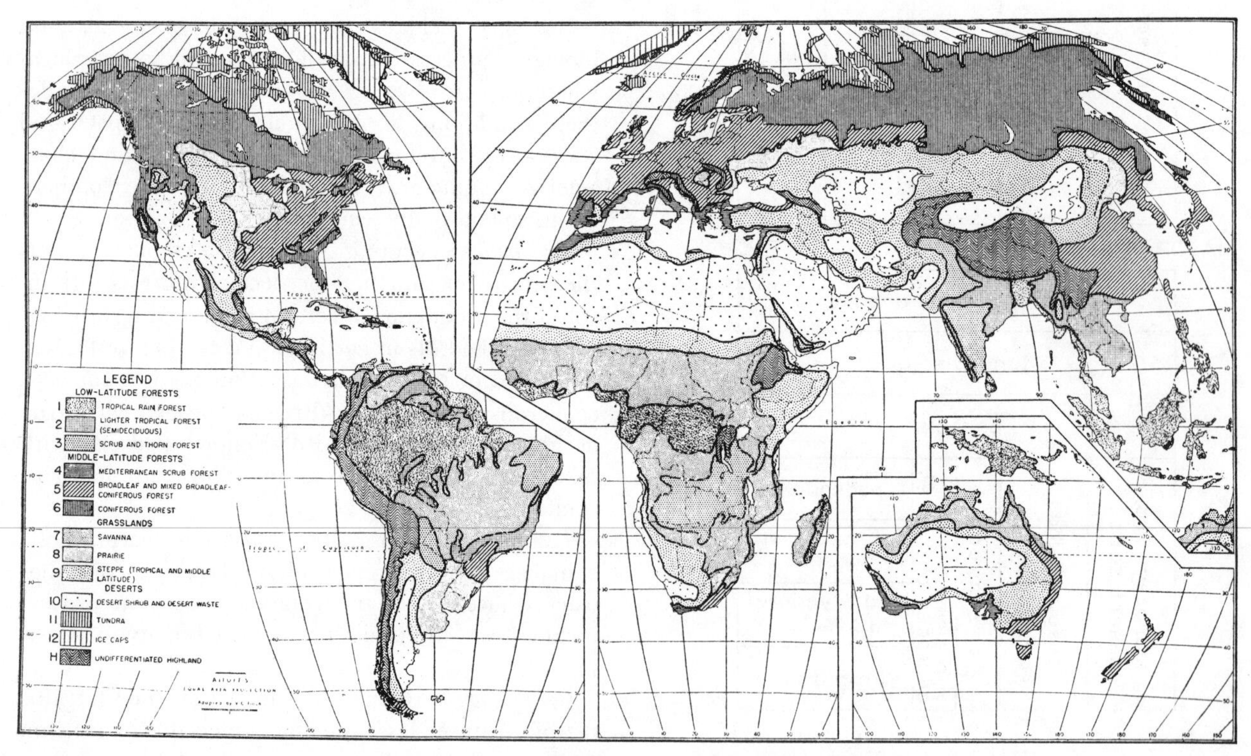

Figure 5.4 World distribution of principal vegetation types. (From *Yearbook of Agriculture,* 1941.)

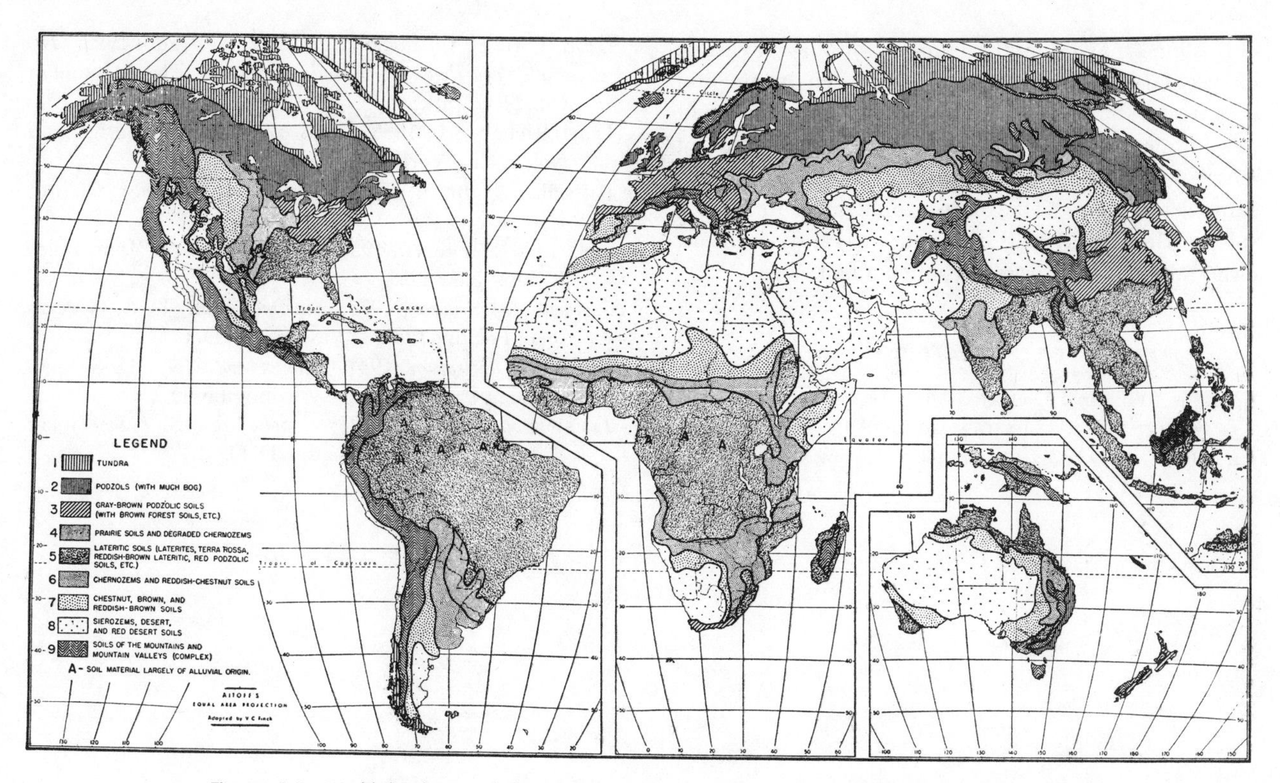

Figure 5.5 World distribution of the principal zonal soil groups. (From *Yearbook of Agriculture*, 1941.)

deep, dark organic horizon above a compact, hard *B* horizon, calcium carbonate hardpan. The dark layer is the basis for this soil sometimes being called black earth. Chernozem regularly grades into Gray-Brown Podsolis, the transition area constituting the Prairie Soils with their tall grasses, True Prairie. Chestnut and Brown soils have more carbonate but less organic material than Chernozems. These two soil types have grassy steppe or brushy vegetation. Sierozem and Red Desert soils contain no organic layer but support a desert vegetation. Sierozem generally has bunchgrasses and Red Desert, desert shrubs and cacti.

Zonal soils, except Tundra, may be placed in two categories. Podsols and Lateritic soils are sometimes grouped as *Pedalfers*, a term emphasizing their aluminum and iron content; and Chernozems, Chestnut, Brown, Sierozem, and Red Desert *Pedocals* to emphasize their calcium content.

INTRAZONAL SOILS

Because these soils are dependent upon local conditions, it is best to treat the three types separately.

Halomorphic Soils. These are the saline and alkali soils of poorly drained, arid regions and of marine deposits. They are light-colored and sometimes display visible evidence of their salt or alkali content. Their vegetation consists of a sparse cover of grasses, forbs, shrubs, and trees that can withstand the high mineral content of the soil.

Hydromorphic Soils. Although these soils are usually found in cool, humid to tropical climates, they can be in any situtation where fresh water accumulates. These soils are usually dark-colored, but they can be light. Their vegetative cover varies, consisting of grasses, sedges, and flowering plants; swamp forest; broad-leaved forests; and tropical forests.

Calomorphic Soils. These soils are in cool to hot, humid to dry climates but reflect a large amount of limestone in their parent materials. They tend to be dark-colored and have a plant cover of grasses and/or broad-leaved trees.

AZONAL SOILS

These have no true profile development; however, there may be some indication of such zonation. Soils of this kind may be in any climate and have a variety of vegetation, depending on local environmental conditions. The vegetation tends to represent developmental stages of the more characteristic plant cover of an area. Such seral stages are considered in some detail later. The main azonal soils are Lithosols, or thin, rocky soils of mountains, and Regosols, either alluvial soils, or sandy, often alkali, soils.

SELECTED READINGS

Emmons, William H., et al., 1960. *Geology: Principles and Processes.* 5th ed. McGraw-Hill Book Co., New York.

Farb, Peter, 1959. *Living Earth.* Harper, New York.

Lyon, T. L., H. O. Buckman, and N. C. Brady, 1952. *The Nature and Properties of Soils.* 5th ed. The Macmillan Co., New York.

Pearl, Richard M., 1956. *Rocks and Minerals.* Barnes and Noble, New York.

Russell, E. John, 1957. *The World of the Soil.* Collins, London.

Waksman, Selman A., 1952. *Soil Microbiology.* John Wiley & Sons, New York.

Yearbook of Agriculture, 1938. *Soils and Men.* U. S. Government Printing Office, Washington, D. C.

Yearbook of Agriculture, 1941. *Climate and Man.* U. S. Government Printing Office, Washington, D. C.

Yearbook of Agriculture, 1957. *Soil.* U. S. Government Printing Office, Washington, D. C.

6 THE ORGANISM

Life Processes and Organization

Life is the most complex phenomenon known to man. This complexity is indicated by the fact that no completely satisfactory definition of life is possible. Yet this chapter proposes to characterize life. Unfortunately, the characterization to be given is in a form that makes living appear very different from nonliving. No attempt is made to show that nonliving things have the same basic processes as do living creatures. Also the question of whether viruses are living or nonliving is not developed. Therefore, the present chapter serves only to introduce the lower part of the life spectrum.

THE NATURE OF LIFE

Living creatures have certain structures and functions that appear to distinguish them from nonliving things, but none of these basic features is unique to life. On the other hand, most organisms display greater development of certain characteristics than do inanimate objects. An examination of those characteristics follows.

ORGANIZATION

Living creatures possess complex structural organization that is associated with even more complex functional relationships. Some of this structure is simple in the sense that it is protoplasmic or unicellular, that is, not composed of many cells, but most living organization does involve cells (multicellular). In multicellular life, groups of cells are intimately joined to perform most life processes. These cells are composed of chemical compounds whose elements are more than 95 per cent carbon, hydrogen, oxygen, and nitrogen. Naturally these same elements are found in nonliving things, but only living creatures generally have such a large proportion of their matter formed from these elements. Also, the organic compounds include the largest and most complex chemicals known; inorganic compounds, in contrast, are mostly small and simple.

Another point of living organization is form and size. Most life is of definite size and shape and any nonliving things are not; however, even inanimate objects are regular enough for their physical aspects to be valuable in identification.

LIFE SPECTRUM

The life spectrum, the range of biological organization, here is arbitrarily assumed to exist and to be composed of ten levels of complexity, *protoplasm*, "*single celled*" (unicellular or acellular), *cells*, *tissues*, *organs*, *organ systems*, *populations*, *communities*, *ecosystems*, and the *biosphere* (Figure 6.1). The first six levels are progressively more complex structural bases of or-

LIVING STRUCTURES	ORGANISM
protoplasm	protoplasmic
cell	acellular (= unicellular)
cells	cellular
tissues	tissue
organs	organ
organ systems	organ system

ORGANISMS

population
community

ORGANISMS plus ENVIRONMENT

ecosystem
biosphere

Figure 6.1 Levels of body and life organization. Organization of living structure in an organism, organisms, and organisms plus their environment.

ganism construction. Protoplasm is any living substance and the cell usually is the fundamental structural unit of protoplasm in most living creatures. Certain organisms have cells grouped into tissues, tissues into organs, and organs into organ systems; however, other life may have protoplasmic, "single celled," cellular, tissue, organ, or organ system bases, or grades, of structure. Therefore, the first six levels of the life spectrum are either possible grades of plant and animal construction, or progressively more complex structural units in an animal with organ systems. One should realize that all of these grades of structural organization really are protoplasmic because all living structure is protoplasm, but protoplasmic organization here is limited to cell-like structure that does not clearly display a complete nucleus (see Monera, p. 127).

The last four levels refer to ever more complex interrelations between organisms and their environment. A population is a species or a portion of a species. A community is all populations in a definite geographic area. An ecosystem is a functional relationship, specifically the complex of creatures interacting with one another and their physical environment. It may be considered a community and its environment and implies dynamic activity within and between each. The biosphere is the part of the earth containing all ecosystems, the zone of life.

IRRITABILITY AND ADAPTATION

Irritability is that property of an organism or cell which causes an appropriate reaction to sudden changes in the external or internal environment. It includes sensitivity to the changes (stimuli), and stimulation or excitation by them. When stimulation takes place, the stimulus is transported to an appropriate center of reaction, and the center brings about a response which has some relation to the original stimulus. This response is temporary and is followed by a return to so-called normal conditions.

Stimuli need not always cause responses. Repeated responses to stimuli produce fatigue, a state in which an organism can no longer react until its body processes recover from overstimulation. Other inhibition of response can come from repetition of the same stimulus, which soon is ignored although the organism is physically capable of reacting. In contrast to these actions of life, nonliving objects usually have the same response to a given stimulus and do not display inhibition.

Irritability in some measure overlaps *adaptation*, which is segregated into two other phases of activity, *adjustment* and *specialization*. Adjustment is the process in which a plant or animal in its own lifetime gradually builds up a functional balance with an environment factor. In specialization, the species as a whole through chance evolves a hereditary balance with its environment. Although this contrast between adjustment and specialization is possible, fundamentally both have a hereditary basis in the past evolution of a species. If adjustment were without any hereditary basis and came about by chance alone, most organisms would perish at their first contact with any sudden change in their surroundings.

AUTONOMOUS MOVEMENT

Although commonly believed to be unique to animals, self-controlled movement is found in other life. For example, many bacteria, blue-green algae, and protozoans are completely independent, freely moving creatures; even certain vascular plants react to a stimulus by moving their leaves and, sometimes, their stems.

Organisms also have movements that are identical to those of nonliving things, but such motions are not strictly autonomous. They are the consequences of external forces being applied to an object. For example, both a rock and an animal may roll down a hill as a result of the force of gravity.

NUTRITION

The nutrition of organisms is of two main types, *autotrophic* and *heterotrophic*. Both types provide the same thing, materials that organisms must have for energy, growth, and repair, the sources of all life processes. Autotrophic organisms need only relatively simple inorganic materials for these functions; heterotrophic creatures require more complex organic compounds.

Autotrophs are of two types, *chemosynthetic* and *photosynthetic*. Chemosynthetic autotrophs build all their nutrients from environmental materials without the aid of chlorophyll. Photosynthetic autotrophs have chlorophyll which traps sunlight, most frequently, to allow the combination of carbon dioxide and water into simple sugar in the process called *photosynthesis*. Some photosynthetic autotrophs use compounds other than carbon dioxide or water.

Heterotrophs are of six types. *Saprophytes* need relatively simple organic compounds that they get from dead or decaying matter. *Scavengers* require complex organic compounds that likewise are obtained from dead or decaying organic remains. *Parasites* often use simple organic compounds in the form in which they are taken from the host; however, some parasites are similar to predators (carnivores) in that both ingest complex organic compounds which must be digested before metabolism. The remaining nutrient types (*carnivores*, meat-eaters; *herbivores*, plant-eaters; and *omnivores*, mixed plant and animal eaters) are often grouped as *holozoic*. Often the scavenger and holozoic organisms are bulk feeders and other feeding types extract only certain chemicals from their source of food.

REPRODUCTION

Racial perpetuation is not simply of two major types, sexual and asexual, but it is convenient to consider two types. In sexual reproduction there is fusion of two nuclei, each from a different specialized sex cell called a *gamete*. The diagnostic feature of sexual reproduction is the fusion of two nuclei within a single cell called a *zygote*. Asexual reproduction, then includes any reproductive process not including fusion of nuclei from two parents.

Unfortunately the terminology of reproduction was developed before much was really known about the subject. Therefore, designations for reproductive structures and functions often are loosely applied. The glossary shows much of this unfortunate multiplicity in term meanings. In the following discussion an attempt is made to avoid this pitfall to learning.

ASEXUAL REPRODUCTION

Asexual means of racial perpetuation are mechanisms limited to individual cells or organisms (Figure 6.2). Interparental crosses do not exist. For this reason offspring are of much the same appearance as their parents; generally an individual has the same gene composition as its parent. The types of asexual reproduction are similar whether they occur in a cell or an organism, but the diagnosis of types is related, in part, to cell or organism reproduction.

Fission and Fragmentation. Fission is cell division whether it occurs in the cell of a multicellular organism or in the cell-like structure, perhaps cell, of an entire organism as in the Monera and many Protista. Fission produces two essentially equal daughter cells from a single cell. When fission stops at this point it is called *binary fission*, but if each of the daughter cells also undergo fission, the process is called *multiple fission*. Multiple fission in its simplest form produces four cells from one, but cell division often will continue in a prolonged sequence until a great many cells, still called daughter cells, are formed.

Fission does not imply any mechanism of cell division, but two types of fission occur, mitosis and amitosis. *Mitosis* is nuclear division diagnosed by complex chromosomal movement and exact duplication of each chromosome of the original cell. (Chromosomes originate in a cell's nucleus and bear the units of heredity, genes.) In this simple cell division the single parent cell goes through a process whereby the original two sets of chromosomes ($2n$) or perhaps the single parental set (n) are each duplicated, doubling the original chromosome number, and then the parent cell divides, producing two daughter cells, each cell with the same number of chromosomes as its

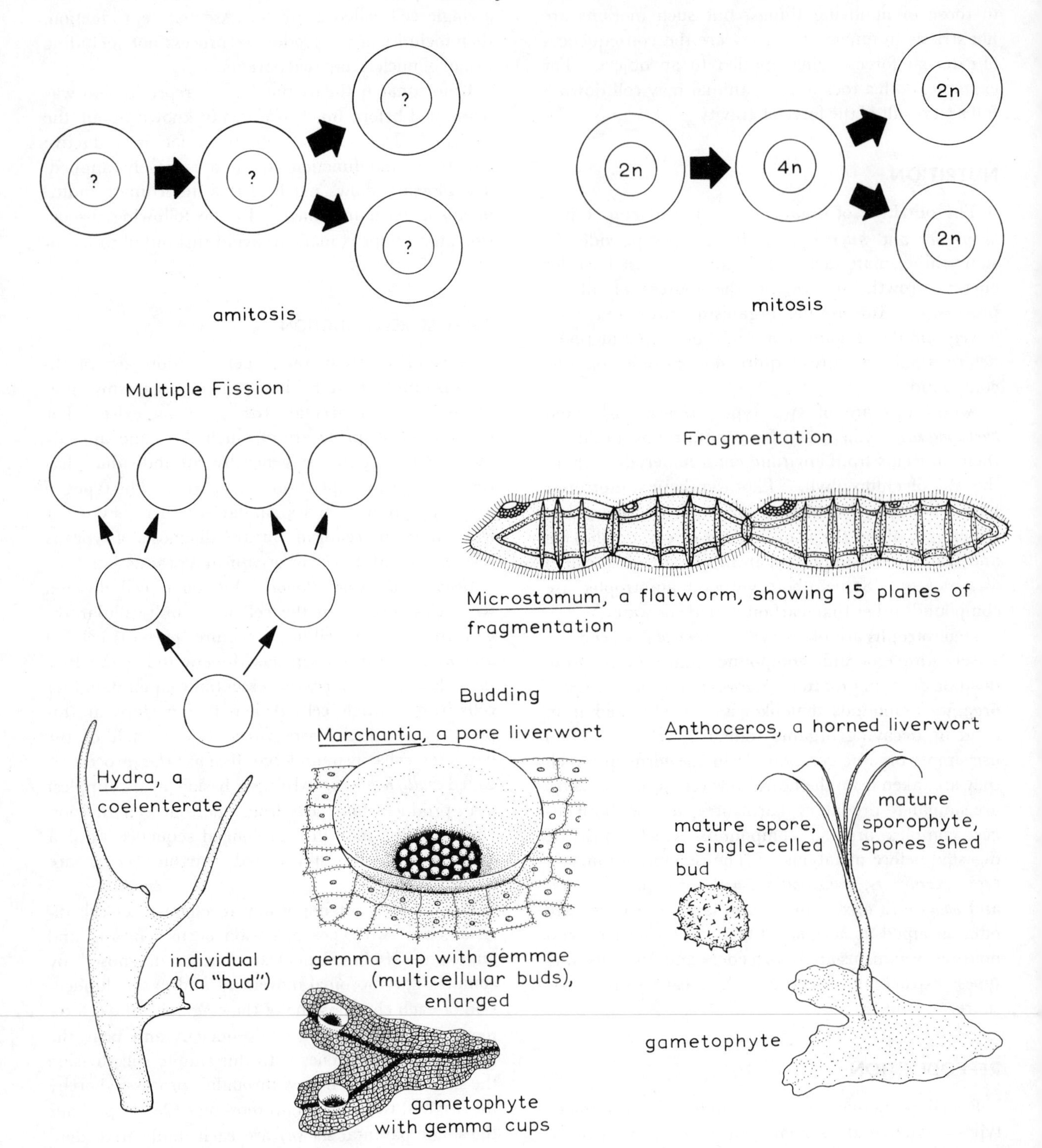

Figure 6.2 Types of asexual reproduction.

parental cell. This is the reproductive process found in many "single-celled" organisms, including some algae and protistans. Mitosis also is the process leading to cell increase and to growth in multicellular life. The consequence of mitosis is two cells, each with a gene composition identical with that of the parental cell.

Amitosis probably has the same consequence as mitosis; hence the process from a hereditary point of view may be identical to mitosis. However, amitosis is recognized because it is fission in which there is segregation of nuclear material rather than structures that can be recognized as chromosomes. Amitosis is the typical reproductive process in the Monera.

Fragmentation is the breaking apart of a multicellular organism in such a way that each segment can grow into a small replica of the adult. The process of growth from a fragment is called *regeneration* and is found throughout the plant kingdom, but it is most typical of the simpler structured plants and animals. In general, the less complex an organism, the less strict are the requirements on the nature of a fragment for regeneration to follow.

Budding. Budding is an unequal division in which an offspring or a structure that can develop into an offspring grows from the surface of a parent, differentiates, and finally separates from the parent. In the case of the offspring budding, the offspring is a small replica of the parent. In the case of the structure, growth and differentiation are necessary to produce a miniature parent.

Budding of miniature offspring occurs throughout the protists and plants and in some animals, especially coelenterates, ectoprocts, entoprocts, pterobranchs, and tunicates. In the protists, because most are unicellular, budding often is a kind of fission. In most plants and animals budding offspring may be best treated as a specialized kind of growth. It is a mitotic phenomenon in which all cell divisions contribute to the formation of a single daughter individual that during development is a parasite upon its parent.

The formation of a true *bud*, a single cell, occurs mostly in higher plants. A true bud is limited to an asexual reproductive cell that develops directly into an adult. Unfortunately, the term "bud" often is applied to early stages of miniature offspring budding in animals and to certain multicellular plant structures like the gemma of bryophytes, flower buds, and leaf buds. Multicellular animal buds are found in sponges (gemmule) and ectoprocts (statoblast) and also grow into a miniature adult. Gemma give rise to an individual identical with the parent. Flower and leaf buds are not asexual reproductive structures. Rather, they are developmental flowers or leaves.

The single-celled or true bud usually associated with plants is called a *spore*. However, this *true* spore is quite unlike most other true buds. Other buds usually reproduce an individual that is a copy of the parent, but spores produce entirely different individuals. A spore forms from an adult called a *sporophyte* and typically grows into an entirely different looking adult called a *gametophyte*. More precisely, a sporophyte is a spore-producing organism which alternates with a sex cell- (gamete-) producing organism, a gametophyte. The occurrence of two kinds of adults that regularly are of unlike appearance often is difficult to appreciate. Although many errors are introduced by the analogy, think of the two adults in the life cycle of a single species as being comparable to a worm and a human. In other words, in such a life cycle an adult worm would produce a bud that would grow into an adult human and a man and woman would produce a fertilized egg that would develop into a worm. The incidental error that might be created by an extension of this analogy can be corrected when the kinds of life cycles, particularly the generalized life cycle, are examined.

Asexual Organismic Reproduction. When restricted to organisms, asexual reproduction is of two types, vegetative reproduction and sporulation. *Vegetative reproduction* includes all asexual types except that involved in the formation of true buds, *sporulation*. Therefore, vegetative reproduction includes fission in the Monera and Protista, the budding off of entire organisms or multicellular structures in plants and animals, and fragmentation of plants and animals. Fragmentation in certain plants, especially bryophytes, arises from decay of parts between groups of interconnected adults, the interconnected adults having originated by budding.

SEXUAL REPRODUCTION

Sexual reproduction was defined as the process dependent upon the fusion of two parental nuclei, each from a different and specialized sex cell called a "gamete." In addition, each gamete contains a single chromosome set (n) and nuclear fusion results in a fertilized egg, or zygote, having two sets of chromosomes ($2n$), one set coming from each parent. The union of parental gametes is called *fertilization.*

The origin of gametes with one set of chromosomes, directly or indirectly, from a parent with two sets of chromosomes necessitates a type of cell division called *meiosis.* Meiosis is a process in which a cell with two sets of chromosomes produces daughter cells with one set of chromosomes. The significance of meiosis in our present discussion is that it compensates for the doubling effect of fertilization.

Meiosis can occur in various stages of a life cycle. For example, in man meiosis produces sex cells, male sperms and female eggs. However, in plants having sporophyte and gametophyte generations, meiosis produces spores. Then these spores grow into gametophytes and sex cells are formed by mitosis. Therefore, meiosis may be somewhat remote from sexual reproduction.

Under the heading of sexual reproduction, associated phenomena may be distinguished (Figure 6.3).

Isogamy and Heterogamy. Isogamy is the union of two gametes of like size and structure, *isogametes.* Neither gamete is distinguishable as egg or sperm but functionally there are two parental gametes. The process occurs in organisms of simpler form, such as the algae.

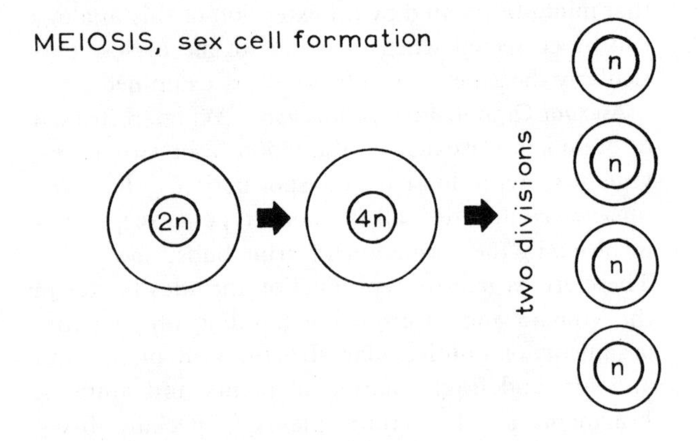

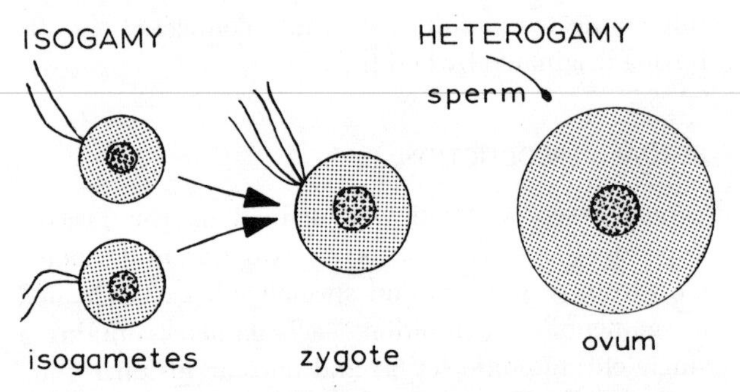

Figure 6.3 Types of sexual reproduction.

Most sexually reproducing plants and animals display heterogamy, a condition wherein egg and sperm, or *heterogametes,* can be distinguished. The egg is generally larger, spherical, and nonmotile; the sperm is usually smaller, elongate, and highly mobile.

Sexuality. In sexual reproduction with heterogamy, a species may be *biparental* with separate male and female sexes, or be *hermaphroditic* with individuals containing both male and female sex organs. Hermaphrodites are sometimes capable of fertilizing their own eggs (e.g., flukes), but most require cross-fertilization between two individuals. Some hermaphrodites do not display both sexes at the same time. An oyster, for example, may start life as a male and later become a female. All of these processes are sexual.

Allied to sexual reproduction because it probably represents a breakdown of the process is *parthenogenesis.* Commonly called "virgin birth," this is the development of an egg without prior fertilization. Because there is no fusion of unlike gametes, it is not sexual reproduction. It is commonest in protistans and algae but is found in many higher plants and in animals. It may be the only reproductive process known in a particular organism, or it may alternate with sexual processes in the same organism. In bees fertilization produces females and parthenogenesis males, but in many aphids unfertilized eggs develop and form either females, or males and females, depending upon the season of the year. At certain times some of these aphids reproduce sexually, but other species of aphids are strictly parthenogenetic.

Alternation of Generations. This is a regular cycle of interchange of structurally distinct adults, one reproducing sexually and the other asexually. The asexual generation is derived from and gives rise to the sexual generation, hence the alternation. Therefore, only every other generation reproduces by the same means and has the same physical appearance. In many plants this is what involves a sporophyte and a gametophyte, two kinds of adults, in a single species. In animals, alternation of generations is typical of the coelenterates, but the asexual reproduction is by the budding of organisms rather than true buds.

Fertilization Site. The actual place of fertilization

may be internal, within the parent's body, or external, in the medium. As a general rule, external fertilization is typical of aquatic life and internal of terrestrial life, but there are exceptions. The marine squids, octopuses, and barnacles carry on internal fertilization even though they are aquatic, and in aquatic salamanders, the male lays a packet of sperm on the substrate, the female picks it up, and fertilization is internal.

LIFE CYCLES

The history of the developmental, reproductive, and any other stages that exist in an organism is called a life cycle or life history. For convenience, life cycles may be segregated into two types, asexual and sexual; however, there are different kinds of each, and both types can be united in the life history of a single species. Also, there is no general kind of life history that is unique to any of the kingdoms.

The various life cycles are related to adults of two chromosomal types. Adults may have one set of chromosomes (symbol n and called *haploid*) or two sets of chromosomes (symbol $2n$ and called *diploid*). It will be seen that there is no over-all direct relationship of either meiosis or mitosis with sexual or asexual reproduction.

Although many kinds of life cycles are recognized, all can be derived from a single generalized, but probably not the ancestral, cycle that includes a sexual and an asexual phase. In all these life histories the various stages have one or two sets of chromosomes, n or $2n$. The presence of the haploid or diploid condition is organized so cycles might have both a *haplophase* and a *diplophase*, or, perhaps, only one of these phases. When both phases occur, only one may have an adult (*haplobiontic*), or each phase may include an adult (*diplobiontic*). In addition, a life cycle might possess one or more stages where asexual reproduction occurs and brings about either the duplication of the stage having such reproduction or the production of an earlier or later stage in the cycle. If these variations are kept in mind, one sees that the accompanying figure is no more than a generalized life cycle (Figure 6.4).

In Figures 6.4 through 6.7 at least part of each life cycle indicates vegetative reproduction. The fact that this reproduction normally is not an essential step in the life cycle is indicated by its starting from and ending at the same stage of the life cycle. The only place

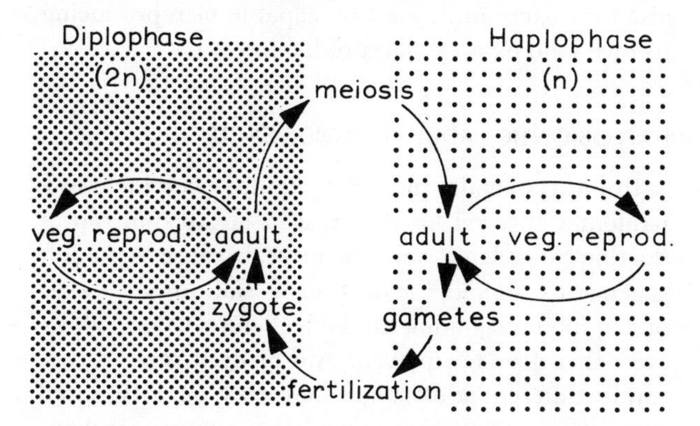

Figure 6.4 The generalized, or diplobiontic, life cycle.

where it always is essential is in the asexual cycle (Figure 6.7).

So far we have considered asexual reproduction only as a secondary part of a given life cycle. We have treated it as secondary in the sense of not mentioning it in the inner circle of a cycle. However, this need not be the case. The production of spores is an asexual process and usually is primary because it often is limited to the inner circle of a cycle. Therefore, primary asexual reproduction generally is by sporulation and secondary asexual reproduction generally is by vegetative reproduction.

DIPLOBIONTIC CYCLE

This generalized life cycle is diagnosed by the two different, n and $2n$, adults, the reason for its characterization as diplobiontic. The other term for the cycle, *diplohaplontic*, also refers to the diploid and haploid adults. Such a cycle contains a distinct alternation of generations, because there are a sexual and an asexual phase and the two kinds of adults often are distinguishable from one another. Diplobiontic cycles are most characteristic of plants; in the plant kingdom the diploid adult is the sporophyte and the haploid adult is the gametophyte.

Note that meiosis does not produce gametes. In plants having sporophyte and gametophyte generations, the diploid sporophyte forms haploid spores by meiosis. These spores germinate by mitosis into a sexual generation, the haploid gametophyte. The gametophyte produces haploid gametes by mitosis. After gamete fusion (sexual reproduction) and diploid zygote formation, mitosis again is involved in development from zygote to diploid adult sporophyte. Note also that each adult may be capable of reproducing its own kind by asexual reproduction.

HAPLOBIONTIC, ADULT DIPLOID, CYCLE

In most animals, the life cycle does not include a haploid adult and for that reason no asexual reproduction by such a form. Therefore, because any adult is generally diploid, the life cycle is said to be *diplontic* or haplobiontic, adult diploid (Figure 6.5). However, this does not prevent two or even more structurally different adult stages from existing. Repeated asexual reproduction can give rise to many such haplobiontic adults. For this reason, "haplobiontic" refers to a single chromosomal complement in adults, either one set or two, and not necessarily to a single adult stage. When adults are haplobiontic the asexual reproduction phase may or may not be present. However, when the cycle is present in diploid animals such as coelenterates, the different appearing adults already mentioned can occur. However, these adults differ from those of the generalized cycle. For example, the zygote of coelenterates generally forms a diploid adult which asexually reproduces by budding a somewhat plantlike colony of diploid adults. This colony includes specialized individuals that bud diploid jellyfishlike adults. The jellyfishes continue the life cycle by entering the sexual phase at the stage of meiosis, males producing sperms and females eggs, and finally through fertilization of eggs zygotes are formed. Therefore, adequate portrayal of certain coelenterate modified haplobiontic, adult diploid, cycles would show an asexual colony (adults) being derived from the zygote, and the colony giving rise to

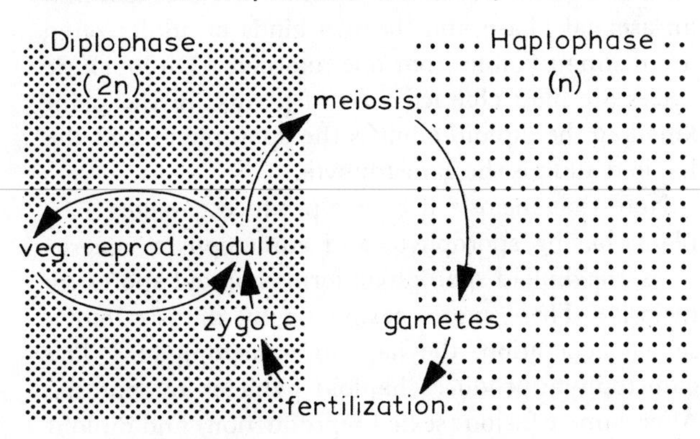

Figure 6.5 The haplobiontic, adult diploid, life cycle.

jellyfish adults. Also, all adult coelenterates would be diploid.

HAPLOBIONTIC, ADULT HAPLOID, CYCLE

In plants, especially, the diplophase of the generalized life cycle might be suppressed (Figure 6.6). This means that the cycle is modified into a haplobiontic type, but the adult or adults are haploid. The other term applied to this cycle in reference to the haploid adult is *haplontic*.

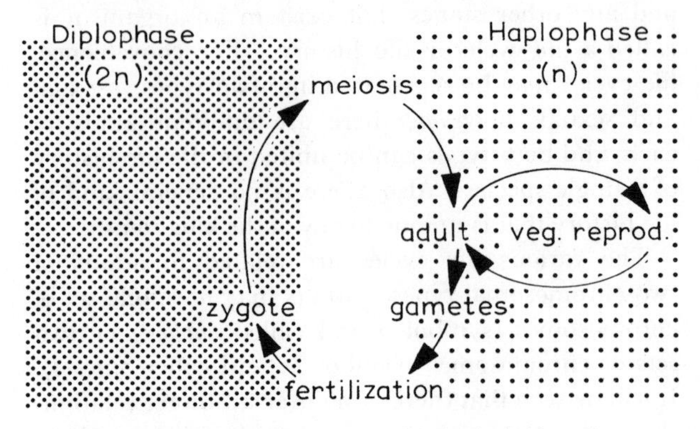

Figure 6.6 The haplobiontic, adult haploid, life cycle.

ASEXUAL CYCLE

The last major kind of life cycle, the asexual cycle, is most difficult to relate to the generalized, or diplobiontic type. However, the asexual cycle can be interpreted as an extreme contraction of the generalized cycle. In the asexual cycle, all stages except the adults and asexual reproduction of like adults are absent. As a consequence, there is an asexual cycle, adult diploid representing the generalized diplophase and an asexual cycle, adult haploid representing the generalized haplophase (Figure 6.7).

The various kinds of life cycles are found within many phyla in both the plant and animal kingdoms. However, different groups of organisms reveal definite tendencies toward one or more of the major types. Asexual cycles of both kinds are most typical of bacteria and blue-green algae. Haplobiontic, adult haploid, cycles are most often encountered in protozoans and certain fungi. The haplobiontic, adult diploid kind is the "typical" cycle in animals, but it also has spotty occurrence in the protozoans, fungi, and plants. Finally, the diplobiontic cycle is widely

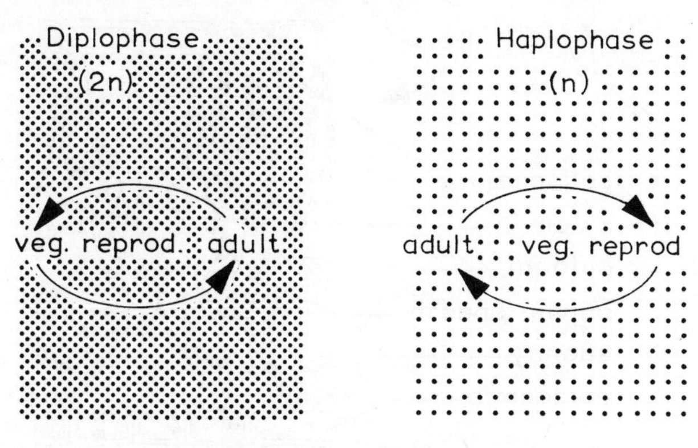

Figure 6.7 The asexual life cycles.

distributed throughout protistans and plants but is more typical of plants.

LIVING STRUCTURE

As already stated, the lower levels of the life spectrum deal with the structural organization of protoplasm in living creatures. In the order of increasing complexity this structure includes incompletely differentiated protoplasm, "single cells," cells, tissues, organs, organ systems, and organisms. However, this structural spectrum should not be interpreted to mean that all organisms are composed of protoplasm organized into cells, the cells into tissues, the tissues into organs, the organs into organ systems, and the organ systems into a single organism. Such an arrangement is found only in animals of complex structural form. Blue-green algae, bacteria, protozoans, fungi, and sponges have no features more complex than cells, yet all are organisms. In addition, there are plants and animals whose organization does not go beyond that of tissues or organs, and only certain animals have organ systems.

PROTOPLASM

Protoplasm is living substance and is found in all living structures. When not found in specialized cells, it usually is a translucent or transparent, usually grayish, slimy, jellylike, complex chemical substance. Between 95 and 99 per cent of protoplasm is composed of the elements carbon, hydrogen, oxygen, and nitrogen. The remaining small percentage consists mostly of the elements sulfur, phosphorus, potassium, iron, magnesium, calcium, manganese, sodium, chlorine, zinc, boron, copper, and molybdenum—a fact that serves to emphasize its complexity.

The structure of bacteria and blue-green algae is most like that of undifferentiated protoplasm. In other words, these organisms lack true cells. For this reason it is convenient to emphasize bacteria and blue-green algae structure as protoplasmic.

CELLS

Cells are the fundamental structural unit, or building block, in most organisms. They are as variable in shape as are the sources from which they are derived. Ideally, perhaps, each cell should be a sphere, but the forces of compression and adhesion holding them together in a multicellular body mold their shape; and cells of special function usually express their function in a particular shape modification that is an adaptation for greater efficiency.

Cells, then, are variable. They vary in structure not only when they are the components of a multicellular organism, but also when one appears to constitute the entire body of an apparently single-celled (acellular or unicellular) organism. Although structural differences do exist, all cells—protistan, plant, and animal—are usually composed of a *cell membrane*, *cytoplasm*, and *nucleus*, and are similar. The cell membrane is a living structure. It provides some protection and support, especially to animal cells; more important, it regulates the movement of materials between the inner parts of the cell and the outer environment. Cytoplasm consists of essentially undifferentiated protoplasm and specialized structures that contribute to cellular metabolism. The nucleus is the coordinating or directing center of all cell activity, including reproduction, and contains the hereditary units (genes) that are usually borne on bodies called chromosomes.

The principal differences between plant and animal cells (Figure 6.8) stem from three additional structures in plant cells: a *cell wall*, *plastids*, and a large *central vacuole* in the cytoplasm. A cell wall is composed of nonliving material, mostly cellulose; it is a somewhat elastic but tough and strong, protective and supportive, outer layer of the cell. This structure is mostly impervious to the passage of materials; however, holes in the cell wall allow the free passage of substances into and out of the cell. Plastids are often

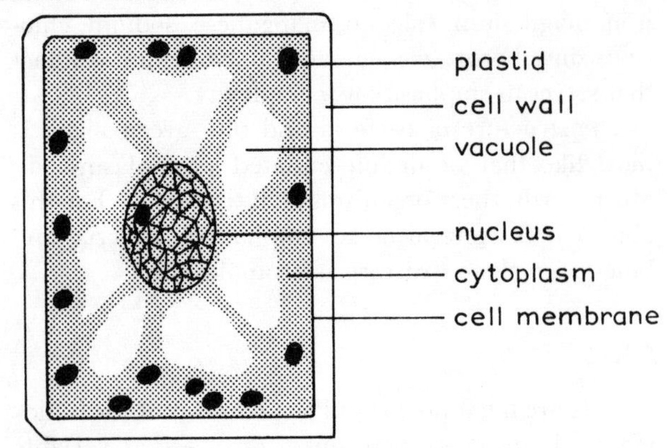

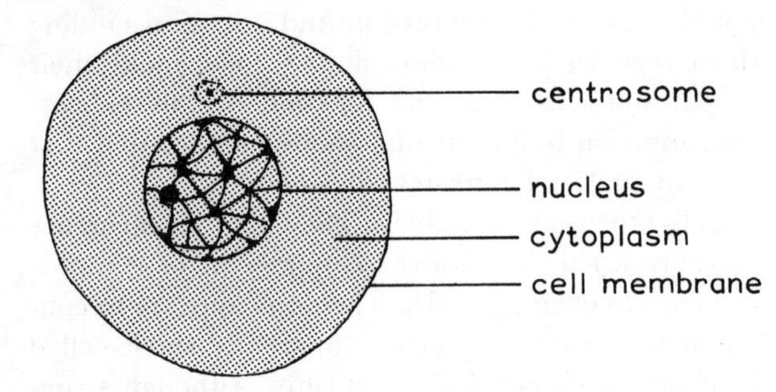

Figure 6.8 Comparison of a plant and an animal cell, highly schematized.

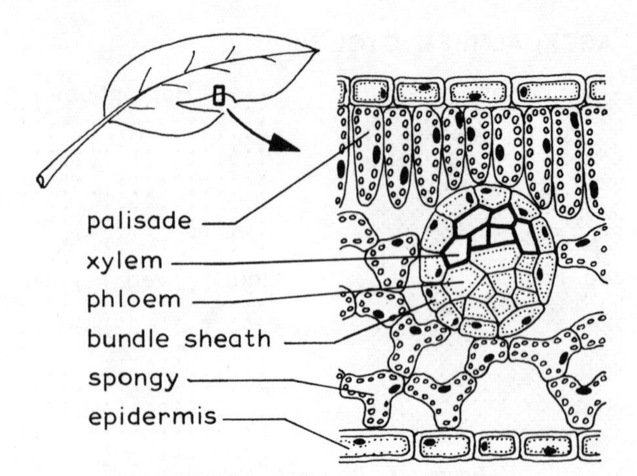

Figure 6.9 A vascular plant leaf, an organ, and some of its tissues. Palisade, spongy, and bundle sheaths are different tissues modified from the simple permanent tissue type called parenchyma. Epidermis is a simple permanent tissue. Xylem and phloem are the complex permanent tissues forming the framework of the vessels of vascular plants. The rectangle on the cut leaf blade indicates the site of the leaf cross-section.

the site of photosynthesis (they usually contain chlorophyll) and food storage. Vacuoles may be related to cell gas and water functions.

TISSUES

Cells that have essentially the same structure and function when organized into a single unit are a tissue. Because tissues are found only in multicellular organisms and such plants and animals are quite unlike one another, plant and animal tissues are classified differently.

Plant tissues are of two types, growing and permanent (Figure 6.9). Growing tissues contribute to the development of increased size and new structures. Permanent tissues are further subdivided into two groups. The simple permanent tissues are composed largely of a single kind of cell. These tissues are of approximately five kinds that function in protection, support, and/or nutrition of plants. The complex permanent tissues, *xylem* and *phloem*, are arrangements of several kinds of cells. Together xylem and phloem form the *vascular bundles* which function in transportation of materials dissolved in water, but they are found together only in the vascular plants, the Tracheophyta. The only permanent tissues found outside the Tracheophyta are phloemlike and are in the brown algae. Xylem and phloem are both supportive tissues; xylem conducts water and dissolved material mostly upward and phloem conducts nutrients chiefly downward.

Animal tissues are also of two major types, reproductive and body. The reproductive tissues form the reproductive cells, or gametes. The body tissues are epithelial, or covering; connective, or supporting; muscular, or contracting; and nervous, or coordinating.

ORGANS

An organ is a group of tissues that performs a particular function. Organs in plants tend to be simpler structurally and of fewer kinds than those in animals. Fully developed plant organs are found only in the Subkindom Embryophyta, the embryo plants. These plants have true organs of four kinds: roots, stems, leaves, and reproductive organs (often grouped into flowers or cones). The functions of roots include anchorage and support of plants, absorption of water and dissolved nutrients from the soil, conduction of materials to the stems, and food storage. The functions of stems include conduction of materials from roots to leaves and from leaves to roots, production of leaves and reproductive organs, plant support, and food storage. The primary function of leaves is food manufacture; they are the primary site of photosynthesis.

Certain brown and red algae have structures that approach, but are not, organs. These structures are *holdfasts*, *stipes*, and *blades*. Holdfasts are rootlike structures, but their only function is support of the plant; stipes are stemlike stalks that have little complexity in comparison to stems; blades are leaflike but, again, are not as complex as leaf blades.

The multicellular animals range from those with no organs to forms that show a great many complex organs. This range of variation does not lend itself to a meaningful classification of organs per se. The animal units of classification are organ systems.

ORGAN SYSTEMS

Organ systems are groups of organs that provide an over-all function and are found almost exclusively in the animal kingdom. Plants are assumed not to surpass the organ basis of organization, because most of their separate parts are organs. However, flowers and most cones are organ systems. In the multicellular animals one or more of the following ten organ systems may be found:

(1) *Integumentary* provides the body covering which affords protection from the environment. (2) *Skeletal* supplies levers for movement and structures for protection and support. (3) *Muscular* allows movement and locomotion. (4) *Digestive* receives food and transforms it to usable nutrients. (5) *Circulatory* transports materials throughout the body. (6) *Respiratory* exchanges gases between the organism and its environment, or is a means of obtaining oxygen and removing carbon dioxide. (7) *Excretory* disposes of excess fluid and metabolic wastes. (8) *Nervous* coordinates body processes. (9) *Endocrine* chemically coordinates body processes. (10) *Reproductive* perpetuates a species by the production of new individuals.

ORGANISMS

The single plant or animal is most often the basic independent unit of life. Units smaller than the organism are incapable of living by themselves, but individuals may be grown together into colonies. Many colonies are composed of individuals each of which could perform all life processes, but some animal colonies are formed of different kinds of specialized individuals. In such specialized colonies marked division of labor can occur, individuals have unique functions, and few if any of the distinct types can survive alone. For example, a colony might be made up of individuals that feed for the entire group, others that do nothing but reproduce, and some that are strictly protectors of the colony. In such cases all types of individuals may be necessary for life to exist. When division of labor is this strict, the organisms are often physically attached to one another into a single structural unit.

In addition to being either solitary or colonial, individuals are either sedentary or free-living. Most multicellular plants and many animals are fixed to soil, rocks, or some other substrate, at least during their adult life. In these sedentary creatures only certain stages of the life history, but not the adult stage, are motile. Free-living creatures, on the other hand, are motile during most, if not all, of their life cycle.

ORGANISM AND ENVIRONMENT

Each creature is subjected to many environmental variables that largely determine its function and place within its surroundings. The organism's basic heredity establishes its over-all ability to cope with variations within and among the physical and biological features of its surroundings. Its reactions with these environmental factors must still permit its receiving all the necessities of life—especially suitable food, shelter, and conditions for reproduction.

The variations of organisms and environments working together as a dynamic interacting phenomenon demonstrate that no organism is independent of its physical or biological surroundings. Their dependence is summarized by the concept of a *web of life* in which an organism is affected by its physical environment and by other organisms acting as enemies, competitors, or food. From all this, the obvious assumption can be made that an organism is usually found in a locality having conditions, within limits, that allow the performing of its life processes.

An additional organism–environment concept is the *balance of nature*. This generalization refers to the dynamic interrelationships that tend toward equilibrium in nature. Although there is an ever-changing association among such things as the number of organisms, the main activities of plants and animals, the amount of food, and the environmental conditions, a dynamic balance is still maintained. The equilibrium is the consequence of the interaction of two things, *biotic potential* and *environmental resistance*. The biotic potential is the amount of increase in organisms that would occur if all offspring were to survive. Environmental resistance is the biological and physical restriction upon number of individuals that causes the balance of nature. Environmental resistance occurs in the form of competition, predation, disease, food supply, and extent of suitable habitats. Therefore, the balance of nature refers to the fact that each habitat has a *carrying capacity*, or saturation level, insofar as the number of organisms it can support is concerned. There is an equilibrium about which fluctuations occur.

SELECTED READINGS

Galston, A. W., 1961. *The Life of the Green Plant.* Foundations in Modern Biology Series. Prentice-Hall, Englewood Cliffs, N. J.

Griffin, D. R., 1962. *Animal Structure and Function.* Modern Biology Series. Holt, Rinehart & Winston, New York.

McElroy, W. D., 1961. *Cellular Physiology and Biochemistry.* Foundations of Modern Biology Series. Prentice-Hall, Englewood Cliffs, N. J.

Ray, P. M., 1963. *The Living Plant.* Modern Biology Series. Holt, Rinehart & Winston, New York.

Simpson, G. G., et al., 1957. *Life.* Harcourt, Brace & World, New York.

Swanson, C. P., 1960. *The Cell.* Foundations of Modern Biology Series. Prentice-Hall, Englewood Cliffs, N. J.

Weisz, P. B., 1963. *The Science of Biology.* McGraw-Hill Book Co., New York.

Wilson, G. B., and J. H. Morrison, 1961. *Cytology.* Reinhold Publishing Corp., New York.

7 CLASSIFICATION, PHYLOGENY, AND EVOLUTION

The Groups and Ancestry of Organisms

Phylogeny is the study of the history of life, especially the evolutionary interrelationships and ancestry of living organisms. On the basis of our present knowledge of phylogeny, we can place living things into convenient categories or groups. In this chapter we will examine the methods by which organisms are classified into *taxonomic categories* and the method of naming those categories, *nomenclature*.

To understand the basis for classification of organisms we must examine the *principles of organism complexity*, the *origin of life*, the *physical and biological history* of the earth, and the changes, or *evolution*, of life on our planet.

CLASSIFICATION AND TAXONOMY

There are over a million species of living organisms in the world today. Needless to say, it is impossible for anyone to know all of them. Yet, for various reasons, man is a great labeler. He appears to have a passionate desire to name things, a characteristic that seems to obscure and all too often to satisfy his ignorance. Probably since the time of the earliest humans, names have been applied. Perhaps, in order to simplify things and arrange them in his mind, ancient man attempted many schemes of classification.

Man's efforts to name organisms led to the science of taxonomy, the grouping of organisms. Early schemes were purely matters of convenience, using such things as habits and habitats to group animals together. According to that now-defunct system whales, seals, and porpoises would be grouped with fishes. Today, biologists do their best to determine animal *ancestry* and *relationships* and to use that information for purposes of classifying. In modern taxonomy, the whales, seals, and porpoises are classified with mammals. Even today, however, the complexity of known phylogeny may necessitate a classification of pure convenience; known evolution may be too intricate to be shown by modern or any relatively simple means of classification. In spite of this possibility, the modern biologists' attempts to use relationships to form groups have resulted in the most convenient, especially for learning and remembering, and most informative scheme to date.

TAXONOMIC CATEGORIES

The basic unit of taxonomy is the single kind of organism, or *species*. (The term "species" is both singular and plural; the word "specie" means coined money.) A species may seem to be a very definite thing. Everyone recognizes dogs, cats, cows, and horses as species because each group is unique and easily distinguished. However, these well-known animals present a warped view of conditions in nature. Perhaps the best way of contemplating a species is to think of its existence in view of the death of many of its ancestors. For example, the African and Indian elephants are two similar but different species that are related through common ancestry; if time could be ignored and the ancestors and all intermediate types to these two species were living today, one would find it impossible to separate the elephants into two species. For this reason, if one considers the known possibility of two living, geographically isolated groups of organisms that possess similar form and habits, the problem of determining what is and what is not a distinct species can be appreciated. Although past life does not exist to create problems in species definition, some very closely related living organisms cause the same sort of difficulty. What then is a species? The common idea, gathered from the less complex kinds of species, is that a species is a group of organisms freely reproducing with one another but reproductively isolated from all other groups of organisms. For many purposes this is a satisfactory way of thinking of a species.

Categories above the species are strictly for convenience and may not be accepted by all biologists. For example, within a single family the number of genera recognized by different biologists may range from five to ten. This occurs because individual higher categories are never equivalent when applied to different groups, no matter how hard a biologist might try for uniformity. Uniform higher categories are impossible, because evolution does not produce units of distinct and discontinuous size; rather, the consequence of evolution is a continuous variation in the size and complexity of different units. In spite of this, larger categories are valuable when they represent natural groups; hence, the primary criterion for any of these larger groups is common ancestry and the larger the category, the more organisms are included. Similar species with common ancestry are grouped into *genera* (singular *genus*), genera into *families* (singular *family*), families into *orders*, orders into *classes*, classes into *phyla* (singular *phylum*), and phyla into *kingdoms*. Depending on the classification scheme, there are two kingdoms, Animalia and Plantae; three kingdoms, those two, plus Protista; or four kingdoms, the preceding three, plus Monera. It should be noted that botanists tend to use the term *division* instead of phylum. Technically speaking, the term "phylum" should be reserved for animals and the term "division" for plants; however, phylum is acceptable and is used here for plants, animals, monerans, and protistans.

Many categories below the species level may be recognized. However, only *subspecies* and *variety* have much use and meaning. The subspecies designation is restricted mostly to animal species. In its usual meaning it refers to a geographic race that has some structural or other difference from the rest of its species. A variety, a plant subunit of the species, can be a structural variant without regard to distribution, a structural variant forming a geographic race, a structural variant sharing the range of other variants of the same species, or a color or habit (form of growth) variant.

The species and other categories already mentioned are the basis of a framework within which one can start with a very large group, such as a phylum, and work down through finer groupings, all attempting to show relationship and usually assuming *common ancestry*, until the individual organism is distinguished. In some cases, and to obtain additional groups, the species and higher categories are further subdivided or grouped by the addition of the prefixes *sub-* and *super-* (respectively, something less than and something more than the group so designated). Also, *infra-* may be used as a unit just below *sub-*. The subspecies is an example of this type of division. Also, such categories as *tribe* and *variety* assume particular places in the heirarchy of biological classification. In certain detailed taxonomic studies special categories (e.g., cohort, brigade, legion, and section) are created and defined to fulfill special needs. These latter categories always must be defined, because they do not possess a standardized position in the taxonomic heirarchy.

An example of the categories generally used to classify modern man are as follows:

- Kingdom Animalia
  - Subkingdom Eumetazoa
    - Phylum Chordata
      - Subphylum Vertebrata
        - Superclass Tetrapoda
          - Class Mammalia
            - Subclass Theria
              - Order Primates
                - Suborder Anthropoidea
                  - Family Hominidae
                    - Genus *Homo*
                      - Species *sapiens*
                        - Subspecies *sapiens*

A general term to refer to any taxonomic category is useful. A single taxonomic category is called a *taxon* (plural, *taxa*).

NOMENCLATURE

Nomenclature is the scientific naming of organisms. Scientific names for species (generally considered "the scientific name") are binomial, consisting of both the generic and specific names. Man belongs to the genus *Homo* and species *sapiens*. His scientific name, a combination of the generic and specific names, is *Homo sapiens*. Parenthetically we must avoid possible confusion. There are two meanings of "specific name." So far we used this term to indicate a single word in a binomial. However, "specific name" also can mean "the binomial scientific name" of a species. For example, the specific name of man is *Homo sapiens*. Moreover, unless one is referring separately to binomial components, the scientific name always is two words.

When written or printed, scientific names must conform to certain set procedures. Notice that the generic name is capitalized and the second word is uncapitalized. This standard procedure is always followed in this book and is essential for animal designations. In some botanical names it also is proper to capitalize the second word; however, it is always correct to capitalize only the first word, the generic name. In addition, specific names must be either underlined, italicized, or printed in boldface type. Often the last name, or an abbreviation of the last name, of the biologist who proposed the organism's name is appended to the scientific name, as in *Homo sapiens* L., the L. being an abbreviation of Carl von Linne ("Linnaeus"), who proposed the scientific name for man. Sometimes the biologist's name is included in parentheses; this means that there has been a change in the name originally applied (see "Name Changes" below). Finally, the names may come from Latin, Greek, or any other language, or have meaningless derivation; however, all must be latinized, as *californica* or *californicus* for California and *washingtonii* or *washingtonia* for Washington. Higher taxa names have the same origin as specific names and are always capitalized but require no special printing or writing. The taxon designation is capitalized only when combined with a scientific name (e.g., Family Hominidae).

Subspecific or varietal recognition necessitates the formation of three names, a trinomial. The subspecies of modern man is *Homo sapiens sapiens*—more simply, *Homo s. sapiens*. The specific name is abbreviated in the previous manner when it is the same as the subspecific name. Further abbreviation is possible if a name follows its nonabbreviated form. For example, if the scientific name of Neanderthal man (assuming Neanderthal and modern man belong to the same species, a premise most biologists do not accept) were to follow in written text the above scientific name for modern man, the Neanderthal's could be written *H. s. neanderthalensis*. However, if the Neanderthal's scientific name did *not* follow that of modern man or of another member of the same genus and species, the correct nomenclature would be *Homo sapiens neanderthalensis*.

The writing of varietal names is somewhat different. For example, a particular variety of the California poppy is *Eschscholtzia californica* var. *crocea*. Notice that the word "variety" is abbreviated and that the variety name, like the subspecific, is written in the same manner as specific names. Abbreviation of part of variety names, actually individual genus or species names, is possible only if the variety follows other members of the same species or genus. For example, after *Eschscholtzia californica*, a poppy, these abbreviations are possible: *E. c.* var. *peninsularis* for *Eschscholtzia californica* var. *peninsularis* and *E. caespitosa* var. *hypecoides* for *Eschscholtzia caespitosa* var. *hypecoides*, a different species. In no event are any of these abbreviations possible unless they follow directly a complete writing of the word or words that are abbreviated.

NAME ENDINGS

Certain taxa of plants and animals tend to have uniform endings because of rules for naming. Although exceptions to these rules are permitted on the basis of pre-rule common usage, the following taxa usually have the endings shown:

	Plants	*Animals*
Order	-ales	
Suborder	-ineae	
Superfamily		-oidea
Family	-aceae	-idae
Subfamily	-oidea	-inae
Tribe	-inae	-ini

NAME CHANGES

In general, scientific names are quite stable. However, there are circumstances under which scientific names can be changed. The two main sources of redesignations are *taxonomic revisions* and the *law of priority*. In part, the law of priority states that the first name given a species shall be its scientific name.

Changes due to taxonomic revision generally reflect scientific progress. They are based upon new interpretation of biological relationships as a result of study of one or more species. This can cause one or more of three possible name changes: (1) A species must be transferred from one genus to another, so the generic name becomes different. (2) It is discovered that what had been considered two species is a single species, so one specific name must be dropped, or synonomized, and the first given name be established for the species as a whole (law of priority). (3) What was thought to be a single species is found to be two or more species, in which case new specific names are given to each of the new species. All of these examples are "scientific changes of names."

Reassignments due to the law of priority alone are the common example of "nomenclatorial changes in names." These changes often are criticized because they do not stem from new knowledge or scientific progress. The technicalities in relation to the law of priority and to other bases for nomenclatorial changes in names are extremely complex. However, a simple example of a replacement according to the law of priority would involve a generic and/or specific name's being superseded because a properly and earlier applied name is found. In spite of the fact that these alterations do cause difficulty and exasperation, they are an aspect of the very thing that yields the great stability characterizing most scientific names.

PHYLOGENY

The evolution of monerans, protistans, plants, and animals followed, in each case, certain major "steps" in the development of structural complexity that now are indicated by the fossil record and development of living creatures.

The evidence of these steps is the basis in this book for the grouping of phyla into four kingdoms. The grouping to be presented in the chapters that follow does not seem to follow any authority on classification exactly, but is closest to the over-all proposal of Weisz. In spite of its "unusual" nature, the classification used here should not cause difficulty in the use of other books. The animal phyla follow the widely used classification of Hyman, with the exception that Phylum Protozoa is not included. The phyla here included under Kingdom Protista, Subkingdom Protozoa are often considered subphyla or classes by other classifiers.

Phyla other than those currently placed in the Animal Kingdom and Protozoa are identical with those proposed by most botanists.

MONERA, PROTISTA, AND PLANT COMPLEXITY

According to our assumptions the earliest steps in organism evolution were associated with the increasing complexity of protoplasm (Figure 7.1). First was the differentiation of protoplasm itself, the *Monera stage*. Second was a further tendency toward the organization of definite cell-like structure, the *earliest Protista stage*. This segregation of nucleus, cytoplasm, and cell membrane created the component parts of what later became true cells. A cell-like body that is an entire organism is said to have *acellular* or *unicellular* organization. The third step was formation of complex cell-like structure, including a distinct cell wall, plastids, and many different ctyoplasmic pigments associated with the plastids; this, the *later Protista stage*, is still represented by living chlorophyll-bearing, flagellate protists. In the fourth step, complexity continued as single acellular organisms gave rise to colonial ones, the *colonial Protista stage*. Finally, colonial protists, probably chlorophyll-bearing flagellates, gave rise to multicellular life, hence true cellular organization and the *Plant stage;* possibly even later, other protists, perhaps both flagellates and ciliates, evolved into other multicellular life, the *animals*. The great importance of multicellularity was that it became the primary impetus to further increase in size and complexity of life.

REPRODUCTIVE MECHANISMS

The first life very likely reproduced asexually by fission or perhaps a simpler mechanism. However, it is thought that prior to multicellularity, sexual reproduction was derived from asexual means. Then

PROTOPLASMIC

a blue-green alga,
Cyanophyta

a bacterium,
Schizophyta

ACELLULAR

a green flagellate,
Mastigophora

a slime mold,
Myxomycophyta

CELLULAR

a sponge,
Porifera

a green alga,
Chlorophyta

TISSUE

a liverwort,
Bryophyta

a jellyfish,
Coelenterata

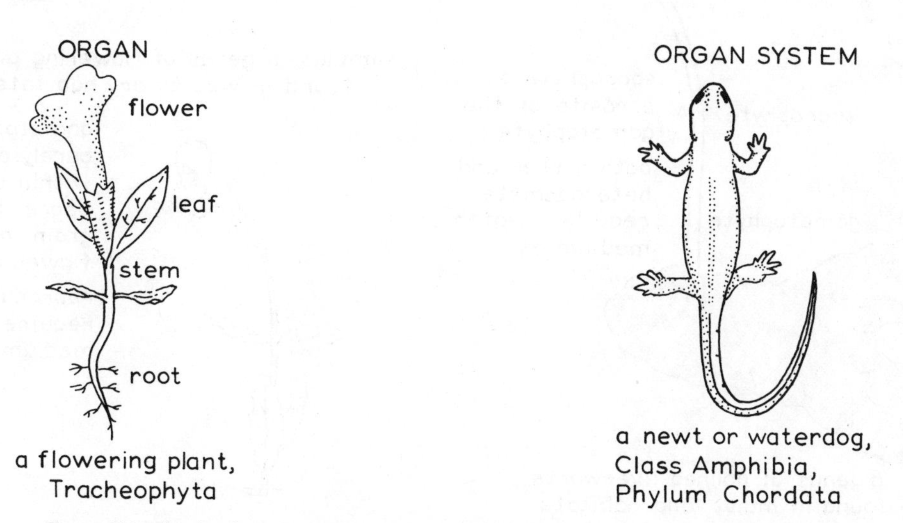

Figure 7.1 Grade of organism organization as exemplified by certain creatures possessing the various structural levels of complexity. The flower in the flowering plant is a group of organs, an organ system.

the next step was the development of alternation of generations. In this reproductive scheme an asexually reproducing sporophyte produced spores that germinated and then matured into a sexually reproducing gametophyte. Using the plant terms *sporophyte* and *gametophyte* stresses the early origin of the generalized life cycle. The fertilization of gametes from different gametophytes produced a zygote which differentiated into a sporophyte. In the early stages of multicellular evolution the cellular gametophyte reached an equal footing, especially insofar as size is concerned, with the cellular sporophyte. Therefore, reproduction soon was integrated with an increased grade of organization and plant origin.

AQUATIC TO TERRESTRIAL LIFE

Plant habitat changes from water to land most likely were related to those of plant grade of organization and reproduction. It is here assumed that the following events took place: There was increased complexity in the sporophyte and simplicity in the gametophyte; however, fertilization still required a water medium (Figure 7.2). In the next step the sporophyte developed various tissues for body support and transport of nutrients. These tissues were veins or vessels, structures unique to the vascular plants. In addition, vascular plants became differentiated into vegetative and reproductive parts, the reproductive structures being cones and flowers. Once the sporophyte became longer lived, cones and flowers could form seeds in which the gamete could produce another sporophyte. This step constituted the start of a series of further land adaptations. Associated with seeds was the carrying of sperm in wind-blown pollen. This reduced the need of a water environment for the fertilization of eggs. Subsequent steps were progressive decrease in gametophyte size and

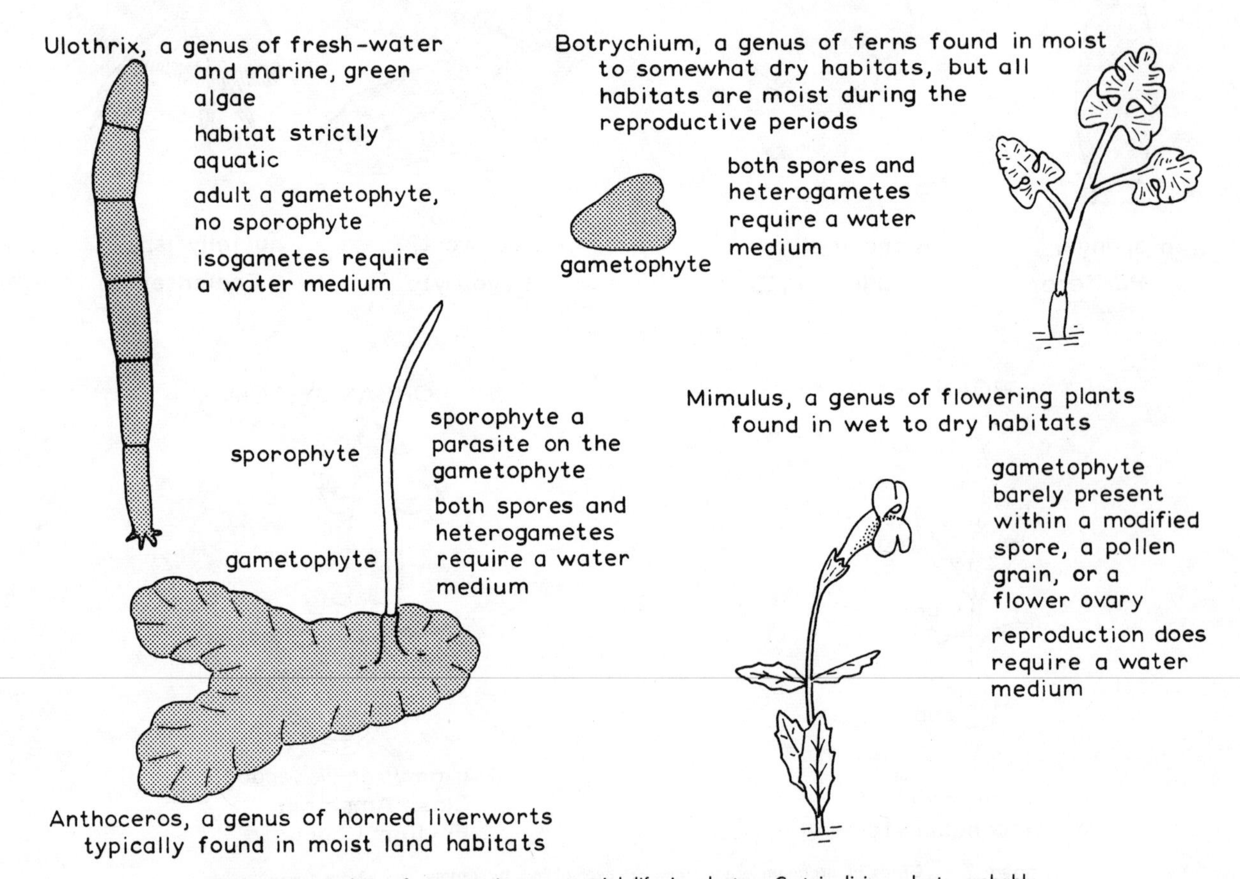

Figure 7.2 Evolution from aquatic to terrestrial life in plants. Certain living plants probably resemble (in structure and habitat) some of the ancestors that actually accomplished the original transition from ocean to land. Some of these living creatures are portrayed. The water medium required by *Mimulus* is internal or in the plant rather than external or in the environment.

increase in sporophyte size with an over-all general increase in plant size. Final land specializations were two in number: (1) still greater freedom from dependence upon water when seed plants obtained pollen tubes for fertilization and (2) the developmental series of seed plants from trees to shrubs, to herbs, and finally to annuals from perennial plants. This developmental sequence was associated with the evolution of dormant seeds.

The above assumptions of "major steps" provide a basis for segregation of the main taxa of the Kingdoms Monera, Protista, and Plantae.

Kingdom Monera—protoplasmic organization, nucleus incompletely developed; reproduction chiefly, probably strictly, asexual

- A. Chlorophyll absent; chiefly parasitic
  PHYLUM SCHIZOPHYTA (Bacteria)
- B. Chlorophyll present; chiefly free-living
  PHYLUM CYANOPHYTA (Blue-green Algae)

Kingdom Protista—unicellular to cellular organization, nucleus completely developed; reproduction asexual and sexual; chiefly aquatic, require water medium for fertilization; chlorophyll present or absent

SUBKINGDOM PROTOZOA—unicellular organization, often colonial; chlorophyll only in some flagellates

- A. Locomotion by one or more whip-like structures (flagellae)
  PHYLUM FLAGELLATA (= MASTIGOPHORA) (Flagellates)
- B. Locomotion and food capture by irregular, elongate body extensions (pseudopodia) that are created by protoplasmic flow
  PHYLUM SARCODINA (= RHIZOPODA)
- C. All internal parasites; without any means of locomotion
  PHYLUM SPOROZOA
- D. Locomotion by a more or less extensive covering of hair-like structures (cilia), or organism possesses sucking tentacles and regularly is attached by a stalk to the substrate
  PHYLUM CILIOPHORA (Ciliates)

SUBKINGDOM FUNGI—unicellular to cellular with incipient tissue formation; locomotion by flagellae or pseudopodia, or non-motile; chlorophyll absent

- A. Body multinucleate, essentially naked protoplasm
  PHYLUM MYXOMYCOPHYTA (Slime Molds or Fungi)
- B. Unicellular, cellular, or approach greater complexity, usually filamentous
  PHYLUM EUMYCOPHYTA (True Fungi)

Kingdom Plantae—cellular, tissue, or organ organization; chlorophyll typically present; characteristically nonmotile as adults; most require an external water medium for fertilization

SUBKINGDOM ALGAE—cellular and tissue organization, sometimes unicellular; chiefly aquatic, require a water medium for fertilization; life cycles of all types

- A. Cellular organization or mostly so, some unicellular
  1. Plastids grass green
     a. Without sex organs
        PHYLUM CHLOROPHYTA (Green Algae)
     b. With sex organs
        PHYLUM CHAROPHYTA (Stoneworts)
  2. Plastids usually yellow to brown; cellulose silicified
     PHYLUM CHRYSOPHYTA (Golden Algae)
- B. More complex cellular or tissue organization
  1. Tissues present; incipient organ formation
     PHYLUM PHAEOPHYTA (Brown Algae)
  2. Only approach tissue differentiation
     PHYLUM RHODOPHYTA (Red Algae)

SUBKINGDOM EMBRYOPHYTA—organs present, tissue or organ organization; chiefly terrestrial, moisture required for fertilization; life cycle usually with definite alternation of generations (diplobiontic)

- A. No veins; sporophyte small; in moist areas, require water medium for fertilization; mostly tissue organization
  PHYLUM BRYOPHYTA (Liverworts and Mosses)
- B. Veins present; sporophyte definitely dominant; includes most land plants, fertilization requires that plant have sufficient internal moisture; organ organization
  PHYLUM TRACHEOPHYTA (Vascular Plants)

ANIMAL COMPLEXITY

The trends in animal evolution were and are so many that the structural features of many species are extremely complex. Considering this complexity, it is fortunate that only a few anatomical and other characteristics are needed to separate the phyla and to indicate their possible paths of evolution. The five main features are grade of organization, development, symmetry, body cavities, and segmentation. In discussing them no attempt will be made to imply sequences of events. This is not necessary because the sequence of each is generally believed to be from the simple to the complex.

GRADE OF ORGANIZATION

Animal organization, especially in the simpler types, is somewhat similar to that of plants. This is logical because plants and animals probably were derived from the protists. The first animals may have consisted of a single, multicellular body, but one with all cells much the same; in other words, they were cellular organisms. With time, animal structure became increasingly more complex. Cells became specialized in structure and function; cells of similar structure and function became grouped into tissues, tissues into organs, and finally, organs into organ systems. For this reason animals can be classified according to evolution of their organization as cellular, tissue, and organ system grades. Animals

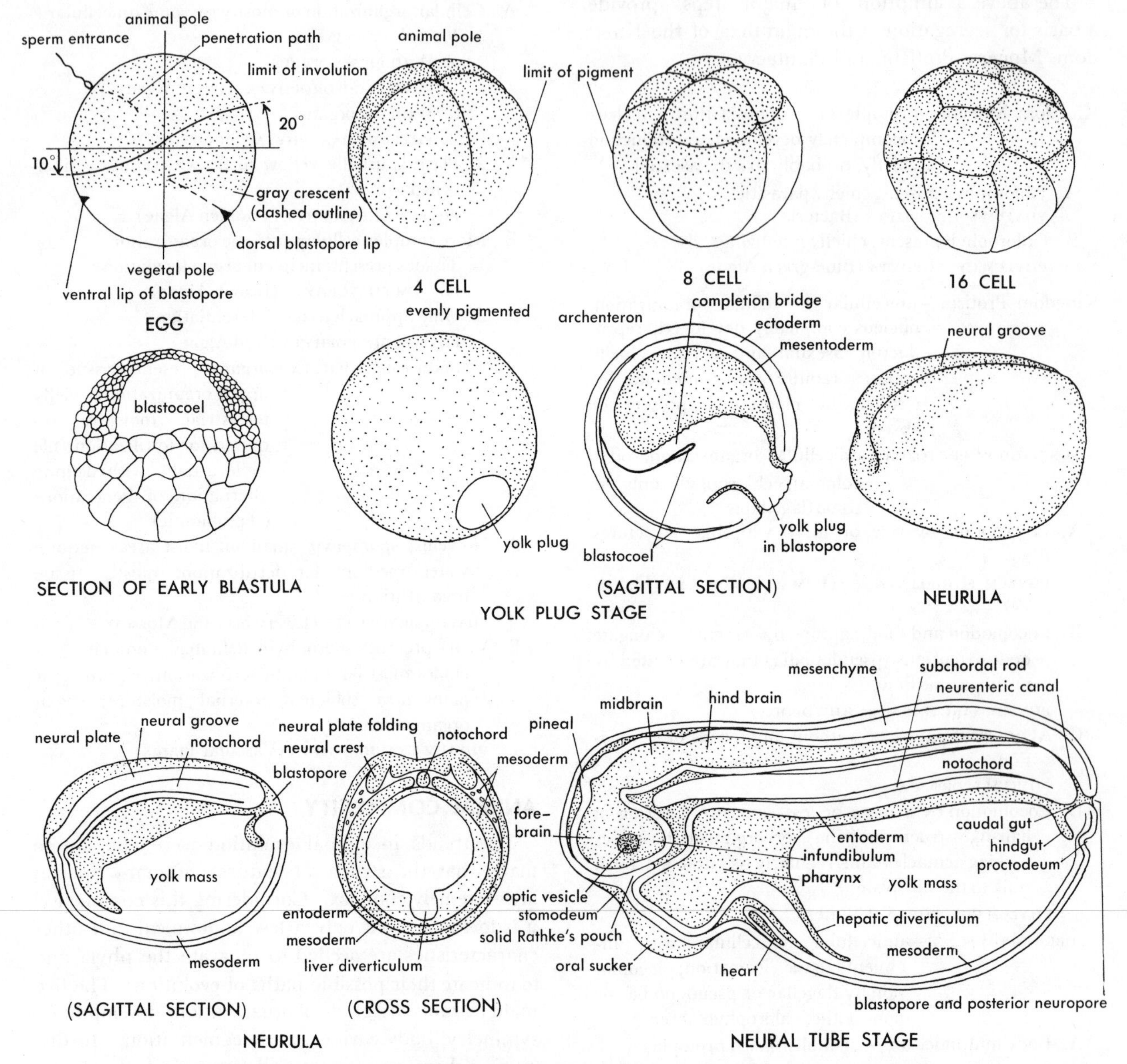

Figure 7.3 Stages in frog development from a fertilized egg to an early tadpole-like stage. Note that this development is strictly from three germ layers. (From Malcolm Jollie, *Chordate Morphology*, Reinhold Publishing Corp., New York, 1962.)

usually are not believed to display an independent organ basis of structure. However, there is sufficient peculiarity of flatworm (Platyhelminthes) structure for some zoologists to describe it as a complex of tissue, organ, and organ system organization, often termed "tissue-organ."

EMBRYOLOGY

Many features of embryonic development are important for understanding of evolutionary history, and for classification of living phyla. Here only the germ layers found in multicellular animals are reviewed. In development, the fertilized egg divides to form a ball of many cells, the *blastula*, which has a cavity, the *blastocoel*. Ultimately these many cells differentiate into two or three layers, *germ layers*, in a so-called gastrula stage (Figure 7.3). The germ layers probably are not strictly comparable in all phyla; however, each germ layer forms certain body structures. The outer germ layer, the *ectoderm*, forms the nervous system and outer coverings of the body; the inner layer, the *endoderm*, forms the lining of the organs of the digestive system; the middle layer, the *mesoderm* (a layer sometimes absent), forms the skeleton, muscles, and circulatory system.

SYMMETRY

Many sponges are asymmetrical, as indicated by one's inability to divide them into two equal, or mirror-image, halves. Other Porifera are essentially *spherical* in their symmetry. A test of this is the ability to divide one of these animals into halves by any cut passing through the center of the ball-like form (Figure 7.4). The Coelenterata, Ctenophora, and Echinodermata have *radial* or *biradial* symmetry; however, that of echinoderms is a secondary evolutionary acquisition from bilateral forms as a result of a sedentary life. Radial symmetry is found in a pie, because an infinite number of cuts through the center and in one plane will produce two mirror images. Biradial symmetry can be likened to a pie with two cherries put on a diameter of the pie and at equal distances from the center. In biradial symmetry there are only two ways of cutting to produce equal halves, one through the centers of the pie and two cherries and the other through the center of the pie and perpendicular to the first possible cut. *Bilateral* symmetry is the commonest and most advanced type. It is found in most of the phyla. Only a single cut is possible if one is to form equal halves, or right and left mirror images.

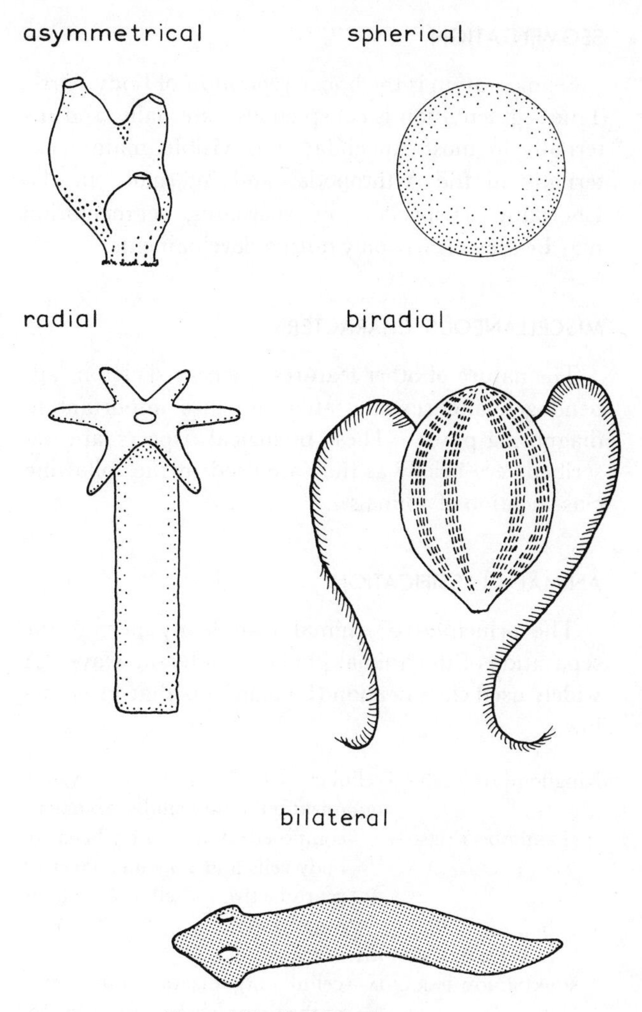

Figure 7.4 The kinds of symmetry.

BODY CAVITIES

Body cavities will be discussed in more detail later. The Ectoprocta through Chordata have true body cavities, or *coeloms*, of two types, *schizocoels* and *enterocoels*. The Mollusca and Arthropoda have reduced coeloms; their body cavity, the *hemocoel*, is so named because blood circulates through it. The Acanthocephala, Aschelminthes, and Entoprocta have so-called false body cavities, *pseudocoels*. Those animals lacking a body cavity are said to be *acoelomate*.

SEGMENTATION

Segmentation is the linear repetition of body parts. True segmentation is conspicuous externally and internally in most Annelida; it is visible mainly externally in the Arthropoda, and internally in the Chordata. Especially in chordates, segmentation may be seen clearly only during development.

MISCELLANEOUS CHARACTERS

The nature of other features, such as skeleton, appendages, and sexual status, are also important in diagnosing phyla. These biological aspects are described very briefly as they are used in the following classification of animals.

ANIMAL CLASSIFICATION

The principles of animal complexity permit the separation of the animal phyla in different ways. A widely used classification (Hyman's) is that given below.

Kingdom Animalia—cellular, tissue, or organ system organization; multicellular animals

SUBKINGDOM MESOZOA—composed of an outer layer of body cells and an inner layer of reproductive cells; cellular organization

PHYLUM MESOZOA (Mesozoans)

SUBKINGDOM PARAZOA—cellular organization, but almost at the tissue level of organization

PHYLUM PORIFERA (Sponges)

SUBKINGDOM EUMETAZOA—tissue or organ system grade of organization

GRADE RADIATA—primarily of radial symmetry; tissue grade of organization with incipient organ systems and mesoderm

A. Symmetry radial, biradial, or essentially bilateral; mouth usually encircled by tentacles; no rows of ciliated plates
   PHYLUM COELENTERATA (= CNIDARIA) (Coelenterates)
B. Symmetry biradial; tentacles, if present, not encircling mouth; 8 rows of ciliated paddle-plates
   PHYLUM CTENOPHORA (Comb Jellies)

GRADE BILATERIA—symmetry bilateral or secondarily radial; organ system grade of construction; mostly with mesoderm of ectodermal origin and usually with a body cavity other than the digestive cavity

A. Acoelomata—region between digestive cavity and body wall filled with cells; no body cavity
   1. Anus absent, poorly developed organ systems, often considered tissue-organ organization
      PHYLUM PLATYHELMINTHES (Flatworms)
   2. Anus present, organ systems present
      PHYLUM NEMERTINEA (= RHYNCHOCOELA) (Ribbon Worms)
B. Pseudocoelomata—space between digestive tract and body wall incompletely lined by cells of mesodermal origin; space is a remnant of a developmental cavity, the blastocoel
   1. Digestive tract absent
      PHYLUM ACANTHOCEPHALA (Spiny-headed Worms)
   2. Intestine essentially straight; anus posterior
      PHYLUM ASCHELMINTHES (Cavity Worms)
   3. Intestine looped; anus near mouth
      PHYLUM ENTOPROCTA (Moss Animals)
C. Eucoelomata—body cavity a true coelom
   1. Lophophorata—with a circular, crescent-shaped or double spiraled, coiled ridge (the *lophophore*) bearing ciliated tentacles; intestine looped, bringing mouth near anus; body cavity a schizocoel.
      a. Colonial, with gelatinous, chitinous, or calcareous encasements
         PHYLUM ECTOPROCTA (= BRYOZOA or POLYZOA) (Moss Animals)
      b. Solitary
         (1) Worm-like
             PHYLUM PHORONIDA (Fan Worms)
         (2) With a bivalve shell
             PHYLUM BRACHIOPODA (Lamp Shells)
   2. Schizocoela—coelom originates as a space in the mesoderm; no lophophore
      a. Unsegmented
         (1) Visceral mass covered by a body fold, the mantle, which secretes a shell; contains a small group having true segmentation.
             PHYLUM MOLLUSCA (Mollusks)
         (2) No mantle; naked; worm-like
             (a) With an eversible proboscis
                 PHYLUM SIPUNCULOIDEA (Peanut Worms)
             (b) No proboscis; mouth ventral
                 PHYLUM ECHIUROIDEA (Echiurids)
      b. Segmented
         (1) No jointed appendages
             PHYLUM ANNELIDA (Segmented Worms)
         (2) With jointed appendages
             PHYLUM ARTHROPODA (Joint-legged Animals)

3. Enterocoela—coelom originates as pouches from the embryonic gut
   a. With secondary, usually five-rayed, radial symmetry
      PHYLUM ECHINODERMATA (Spiny-skinned Animals)
   b. Bilateral symmetry retained throughout life
      (1) Without gill slits or internal skeleton
         (a) Without circulatory or excretory systems
            PHYLUM CHAETOGNATHA (Arrow Worms)
         (b) With both circulatory and excretory systems
            PHYLUM POGONOPHORA (Beard Worms)
      (2) With gill slits or internal skeleton or both
         (a) Without typical notochord (internal skeletal rod) in adult or embryo
            PHYLUM HEMICHORDATA (Acorn Worms)
         (b) Embryo with notochord, gill slits, and dorsal hollow nerve cord; adults with gill slits or vertebral column or both
            PHYLUM CHORDATA (Chordates)

ORIGIN OF LIFE

Because the unifying concept used in treating life is its evolution, a more detailed hypothesis on the origin of life and of the earliest plants and animals must be considered. The hypothesis that is considered here is one favored by many modern biologists, but not all. However, qualifying words or phrases will not be used.

After the earth first solidified, various materials, including water, were in a gaseous state in the early atmosphere. Atmospheric water fell almost constantly as rain, but because of heat from the earth's surface, the raindrops evaporated before reaching the surface. Finally, with additional cooling, the first rain struck the earth's surface and soon the first water came into existence. Owing to almost continuous rainfall and heat, conditions were optimum for the dissolving of materials of the crust and for the reacting of chemical compounds. Present puny efforts of man to duplicate conditions during this phase of earth's history caused the synthesis of amino acids (the building blocks of proteins) and other organic compounds. More recently, one of the essential building blocks of nucleic acid, genetic material, was synthesized by a similar experiment. This is important if one remembers that organic compounds now are made only by living creatures and are part of the chemicals in living flesh.

When the earth finally cooled enough to allow the first permanent bodies of water, there were great varieties of *organic compounds* present; the larger of these compounds existed as so-called *colloidal solutions* in the water (Figure 7.5). Because these solutions included electrically active groups, water accumulated around the surface of individual particles and oppositely charged particles attracted one another. Due to increased size, still larger materials settled and heaped up as complex mixtures called *coacervates.* The coacervates each absorbed water on their surfaces to form a membrane-like external structure. All of these hypothetical steps indicate the origin of individuality, but not of life itself.

From such chemically active individuals, the

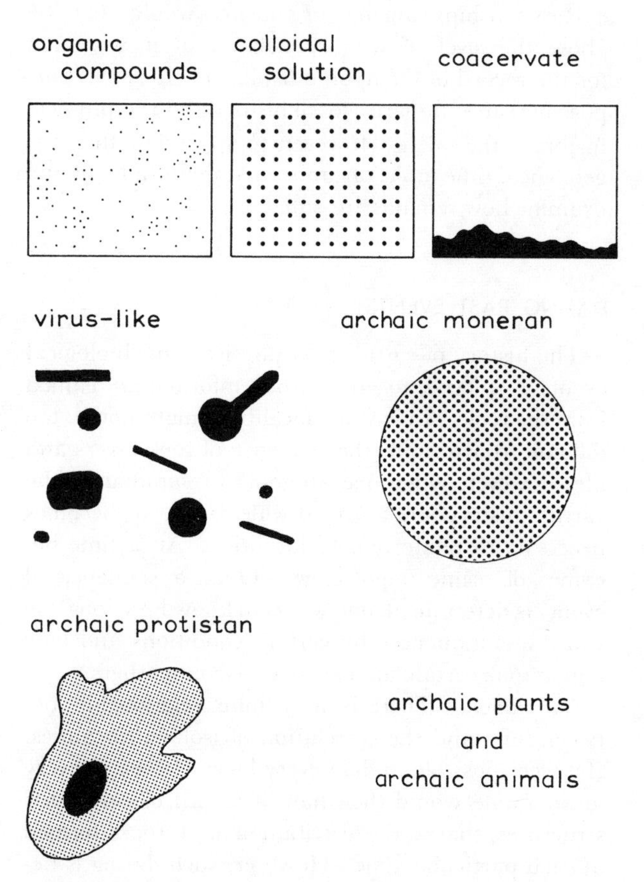

Figure 7.5 Hypothetical sequence in the early evolution of life. Plants and animals most likely had different protistan ancestors.

chemical reactions to complete evolution of a *virus-like* condition are relatively simple. "Living" viruses are chemically similar to a hereditary unit, or gene, of more complex life forms; but probably are not modern descendants of a virus-like stage. Anything causing ancient virus-like creatures to combine with one another would produce organisms like the simplest, present-day bacteria. This *archaic moneran* stage, the first definite life, was not far from evolution into unicellular creatures, the Protista. For example, the living sulfur bacteria may be similar to the ancestral Monera. These sulfur bacteria have a pigment quite similar to chlorophyll, which is capable of carrying on a kind of photosynthesis. From such organisms, it is a small step to the *protistans*, and from protistans, a small step to the origin of the *plant* or *animal* kingdom.

GEOLOGICAL HISTORY

Relationships among organisms would not be above the level of wild speculation if it were not for the record of life upon our planet. It is the purpose here to summarize fossil history and the physical history of the earth. However, to appreciate fully the geological time table, one must first define a fossil and examine how remains are dated.

DATING PAST EVENTS

The history of earth's past physical and biological events is pieced together from information gained from the rocks. In any one locality it might not be too difficult to determine the sequence of rock layers and life; however, when one attempts to summarize the earth's history on a world-wide basis, it becomes necessary to relate remote localities. Also, time becomes of prime importance. Once a sequence of events is determined, one wants to know how long the world was influenced by certain conditions and how long it took certain animals to evolve into others.

Correlation. There is a definite relationship between time and the correlation of isolated localities. If it were possible to date every layer of rock in every locality, one would then have a record of correlated structures; that is, the distribution of all rocks formed at each particular time. However, such dating is beyond the possibility of human accomplishment; there is time only to date a minute sample of the earth's layers of rocks. Therefore, the relating of geological events must be based on some simpler, less time-consuming procedure. The historical geologists call the procedure they now use *correlation.*

Geological correlation is done in three main steps. First, the geologist looks for continuity. He traces the distribution of a particular layer of rock and assumes that all of it was formed at the same time and under similar conditions. This layer he calls a *formation.* Second, he looks for structural similarity among isolated rock layers. If isolated rocks are similar to one another, the geologist considers separately the layer found directly above and the one directly below. Then, if all the upper rock strata seem to be a homogeneous appearing unit, or formation, and so do all the lower layers, it is concluded that each isolated but similar group belongs to one formation. This same general procedure is used in even more complex determination of formations. Finally, the geologist tries to correlate fossils. If these indications of past life are essentially the same in isolated, similar rock layers, he concludes that the remote strata belong to one formation and are approximately of the same age.

Correlation does no more than provide a sequence of past events; it does not tell how long each event lasted or how long ago each started. Therefore, other techniques are required to provide a geological calendar.

Dating. About fifty methods have been used to measure geological time; however, they can be summarized under four main groupings. The first type attempts to date the age of the earth by estimating the past rate of heat loss from the sun or earth and gives an age of about forty million years. However, this age is no longer considered valid, because it is based upon the false assumption that the earth and sun are simple cooling bodies. The second type evaluates erosion rates and provides a similar estimate of the earth's age. Although erosion rate is a fairly accurate technique for approximating the age of recent events, it is little better than the first type for long-range events. The third type uses the rate of deposition of eroded materials. Although no longer acceptable because of unequal rates of deposition at different times, it does imply that the earth is one hundred million years old. The final type, the present one, is by calculation of the amount of radioactive decay of rocks. Age approximation, not only of the earth but also of the features formed since the origin of the earth, is possible because each radioactive material goes through a cycle of decay from one mineral to another. For example, uranium changes to a unique kind of lead that can be distinguished from other lead, and radioactive carbon goes to nonradioactive carbon. The life of any radioactive material is expressed in terms of its "half life," the time necessary for one-half of the substance to decay completely. For uranium the half life is five billion years; for carbon it is 5570 years. However, it takes much more than two half lives for any radioactive material to decay completely. At the end of one half life there is one-half of the original material left; at the end of two half lives, one-fourth; at the end of three, one-eighth; etc.

Many radioactive substances are utilized in the extremely critical techniques of dating. For example, uranium may be used to determine the age of rocks in millions of years, and radioactive carbon may be used for dating fairly recent materials. Although these and other radioactive materials can give accurate dating, generally within 5 per cent of the true age, procedures must be meticulous or considerable error is possible. For example, only an expert technician is capable of selecting the materials for dating. Test rocks must be unweathered. Also there are analysis difficulties, as in uranium dating where primary lead often is mixed in the sample with the lead produced by the radioactive decay of uranium; other radioactive materials may also be present. Therefore, for reliable estimates, many separate determinations, if possible on different radioactive samples, must be made. Although these difficulties exist in all radioactive dating, there is an apparently reliable estimate of the age of the oldest known rocks at over three billion years! This would mean that our planet must be at least four, and probably more, billion years old; many geologists consider four and one-half billion years a reasonable approximation of the age of the earth.

FOSSILS

Fossils give direct or indirect evidence of past life. A fossil can be actual remains of an organism—soft parts, hard parts, or waste products; any impressions or replacements of original substances, such as molds or casts of a once-living creature; or any indication of past life no matter how remote, such as tracks, trails, or burrows. In general, the more recent the fossils the better their condition and the more numerous they are. Naturally, an organism that has just died (technically a fossil) is relatively easy to identify. All the hard and soft parts are present; there is really little basic difference between the dead creature and a living representative of the same species. However, the older a fossil the less it looks like a once-living creature. In the case of many animals, older fossils progressively may consist of defleshed bones in a life-like position, well-preserved but scattered bones, partially broken bones, bone fragments, and hardly recognizable pieces. This tendency for progressive destruction is directly associated with geological processes. Because the amount of geological activity is directly related to time, the older the fossils generally the poorer their condition. From a related point of view, the older the rocks the fewer the indications of past life.

Recency of fossil formation is not the only important aspect of fossil permanence. Different organisms vary in their likelihood of remaining as fossils. It should be no great surprise that the fossils most frequently found are of plants or animals with hard parts. Remains such as bones, shells, or coral deposits are more likely to persist long enough to be preserved and are less likely to be removed either by decay or by geological activities. On the other hand, soft parts are susceptible to complete loss. Soft parts and time worked together to cause the paucity of archaic fossils. The oldest fossil-containing rocks have few fossils because they represent the time of the most simply constructed organisms, species composed almost entirely of soft parts. For example, the first three billion years of earth history included the dawn of life but left hardly any easily recognizable fossils. Rather, this record contains mostly hydrocarbons and other chemical compounds that probably were formed by living creatures. For the next one and one-half billion years of life (Proterozoic Era) fossils still are poor. These fossils are often fragmentary; however, there are recognizable sponges, corals, worms, mollusks, algae, and other groups. Some of these fossils give good evidence for the presence of most to all animal phyla, algae, protistans, and monerans.

A rather recent contribution to the history of life is the study of minute remains such as microscopic reproductive structures (e.g., plant pollen) and microorganisms. Such plant remains, according to some botanists, definitely establish the vascular plants as being with the Proterozoic Era fossils. In fact, the various kinds of fossil evidence allow the generalization that all living phyla likely existed prior to Cambrian times, or more than one-half billion years ago.

GEOLOGICAL TIME TABLE

For convenience, geological time is divided into four time levels (Figure 7.6). The largest category is an *era*. An era contains a particular major *rock group* that represents a time of fairly homogeneous topography and climate and is distinctly separated from rocks of adjacent eras. Eras are subdivided into *periods,* the largest of the units within eras. Each period is diagnosed by having a single *rock system.* Further subdivision may provide individual *epochs,* each having a single *rock series*. Within epochs there is the small time unit, the *age,* which is determined by the basic rock unit, the *stage,* which locally may be represented by one *formation.* Unfortunately, formations often vary a great deal in age from locality to locality, so usually conform to no particular time unit.

Eras prior to the Paleozoic are no longer recognized by many geologists. This entire time often is called the *Cryptozoic Eon* or simply *Precambrian* and is contrasted with the named eras grouped into the *Phanerozoic Eon.* Although one probably should not subdivide Precambrian time because so little is known about it, its named eras are given.

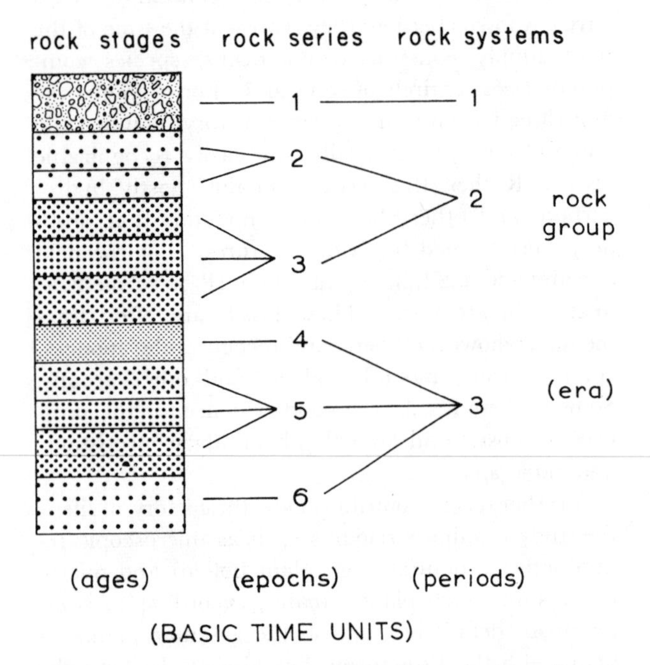

Figure 7.6 The subdivisions of geological time according to rock layers.

Table 7.1 is a geological calendar that barely summarizes the greatest trends throughout geological history. The left-hand portion of the table segregates time levels. These levels are arranged to start with the present and go back through time to the origin of the earth and solar system. Therefore, one can start either at the beginning or at the end of the table, tracing history backward or forward. The middle column sketches physical events of North America, and the final column summarizes the world-wide history of life.

EVOLUTION

Darwin was not the first man to think in terms of one form of life giving rise to another. Thinking about evolution existed in the times of the ancient Greek philosophers, at least as far back as the fifth century B.C. when Empedocles proposed a means whereby organisms spontaneously arose from the earth. However, as far as is known, it was Aristotle (384–322 B.C.) who first proposed that more complex creatures arose from simpler ones. This was a remarkable step toward the truth, but it was not supplemented until the eighteenth century when many individuals began to criticize the then long-prevalent concept of special creation of each species. In 1802, Jean Baptiste de Lamarck (1744–1829) proposed a mechanism by which simpler creatures evolved into more complex ones. According to Lamarck's hypothesis increased use of structures supposedly would cause their greater development, and disuse would result in their atrophy and loss. Therefore, Lamarckian evolution suggested the inheritance of acquired characteristics, that is, that offspring inherit traits developed by their parents. For example, if Lamarckian evolution were true it would mean that if a man exercised and acquired extreme musculature, the man's offspring would have such muscles without any need for exercise. Although Lamarck's ideas were a big step toward a theory of evolution, they are not generally accepted at the present time.

The final significant pre-Darwin contributions to evolution were made by Sir Charles Lyell (1797–1875) and Reverend Thomas R. Malthus (1766–1834). Lyell, an English geologist, related fossils to the geological record in his *Principles of Geology*, the

TABLE 7.1 GEOLOGICAL CALENDAR, INDICATING MILLIONS OF YEARS CHRONOLOGICALLY WITH ERAS AND DURATION OF EACH PERIOD AND EPOCH

PHANEROZOIC EON

Eras	Periods and Epochs			Physical Events (North America)	Life
CENOZOIC (MODERN LIFE)	QUATERNARY	Recent	.01	Postglacial climate; glaciers melting; great stream, flood, and ground water actions; ocean wave and shore current erosion; winds important in dry areas. Rejuvenation to high relief—northeast and Pacific Coast uplift, western mountain vulcanism; general growth; Great Valley a geosyncline since Jurassic; extensive continents.	Rise of man through new stone, bronze, and iron ages. Expansion and restriction of ranges of living organisms to present distributions.
	1	Pleistocene	1	Four glacial and three interglacial warm climates; alpine glaciation and erosion; continental glaciation and effects; many lakes, especially in Great Basin; rivers flooded by melting ice; western canyons excavated; extensive glacial and stream actions. Pronounced western mountain building, including vulcanism.	Stone age men and first modern man (Cro-Magnon). Modern types of plants and animals are dominant. Extinction of many trees and large animals.
	TERTIARY	Pliocene	12	Climate cooling but semiarid; first half marked zonation, and last half like now; western mountain erosion and area sedimentation; some western peneplaination; Great Plains sedimentation. World-wide elevation and restricted seas; most active growth of western mountains; vulcanism especially in Cascades; Rockies and Basin Ranges refaulted; Western Great Basin shears from Sierras; Coast Ranges folding, faulting, and vulcanism.	North and South America connected after isolation since Eocene (?) and mammals known to mingle—extension and expansion of many species. North American horses and elephants approach modern forms. Rise of present organism distribution.
		Miocene	12	Climate with temperature fluctuations in the continuing cooling trend; some erosion due to mountains; California, Gulf and Atlantic Coasts submerged and deposits accumulated; continental erosion. Seas generally restricted; western mountains start forming, widespread vulcanism including northwestern lava fields, start of Cascadian Revolution and growth to Recent.	Advances in mammals, especially horses and elephants; apes appear; peak for mammals. Reduction of forests and retreat of polar flora.
		Oligocene	11	Rapid decline from old warm climate, warm and humid to cooler and drier; erosion in high western mountains and associated local sedimentation; Gulf submerged and sedimentation. Restricted seas, but lands generally lower; some localized western uplift near end.	Archaic mammal extinction; rise of advanced mammals (anthropoids, hoofed and carniverous) and birds. Subtropical forests widely distributed.

TABLE 7.1 GEOLOGICAL CALENDAR (continued)
PHANEROZOIC EON

Eras	Periods and Epochs		Physical Events (North America)	Life
CENOZOIC (cont.)	TERTIARY (cont.)	Eocene 22	Last of maximum warm climates in a cycle of slight cooling then return, start of cooling cycle at end; high mountain stream erosion, perhaps some glaciation in highest Rockies; California and Gulf Coast sedimentation. Most extensive Tertiary seas in California; California mountains active, especially vulcanism; continued Rockies growth.	Dominance of early mammals. Coming of modern invertebrates, birds and mammals. Expansion of modern plants with subtropical forests to polar regions.
63	62	Paleocene 5	Continued slight cooling then return to Cretaceous conditions; physiography much like Eocene but climate cooler and drier with semiarid areas. Seas not as widespread and mountain growth less active, except Rockies.	Reptiles subordinate. Dawn and spread of modern mammals. Modernization of plants.
MESOZOIC (MIDDLE LIFE)	CRETACEOUS	Upper Cretaceous 27	Climates more uniform and warmer than now but slight cooling at end. Seas split North America through Great Plains; Atlantic and Gulf Coasts and much of California submerged, widespread sedimentation; submerged and lowlands of Rockies rise by some vulcanism, then uplift of intermontane plateaus of west and Rockies growth; also Great Plains and eastern uplift and Appalachian Highlands arching.	Great extinction of older groups at the end and into the Paleocene, extinction of ruling reptiles and earliest birds. Mollusks abundant. Continued decrease of gymnosperms; eruption of flowering plants, dominance toward the end.
	72	Lower Cretaceous 45	Temperature generally uniformly high, but climatic diversity and seasonal changes, perhaps some glacial and arid areas, mostly warm and fluctuating. Continent generally low except for continued elevation in Pacific borderlands; seas encroach from Arctic into Canada and from Gulf into Great Plains, also from Pacific into borderlands.	Dinosaur peak, but extinction of some ruling reptiles and earliest birds. Increase of mollusks and dawn of modern invertebrates. Expansion of modern gymosperms; first absolute fossils of flowering plants; decrease of gymnosperms at end.
	JURASSIC 46		Temperature much like Lower Cretaceous, but generally less climatic diversity. Shallow seas in Pacific borderlands and Great Plains, a long erosion cycle for most of the continent. Pacific borderland mountain building from Central America to Alaska, active vulcanism including intrusion of Sierra batholith.	Dawn of birds; spread of archaic mammals: marine, flying, and giant reptiles common. Modern type crustaceans; age of cephalopods (octopus and squid allies); development of higher invertebrates. Older gymnosperms dominant to the dawn of modern types.

TABLE 7.1 GEOLOGICAL CALENDAR (continued)

PHANEROZOIC EON

Eras	Periods	Physical Events (North America)	Life
MESOZOIC (cont.) 230	TRIASSIC 49	Period of temperature rise to Jurassic, but climate more arid than Jurassic, mostly semiarid and arid with widespread deserts, probably wet-dry cycles in temperate climates. Continent rising, east becoming land, but continent generally low and some sea encroachment along Pacific.	Dawn of mammals; ruling reptiles dominant: primitive amphibian extinction. Marine invertebrates decline. Older gymnosperms increase.
PALEOZOIC (OLD LIFE)	PERMIAN 50	Climatic mystery, apparently a violent drop in temperature almost to present conditions and rapid rise almost to past warmth; widespread aridity and Southern Hemisphere glaciation, perhaps some glaciation in the eastern United States; different areas with desert, semiarid, wet-dry cyclic, warm, and frigid climates. Seas invade Texas, southwest, and then Great Plains and area of western mountains, or Cordilleras. Third cycle of world-wide uplift and mountain building, including Appalachian Revolution.	Widespread extinction of older forms of life. Rise of primitive reptiles, mammal-like reptiles, and modern insects. Fossil evidence for most living orders of vascular plants other than the flowering plants. Decline of lycopods and horsetails.
	PENNSYLVANIAN or UPPER CARBONIFEROUS 30	Gradual temperature decline from Mississippian, climate very moist, warm to tropical with little seasonal variation; subtropics move farther northward. Alternate emergence and submergence with extensive epicontinental shallow seas developing many times; great swamps in east contain flora that fossilized to form extensive coal deposits.	Ancient forms of life become rare. Giant insects. More coal-forming plants and continuation of many Mississippian types. Many fern-like plants and gymnosperms forming forests. First definite moss and liverwort fossils.
	MISSISSIPPIAN or LOWER CARBONIFEROUS 35	Generally uniformly warm and mild climate but local moist and wet-dry cycles. Topography low, shallow seas invade much of west and east to continental rise at end; active movements in southern Appalachians and site of Rockies from Utah to Texas; continued folding of New England Acadian mountains; start of great eastern coal deposits.	Dawn of reptiles; amphibians numerous; sharks numerous; rise of insects; many corals. Early coal-forming plants dominant, especially nonflowering vascular plants, including lycopods, horsetails, seed ferns, etc.
	DEVONIAN 60	Temperature drop, then rise to warmer Mississippian conditions; climate generally desert to warm and humid mild, perhaps some glaciation. Widespread seas advance to cover 40% of North America, but withdraw at end. Acadian Mountains form by vulcanism and folding in second uplift cycle.	Dawn of amphibians; age of fishes, many armored types; perhaps first insects; corals and crinoids abundant. First known trees, but mostly primitive plants. First brown algae, "moss," and higher fungi macrofossils.

TABLE 7.1 GEOLOGICAL CALENDAR (continued)

PHANEROZOIC EON

Eras	Periods	Physical Events (North America)	Life
PALEOZOIC (cont.)	SILURIAN 20	Uniformly warm, representing first peak in continuously warming trend that started in Precambrian; climate generally mild and uniform, much like Ordovician, to late desert conditions. Two complete cycles of sea advance and retreat with advances featuring widespread seas; land generally low.	First air-breathing animals invade the land (lungfishes and arthropods). Marine arthropods (sea scorpions) dominant. First insects. Rise of fishes. Many algae, probably still dominant. Expansion of land plants, including vascular plants; first psilopsids.
	ORDOVICIAN 95	Gradual temperature rise to Silurian conditions; climate relatively warm and uniform apparently to area of present Arctic Seas. Greatest North American submergence (over 60%) to sea withdrawal at end. Mountain formation along northern Atlantic Coast of the United States.	First vertebrate fossils (armored fishes). Climax of age of invertebrates and rise of modern types; corals and trilobites abundant; many mollusks, especially cephalopods. First red algae fossils. Probable divergence of vascular and other land plants. Algae still the dominant plants.
620	CAMBRIAN 100	Rapid temperature rise from conditions much like now; perhaps early glaciation to warm with local arid areas. Sea invades much of continent and partially withdraws by the end. Land generally low.	Most to all plant and animal phyla definitely present; all vascular plant subphyla present? Mostly ancient, now extinct representatives of present life; ancient lamp shells and arthropods (trilobites) dominant. Continued marine algae dominance.

CRYPTOZOIC EON

	Possible Subdivisions		Physical Events (North America)	Life
PRECAMBRIAN	ACTUALISTIC ⟶ 2120	Proterozoic Era? 1500?	Climate of repeated glacial and warm moist interglacial periods; near end temperature conditions to the lowest ever known, then start of rapid rise that also characterized the Cambrian. Great sedimentation to second great period of mountain building followed by erosion—loss of many fossils. Dawn of Actualistic Period of geological history—geological processes subject to same laws and conditions as now.	Age of primitive life; marine algac probably the dominant life. Perhaps the final origin of most phyla; definite protozoans, sponges, coelenterates, segmented worms, other worms, and perhaps lamp shells; also bacteria, algae, fungi, and vascular plants (spores) seem to be represented. Probably a time of the early development of all phyla.
	PREACTUALISTIC	Archezoic Era? 2000?	Probably hot to very warm with dense cloud cover and torrential rains to more moderate conditions. First great mountain formation (volcanic) and erosion, some sedimentary deposits. Like Proterozoic in many respects.	Dawn of life? Indications of earliest life: iron deposits by bacteria (?); archaic blue-green algae and archiac fungi fossils (?) at end of era or beginning of Proterozoic; archaic blue-green algae fossils at 2.7 billion years (?)!

TABLE 7.1 GEOLOGICAL CALENDAR (continued)

CRYPTOZOIC EON

Possible Subdivisions			Physical Events (North America)	Life
PRECAMBRIAN (cont.)	PREACTUALISTIC (cont.)			Premise that early life used H_2S and CO_2 in photosynthesis, releasing oxygen to form early version of present atmosphere; H_2S removed.
		Azoic Era?	Birth of the solar system, earth, oceans; first great erosion cycle. Preactualistic Period of geological history—although same fundamental laws operated as now, conditions were so different that natural phenomena were not the same; earliest part had barren rocky lithosphere, and hydrosphere and atmosphere mainly of ammonia, hydrogen sulfide, and water plus some carbon dioxide; photochemical reactions formed the organic compounds which characterized later Preactualistic, prior to the dawn of life.	Inorganic materials to organic compounds that became the basis for life. Probably no living creatures during this era; perhaps the dawn of virus-like compounds.
5120	3000	1000?		

first work to establish definitely a prehistoric record of life. Malthus, primarily a mathematician and economist, wrote *An Essay on the Principle of Population*. This essay suggested that (1) the breeding potential (Malthus referred to man) is much greater than environmental resources; (2) this leads to competition for available materials; therefore, (3) there is a struggle for existence. Malthus pointed out that all this occurs because population increase is geometric, whereas the potential increase in environmental materials is, at best, arithmetic. To summarize, these two men proposed a prehistoric fossil record, portraying gradual change in life; the means of population increase; the presence of competition; and a struggle for existence. These principles of evolution directly lead to five general conclusions that usually are credited to Darwin alone: (1) members of the same species display individual differences, (2) more offspring are produced than can survive, (3) overpopulation leads to competition, (4) competition ends in the survival of individuals that are best suited to their environment (survival of the fittest), and (5) new species arise from survival of the fittest.

In 1858, while Charles Darwin (1809–1882) was gathering evidence to verify these ideas, another naturalist, Alfred R. Wallace (1823–1913), wrote Darwin. In this letter Wallace showed that his years of study of East Indian plants and animals brought him to the same ideas about evolution. Although Wallace's ideas were independently derived, there is little doubt that the ideas were stimulated by his correspondence with Darwin. Wallace's letter led to the now famous Darwin-Wallace essay of July, 1858, which presented their conclusions about evolution before the Linnean Society of London. However, Darwin now is credited as the father of evolution because of his 1859 publication, *On the Origin of Species by Means of Natural Selection*.

Darwinism was a tremendous contribution to modern evolutionary thought. However, certain of his hypotheses were invalid. Competition and struggle for existence do exist, but these factors are not necessarily most intense among individuals of the same species. Of equal and sometimes greater significance are relationships between individuals and their physical environment or their predators, prey, parasites, and/or diseases. Darwinism was right in the concepts of potential increase, competition, and struggle, but did now allow for the importance of multiple environmental factors or even chance alone eliminating members of a single species. Also, there was no mention that population sizes could and do vary tremendously from season to season and year to year. Darwin assumed population sizes to be essentially fixed.

Darwin's ideas on variation were confused by being associated directly with the survival of the fittest. Actually, variation and survival are two distinct things. Variation is primarily due to heredity and environmental influence upon the basic hereditary pattern. Moreover, heredity and changes in heredity (*mutations*) provide the basis for evolution. Heredity and environment together cause the many functional, structural, and behavioral traits that may be beneficial, neutral, or harmful to organisms.

Generally there is a natural selection for the beneficial or neutral traits and against the harmful ones. However, selection is not simply a matter of organisms with the best characteristics surviving and those with the poorest ones dying. Chance has a part to play. Chance alone might cause either the elimination of the best features or the retention of the worst. On the other hand, there is believed to be a direct relationship between value of a feature and survival. This allows one to modify Darwin's ideas and state that organisms with beneficial traits are more likely to survive than individuals with harmful traits.

Darwinism in the strictest sense is no longer completely accepted. The prevalent expanded concept of evolution is called neo-Darwinism. Neo-Darwinism stresses the importance of the basic units of heredity, the genes; it considers the principal source of variation to be gene mutations, and the principle force of the direction of evolution to be natural selection (chance is of much less importance).

Neo-Darwinism, phylogeny, and the principles of evolution all are interrelated. Historically, the interrelations came from the accumulation of evidence for evolution; the development of the science of genetics, which provided the mechanisms for evolution; and the explanation of various characteristics of evolution.

EVIDENCE FOR EVOLUTION

FOSSIL RECORD AND GEOLOGICAL TIME

The record of past life is far from perfect; however, it is more extensive than would be necessary for one to consider evolution a fact rather than conjecture (see Table 7.1). There are good fossil series that portray gradual changes in individual lines of development and probable major lines of past development of the living phyla. The animal record is somewhat better than that of plants in this respect. The animal record shows that the first animals were invertebrates; then came primitive fishes, amphibians, reptiles, and finally birds and mammals.

The fossil record definitely refutes the old idea of catastrophism, that life was created and abruptly destroyed many times. In spite of gaps in the record, fossils indicate trends of gradual to abrupt decline in some past life and of almost simultaneous diversification in others. Many times the number of species living today evolved and later became extinct; however, most of the geological record implies somewhat independent origin and extinction. Although part of this record might suggest catastrophism, different groups of organisms reacted differently during the infrequent times of widespread extinction; while some formers were declining, others were increasing.

ANATOMY

The anatomical evidence for evolution is overwhelming. For example, the subject of comparative anatomy of the vertebrates demonstrates the affinity among vertebrate body systems (Figure 7.7). However, comparative anatomy need not be limited to vertebrates alone. One also can follow the lines of development and like origin of body parts in invertebrates and in plants.

COMPARATIVE PHYSIOLOGY

Like anatomy, body function is important proof of evolution. Physiology is accomplished by chemical processes. In closely related organisms the chemicals and processes are quite similar; the more distantly related the organisms, the greater the differences in physiology.

Important sources of comparative physiological data are blood chemistry tests in which blood proteins are analyzed. The data allow the generalization that the more closely related the species, the more similar the blood chemistry, the more distantly related, the more dissimilar the proteins.

EMBRYOLOGY

The importance of embryology was once overemphasized by the so-called *Biogenetic Law*. This "law" was that *ontogeny recapitulates phylogeny*, that is, the developmental history of an organism recreates the evolutionary history of its ancestors. This premise

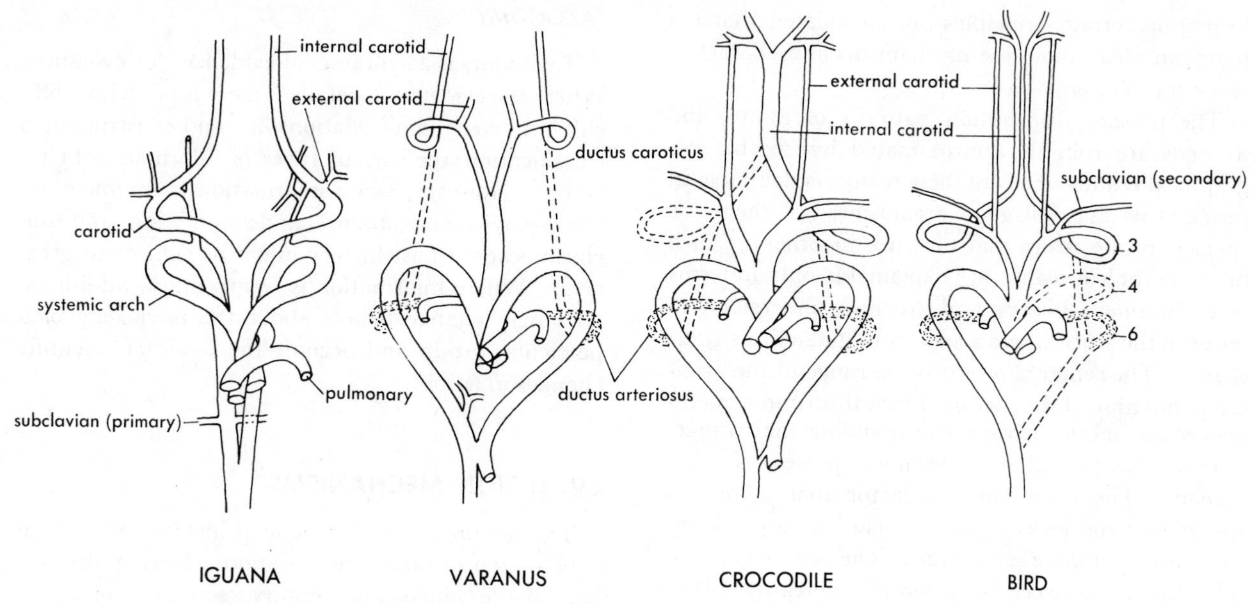

Figure 7.7. Structure of the aortic arches (arteries associated with the heart) in two lizards, a crocodile, and a bird. The variations are due to retention of different ones of the vessels present in early developmental stages of all four animals. (From Malcolm Jollie, *Chordate Morphology*, Reinhold Publishing Corp., New York, 1962.)

assumed that in general embryos repeated ancestral history, although there was elimination of some stages, reduction of others, and perhaps some overemphasis of still others. It completely ignored the possibility that embryos, or developmental stages in general, can have structures or stages of their life history that are adaptations to preadult life. Immature stages are so adapted.

In spite of developmental stage adaptations, embryology does tend to present a picture of relationships (Figure 7.8). Its data also show that closely related forms are similar and more distantly related ones are dissimilar. Also, there is a tendency for embryology to give some portrayal of past evolutionary history. Therefore, one might modify the old Biogenetic Law to read "ontogeny *tends to* recapitulate phylogeny."

BIOGEOGRAPHY

The geographic distribution of plants and animals first caused Darwin and Wallace to accept evolution. In the modern use of biogeography, both present and past distributions of life are studied. From such in-

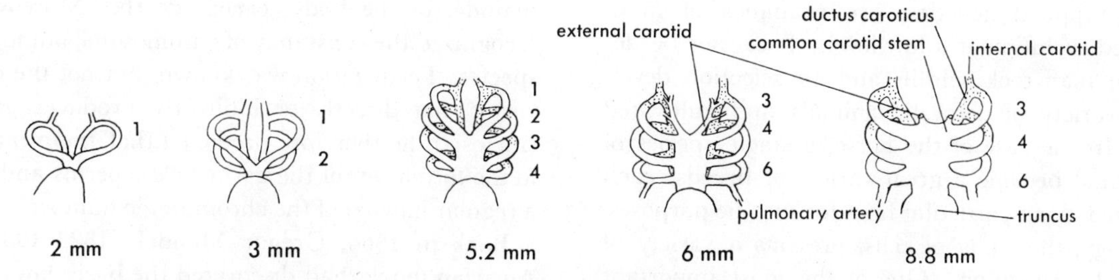

Figure 7.8 Development of aortic arches in man implies path of vertebrate evolution. Although arches 1–6 may all develop, arch 5 often does not. Note that arches 1 and 2 develop, but soon only their base stems are retained in the external carotid artery. Also, in the adult human each third arch becomes the base of an internal carotid artery, the left fourth arch remains as the systemic arch of the aorta and the right fourth arch remains as the subclavian artery, the fifth arch (if it appears at all) is lost, and the sixth arch normally loses much of its use at birth. (From Malcolm Jollie, *Chordate Morphology*, Reinhold Publishing Corp., New York, 1962.)

formation certain principles are formulated that expand our ideas about the mechanisms and characteristics of evolution.

The present distribution patterns of plants and animals are roughly approximated by six biogeographical realms. Each of these realms is definable in terms of its assemblage of organisms, but there are species in one realm that also live in others. Such biogeographical realms are explainable only in terms of evolutionary history and are best understood in terms of the place where a species originated, its *center of origin*. The center of origin is the range of the original population of the species. From this center, members of the species move out, expanding their range, until some aspect of an environment prevents further spread. The environmental factor that stops the spread of a species is a *barrier*, including such things as oceans and large mountains. The ocean is a primary barrier between biogeographical realms. Barriers within realms are instrumental in the evolutionary independence among its species.

Barriers can be biological as well as physical. The general effect of biological barriers is to separate organisms having similar life requirements. Naturally, different species having near identical requirements are going to compete for the same things, and in their struggle for existence be separated geographically, each species occupying the environment in which it does best. Such separation of biologically similar organisms usually involves closely related taxa; hence, there are few known instances of closely related species inhabiting the same geographic area.

GENETICS AND CYTOLOGY

The entire fields of plant and animal breeding, areas of applied genetics, are examples of man-controlled evolution at a low level. It cannot be denied that man took wildlife and by selection developed a variety of domestic animals and cultivated plants. In the case of the horse, a single species of wild animal became a great variety of breeds, each specialized along particular lines for specific purposes.

Cytology, the study of cells, presents a variety of evidence for evolution. One of the most important phases of cytological study is that of chromosome structure. The number, size, and form of chromosomes are used both to investigate and to verify lines of evolution.

TAXONOMY

Taxonomy is a synthesis of evidences for evolution. Where the evidence is detailed, there is often less difficulty in determining relationships and constructing a classification; the various types of information fit together. However, when information is fragmentary, phylogeny is more obscure, and assumptions and conclusions about past history might be subject to great error. Where information is fragmentary, additional data may change beliefs about the phylogeny of a particular group and become the basis for scientific changes in names.

EVOLUTION MECHANISMS

The development of genetic principles offered an explanation of organism variation. During the last half of the nineteenth century, several people, especially Weismann and Naegeli, called attention to the lack of explanation of variation in Darwin's theory. Naegeli, in the earliest days of knowledge about chromosomes, postulated a linear series of determiners (genes) in each chromosome, because of the careful provision in cell division for longitudinal duplication of chromosomes. Weismann, while still comparatively young, was afflicted with near-blindness and had to turn from experimental work to purely imaginative speculation. The results were brilliant. From his work in refuting Lamarckism, Weismann theorized a continuity of the germ plasm. He said that germ cells, as determiners of heredity, are apart from and practically a parasite on the organism. The germ cells, he said, are potentially immortal, perpetuating themselves in each generation, and are unaffected by any changes in the remainder of the body, except death. Moreover, he recognized the constancy of chromosome number in a species. Fertilization was known, but not the cell division that directly or indirectly produces gametes (meiosis); he therefore predicted that there must be, in the formation of the germ cells (sperms and eggs), a regular halving of the chromosome number!

Back in 1866, Gregor Mendel (1822–1884), an Austrian monk, had discovered the basic laws of heredity. However, Mendel's work remained unnoticed until 1900, when a number of individuals "rediscovered" these basic laws. One of the first discoverers pointed out the sudden, spontaneous, discontinuous variations in heredity and called these *mutations*. Later, the work of a great many men studying genetics tied the visible change of traits in mutants to changes in the chromosomes themselves. Therefore, in place of Darwin's infinite variations, biologists now speak of mutations as the basic material of evolution.

This idea of sudden, spontaneous change in heredity emphasizes the importance of an aspect of geographic distribution in evolution. This aspect is the factor of *isolation*. Two groups of the same species may be isolated by a mountain or other barrier. Within each group there is the possibility of different sets of chance mutations arising, being incorporated into the populations, and leading to speciation (Figure 7.9). But final isolation between species is not only geographic; it may be physiological, such as genetic factors limiting cross-fertility or normal development of an embryo; it may be anatomical, such as structure preventing breedings; it may be psychological, such as behavior patterns preventing breeding; ecological, such as environmental barriers preventing different populations' coming together; or seasonal, such as different populations' living in the same space but breeding at different times of the year. However, in all of these isolation mechanisms the basic causes of species formation are genetic change (mutation) and natural selection that first occurs during geographic isolation.

CONTINUOUS DISTRIBUTION

one species

free gene exchange throughout to geographic trends in gene frequencies

DISCONTINUOUS DISTRIBUTION

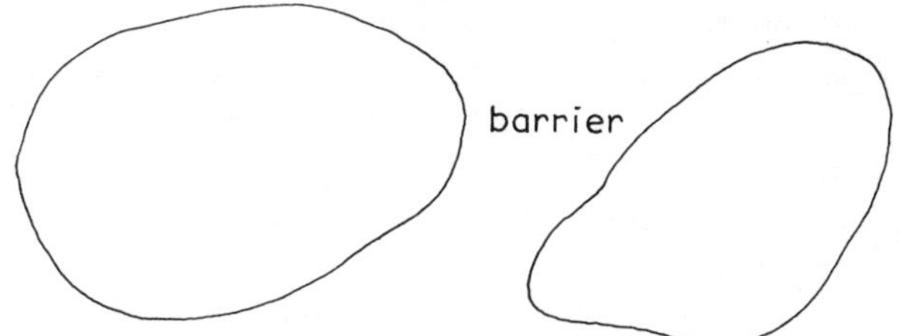

gene mutation and selection occur independently

BARRIER BREAKDOWN

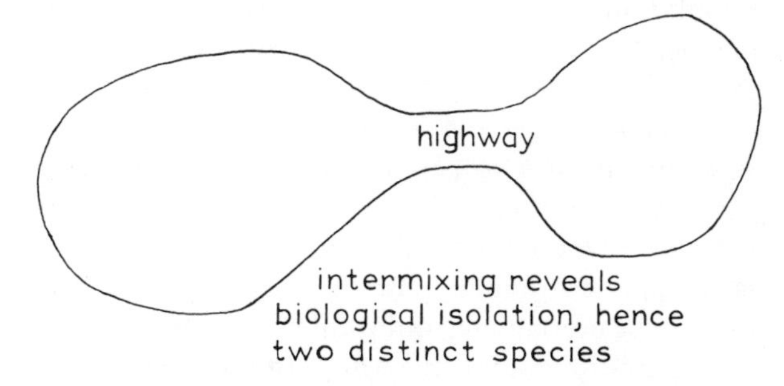

Figure 7.9 Geographic speciation, showing how genetic change during isolation normally is necessary for the origin of new species.

NATURE OF ISOLATION

The different types of isolation work in one or more of three ways. They may prevent mates from meeting, prevent mates from breeding when they do meet, and/or prevent offspring from developing normally. Geographic isolation bars the contact of mates. Physiological isolation keeps offspring from developing normally. Anatomical isolation may physically obstruct breeding. Psychological isolation prevents the fulfillment of courtship activities. Seasonal isolation causes organisms to reach the breeding state at different times. Ecological, or habitat, isolation is a special aspect of geographic isolation.

Isolation mechanisms rarely work independently. Consider the possibilities in two geographically isolated populations of a single species. Independent genetic mutations and selection of mutant genes can take place. Some of these mutations start the development of any to all of the nongeographic isolating mechanisms between the populations. Therefore, if the organisms once again come together because the barrier between them is destroyed, the two groups may interbreed but lack fertility; the offspring may be stillborn, or the young may be less vigorous than normal and die shortly after birth. In other words, some phase of physiological isolation may be present. In addition, some ramification of anatomical, behavioral, and/or seasonal isolation may exist. If one or more of these isolation mechanisms prevents the development of offspring from crosses between the two populations, there is no doubt that at least one new species has evolved; the two old populations of a single species are now two distinct species.

The consequences of isolation can be much more subtle. The primary example of this is the geographic race. Geographic races are groups of populations that replace one another geographically, each race having one or more identifying features. These characteristics may be no more than the greater prevalence of certain traits or they may be unique; however, unique features are unlikely without geographic isolation.

Subtle isolation is found where individual populations of a species are not strictly isolated from one another. Rather, adjacent populations do contact and interbreed with one another; however, in the linear replacement of one race by another there is a subtle factor of isolation between the remote populations. In such cases it is not uncommon to discover that two spatially remote races, although linked by races that freely interbreed with their neighboring races, cannot produce offspring. Moreover, this isolation is not due to some unknown mechanism; normal isolation mechanisms that accumulate over distance can be shown to be the cause. Therefore, the type of isolation that distinguishes species can exist between populations that are somewhat distant from one another but are connected by a complete chain of interbreeding races. This suggests a like means of origin of both races and species.

A special case of subtle isolation of geographic races can be especially confusing locally. If races of the above type form a circular rather than a linear geographic distribution pattern, it is possible for two races to be overlapping, quite different in appearance, and unable to produce offspring. In the area of overlap, the two races behave as good species; however, one can find step-by-step interbreeding of races around the circle of races.

In some cases isolation mechanisms that cause absolute barriers between species and between portions of the same species break down between different species. In such hybridization between species, the offspring may be either unable to develop, less viable and unable to reach reproductive age, more vigorous than either parent but sterile, or viable and able to reproduce. Hybrids that reproduce clearly represent the breaking down of isolation mechanisms. Most of these hybrids produce only a few offspring—so few that both the hybrids and their offspring are extremely rare. However, in plants more than in animals there is a tendency for some interspecific hybrids to contribute to the evolution of one or both of the species that hybridize. A prime example of this is called *introgressive hybridization*, a phenomenon in which hybrid offspring cross back to one or both parents and cause the genes of one parental species to become a part of the gene complement of a portion of the other parental species. Another possible consequence of plant hybridization is the production of new *polyploid* (more than two sets of chromosomes) *species*. The multiple chromosome sets of the hybrids cause low genetic compatibility for crosses with either parent; however, the polyploids often can cross among themselves (hence act as and are a single species). This is not as remarkable as it might seem; genetic mechanisms cause greater potential reproductive success when hybrids cross among their own kind than with either parent type.

SPECIATION

The means of species formation could be of two major types, nongeographic and geographic. *Nongeographic speciation* must occur within the area of the parent species. In animals, it is extremely unlikely; at best it must be a rare phenomenon. The only animal possibilities appear to be in self-fertilizing hermaphroditic or in parthenogenetic forms; however, firm evidence for such speciation does not exist. In plants, a common type of nongeographic speciation was said to come from interspecific hybridization creating polyploid species. Although other types of nongeographic plant speciation are possible, they are probably of minor significance. Therefore, the only kind of nongeograpiic speciation that is of significance happens when plant species hybridize and form polyploids, and the most significant type of speciation is geographic. *Geographic speciation* is the simple case of genetic change and spatial separation allowing the origin of isolation mechanisms.

HIGHER-CATEGORY FORMATION

The origin of new genera, families, orders, classes, phyla, and kingdoms may appear (at least for the kingdoms) as steps so great that some unique mechanism is required. However, there really is no absolute need or proof of such evolution. The fragmentary fossil record does not imply such "big steps" in evolution. The time was available for the necessary developments. The simple process of geographic isolation and mutation during the time represented by a gap could accomplish the changes that are seen in the fossil record. In spite of the fact that no unique type of macroevolution seems necessary to explain life, past or present, some biologists believe that there is evidence suggesting such a unique mechanism.

EVOLUTION CHARACTERISTICS

Many important aspects of speciation and evolution in general contribute to better understanding of the principle.

NATURAL SELECTION

There is little doubt that individual traits can be beneficial, neutral, or harmful to an organism. However, man's judgments of values too often are crude, if not incorrect, owing to his misinterpretation of the influence of traits, and/or his ignoring the total features of the organism. An individual or a species is more than the sum total of its parts; there is a synergistic relationship. Although a single part can have pronounced influence upon the success or failure of an organism, the individual is most often affected by the sum total of its characteristics. In spite of the limitations of man's interpretation, however, there are many features that are apparently beneficial (and so, examples of natural selection) and that are called *adaptive characters* or *adaptations*. When traits are believed neutral or harmful to the species, they are called *nonadaptive characters*.

Industrial Melanism. Some city-dwelling populations of insect species have darkened, presumably an adaptation to smoke in the atmosphere. Supposedly the insects in such areas accumulated chance mutations until their coloration was genetically darker and less conspicuous in the darkened sky. This darkening adaptation is interpreted either as enabling the insect to blend into its environment and be less subject to predation, or as being incidental pigment alterations associated with internal functional changes.

Adaptive Resemblance. Many fairly common structures are believed to be adaptive in nature. *Cryptic coloration* involves colors or patterns that blend the animal into its background. *Warning coloration*, found in animals well suited to repel a potential predator, is conspicuous and advertises the bearer. *Mimicry* in its true form is found in a helpless and desirable prey animal that has the warning coloration of undesirable prey.

Nonadaptive Characters. The existence of traits that are not of distinct benefit to organisms is a debatable subject among biologists. Some can conceive of organisms having characteristics that are not necessarily beneficial, if they are not actually harmful; other biologists cannot. The difference in opinion is possible because it is probably impossible to prove that a particular character is nonadaptive; just because man cannot demonstrate the use of a structure does not mean that the structure is useless. An additional problem in such proof stems from known examples of traits having definite value, but only during a short part of the life cycle. Therefore, it is possible to assemble strong evidence for the value of a particular feature, but impossible to prove one valueless.

PATHS OF EVOLUTION

The processes of evolution allow different paths of evolution. Many of these paths often are contained in a single line of development, either as separate events through time or as simultaneous occurrences.

Ancestors. The ancestors that give rise to new species and even new paths of evolution likely are not extremely specialized, so-called advanced creatures, but are populations (never individuals) of species with rather generalized features. Moreover, they do not always evolve into more complex creatures. For example, parasites usually are structurally more simple than were their ancestors (but they might be considered functionally more complex). A case where ancestors give rise to simpler creatures is called *regression*.

Orthogenesis. Orthogenesis is the well-documented phenomenon of "straight-line evolution." Its apparent verification led to the erroneous belief that there could be a basis for a predetermined direction of evolution (Figure 7.10). Actually, the best-documented records of evolutionary history indicate that strict straight-line evolution probably does not take place, but there are well-known examples in which certain structures became increasingly suited to environmental conditions—at least, that is often the interpretation. Under such circumstances, the gradual refinement of structures through the chance occurrence and fixation of mutations is somewhat directional.

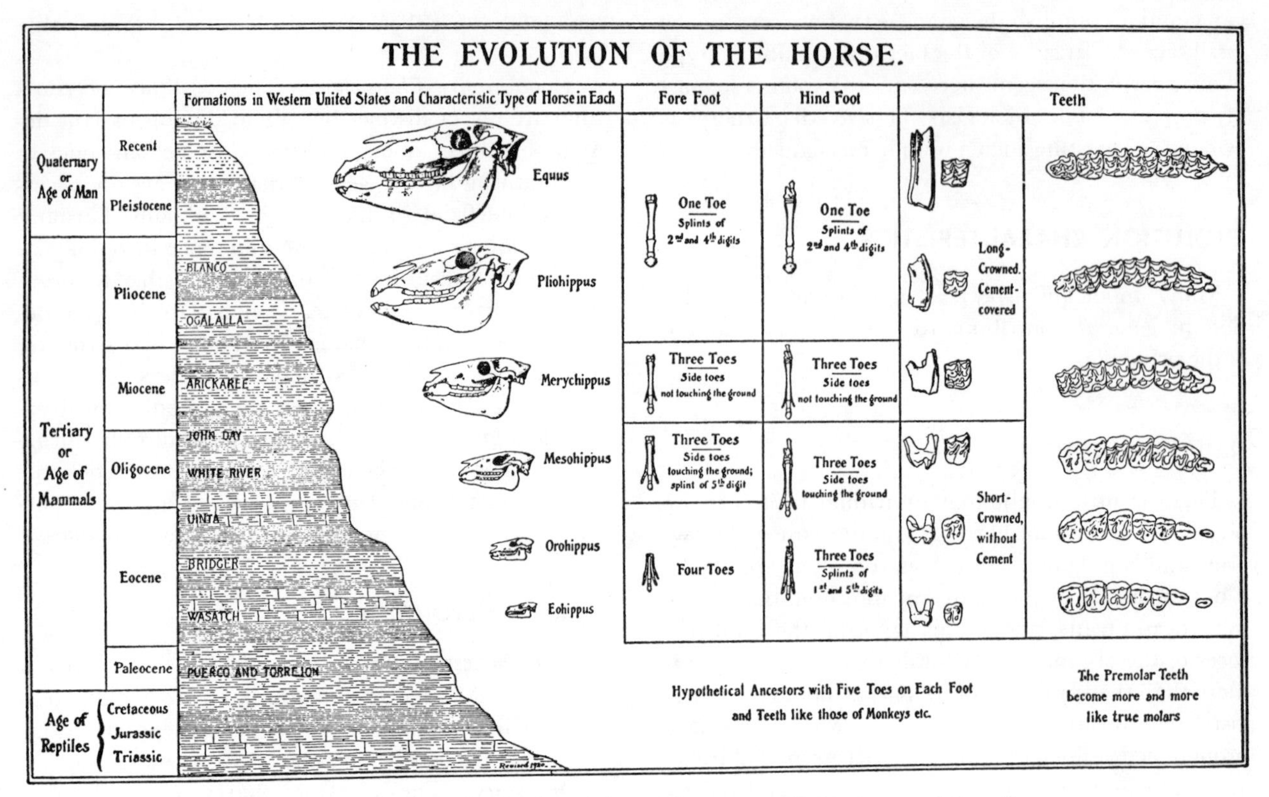

Figure 7.10 Orthogenesis, directional trends in evolution as exemplified by horse evolution. (From W. D. Matthew, *Quart. Rev. Biol.*, vol. 1, 1926.)

Adaptive Radiation. The evolutionary explosion of an ancestral group or groups into several new lines of development (hence, many new higher taxa) is called adaptive radiation (Figure 7.11). It is one of the strongest cases made for "big step" evolution; however, simple neo-Darwinian speciation mechanisms can explain the phenomenon. Adaptive radiation mechanisms can be hypothesized in four steps. First, a potential ancestral group is restricted to a particular environment. It does not occur elsewhere because other organisms, generally representing a much larger taxon, restrict the ancestor's habitat distribution. However, the ancestor could live in vast expanses of these other situations if it were not blocked by the species already in these areas. Therefore, the future ancestor is *preadapted* to other localities; it could exist in certain places, even though it does not occupy them. Second, the competitors, the large taxon keeping the ancestor out of extensive areas, becomes extinct. Third, the ancestor moves into the available localities, which constitute a diversity of habitats. Fourth, different segments of the ancestor become isolated and go through a period of rapid changes because more than the usual number of the chance mutations are of greater benefit in the hereditary complement allowing bare survival. An example of adaptive radiation occurred in the small mammals that lived at the time of dinosaurs and radiated into many mammal types, but only after most of the dinosaurs became extinct.

Extinction. Extinction is one of the great mysteries of the geological record. Generally, only one or a few species die out at a given time; but in a relatively short period, large taxa can be destroyed or even created. However, no past geological and climatic conditions seem to explain the rare times of widespread extinction that tended to wipe out many past taxa or completely changed the nature of the species in some taxa. Only single-species death appears likely to be something inherent within life. For this reason, one of the generally accepted hypotheses proposes that extinction results from the overaccumulation of harm-

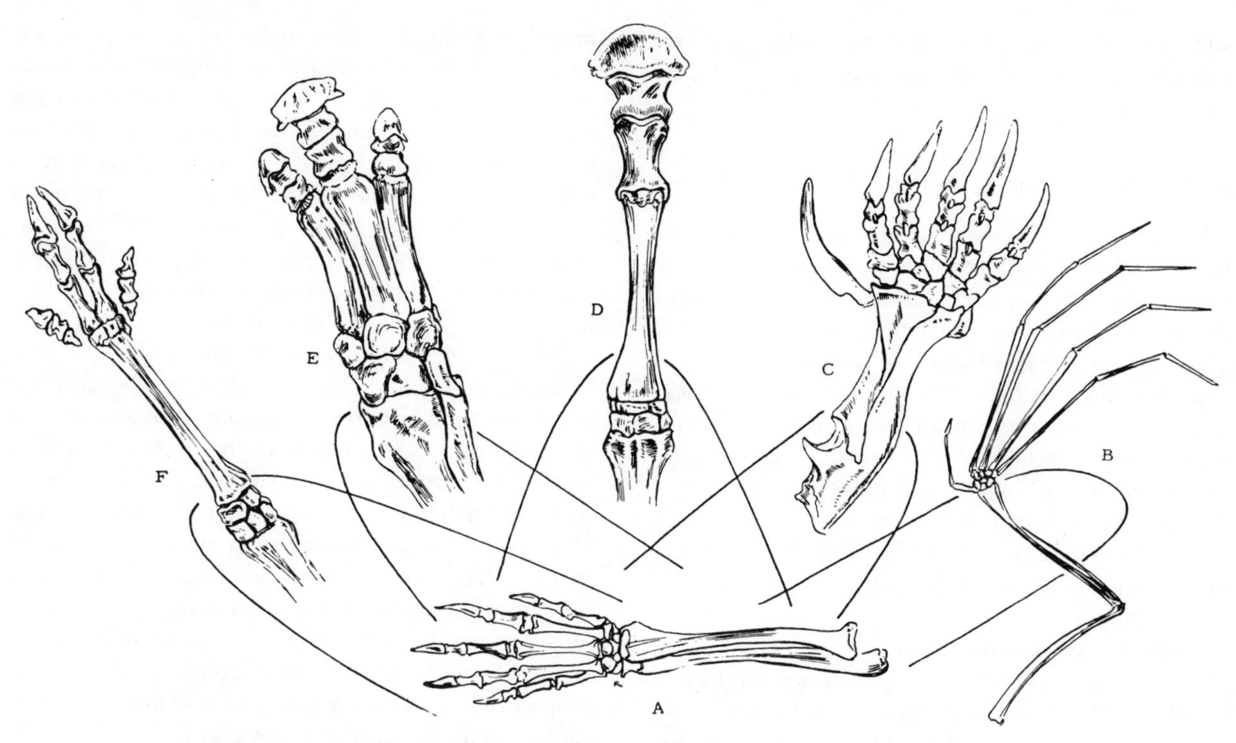

Figure 7.11 Adaptive radiation in the forelimbs of mammals. A, tenrec, a large insectivore with limb structure much like the shrew except for size; B, bat wing; C, mole; D, horse, E, rhinoceros; and F, deer. Each is modified from the primitive form (approximated by the tenrec) by changes of proportion, fusion of parts, or loss of parts. Not drawn to the same scale. (From Edward O. Dodson, *Evolution: Process and Product*. rev. ed., Reinhold Publishing Corp., New York, 1960.)

ful, or lethal, genes. But this does not explain widespread extinction, a biogeographic subject discussed later.

Adaptive Convergence and Parallelism. A general impression is that the more closely allied the organisms, the more similar their appearance, and the more distantly related, the less similar their appearance. One can well ask, what is meant by related? For present purposes, let it imply time. Using time alone as a basis for affinity does not allow strict association between structural differentiation and kinship. For example, adaptive radiation and orthogenesis affect degree of relationship, and convergence and parallelism present additional problems. Convergence is the tendency for different lines of evolutionary development to approach one another. This means that ancestors quite remote and different from one another can give rise to populations that are more similar structurally and functionally and give the impression of similar or identical ancestry. Parallelism causes less difficulty. It is the continuation through time of a particular amount of differentiation between two or more lines of evolutionary development, and causes the time of common ancestors to appear less remote than it was.

Both convergence and parallelism are associated easily with environmental conditions. Convergence exists when, for some reason, organisms occupy either the same environments or environments approaching one another. Parallelism takes place when environments maintain an equivalent differentiation throughout a period of geological time.

TEMPO

The speed of evolution is highly variable. There are periods of geological time when most life had a relatively high, moderate, or low rate of evolution; most frequently, however, different groups of organisms evolve at different rates, from very slowly to very rapidly. This does not mean that the speed of evolution is constant in a line of development or even in a single species. Any species, and especially, any line of development, can display the gamut of tempo during its evolution.

DISTRIBUTION PHENOMENA

Evolution of species and larger taxa is to a great extent a reflection of distribution. Biogeography was already mentioned as the primary basis for the origin of a theory of evolution. Actually, two aspects of distribution, barriers and highways, are most influential upon evolution. A barrier is any condition, physical or biological, that prevents an organism from expanding its range. A highway, or bridge, is most easily considered a somewhat unfavorable environmental situation but one that still allows the passage of an organism onward to a favorable habitat. Therefore, barriers cause isolation, and highways, in part, prevent isolation.

Highways are of three kinds, *corridors*, *filter bridges*, and *sweepstake routes*. A corridor is a geographically broad, fairly long-existing connection between two favorable environments; a corridor may be a favorable habitat. A corridor now exists between Europe and Asia. One often speaks of an influential corridor in the past tense. "It was a broad, favorable area that explains the present isolation of two groups of the same species, or species that evolved from the once broadly ranging species." A filter bridge is narrower and less permanent than a corridor and contains conditions that allow only certain species to pass between the two similar environments; corridors, on the other hand, enable many species to pass rather freely. A filter bridge now exists between the Americas. Sweepstakes routes are not real highways in the physical sense; rather, they are paths along which some individuals of one or a few species pass by chance alone. The path is only in one direction, and the passage is not possible for the species as a whole. Barriers and highways are best contrasted by examining island and continental organisms.

Continental Organisms. Distributional phenomena are apparent in the evolutionary history of species in general. When a new species finally is formed from a pre-existing population of another species, of necessity the new taxon is restricted in its distribution, it is geographically limited to its *center of origin*. The next phase of development, if the organism does expand at all prior to extinction, is movement from the center of origin via highways. Eventually, all points in the expanding "circle" of the species range will encounter barriers. For a while, at least, the species does not expand its distribution. Later, a highway—perhaps only a sweepstakes route—will allow the passage of individuals into a new area. If sufficient numbers reach the new locality and the invaded area is favorable, the species will increase in numbers and again start a cycle of range expansion. In this case, the new locality is termed a *center of dispersal*.

Some time later, geological changes occur and cause environmental changes. If the geological cycle is not too rapid but still exterminates the species, the following cycle of events is likely: Barriers such as arms of the ocean may split the range of the species without much influence on the separated populations. However, the cycle of extinction itself is more dramatic. The species first becomes less and less numerous in various parts of its range. Then it no longer occurs in many places, and the distribution is island-like with populations remaining only in geographically separated areas, perhaps including true islands. Finally, only a single population of the organisms exists; then, even this is no longer present and the group becomes another fossil species.

The evolutionary history of a species might fall far short of the above history of the more detailed types. Also, the actual history might be modified by certain peculiar circumstances. For example, the horse has its center of origin in North America and a center of dispersal in eastern Asia. During the last glacial age, the horse became extinct in North America but survived in Asia.

Island Organisms. From an evolutionary point of view, there is only one important kind of island, the *biological island*. Biological islands are of two general types, geographical and ecological. A geographic island is an island in the usual sense; however, only those having organisms isolated from their relatives on adjacent land are true biological islands. An ecological island is an isolated habitat such as an alpine environment that is remote from like mountain communities. Therefore, biological island life is not found on all geographic islands and is not limited to such areas. On the other hand, biological islands of any kind possess common characteristics, so that one can describe conditions of suitable geographic islands that will apply to ecological ones as well.

Although geographic island organisms typically

resemble those of nearby land and probably evolved from the continental forms, island creatures frequently are different from their mainland ancestors. The main reason for the divergence is believed to be a general lack of competition on the islands, where species frequently have no predators and/or competitors. Under such conditions, a phenomenon called *genetic drift* may exist. Owing to the general reduction of the normal unfavorable environmental conditions, selection may be weak; and, rather than maintaining and further developing the continental adaptations, organisms may drift into a less adaptive evolution.

Islands, however, can be extremely severe habitats. Chance island immigrants might require much the same food and shelter, interspecific competition may develop, and one or more of the competing species may become extinct. On the other hand, most competitors might survive if chance mutations allow fairly rapid rates of evolution. Hence, fairly recent island derivatives of continental species can evolve so much as to appear greatly divergent from their relatives.

Endemism. An *endemic* is a species with a fairly restricted but continuous range. Any species limited to one island is an endemic (unless the island is extremely large), and so is any species still restricted to its center of origin. However, when a center of dispersal is first formed, and even if this population is of endemic size, it is not endemic because of the parent population. The final endemism of any species is found in the last, single, small population just prior to extinction.

Many species display the same endemism, if all share an identical, small geographic range. The area they occupy is called an *endemic area*. Examples of such areas are found in some islands and high mountains. If an endemic area represents the final population of a formerly more wide-ranging species now on the road to extinction, the locality is called a *relict area;* however, a relict area can be any kind of living historical community, not only an endemic one.

SELECTED READINGS

Andrews, H. N., Jr., 1961. *Studies in Paleobotany*. John Wiley & Sons, New York.

Bates, M., and P. S. Humphrey, 1957. *The Darwin Reader*. The Macmillan Co., New York.

Benson, L., 1957. *Plant Classification*. D. C. Heath, Boston.

Bonner, D. M., 1961. *Heredity*. Foundations of Modern Biology Series. Prentice-Hall, Englewood Cliffs, N. J.

Bowen, R. N. C., 1958. *The Exploration of Time*. Philosophical Library, New York.

Dobzhansky, T., 1955. *Evolution, Genetics and Man*. John Wiley & Sons, New York.

Dodson, E. O., 1960. *Evolution: Process and Product*. rev. ed. Reinhold Publishing Corp., New York.

Dunbar, C. O., 1960. *Historical Geology*. 2nd ed. John Wiley & Sons, New York.

Fenton, C. L., and M. A. Fenton, 1958. *The Fossil Book*. Doubleday & Co., Garden City, N. Y.

Griffin, D. R., 1962. *Animal Structure and Function*. Modern Biology Series. Holt, Rinehart & Winston, New York.

Hanson, E. D., 1961. *Animal Diversity*. Foundations of Modern Biology Series. Prentice-Hall, Englewood Cliffs, N. J.

Hardin, Garrett, 1959. *Nature and Man's Fate*. Holt, Rinehart & Winston, New York.

Huxley, J. S., 1942. *Evolution: The Modern Synthesis*. Harper, New York.

Hyman, L. H., 1940. *The Invertebrates*. Vol. 1: *Protozoa through Ctenophora*. McGraw-Hill Book Co., New York.

Levine, R. P., 1962. *Genetics*. Modern Biology Series. Holt, Rinehart & Winston, New York.

Life Editorial Staff and Ruth Moore, 1963. *Evolution*. Time Inc., New York.

Matthews, W. H., 1962. *Fossils: An Introduction to Prehistoric Life*. Barnes & Noble, New York.

Mayr, E., E. G. Linsley, and R. L. Usinger, 1953. *Methods and Principles of Systematic Zoology*. McGraw-Hill Book Co., New York.

Merrel, D. J., 1962. *The Modern Theory of Evolution, Evolution and Genetics*. Holt, Rinehart & Winston, New York.

Romer, A. S., 1945. *Vertebrate Paleontology*. 2nd ed. The University of Chicago Press, Chicago.

———. 1959. *The Vertebrate Story*. 4th ed. The University of Chicago Press, Chicago.

Ross, H. H., 1962. *A Synthesis of Evolutionary Theory*. Prentice-Hall, Englewood Cliffs, N. J.

Savage, J. M., 1963. *Evolution*. Modern Biology Series. Holt, Rinehart & Winston, New York.

Shrock, R. R., and W. H. Twenhofel, 1953. *Principles of Invertebrate Paleontology*. McGraw-Hill Book Co., New York.

Simpson, G. G., 1949. *The Meaning of Evolution*. Yale University Press, New Haven, Conn.

———. 1953. *Life of the Past*. Yale University Press, New Haven, Conn.

———. 1953. *Evolution and Geography. An Essay on Historical Biogeography with Special Reference to Mammals*. Oregon State System of Higher Education.

Sistrom, W. R., 1962. *Microbial Life.* Modern Biology Series. Holt, Rinehart & Winston, New York.

Stirton, R. A., 1959. *Time, Life, and Man: The Fossil Record.* John Wiley & Sons, New York.

Tax, S., ed., 1960. *Evolution after Darwin.* Vol. 1: *The Evolution of Life.* Vol. 2: *The Evolution of Man.* Vol. 3: *Issues in Evolution.* The University of Chicago Press, Chicago.

Tippo, O., 1942. A Modern Classification of the Plant Kingdom. *Chronica Botan.*, 7:203–206.

Wallace, B., and A. M. Srb, 1961. *Adaptation.* Foundations of Modern Biology Series. Prentice-Hall, Englewood Cliffs, N. J.

Weisz, P. B., 1963. *The Science of Biology.* 2nd ed. McGraw-Hill Book Co., New York.

Worth, C. B., and R. K. Enders, 1955. *The Nature of Living Things.* The New American Library (Signet Book Ks 326), New York.

8 KINGDOMS MONERA AND PROTISTA

Simple Life

In this taxonomic classification the Kingdom Monera includes the bacteria and blue-green algae; the Kingdom Protista includes four phyla classified by some taxonomists as one-celled animals (protozoans) plus the slime molds and the true fungi. Of these, only the true fungi are so conspicuous that they are commonly observed in nature. (Mushrooms, plant rusts and smuts, and bread mold are examples of true fungi.) However, many species of monerans and protistans are macroscopic; the reader probably has observed many of them, even if he did not know what they were.

Monera and Protista probably are closely related; however, the time of common ancestry is remote, perhaps well over a billion years ago. Both kingdoms contain many species that appear to be single-celled organisms whose primary organization is within a single mass of protoplasm. Although their organization may appear almost identical, monerans are not as complexly organized as are the protistans (e.g., monerans have no distinct central cell body, or nucleus, and protistans have a highly organized nucleus), this contrast from lower to higher complexity probably reflects a major step in the early evolution of life. It is likely that the Monera organization of today represents one of the steps prior to the complex organization found in most Protista and in most true cells found in plants and animals. The Monera are believed to be derivatives of the step in the origin of life where groups of individual hereditary units, or genes, were clumped into larger groups. This nuclear material stage likely preceded chromosomes containing genes and a distinct nucleus—that stage now represented by Protista. Therefore, though superficially similar, from a structural point of view the Monera and the Protista are very different. This difference is implied by treating the Monera as having protoplasmic organization and the Protista as having acellular (or unicellular) organization.

VIRUSES

Prior to discussing the Monera and Protista, we will outline the problem created by viruses. Viruses are important because they are disease-producing agents. In man viruses cause many serious disorders, including poliomyelitis, influenza, and chronic hepatitis. In addition to this they are of some concern in the origin of life and even in the question of what is life.

Diagnosis: complex chemical organization without indication of cell-like structure; chemicals are mostly

TAXONOMIC SUMMARY

Viruses (L. *virus*, slime or poison)—viruses
Kingdom Monera (Gr. *moneres*, single)—monerans
Phylum Schizophyta (Gr. *schizo*, cleave + *phyton*, plant)—bacteria
Phylum Cyanophyta (Gr. *kyanos*, blue + *phyton*)—blue-green algae
Kingdom Protista (Gr. *protistos*, first of all)—protistans or protists
Subkingdom Protozoa (Gr. *protos*, first + *zoon*, animal)—protozoans
Phylum Flagellata (L. *flagellum*, little whip)—flagellates
Phylum Sarcodina (Gr. *sarcodes*, fleshy)—sarcodines
Phylum Sporozoa (Gr. *sporos*, spore + *zoon*)—spore animals
Phylum Ciliophora (L. *cilium*, eyelid + *phoros*, bearing)—ciliophorans
Class Ciliata (L. *cilium*)—ciliates
Class Suctoria (L. *suctus*, sucking)—suctorians
Subkingdom Fungi (L. *fungus*, a mushroom or fungus)—fungi
Phylum Myxomycophyta (Gr. *myxa*, mucus + *mykes*, fungus + *phyton*)—slime molds or fungi
Phylum Eumycophyta (Gr. *eu*, good + *mykes* + *phyton*)—true fungi
Class Phycomycetes (Gr. *phykos*, alga + *mykes*)—algal fungi
Class Ascomycetes (Gr. *askos*, bladder + *mykes*)—sac fungi
Class Basidiomycetes (Gr. *basis*, pedestal + *mykes*)—club fungi
Lichens (Gr. *leichen*, lichen)—lichens

nucleic acids in a covering of protein; size ultramicroscopic, from about 15 to 450 millimicrons (25 million millimicrons equals 1 inch); shape approximately spherical, rod-like, tadpole-like or polyhedral; all known forms are obligate parasites (within their host's cells) and act as disease-producing agents; probably parasitize all kinds of life; many can be crystallized; multiply very rapidly after entering a host cell by a process in which virus nucleic acids cause the host's cell to form virus chemical compounds, finally the virus compounds are assembled into virus particles and the particles are released as viruses when the host cell is destroyed; viruses' activities may be the cause of cancer.

The viruses are a group that most classifiers of life might like to ignore. One cannot satisfactorily answer the question of whether they are living or nonliving. The problem may be centered around viruses containing nucleic acids. Nucleic acids have three properties which characterize life. First, these acids are chemical information carriers. Through their chemical properties, they contain the plans for synthesizing proteins. More specifically they are hereditary units or genes that provide the genetic code or plan of chemical reactions that determine the eventual traits of an organism. Second, nucleic acids are capable of making exact copies of themselves. This is the ability that allows genes to duplicate themselves. Finally, although nucleic acids are extremely stable compounds (they generally are not altered in most earth environments), on rare occasions minor changes in chemical structure can take place. Such changes are the source of gene mutation, hence evolution. Therefore, viruses contain the materials that control evolution and they are able to mutate and evolve.

Because the properties of nucleic acids are characteristic of organisms, it is difficult to separate viruses from life. However, a virus appears to be much less than any organism. For example, some viruses definitely originate from nucleic acids that become separated from certain cells. Although all viruses may not have been formed from cell fragments, it is difficult to imagine those viruses that originate as fragments being complete organisms. Also, it seems impossible for one organism to be the parent of a remotely related individual.

The activity of viruses leads to further difficulty in diagnosing their living or nonliving status. Viruses in air or water are inert and seemingly nonliving. However, upon contacting a cell or cell-like organism viruses become active. The virus attaches to the host's surface and injects its nucleic acids into the host. Once inside the host cell the nucleic acids use the cell's materials to form identical nucleic acids. Next the nucleic acids apparently combine into groups and each group creates a protein covering. Therefore, each grouping of nucleic acids within a protein covering is a new virus. Finally, the viruses leave the host cell, often destroying the host in the process.

Another problem is how viruses fit into the scheme of past evolution. Biologists generally agree that modern forms are relatively complex and that archaic viruses probably were far simpler, perhaps no more than pure groupings of nucleic acids. However, their origin is a subject of debate. Some biologists believe viruses are living descendants of the early evolution stage prior to the organization of cell-like structure. This would mean that viruses are older than monerans. Other biologists, perhaps most, do not place viruses in the main evolutionary stream of life. Rather, these biologists assume that viruses represent an early escape of nucleic acids from living organisms, perhaps archaic monerans. In spite of this disagreement, it is regularly assumed that a nucleic acid or virus-like stage did occur during the origin of life. Therefore, to some biologists viruses probably are descendants from that stage; to other biologists viruses just happen to resemble the nucleic acid stage.

Even if one could assume that viruses do represent a step in evolution prior to the origin of Monera, one still does not solve the problem of their being living or nonliving. Possession of the life characteristics due to the presence of nucleic acids is counterbalanced by their lacking either the chemical complexity associated with definite living substance, protoplasm; the cell-like structure (other than nuclear material) found in definite organisms; or the organization one can call an organism. Moreover, this statement would be accepted by most biologists who prefer to consider viruses living.

MONERA

The Monera are the oldest known kind of life. The oldest known fossils seem to be monerans, perhaps blue-green algae. These early forms probably were different in many respects from any living group of organisms, even living blue-green algae (Cyanophyta). However, the gross structure of the oldest fossils, dated at no less than 2.7 billion years old,* is said to be much the same as that of present Cyanophyta. Likely fossils of organisms that appear to represent bacteria, blue-green algae, and fungi have also been found; they are slightly less than 2 billion years old. The bacteria and blue-green algae are fairly well represented in deposits from this latter time onward.

Because the archaic Monera seem complex, the origin of life might date back some 4 billion years. According to recent approximations this would place the origin some one billion years after the formation of our planet, perhaps soon after the origin of the oceans. As indicated on the geological calendar (Table 7.1, p. 109), the earliest conditions of the earth often are assumed to have been quite unlike those of today. When the earth first solidified, the land was bare rock and the atmosphere probably had only a trace of oxygen. The air, perhaps, was primarily poisonous ammonia and hydrogen sulfide, but had carbon dioxide and water vapor as well. When these gases cooled and the first oceans formed, the chemicals necessary for life to form most likely were present.

There is good evidence to suggest that this radically different set of geological conditions, the Preactualistic Phase, continued in progressively less intense form up to a little less than 2 billion years ago. At this time the light ammonia and hydrogen sulfide gases already had been used by organisms or lost to space and probably little more than the present concentrations of these gases remained.

Because the Preactualistic atmosphere had little or no oxygen, the earliest forms of life had to be much like some present-day bacteria. These modern bacteria form their own foods from basic materials without using oxygen, and some cannot even exist in oyxgen. If the first life was the same as this group of living bacteria, during the Preactualistic Phase the organisms could have lived in direct contact with the early, oxygen-free atmosphere.

The loss of ammonia and hydrogen sulfide from the

*Ahrens, L. H., 1955. Geol. Soc. America, Special Paper, 62.

atmosphere, plus the replacement of these compounds by oxygen, set the scene for the extinction of many ancient organisms and the success of those mutants that could survive within an oxygen medium. In this earliest Actualistic Phase a small amount of oxygen probably existed because lightning continually changed water vapor into its component parts of hydrogen and oxygen.

Present-day Monera, then, probably are a remnant of life that dominated the past. However, this is not meant to imply that living forms are "living fossils," in the sense of existing some two or more billion years. Rather, living Monera probably are the product of eons of evolution. Many specialized types, especially those closely adapted to relatively recent geological conditions, show that the Monera have not stood still since ancient times. On the other hand, reference to the diagnoses of the two living phyla does indicate how simple are most living monerans in contrast to other living groups. Even a brief comparison of the bacteria and blue-green algae with the protistans will show various differences. In such a comparison, one must realize that the seemingly simple differences actually represent marked divergences in microscopic structure. Before reading the rest of this chapter, review the structures in cells (Figure 6.8, p. 92), the life cycles (Figures 6.4 through 6.7, pp. 89–91), and nutrition types (p. 85).

SCHIZOPHYTA (Bacteria)

Diagnosis: protoplasmic organization, cell-like and mostly solitary but some are colonial; solitary individuals are spherical (cocci), short rods or cylinders (bacilli), or corkscrew-like (spirilla); colonial forms are chain-like or hair-like (filamentous), but a few have a definite terminal spore-producing structure (sporangium) similar to that of the slime molds (Myxomycophyta); excluding the viruses, bacteria are the smallest living creatures (Figure 8.1).

Structure: nucleus simple, incompletely developed, without complex internal structures and not delimited by a nuclear membrane; cytoplasm with neither plastids, one or more central vacuoles (structures present in most green flagellates and algae), nor other complex structures that are found in most plants (Figure 6.8); cytoplasmic pigments present or absent, but probably not of the type present in green flagellates and algae; chlorophyll present in a special form (bacteriochlorophyll) and involved

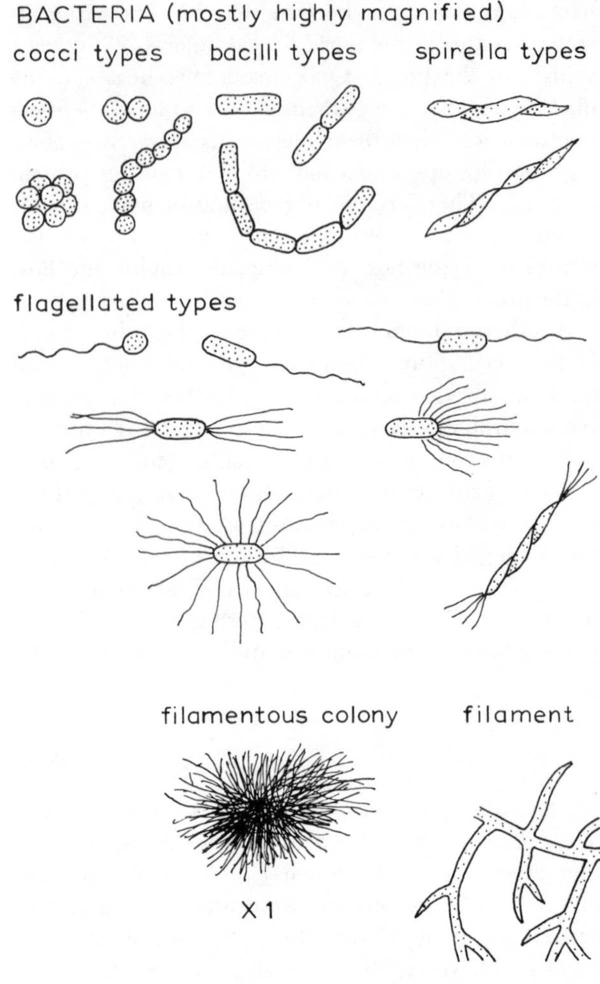

Figure 8.1 Bacteria types.

in photosynthesis (a particular type without the release of oxygen); only about one-third are pigmented with bacteriochlorophyll or some other substance; most have a cell wall; simple, thread-like locomotor structures (flagellae) may be absent or one, two, or several may be present.

Nutrition: all types except holozoic are known.

Reproduction: mostly asexual by cell division without the segregation of chromosomes (amitotic); some forms produce spores that are more resting cells than true spores (a usually single-celled, asexually reproducing structure); bacterial spores are formed and persist in unfavorable environmental conditions; the few complex bacteria form true reproductive spores at the end of a hair-like filament or in a specialized spore-producing sporangium; typical sexual reproduction with zygote formation does not occur, but processes with the exchange of hereditary materials exist in some species.

Occurrence: widely distributed in land, water, and air; many are parasites of plants and animals and others are saprophytes, generally involved in the process of decay; some are only in oxygen-free conditions but most require oxygen; more than 1000 species.

The bacteria are an ecologically diverse assemblage of organisms that live in moist to aquatic media. They are widely distributed in air, water, and soil and within and upon organisms. However, both as a group and often as individual species, owing to their ability to disperse via air and water currents, they are cosmopolitan. Their ecology may be examined in terms of their nutrition and physiology. Many species require only inorganic materials and photosynthetic or chemosynthetic processes solve their nutritional needs. In photosynthesis, oxygen never is involved; e.g., certain sulfur bacteria use hydrogen sulfide, sulfur, or thiosulfate with carbon dioxide, in the presence of light, to form simple sugar (actually cell materials in the proportion CH_2O). The other species require simple to complex organic compounds which they gain by loose to rigid saprophytic and parasitic behaviors and functions. Perhaps more remarkable yet, many species can adjust their metabolic needs to a variety of environments, some individuals running the gamut of autotrophic and heterotrophic nutrition types.

Further indication of metabolic plasticity is found in their reaction to oxygen in their environment. Some bacteria can live in situations ranging from no oxygen to high oxygen content. Others rigidly require the presence or absence of oxygen.

Nutritional activities allow a convenient appraisal of the most significant activities. Some bacteria, such as those in the soil, ocean oozes, and surface waters, are extremely important geomorphic agents. With certain blue-green algae and fungi they accomplish most of the transformation of organic matter to sedimentary rock deposits. Most are extremely important in generating carbon dioxide into the atmosphere. They are prime oxidation agents in biogeochemical cycles, those using oxygen to change ammonia to nitrite and nitrite to nitrate (nitrifying bacteria); hydrogen to water; sulfide to sulfur, sulfur to thiosulfate, and thiosulfate to sulfate; and ferrous iron to ferric iron; all processes involved in decomposing or transforming compounds and in cycling protoplasmic elements to plants. Also, the above reactions may be reversed by other bacteria (e.g., nitrate to nitrogen by denitrifying bacteria). In addition, certain species gain energy by regularly simplifying a variety of organic compounds by fermentation. Finally, are their close relationship with other organisms. For example, they are beneficial to plants of the pea family (in forming root nodules, bacteria enable the plants to use atmospheric nitrogen in a process called nitrogen fixation) and to hoofed mammals (stomach-inhabiting bacteria enable digestion and fermentation of plants otherwise indigestible). However, many cause plant and animal diseases. Bacterial agents of human disease cause plague, cholera, whooping cough, dysentery, tuberculosis, scarlet fever, tularemia, pneumonia, diptheria, syphilis, and gonorrhoea. Yet, most bacteria are beneficial. For example, they allow man to preserve food by pickling and fodder by ensilage; to produce vinegar; to dispose of sewage; to manufacture a variety of sour milk products; to obtain food from plants (most plants could not obtain their nutrients without bacterial decomposition and transformation of pre-existing organic compounds); to prepare various alcoholic beverages; to produce antibiotics (e.g., aureomycin, streptomycin, and chloramphenicol), vitamins, and enzymes; and, perhaps most important, to learn about the fundamental workings of life itself.

CYANOPHYTA (Blue-green Algae)

Diagnosis: protoplasmic organization; some are solitary and cell-like, but most colonial or simple "multicellular"; most are sheathed by a jelly-like material; solitary species are nonmotile and free-living or live upon objects, generally fixed and spherical or globular; colonial forms are "one cell" thick and flat, spherical and hollow, massive and cubical, or formless; "multicellular" types are filamentous (thread-like) in the form of simple bead-like or spiral threads or of branching threads; some filamentous forms are colonial rather than multicellular; no indication that tissue-like material is formed (Figure 8.2).

Structure: individuals distinct or in a common jelly-like mass; without a distinct central body (nucleus) surrounded by a typical nuclear membrane, probably no membrane of any kind; chlorophyll and pigments not in chlorophyll-containing

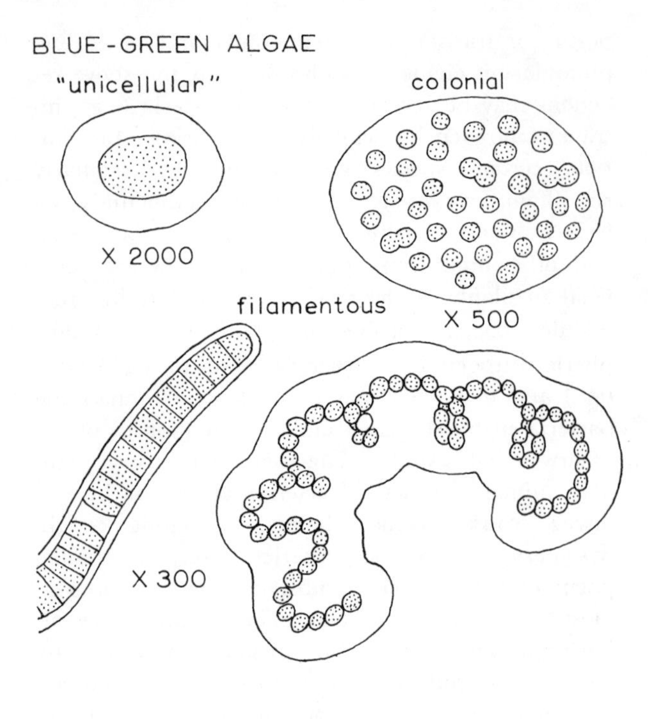

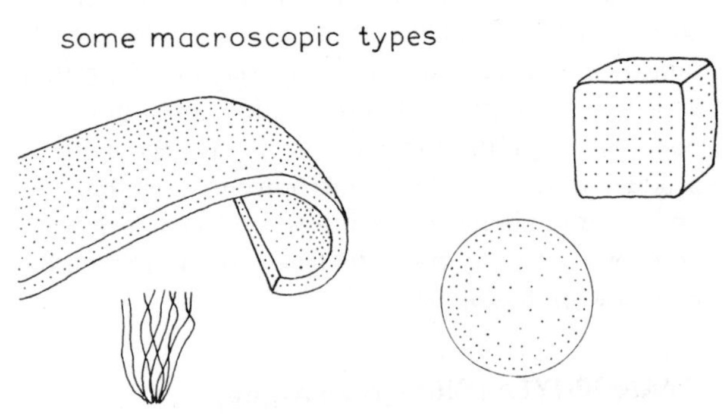

Figure 8.2 Blue-green algae types.

bodies or pigment-containing bodies called plastids; from none to many small central vacuoles (probably not true vacuoles); cell wall usually two-layered; no flagellae but waving, gliding, and circular movements are fairly common.

Nutrition: primarily photosynthetic; some carry on chemosynthesis.

Reproduction: asexual by division (amitotic by constriction of the body, probably never mitotic but some species apparently segregate chromosome-like bodies), by fragmentation of colonies or filaments, or by spores; sexual processes are unknown if present at all.

Occurrence: mostly fresh water, floating, attached to objects, or bottom dwelling; some are marine and distributed as the fresh-water forms; others form layers upon moist rocks or soil or are under ground; others occur in hot springs that approach the boiling point, many of the species in mineral springs causing calcium and other carbonates to be precipitated; a few are enslaved within other algae, protozoans, and fungi; some combine with fungi to produce lichens; some are parasitic; about 2500 species.

Do not expect to recognize blue-green algae by a constant color clue. In nature, only about half are blue-green; the others are purple, red, orange, green, blue, or some intermediate hue. Some are black.

Many are microscopic, occurring as individuals in fresh or salt water plankton. Others are fairly conspicuous, globular or encrusting, jelly-like to leathery masses upon objects. Most are nonmarine. On rocks or soil they may be the first invading organisms. They are particularly suited (owing to their photosynthetic capabilities) to invading rocks and starting the process of soil formation. Many appear to sustain themselves by exclusive use of inorganic materials. Such Cyanophyta can be observed in the free-living state and along their margins they may be invaded by fungi. Such a fungus is entrapping, perhaps enslaving, the blue-green alga cells; eventually, an intimate organization of alga cells and fungus filaments will produce a single, integrated structure, a lichen. Therefore, although lichens often are the first "organisms" to invade a bare rock, blue-green algae can cause lichens to be the second stage.

Like bacteria, blue-green algae are cosmopolitan but closely tied to moist environments. Certain soil inhabitants especially resemble bacteria. These Cyanophyta range several feet down in the soil where they either are dormant, or are saprophytic like the associated bacteria. Higher in the soil, with bacteria some are involved in nitrogen fixation. In fact, some apparent bacteria may actually be blue-green algae that have lost their chlorophyll.

Their importance in water, fresh or salt, tends to be minimized. Aquatic species, along with true algae in the ocean and various aquatic plants in fresh water, are primary producers. All these organisms, through photosynthesis, are the primary converters of inorganic materials to nutrients and producers of oxygen in aquatic areas.

These monerans seem as ecologically significant and perhaps as numerous in arctic habitats. Here, both salt and fresh waters feature a diversity of species; however large organisms appear definitely reduced in individuals and species. Some species even grow upon glacial ice and others upon mud to almost dry soil.

Some species grow within or upon other organisms. A few occur in man's intestinal tract. Some occur upon the shells of turtles or aquatic arthropods. Others may be found upon and provide color to the hair of arboreal mammals, especially sloths. Certain unicellular forms are within and occasionally may parasitize protozoans, sponges, and coelenterates. Some can be found upon or within plant leaves and roots.

The blue-green algae are of economic importance. Perhaps their only benefits exist in the food and oxygen they provide other organisms and in the source of biological information they provide to biologists and naturalists. Unfortunately, their primary relationship with man is detrimental. The various floating species form sticky scums that cover many bodies of fresh water. Such scums contribute to noxious odors and disagreeable tastes in water supplies. When abundant, the decaying individuals may produce poisons and deplete oxygen to the point of killing fish and other aquatic organisms. Even livestock and water fowl may die if they drink water containing the poisons.

PROTISTA

With the dawn of the Actualistic Phase of geological history, the scene was set for the evolution of more modern types of organisms. Probably both the protozoan and fungi subkingdoms of protistans were derived from the monerans. Perhaps the origin of protistans was very rapid. The first protistans probably were photosynthetic flagellates (ancestral protozoans) and archaic representatives of the true fungi. However, where and from what did they originate? There can be little doubt that the ocean was the site of protistan origin. Also, it is believed that either the protistans had a single moneran ancestor, or the flagellates evolved from the early blue-green algae and the fungi from the early bacteria. Only assuming a single origin of protistans from monerans would satisfy the common ancestor requirement for a Kingdom Protista. Although this possibility is followed in the scheme of classification, it appears more likely that the protozoans and fungi originated independently. Belief in separate origins is based on observation of present Monera and Protista and on a very scanty, almost useless fossil record. For such a double origin of protistans two moneran groups must, over a great period of time, have developed a well-organized nucleus and other features to make the transition from protoplasmic to unicellular organization. Actually the two similar but independent transitions would not have had to be great. The first two groups of protistans could have been little more than strange, archaic, blue-green algae (ancestral flagellate protozoans) and bacteria (ancestral fungi), and evolution from there on would have been a relatively simple matter. Therefore, although admitting the likelihood of two protistan ancestors, we retain our classification for convenience in emphasizing levels of organization.

PROTISTA AS PLANTS OR ANIMALS

In the taxonomic classification of most botanists and zoologists, the phyla here assigned to the Kingdom Protista are considered members of the plant or animal kingdoms, rather than being classified separately. That solution is possible and satisfactory for many taxa. The protistans Sarcodina, Sporozoa, and Ciliophora are in most classifications treated as animals, members of the animal phylum Protozoa. They lack chlorophyll, and so are unlikely to be confused with plants. The true fungi (Eumycophyta) can be considered members of the plant kingdom. However, some of the Flagellata (those bearing chlorophyll) and all of the slime molds (Myxomycophyta) can be classified as either plants or animals. Today many botanists distribute the confusing flagellates throughout many phyla of algae and the slime molds in a single phylum allied to the fungi; zoologists, on the other hand, place both groups in the Phylum Protozoa, the green flagellates as a subclass of a Class Flagellata and the slime molds as a group of the Class Sarcodina.

As mentioned earlier, the protistans and monerans, except for differences in basic organization, might be classified as a single kingdom. Some taxonomists consider them as such, for many reasons. For example, certain bacteria and the slime molds appear very closely related, so close that even experts can be perplexed by their true relationships. In addition, it was already mentioned that the slime molds are allied to the Sarcodina. However, they are treated as separate kingdoms in this book because it seems convenient to stress organizational differences that imply two major steps in evolution. Once Protista is considered as a kingdom, the six phyla assigned to it must be included, since they most likely represent a closely knit phylogenetic group.

If inclusion in a taxonomic system of a separate Kingdom Protista tends to simplify the understanding of organism evolution, why is this taxon often avoided in textbooks and elsewhere? There is no simple answer to this question. Perhaps the answer is that too little is known of the fossil record of protistans. The phylogeny of the group is based largely upon conjecture about the implications of various structures in living creatures. Unfortunately, this may not provide a true picture of protistan phylogeny; analyses of structures in living organisms, no matter how detailed, do not reveal a single possible path for their past evolution. Present features often contradict one another in any interpretation of their evolution. Such contradiction is understandable because only certain structures reflect evolutionary trends, whereas others portray adaptations to environments. In other words, similar features in protistans can be due to common evolutionary history or to a common environmental history. In like habitats, chance hereditary changes and selection of the changes would be likely and would lead to similar-appearing creatures. Moreover, it is very difficult, if not impossible, to be sure whether any particular similarity is due to common environment or to common ancestry. This is the case with similarities among any creatures where a fossil record is poor or absent.

SUBKINGDOM PROTOZOA
(Protozoans)

Although frequently called simple and primitive, living members of the protozoans have evolved separately through eons of time to their present form. Their simplicity and primitiveness exist only in their physical resemblance to the most archaic protists.

Living protozoans include the flagellates, which often are believed to approximate the ancestors of all other protozoans and of members of the plant and animal kingdoms. It is thought that archaic flagellates gave rise to most living protozoans, to sponges (Porifera), and to green algae (Chlorophyta) via innumerable ancestral forms. Also, in one hypothesis of the origin of the animal phyla Mesozoa and Coelenterata, the flagellates are believed to have been ancestors. However, both coelenterates and mesozoans could have originated otherwise.

Diagnosis: body cell-like but the single protoplasmic mass is an organism; hence, protistans are structurally and functionally somewhat unlike true plant or true animal cells; nucleus differentiated, complete and complex, unlike the simpler structured Monera counterpart.

Structure: symmetry of all types; small, solitary or colonial creatures; most are microscopic, but a few are visible to the naked eye; occur in most land, freshwater, and marine habitats as sessile, or free-living forms; many aquatic forms contribute to plankton; many are internal or external parasites of plants, animals, and other protistans; cell division regularly by mitosis or meiosis, amitosis uncommon or absent.

Protozoans are assumed to be acellular by many biologists because the "cells" of these creatures are the organism and often contain certain complex structures that are not found in the cells of multicellular life. Many of these complex protozoan structures have functions that are similar to the organs of animals. For this reason, the complex structures are called *organelles*, literally "little organs."

Many other biologists would not consider protozoans acellular; rather, they would call them single-celled animals that occur either singly or colonially. Their reasoning is that *cell* is a structural designation, and even if specialized, the protozoans possess the structures which fit the name "cell." (In fact, many biologists assume monerans are cells.) Moreover, some cells in multicellular organisms display great complexity. However, even this group of biologists agrees that there is a functional distinction between the protozoan structure and the cell of a plant or animal. The protozoan is functionally an organism; generally plants and animals have unlike cells for unlike functions.

The disagreement among biologists need not be

of primary concern here. However, it shows that a seemingly simple thing such as structural type is not agreed upon in a group of creatures that are quite numerous and are studied a great deal. No matter what view makes the most sense to you, if you wish to be correct, refer to the protozoans as *organismal* rather than as either unicellular or acellular. You could be even more descriptive by calling these creatures "organismal, cell-like protists."

FLAGELLATA (= MASTIGOPHORA) (Flagellates)

Diagnosis: characterized by one or more whip-like flagellae that provide a typical locomotion; flagellae present during one to all stages of the life cycle; individual's shape mostly fixed—oval, spherical, or elongate; shape maintained either by a firm external pellicle that normally is ridged spirally or longitudinally, or by armor, plates, cases or shells; those species without firm body coverings change shape by a flowing of their cytoplasm (pseudopodia allowing amoeboid movement) and if they lack flagellae these protistans resemble the Sarcodina; occur as individuals or colonies, colonial forms branching or held together by a jelly-like material or cellulose; may be motile or nonmotile, nonmotile species generally attached by a stalk or enclosed by a jelly-like mass (Figure 8.3).

Structure: individuals distinct or without cell membranes or cell walls, so nuclei are in a continuous cytoplasm; nucleus complete and complex, one to many per individual, but no nucleus is especially larger than any others (see Ciliophora); cytoplasmic pigments when present include green chlorophyll in plastids, but the green is sometimes masked by a dense red in the cytoplasm; possible organelles (complex structures) include flagellae, plastids, vacuoles, an eyespot or stigma, trichocysts, and various rods and fibers of unknown function; flagellae usually one or two, also more or none during certain stages of the life cycle; flagellae are the principal source of locomotion and food gathering, or of food capture by entangling; locomotion also may involve a worm-like movement; plastids, when present, are variously shaped and constitute the site of photosynthesis; contractile vacuoles, generally two, rarely more, are near flagellae bases; contractile vacuoles commonly present in fresh-water species, absent elsewhere, function in excess water removal; contractile

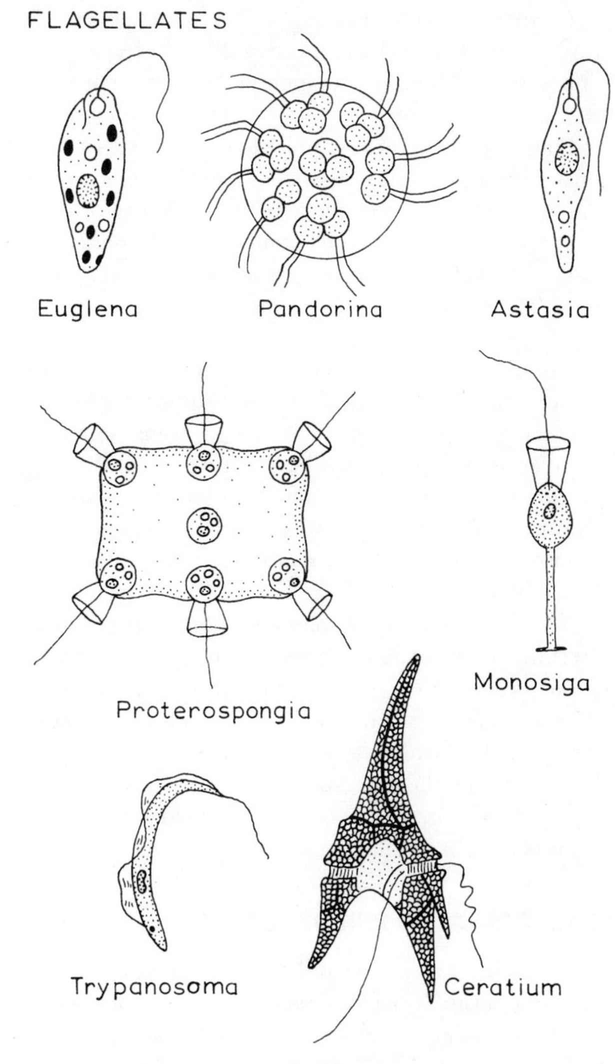

Figure 8.3 Flagellate types, all microscopic.

vacuoles without contributing canals or vacuoles as in ciliates; nonflagellate species often have a large central vacuole; stigma, a red spot that is light sensitive, is typically associated with a gullet that contains the basal part of a flagellum; trichocysts (mostly ciliate organelles) may be discharged as long threads that may be used to attach, to capture food, or to defend against predators.

Nutrition: photosynthetic, chemosynthetic, or holozoic.

Reproduction: mostly asexual by binary fission; also asexual by fragmentation and multiple fission; some are sexual and display either diplobiontic or one of the haplobiontic life cycles; in many species the life cycle is complex.

Occurrence: with diatoms (Chrysophyta) constitute the most typical and numerous life in fresh-water and marine plankton; also include many parasites.

Flagellates get their name from the possession of one or more whip-like organelles, the flagellae, which are locomotor and feeding structures. Many of these protists possess chlorophyll and some of them even have cell walls. For these reasons they are plant-like. The chlorophyll allows the typical plant process of photosynthesis.

The flagellates are believed to approximate most closely the ancestors of plants and animals. Within the living flagellates one can find a transition from cell-like to multicellular-like creatures. Also, there is division of labor among a colony's "cells," a feature of most multicellular animals (Eumetazoa) whose individual cells, tissues, or organs have different functions.

The flagellates are of major economic importance. Certain of them cause diseases of man and animals, perhaps the most serious human disorder being African sleeping sickness. Termite-inhabiting flagellates enable termites to obtain nutrients from wood by performing the early stages of digestion. The "red tides" that poison seafoods are fantastic concentrations of certain flagellates.

SARCODINA (= RHIZOPODA)

Diagnosis: characterized by flowing extensions of the cytoplasm (pseudopodia) for locomotion (amoeboid movement) or feeding; worm-like movement, as in some flagellates, is also found; individual's shape irregular or spherical; simple to complex skeletons or shells may be present; many bear flagellate young or, in certain conditions, gain flagellae (hence cannot be easily segregated from the flagellates); most are solitary, mobile, and free-living creatures, but some are colonial, sedentary, and/or parasitic (Figure 8.4).

Structure: individuals regularly distinct, with a cell membrane but without a cell wall; nucleus complete and complex, one to many per individual but none especially larger than the others; chlorophyll absent; contractile vacuoles, one to several but without contributing canals or vacuoles as in ciliates, are found in fresh-water species; organization typically less complex than that of the flagellates; no pellicle, plastids, stigma, or trichocysts.

Nutrition: holozoic, saprophytic, or parasitic.

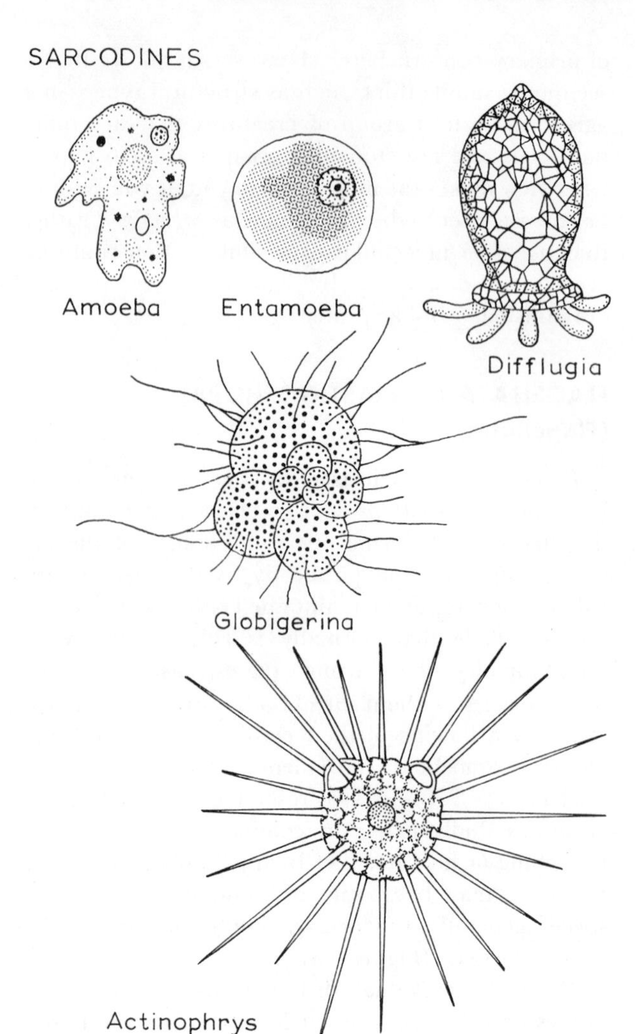

Figure 8.4 Sarcodine types, all microscopic.

Reproduction: mostly asexual by binary fission; also asexual by multiple fission and plasmotomy (cell division without mitosis that is somewhat analagous to fragmentation; limited to multinucleate species); sexual processes as in Flagellata.

Occurrence: fresh-water, marine, and moist terrestrial habitats; many parasitic species are known.

Sarcodina includes the amoeboid forms, those that move and capture food by projecting their protoplasm in the direction traveled or toward prey. This phylum is closely related to the flagellates—so close, in fact, that some species are shifted between the two phyla as various workers advance their interpretations of life cycles. Both phyla show the alternation of sexual and asexual generations.

Perhaps the most important amoeba is *Entamoeba histolytica*, the protozoan that produces amoebic dysentery in man. Other sarcodines, especially the radiolarians and foraminiferans, secrete shell-like structures. The foraminiferans are used by petroleum geologists to identify oil-bearing layers of rocks, and some fossil species occur in rocks more than one-half billion years old.

SPOROZOA

Diagnosis: fixed and motionless or possessing amoeboid movement; some display worm-like or less marked gliding body movements; individuals rounded or oval to elongate or worm-like; all are parasites (mostly internal) that move as "spores" (resistant encasements of zygotes or young) from host to host (Figure 8.5).

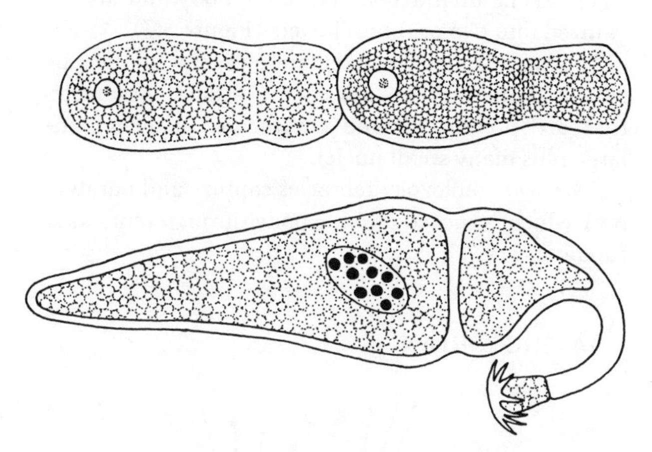

Figure 8.5 Sporozoan types, all microscopic.

Structure: individuals regularly distinct with a cell membrane, no cell wall, but rarely with adhesive organelles; nucleus complete and complex, generally one per individual except during multiple fission; organelles normally absent.

Nutrition: strictly parasitic by body surface absorption.

Reproduction: both asexual and haplobiontic, adult haploid, life cycles; both cycles regularly involve multiple fission and complex stages.

Occurrence: parasitic, most species within the cells of their host; many cause disease.

The "spore animals" all are parasites of other creatures, mostly animals. Sporozoans have a complex life cycle with sexual and asexual stages. They get their name from the asexual cells, or spores, they produce during part of their life cycle. Like the spores of most protozoans those of sporozoans serve to protect the organism during an unfavorable period, in the present instance that involving the movement from one host to another. Among the more important creatures in this class are those causing malaria; mosquitoes transport these protozoans from infected to other humans.

CILIOPHORA

Diagnosis: protozoans bearing hair-like organelles (cilia) during some to all stages of the life cycle; cilia typically are numerous and in rows over the body; never amoeboid like Sarcodina and certain other protozoans; normally with one nucleus larger than the others.

CLASS CILIATA (Ciliates)

Diagnosis: individual's shape fixed, spherical to elongate; shape usually fixed by a firm external pellicle that normally is diagonally or longitudinally grooved; often each groove is a site for attachment of a row of cilia, but when pellicle sculpturing bounds squares or other geometric forms, one or two cilia are within the confines of the sculpturing; characterized by cilia being present throughout the life cycle; cilia are agents of movement and other functions; ciliates are mostly solitary and motile but some species occur as sessile, branching colonies; many are parasites (Figure 8.6).

Structure: individuals regularly distinct, often with a clearly differentiated external pellicle; nuclei complete and complex, at least one larger than the others; no chlorophyll or eye spot (stigma), but ciliates constitute the most complexly organized protozoans; trichocysts present (see Flagellata) and very complex; cilia occur singly or united into complex structures that help capture prey by propelling food to a gullet, or that aid in swimming or crawling; some cilia probably are sensory; possess a complex body-coordinating structure; many have organelles providing movements much as do muscles; contractile vacuoles with contributing canals and/or vacuoles; food gathering often involves structures such as mouth and gullet.

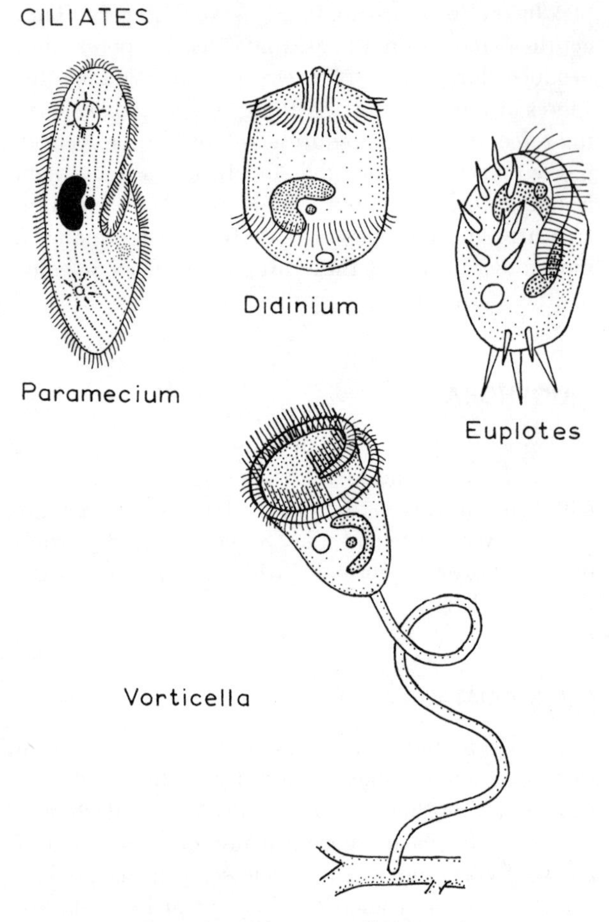

Figure 8.6 Ciliate types, all microscopic.

Nutrition: mostly holozoic, some hunting their prey and others creating currents that bring the prey to them.

Reproduction: asexual usually is by binary fission in which resistant cysts are formed to endure unfavorable environmental conditions; also probably by budding; sexual reproduction usually involves a unique process; life cycle perhaps mostly haplobiontic, adult diploid.

Occurrence: abundant in the ocean and in fresh water; some are parasitic; aquatic forms are among the primary predators of the microscopic world.

The ciliates are named for their hair-like locomotor structures. Cilia are part of a coordinated locomotor system composed of complex organelles. Many ciliates are free-living forms that can be found in almost any waters; others live in or upon other animals. Most ciliates have both sexual and asexual phases in their life cycles.

Of particular interest in ciliates and suctorians is conjugation, a reproductive process involving the temporary coupling of two individuals. This process occurs during meiosis and leads to cross-fertilization by the exchange of nuclei that act as gametes. Conjugation is considered sexual reproduction although there is no permanent fusion of cells.

CLASS SUCTORIA (Suctorians)

Diagnosis: young resemble ciliates; adults spherical, oval, inverted conical or branched protozoans fastened either by a stalk or directly to living or nonliving aquatic objects; adults with food-getting tentacles that either cover the body or are concentrated at the unattached end of the body and are organized into two or three clusters (Figure 8.7).

Structure: much as in ciliates, except for lacking cilia and most organelles in the adults; organelles that are present include contractile vacuoles; one large plus many small nuclei.

Nutrition: holozoic; tentacles capture and paralyze prey which is sucked into the body through tentacular canals.

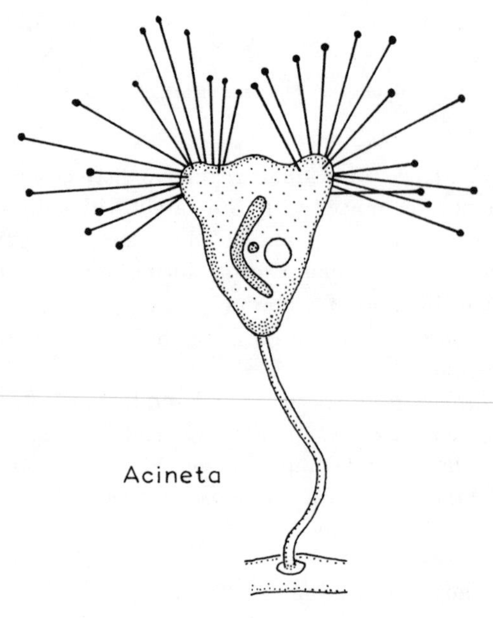

Figure 8.7 A suctorian, microscopic.

Reproduction: asexual budding and conjugation are common; encystment regularly takes place and is related to an unfavorable period; an asexual life cycle appears most typical.

Occurrence: regularly found in the ocean and in fresh water, generally upon living or nonliving objects; some are parasitic.

The ciliated, free-living, young suctorians resemble ciliates. After swimming for a while the young lose their cilia and change into an attached adult stage. The adults usually are attached to objects by a contractile stalk.

SUBKINGDOM FUNGI

In the two phyla here considered, the slime molds (or slime fungi) constitute the Phylum Myxomycophyta and the true fungi (including the algal fungi, sac fungi, and club fungi) constitute the Phylum Eumycophyta. Also treated here are the lichens.

The limits and relationships of most protists are a subject of much controversy, the consequences of an already mentioned poor fossil record. The controversy extends to the present groups. Some biologists believe that the slime molds, true fungi, and even the bacteria represent subphyla of a single phylum, hence had a common ancestor. At the other extreme are biologists who would segregate the slime molds, each of the three true fungi classes, and the bacteria into individual phyla. The present interpretation of relationships, then, assumes a common ancestor for all fungi.

Division of the Subkingdom Fungi into two phyla shows where common ancestry is less likely to be present. There is good evidence that slime molds are unrelated to true fungi; slime molds may have evolved from the Sarcodina and true fungi from the Flagellata. Under the present interpretation it is assumed that the evidence for single origin of a Subkingdom Fungi from the earliest Protista is true. In the case of the true fungi, there are apparent fossils from the dawn of Actualistic times, almost two billion years ago.

The Subkingdom Fungi includes the majority of plant-like creatures that do not contain chlorophyll and do not belong to the Kingdom Plantae. Only the bacteria share this plant-like nature and lack of true chlorophyll. For this and other reasons, bacteria sometimes are classified as fungi. However, fungi possess single-cell or more complex organization and have their basic structure in the form of hair-like filaments called *mycelia.*

Diagnosis: organization unicellular to simple cellular; nucleus differentiated, complete and complex; generally plant-like, most possess definite cell walls and are nonmotile; chlorophyll absent; structure usually hair-like (filamentous); cell division regularly by mitosis or meiosis, amitosis less common.

MYXOMYCOPHYTA (Slime Molds or Slime Fungi)

The slime molds are truly remarkable creatures. For much of their life cycle they are very much like flagellates (Figure 8.8). A motile, flagellate *swarm cell* is released from a spore. These swarm cells (or swarm spores) move about by means of their flagellae and engulf food by surrounding it with protoplasmic projections of their cell body. The swarm cells then become more spherical in shape and lose their flagella, becoming Sarcodina-like *myxamoebae.* These myxamoebae divide mitotically to provide *gametes.* Gametic fusion and *zygote* formation start the development of a multinucleate protoplasmic mass, or *plasmodium.* The plasmodium might still be considered animal-like because it is slow moving. However, the plasmodium soon becomes nonmotile and

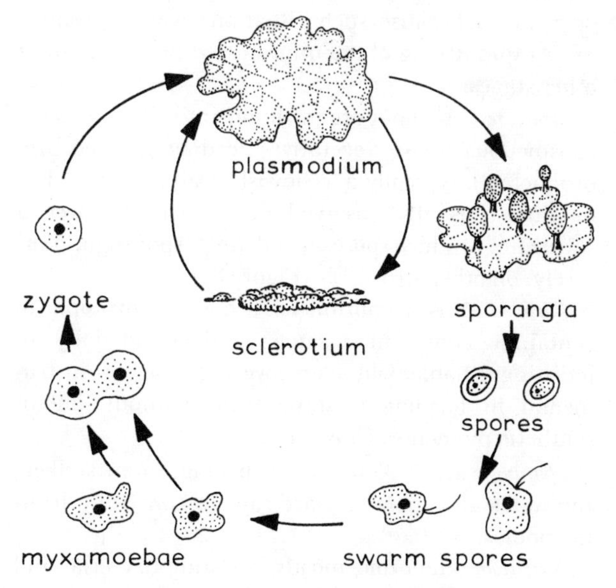

Figure 8.8 Life cycle of a typical slime mold.

forms plant-like *sporangia* which later form *spores*. In some circumstances the plasmodium does not form sporangia immediately. If food and/or moisture are limited, a resting stage (*sclerotium*) is assumed until the return of favorable conditions.

Most slime molds feed upon dead and decaying materials. Unfortunately, the forms are rarely observed. These creatures are quite intricate and beautiful, but to appreciate this fact one must first recognize and know where to find them. They generally range from the size of a dime to that of a dinner plate. When growing, they appear slimy and moldy to the naked eye. More specifically, they are a naked mass of usually yellowish or whitish slimy protoplasm that moves in a slow creeping motion. Although such a description is unlikely to imply much in the way of beauty, appropriate magnification (in some cases even a hand lens) reveals an intricacy of pattern that is pleasing to the eye. However, this is neither the only nor the most pleasing structure of these fungi. When dry, they tend to assume a lacy pattern and have erect spore-producing structures arising from this pattern.

To find slime molds, one must look through dead, preferably decaying, leaves and wood. An especially likely site is the interior of a decaying, wet log. These habitats are an indication of the most likely areas, namely below the substrate, where these creatures can be found. Their habitat is explained on the basis of their lacking chlorophyll and any type of photosynthetic nutrition. Also, it appears that they shun open areas because such situations would promote more rapid drying of the unprotected plasmodium or other stages.

Structure: without organization into definite cells; conspicuous phase vegetative (feeding but not reproductive), typically a yellowish visible mass (plasmodium), usually observed flowing slowly over a substrate; produce spores in a definite sporangium or, rarely, on other structures (Figure 8.9).

Plasmodium is a multinucleate mass of protoplasm containing contractile vacuoles and bounded by an indistinguishable jelly-like covering that is instrumental in forming a slime trail; without photosynthetic pigments of any kind.

Sporangia are 1/25 to 2/5 inch long; often stalked, the stalks and sporangia are said to constitute fruiting bodies.

Nutrition: holozoic, mostly ingesting bacteria, and saprophytic on decaying vegetation.

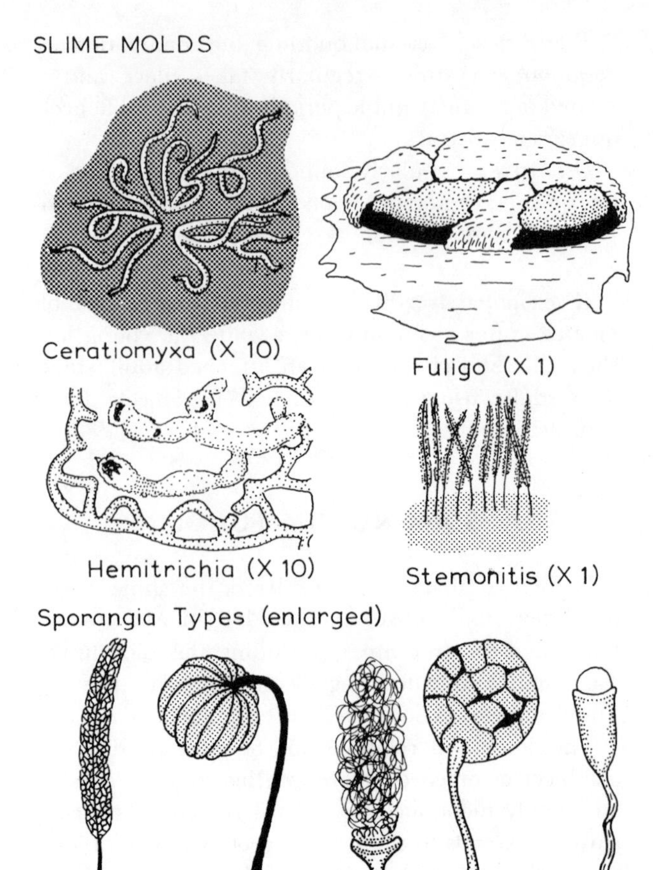

Figure 8.9 Representative slime molds, showing plasmodia with sporangia or other spore-forming structures.

Life cycle: typically with a sequence of stages (see Figure 8.8).

Occurrence: terrestrial in moist situations, mostly in decaying vegetation (especially inside dead wood or within dead surface leaves) or in the dung of herbivorous animals; rarely seen upon the surface except when approaching or within the sporangia-bearing stage; also a few parasitic forms mostly upon vascular plants but also algae and true fungi; about 500 species.

EUMYCOPHYTA (True Fungi)

Fragmentary fossils imply the presence of the first fungi some two billion years ago during the "Age of Monera." The same fossils could include flagellates but the remains do not definitely establish their presence at that time. Therefore, fungi may be more ancient than flagellates and the fungi might have evolved from the bacteria. This creates a problem because the archaic protistans often are believed to have been flagellates. However, bacterial origin of the fungi was suggested long before the fossil indication. In fact, many botanists include the bacteria and true fungi in the same phylum; however, any relationship between the two groups seems too remote to make a single-phylum grouping meaningful. In addition, joining the bacteria with the fungi would minimize the importance of the Monera.

Although there is some disagreement about the true status of the Eumycophyta, there appears to be adequate evidence for placing the three classes that follow into a single phylum. Not only do the structures of the three groups show close relationship and the possibility of straight-line evolution from Phycomycetes to Ascomycetes to Basidiomycetes, but the fossil record implies the same temporal sequence in the three classes.

Like the slime molds, true fungi lack both chlorophyll and the process of photosynthesis. For this reason, many fungi are found in areas of darkness, for example, underground and in caves. Other fungi are quite inconspicuous, and neither their structures nor other indications of their presence are likely to be noticed. Still others are noted mostly by their effects upon the plants or animals they parasitize. Most of the conspicuous algal fungi have the appearance of molds and are found either upon dead plants and animals in water or upon dead insects and organic remains on land. For details of the sac and club fungi, one should study the synopses of the classes.

Structure: generally simple and usually multicellular (cellular organization), but also species with one to many nuclei and typically not filamentous (unicellular); multicellular forms mostly filamentous, the hair-like filaments sometimes organized into moldy-looking masses or visible fruiting bodies; fruiting bodies normally spherical, oval, or shaped like a pear, funnel, cup, umbrella (toadstools or mushrooms), hoof, cushion, disc, club, branching tree or coral, or quite irregular; filaments spread over substrate or branch within living or dead organic matter; usually without any tendency toward tissue formation.

Cells are distinct or without cell walls, so nuclei are in a continuous cytoplasm; when distinct, cells may have one to many nuclei; nuclei complete and complex; cytoplasm without photosynthetic pigments; cell walls often absent; when present, they are usually chitinous, sometimes having cellulose; flagellae absent, or one or two in some Phycomycetes spores.

A single filament is called a *hypha;* a mass of hyphae, a *mycelium.*

Fruiting bodies are usually limited to sexual spore production, but asexual spore-producing types are known.

Nutrition: parasitic or saprophytic; both types found throughout the phylum.

Reproduction: asexual occurs by fragmentation, budding, mitosis, and spore production; sexual reproduction and parthenogenesis also occur.

Life cycle: very complex (Figures 8.11, 8.13, and 8.15); probably all types occur; generally there is an alternation of haploid and diploid phases (if not generations) and a true diplobiontic cycle; many fungi have an asexual cycle associated with a sexual cycle, both cycles stemming from and generally returning to a vegetative stage (often a mycelium).

In the *asexual cycle* a vegetative stage (usually a mycelium) forms spore-producing structures; spore-producing structures form asexual spores; asexual spores produce the vegetative stage or transform directly into gametes.

In the *sexual cycle* the vegetative stage usually forms structures which directly or indirectly form gametes; then gametic fusion (fertilization) or parthenogenesis occurs, followed later by nuclear fusion and zygote formation; then the zygote may go into either a resting-spore or a sporangium stage prior to meiosis and the vegetative structure development; or these stages are accompanied by the development of a fruiting body; and finally, some fruiting-body hyphae produce sexual spores which germinate into a filament mass (vegetative mycelium); still other variations occur.

The sexual cycle usually contains a *perfect stage,* one in which structures (often fruiting bodies) related to zygote formation and meiosis occur. Fungi without such a stage are grouped as Imperfect Fungi.

Occurrence: widespread as parasites on plants and animals and as saprophytes on organic remains; include about 1300 Phycomycetes, about 15,000 Ascomycetes, and about 15,000 Basidiomycetes.

Although the fungi include the most conspicuous protistans, some are microscopic, unicellular or multicellular species. The more conspicuous forms usually are called slime molds, molds, smuts, rusts, puffballs, earthstars, or mushrooms. These generally are discovered growing upon plants or organic remains on the ground. However, one should recognize more groups for adequate appreciation of the taxon (see below).

This is a cosmopolitan subkingdom and certain individuals also approach a world-wide distribution. They can be found in salt and fresh water, in moist areas, and in soil. Many occur as external or internal parasites. The only serious restrictions on their distribution are temperature and moisture. At temperatures over 86°F most cease growth. Optimum functions usually occur between 68° and 79°F. Also, some moisture is required for them to complete their life cycles. In spite of this, they occur in arctic and desert areas but appear to be less abundant in these environmental extremes.

These organisms contain no chlorophyll and most definitely are consumers rather than producers of nutrients. Their main ecological roles are saprophytic, breaking down organic remains, or parasitic, often causing mild reactions, disease, or even death to their hosts. Parasitic fungi apparently infest all major taxa, but most parasites also can live upon organic remains. Therefore, their function in any community is allied to that of other organisms with heterotrophic nutrition.

In addition to some being associated with certain blue-green or green algae as lichens, other fungi form a *mycorrhiza* association with higher plant roots. Fungi filament penetration of root cells (but only the surface layer) is a fundamental part of this association. In some cases at least, it appears that the association enables transfer of certain soil nutrients to the plants and that plant cells digest and gain nutrients from fungal filaments. Also, it seems that fungi filaments gain nutrients from the plant roots. Therefore, on occasion, the relationship might be beneficial to both participants; but in other cases the fungus acts like a parasite.

Due to their saprophytic activities, they may destroy man's stored goods, especially food. Also, they are agents of most known plant diseases, especially various blights, mildews, wilts, scabs, blunts, rusts, and smuts. Fungi cause some potentially fatal diseases in man but are better known as agents of skin infections like ring worm and athlete's foot. However, as a group, they are extremely beneficial They produce various chemicals important as drugs (e.g., penicillin and cortisone), vitamins, enzymes, baking and brewing agents, and cheese-producing materials (e.g., chemicals that form blue and other cheeses). The larger fleshy fungi, mushrooms including truffles and puffballs, are human food. Also, the fungi provide biologists with many clues as to the basic workings of life processes.

CLASS PHYCOMYCETES (Algal Fungi)

Diagnosis: filament mass (mycelium), when present, is without cross structures separating nuclei, except where reproductive structures are formed; without fruiting bodies; most produce both sexual and asexual spores in sporangia; sporangia are absent in other true fungi; sporangia often contribute distinctive specks to mycelia; sporangia sexual spores possess no, one, or two flagellae; flagellae absent in other true fungi (Figure 8.10).

ALGAL FUNGI

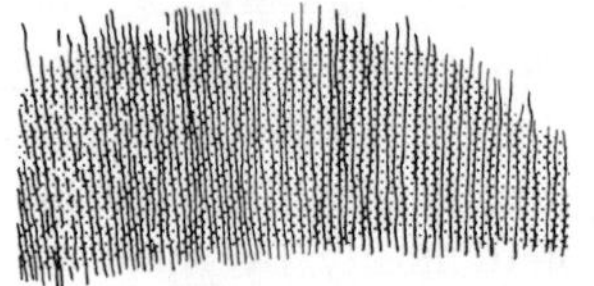

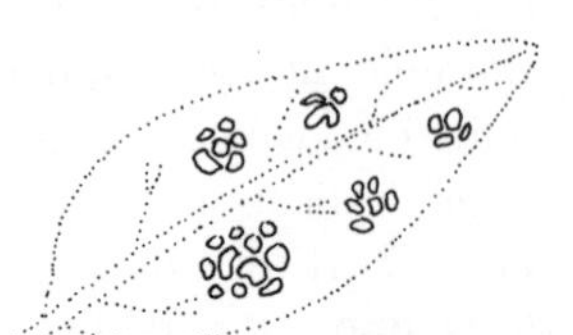

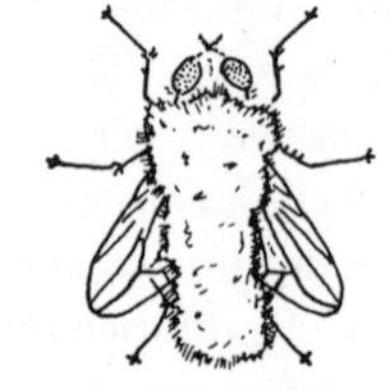

Figure 8.10 Conspicuous algal fungi, about natural size.

Structure: unicellular forms without a filament mass (the entire cell commonly transforming to the next stage), but either with a few anchoring structures, or with a much abbreviated mycelium; filamentous forms possess a true mycelium of branching hyphae; visible structures normally are powdery or moldy appearing; no fruiting bodies produced.

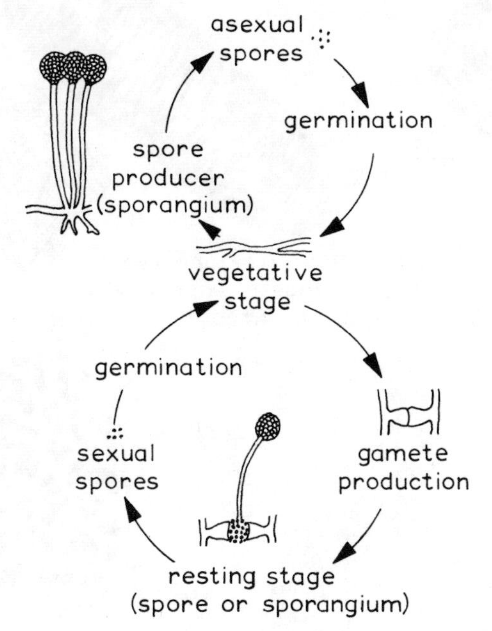

Figure 8.11 Algal fungi life cycle as typified by the bread mold, *Rhizopus*.

Life cycle: mostly of a single type involving a sexual and an asexual cycle united in a vegetative mycelium (Figure 8.11).

CLASS ASCOMYCETES (Sac Fungi)

Diagnosis: cellular (often multinucleate) and usually filamentous; mycelium when present with individual cells regularly defined by chitinous cell walls; typical structure a sexual cycle spore (ascospore) produced in a sac-like ascus that forms a definite number, usually eight, of ascospores (sporangium gives rise to an indefinite number); many have a multicellular, often visible, sexual fruiting body often approaching tissue organization; flagellae absent (Figure 8.12).

Structure: unicellular forms (mostly yeasts) have little or no mycelium; filamentous forms have a true mycelium, often organized into conspicuous fruiting bodies; visible forms are generally powdery, moldy, or some form of macroscopic fruiting body; the vegetative mycelium may be a compact, cushion-shaped, visible structure.

Life cycle: assumes many complex forms (Figure 8.13); major types involve a sexual and an asexual cycle (generally with the production of hyphae during the sexual phase as well as the vegetative mycelium), a strictly sexual cycle with ascospores forming the vegetative mycelium which in turn forms "gametes," and two major variations without any vegetative mycelium.

CLASS BASIDIOMYCETES (Club Fungi)

Diagnosis: cellular and usually filamentous as in Ascomycetes; typical structure a sexual cycle spore (basidiospore) produced in a vaguely club-like basidium that forms a definite number, usually four, of basidiospores; basidium may form a vegetative mycelium directly (mostly in smuts); mycelium often more developed than that in Ascomycetes; often with a fruiting body that approaches tissue organization; flagellae absent (Figure 8.14).

Structure: species without a fruiting body usually are observed as a colored powder (rusts) or black powder (smuts), the spores; gross form of fruiting bodies vary but are similar to those found in Ascomycetes.

Life cycles: cycles are extremely complex, but can be reduced to four major types (Figure 8.15); two types occur in the fruiting-body-producing forms, (the so-called higher club fungi), one type in the rusts (many of which are parasitic upon two different plants during their life cycle), and the last type in the smuts.

MUSHROOMS VS. TOADSTOOLS

Contrary to popular belief, there is no way of being sure that a particular fleshy fungus is a mushroom or a toadstool. That is, one cannot be certain whether a particularly shaped member of the fleshy club fungi is nonpoisonous or poisonous. Certain species of these fungi may be perfectly edible at some times and poisonous at others. However, there are certain distinctive, always safe mushrooms that one can eat and others that are always poisonous. Therefore, the so-called distinction between mushrooms and toadstools has no real meaning. Although there is some confusion in the application of common names to club fungi, most of the *fleshy club fungi* called mushrooms can be assigned to one of a few growth forms (Figure 8.16). However, the same growth form can occur in three different families, the pore (with fine holes or teeth), gill (with blade-like gills), and tooth (with pricks or tooth-like structures) fungi. Also, these mushrooms belong to the same or-

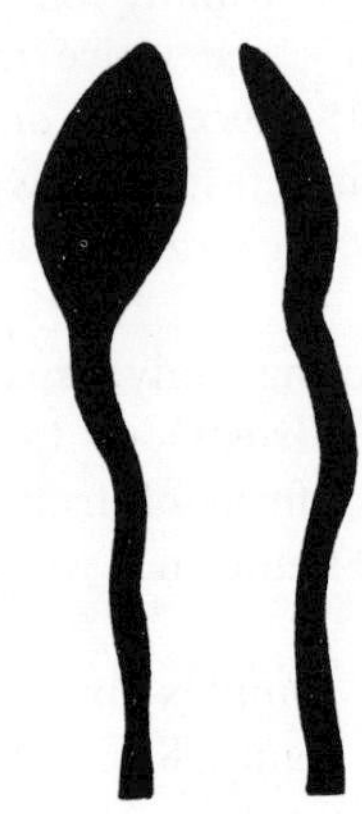

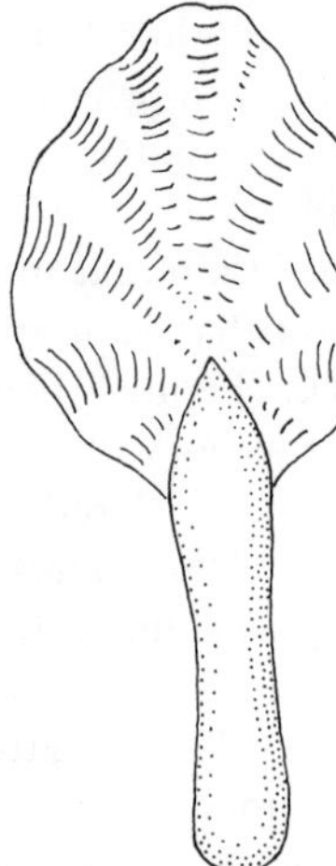

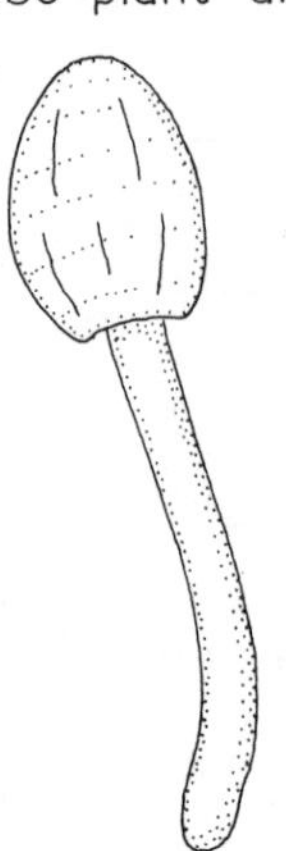

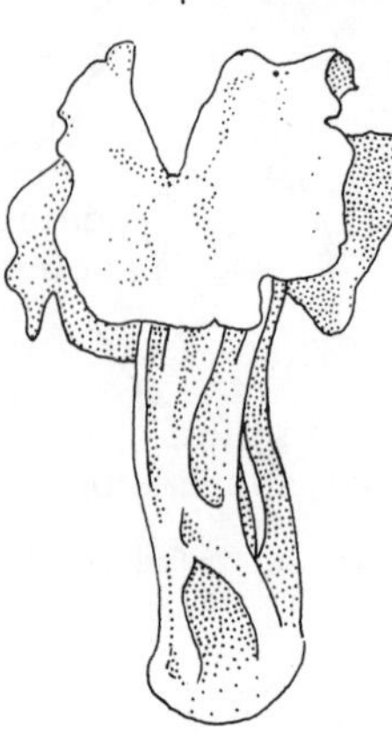

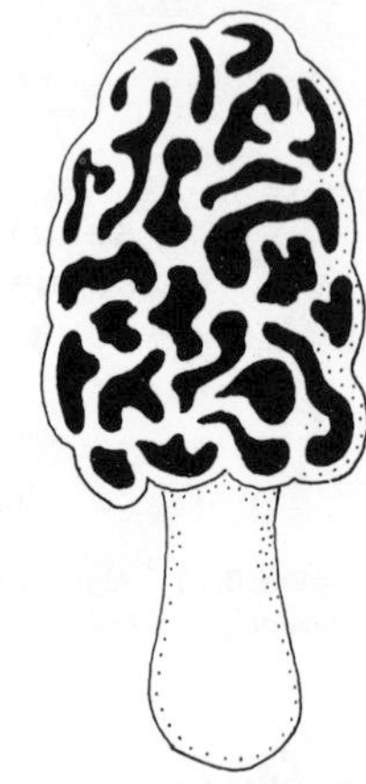

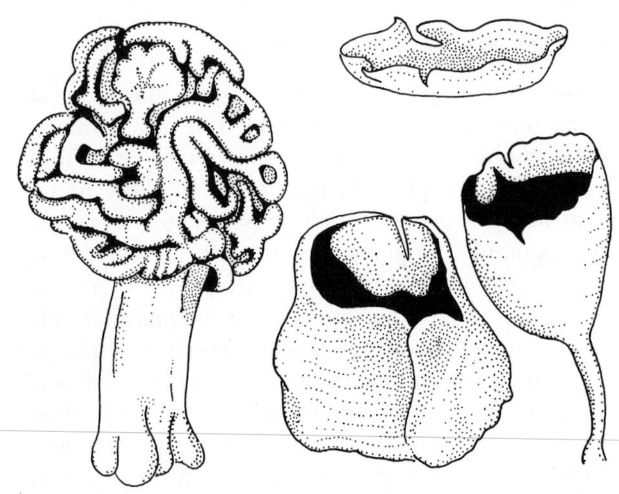

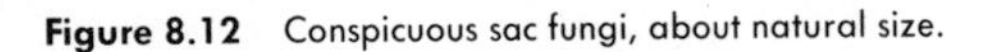

Figure 8.12 Conspicuous sac fungi, about natural size.

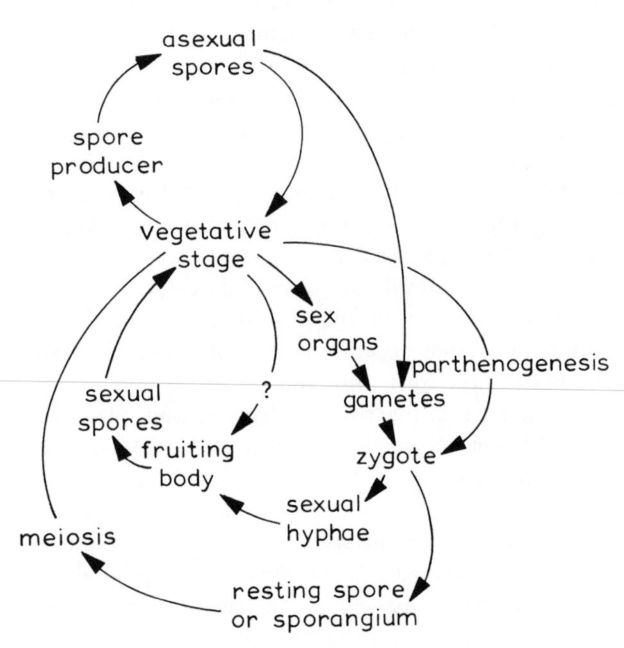

Figure 8.13 Generalized life cycle of the sac fungi.

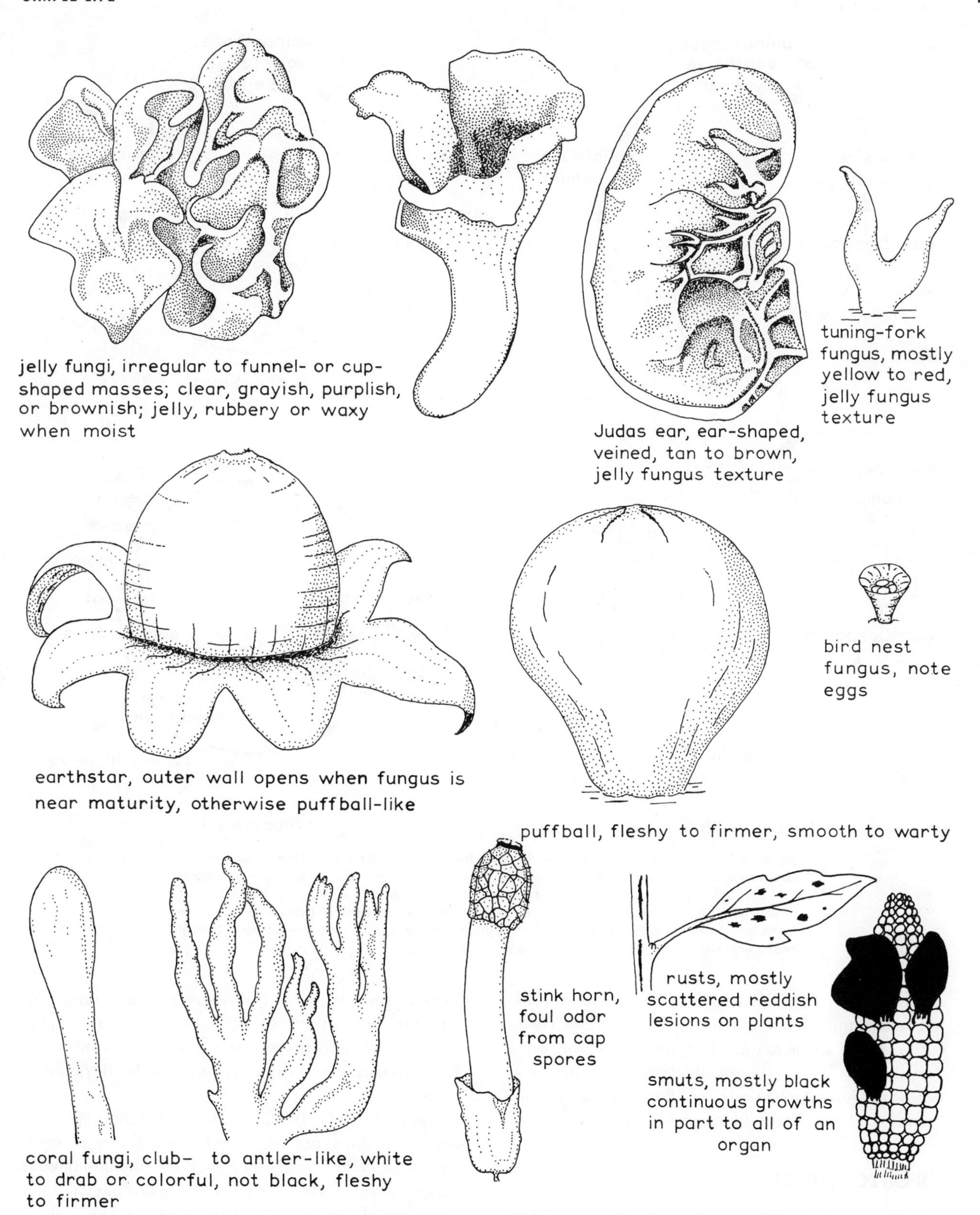

Figure 8.14 Conspicuous club fungi, exclusive of mushrooms, about natural size. Truffles, a rarely encountered, edible, underground type are not shown.

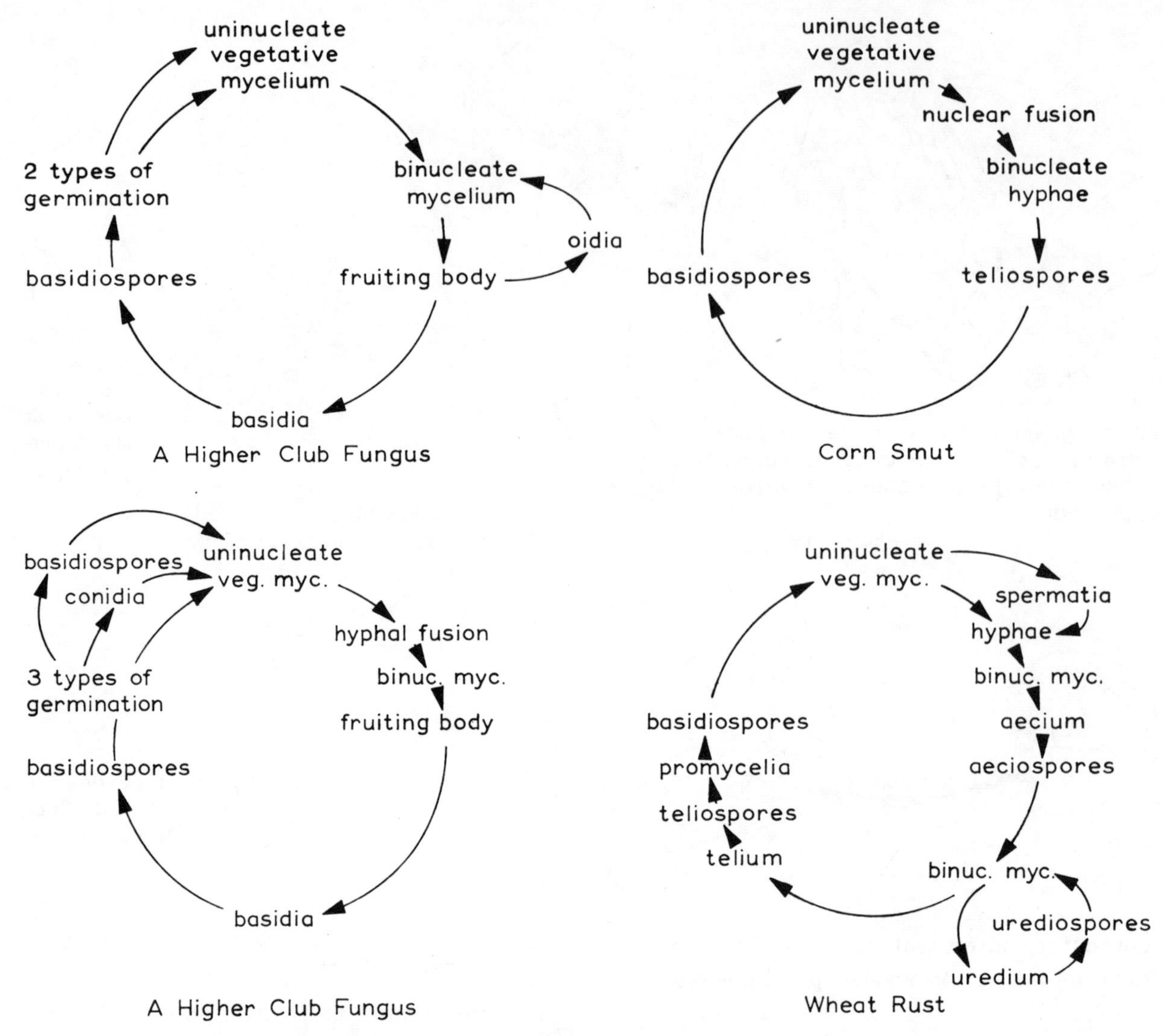

Figure 8.15 Generalized life cycle of the club fungi. The various club fungi spores include haploid basidiospores and conidia and diploid aeciospores, oidia, teliospores, and urediospores. Typically, the basidiospores constitute the stage that disperses these fungi. In corn smut, basidiospores infest new corn plants. In wheat rust the aeciospore through basidiospore-formation stages normally occur on a grain plant, usually wheat, and basidiospore through aeciospore-formation stages on a barberry plant.

der as some of the club fungi shown in Figure 8.14. Therefore, mushrooms do not represent either clear-cut taxa or a single taxon. In spite of this, the word "mushroom" is a convenient designation for any fleshy fungus, Ascomycete or Basidiomycete, and "toadstool" may be useful for umbrella-shaped forms.

IMPERFECT FUNGI

Fungi without known perfect stages once were grouped into a Class Deuteromycetes. However, as time goes on, more and more of these fungi are found to have a perfect stage. The discovery of perfect stages usually places such organisms in the Class Ascomycetes, but many were found to be Basidiomycetes.

Approximately 10,000 species of fungi still are without known perfect stages, and there is good reason to believe that some of these do not have a perfect stage. An often quoted example of such fungi are the ones that cause athlete's foot. This group of species, collectively called *Epidermophyton*

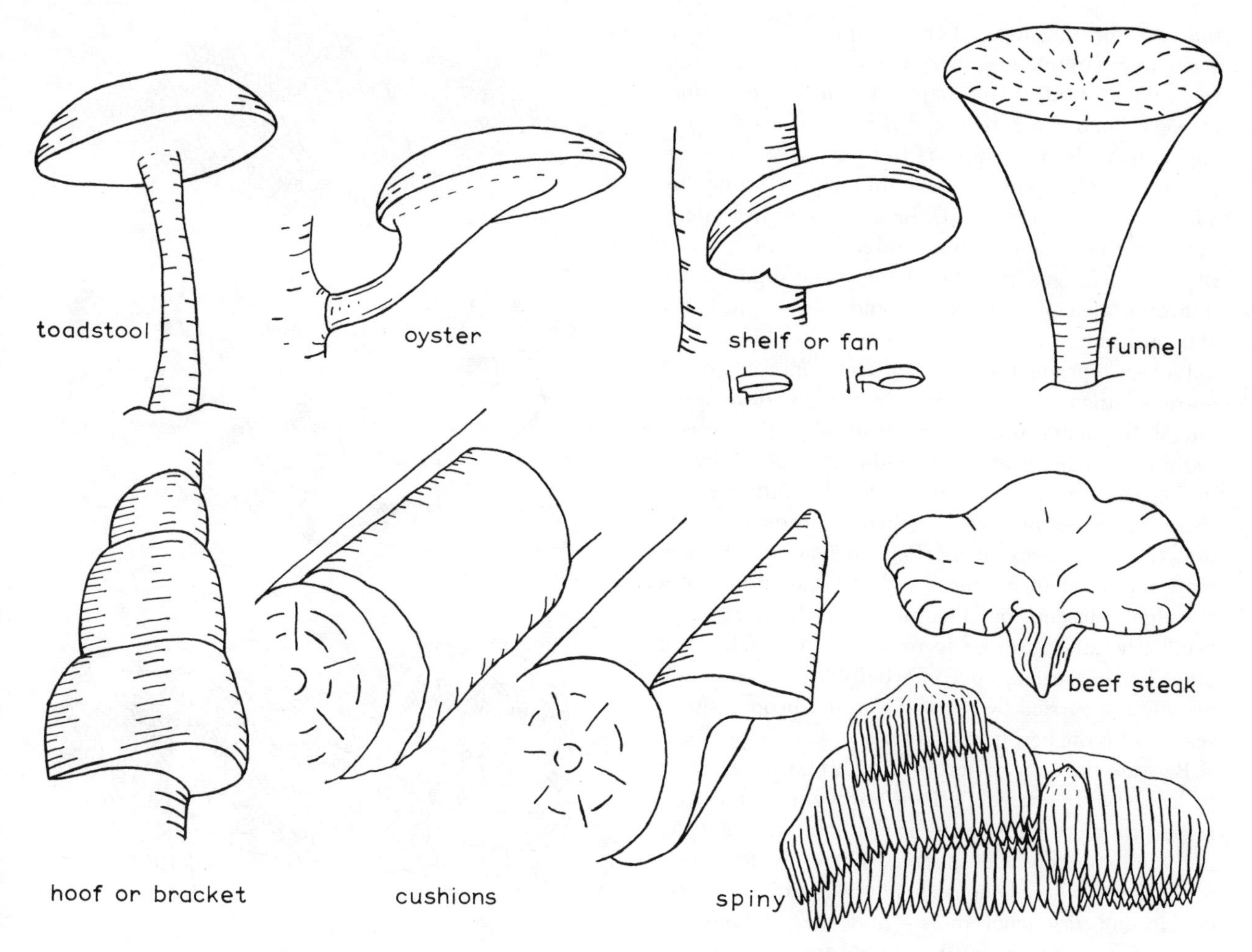

Figure 8.16 Mushroom types, about natural size for some members of each type, but many species get much larger than those shown.

floccosum, provide an example of the form-species in its form-genus. Because imperfect fungi lack perfect stages, they often cannot be adequately separated from one another, hence may be diagnosed on the basis of diseases they cause.

LICHENS

Lichens are of ecological importance because they usually represent the first living things to grow upon rocks. Although lichens represent combinations of algae and fungi, not all algae and fungi form lichens. The only true algae found in lichens are the Chlorophyta; however, the blue-green algae (Cyanophyta) also form lichens. Therefore, "algae" in the present discussion will include the moneran Phylum Cyanophyta as well as the plant Phylum Chlorophyta.

The known lichen-forming fungi are found only in the Ascomycetes and Basidiomycetes. As far as is known, these particular fungi are strictly lichen-forming, hence are completely dependent upon the lichen association for their food and always benefit from the relationship. In some cases at least, lichen-forming fungi supply necessary moisture and, perhaps, growth-stimulating substances to the algae, which are trapped and included within a lichen. However, whether or not algae benefit from being associated with fungi, the relationship is essentially one of algal enslavement, a free-living alga being "entrapped" by a fungus.

All lichens once were accepted as examples of mutualism, the assumption being that both the alga and fungus always benefited from the association. However, there is reason to doubt that such is always the case for the alga. For example, when lichens occur in environments where the alga could not survive alone, both plants are obviously benefiting. However, in other instances, it is not obvious that the alga is helped. This appears to be the case when an alga is both free-living and, within inches, confined by a fungus. At the very least, the alga could live alone, but in such a case the fungus might even be a parasite. The fungus may be shading the alga, hence retarding alga photosynthesis, and may be utilizing alga nutrients.

Lichen reproduction is often the consequence of normal fungal reproduction in which developing fungal filaments probably entrap algae; however, within a lichen, algal reproduction normally is limited to asexual mitosis. On the other hand, there is a process by which lichens reproduce lichens directly. This asexual mechanism features the formation of a small fragment of lichen composed of a few algal cells entrapped within a mycelium. Such reproductive structures are formed inside the lichen but grow to the surface, become ball-like, detach, and usually are carried by the wind until a proper site is reached for the new lichen to grow.

Because lichens can become dormant, they are able to withstand severe, periodic drought. For this reason they are important early inhabitants of rocks and are extremely widespread. There are few areas in the world where lichens cannot be found. They occur in hot dry, cool moist, and even frozen environments. Frequently they grow upon objects, especially living and dead plants.

Although the combination of algae and fungi constitutes a unique growth form with functions all its own, lichens are not a natural grouping of organisms. This does not mean that the lichen-forming fungi, especially, show little specialization or evidence of evolution toward the lichen way of life. Actually, such evolution did occur and must have taken some time. However, evolution was not of single lichen species; rather, remotely related fungi and "algae" were involved. Therefore, any classification of the group as a whole has no phylogenetic meaning. For this reason, classification of lichens is strictly for the convenience of specialists, and the growth-form segregation of lichens into crustose, foliose, and fruticose types is sufficient for most naturalists (Figure 8.17).

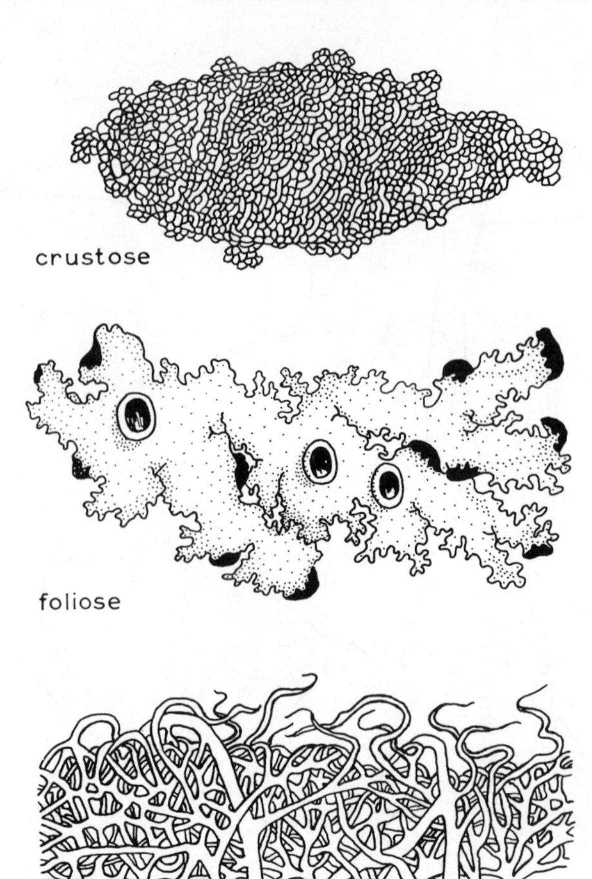

Figure 8.17 Lichen types, about natural size, but many kinds are much larger. Crustose and foliose types are shown from above, fruticose from the side.

Crustose lichens grow in thin crusts and usually occupy the driest habitats. Foliose lichens often are somewhat encrusting but are more elevated from the substrate, generally display a pattern of two-forked branching, and sometimes vaguely resemble leaves. They generally require more water than do crustose but less than fruticose lichens. Fruticose lichens are upright or hanging, and often are confused with and called mosses.

SELECTED READINGS

Alexopoulos, C. J., 1962. *Introductory Mycology.* 2nd ed. John Wiley & Sons, New York.

Christensen, C. M., 1946. *Common Fleshy Fungi.* Burgess Publ. Co., Minneapolis, Minn.

Edmondson, W. T., ed., 1959. *Ward and Whipple's Fresh-water Biology.* 2nd ed. John Wiley & Sons, New York.

Fergus, C. L., 1960. *Illustrated Genera of Wood Decay Fungi.* Burgess Publ. Co., Minneapolis, Minn.

Jahn, T. L., 1949. *How to Know the Protozoa.* Wm. C. Brown Co., Dubuque, Iowa.

Krieger, L. C. C., 1947. *The Mushroom Handbook.* The Macmillan Co., New York.

Manwell, R. D., 1961. *Introduction to Protozoology.* St. Martin's Press, New York.

Palmer, E. L., 1949. *Fieldbook of Natural History.* McGraw-Hill Book Co., New York.

Ramsbottom, J., 1953. *Mushrooms and Toadstools.* Collins, London.

Sistrom, W. R., 1962. *Microbial Life.* Modern Biology Series. Holt, Rinehart and Winston, New York.

Smith, A. H., 1958. *The Mushroom Hunter's Field Guide.* University of Michigan Press, Ann Arbor, Mich.

Smith, G. M., 1955. *Cryptogamic Botany.* Vol. 1: *Algae and Fungi.* McGraw-Hill Book Co., New York.

9 SUBKINGDOM ALGAE

Lower Plants

The plant kingdom, as here restricted, is fairly easy to define if rare exceptions to the rule are ignored. Plants are organisms with cellular, tissue, or organ organization in which the individual cells contain a cell wall, chlorophyll in plastids, and a central vacuole. Among the Protista certain flagellates have the latter structures in their single, cell-like bodies. In the classification followed here, the Kingdom Plantae is divided into two subkingdoms, Algae and Embryophyta.

In the rare exceptions to an absolute definition of the plants all criteria break down. However, one can consider the exceptions in relation to level of organization alone. No algal phylum is without unicellular members. (Some algae even have organs.) The unicellular forms cannot be separated from protistans by simple means. However, detailed study definitely relates these problematical species to algae rather than to protistans.

The presence of exceptions to the level of organization definitions of phyla can be perplexing as well as frustrating. Previous exceptions were noted (e.g., tissue-like fungi) and further exceptions will occur. Rather than being frustrating to the biologist, these exceptions are welcomed. They serve as another item supporting the principle of organic evolution. Although we might not logically expect transitional forms, "missing links," their representation in living species is useful in ascertaining phylogenies or "trees of life."

Unfortunately, exceptions in the form of "missing links" are all too few. This is indicated by lack of agreement on the phylogenetic position of the Algae.

ALGAL CLASSIFICATION AND PHYLOGENY

Some biologists prefer to include Algae as a taxon in the Subkingdom Thallophyta (Gr. *thallos*, a young shoot + *phyton*, a plant), which also includes the taxa Monera, chlorophyll-bearing Flagellata, and Fungi. However, since it is now believed unlikely that the Thallophyta constitute a natural grouping of life (that is, thallophytes probably were not derived from a common ancestor), that grouping will not be followed here.

In spite of the doubtful evolutionary significance of the Thallophyta, the terms *thallophyte* and *thallus* are often used in describing the simple structure of certain organisms, specifically the Monera, Protista, and Algae and the gametophyte generation of the Bryophyta (mosses and liverworts). A thallus is a structure in which there is little tissue or organ differentiation. More specifically, a thallus has none of the following structures: true roots, stems, leaves, complex

TAXONOMIC SUMMARY

Kingdom Plantae (Eng. *plant*)—plants
Subkingdom Algae (L. *algae*, seaweeds)—algae
Phylum Chlorophyta (Gr. *chloros*, green + *phyton*, plant)—green algae
Phylum Charophyta (Gr. *chara*, delight + *phyton*)—stoneworts
Phylum Chrysophyta (Gr. *chrysos*, gold + *phyton*)—golden algae
Phylum Phaeophyta (Gr. *phaios*, dusky + *phyton*)—brown algae
Phylum Rhodophyta (Gr. *rhodon*, red + *phyton*)—red algae

spore-forming sporangia, multicellular sex organs (except in the Charophyta), embryo stages, or any structure characteristic of animal organization.

The algae probably are a natural group, all having common ancestry from among the archaic chlorophyll-bearing Flagellata. In this hypothesis it is assumed that the green algae (Chlorophyta) originated from the green, or chlorophyll-bearing, Flagellata and that the early green algae were ancestral to other algae. Three lines of evolution are assumed from the archaic green algae. In one line of development, the Chlorophyta continued from their archaic ancestors but also gave rise to a poorly defined phylum, the Charophyta (stoneworts), and possibly to all other plant phyla. In a second line, the Rhodophyta (red algae) evolved. In the final line, the Chrysophyta (golden algae) and the Phaeophyta (brown algae) were derived. The possibility of such a series of happenings can be appreciated by contrasting the features of the different groups of algae.

There are other possible origins for the algae. For example, each line of development, or even each phylum, may have had independent origin from among the green flagellates. Also, the Rhodophyta may have had an entirely separate origin. Instead of a green flagellate ancestry the red algae may have evolved from the blue-green algae.

This confusion of origin again is the consequence of a poor fossil record. Although many algal fossils appear to be well preserved, the remnants of these simple creatures are far from being adequate. This statement may be difficult to accept if one has seen what appear to be excellent algal remains. However, the problem is not simply one of general structure. Such things as minute organization, including types of pigments, chlorophyll, and food reserves, must be known in order for the pattern of algal evolution to be disclosed. Therefore, although the time from the first conspicuous life through the Ordovician is called the Age of Algae, many of the known algal fossils cannot be identified. However, the green algae are known from the Precambrian, brown and red algae appear to be represented in the Cambrian, stoneworts in the Devonian, and diatoms in the Triassic. In addition, in Precambrian and Cambrian deposits there are remains of complex alga-like creatures, the very conspicuous reef-building stromatolites. As one might expect, the exact nature of the stromatolites is not known. They might have included remotely related taxa, or they may not have been single creatures. It still is suggested that they were lichen-like combinations of red algae and blue-green algae.

ALGAL ECOLOGY

Algae most frequently are found in bodies of water. They form the dominant flora of the ocean; few marine plants are not algae. About the only exception to a completely algal flora in the seas is the eel grasses. The eel grasses are vascular plants, or Tracheophyta, that can be diagnosed by their green, reed- or grass-like leaves that arise from a dark brown, underground, slender rootstock. The rootstock is an underground stem that bears many true roots. No marine algae have such a creeping rootstock or such differences in color between leaf-like and root-like structures. Marine algae usually are called seaweeds, and the word "kelp" refers to the large, coarse marine algae (mostly brown algae).

Many other algae are found in fresh water. Most of these plants create, along with certain Cyanophyta, various "scums" in the water, but the Charophyta, or stoneworts, form complex structures comparable to those of certain marine algae—again, no true roots are found. However, not all algae are aquatic or even semiaquatic. Many species are found in moist or semimoist terrestrial areas, for example, soil, rocks, or tree trunks. As mentioned in Chapter 8, certain green algae (and some blue-green algae among the Monera) occur in combination with fungi in a growth form called a lichen.

Being plants, the primary ecological role of algae is production of food, naturally, by photosynthesis. In fulfilling this role algae are most important in aquatic situations—at least they are the most abundant and widespread plants there. Green algae occur in all seas and in most fresh-water habitats. They are most numerous and probably influential in fresh water. Many occur in moist land environments (e.g., some grow upon rocks, trees, ice or snow). Red snow is caused by greens that have a red pigment masking their chlorophyll. Some even grow upon animals and plants. With blue-green algae, a few provide external coloring to arboreal animals. Many aquatic species also color the eggs, larvae, or adults of aquatic animals. For example, some fresh-water greens, add color to, apparently gain carbon dioxide from, and perhaps provide greater oxygen to the eggs of certain amphibians. Such algae usually are not parasites, they generally use the host organism merely as a site of attachment. However, some green algae are plant, especially leaf, parasites.

Diatoms are microscopic. In both fresh and salt water, with certain flagellates, they usually are so numerous as to be the primary food-producing organisms in their habitat. For this reason, aquatic animals often are dependent upon the existence of these plants. Some diatoms can survive in perpetual darkness if certain simple, organic compounds (e.g., glucose) are present. Such species live heterotrophically. At least one species (*Nitzschia putrida*) lacks chlorophyll, hence must always live by heterotrophic means. In addition, probably all extract silica from their aquatic medium to construct a two-part cell wall, or shell, reminiscent of the two halves of a pill box (one "box" fits tightly within the other). Therefore, when diatoms die their silica shells accumulate to form diatomaceous ooze; upon compaction, the ooze becomes a rock called "diatomaceous earth" or "diatomite."

Brown algae are almost exclusively marine; in fact, there is disagreement as to whether the so-called fresh-water forms are indeed brown algae. They include the largest algae; some surpass 100 feet in length. All sizes can be found in all oceans but browns are especially abundant in cold and temperate seas of the Northern Hemisphere. Near many coasts, they are the most abundant and conspicuous plants. Here, they often form extensive "forests," kelp beds.

About 7 per cent of the red algae occur in fresh water; the rest probably are marine. They are most numerous in subtropical and tropical waters but extend to depths of maximum light penetration in all seas, often to the 600-foot level. Species occurring in fresh and intertidal waters are less likely to be red than are the deep-sea forms. In addition to being food producers, additional ecological significance comes from the coraline red algae. These plants are more significant calcium carbonate contributors to reef formation than are corals. Some reds grow upon others and a few of these appear semiparasitic.

The marine algae normally have distributions limited to particular latitudes, oceans, or coasts. For this reason, one can speak of climatic, oceanic, or regional algal floras. These plants generally have structures and functions that enable survival in surf. Also, many can withstand short periods of drying. Partly for these reasons, marine forms are mostly intertidal.

Most fresh-water algae are cosmopolitan, owing to dispersal by such things as winds and the muddy feet of birds. However, light, temperature, and water chemistry place some restriction upon their potential ranges. The greatest number of individuals and species exists in slightly alkaline, quiet waters that are rich in such things as nitrates and phosphates. Only a few species occur or are restricted to rapid-moving fresh waters. Waters that are acid or poor in nutrients also have few algae.

The need for nutrients points out that algae are like other plants. Different algae (in fact, different plants) have unlike requirements in amounts and kinds of vitamins, growth-promoting substances, and trace elements. Many of these nutrients are synthesized by bacteria or blue-green algae, some even by other true algae.

CHLOROPHYTA (Green Algae)

Structure: typically cellular organization, but also unicellular and independent or colonial; mostly grass-green plants; unicellular forms mostly of fixed, oval to spherical form; colonies of small cell clusters in the form of discs, large and irregular masses, or hollow spheres; multicellular structure of filaments (simple and hair-like or branching), flat and thin sheets (continuous or somewhat narrow and branching), hollow tubes, or solid cylinders (simple to many-branched to feather-like), and some resemble vascular plants; those resembling vascular plants possess leaf, stem, and root-like structures; some even have an erect axis with whorls of branches from top to bottom or only at the top; structures display some tendency toward cellular differentiation but no tissues are present (Figure 9.1).

Cells: distinct or without cell walls so nuclei are in a continuous cytoplasm; nucleus complete and complex, one to many per cell; cytoplasmic pigments normally in grass-green plastids; one or more large central vacuoles; cell wall mostly two layers, the inner firm, mostly cellulose layer and the outer gelatinous layer; certain stages generally with flagellae.

Nutrition: mostly photosynthetic.

Reproduction: *asexual* by mitosis (unicellular species), fragmentation (colonial and filamentous types), and spore production; some species form spores similar to those of the Cyanophyta; others also form mobile, flagellate spores in a cell modified as a spore-producing structure (sporangium); in a very few cases gametes develop without first being fertilized; *sexual* involves diplobiontic and both haplobiontic life cycles; life cycles either are of both gametophyte and sporophyte being single-celled or multicellular, or are of one generation being suppressed to a phase and the other being "the plant"; diplobiontic cycles have both generations of the same or different form and independent plants or one generation growing upon the other; gametes are of the same form or different form with distinct eggs and sperms.

Occurrence: approximately 90 per cent fresh water and 10 per cent marine; most marine forms are intertidal and attached to rocks; most fresh-water species are submerged; also in moist land habitats and upon other algae, plants, and animals; some saprophytes, parasites, and lichen formers; about 6500 species.

CHAROPHYTA (Stoneworts)

Structure: multicellular and macroscopic, greenish plants consisting of simple root-like "hairs"; of an erect, stem-like, branching axis; and of branches (often leaf-like) arranged in whorls at interrupted points on the axis; structure and pattern of development from a single cell is suggestive of horsetails; plant often heavily covered with calcium carbonate, origin of their common name; some cellular differentiation, but no true tissues; sex organs are present (Figure 9.2).

Cells: distinct, complete and complex with cell walls; structure much as in Chlorophyta; flagellae absent except in sperm.

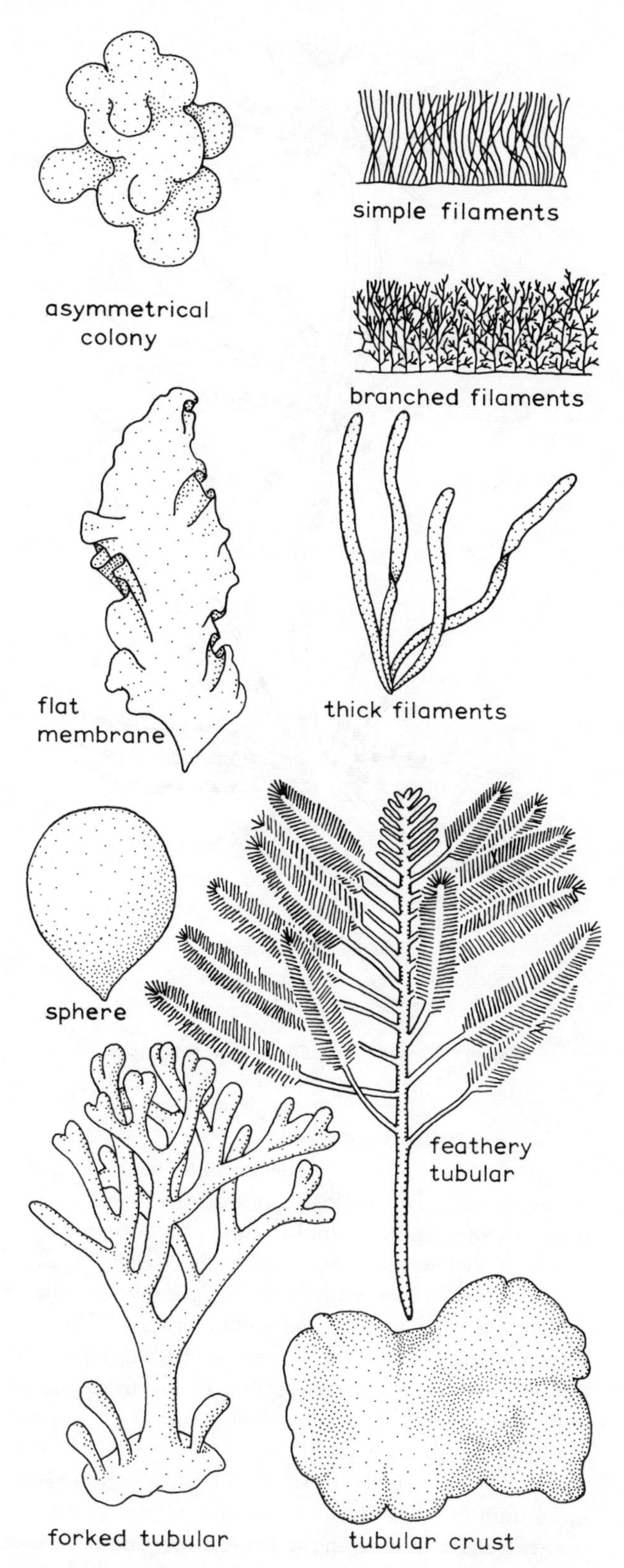

Figure 9.1 Green algae types, about natural size, but the flat membrane, thick filament, and forked tubular types often are much larger.

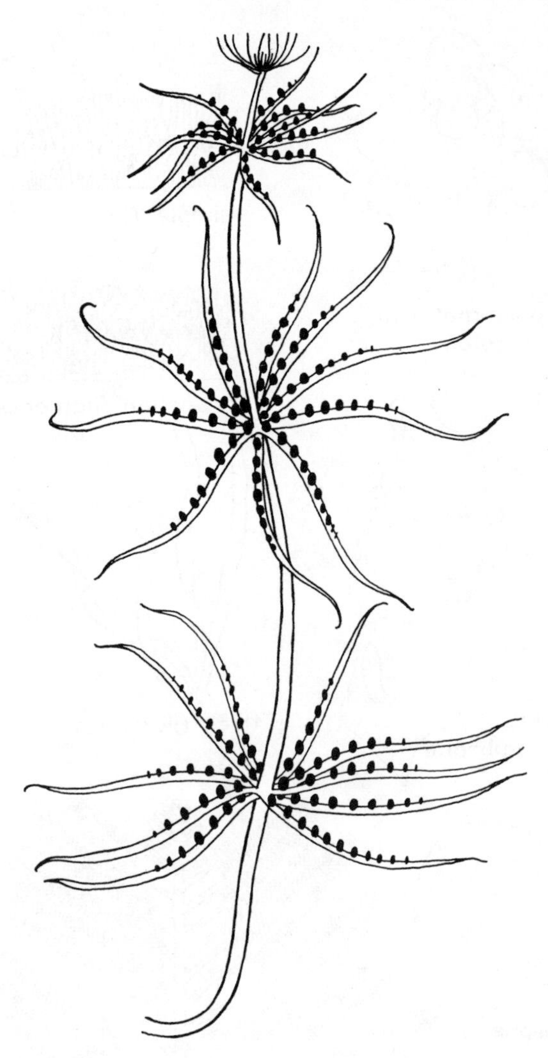

Figure 9.2 A stonewort, *Chara*, about natural size.

Nutrition: photosynthetic.

Reproduction: *asexual* by special buds or *sexual* with sperm produced in male sex organs and eggs in female sex organs (both multicellular sex organs are generally visible and borne upon the "leaves"); sex organs green when young, male organs becoming orange-red when mature and female organs blackish-brown when fertilized; sperm are flagellate, fertilization is internal; female sex organ drops from plant and develops on fresh-water substrate; life cycle haplobiontic, adult haploid.

Occurrence: mostly fresh water and submerged upon muddy or sandy bottoms in shallow, standing water, frequently forming dense growth; best development in clear, hard (usually calcium carbonate) fresh water; plants commonly become encrusted with calcium carbonate, hence become an important source of marl (see p. 73) deposition; only a few species are found in brackish water; about 250 species.

CHRYSOPHYTA (Golden Algae)

Structure: mostly unicellular or loosely colonial, also cellular, usually microscopic, and filamentous; form often tends to be amoeboid (see Sarcodina, p. 134) and solitary, or consists of joined, immobile cells with a firm cell wall; cells tend to be naked or in an enveloping membrane; filamentous species are simple and hair-like or branched and tree-like; no tissue tendencies.

Cells: cells normally distinct, with one to many nuclei; nucleus complete and complex; cytoplasmic pigments normally in yellowish-green to golden-brown, lens- or disc-shaped plastids; pigments also absent; vacuoles often none, or one or more contractile or noncontractile and normally central ones; with or without cell walls; cell walls, when present, often with little cellulose, usually silicified, commonly of two overlapping parts; flagellae none, one, or usually two unequal and dissimilar ones.

Nutrition: mostly photosynthetic, but most types are represented.

Reproduction: *asexual* by mitosis, fragmentation, and spore production; spores include Cyanophyta and Chlorophyta types; some plants develop their spores in sporangia; some plants produce spores of a unique, somewhat complex type; *sexual* processes in forms other than diatoms are mostly in a seemingly haplobiontic, adult haploid, life cycle; however, diatoms are diplobiontic.

Occurrence: include a few, mostly fresh-water Chloromonadophyceae of uncertain relationship; about 400 mostly fresh-water or damp soil, but a few marine Xanthophyceae (yellow-green algae); and perhaps 10,000 aquatic Bacillariophyceae (diatoms).

PHAEOPHYTA (Brown Algae)

Structure: cellular or tissue organization, branching filaments to more complex; light olive brown to dark brown plants; gametophytes and/or sporophytes vary from minute, irregular groupings of a few cells to complex structures with leaf-like (blades), stem-like (stipes) and root-like (holdfasts) parts resembling some Chlorophyta; stipes generally cylindrical, round or flattened, solid or hollow, simple or branched, erect structures; stipe branching and tree-like to feather- or fern-like; blades generally thin, tongue-like, leaf-like, disc-like, or membranous; blades normally arising all along stipe, sometimes only from the top (one such form looks vaguely palm-like); holdfasts typically a mass of cylindrical, often partially at least fused, structures that attach the plant to the substrate; very simple tissues are present (Figure 9.3).

Cells: mostly complete and in contact with one another, but often with some open spaces between parts of adjacent cells; nucleus complex and complete; cytoplasm pigments in plastids; nonreproductive cells usually contain many small vacuoles, rarely a single large one; cell walls generally present and of two layers (outer gelatinous layer commonly of a substance called algin, inner firm layer largely cellulose); flagellae limited to motile reproductive cells, regularly two and dissimilar.

Tissues: one type, parenchyma, characterized by the presence of relatively unspecialized cells; brown algae parenchyma lacks the intercellular spaces and central vacuoles of land plant parenchyma; parenchyma cells are found throughout the plant; in some forms there are crudely organized phloem cells, the basic units for one of the tissues, phloem, that forms the vessels of vascular plants.

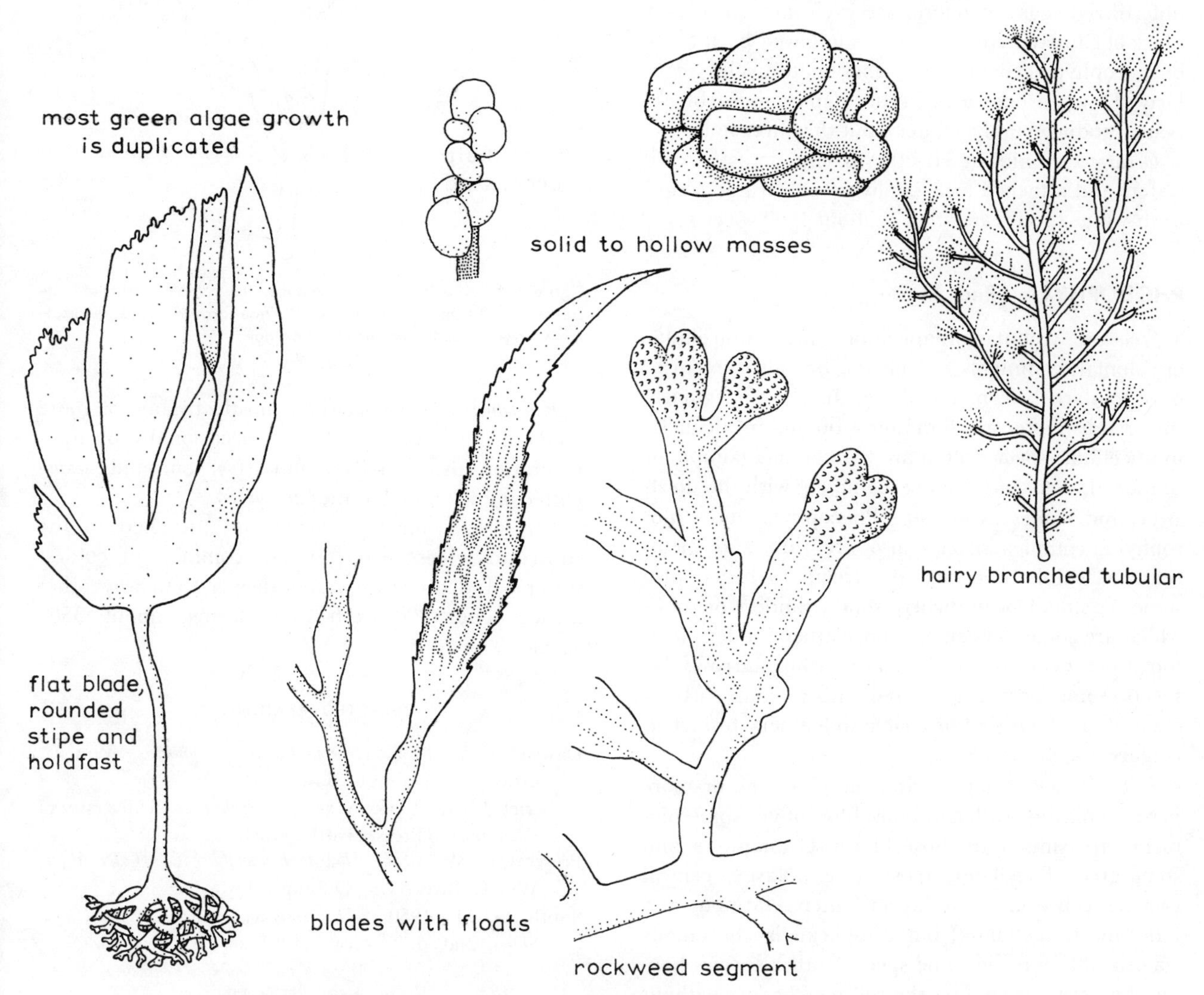

Figure 9.3 Representative brown algae. Brown algae types include species that run the gamut of green algae growth forms. Most brown algae grow very large.

Reproduction: chiefly sexual in a complex diplobiontic life cycle in two of the three classes; the remaining class has little or no indication of a gametophyte, the life cycle being essentially haplobiontic, adult diploid; diplobiontic cycles are characterized by like or unlike gametophytes and sporophytes; some cycles are obligate (the sporophyte must give rise to the gametophyte directly and vice versa), but others are not obligate; nonobligate cycles involve the sporophyte giving rise to neutral spores which develop into another sporophyte, and many sporophyte generations occur before gametophytes are produced; each sporophyte generation usually has a spore-producing sporangium; nonobligate cycles often also feature one gametophyte generation giving rise to another from unfertilized eggs; therefore, the cycle may involve a block of gametophyte generations followed by a block of sporophyte generations; nonobligate cycles regularly show seasonal associations (sporophyte blocks being produced in the winter), but they may not.

Occurrence: almost strictly marine, mostly cold waters and attached to a nonliving substrate; 3 rare fresh-water species are known; about 1500 species.

RHODOPHYTA (Red Algae)

Structure: cellular organization, rarely unicellular or colonial; commonly red plants, but also greenish, olive to dark brown, purple, or blackish (regularly turn reddish after a few minutes' boiling in alcohol); multicellular species often are filamentous (simple or branched) and often more complex with holdfast, stipe, and blades as in some Phaeophyta and Chlorophyta; complex species also are thin and membranous, solid, branched, or irregular sheets; also some are simple or branched, solid cylinders or tubes which are sometimes small and feather- or fern-like, sometimes cylinders or tubes are within narrow, flat sheets; some forms are covered with calcium carbonate and are encrusted or coarse to feathery branched (Figure 9.4).

Cells: nuclei complete and complex, one or more per cell; plastids with a unique chlorophyll; some pigments are similar to those of the Cyanophyta and some green flagellates; most have a large, central vacuole; cell wall of two layers (outer gelatinous and inner mostly cellulose) but cytoplasm is continuous via cell wall pores in some species, other species having the pores covered by the cell membrane; without flagellated cells of any kind.

Nutrition: probably strictly photosynthetic.

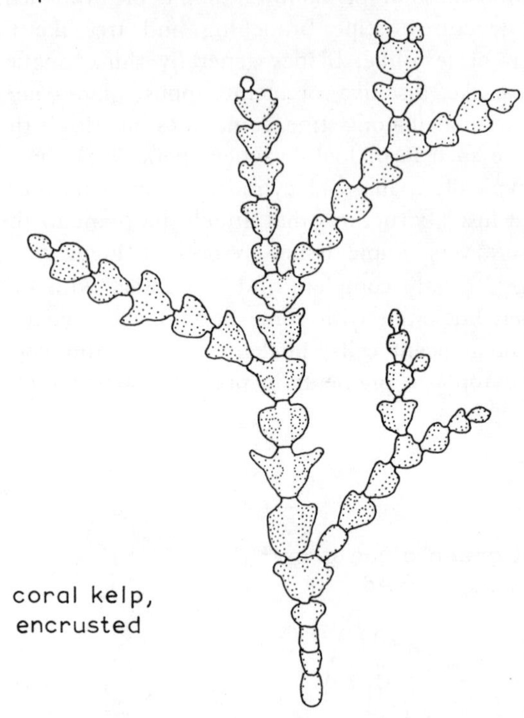

Figure 9.4 A unique red algae type, the calcium carbonate encrusted coral kelp, *Corallina.* Red algae growth forms duplicate those shown for both green and brown algae.

Reproduction: *asexual* rare, mostly by one or more kinds of nonmotile spores, but occasionally by fragmentation (usually kills plant parts); commonly *sexual* with complex diplobiontic life cycles.

Occurrence: mostly marine and attached to the substrate, widespread (but not common in coldest waters) and occur in waters deeper than any other algae; about 200 fresh-water forms; about 3500 species.

SELECTED READINGS

Dawson, E. Y., 1956. *How to Know the Seaweeds.* Wm. C. Brown Co., Dubuque, Iowa.

Guberlet, M. L., 1956. *Seaweeds at Ebb Tide.* University of Washington Press, Seattle, Wash.

Prescott, G. W., 1954. *How to Know the Fresh-Water Algae.* Wm. C. Brown Co., Dubuque, Iowa.

Smith, G. M., 1950. *The Fresh-water Algae of the United States.* 2nd ed. McGraw-Hill Book Co., New York.

———. 1954. *Marine Algae of the Monterey Peninsula.* Stanford University Press, Stanford, Calif.

———. 1955. *Cryptogamic Botany.* Vol. 1: *Algae and Fungi.* McGraw-Hill Book Co., New York.

10 PHYLUM BRYOPHYTA

Lower Land Plants

The bryophytes probably are the most recently evolved phylum. The oldest known moss and liverwort fossils occur in Pennsylvanian rocks, and thus are about 300 million years old. Other phyla generally have remains at least 400 million years old, and most are much older than that.

Bryophyte features imply their relationship to the vascular plants. Although bryophytes lack true roots, stems, and leaves, their body parts and life cycle are similar to those of the vascular plants; also moss and liverwort gametophytes often resemble those of the more primitive vascular plants. For this reason, the Bryophyta and Tracheophyta regularly are united as the Subkingdom Embryophyta and are commonly called "embryo plants" or "land plants." Prior to discussing liverworts and mosses, we will further examine their possible affinity to the Tracheophyta.

SUBKINGDOM EMBRYOPHYTA (Land or Embryo Plants)

Although the fossil record shows little that can be construed as evidence for a common ancestry of the two Embryophyta phyla (Bryophyta and Tracheophyta), these plant groups do have various features in common.

It should be mentioned that the expression "land plants" is deceiving. Many Algae are land plants in the sense that they are plants and are terrestrial, not aquatic. Conversely, many Embryophyta are aquatic, some being completely submerged, and a few are marine. However, the Algae do not comprise the vast majority of the terrestrial flora as embryophytes do. For this reason, and because embryophytes were the most successful plants to invade the land, the use of "land plants" as a descriptive common name for this subkingdom is justified.

Diagnosis: tissue or organ organization; individual cells of generalized to specialized types derived developmentally from generalized cells; generalized cells with nuclear, cytoplasmic, and cell wall components essentially the same as in the Chlorophyta; body organization of tissues with tissue layering (Bryophyta) or organs (Tracheophyta) in the sporophyte; organ systems are not typical of entire land plants but occur in the form of cones or flowers; asexual reproduction without spore formation; life cycle diplobiontic with definite alternation of generations and with sporophyte showing progressively more complex development until the embryo sporophyte is not a parasite upon the gametophyte (some Rhodophyta have parasitic sporophytes, but not a definite embryo stage); mostly terrestrial.

Reproduction: definite sporophyte and gametophyte generations. *Asexual spores* (produced by mitosis) never are formed; the only spores are formed by the sporophyte and are sexual spores (produced by meiosis); *asexual reproduction* mostly in gametophyte

TAXONOMIC SUMMARY

Kingdom Plantae (Eng. *plant*)—plants

Subkingdom Embryophyta (Gr. *embryon*, embryo + *phyton*, plant)—land plants
Phylum Bryophyta (Gr. *bryon*, moss + *phyton*)—bryophytes
Class Anthocerotae (Gr. *anthos*, flower + *keras*, horn)—horned liverworts
Class Hepaticae (Gr. *hepar*, liver)—liverworts
Class Musci (L. *muscus*, moss)—mosses
Order Andreales (after J. Andreae, a German apothecary)—rock or black mosses
Order Sphagnales (Gr. *sphagnos*, kind of moss)—peat mosses
Order Bryales (Gr. *bryon*)—mosses

but also in sporophyte; processes mostly as in algae; *sexual reproduction* limited to gametophyte and similar to many algae.

Life cycle: regularly a definite alternation of generations (diplobiontic life cycle) with sporophyte embryo developing as a gametophyte parasite to gametophyte developing as a sporophyte parasite; sporophyte producing spores which develop into the gametophyte —gametophyte forming male and female sex organs, male organs often forming flagellate, mobile sperm, and female organs forming nonflagellate eggs; fertilization in the female sex organ; sporophyte development from a fertilized egg in the female sex organ.

Nutrition: photosynthetic, except for developing sporophyte and some special types in tracheophyte gametophytes; a few holozoic (saprophytic and parasitic) exceptions occur.

Occurrence: about 20,000 fresh-water, wet soil, moist soil, and rock inhabiting bryophytes; about 200,000 mostly terrestrial but also many fresh-water and a very few marine tracheophytes.

GENERALIZED CELL

Like Chlorophyta; nucleus complete and complex; chlorophyll and cytoplasmic pigments in plastids; flagellae, when present, limited to sperm.

GAMETOPHYTE

Structure: typically simple, mostly a single tissue layer to about three distinct tissues, and much like membranous algae organization and form; in mosses structure approximates that of leaves, stems, and abbreviated roots, but these organs are sporophyte structures; size and structure progressively reduced in more complex plants to ten cells in flowering plants (Class Angiospermae); sex organs multicellular in the simply organized subphyla (shared only with Charophyta) but not in the angiosperms.

Reproduction: *asexual* mainly by budding and fragmentation; merely slight modifications of processes found in algae and protists; *sexual* not unique, involves motile, flagellate sperm and larger, nonflagellate eggs in the bryophytes to more specialized gametes in some tracheophytes.

SPOROPHYTE

Structure: unique; generally complexly organized with at least two tissue types (usually more) and incipient organ formation (Bryophyta capsule, stalk, and foot) to definite organ formation (Tracheophyta leaves, stems, and roots); more complex than any Algae; typically differentiated into aerial parts (capsule and stalk, or leaves and stems) and subterranean parts (roots), or a part analogous to roots (foot) is embedded in the gametophyte; aerial parts often bearing a complex spore-forming organ, the sporangium (bryophytes and simpler tracheophytes). *Note:* Bryophyte "leaves," "stems," and "roots" when present, as in mosses, are gametophyte structures that are not organized as complexly as the true leaves, stems, and roots (sporophyte structures) of tracheophytes; hence calling these bryophyte structures "leaves," "stems," or "roots" really is incorrect.

Tissues: unique aspects normally include an outer epidermis with scattered unique openings (stomata, for gaseous exchange between the atmosphere and internal tissues), each stoma bounded by two specialized cells (guard cells) that open and close the stoma; specialized conducting tissues include the columella (bryophytes) and stele (tracheophytes) and usually are present; columella has thick-walled, elongate cells and stele has at least xylem and phloem; xylem is largely water-conducting and phloem is food-conducting; stele also is called a vein or central cylinder; phloem without xylem is found in the brown algae (Phaeophyta).

BRYOPHYTA (Mosses, Horned Liverworts, and Liverworts)

Structure: generally tissue organization in two generations, sporophyte and gametophyte; gametophyte generation of one or two phases; single phase is the simple to branched or leafy membranous gametophyte present in horned liverworts (Anthocerotae) and most liverworts (Hepaticae); two phases include a filamentous to membranous stage (protonema) which buds one or more branched leafy stages (gametophores) found in a few liverworts (Hepaticae) and in the mosses (Bryales); gametophytes photosynthetic, normally simply organized of one or more tissue layers into a variously organized flat membranous sheet or into a branched stem-like structure bearing "leaves"; gametophyte "roots" are simple, short, hair-like structures; the gametophyte usually is the larger and more conspicuous generation; sporophyte may be partly photosynthetic, but is wholly or partly dependent upon the gametophyte for its nutrition, often complexly organized with about four differentiated tissue layers into a specialized spore-forming sporangium (capsule) that may or may not be supported by a stalk that is joined to the gametophyte by a foot, usually no more than a few inches long.

Tissues: many types present, but no vascular (xylem and phloem) tissues organized into veins as in the vascular plants.

Nutrition: typically photosynthetic, but sporophyte is essentially a parasite upon the gametophyte.

Reproduction: asexual generally involves gametophyte fragmentation (mostly by death of parts connecting surviving parts), gametophyte production of specialized areas along its margin, and gametophyte formation of special structures called gemmae; no spore formation; *sexual* involves sperms and eggs and the production of spores; gametes usually form in unlike male and female multicellular sex organs.

Life cycle: diplobiontic, with alternation of generations well developed (Figure 10.1); mature sporophyte sporangium (capsule) sheds spores, the spores germinating into a gametophyte generation (if two phases, protonema germinates into a gametophore); mature gametophytes develop male and female sex organs either on the same or different plants; sperms are shed and require water to reach the female sex organ; fertilization produces a zygote which by mitosis forms first an embryo and then an adult sporophyte; the inner layer of the sporophyte capsule, by meiosis, forms spores; generally moisture absorption is necessary to create the pressure needed for the capsule to open and shed its spores; spores typically must be shed into water to be transported and to germinate into a gametophyte (or a protonema which buds off gametophores).

Occurrence: normally found in moist areas, but range from fresh-water situations to dry rocks; about 20,000 species.

The bryophytes are sometimes treated as two phyla, the Bryophyta, or mosses, and the Hepatophyta, or horned liverworts and liverworts. No matter which interpretation is preferred, it is generally agreed that these plants originated from algae and most likely from the Chlorophyta. Therefore, if two phyla are recognized, each phylum is assumed to have evolved from algae independently.

The origin from the Chlorophyta is assumed for various reasons, but especially because bryophytes and green algae share the same photosynthetic and other pigments. The similarities can be appreciated by comparing the Bryophyta and Chlorophyta synopses. However, it should be noted that the Charophyta also bear the same similarities plus sex organs, structures found in the Bryophyta but not in the Chlorophyta. In spite of this, the Chlorophyta still tend to be favored as ancestors because of their generalized nature, especially that of the primitive forms, and the fact that the Charophyta, both living and fossil, appear to be specialized. Experience would imply that such specialized forms are not likely to be ancestral to other groups of organisms. Therefore, the ancient Chlorophyta remain as the best possible ancestors of the Bryophyta, but this does not mean that either the Charophyta or even other algae can be exempt from ancestral contention.

At one time the bryophytes, especially the horned liverworts, were believed ancestors of the Tracheophyta, or vascular plants. Although this theory is no longer favored by most botanists (present information tends to make the possibility of such a relationship remote), one can find a definite similarity in the gametophytes of these groups.

If there is any close relationship between the phyla of land plants, this evolution is unlikely to be from Bryophyta to Tracheophyta. Rather, the fossil record almost demands the opposite ancestry; fossils imply that the tracheophytes are older than the bryophytes. Moreover, there is some slight chance that tracheophytes were ancestral to bryophytes. This chance is

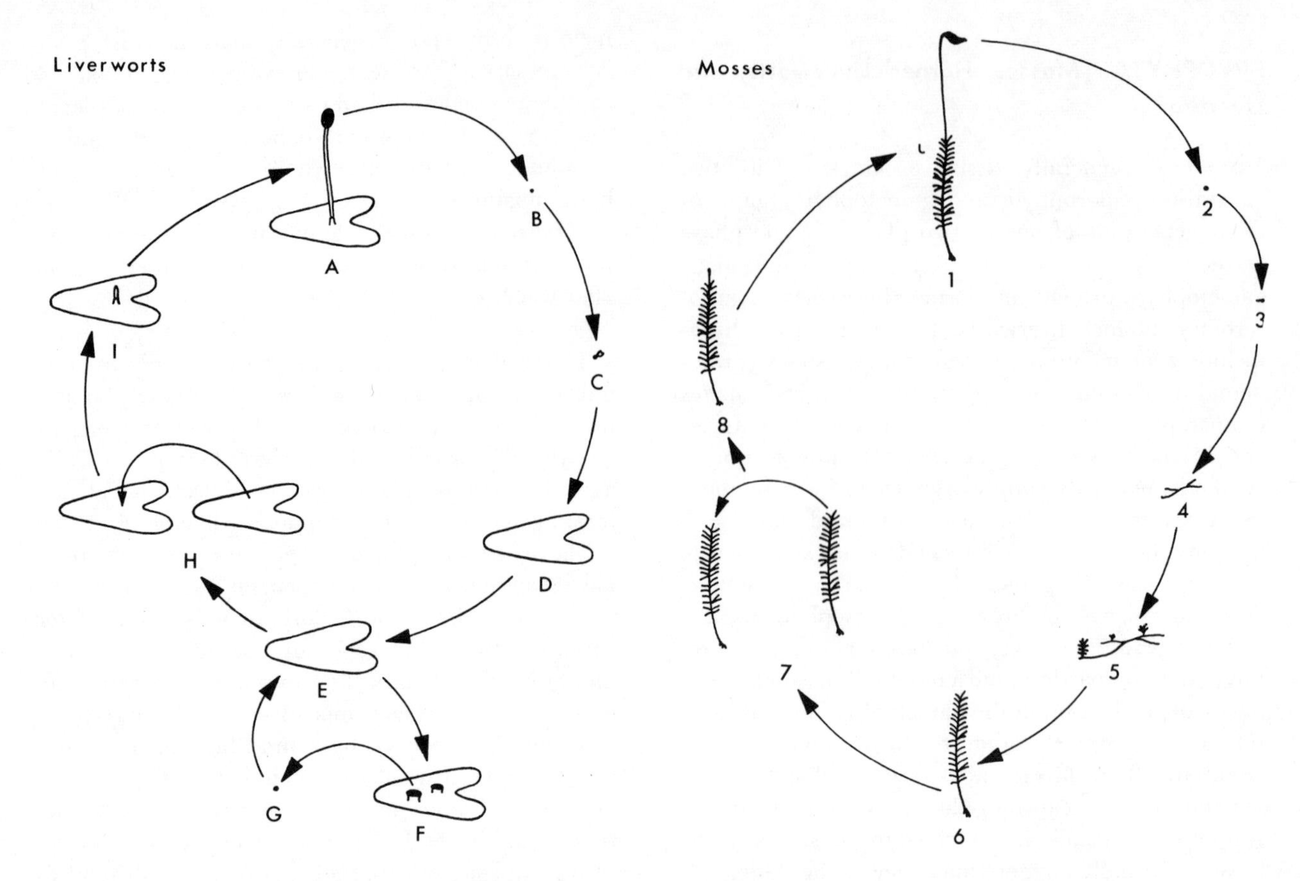

Figure 10.1 Bryophyte life cycles. *Liverworts:* A, mature sporophyte on gametophyte; B, spore shed from sporophyte's sporangium; C, spore germinating into a gametophyte; D, mature gametophyte; E, gametophyte ready to form either sex organs or cupules; F, gametophyte with cupules prepared to shed gemmae; G, gemma prepared to germinate into a gametophyte; H, mature male and female gametophytes containing mature sex cells in their sex organs, the path of sperm to the female sex organ (to fertilize an egg) is indicated; I, after fertilization, the fertilized egg (zygote) develops into an embryo sporophyte which germinates from and remains partly within the female sex organ.
Mosses: 1, mature sporophyte on gametophyte (gametophore); 2, spore shed from the sporophyte's sporangium; 3, sporophyte germinating into a protonema; 4, protonema; 5, protonema with buds and immature gametophore; 6, mature gametophore; 7, mature male and female gametophores containing mature sex cells in their sex organs, the path of sperm to the female sex organ is indicated; 8, after fertilization, the zygote develops into an embryo sporophyte.

not denied by the fossil record, which implies land plants became somewhat complex due to occupying land habitats. Then, some of these land inhabitants might have invaded coastal marshes. After some time, these marsh invaders could have evolved into simplified plants called psilopsids, three of which live today. Therefore, if the trend toward simplification continued, the product of evolution could have been the bryophytes.

The mosses are the most frequently encountered bryophytes because mosses range from moist to dry habitats. Typically, certain mosses are found either as a developmental stage in the formation of a stable plant community, specifically a stage that is usually intermediate between lichens and herbs, or as a layer in a stable community. Liverworts and horned liverworts usually are not common because they tend to be restricted to aquatic, semiaquatic, or moist areas; however, in certain localities they are more common than mosses.

CLASS ANTHOCEROTAE (Horned Liverworts)

Diagnosis: gametophyte a thin, somewhat membranous sheet, flattened from top to bottom and having embedded male and female reproductive

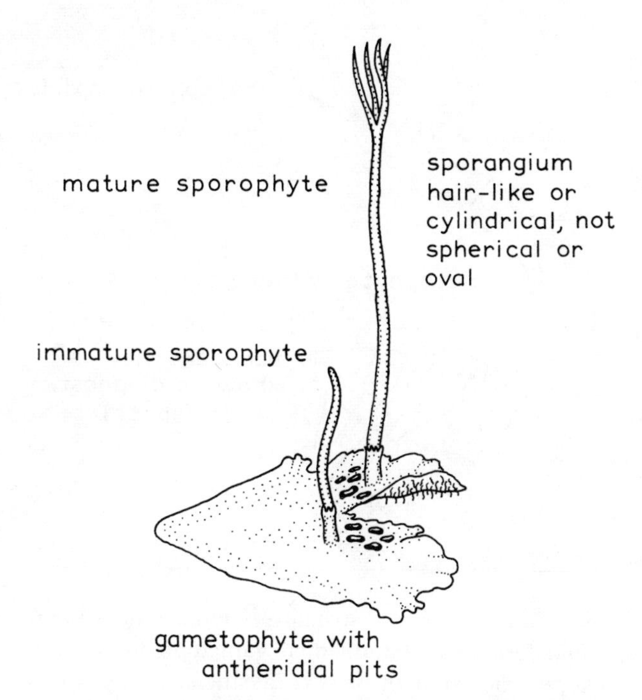

Figure 10.2 *Anthoceros, a hornwort or horned liverwort.*

organs; sporophyte with an area of continuous cell division, hence growth, near its base (Figure 10.2). Anthocerotae is distinct from the Class Hepaticae in that the sporophyte is relatively large, persistent, and contains cells with chlorophyll, columella tissue, stomata, and a continuous growth region; sporophyte capsule (sporangium) is wire-like and not distinct from the foot.

Occurrence: about fifty living species in a single Order Anthocerotales; all tend to be limited to moist soil.

GAMETOPHYTE

Structure: membranous; generally a 1 × 1 inch sheet, mostly lobed or divided (often repeatedly equal forking to form extensive masses), with many unicellular unbranched "roots" on the under surface; in extensive masses each extreme of a branch or lobe continues to grow; mature gametophytes are near the end opposite the growing end; mature gametophytes generally are dying and sloughing away at a rate approximating that of new growth; dying and sloughing results in a separation of individuals whenever points of forking are destroyed (a method of asexual reproduction); most species have male and female sex organs embedded within the same gametophyte; in other species sex organs are embedded in separate and slightly different looking male or female gametophytes. Male sex organs occur singly or grouped on short stalks in chambers within the thallus. Female sex organs occur singly and are not sharply differentiated from the surrounding vegetative tissue of the thallus.

Reproduction: asexual reproduction mostly by the process of dying and sloughing, but also by formation of marginal thickenings that develop protective coverings (product regenerates a new gametophyte); in *sexual reproduction* sperm form in male sex organs and swim through water to the egg in the female sex organ, fertilization produces a zygote which develops into an embryo sporophyte.

SPOROPHYTE

Structure: a basal foot continuous with a 1- or 2-inch wire-like capsule (a sporangium); the foot and the base of capsule are in a thin upward extension of the gametophyte.

In the capsule spores mature from top to bottom; then the capsule splits along one to four "lines," and finally the split capsule parts either separate from the top downward or separate and bow out from a point just below the united tip.

The foot is a bulb-like structure that anchors the sporophyte to the gametophyte by fitting into a "socket" of the gametophyte. The socket provides a site for the sporophyte to absorb water and nutrients from the gametophyte.

The horned liverworts, or hornworts, include five or six genera of world-wide plants. However, wherever they occur they usually are localized in moist, temperate situations. Normally, they inhabit disturbed, acidic soil but they may be found upon rocks or trees. Like liverworts and mosses, they are affective in holding moisture and retarding soil erosion.

Hornworts are unique bryophytes owing to the chlorophyll in their sporophyte. Moreover, their gametophyte often is invaded by blue-green algae, so rather than being green they assume a dark green hue. In addition, they feel greasy. Although some of the blue-green algae are able to fix nitrogen, thus providing nutrients to their horned liverwort hosts, some at least appear to inhibit hornwort growth.

CLASS HEPATICAE (Liverworts)

Diagnosis: gametophyte sometimes membranous as in horned liverworts, but mostly leafy; reproductive organs range from partially embedded to stalked;

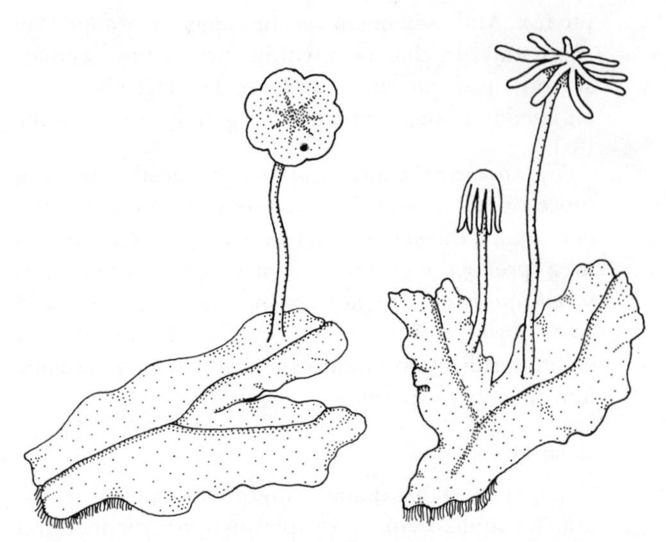

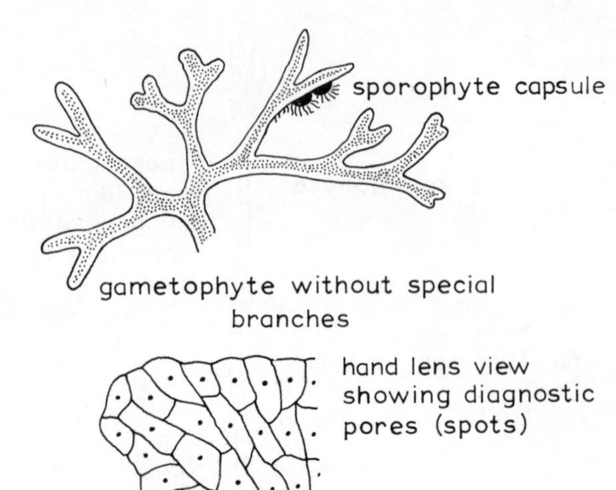

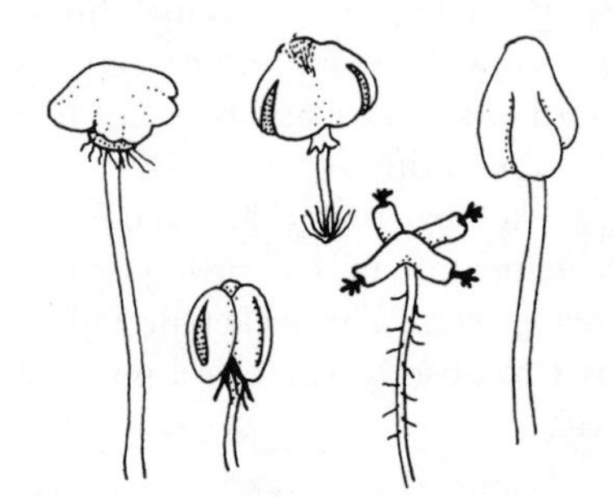

Figure 10.3 Pore liverwort types, slightly enlarged. Antheridial pits are the sites of male sex organs.

leafy structures are nearly always flattened, are almost always in two or three rows, without a distinct midvein; spore germination either not forming a moss type gametophyte (protonema) or, at best, only a rudimentary one; sporophyte a single, mostly stalked capsule (a sporangium) without a region of constant growth; sporangium (capsule) without moss structures such as a well-formed lid or a ring of "teeth" surrounding the opening; capsule opening by valves (Figures 10.3 and 10.4).

Occurrence: about 5000 species; distribution essentially world-wide, from completely aquatic situations to moist soil.

THALLOSE GAMETOPHYTE

Structure: often sheet-like, lobed or divided, but parts also narrowly linear; either with equal-forked branching and gross structure compact or without equal forking and individual gametophytes tongue-like; surface smooth or with a single midrib which usually is forking and conforms to the equal-forking growth pattern; vegetative reproduction includes the dying and sloughing process; most species have the male and female organs upon different gametophytes; reproductive organs either upon the gametophyte surface or at the end of stalks. Male sex organs variously organized; in urn-shaped enclosing structures and mostly concentrated in the center of the gametophyte; in sac-like structures along the midrib; in fringed, scale-like structures that join into fringed structures along the midrib; also, in a specialized portion of the gametophyte, an upright structure composed of a stalk that bears a terminal disc-like body which contains the male organs. The female sex organs are variously organized and generally similar to male sex organs.

Reproduction: asexual, as in Anthocerotae, some also by gemmae formation; gemmae formed inside a part of the gametophyte that is modified into a cup-like structure (gemma cup or cupule); inside of cup generally producing stalked, lens-like gemmae which are transported by water to a site for growth of a new gametophyte; *sexual reproduction* typically as in Anthocerotae.

LEAFY GAMETOPHYTE

Structure: composed of a simple or branched stem-like structure with leaf-like parts but without vascular tissue (xylem and phloem); leaves commonly in two lateral rows plus one row of underleaves; lateral

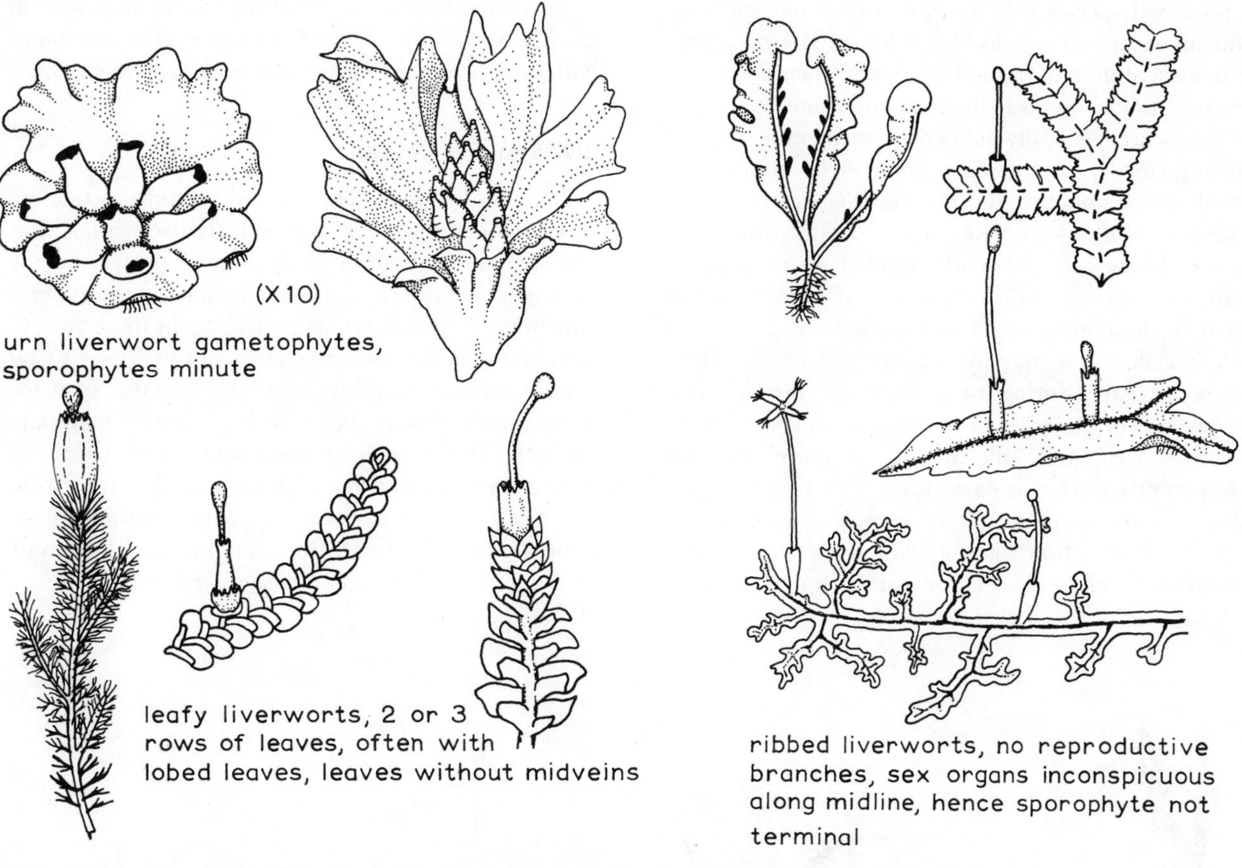

Figure 10.4 Liverwort types exclusive of pore liverworts, about natural size except for the two urn liverworts.

leaves (see Figures 11.3 and 11.4) regularly alternate and sessile (rarely opposite), flattened, entirely without midribs (a very few with elongate cells giving a semblance of a midrib), and variously shaped; lateral leaves entire, notched, two-cleft, two-lobed, or more complexly cleft, lobed, or divided; when leaves are largely separated into two parts, one part often is smaller and folded under the larger part, or underfolded part is larger and plant appears to have four leaf rows; underleaves may be absent or may be as large as lateral leaves; a few aquatic species have leaves or leaf parts bladder-like; leaves with or without gemmae cups; if present, gemmae cups usually are near tips of young leaves; gametophytes with male and female organs on one or separate plants. Male sex organs nearly always in the axil (angle formed by leaf upon stem) of lateral leaves, some on the underleaves; sex-organ-bearing leaves generally organized into a cone-like structure. Female sex organs are normally at the end of the stem in the region of growth, also, on growth region of a normal branch or on a special branch; sex-organ-bearing leaves form a bud-like structure resembling that of early developing leaves.

Reproduction: *asexual*, drought may kill all plant parts except the growth regions at the ends of stems; gemmae are produced in some forms; *sexual*, generally as in Anthocerotae.

SPOROPHYTE

Structure: consisting of a capsule with or without a stalk and foot. In the capsule spores normally mature at the same time. Then the capsule opens along two or more valves, usually four. The stalk and foot grow rapidly but do not develop until after the spores mature. The end of stalk and foot growth is followed by immediate capsule opening (typically into petal-like segments) and shedding of spores.

Most liverworts inhabit moist, generally disturbed areas. They almost encompass our globe, ranging from frigid to tropical areas. In the Arctic, there are about 300 species that appear to be ecologically influential, especially in localized floras. However, they are most abundant in the tropics and their secondary distribution center is in the temperate zone.

Moisture generally influences their range. One genus, *Riella*, is the only completely submerged, fresh-water aquatic. Forms like *Riccia* are floating aquatics. Others are found in marshes, swamps, and bogs. Many occur on moist, shaded, steep slopes of cliffs or ravines. Still others are in forests on tree trunks, decaying logs, or the ground. Especially in California, a few may live in semiarid areas. Here, they are active during the moist season but all structures, except the growing region and asexually reproductive structures, die during summer drought. Apparently none are parasites. The Genus *Cryptothallus* is the only bryophyte known to lack chlorophyll. These liverworts apparently gain nutrients from an intimate association with a fungus (mycorrhiza).

Further information on liverworts is included in the discussion of mosses. Liverworts often are found with mosses and display similar ecological reactions.

CLASS MUSCI (Mosses)

Diagnosis: spores develop into protonema (a simpler protonema occurs in some leafy liverworts), and protonema usually forms one or more leafy gametophores (generally the conspicuous part of the plant); gametophore leaves typically develop in three (rarely two) rows, but growth regularly causes leaves to be spirally arranged; protonema and usually gametophores anchor to a substrate and absorb materials from the substrate by multicellular hairs (none in Sphagnales); protonema and gametophore constitute two phases of the gametophyte generation; gametophores resemble lycopsids (see Figures 11.8 and 11.10), but lack vascular tissues and roots (Figure 10.5).

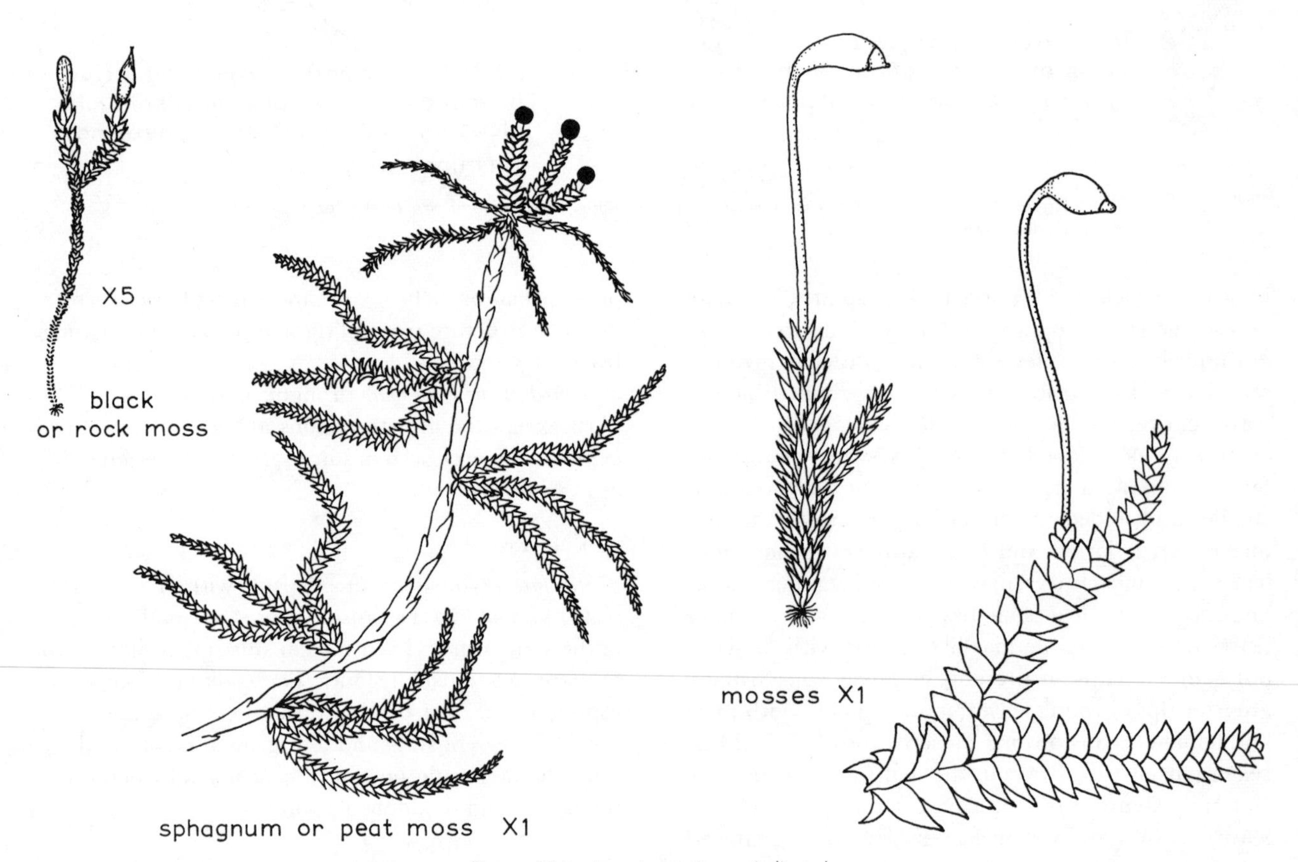

Figure 10.5 Moss types; sizes as indicated.

Occurrence: about 14,000 species of world-wide distribution; habitats range from completely aquatic and submerged to very arid; typically are inhabitants of drier areas, especially as an unstable plant community upon rocks and as a group of plants upon tree trunks.

PROTONEMA

Resemble Chlorophyta in their organization; each forms one to many buds, each bud germinating into a gametophore.

GAMETOPHORE

Structure: normally attached to substrate; main branches either erect or prostrate and erect; prostrate branches form erect shoots which remain when prostrate branches die; branches with leaves; many species with leaves forming gemmae and/or with protonema or root-like hairs forming usually dormant gemmae (gemmae developing into gametophore only after detached); sex organs occur among branch tips or on short stalks from main stem; sex organs either in a single cluster, or in separate clusters on the same branch, on separate branches, or on separate plants.

Leaves: variable; assuming most of the shapes of the true leaves of higher plants (see Figure 11.4); midribs when present are narrow and single, double, forked, or very broad; midribs vary from not reaching the apex to extending beyond as a hair-like structure; leaves spirally arranged on branches, some leaves appearing to lie in two rows (as in leafy liverworts) but are spirally inserted upon the branches.

Reproduction: reproductive organs develop from the upper leaf cells; a male organ develops along with one or more other cells that become larger, thicker-walled, and more transparent to form a lid (operculum); male organ usually requires moisture accumulation for pressure to open the operculum and release sperm; female organ enlarges with sporophyte growth, becoming a calyptra which is sporophyte-enveloping, but the sporophyte growth finally tears off the upper calyptra (calyptra usually covers sporophyte capsule until capsule is nearly mature); the torn calyptra may continue to develop and form a prominent cap; *asexual reproduction* by leaf gemmae, protonema and "root" gemmae, and by upright branches growing when the prostrate branches die; *sexual reproduction* follows same general pattern found in all bryophytes.

SPOROPHYTE

Structure: a capsule, commonly supported by a slender, short to long stalk, and a foot; sporophyte does not persist long in the Sphagnales; capsule normally covered for some time by a hood-like calyptra; the capsule typically is an urn (main body) with an apical opening that is often surrounded by a fringe of fine "teeth" which project inward when wet and outward when dry and the spores discharge; most urns are capped by a circular lid (operculum), but the urn and operculum are separated by a layer of cells; drying and shriveling (perhaps moisture pressure also) of the layer of cells and the lower operculum sheds the operculum—but some species lack an operculum; the calyptra and/or operculum may be present or absent when the spores are shed; spores are shed when the mature capsule (1) opens by splitting lengthwise, crosswise, or irregularly (Bryales); (2) opens explosively often shooting operculum and spores into the air (Sphagnales); or (3) opens mostly along four regular lines (Andreales).

There are more than twice as many mosses as all other bryophytes. Mosses are widely distributed upon moist surfaces from pole to pole. They range from inconspicuous, thread-like masses (protonema) to erect, fern-like plants almost 2 feet tall. Some large specimens hang from trees or rocks, but the largest (about 7 feet long) are the aquatic peat mosses. Although the larger forms are potentially confusing (they resemble spike or club mosses and ferns), mosses have only root-like hairs, never roots. The vast majority of species occur as tufts or extensive cushions or mats on rocks, soil, or trees.

Being bryophytes, mosses are dependent upon moisture for sexual reproduction. However, they persist in frigid and desert habitats. They have remarkable abilities to survive freezing and desiccation. Along with liverworts, they comprise an ecologically influential part of localized Arctic floras. Although they are like other bryophytes in not being marine, some mosses persist in brackish waters. Therefore, only flowering plants display a greater range of environments. However, mosses regularly grow in habitats too severe for flowering plants.

Temperate areas often have abundant mosses and liverworts. In the Pacific Northwest and other areas of high rainfall, they become so dense on rocks, soil, and trees as to be called "moss forests." Above timberline they may grow with other plants or be the only plants. In frigid areas, only lichens appear to equal (perhaps sometimes surpass) their hardiness. Therefore, it might not be surprising that alkalinity or acidity of a substrate often appears most influential in limiting their distribution. In fact, particular mosses and liverworts normally indicate the acid, alkali, or mineral nature of their substrate.

Perhaps the greatest significance of mosses and, less frequently, liverworts is the regularity of their occurrence as a developmental stage in the formation of stable plant communities. In most areas, a moss community appears between a lichen and an herb community. The mosses normally are on fine but thin rock particles before any soil has formed.

ORDER ANDREALES (Rock, or Black, Mosses)

Gametophyte: of two phases, protonema and gametophore; each protonema broadly membranous, each normally forming several gametophores; gametophore leaves blackish or very dark, but sometimes fading to reddish brown or brown; leaves small, frequently crowded, smooth to warty, with or without midribs; leaves typically more rigid (actually stiff) and resistant to heavy rains (and perhaps desiccation) than those of other bryophytes; branches equal-forking or clumped.

Sporophyte: dark and small; of capsule and false foot, without a distinct stalk; mature capsule opening by four longitudinal lines.

Occurrence: minute plants (up to 0.4 in. tall); erect, forming dense tufted or cushion-like clumps; especially on granitic or slaty rocks (not on calcareous rocks) of high alpine and subalpine mountain communities and lower frigid areas; about 100 species.

ORDER SPHAGNALES (Peat Mosses)

Gametophyte: of two phases, protonema and gametophore; protonema broadly thallose, each forming a single gametophore; gametophore leaves whitish or light green but sometimes reddish tinged or yellowish to reddish brown, size variable, frequently crowded, without midribs, water-storing cells present, and every fourth leaf usually below a group of branches; some branches drooping, others erect; mature gametophore without attachment hairs of any kind; reproductive organs resemble those of some leafy liverworts.

Sporophyte: dark and small; of capsule and false foot, without a distinct stalk; mature capsule opening by a lid.

Occurrence: plants up to 7 feet long, generally intertangled with one another, often packed into dense masses that will support humans; common in moist to aquatic situations that lack calcium, in cool temperate to arctic climates, especially common in glacially formed lakes; about 300 species.

ORDER BRYALES (Mosses)

Gametophyte: of two phases, protonema and gametophore; protonema mostly filamentous, rarely broadly membranous; gametophore leaves yellow-green, green, dark green, or blackish, size variable, crowded to open, with or without a narrow or broad midrib; branching variable but not arranged in close groups.

Sporophyte: often greenish and larger than other Musci; of capsule, foot, and stalk; mature capsule usually opening by a lid, or opening irregularly.

Occurrence: mostly a few inches tall, minute to about 24 inches; erect, prostrate, or ascending; widely distributed from dry to aquatic situations, mostly in moderately moist situations; about 14,000 species.

SELECTED READINGS

Bodenberg, E. T., 1954. *Mosses: A New Approach to the Identification of Common Species.* Burgess Publ. Co., Minneapolis, Minn.

Campbell, D. H., 1918. *Structure and Development of Mosses and Ferns.* The Macmillan Co., New York.

Conard, H. S., 1944. *How to Know the Mosses.* Wm. C. Brown Co., Dubuque, Iowa.

Frye, T. C., and L. Clark, 1937–1947. *Hepaticae of North America.* University of Washington Press, Seattle, Wash.

Grout, A. J., ed., 1928–1934. *Moss Flora of North America.* Publ. by the editor.

Grout, A. J., 1947. *Mosses with a Hand Lens.* 4th ed. Publ. by the author.

Palmer, E. L., 1949. *Fieldbook of Natural History.* McGraw-Hill Book Co., New York.

11 PHYLUM TRACHEOPHYTA

Higher Land Plants

To most people the word "plant" means *vascular plant*. Of the less than 250,000 known plant species about 200,000 are tracheophytes. Almost always, tracheophytes are man's source of plant food, are the distinctive organisms that give the appearance of a community, and are the plants in gardens. Moreover, they are the primary source of food for almost all strictly terrestrial animals.

We might compare the position of tracheophytes in the plant kingdom to that of arthropods in the animal kingdom. In sheer numbers and bulk of species, perhaps even of individuals, vascular plants are not equaled by any other group of plants.

Tracheophyte evolution probably started from the green algae. The hypothesis accepted here is as follows: Upon origin of archaic tracheophytes from green algae, early evolution produced three persistent, separate, somewhat equivalent major taxa, the subphyla Lycopsida, Sphenopsida, and Pteropsida. However, complication was an early feature in the evolution of all three subphyla. Although each subphylum first gained some complexity in structure and function, each then evolved in two directions. One direction was toward a coastal marsh existence and involved simplification of previously gained complexity; the other was toward an inland or truly continental existence and involved further complexity of previous features. The coastal marsh inhabitants are first found in Silurian deposits, but continue in good numbers up through the Devonian. This Silurian through Devonian evolution featured greater simplification, presumably closer adaptation to the coastal marsh habitats. After the Devonian most became extinct; only three species live today.

The coastal plants are called psilopsids and often are recognized as a major taxon (here Subphylum Psilopsida). However, if psilopsids are what recent evidence indicates, that is, members of three subphyla, they are not a natural group. For example, the living members most likely are ferns. In spite of all this, living psilopsids are treated here as a subphylum—their fern alliance probably would be shown best if they were considered a subclass under the Class Filicineae (other living ferns would form a second subclass). The justification for considering them a subphylum of vascular plants and not a subclass of ferns is to emphasize a distinct trend in early land plant evolution, an unusual trend for simplification, and to follow the usual taxonomic assignment of psilopsids. Apparently, living psilopsids have never been formally assigned to the ferns.

How, then, are we to explain the present subphyla? The living Lycopsida and Sphenopsida each could be descendants of a continental line, the coastal marsh line of both subphyla now being extinct. Pteropsida is more difficult to explain. Its coastal marsh line now apparently has two representatives, one of Devonian simplicity in the psilopsids and the other

TAXONOMIC SUMMARY

Kingdom Plantae (Eng. *plant*)—plants
Subkingdom Embryophyta (Gr. *embryon*, embryo + *phyton*, plant)—land plants
Phylum Tracheophyta (Gr. *tracheia*, windpipe + *phyton*)—vascular plants
Pteridophytes (Gr. *pteris*, fern + *phyton*)—fern plants
Subphylum Psilopsida (Gr. *psilo*, slender + *opsis*, appearance)—psilopsids
Class Psilotae (Gr. *psilo*)—whisk ferns and allies
Subphylum Lycopsida (Gr. *lykos*, wolf + *opsis*)—lycopsids
Class Lycopodae (Gr. *lykos* + *pod*, foot)—lycopsids
Order Isoetales (Gr. *isos*, equal + *etes*, association)—quillworts
Order Selaginellales (L. *selago*, kind of shrubby plant)—spike mosses or small club mosses
Order Lycopodiales (Gr. *lykos* + *pod*)—club mosses
Subphylum Sphenopsida (Gr. *sphen*, wedge + *opsis*)—sphenopsids
Class Equisetae (L. *equus*, horse + *setae*, bristles)—horsetails and scouring rushes
Order Equisetales (L. *equus* + *setae*)—horsetails and scouring rushes
Subphylum Pteropsida (Gr. *pteris* + *opsis*)—pteropsids
Class Filicinae (L. *filic*, fern)—ferns
Order Ophioglossales (Gr. *ophis*, snake + *glossa*, tongue)—adder's tongue and grape ferns
Order Marattiales (after J. Maratti, Tuscan botanist)—tropical ferns
Order Filicales (L. *filic*)—true ferns
Order Marsileales (after L. F. Marsigli, Italian botanist)—water ferns
Order Salviniales (after A. Salvini, Italian scholar)—floating and mosquito ferns
Spermatophytes (Gr. *sperma*, seed + *phyton*)—seed plants
Gymnosperms (Gr. *gymnos*, naked + *sperma*)—gymnosperms
Class Cycadae (Gr. *kykas*, coco palm)—cycads and fossil allies
Order Cycadales (Gr. *kykas*)—cycads
Class Ginkgoae (Chinese *yin*, silver + *hsing*, apricot)—ginkgos
Order Ginkgoales (Chinese *yin* + *hsing*)—maidenhair tree or ginkgo
Class Coniferae (L. *conus*, cone + *fero*, to bear)—conifers and allies
Order Coniferales (L. *conus* + *fero*)—conifers
Order Taxales (L. *taxus*, yew tree)—yews
Order Gnetales (Malay *gnenom*, name for plant)—*Ephedra* and allies
Angiosperms (Gr. *angos*, vessel + *sperma*)—flowering plants
Class Angiospermae (Gr. *angos* + *sperma*)—flowering plants
Subclass Dicotyledoneae (Gr. *di-*, two + *kotyledon*, cup-shaped cavity)—dicots
Subclass Monocotyledoneae (Gr. *mono*, one + *kotyledon*)—monocots

of a trend to present complexity in the ferns, Class Filicineae. The remaining pteropsids, then, are assumed to be living descendants of the interior line. Support is given these premises by a very recent fossil, *Archaeopteris*, a fern-like tree having a large trunk. This Devonian "missing link" has fern-like leaves and reproductive structures on a trunk much like that of early spermatophytes. It is assumed that *Archaeopteris* represented the interior line of ancestral spermatophytes, but at a time predating the evolution of true seeds.

Among the spermatophytes the first main radiation probably provided the classes Cycadae, Coniferae, and Ginkgoae; on the other hand, the Coniferae and Ginkgoae may have evolved from definite Cycadae. Although Angiospermae origin is not clear, their ancestors probably evolved from the Coniferae.

TRACHEOPHYTA (Vascular Plants)

Diagnosis: comprise the vast majority of plants in the form of trees, shrubs, and herbs; contain gametophyte and sporophyte generations; gametophyte generally smaller than the sporophyte and functionally independent in lower taxa but a sporophyte parasite in the higher taxa; gametophyte organization varies from a cylindrical body with some tissue organization, to a membranous structure reminiscent of certain liverworts and horned liverworts, to a single cell; sporophyte functionally independent at maturity, containing vascular tissues (central cylinder, veins, or stele) and many other tissues grouped into organs; organs especially in the form of leaves, stems, and roots (roots absent in Psilopsida); over-all structure associated with whether plants produce a single kind of spore or two kinds of spores (apparently the ancestral condition); two-spore species produce male spores (smaller) which form a strictly male gametophyte and female spores (larger) which form a strictly female gametophyte; living "primitive" species generally with one spore (includes Psilopsida; Lycopsida, except for certain fossil orders, the Isoetales and the Selaginellales; Sphenopsida, except for a few fossil forms; Filicineae, except for certain fossils and the Marsileales and, probably, the Salviniales).

The life cycle of Tracheophyta involves a haploid spore (one set of chromosomes) which develops into a haploid gametophyte. The gametophyte may or may not constitute a distinct plant that is independent of the sporophyte. Gametophytes produce sperm and eggs, and a sperm fertilizes an egg to form a diploid zygote (two sets of chromosomes). The zygote divides mitotically, producing a diploid embryo sporophyte which eventually develops into the mature sporophyte. The mature sporophyte completes the life cycle when it produces haploid spores. Therefore, the life cycle is diplobiontic with two adult generations, gametophyte and sporophyte (Figure 11.1).

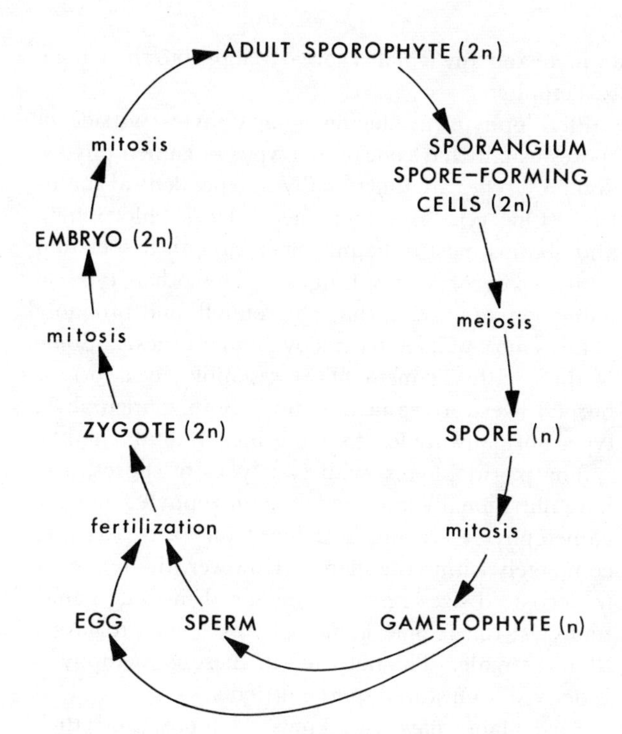

Figure 11.1 Life cycle of vascular plants, simplified to the point of being suitable for bryophytes also.

GAMETOPHYTE

In all subphyla except the three species constituting the living psilopsids, there is a tendency toward reduction in size, complexity, and duration of the gametophyte generation (see the many life cycle diagrams in the remainder of this chapter). Therefore, the known gametophyte reductions in lycopsids, sphenopsids, and pteropsids are a case of distinct parallel evolution because each group has evolved in its own way to a simplified gametophyte. This parallel and apparently directional evolution (orthogenesis) seems to be explained by a past need for all land plants that survived to assume a more terrestrial existence. This probably is the case because gametophytes are relatively more fragile and susceptible to environmental extremes than are sporophytes. The gametophyte is less able to do without water than is the sporophyte. Moreover, this "gametophyte problem" apparently was solved in the same general way. In each subphylum, reduced size and complexity enabled a much shorter gametophyte generation and, therefore, less dependence upon the dangers of varying climatic and/or environmental conditions. The culmination of this line of development is found in the angiosperms where the male gametophyte is reduced to a single cell within a pollen grain and the female gametophyte is reduced to an embryo sac within the ovule of a flower structure, the pistil. However, in both cases the gametophytes still are associated with modified spores.

More specifically, the non-seed-producing plants (pteridophytes) that form only one kind of spore regularly develop part to all of their gametophytes outside the spore, but seed plants (spermatophytes) and pteridophytes forming two types of spores not only tend to produce distinct male and female gametophytes, but the gametophytes when mature are largely to completely within the spores. In this latter process, any male spore develops into the male gametophyte and any female spore develops into the female gametophyte.

Pteridophytes producing gametophytes outside of spores usually have one of two types of gametophytes, and both types are functionally independent at maturity. One type is subterranean, lacks chlorophyll, and obtains most of its nutrients from an association with a Phycomycetes fungus. The other type of gametophyte is aerial, has chlorophyll, and probably obtains most of its nutrients by photosynthesis. Some of these latter gametophytes resemble liverwort or horned liverwort gametophytes. Both gametophyte types normally are less than one inch in total length.

The pteridophytes, with two types of spores, also have nutritionally independent gametophytes, but the gametophytes are much reduced and are partly to completely within the spores. However, the tendency to decreased size is more pronounced in male gametophytes; the female gametophytes often are larger than the male. The nutrition in these gametophytes is derived from stored spore nutrients.

Seed plants have two kinds of spores and their gametophytes are extremely reduced and confined within spores or modified spores. Also, the gametophytes complete the tendency toward reduction in size and become entirely parasitic upon the sporophyte. In flowering plants the gametophytes are much reduced, sex organs are not developed, and the gametes are produced directly.

SPOROPHYTE

The zygote formed from fertilization of an egg by a sperm is the first cell in the sporophyte generation. This zygote develops into an embryo sporophyte. Further development then comes from growth in certain regions that usually are at the tips of root and stem branches or in axillary buds. A bud is a bit of such growth region tissue that is covered, partly to completely, by overlapping leaves. An axillary bud is merely a bud that is in a leaf axil, the small angle formed by a leaf stalk and a stem.

The adult sporophyte regularly has shoots (or stems), leaves, and roots, but there are no roots present in known psilopsids. Moreover, one of the two living genera of Psilopsida lacks leaves other than reduced ones associated with the spore-producing structures (sporangia). All tracheophytes have distinct or much reduced and barely indicated sporangia whose function is to form the spores that grow into a gametophyte.

ROOTS

Roots, as opposed to stems, usually are underground structures but this is a poor distinction (Figure 11.2). Actually, the fundamental differences between roots and stems are less obvious than mere position. Roots can be distinguished as follows: (1) They function primarily in the absorption of dissolved materials and water from the substrate and in the anchorage of plants. (2) Their apex is a meristem, or region of growth, but this apex is typically covered by a root cap. (3) Root axes are usually naked and without superficial appendages other than epidermal outgrowths in the form of root hairs. (4) The axes are neither segmented nor jointed by nodes, so there is no root axis separation into nodes and internodes. (5) Root branches originate irregularly and from internal tissues. (6) Vascular tissues usually are not organized into vascular bundles consisting of primary xylem and phloem on alternating radii. (7) An endodermis usually surrounds the stele.

SHOOTS (STEMS)

In contrast to roots, stems (Figure 11.2) serve the following purposes: (1) They are primarily for support, but are generally involved in photosynthesis, storage, and reproduction. (2) Their apices are an uncapped growing region which forms primary stem tissues plus superficial appendages in the form of leaves. The leaves complete development in an orderly sequence toward the growing region and at distinctive differentiated regions called nodes. Adjacent nodes define an interveining internodal region. (3) Branches are present, but they tend to originate regularly from a superficial mass of growing tissue that remains in the axils of leaves (axillary buds). (4) Vascular tissues regularly are organized into vascular bundles of primary xylem and phloem on the same radii from the stem center. (5) An endodermis may or may not be present.

LEAVES

Leaves, the primary food-producing, or photosynthetic, organs of most plants, usually are formed and organized at the nodes of shoots. Their arrangement, probably in phylogenetic sequence, can be spiraled, alternate (merely a reduced spiral arrangement), opposite, or whorled (Figure 11.3). The terms "spiraled" and "alternate" are often used interchangeably; however, alternate may be reserved for single leaves at each node so inserted that all leaves follow

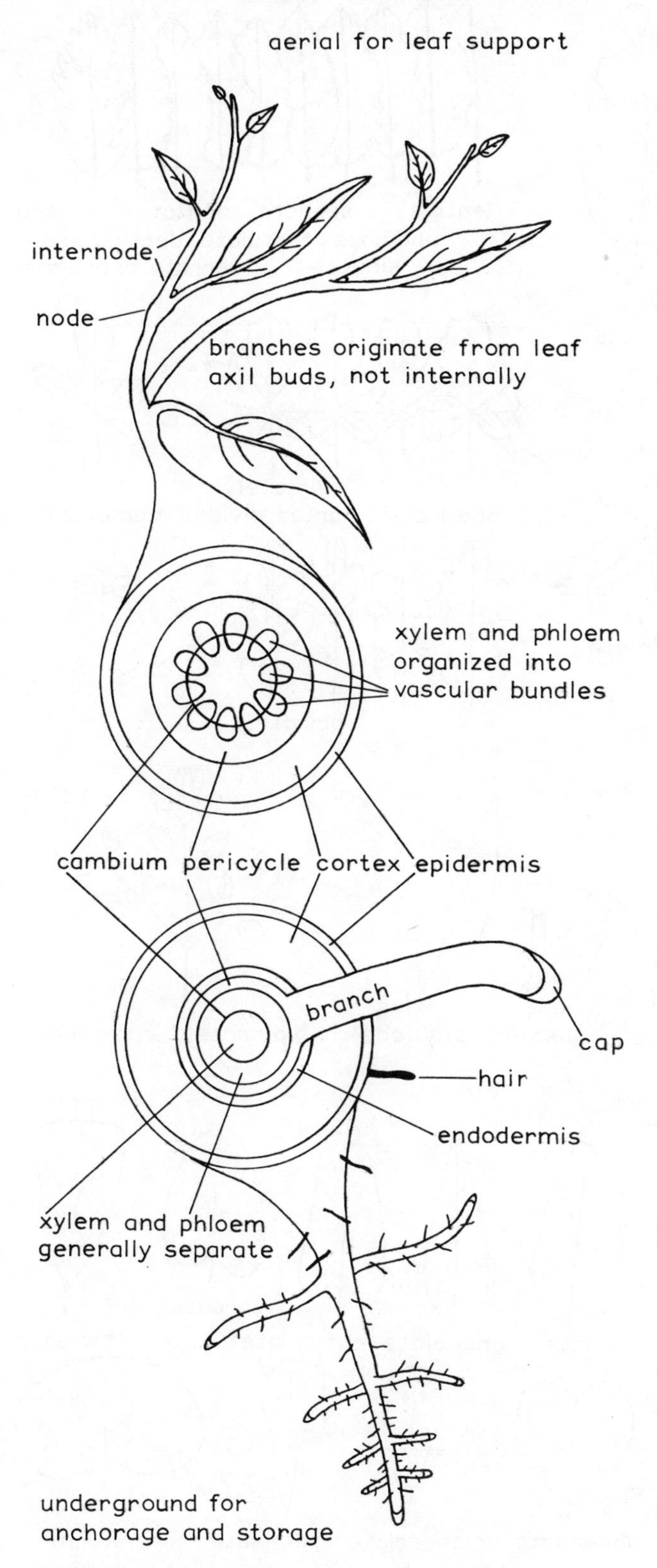

Figure 11.2 Roots vs. stems. Diagram shows the general arrangement, but not the details of unlike structures.

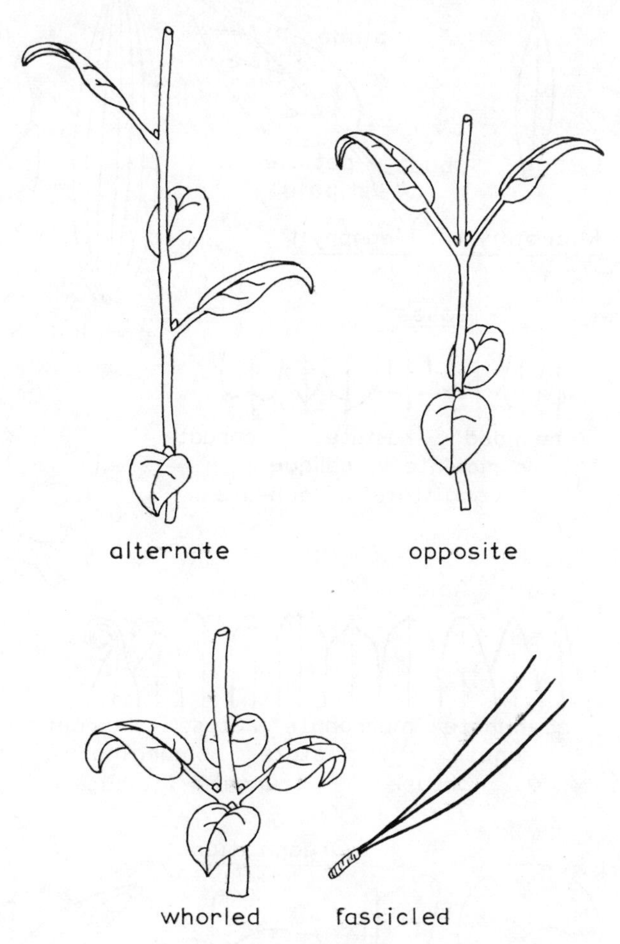

Figure 11.3 The basic arrangements of leaves upon stems.

a spiral pattern either up or down the stem. Opposite refers to opposite pairs of leaves at each node, with adjacent nodal pairs usually being at right angles to one another. Whorled designates three or more, usually geometrically inserted, leaves at each node.

Tracheophyte leaves are of two phylogenetically significant major types, microphylls and megaphylls. Microphylls commonly are small, but not necessarily so. They are diagnosed by a single vein (stele) entering from the stem and forming an unbranched midvein that goes to the leaf apex. In contrast to megaphylls, microphylls usually are smaller and less differentiated or modified.

Megaphyll (or macrophyll) venation ranges from simple forking patterns to a network of small veins that connect the primary veins. The pattern of the primary veins define pinnate, palmate, and parallel venation (Figure 11.4). Pinnate venation consists of a prominent central, longitudinal, main midvein and

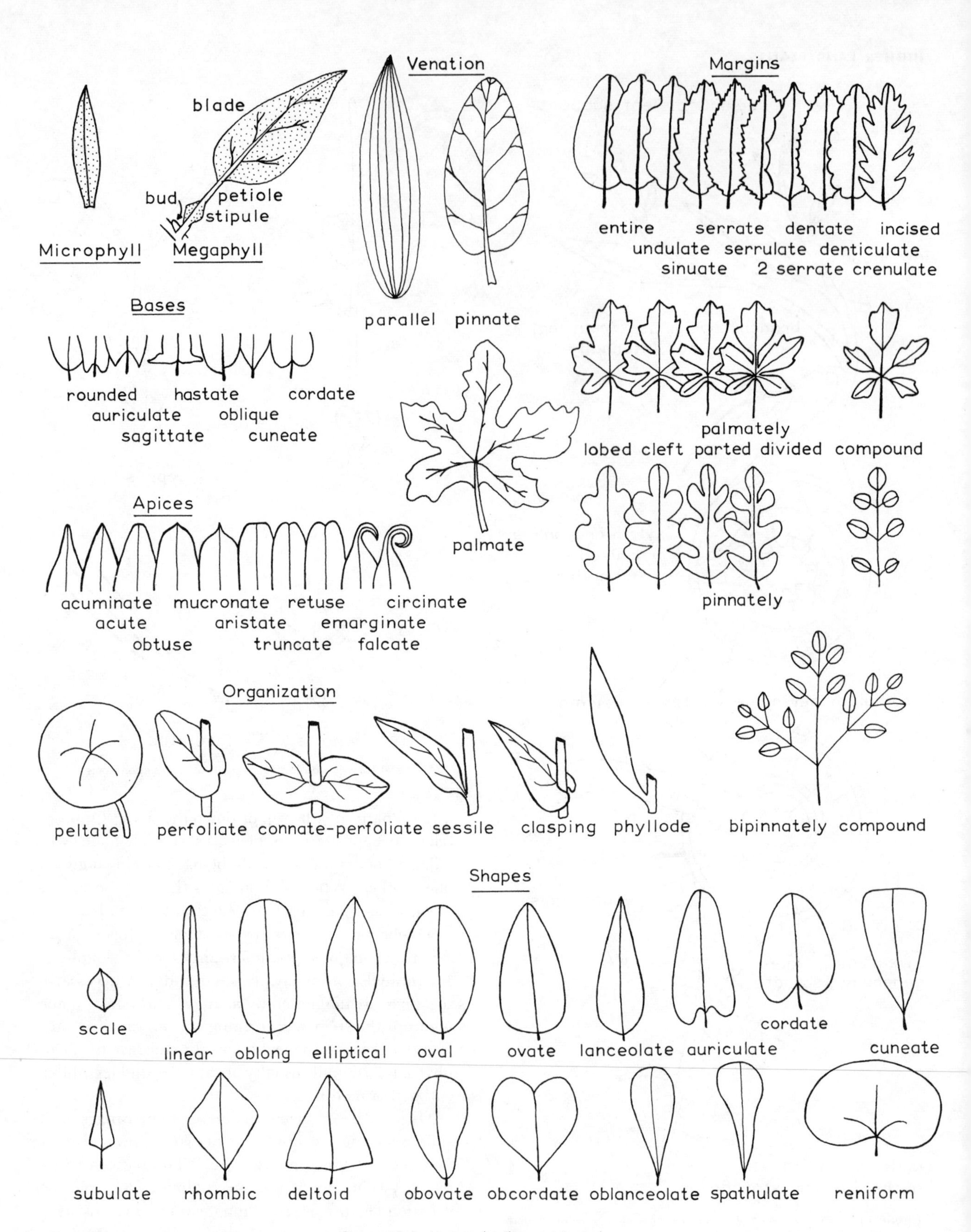

Figure 11.4 Various details pertaining to leaves.

alternate or opposite primary branches to the margin. Palmate venation consists of several central, main veins that fan out from a point at the base of the leaf blade, each main vein usually being pinnately veined. Parallel venation shows either many main parallel veins running from the leaf blade base to apex, or many main veins arching from the base (and perhaps from a short, large vein that originates from the base) to the apex.

Megaphylls usually consist of three main parts. The expanded part of the leaf is the terminally located blade. The blade is often connected to a node by a stem-like leaf structure, the petiole. Regularly near the base of the petiole, there is one, perhaps two, blade-like structures, the stipules.

The structure of leaves, especially megaphylls, often is important in the identification of individual kinds of plants. So that the reader may obtain some idea of structural diversity, and also as an aid to use of plant identification manuals, the form of leaves as to margins, outlines, bases, apices, and general organization is presented (Figure 11.4).

The following types of *leaf margins* can be recognized: *entire*, even and continuous, not cut or divided in any way; *undulate*, slightly wavy; *sinuate*, strongly wavy; *serrate*, saw-toothed, the "saw points" being nearest to the leaf apex; *serrulate*, finely saw-toothed; *doubly serrate*, saw-toothed pattern superimposed upon a larger saw-toothed pattern, generally serrulate upon serrate; *dentate*, pointed-toothed, the points generally being at the center of the "tooth" and not directed toward the leaf apex; *denticulate*, slightly and finely toothed; *crenate*, rounded-toothed; *crenulate*, finely rounded-toothed; *incised*, deeply and sharply cut or slashed, commonly double serrate to an extreme; *lobed*, typically steep but wave-like or finger-like cuts, cuts less than halfway to the midrib of the blade (pinnate) or less than halfway to the point of origin of the palmate veins that course down the middle of each lobe (palmate); *palmately lobed*, lobes radiate from a common point normally at the base of the blade; *pinnately lobed*, lobes arranged oppositely or alternately along the single midvein of the blade; *parted*, deeply cut, incised, or lobed more than half way, either palmately or pinnately; *divided*, parted completely to the base; *compound*, a step beyond divided, separated parts palmately or pinnately arranged leaf-like structures (leaflets) having blade-like and petiole-like parts; *leaflets*, can have any of the margins found in leaves; *decompound leaves*, leaves that are compounded two or more times.

Although leaves are simple, compound, or decompound, decompound leaves are often considered in more detail. Leaves that are twice compounded are usually recognized as being *bipinnate*. Those that are three times compounded are usually *tripinnate*. The limits of a single leaf are diagnosed by the site of the axillary bud.

The following types of *leaf outlines* usually are recognized: *scale-like*, regularly small and triangular; *linear*, needle-like or long and quite narrow; *oblong*, longer than broad but with parallel sides, similar to linear but broader; *elliptical*, like a flattened circle but with pointed apex and base; *oval*, broadly elliptical, with rounded apex and base; *ovate*, egg-like, broader at the base than at the apex, both ends rounded; *lanceolate*, like ovate, but the apex is drawn out into a point; *auriculate*, with the base having a lobe on each side of the midrib ("eared"); *cordate*, heart-shaped with broader part toward the base and the cleft of the "heart" inserted in the petiole; *cuneate*, wedge-shaped, triangular with the triangle base at the leaf apex and the triangle apex at the leaf base; *obovate*, like ovate, but the broader part is at the apical end; *obcordate*, like cordate, but the broader part and cleft are toward the apex; *oblanceolate*, like lanceolate, but the point is inserted into the petiole; *spatulate*, apical part oblong but basal part narrower; and *reniform*, kidney shaped. Often more than one of the above terms is required to describe leaf outlines. Such compound descriptive terms frequently are hyphenated (e.g., *oblong-ovate*).

The following types of *leaf bases* often are mentioned in plant keys: *rounded; auriculate; sagittate*, arrow-like, generally appearing in a lanceolate leaf in which a triangular portion of the base is missing; *hastate*, arrow-like but the basal lobes are turned outward; *oblique* or *unequal*, slanting, the portions of the blade on either side of the midrib do not meet at the same point; and *cuneate*, wedge-shaped. The terms sagittate and hastate, like auriculate and cuneate, often are applied to leaf outlines as well as leaf bases.

The common types of *apices* are as follows: *acuminate*, gradually tapering to a point; *acute*, sharply angled and pointed, not tapering; *obtuse*, rounded to blunt; *mucronate*, generally obtuse but with a slight extension of the midrib causing a blunt point at the apex; *cuspidate*, apex extension tooth-like; *aristate*, like mucronate, but extension is longer and sharper to hair-like; *truncate*, appearing to be cut off squarely; *retuse*, apex with a shallow notch; *emarginate*, apex with a well-defined notch; *falcate*, apex curving, sickle-shaped; and *circinate*, falcate-like tip almost forms a complete circle.

The following *organizations or modifications of leaves* are of importance in identification: *peltate*, a leaf in which the petiole is inserted to some part of the lower surface of the blade rather than to the blade base or margin; *perfoliate*, an organization where the leaf blade entirely surrounds a stem; *connate-perfoliate*, where two leaf bases are joined together in such a manner as to surround a stem; *sessile leaf*, one without a petiole, typical of perfoliate, connate-perfoliate, clasping, and certain other leaves; *clasping leaf*, the base of a sessile leaf blade is inserted and extends only partly around a stem; *rachis*, leaf without a blade, the petiole (phyllode) and perhaps the stipules constituting the leaf; and *spine*, generally a sharply pointed rachis, a modified leaf and not a modified stem, or thorn.

PTERIDOPHYTES (Fern Plants)

Some botanists consider Tracheophyta to include two phyla, the fern plants, Pteridophyta, and seed plants, Spermatophyta. Although such a grouping no longer emphasizes apparent phylogeny because each group probably does not trace back to a common ancestor, the terms still are useful. The pteridophytes include those tracheophytes that do not form seeds. Therefore, the fern plants include three subphyla, Psilopsida, Lycopsida, and Sphenopsida, plus one class (Filicineae) of the Subphylum Pteropsida. The spermatophytes include the four remaining classes of Pteropsida, the Cycadae, Ginkgoae, Coniferae, and Angiospermae.

The pteridophytes are further characterized as follows:

Diagnosis: generally moss-like or fern-like; leaves either without veins, with a single vein (leaves called microphylls), or with branched veins (megaphylls); stem and root development poor to moderately complex, an underground stem (rhizome) usually is present; sporangia produce one or two kinds of spores; when two spores are formed, smaller ones produce male gametophytes but are not modified as pollen grains and larger spores produce female gametophytes but are not involved in ovule or seed formation; sperm is formed and released from a male sex organ, fertilization commonly features flagellate sperm moving through water to the female sex organ, a zygote forms in the female gametophyte, the sporophyte embryo develops, and the sporophyte normally matures without a resting stage; the primary means of fern plant diagnosis is the lack of seed production.

Subphylum PSILOPSIDA (Whisk Ferns, etc.)

Diagnosis: known from Silurian to Recent; perennial herbs mostly to about three feet tall, shrubby and erect or grow upon plants and hang downward; sporophyte with simple organs, with or without leaves, with a branching aerial stem and an underground stem (rhizome), rhizome generally giving rise to multicellular filaments; roots are absent; leaves when present often lack veins, are small and arranged alternately along stems; sporophyte organs typically have veins throughout; spore-forming organs (sporangia) are at the apex of minute branches; spores of one type; both sporophyte and gametophyte are functionally independent at maturity; living gametophytes inconspicuous, ordinarily a branched cylindrical structure containing multicellular sex organs on the same plant (Figure 11.5).

Occurrence: three living species: *Tmesipteris tannensis*, either hanging from other plants (mostly on tree ferns), or a ground form in deep humus is leaved, 2 to 10 inches long, and is found in Australia, New Zealand, and the adjacent South Pacific islands. *Psilotum nudum* and *P. faccidum*, the whisk ferns, are sparsely leaved subtropical to tropical plants of both hemispheres and either are upon tree ferns or coconuts, are found in soil under trees, or are found upon rocks and even on open ground. The whisk ferns may be dwarfed and only 2 to 3 inches high, or may attain their full growth of 30 to 40 inches. Only *P. nudum* enters the United States, and only in the state of Florida.

GAMETOPHYTE

Structure: unknown in fossils; living forms small, up to about 1 inch long; commonly are equally forking or irregularly branching cylinders that resemble

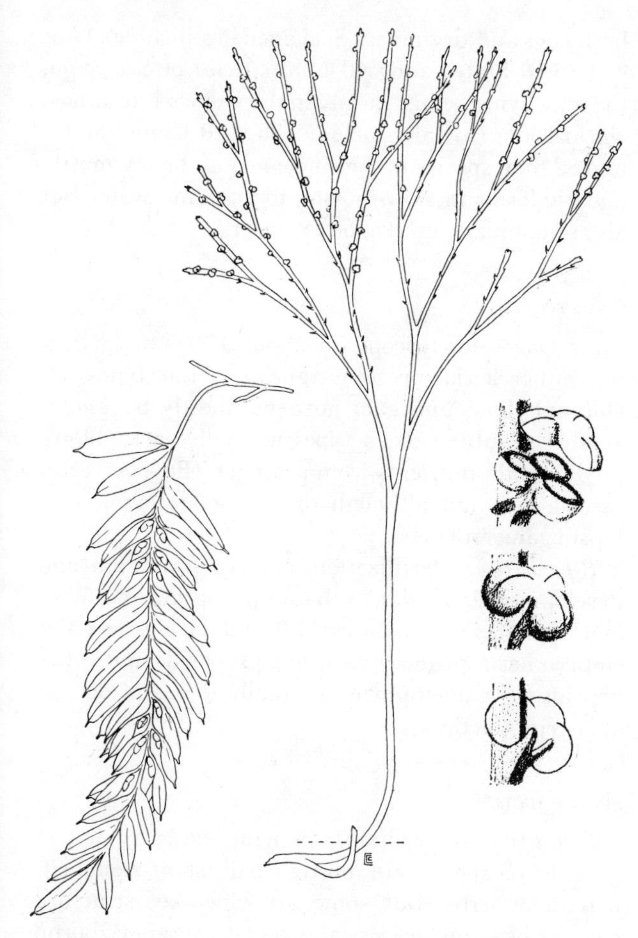

Figure 11.5 The two living psilopsid genera, *Tmesipterus* (left, slightly less than natural size) and *Psilotum* (center, slightly less than natural size, and right, enlarged sporangia). (Used by permission, from Arthur Cronquist, *Introductory Botany*, Harper, New York, 1961.)

the sporophyte rhizome; sex organs develop from single cells, male organs are globular to hemispherical and female organs, are necked and flask-like; gametophyte aerial or subterranean but usually brown and without chlorophyll, nutrition involving a fungus (Phycomycete).

Reproduction: flagellate sperm swim through water from a male sex organ into the female organ neck and to the egg; mitotic division of the fertilized egg (zygote) takes place and the embryo soon differentiates into a bottom foot and an upper shoot; the shoot develops into the mature sporophyte; when the shoot functions independently, a layer of cells forms between the shoot and foot; such layers in any plant are for the separation of parts; in psilopsids, foot and shoot are separated; after some time the gametophyte dies and decays (Figure 11.6).

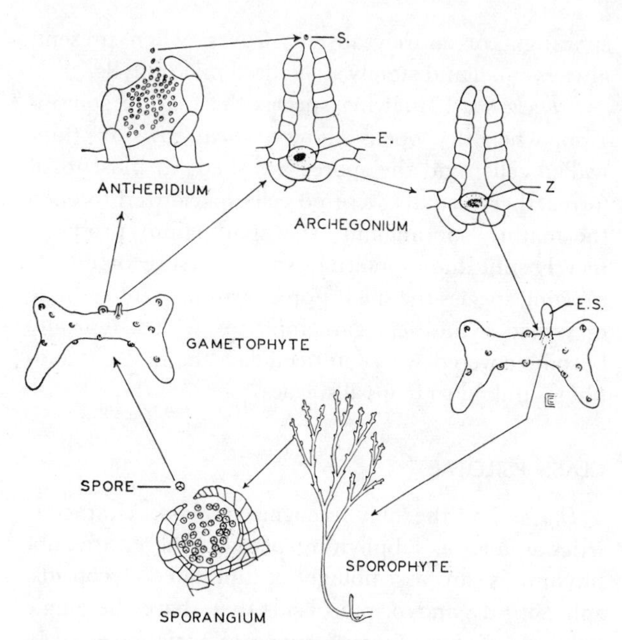

Figure 11.6 Life cycle of *Psilotum*, the whisk fern: e., egg; e.s., embryo sporophyte; s., sperm; z., zygote. (Used by permission, from Arthur Cronquist, *Introductory Botany*, Harper, New York, 1961.)

SPOROPHYTE

Structure: fossils to about 10 feet tall, living forms to about 2 feet tall; herbaceous perennials; with stems, including underground rhizomes, and leaves (leaves well developed in only one of the three living species), but without roots; sporangia mostly on branch ends, terminating ordinary branches in most fossils but on short specialized branches in living forms; leaves at the base of minute sporangia branches in living forms cause sporangia to appear to be in the axils of leaves.

Sporangium: a two- or three-lobed (three-lobed is the only species in the United States), semiglobular structure; if truly lobed, sporangia represent the fusion of two or more individual sporangia (see Marattiales in the Class Filicineae) and each sporangial lobe is essentially a single sporangium; all spores of the same size and shape; in known fossil forms the sporangia are definitely single and range from little more than a fertile portion of a terminal shoot to a definite sporangium.

Stems: branched, green, and photosynthetic in living species; in all species branching is mostly equal forking; rhizome only slightly differentiated at most; often turned upward and gives rise to regular stems.

Leaves: either present and alternate upon stem, restricted to the base of the shoot or to the vicinity of sporangia, or entirely absent; leaves, when present, always small and simply structured microphylls.

Reproduction: in living species the mature sporangium when dry opens along vertical rows of thin-walled cells, and the spores are shed; in most fossil forms, there usually were no cells specialized to open the mature sporangium; the sporangium probably merely split due to internal water pressure or decay; in living species the shed spores germinate into simple or forked cylindrical gametophytes which typically become covered with multicellular "hairs"; gametophytes unknown in fossil species.

CLASS PSILOTAE

Diagnosis: the only recognized class; characteristics as for the subphylum; perhaps the entire subphylum is an assemblage of unrelated lycopsids, sphenopsids, and/or pteropsids that share the single attribute of simplification owing to their ancestry in freshwater to semiaquatic, commonly marshland, habitats.

Subphylum LYCOPSIDA (= LEPIDOPSIDA; MICROPHYLLOPSIDA) (Club Mosses, Spike Mosses, and Quillworts)

Diagnosis: known from Cambrian to Recent, represented by the oldest apparent vascular plant known, *Aldanophyton* of the Cambrian; modern forms perennial herbs; fossil forms included trees; sporophyte with simple organs, microphyllous leaves, simple or branching stem, and roots; leaves alternate or opposite along the stem, rarely, whorled at the nodes; sporophyte organs usually containing veins throughout; sporangia occur singly on the under or upper surface of leaves and produce one or two kinds of spores; sporophyte and gametophyte both functionally independent at maturity; gametophytes of living species small but visible, but mostly subterranean and essentially a membranous sheet with multicellular sex organs (upon the same plant in one-spore species, upon separate male and female gametophytes in two-spore species); or gametophyte much reduced and confined within a spore.

Occurrence: living forms in three orders; Lycopodiales include about 15 United States and 200 total members of the genus *Lycopodium* and one Australian species of *Phylloglossum*, most species being inhabitants of warm, moist, tropical areas, but some found in both cool and dry areas; Selaginellales include about 25 United States and 500 total species of *Selaginella*, the only living genus, mostly in the tropics but almost world wide; Isoetales include about 20 United States and 80 total species in the single genus, *Isoetes*, mostly aquatic forms in slow-moving to standing water but also semiaquatic in temporary waters.

GAMETOPHYTE

Structure: microscopic to about 1-inch in diameter; either aerial or subterranean; aerial types are chlorophyllous and gain nutrients mostly by photosynthesis; subterranean types normally lack chlorophyll, obtain nutrients from a fungus (Phycomycete) association, and although distinctive, resemble psilopsid gametophytes.

Reproduction: fertilization, embryo formation and development is similar to that of psilopsids and other pteridophytes (see Figures 11.9 and 11.11), but the embryo has a primary root; like psilopsids and sphenopsids the gametophyte eventually dies and decays after reproduction.

SPOROPHYTE

Structure: many fossil trees with leaves a few feet long; living species are mostly small, short-stemmed, perennial herbs, but some are vine-like; structure consists of stems, leaves, and roots; sporangia borne singly upon the upper surface of a leaf and either near or within the leaf axil.

Sporangia: most are on undifferentiated leaves; in some, leaves are somewhat modified and grouped into a cone that produces spores of one or two types.

Stems: simple or branched, green and photosynthetic; branching often equal forking, but straight main stems do occur; organized similar to, but more complex than, the psilopsids.

Leaves: present and mostly alternate or opposite, rarely whorled; narrow, typically small and with a single, rarely two, unbranched midveins (microphylls) otherwise of generalized structure; all except a fossil order and the Lycopodiales have a ligule (a small scale-like appendage on the upper surface near the leaf axil) and are called ligulate (see Figures 11.7 and 11.8), fossil order and the Lycopodiales are eligulate; ligule might represent an undeveloped branch; the term *ligule* refers to any tongue-like structure, so the word does not necessarily refer to the same structure in all plant groups.

Roots: the primary root usually disappears before the sporophyte matures, the mature roots forming adventitiously from stem internal tissues or from unique, peculiar, prop-like, equal-forking organs found at underground points of stem branching (rhizophores, Figure 11.7); roots are mostly simple, sometimes equal-forking.

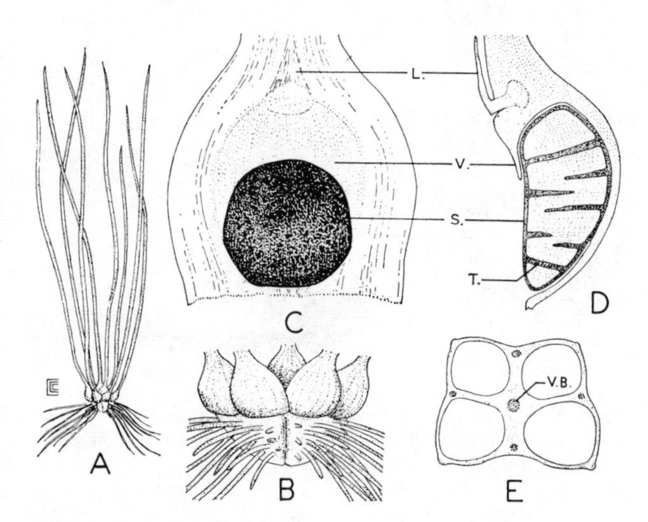

Figure 11.7 *Isoetes,* a quillwort. A, habit (× ½); B, rhizophore, with roots and leaf bases (× 2½); C, sporangium-bearing leaf, inner surface view of base (enlarged); D, sporangium-bearing leaf, side view in long section at base (enlarged); E, cross-section of leaf (enlarged); l., ligule; s., sporangium; t., trabecula; v., velum; v.b., vascular bundle. (Used by permission, from Arthur Cronquist, *Introductory Botany,* Harper, 1961.)

Reproduction: if only one single kind of spore is formed, spore development ends in a gametophyte having both sex organs; if two kinds of spores are formed, separate male and female gametophytes of highly variable form and organization develop.

CLASS LYCOPODAE

Diagnosis: the only recognized class; represented by macrofossils since Cambrian times; characteristics as for the subphylum.

ORDER ISOETALES (Quillworts)

Diagnosis: known from Triassic to Recent; fossil species up to 6 feet tall, composed of an erect, unbranched axis upon a lobed, unbranched rootstock that bore rootlets similar to those of a fossil order (Lepidodendrales); upper part of axis with numerous, long and narrow, spirally arranged, ligulate leaves; axis capped by a single, strictly male or female cone, hence plants strictly male or female; living species essentially "shrunk" from the fossil species to small, aquatic or semiaquatic, sedge or rush-like, perennial herbs; living structure consisting of quill-like, entire, simple, ligulate leaves; leaves arising from an inflated but flattened axis which is usually underground; lower part of axis a two or three-lobed rootstock; lower axis with many equal-forking roots; outer leaves bearing sporangia forming female spores and inner leaves bearing sporangia forming male spores, but lowermost leaves sterile; sporangia occur singly, on inner (upper) side of leaf between ligule and the leaf base, are covered by a membrane, and are incompletely divided by partitions; male gametophyte formed within a male spore; female gametophyte starts forming within a female spore, but the female spore generally breaks before complete female sex organ formation, so the female organ extends beyond the spore confines (Figure 11.7).

ORDER SELAGINELLALES (Spike Mosses, or Small Club Mosses)

Diagnosis: known from Pennsylvanian to Recent; both fossil species and members of the single living genus, *Selaginella*, are of much the same appearance; certain fossil species produced seed-like structures but not true seeds; modern forms are mostly smaller than fossil taxa and resemble club mosses, mostly perennial herbs, a very few delicate annuals; some are erect and shrubby; others are prostrate creepers that form tufts, mounds, or mats and resemble mosses, but have roots; some are fern-like and have a conspicuous underground stem (rhizome); leaves are mostly less than ⅕-inch long, spirally arranged, sometimes in four distinct rows, and ligulate; roots grow from leafless root stocks; sporangia always develop in cones; two kinds of spores; male gametophyte forms completely within male spore; female gametophyte essentially as in Isoetales (Figures 11.8 and 11.9).

ORDER LYCOPODIALES (Club Mosses)

Diagnosis: known from Pennsylvanian to Recent; ours mostly trailing or creeping, also erect, perennial herbs; somewhat moss-like, general form of some causes them to be called "ground pines"; branching mostly equal-forking to approaching a straight main stem; leaves commonly under 1 inch, eligulate, and usually spiralled on stem (but also whorled, opposite, or alternate, and sometimes in rows); leaves range from scale-like to needle-like but generally over $\frac{1}{5}$-inch long; roots form along creeping stems or grow down from erect stems; most sporangia are on leaves that are either organized into cones or are ungrouped leaves that may be confined to "fertile areas" or scattered on the sporophyte; one spore type, the spore developing into a vaguely carrot-like, $\frac{1}{8}$- to $\frac{3}{4}$-inch gametophyte bearing both male and female sex organs (Figures 11.10 and 11.11).

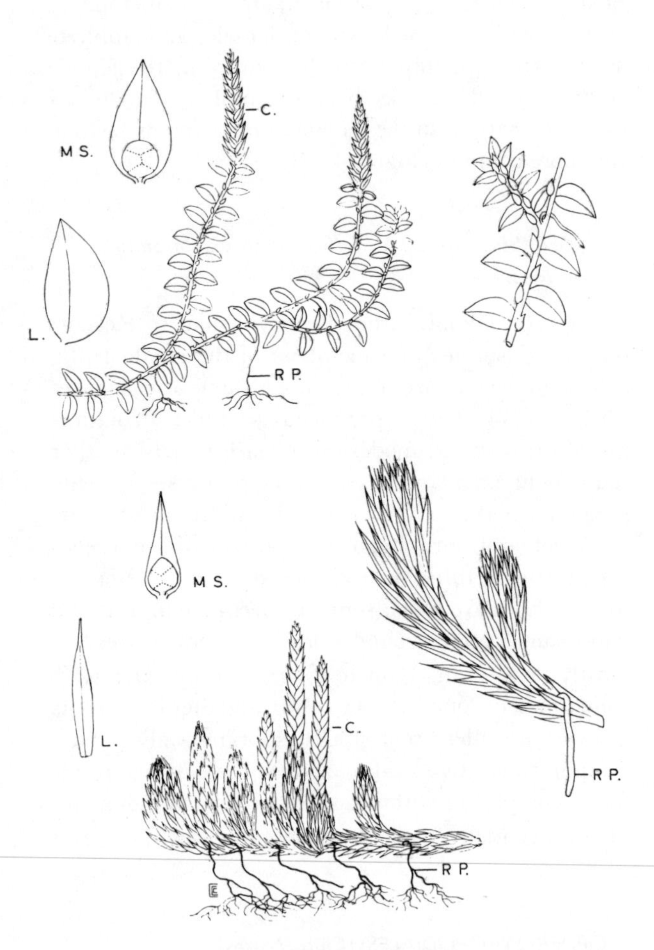

Figure 11.8 *Selaginella,* two species of spike mosses; habit (about natural size); branches (x 3); sporangium-bearing and vegetative leaves (enlarged); c., cone; l., leaf; ms., leaf-bearing sporangium that forms female spores; rp., rhizophore. (Used by permission, from Arthur Cronquist, *Introductory Botany,* Harper, New York, 1961.)

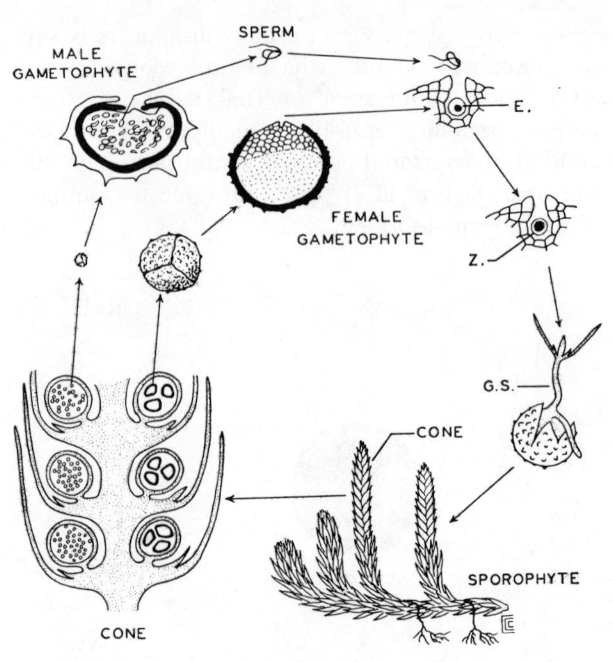

Figure 11.9 Life cycle of *Selaginella:* e., egg; g.s., germinating sporophyte; z., zygote. (Used by permission, from Arthur Cronquist, *Introductory Botany,* Harper, New York, 1961.)

Subphylum SPHENOPSIDA (= ARTHROPSIDA; CALAMOPSIDA) (Horsetails and Scouring Rushes)

Diagnosis: definite fossils date back to Middle Devonian; most fossils resemble the single, living genus, *Equisetum*; living species are perennial herbs with microphylls, but some fossils had leaves with branched veins (macrophylls); stems are ribbed, simple or branched, jointed, and have distinct nodes and elongate internodes; roots are present; the leaves are never alternate, but leaves and branches alternate with one another at the nodes; sporangia are in cones organized from specialized stalks; spores of one kind (includes *Equisetum*), or rarely two kinds (some fossils); both sporophyte and gametophyte are functionally independent at maturity; living gametophytes are inconspicuous and have both sex organs on the same plant (probably were on separate plants in two-spore fossils) (Figure 11.12).

Occurrence: about 20 living species in the genus *Equisetum* of the order Equisetales; almost cosmopolitan, but not in Australia; mostly in wet areas, also shallow water emergents to well-drained soil.

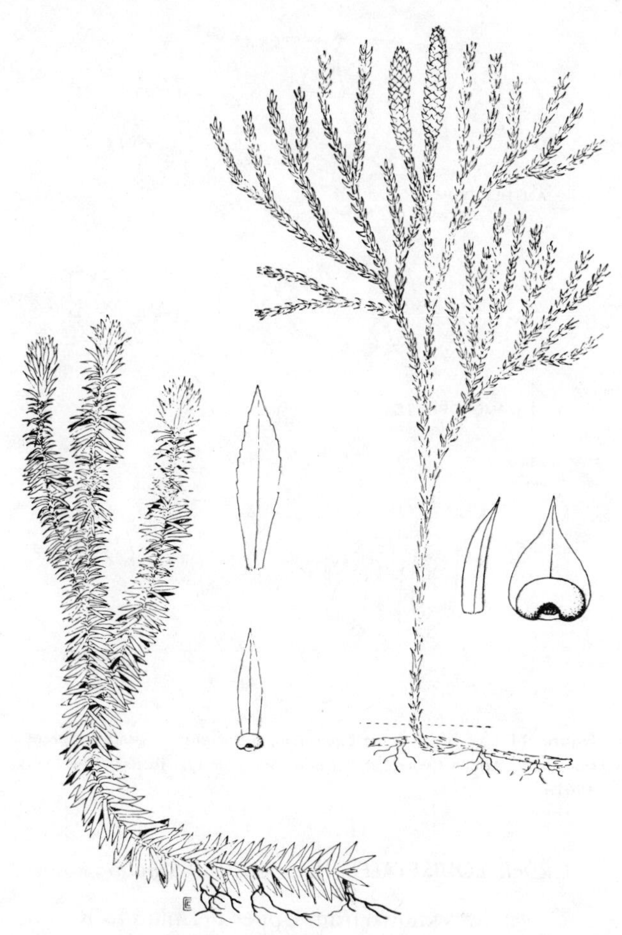

Figure 11.10 Club moss, *Lycopodium*, types. Left, *L. lucidulum* (x ½) with enlarged sporangium-bearing and vegetative leaves. Right, *L. obscurum* (x ½) with enlarged sporangium-bearing and vegetative leaves. (Used by permission, from Arthur Cronquist, *Introductory Botany*, Harper, New York, 1961.)

GAMETOPHYTE

Structure: *Equisetum* is minute to (rarely) 1 inch, generally on damp ground, and contains chlorophyll; mature plant an irregular cushion-shaped structure attached to the substrate by "hairs"; sex organs multicellular and similar to those in the quillworts (Isoetales).

Reproduction: similar to other pteridophytes; gametophyte after a period also dying and decaying.

SPOROPHYTE

Structure: many fossil trees with large and sometimes branched leaves; living species herbaceous to shrubby, surface tissues often containing silica (once used for scouring), mostly under 3 feet, South American vine to 36 feet; composed of finely grooved, jointed stems, whorled leaves (living forms microphylls), and roots originating from underground stems (rhizomes); sporangia on specialized stalks, stalk apex organized into a cone; details to emphasize *Equisetum*.

Sporangium: many sporangia are on each cone scale, and the cone scales are grouped into closely set whorls upon a central axis, to form a cone at the end of the axis; the axis is on a vegetative stem or a strictly fertile, non-chlorophyllous stem arising from a rhizome.

Stems: simple or branched, green, and photosynthetic; unique in having whorls of branches originate from the nodes, distinct joints at the nodes (the internodes being elongate and ribbed or longitudinally grooved); and a constantly growing base of each node which allows disjointing at the nodes; stem anatomy, especially vein organization, is unique.

Leaves: whorled, arising from joints, or nodes, and aligning with an underlying internodal rib; typically are narrow, less than an inch long, have a single unbranched midvein (microphylls), have generalized structure but little or no chlorophyll, and have the lateral margins of adjacent leaves fused except at the tips; a ring of fused leaves forms a protective leaf sheath around each stem joint (a growing part of the stem); leaves often were more generalized in fossil species; microphylls, except in a few fossil forms.

Roots: originate at the nodes of an underground

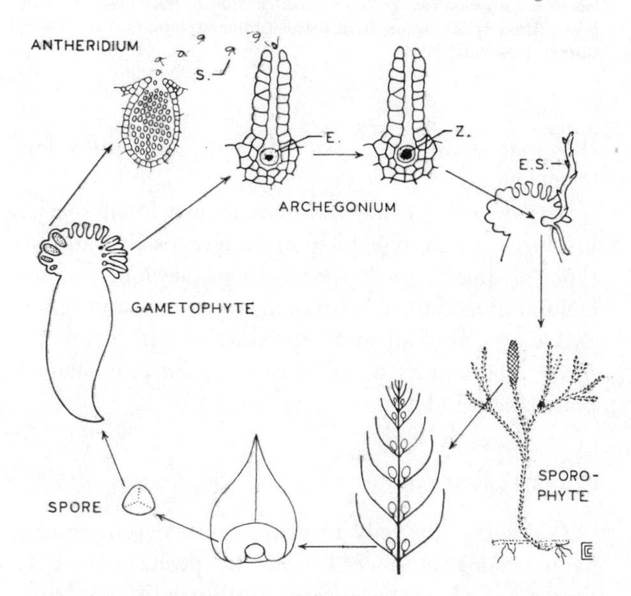

Figure 11.11 Life cycle of *Lycopodium*, a club moss: e., egg; e.s., embryo sporophyte; s., sperm; z., zygote. (Used by permission, from Arthur Cronquist, *Introductory Botany*, Harper, New York, 1961.)

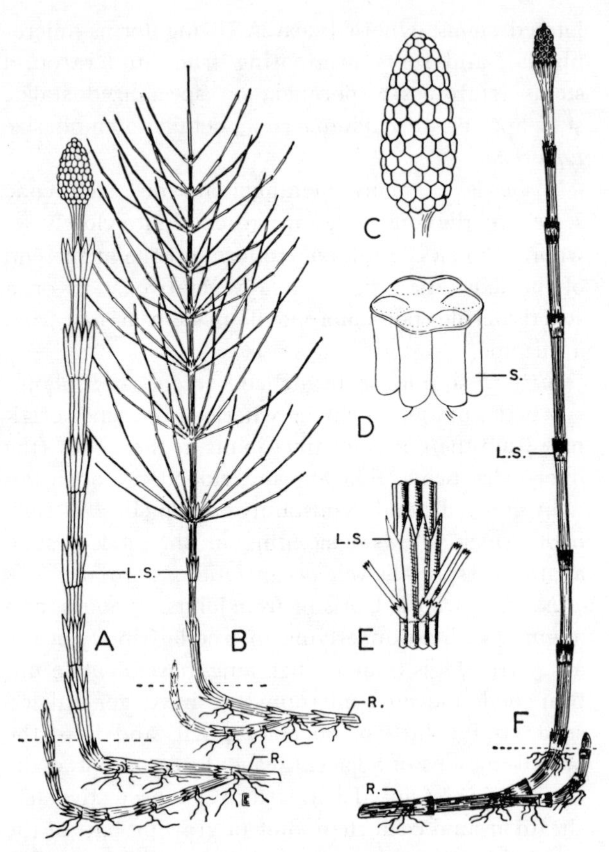

Figure 11.12 *Equisetum.* A–E, *Equisetum arvense,* a horsetail: A, fertile shoot (x ¾); B, sterile shoot (x 1½); C, cone (x 1½); D, sporangium-bearing unit of a cone (x 18); E, part of the stem (x 2½). F, *E. hiemale,* a scouring rush (x ⅕); l.s., leaf sheath; r., rhizome; s., sporangium. (Used by permission, from Arthur Cronquist, *Introductory Botany,* Harper, New York, 1961.)

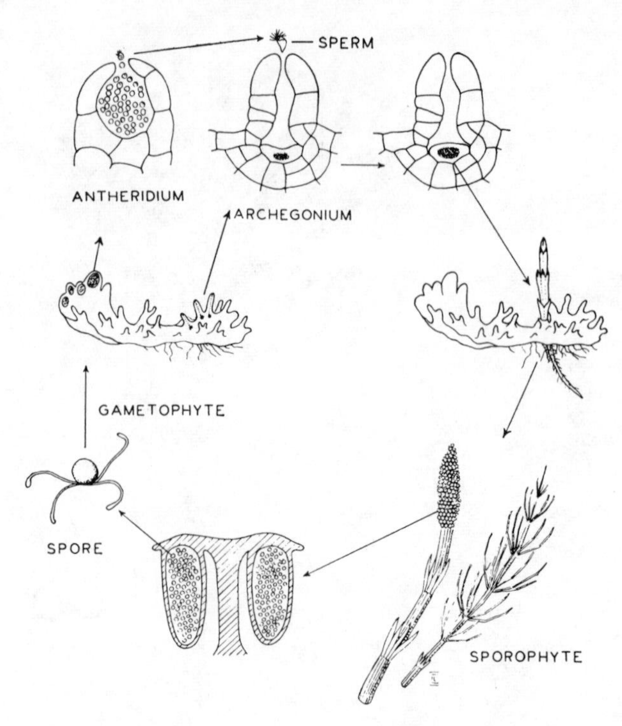

Figure 11.13 Life cycle of *Equisetum,* a horsetail. (Used by permission, from Arthur Cronquist, *Introductory Botany,* Harper, New York, 1961.)

rhizome; regularly are short, simple, or with a few branches.

Reproduction: living and most known fossil species produce a single type of spore; a few fossils had two types of spores; single-spore species develop a multicellular gametophyte with both sex organs, an organization typical of all such reproductive types; gametophyte commonly a membranous, cushion-shaped body (Figure 11.13).

CLASS EQUISETAE

Diagnosis: the only recognized class; represented by macrofossils since Lower, or perhaps Upper, Devonian; characteristics as outlined for the subphylum.

ORDER EQUISETALES (Horsetails and Scouring Rushes)

Diagnosis: known from Upper Permian to Recent; characters as emphasized in the subphylum account.

Subphylum PTEROPSIDA (Ferns, Cycads, Ginkgos, Conifers, and Angiosperms)

Diagnosis: definite fossils from Devonian to Recent; commonly perennial herbs or trees, also annuals; leaves usually pinnately compound or decompound, rarely simple, always megaphylls; leaves typically alternate, often radiating from the apex of an aerial stem, and frequently large and conspicuous; stem short and underground to aerial, unbranched to branched; sporangia borne upon leaves or modified leaves; spores of one or two kinds; gametophytes small to minute, often distinctly male or female, with or without distinct sex organs; with or without seeds; an extremely variable group.

Occurrence: over 200,000 living species of worldwide occurrence and in almost every conceivable habitat for a plant.

GAMETOPHYTE

Structure: ranges from a structure with a midrib in the center of a heart or butterfly-shaped membrane having sex organs (reminiscent of certain liverworts and horned liverworts) to both gametophytes being much reduced, without distinct sex organs, and essentially within the parental spores (the male gametophyte forming a resting stage, called a pollen grain and the fertilized female gametophyte becoming part of a seed).

Reproduction: ranges from conditions similar to other pteridophytes to a complex process involving seed production.

SPOROPHYTE

Structure: herbs, shrubs, and trees; leaves simple, compound, or decompound, generally alternate to radiating at the apex of a simple aerial stem; sporangia simple to grouped into complex structures.

Sporangium: ignoring angiosperms, generally upon leaves to associated with modified leaves in the formation of cones; sporangia occur either singly and somewhat scattered, characteristically clustered but not fused, fused together into a nut-like structure, or male spore-forming sporangia are grouped into male cones and female spore-forming sporangia are grouped into female cones; see flower organization in Angiosperms.

Stems: ranging from unbranched to complexly branched rhizomes; to unbranched, equally forked, or irregular branched aerial stems; arranged into nodes and internodes; growth primarily from an apical growth region, but also from axillary buds at the nodes.

Leaves: simple, compound, or decompound; margins generally pinnatified, also otherwise including entire; arrangements include one or more leaves as the only aerial portion of many plants, leaves alternate on aerial stems, or leaves terminal and radiating from the aerial stem apex; basic leaf arrangement is typically alternate; certain leaves become fertile and usually differentiate into hardly leaf-like sporangia-bearing structures that are sometimes organized into separate male and female cones.

Roots: mostly present; often of a fibrous nature.

Reproduction: either a single kind of spore is formed and usually develops into a bisexual gametophyte reminiscent of the midribbed liverwort gametophyte; or two kinds of spores are produced, the smaller one developing into a male gametophyte and the larger one developing into a female gametophyte; or two kinds of spores are produced, the smaller one developing into a male gametophyte within its spore wall and the larger developing into a female gametophyte within its spore wall, the female gametophyte and spore being involved in seed production (see spermatophyte characteristics); also see angiosperms.

CLASS FILICINEAE (Ferns)

Diagnosis: known from definite early Lower Devonian fossils; range in structure from the earliest fossils which approximated the psilopsid structure to the complex ferns of today; leaves commonly alternate and pinnatified; stems often entirely underground, a simple or branched rhizome; sporangia mostly upon the undersurface of leaves, but variously distributed; sporangial organization highly variable, primitively occurring singly, now frequently organized into closely set but not fused groups of definite shape (sori) which may have a protective covering (indusium) and are upon a specialized raised portion of the leaf (receptable); in Marattiales sporangia are fused (see living psilopsids), and in Marsileales and Salviniales are represented by modified leaves formed into a nut-like structure (sporocarp); spores of one or two kinds, but the two kinds of spores are typically similar in appearance; both gametophyte and sporophyte are functionally independent at maturity; gametophyte small and inconspicuous to minute and approaching being contained within a spore, mostly with chlorophyll and free-living upon the surface of the ground; also free-living but without chlorophyll and underground, some female gametophytes within a female spore and obtain nutrients from spore food reserves (Figure 11.14).

Occurrence: about 10,000 living species, all but about 260 being true ferns (Order Filicales); mostly in moist, warm, temperate and tropical areas but extending to dry and cold climates as well.

ORDER OPHIOGLOSSALES (Adder's-tongue and Grape Ferns)

Diagnosis: indefinite fossil record, Permian (?) to Recent; perennial herbs of small to moderate size, generally in forests or open areas; sporophyte stem short and fleshy, often underground; roots thick and fleshy, mostly simple; leaves simple or pinnately com-

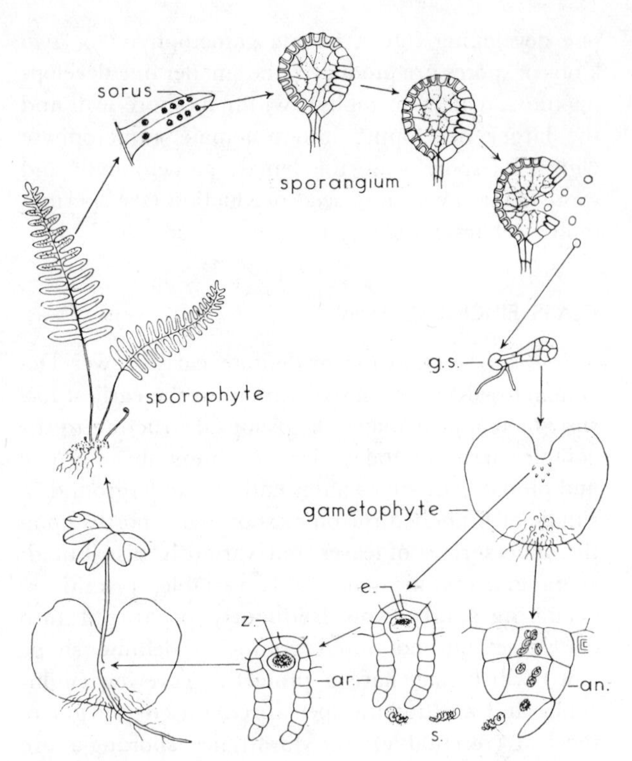

Figure 11.14 Life cycle of a fern; an., male sex organ; ar., female sex organ; e., egg; g.s., germinating spore; s., sperm; z., zygote. (Used by permission, from Arthur Cronquist, *Introductory Botany*, Harper, New York, 1961.)

pound, generally only one present; fertile leaves of two parts, a lower sterile, or vegetative, leafy segment and an upper, sporangia-bearing segment or spike ("adder's tongue"); leaf not unrolling with growth, petiole with clasping stipules; one spore type, gametophyte bisexual, inconspicuous, underground, without chlorophyll, and worm-like, its nutrition involving a fungus relationship (Figure 11.15).

Occurrence: three genera in a single family, Ophioglossaceae; one species of *Helminthostachys* in the Indo-Malayan region; about 28 species of *Ophioglossum* (adder's-tongue ferns) and about 23 species of *Botrychium* (grape ferns) of world-wide distribution; all small to average sized perennial herbs, some evergreen, mostly of moist tropical and temperate forests; fossils unknown.

ORDER MARATTIALES (Tropical Ferns)

Diagnosis: known from Pennsylvanian to Recent; about 145 living, perennial herbs to tree-like forms of the tropics, mostly forest plants that closely resemble the Filicales in gross appearance but have many Ophioglossales characters; stems reduced to rhizomes or erect tuberous trunks; leaves large and pinnate, sometimes simple but mostly compound or decompound; some leaves resemble those of cycads; leaves have clasping stipules and unroll with growth; sporangia either are free but grouped (into sori), or are fused (see psilopsids); sporangia on upper surface of leaves; one kind of spore; gametophyte bisexual, conspicuous (mostly over 1 inch long), chlorophyllous, flat, and ribbon- or heart-shaped (Figure 11.16).

Figure 11.15 A grape fern, *Botrychium* (left), and an adder's tongue fern, *Ophioglossum* (right). (Used by permission, from *Comparative Morphology of Vascular Plants* by Adriance S. Foster and Ernest M. Gifford, Jr. San Francisco: W. H. Freeman and Co., 1959.)

Figure 11.16 *Marattia, a tropical fern.* (Used by permission, from *Cryptogamic Botany*, vol. 2, by Gilbert M. Smith. Copyright 1955. N. Y.: McGraw-Hill Book Co.)

ORDER FILICALES (True Ferns)

Diagnosis: known from Pennsylvanian to Recent; variable occurrence and growth habit; United States species are perennial herbs, mostly fern-like but ranging from creeping to climbing plants of moss-like to tree-like form; stems commonly underground and branched; leaves unroll with growth and are variable, mostly large but either simple, compound, or decompound and often pinnatified; sporangia mostly upon margin or under surface of leaves, occurring singly or in groups (sori); sori with or without a protective covering (indusium); one spore type; gametophyte usually bisexual, generally inconspicuous ($1/16$ to $1/2$ inch), above ground, membranous, and chlorophyllous (Figure 11.17).

Occurrence: about 10,000 species forming several families of world-wide distribution; perennial herbs to trees, rarely annuals, mostly of moist climates and/or moist habitats, some in dry areas.

ORDER MARSILEALES (Water Ferns)

Diagnosis: fossil record obscure; aquatic or semi-aquatic forms that are not at all fern-like; primarily a creeping rhizome bearing filamentous or clover-like leaves; sporangia in modified nut-like structures (sporocarps) at or near the base of the leaf petioles; two spore types, producing much-reduced male and female gametophytes that approach those of seed plants (Figure 11.18).

Occurrence: three genera of perennial herbs in a single family, Marsileaceae; one species of *Regnillidium*, a South American form characterized by bilobed, simple leaves; six species of *Pilulária* in northern Africa, Europe, Australia, and America (one American species, *P. americana*, the pillwort) characterized

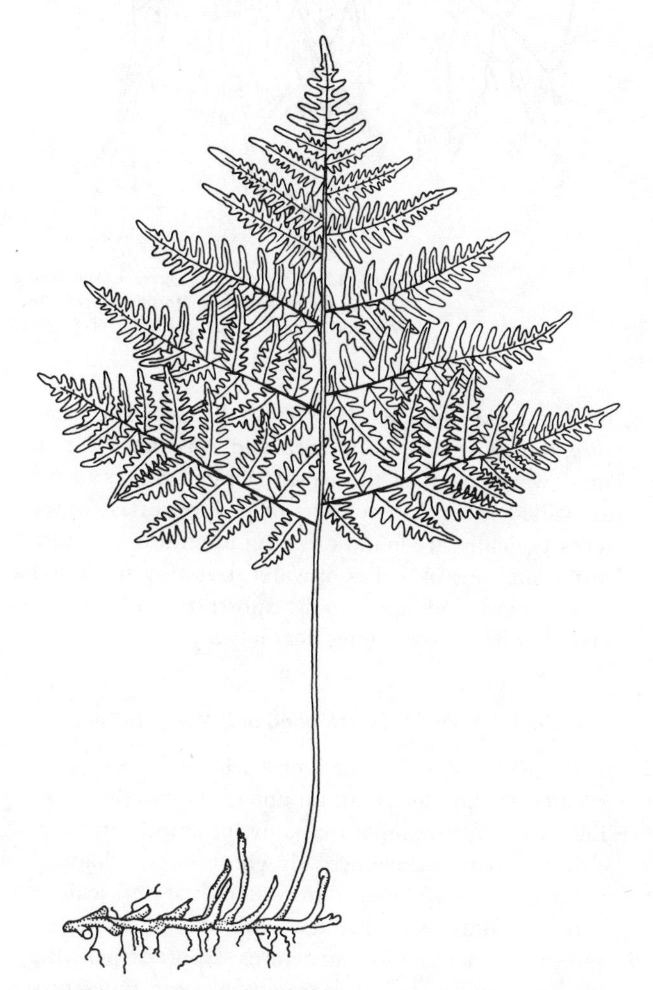

Figure 11.17 *Pteridium, a true fern.* (Used by permission, from *Cryptogamic Botany*, vol. 2, by Gilbert M. Smith. Copyright 1955. N. Y.: McGraw-Hill Book Co.)

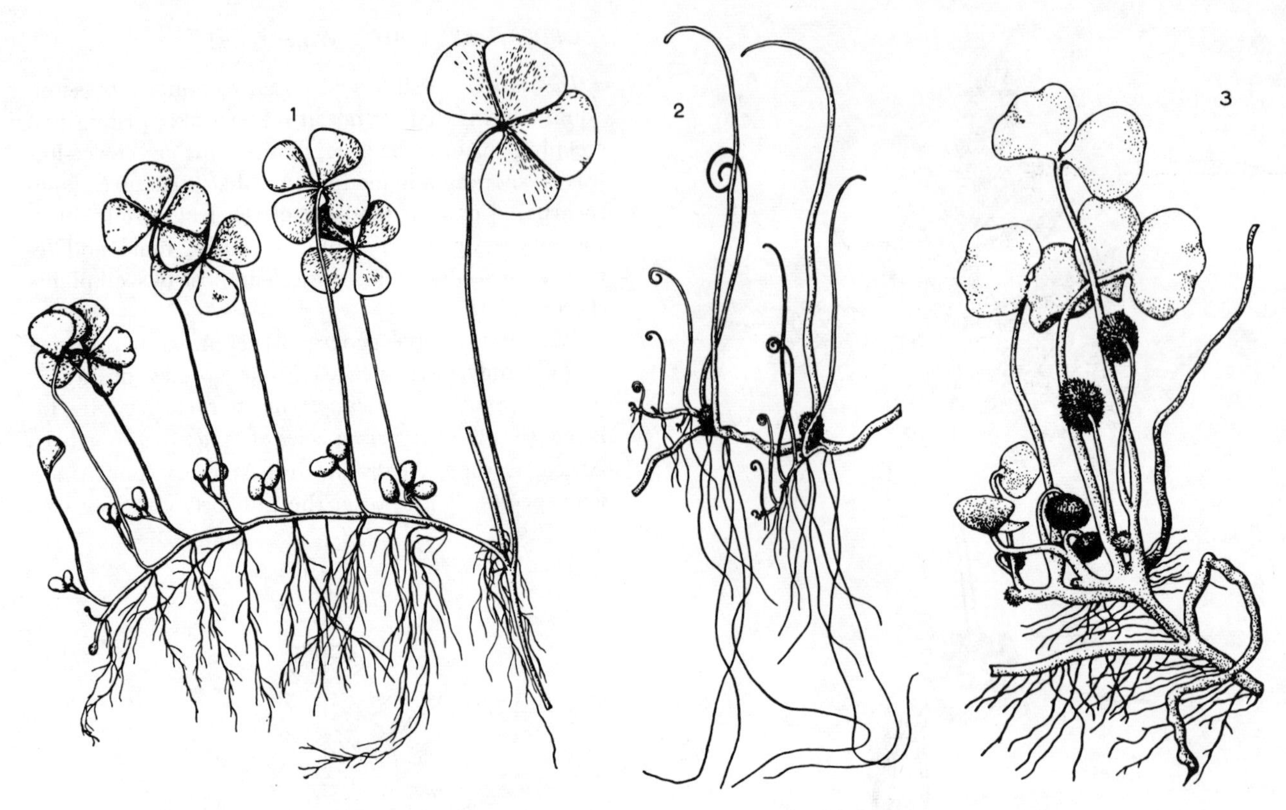

Figure 11.18 Water fern types: 1, *Marsilea;* 2, *Pilularia;* and 3, *Regnellidium.* About natural size. (Used by permission, from *Morphology of Vascular Plants; Lower Groups, Psilophytales to Filicales* by Arthur J. Eames. Copyright 1936. N. Y.: McGraw-Hill Book Co.)

by a hair-like, bladeless leaf; about 40 species of *Marsilea*, mostly in tropical Africa and Australia, but in most warm parts of the world (United States forms are called either water clovers or pepperworts); water ferns typically are found creeping upon the substrate at the margins of bodies of water, but also are found in wet mud and upon moist substrates; plants are erect but leaves sometimes float in water.

ORDER SALVINIALES (Floating and Mosquito Ferns)

Diagnosis: fossil record obscure; like the Marsileales are no more than an unfernlike family of the Filicales; both are separated only for emphasis; plant either a floating rhizome with whorls of two floating, inflated leaves and one underwater dissected leaf, or a rooted branched rhizome with moss-like leaves; sporangia in modified structures (sporocarps) that are associated with the leaves; two spore types producing much reduced male and female gametophytes (Figure 11.19).

Occurrence: two genera of mostly perennial herbs (one species of each genus is an annual) in a single family, Salviniaceae; all are floating aquatics of warm temperate and tropical regions but none are in Europe; about 10 species of *Salvinia* (floating ferns), 1 in the United States, and 6 species of *Azola* (mosquito ferns), 1 in the United States.

SPERMATOPHYTES (Seed Plants): Gymnosperms and Angiosperms

Diagnosis: plants that produce true seeds; the leaves are often large, relatively complex and branched-veined (megaphylls), the stems and roots are usually well developed; the veins are complex; branching is mostly from a straight main stem but often is modified into an irregular type; sporangia producing two kinds of spores; differ from other two-spore-type plants by greater reduction in the male and female gametophytes and by some features in the sporophyte embryo; smaller spores develop into dis-

Figure 11.19 Floating and mosquito ferns. *Salvinia*, a floating fern: 1, habit. *Azolla*, a mosquito fern: 2, natural size; 3, enlarged; 4, enlarged leaf. (Used by permission, from *Morphology of Vascular Plants; Lower Groups, Psilophytales to Filicales* by Arthur J. Eames. Copyright 1936. N. Y.: McGraw-Hill Book Co.)

tinctive male gametophytes (pollen grains) which are shed, and larger spores into a distinctive female gametophyte; both gametophytes develop within their spores and complete their final development in the larger female spore; shed pollen reaches the female gametophyte, sperm fertilizes egg or eggs, the zygote develops into an early embryo which soon stops development and enters a resting stage; the resting embryo plus other tissues form a structure called a seed (Figure 11.20).

Seed production: The *female sporangium* produces a single female spore which develops into the female gametophyte; female sex organs may or may not develop; within the female gametophyte an egg or eggs forms; the egg is replaced by an ovule composed of egg, sporangium wall (called nucellus), and one or two surrounding layers of tissue (integuments); integuments have a small opening (micropyle) at either the sporangium stalk or opposite end of the ovule; through this opening fertilization can occur.

The *male sporangium* (called a pollen sac) produces many small spores, each developing into a resting stage of a male gametophyte (a pollen grain, composed of inner gametophyte surrounded by an outer protective wall, wall is the spore wall and is usually two-layered); the pollen grain wall often has variable but distinctive shapes and markings; in a pollen grain the male gametophyte without first differentiating into a sex organ produces sperm; later and upon contact of pollen grain and ovule, the pollen grain develops an outgrowth, or pollen tube, which digests its way through the intervening ovule tissues and deposits the sperm.

In seed development fertilization occurs, a zygote results, and the embryo grows slightly. Then the embryo enters a brief to prolonged resting stage, which lasts until germination. Finally, the embryo sporophyte, female gametophyte, and ovule (three generations) form the seed. Seed formation is essentially completed when the integuments become the protective outer layer, or seed coat, of the seed. Seeds either germinate immediately, the apparent primitive ancestral condition, or assume a resting stage prior to germination. In some cases germination starts only after certain environmental influences.

Classification Note: As mentioned earlier, biologists once classified spermatophytes as a phylum distinguished from the pteridophytes. It was also mentioned previously why spermatophytes and pteridophytes are no longer usually considered natural groupings of plants. In this older system of classification two classes, the Gymnospermae and Angiospermae, also were recognized. Although none of these groups now tend to be recognized in the older sense, tracheophytes are regularly labeled as "pteridophytes" or "spermatophytes" and spermatophytes as "gymnosperms" or "angiosperms." It will be seen that the term "angiosperm" still applies to a natural group but not one equivalent to gymnosperms.

The gymnosperms include all seed plants except the Class Angiospermae, or flowering plants. They

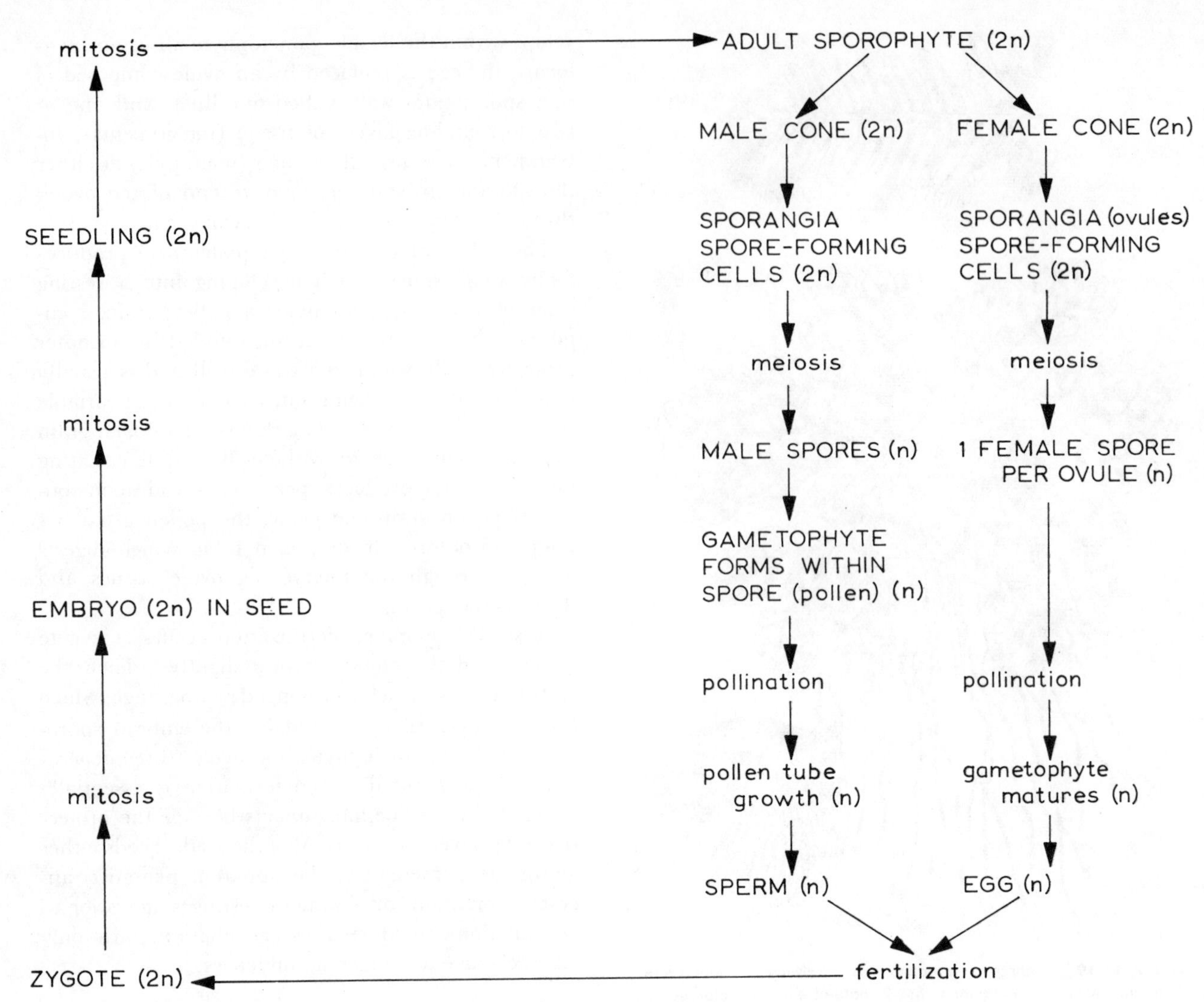

Figure 11.20 Spermatophyte life cycle, generalized as found in gymnosperms.

are distinguished from flowering plants by the absence of complex flowers (but flower-like structures are present in some), by pollen being transported strictly by the wind and only accidentally by organisms or water, by the pollen tube being inserted directly into the micropyle rather than having to grow through tissues, by a single fertilization involving a sperm and an egg rather than by double fertilization in which the second process involves formation of a seed nutrient (endosperm), and by seeds being formed naked rather than enclosed in a "vessel."

"Gymnospermae" is an artificial taxon in that contrasting gymnosperms with angiosperms implies equivalent taxa. Actually it appears most likely that the gymnosperms arose first, and one gymnosperm group later gave rise to the angiosperms. Also, the gymnosperms appear to represent three major lines of development (three classes) and the angiosperms one line of development from the gymnosperms.

CLASS CYCADAE (Cycads and fossil allies)

Diagnosis: known from early Mississippian (indefinitely from Upper Devonian) to Recent; plants generally fern-like to palm-like; leaves mostly large, unfolding with development and pinnatified (because of definite fern appearance leaves are often called fronds); stems mostly above the ground or visible at the surface, sometimes an underground rhizome; stem unbranched or branched; sporangia produce two kinds of spores and are on modified leaves as in ferns; gametophyte functionally dependent upon the sporophyte (as in conifers), so the gametophyte and its contained embryo sporophyte are parasitic upon the old sporophyte, and all three generations contribute to seed formation.

ORDER CYCADALES (Cycads)

Diagnosis: known from Triassic to Recent; only one United States species; generally resemble small tree ferns or palms, but up to 60 feet tall; leaves typically palm-like, firm, spiny-tipped, and pinnately compound; leaves unfolding with development and resulting in a radiating crown of leaves at the apex of an aerial stem; stem regularly simple and aerial, but sometimes simply branched, lower stem covered by stiff remnants of leaf petiole bases; some stems are underground and tuberous; sporangia separated into male and female cones, but no male cone in the genus including the United States species; rather, sporangia upon modified leaves grouped in a loose crown; cones mostly at a stem apex and above an axillary bud; male and female cones on separate plants (Figure 11.21).

Occurrence: about 65 tropical and subtropical species, one in Florida; represent the remnants of a once much larger group.

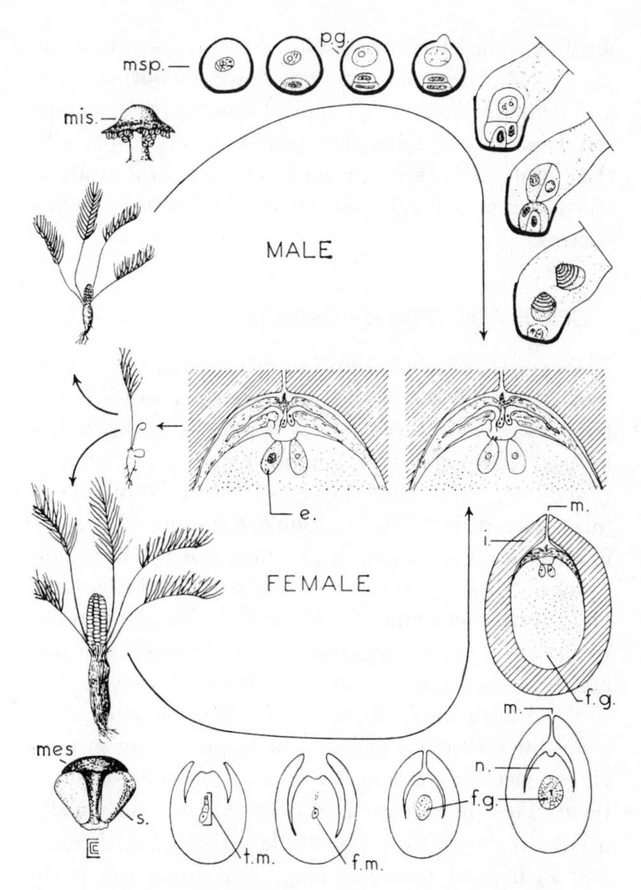

Figure 11.21 Life cycle of *Zamia*, a cycad: e., female sex organ with fertilized egg; f.g., female gametophyte; f.m., functional spore; i., integument; m., micropyle; mes. and mis., sporangium-bearing leaves; msp., male spore; n., nucellus; p.g., pollen grain; t.m., four spores; s., sporangium. (Used by permission, from Arthur Cronquist, *Introductory Botany*, Harper, New York, 1961.)

CLASS GINKGOAE (Maidenhair Tree)

ORDER GINKGOALES

Diagnosis: known from the Permian (indefinitely from Pennsylvanian and even Upper Devonian) to Recent; one living species *Ginkgo biloba*, native to China; but probably no longer occurs in the wild; commonly large trees to over 100 feet tall and with bases 4 feet wide; typically consisting of a straight central axis, but erect to drooping lateral branches usually start from near the ground level (branches approach the diameter of the central axis), sometimes tending toward a basal trunk and many branches; leaf blades wedge-shaped or fan-like, 1 to 2 inches long, petiole somewhat longer; leaves deciduous and resembling maidenhair ferns (*Adiantum*), mostly upon short shoots and not upon the main branches; two spore types, plants male or female; males with cones similar to those of cycads; females without typical cones, female "cone" consisting of a long stalk, stalk apex mostly with two ovules (one usually degenerates), base of each ovule surrounded by a "collar"; mature seeds with a fleshy covering ("apricot-like") (Figure 11.22).

CLASS CONIFERAE (Conifers and allies)

Diagnosis: known from Mississippian to Recent; generally much like the Cycadae except that the leaves are generally small, simple, and not bipinnate (some *Ginkgo* leaves are divided many times); mostly trees with stems and roots similar to the Cycadae; two spore types like the Cycadae, but sporangia appear to be borne upon structures that never develop through a leaf stage (however, even if this were true, the conifer condition could represent no more than a developmental "short cut") (Figure 11.23); in modern forms, female cones are complex and unlike the simple cycad cones, but the male cones of both cycads and conifers are similar; typical cones are absent in the Taxales and Gnetales; certain forms, especially the Coniferales, have special resin ducts and resin, a character apparently shared only with the angiosperms.

ORDER CONIFERALES (Conifers)

Diagnosis: known from Lower Permian to Recent; mostly trees in the form of well-known pines (*Pinus*), larch (*Larix*), spruce (*Picea*), hemlocks (*Tsuga*), firs (*Abies*), redwood (*Sequoia*), cypress (*Cupressus*), juniper (*Juniperus*), plus distinctive Southern Hemisphere forms like Bunya-Bunya, monkey puzzle, and Norfolk Island pine (*Araucaria*), certain Australian region "pines" (*Agathis*), and the widely cultivated Southern Hemisphere fern pines (*Podocarpus*); a few are shrubs; trees with a distinctive central trunk and smaller lateral branches (similar to most fossil forms) to 300 feet tall with bases 20 feet wide in redwoods; considerable secondary tissue growth, producing growth rings reflecting wet and dry seasons (annual rings can be used to approximate past climate); leaves typically needle-like or narrow (mostly less than ⅛ inch wide and ½ inch to 6 inches long), but some are fairly broad and almost have true parallel venation; some leaves are minute and scale-like, none are fan-shaped as in ginkgos; leaf arrangement is normally alternate in a close spiral, but both opposite and whorled arrangements occur; various modified leaf arrangements exist, some leaves are on specialized short shoots and others are bound together at the base by a membranous bundle sheath, or fascicle, that is formed from leaves fusing; sporangia arranged in male or female cones, differing from other living orders by the presence of distinct cones; male cones about ¼ inch to 4 inches long; female cones about 1 to 20 inches long; female cones typically woody (*Pinus*) or at least parchment-like (*Sequoia*) in consistency, but certain forms (*Juniperus*) are almost fleshy and berry-like (Figure 11.24).

Occurrence: about 300 living species, mostly in temperate and cold temperate climates but occurring from Arctic to Antarctic Circles; represent remnants of a once much larger group.

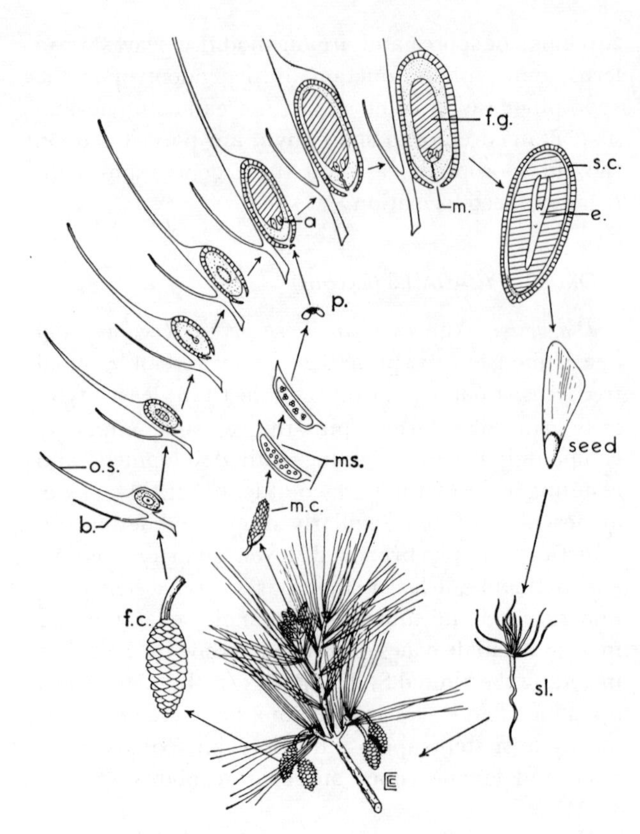

Figure 11.23 Life cycle of a pine, *Pinus:* a., female sex organ; b., cone scale; e., embryo; f.c., female cone; f.g., female gametophyte; m., micropyle; m.c., male cone; ms., male sporangium in cone scale; o.s., egg-bearing part of cone scale; p., pollen grain; s.c., seed coat; sl., seedling. (Used by permission, from Arthur Cronquist, *Introductory Botany*, Harper, New York, 1961.)

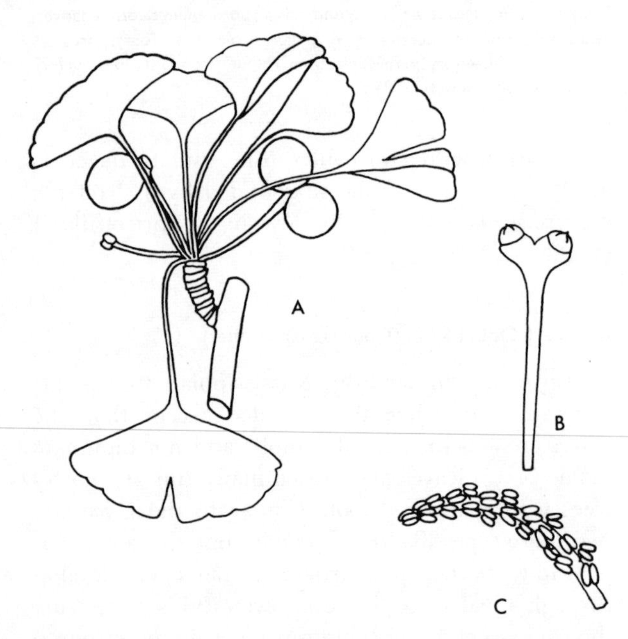

Figure 11.22 The maidenhair tree, *Ginkgo:* A, fruiting branch; B, female branch with two developing ovules; C, male branch or cone.

Figure 11.24 Conifer types: 1, knobcone pine, *Pinus attenuata;* 2, western larch or tamarack, *Larix occidentalis;* 3, Sitka spruce, *Picea sitchensis;* 4, western hemlock, *Tsuga heterophylla;* 5, Douglas fir, *Pseudotsuga menziesii;* 6, white fir, *Abies concolor;* 7, bigtree or giant redwood, *Sequoiadendron gigantea;* 8, incense cedar, *Libocedrus decurrens;* 9, western red cedar or arborvitae, *Thuja plicata;* 10, Monterey cypress, *Cupressus macrocarpa;* 11, Utah juniper, *Juniperus utahensis.* (Redrawn from *Forest Trees of the Pacific Slope* by George B. Sudsworth. Washington, D. C.: USDA, 1908.)

ORDER TAXALES (Yews)

Diagnosis: known from Jurassic to Recent; generally large trees to about 90 feet tall and with bases over 3 feet wide; commonly consisting of a straight central axis above a branching root system, the trunk scaly or fissured and the top half bearing branches that often droop; lateral branches bearing spirally arranged, simple, entire, lanceolate, and stiff parallel-veined leaves, ½ inch to 3 inches long; without typical cones; two to eight sporangia in a flower-like arrangement; male sporangia normally stalked and stamen-like, borne singly or in spike-like arrangements in the leaf axils; female sporangia contribute to ovule formation, but the general structure is only vaguely pistil-like; seeds with a fleshy covering; plants male or female (Figure 11.25).

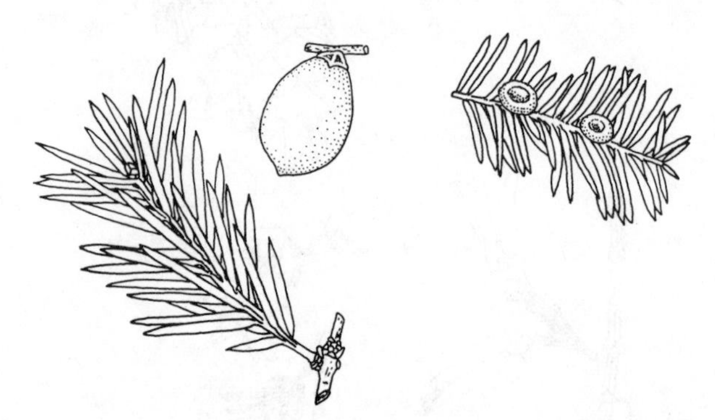

Figure 11.25 Yew types. Left, California nutmeg, *Torreya californica*. Right, western yew, *Taxus brevifolia*. (Redrawn from Sudsworth.)

Occurrence: about 15 species in 3 genera; *Austrotaxus* is limited to New Caledonia; *Torreya* has one species in western Florida, one in California and probably three in China and Japan; *Taxus* (yews) has one western United States, one eastern United States, and probably six other species, the genus being represented on all continents except South America and Australia.

ORDER GNETALES

Diagnosis: composed of three genera, *Gnetum*, *Ephedra*, and *Welwitschia*, probably only remotely related and not in the same order; angiosperm-like in vein arrangement and *Gnetum* with habit and leaves like the Subclass Dicotyledoneae; no resins (found in many gymnosperms); male and female cones compound and flower-like (especially the male cone of *Welwitschia*); *Gnetum* reproduction involving a structure similar to an angiosperm embryo sac; embryos with two embryo leaves, and leaves in opposite pairs.

Welwitschia, only one living species, is found in the desert and semidesert areas of coastal southwestern Africa. It is one of the truly strange plants, composed of two large (to about 6 feet long), strap-like, often apically frayed leaves inserted upon opposite sides of the barely exposed part of the woody stem. The barely exposed part of the stem is a concave disc up to 4 feet in diameter; the disc margin bears many-branched fertile shoots about 6 inches tall, each shoot containing many cones. The underground stem is long, large, and tuberous. Some plants apparently live more than 100 years.

Gnetum is represented by about 30 species in the forests of the world's tropics. They are mostly climbers, but a few are trees or shrubs. The leaves and habits are much like those of certain climbing, shrub or tree, dicot angiosperms.

Ephedra contains about 35 species; generally cosmopolitan in semidesert to desert areas. Most species (including those in the United States) are twiggy, often green-stemmed (young stems) shrubs with two opposite, or three whorled, scale-like, inconspicuous leaves at the nodes (Figure 11.26). They may also be tree-like or climbing. Plants are mostly male or female, cones compound and flower-like.

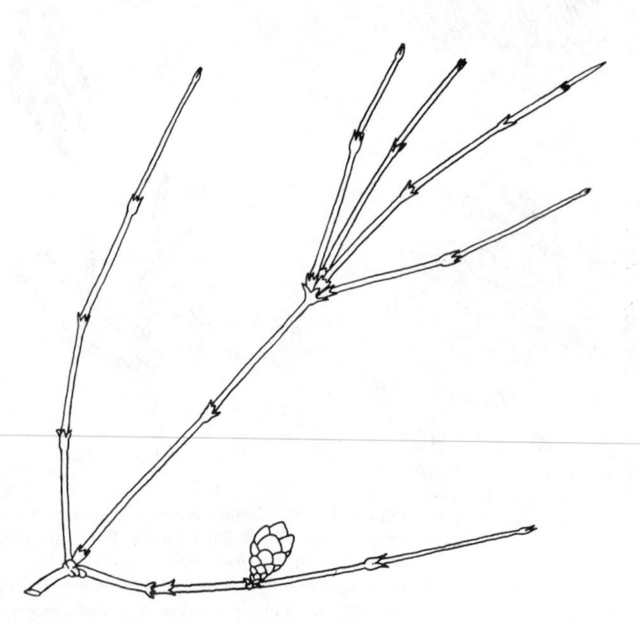

Figure 11.26 *Ephedra*, the only United States genus of the Order Gnetales (x ½).

CLASS ANGIOSPERMAE (Flowering Plants)

Diagnosis: definite remains no older than Lower Cretaceous but questionable forms back to Mid- to Upper Triassic; the most abundant group of living plants; habit and growth form various, trees, shrubs, and herbs; herbs perennial, biennial, and annual; a natural group of seed plants distinguished from the somewhat artificial group of gymnosperms primarily by reproductive structures; angiosperms are unique in the possession of true flowers; in pollen being specialized for transportation by water and organisms as well as by wind; by the pollen tube having to travel through several parts of a central floral structure (pistil) to reach the opening (micropyle) of the ovule; by a process of double fertilization involving the formation of a nutritive tissue (endosperm), as well as the zygote; by the ovules (and seeds) being formed within "vessels" (modified leaves) instead of "naked" (upon the surface); by gametophyte development generally being much more abbreviated; by gametophytes typically being smaller, simpler structured, and without definite sex organs; by embryos being nourished by endosperm; and by the seeds being enclosed within fruits. Include two major groups. Subclass Dicotyledoneae (dicots) and Subclass Monocotyledoneae (monocots) whose features are contrasted in Figure 11.27.

The "vessel" enclosing the ovule has nothing to do with the veins, or xylem or phloem; rather it is part of a structure called a carpel, which in turn is the prime component of a pistil. A simple pistil is composed of a stigma (pollen receiver), a style (a connecting link), and an ovary (ovules, hence seeds, are formed inside). A compound pistil is formed by fusion of simple pistils into a single structure. Each simple pistil, or unit of a compound pistil, is a carpel (a modified female sporangium-bearing leaf). Therefore, both ovules and young seeds are enclosed in the ovary portion of a single carpel, so either the ovary or entire carpel can be considered "the vessel."

The *fruits* are the containers of mature seeds. Fruits

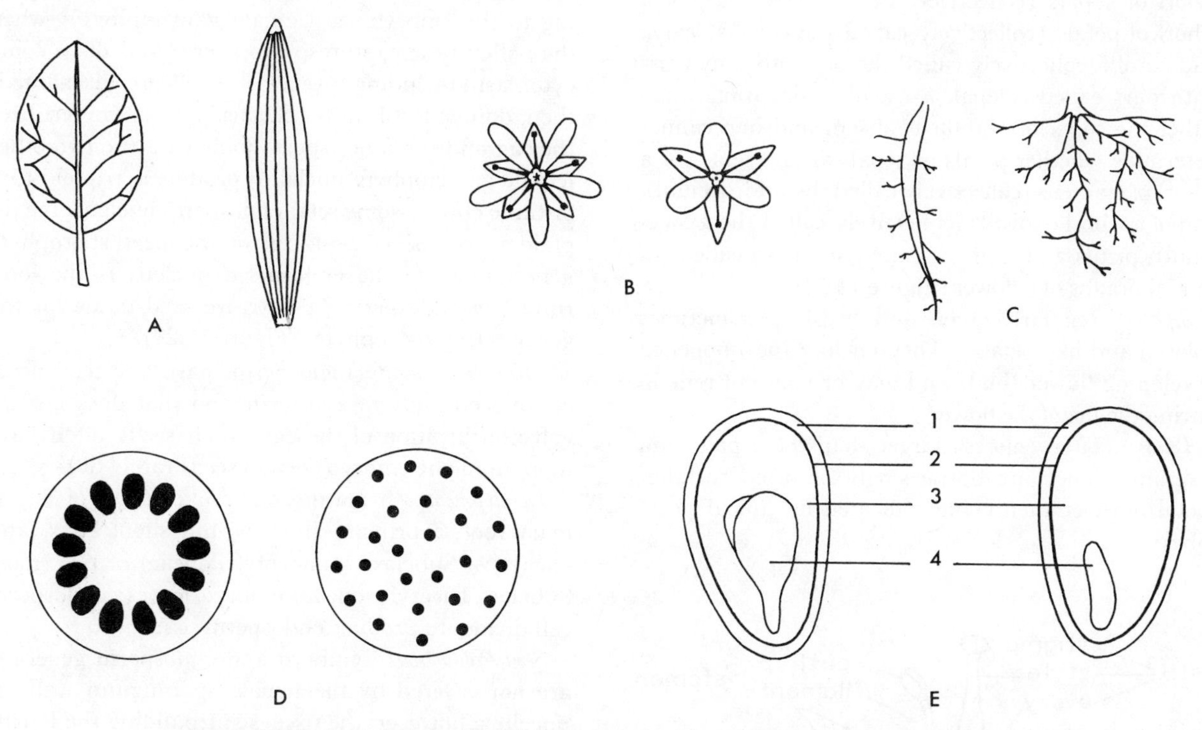

Figure 11.27 Dicots (Subclass Dicotyledoneae) to the left contrasted with monocots (Subclass Monocotyledoneae) to the right of each pair of diagrams: A, net venation vs. parallel venation of leaves; B, flower parts usually in fives (also twos and fours) vs. in threes (or multiples of three); C, usually with taproots vs. with fibrous roots; D, vascular bundles in a single cylinder (forming a growth ring each year) vs. scattered (no cambium to form annual rings); E, embryo with two developmental leaves vs. with one developmental leaf—(1) seed coat, (2) sporangium wall or nucellus, (3) endosperm, and (4) embryo. (Modified from various sources.)

are derived from a single carpel or groups of carpels and sometimes from other floral parts as well.

Occurrence: include the vast majority of living plants; about 200,000 living species found throughout the world; mostly land plants and free-living, but there are epiphytes, parasites, animal predators in the form of certain species that utilize mostly insects as food, as well as many freshwater and even a few marine forms.

FLOWER

May be no more than a group of modified leaves, only certain kinds with sporangia. This interpretation is generally accepted for various reasons. For example, parasitized flowers often form into a group of leaf-like structures. A flower is one of the few organ systems found in plants.

Structure: commonly borne upon an inflated part (receptacle) of a special flower stalk (pedicel); typically composed of four whorls of distinctive parts; from outermost to innermost whorls, composed of a whorl of sepals (collectively called the calyx), of a whorl of petals (collectively called the corolla; calyx and corolla collectively called the perianth; any perianth part called a tepal, a useful designation when either the calyx or corolla is absent and one cannot determine whether petals or sepals are present), of a whorl of stamens (collectively called the androecium), and of a whorl of pistils (collectively called the gynoecium); pistils and stamens comprise the so-called essential organs of a flower (Figure 11.28).

Sepals: regularly green and leaf-like, sometimes colored and like petals. They enclose the unopened developing flower (bud) and may or may not remain during the life of the flower.

Petals: often colored, larger than the sepals, and fragrant. They are borne singly or fused together (petal number then being indicated by apical petal lobes).

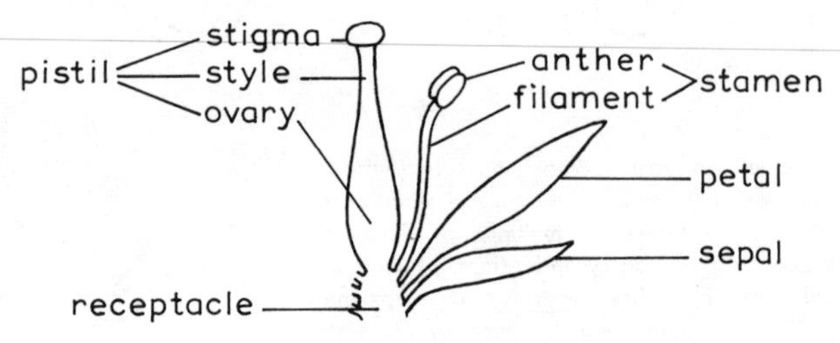

Figure 11.28 Parts of a flower.

Stamens: vary greatly in size and organization; each usually consists of two parts, anthers, containing one or more, usually four, male sporangia called pollen sacs and a sterile, hair-like filament (or stalk) that attaches the anther to the receptacle.

Pistils: basic unit the carpel. They are either simple and composed of a single carpel, or compound and composed of two or more fused carpels. Each carpel (pistil unit) of a compound pistil usually can be distinguished either by cross-sectioning the ovary and counting the number of ovary partitions, or by counting the number of style or stigma lobes.

SEED FORMATION

Fertilization: pollen is specialized to travel by wind, organisms (mostly insects), and/or water; normally mechanisms prevent self-pollenation by a plant; flower stigma secretes a sticky, sugary fluid which catches and perhaps stimulates pollen germination; upon contacting a stigma, a pollen grain germinates, growing between stigma cells, down the style (often a hollow structure), generally enters an opening to the embryo sac (female gametophyte); when the pollen tube ruptures, two sperm and often some cytoplasm including a vegetative cell are discharged; then, double fertilization because one sperm fertilizes the egg and the other sperm joins with the two other female gametophyte nuclei to produce a triploid (3n, or three chromosome sets) endosperm nucleus; the diploid zygote is the first cell of the next sporophyte generation and the endosperm nucleus is the forerunner of endosperm (a nutritive seed tissue for the germinating sporophyte) (Figure 11.29).

Apomixis: some angiosperms have a special process of seed and embryo formation that does not involve fertilization of the egg; such seeds often have more than one embryo (sexual seeds rarely do).

Development: a mature embryo consists of a primary root, a primary shoot with a shoot apex, and one (most Subclass Monocotyledoneae) or two (most Subclass Dicotyledoneae) embryo leaves; endosperm cell divides to produce endosperm tissue.

Seed Production: embryo and endosperm generally are not covered by the female sporangium wall, or nucellus; however, the tissues surrounding the female sporangium (integument) generally become thick, layered, and form a very hard seed coat.

Fruits: seeds are usually covered by the ripened ovary wall and often certain other ripened structures.

Germination: seeds normally require a resting

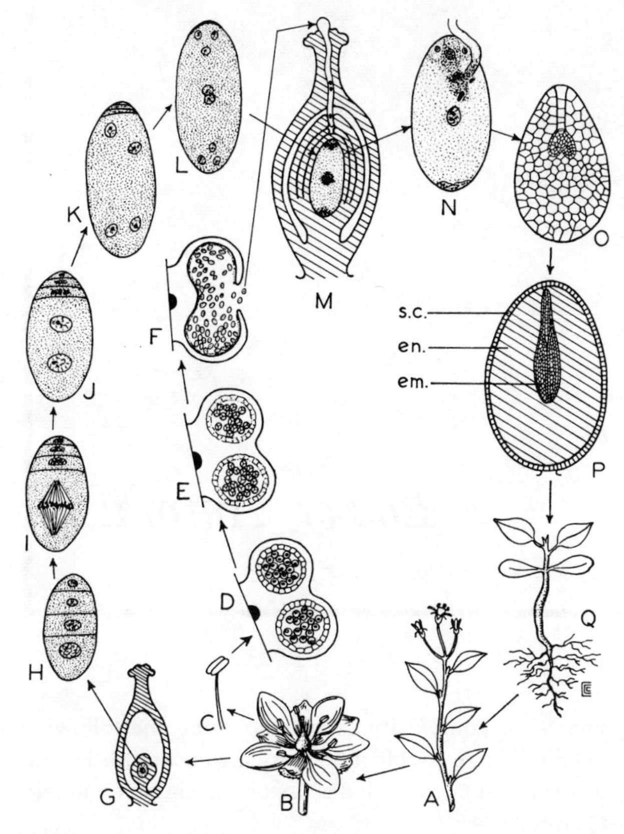

Figure 11.29 Life cycle of an angiosperm. A, mature sporophyte; B, flower; C, stamen; D-F, development of pollen; G, pistil; H-L, development of embryo sac; M, growth of the pollen tube toward the embryo sac; N, release of the sperms into the embryo sac; O, developing embryo and endosperm; P, mature seed; Q, seedling: em., embryo; en., endosperm; s.c., seed coat. (Used by permission, from Arthur Cronquist, *Introductory Botany*, Harper, New York, 1961.)

stage before germination is possible; otherwise, essentially as in the Conifierae.

SPOROPHYTE

Structure: various; include perennial trees, shrubs, and herbs, plus biennial and annual herbs.

Sporangium: included in flowers; male sporangia in the anthers and female sporangia functionally represented within the ovule.

Stems: range from structures similar in their heavy, secondary growth to the conifers, to herbaceous types with little or no secondary growth.

Leaves: run the gamut of structural complexity more than do the leaves of any other group of plants; are frequently modified or specialized appendages with distinct names; most Monocotyledoneae have parallel venation and most Dicotyledoneae have net venation.

Roots: mostly as in other spermatophytes.

Reproduction: male plants produce male spores in the form of pollen grains; fertilization takes place within the ovule in an ovary of a flower.

SELECTED READINGS

Benson, L., 1957. *Plant Classification.* D. C. Heath & Co., Boston.

Chamberlain, C. J., 1935. *Gymnosperms: Structure and Evolution.* The University of Chicago Press, Chicago.

Foster, A. S., and E. M. Gifford, 1959. *Comparative Morphology of Vascular Plants.* Wm. Freeman Co., San Francisco.

Galston, A. W., 1961. *The Life of the Green Plant.* Foundation of Modern Biology Series. Prentice-Hall Inc., Englewood Cliffs, N.J.

Lawrence, G. H. M., 1951. *Taxonomy of Vascular Plants.* The Macmillan Co., New York.

Moldenke, H. N., 1949. *American Wildflowers.* D. Van Nostrand Co., Princeton, N. J.

Palmer, E. L., 1949. *Fieldbook of Natural History.* McGraw-Hill Book Co., New York.

Platt, R. H., 1942. *This Green World.* Dodd, Mead & Co., New York.

Ray, P. M., 1963. *The Living Plant.* Modern Biology Series. Holt, Rinehart & Winston, Inc., New York.

Scientific American Book, 1949. *Plant Life.* Simon & Schuster, New York.

Weisz, P. B., and M. S. Fuller, 1962. *The Science of Botany.* McGraw-Hill Book Co., New York.

Note: Identification of vascular plants requires special knowledge and the use of various locally oriented books or monographs called floras.

12 MESOZOA THROUGH ENTOPROCTA

Lower Animals

When the Protozoa are considered members of the Kingdom Protista, the animal kingdom is easily separated from the plant kingdom. Animals lack chlorophyll, cells containing a cell wall, plastids, and a central vacuole. However, some similarity of animals and plants is implied in the chemical resemblance of the animal blood pigment, hemoglobin, to chlorophyll.

Many other differences often exist between plants and animals. Only animals have the following as well-developed tendencies: mobility, holozoic nutrition, fixed structure, marked responses to stimuli, body fluids resembling sea water, and structures and functions that tend to maintain a constant internal body environment. In addition, animals almost invariably have a haplobiontic, adult diploid, life cycle. However, an alternation of generations in which one adult is produced by asexual reproduction also occurs. Therefore, for practical purposes, animals lack a gametophyte generation. By analogy, one might say that almost all adult animals are comparable to a plant sporophyte.

In our classification of the animal kingdom, we will consider first two groups that are characterized by cellular organization (Mesozoa and Porifera) and two phyla whose differentiation lies in tissue organization (Coelenterata and Ctenophera). All of the remaining phyla possess organs grouped into organ systems of increasing complexity. Before reading the following detailed diagnosis of animal phyla, you would do well to review the general discussion of classification in Chapter 7.

CELLULAR ORGANIZATION: MESOZOA AND PORIFERA

The cellular animals encompass two subkingdoms. The Subkingdom Mesozoa includes a single phylum, also called Mesozoa, and the Subkingdom Parazoa likewise includes a single phylum, the Porifera.

MESOZOA

Diagnosis: cellular, organization; symmetry radial or bilateral; minute, up to about 0.4 inch long; cellular organization consists of an outer layer of cells or of nuclei not separated into individual cells and an inner layer of one or more reproductive cells; the two cell layers not comparable to ectoderm and endoderm; life history complicated, with an alternation of generations; internal parasites; two orders, one parasitic in the kidneys of squids and octopuses, the other in the internal spaces and tissues of various invertebrates (flatworms, ribbon worms, brittle stars, segmented worms, and clams) (Figure 12.1).

Kingdom Animalia (L. *animalis*, animate)—animals
Subkingdom Mesozoa (Gr. *mesos*, middle + *zoon*, animal)—mesozoans
Phylum Mesozoa (Gr. *mesos* + *zoon*)—mesozoans
Subkingdom Parazoa (Gr. *para*, beside + *zoon*)—parazoans
Phylum Porifera (L. *porus*, passage + *fero*, to bear)—sponges
Class Calcarea (L. *calcarius*, pertaining to lime)—calcareous sponges
Class Hexactinellida (Gr. *hex*, six + *aktinos*, rayed + *ella*, diminutive ending)—glass sponges
Class Demospongia (Gr. *demas*, frame + *spongos*, sponge)—frame sponge
Subkingdom Eumetazoa (Gr. *eu-*, true + *meta*, among + *zoon*)—eumetazoans
Grade Radiata (L. *radiatus*, rayed)
Phylum Coelenterata (Gr. *koilos*, hollow + *enteron*, gut)—coelenterates
Class Hydrozoa (Gr. *hydra*, mythical water serpent + *zoon*)—hydrozoans
Order Hydroidea (Gr. *hydra* + *-oideos*, type or form of)—hydroids
Order Hydrocoralina (Gr. *hydra* + *korallion*, coral + L. *-ina*, like)—hydrocorals
Order Trachylina (Gr. *trachys*, rough + L. *-ina*)—hydromedusae
Order Siphonophora (Gr. *siphon*, siphon + *phoros*, bearing)—siphonophores
Class Scyphozoa (Gr. *skyphos*, cup + *zoon*)—jellyfishes
Order Stauromedusae (Gr. *stauros*, a cross + *medousa*, mythical monster)—sessile jellyfishes
Order Cubomedusae (Gr. *kybos*, a cube + *medousa*)—jellyfishes
Order Coronatae (L. *corona*, a crown + *medousa*)—jellyfishes
Order Discomedusae (Gr. *diskos*, a disc + *medousa*)—jellyfishes
Class Anthozoa (Gr. *anthos*, flower + *zoon*)—sea anemones and corals
Subclass Alcyonaria (Gr. *alkyon*, the kingfisher + L. *-aria*, like)—false corals
Order Stolonifera (L. *stolonis*, a shoot or branch + *fero*, to bear)—stolon corals
Order Telestacea (Gr. *telestes*, a poet)—false stolon corals
Order Alcyonacea (Gr. *alkyon*)—soft corals
Order Gorgonacea (L. *gorgo*, mythical monster)—horny corals
Order Pennatulacea (L. *pennatulus*, winged)—sea pens and allies
Subclass Zoantharia (Gr. *zoon* + *anthos* + L. *-aria*)—sea anemones and corals
Order Actinaria (Gr. *aktinos*, rayed + L. *-aria*)—sea anemones
Order Madreporaria (NL. *madre*, mother + *-pora*, pore + L. *-aria*)—stony corals
Order Zoanthidea (Gr. *zoon* + *anthos*)—false sea anemones
Order Ceriantharia (Gr. *keras*, horn + *anthos* + L. *-aria*)—tube anemones
Phylum Ctenophora (Gr. *ktenos*, comb + *phoros*, bearing)—comb jellies
Grade Bilateria (L. *bi-*, two + *lateralis*, side)
Acoelomata (Gr. *a-*, without + *koilos*, hollow)
Phylum Platyhelminthes (Gr. *platy*, flat + *helminthes*, worms)—flatworms
Class Turbellaria (L. *turbella*, a disturbance + *-aria*)—free-living flatworms
Class Trematoda (Gr. *trematodes*, with holes)—flukes
Class Cestoda (Gr. *kestos*, girdle)—tapeworms
Phylum Nemertea (Gr. *nemertes*, mythology, a nereid)—ribbon worms
Pseudocoelomata (Gr. *pseudes*, false + *koilos*, hollow)
Phylum Acanthocephala (Gr. *acanthos*, spine + *kephale*, head)—spiny-headed worms
Phylum Aschelminthes (Gr. *askos*, cavity + *helminthes*)—cavity worms
Class Rotatoria (L. *rota*, wheel)—rotifers or wheel animalcules
Class Nematomorpha (Gr. *nema*, thread + *morphe*, shape)—horsehair worms
Class Nematoda (Gr. *nema*, thread)—roundworms
Class Gastrotricha (L. *gaster*, stomach + *trichos*, hair)—fork-tailed worms
Class Kinorhyncha (Gr. *kineo*, to move + *rhynchos*, snout)—spiny-crowned worms
Class Priapuloidea (Gr. *priap*, phallus + *-oideos*, type or form of)—club worms
Phylum Entoprocta (Gr. *entos*, inside + *proktos*, anus)—entoprocts or moss animals

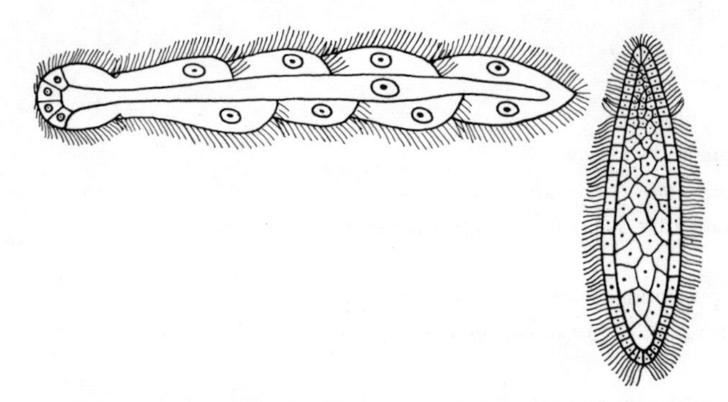

Figure 12.1 Two types of mesozoans. Drawn to indicate both external and internal structure: *Dicyema* to the left and *Rhopalura* to the right. (Modified from various sources.)

We have already examined the conflicting ideas of biologists on the structure of the Protozoa; the additional fact that scientists do not agree on the phylogenetic position of the Mesozoa might cause the reader to believe that biologists are an argumentative group. If one is more serious about the various controversies in biology, he realizes that they exemplify a dictum of science: nothing should be accepted as fact whenever there is room for disagreement. All possible explanations of any phenomenon must be considered.

Some zoologists believe that mesozoans are a degenerate group of free-living flatworms. The idea that they might be degenerate flatworms stems from their being parasites and their simplified flatworm-like structure. Moreover, parasites tend to become structurally simplified, often losing many of their organs. Many parasites are little more than nutrient-absorbing, reproductive organs. Other zoologists believe that mesozoans are exactly what they appear to be, a group that lies structurally between the Protozoa and the Eumetazoa—hence their name, "middle animals." This latter interpretation has gained favor because mesozoan surface cells, which have the ability to engulf and digest food, are far removed from the kind of cells found in flatworms. Furthermore, one might say that these animals resemble some ciliate protozoans: both groups have cell-like structure, or cells that ingest and digest food; have cilia throughout much of their life history; and have an internal layer of specialized, reproductive "cells."

The Mesozoa are also of interest because they have two cell layers that are not comparable to germ layers and have one or more life cycle stages that are unknown. For example, in one order, parasitic in octopuses and squids, only the sexual cycle is known; an asexual cycle, which seemingly must exist, is not known.

PORIFERA (Sponges)

Diagnosis: cellular organization; symmetry radial or asymmetrical; occur as thin flat crusts, plant-like branches, and vase-like globular or irregular masses; colors range from gray to drab to brilliant red, orange, yellow, blue, violet, or black; adults attached to rocks or other objects; without mouth or organs of any kind; body permeated with pores, canals, and chambers through which a water current flows; body generally rigid and spiny or velvety to the touch, rarely slimy; marine, except for one fresh-water family.

This phylum may be confused with the Ectoprocta, Entoprocta, some Chordata (tunicates), and some Algae. Sponges, however, usually have one or more visible openings, depending upon solitary or colonial forms; the other phyla do not. Also, sponges tend to be unique in having readily visible internal cavities. Individuals in a sponge colony mass are rarely discernable, but Ectoprocta, Entoprocta, and the Tunicata usually are, even though individuals in Ectoprocta, Entoprocta, and Tunicata may be minute. The Algae form smooth, usually rock-like and purplish crusts.

The sponges are many-celled animals, but unlike all other multicellular animals (except the Mesozoa) sponge cells are not combined into tissues. The individual cells function much like members of a protozoan colony, so sponges are organized on a cellular basis. These and other features have caused them to be classified as the Subkingdom Parazoa, "beside animals," implying that they stand beside rather than among the other animals.

Simple, solitary, adult sponges are vase-like, sedentary animals (Figure 12.2). They possess, in certain surface cells, pores that lead into a large central cavity which has a single, large, mouth-like opening to the exterior. The central cavity is lined by flagellate cells with the whip-like structures surrounded by a collar. These cells produce a current into the central cavity through the surface pores and out of the cavity through the large opening. This simple organization is called the *ascon* type. In the more complex organizations the current-producing cells are found not in the central cavity, but in special cham-

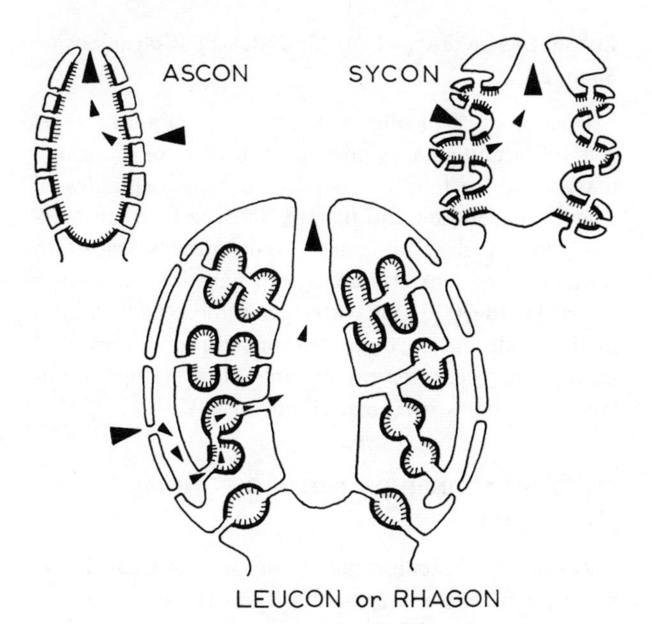

Figure 12.2 Types of canal systems in sponges.

bers of greater and greater complexity. In the *sycon* type the pores are sunk into chambers that are in turn parallel to the chambers where all the current-producing cells are located. The *leucon* type displays still greater ramification of chambers with further withdrawal of the current-producing cells from the central cavity. Most sponges are not solitary, but occur as interconnected individuals (e.g., the common encrusting forms).

The anatomy of the simplest sponge type is most easily studied through the microscope. The outer layer is composed of flattened cells. Within is a jelly-like, nonliving layer containing living, wandering, *amoeboid cells*, so-named because of their resemblance to *Amoeba*, a protozoan. These amoeboid cells carry on many of the life processes of the sponge. They form spine-like, calcareous or siliceous *spicules* (spicule composition and shape are used to characterize the classes of sponges). Amoeboid cells also secrete horny *spongin*, the material of the bath sponge and certain other complex sponges. Both spicules and spongin when present form a sponge's skeleton. The inner layer of a simple sponge is principally current-producing cells. Besides creating a water current, these cells capture microscopic food organisms. The resulting nutrients are probably distributed to the sponge by amoeboid cells. An additional cell type, the already mentioned pore cell, contains a canal throughout its length. Pore cells are so oriented that the canal leads from the exterior to the central cavity, forming the surface pores. Pore cells and these current-producing cells are found in no other multicellular animal. Current-producing cells, however, exactly resemble certain free-living protozoans, some flagellates. Because of this and the strange development of sponges, some zoologists believe that sponges had flagellate ancestors, but arose separately from other multicellular animals. Although the microscopic anatomy of sponges reveals contractile cells around the mouth-like, large, external opening, sponges lack any specialized nerve, muscle, or excretory cells (Figure 12.3).

Sponges are primarily marine animals found from tide pools to the ocean deeps. They are extremely varied in appearance and assume various flat, globular, and branched shapes. Most adults are attached to living or nonliving objects in the sea; however, a few species do not grow on objects. Those sponges growing upon animals may, in a sense, be motile. For example, some sponges grow around snail shells that frequently contain hermit crabs rather than the living snail; other species grow upon crabs. The only group of nonmarine sponges is the strictly fresh-water Family Spongillidae. Spongillidae grow as small to fist-sized, irregular masses on plants or nonliving objects in streams, ponds, and lakes. Their basic colors are yellow and brown, but some are green owing to the presence of microscopic, chlorophyll-bearing flagellates or green algae.

Reproduction in sponges is both asexual and sexual and generally different from that of other groups of animals. Asexual reproduction occurs by budding of individuals and *gemmule* formation. In budding, the parent sponge remains an entity while a bulge in the body wall grows to form a new individual. Gemmules are formed in the jelly-like layer when clumps of amoeboid cells are surrounded by a heavy, resistant *cyst* wall. This latter type of reproduction is more common and seemingly more valuable to fresh-water sponges, because ponds may freeze in winter or dry in summer and the resistant cysts make survival until a favorable period possible. Sexual reproduction also involves the amoeboid cells, which in different individuals give rise to a single egg or to many sperm. The sperm are liberated and swim in the sea water. If fertilization is completed, the sperm must first enter through a pore cell of another sponge, then be engulfed (like food) by the current-producing cells which then become amoeboid, and finally be trans-

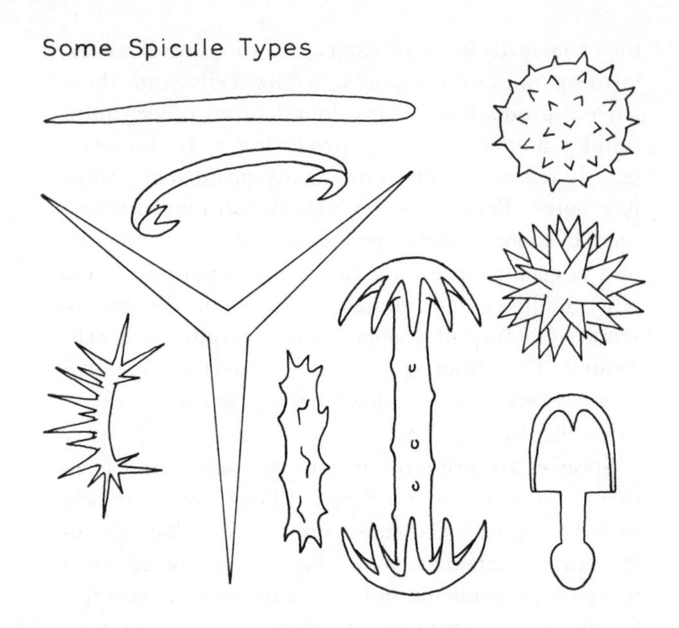

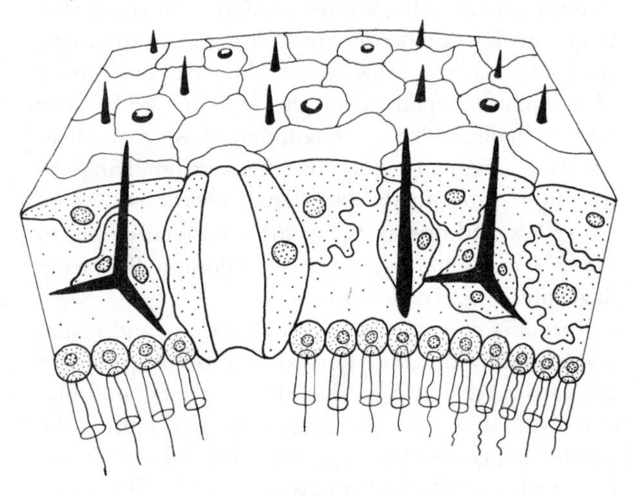

Figure 12.3 Sponge structure.

ferred by the amoeboid cell to an egg to effect fertilization. Development in part resembles that of certain colonial flagellate protozoans.

Regeneration of parts is found in many parts of the animal kingdom, but no other animals can match the amazing powers of the sponges in this respect. One may separate the cells of a sponge by straining them through fine cloth. In a suitable medium, whenever a sufficient number of cell types get together, the cells reorganize to form a new sponge.

CLASS CALCAREA (=CALCISPONGIAE) (Calcareous Sponges)

Diagnosis: typically solitary or colonial vase-shaped organisms; some form bushy or compact masses, and a few have stalk-like bases; spicules of calcium carbonate and usually causing a bristly surface; mostly drab, inconspicuous animals less than 6 inches long; strictly marine organisms occupying intertidal to 3000-foot waters, are most likely found in tidepools either on rocks or within cracks and crevices in rocks, or on marine algae (kelp) holdfasts (root-like structures) (Figure 12.4).

CLASS HEXACTINELLIDA (=HYALOSPONGIA) (Glass Sponges)

Diagnosis: spicules glassy or siliceous, and six-rayed; mostly solitary, cylindrical, vase-, urn-, or funnel-shaped animals, but some are curved, flattened, or branched; most are 4 to 12 inches long; but some are 3 feet long; strictly marine, from 300 feet to 3 miles deep (Figure 12.4).

CLASS DEMOSPONGIA (Frame Sponges)

Diagnosis: three subclasses: Tetractinellida, a shallow-water marine group, lack fibrous spongin and either lack spicules or have four-rayed siliceous ones; Monaxonida, a mostly shallow-water, marine group, but extend to over 3-mile depths and include a fresh-water family; possess toothpick-like siliceous spicules and some have spongin; Keratosa, usually a shallow-water, hard marine bottom group, strictly marine, include the bath or commercial sponges; skeletons all fibrous spongin (Figure 12.4).

RADIATA: COELENTERATA AND CTENOPHORA

The body plan and organization of the Mesozoa and Porifera are based directly on the cell. We now approach another type of complexity, animals whose differentiation can be summed in the tissue. Two phyla, the Coelenterata and the Ctenophora, display this organization. These and all the remaining phyla are members of the Subkingdom Eumetazoa; however all except the Radiata possess definite organs. The

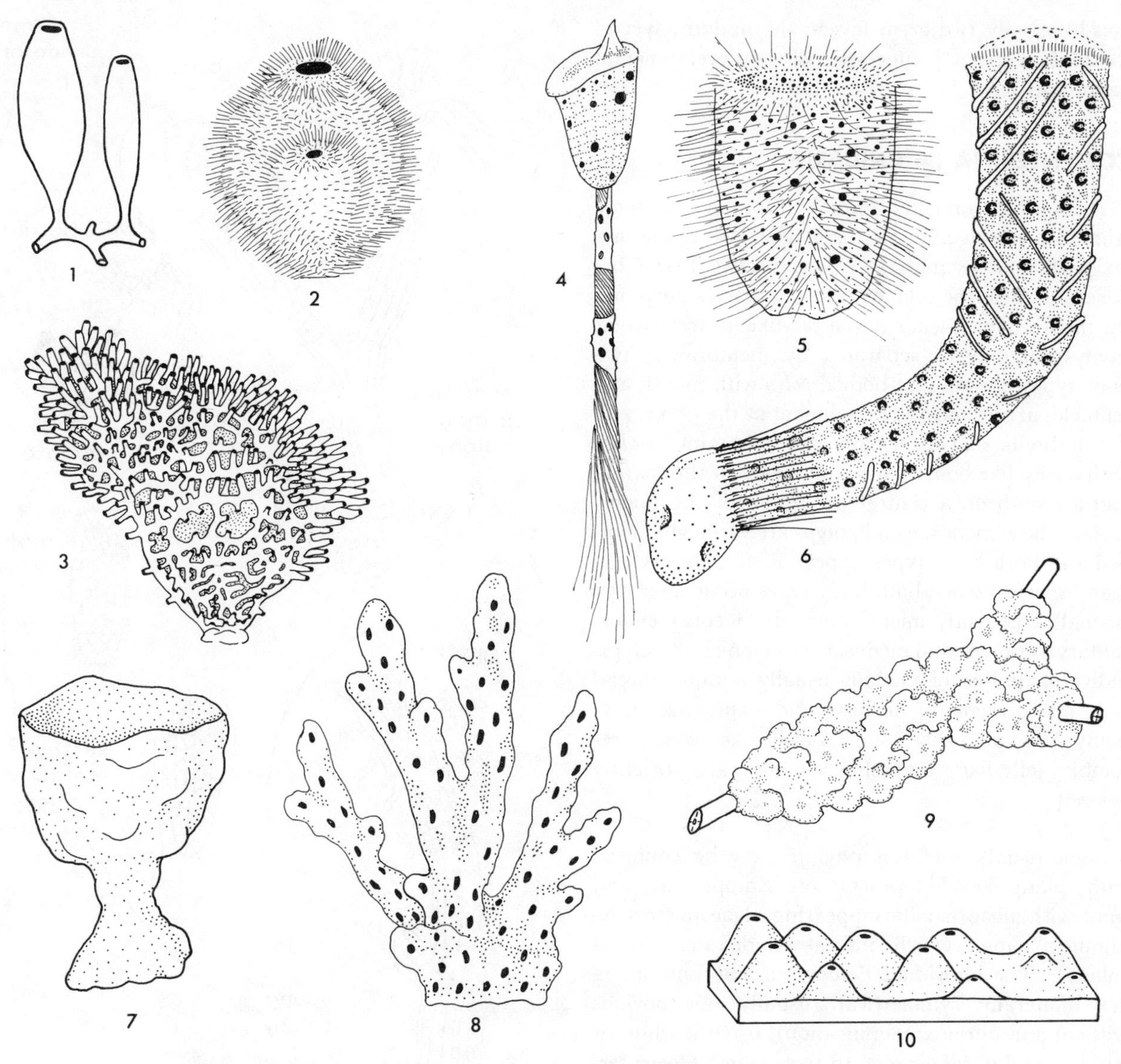

Figure 12.4 Sponge types. Class Calcarea: 1, *Rhabdodermella*, a vase sponge; 2, *Leuconia*, a bristle sponge; 3, *Leucosolenia*, an antler sponge. Class Hexactinellida: 4, *Hyalonema*, a glass rope sponge; 5, *Staurocalyptus*, a glass goblet sponge; 6, *Euplectella*, Venus's flower basket. Class Demospongia: 7, *Poterion*, Neptune's goblet; 8, *Chalina*, a finger sponge; 9, *Spongilla*, a freshwater sponge; 10, *Haliclona*, an encrusting sponge. (4, 5, and 7 modified from various sources.)

group Eumetazoa implies that all its phyla have a common ancestry.

The relationships within the coelenterates is believed very important in the ancestry of Eumetazoa. First, and because of their ciliated larva, it is often assumed that the coelenterates originated from a ciliated or perhaps flagellated ancestral protozoan. According to this hypothesis, the "first" coelenterate was a primitive medusan (jellyfish). This jellyfish, in turn, is considered the ancestor of all coelenterates. From this stem jellyfish, and quite early, were derived a hydromedusan-like animal that was probably close to being the ancestor of all coelenterates and, also, of all Eumetazoa. This assumption is based on such things as hydromedusan structure resembling a developmental stage of the Eumetazoa, for example, hydromedusan tissues contain most of the cell types found in Eumetazoa. Moreover, although coelenterates have only two germ layers, the middle layer of the adult is strongly suggestive of the developmental mesoderm of the Eumetazoa.

COELENTERATA (= CNIDARIA)

Diagnosis: symmetry radial, biradial in some Anthozoa (corals and sea anemones); two tissue layers with some semblance of connective tissue between; no head or segmentation; tentacles surround the mouth, which leads into a sac-like gastrovascular cavity that may be separated by membranes; two body types, the tubular-bodied *polyp* with mouth and tentacles at one end and attachment at the other, and the umbrella-shaped, usually free-swimming, *medusa* with a jelly-like body, having tentacles on the margin and a mouth on a central projection of the undersurface; both medusae and polyps are variously modified and both body types appear in the life cycle of many species; when both body types occur, one type is small, frequently microscopic, and inconspicuous; solitary as polyps and medusae, or colonial as polyps, individual polyps of a colony usually minute; thread cells are present for defense and capturing prey; many look plant-like, some flower-like, others resemble jelly-like umbrellas; many are brightly colored.

Some members of this phylum may be confused with plant-like Ectoprocta or Entoprocta, and some with algae (similar-appearing algae possess no minute "cups" which indicate individuals of a colony). The individual Ectoprocta and Entoprocta are bilaterally symmetrical (usually not obvious without appropriate magnification), usually white or whitish, and usually rough to the touch. Coelenterates are found in both marine and fresh waters.

The tissue basis of organization in coelenterates implies that the tissues, as such, carry on body functions and definite organs are not formed. Division of labor is found in some colonial forms; different individual animals within a single colony are specialized for various different functions, such as feeding, defense, and reproduction. Here one might consider individuals as taking the place of definite organs.

These animals possess a common plan of structure that is expressed in two ways, the *polyp* or the *medusa* (Figure 12.5). In both types, at one end a single opening functions as both mouth and anus. This opening leads into a central cavity within both types of animals. Functionally, the central cavity is called the *gastrovascular cavity* because it is the site of some of the digestive processes and its large size and branchings give it the effect of a circulatory system. The mouth is often at the end of a cone of tissue and, except in a very few cases, is surrounded by a ring of *tentacles*.

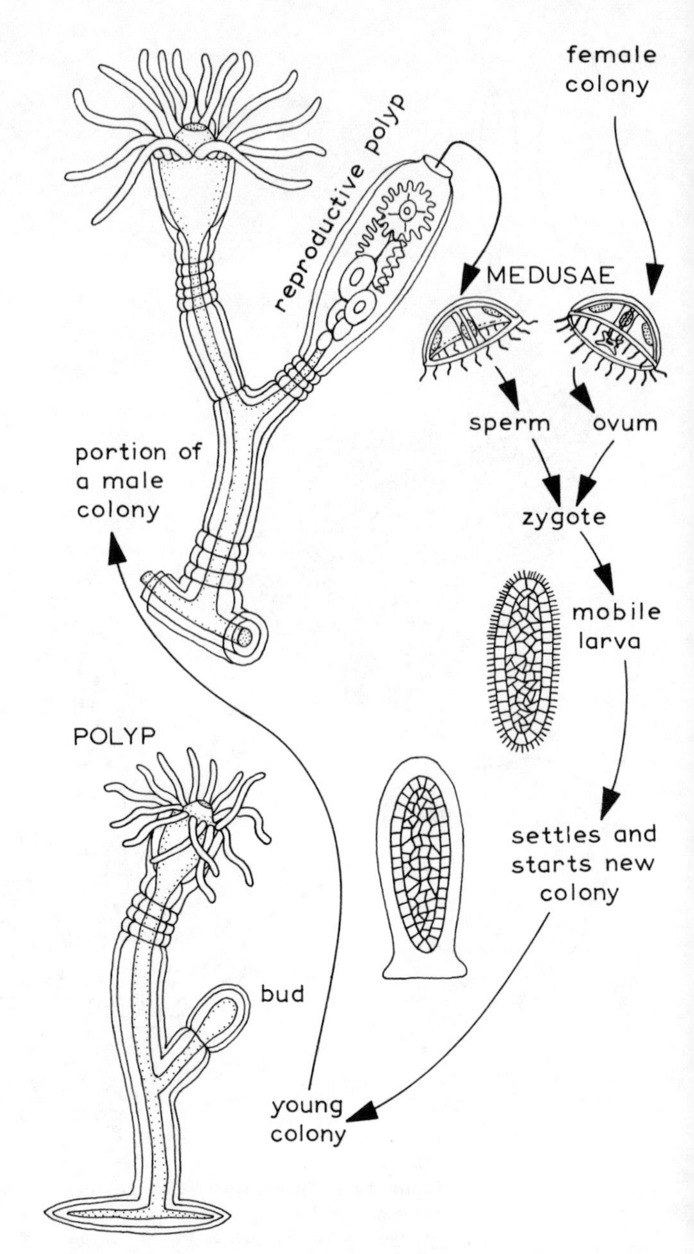

Figure 12.5 Life cycle of the marine colonial hydroid, *Obelia*, showing both medusa and polyp stages and alternation of generations. Variably enlarged and highly diagrammatic.

Coelenterates have two tissue layers, an outer and an inner. Between the two is material which is mostly jelly and in some forms approaches the status of a third tissue layer. Among these layers are several specialized types of cells. There are special outer layer cells which form the thread cells (*nematocysts*) which by stinging, tangling, or other means are used in food capture and defense. Certain T-shaped cells located in the outer and inner layers provide protective and muscle-like tissues—contractile fibers within the cross arm of the T—are responsible for the movements of the body. Of the other cell types found, perhaps the nerve cells are most interesting. These nerve cells are unique; many of them connect into the so-called "nerve net" in which nerve impulses pass in both directions over any individual nerve fiber, a phenomenon unknown elsewhere in the animal kingdom.

Coelenterate reproduction may be asexual by budding, or sexual. Very often the life history is a regular succession of sexual and asexual reproduction, with the sexual generation represented by the medusoid form and the asexual by the polyp form. The hydrozoan *Obelia* is an example of a species displaying this alternation of generations. The fertilized egg develops into a ciliated larva. Settling to the bottom, the larva differentiates and grows to a polyp form from which a whole colony arises by budding. Some of the specialized individuals in the polyp colony give rise to medusae by budding. These medusae are male or female and generally all the medusae produced by one colony are of one sex. The medusae float free in the water and enter the sexual stage by producing eggs or sperm. Slightly different life cycles occur in other coelenterates and represent condensations through loss of some of the stages or dominance of others.

CLASS HYDROZOA

Diagnosis: solitary or colonial; both asexual polyps and sexual medusae present, but one form often is suppressed; polyps without vertical membranes partitioning the gastrovascular cavity; medusae with a velum (a shelf-like membranous ring attached to the inner margin of the "umbrella"); almost entirely marine, but there are a few fresh-water species (the only nonmarine coelenterates); although not rare, the fresh-water species tend to be overlooked (Figure 12.6).

ORDER HYDROIDEA (Hydroids)

Diagnosis: solitary or colonial plant-like animals; polyp generation well developed, medusae if present are small; marine and fresh water.

These animals give the appearance of sedate, plant-like creatures. Although the purely reproductive individuals of any colony appear harmless, other individuals of colonies and the solitary species are predators of the microscopic world. These feeding individuals use their thread cells to spear or "rope" their prey and then, using their tentacles, collect their potential food and carry it to be devoured by the mouth.

Most hydroids are found growing on or among seaweeds. Many kinds can be encountered in intertidal areas, perhaps the most conspicuous being the feather-like colonial species called sea plumes.

ORDER HYDROCORALINA (Hydrocorals)

Diagnosis: colonial, with the polyp form dominant but also with a massive, calcareous skeleton of coral through which two kinds of polyps protrude; marine.

Although their behavior resembles that of the hydroids, hydrocorals are not as likely to be encountered, because most are deep-water forms. However, they are fairly common along the Gulf of Mexico. In Florida, the stinging coral (*Millepora*) is attached to reefs and is of concern to swimmers; this hydrocoral possesses powerful stinging cells. Along the coast of California, there is a purple hydrocoral (*Stylantheca*) that sometimes can be found encrusting rocky ledges at very low tide levels.

None of these animals are true corals. True corals are members of the Class Anthozoa.

ORDER TRACHYLINA (Hydromedusae)

Diagnosis: polyp generation reduced or absent, the medusa being the dominant form; many do not possess any polyp stage, the stage prior to the medusa being a parasite on the parent or another species of hydromedusan; marine and fresh water.

These predators of microscopic animals and protistans are seldom found by amateur collectors. However, in quiet waters on overcast days one might

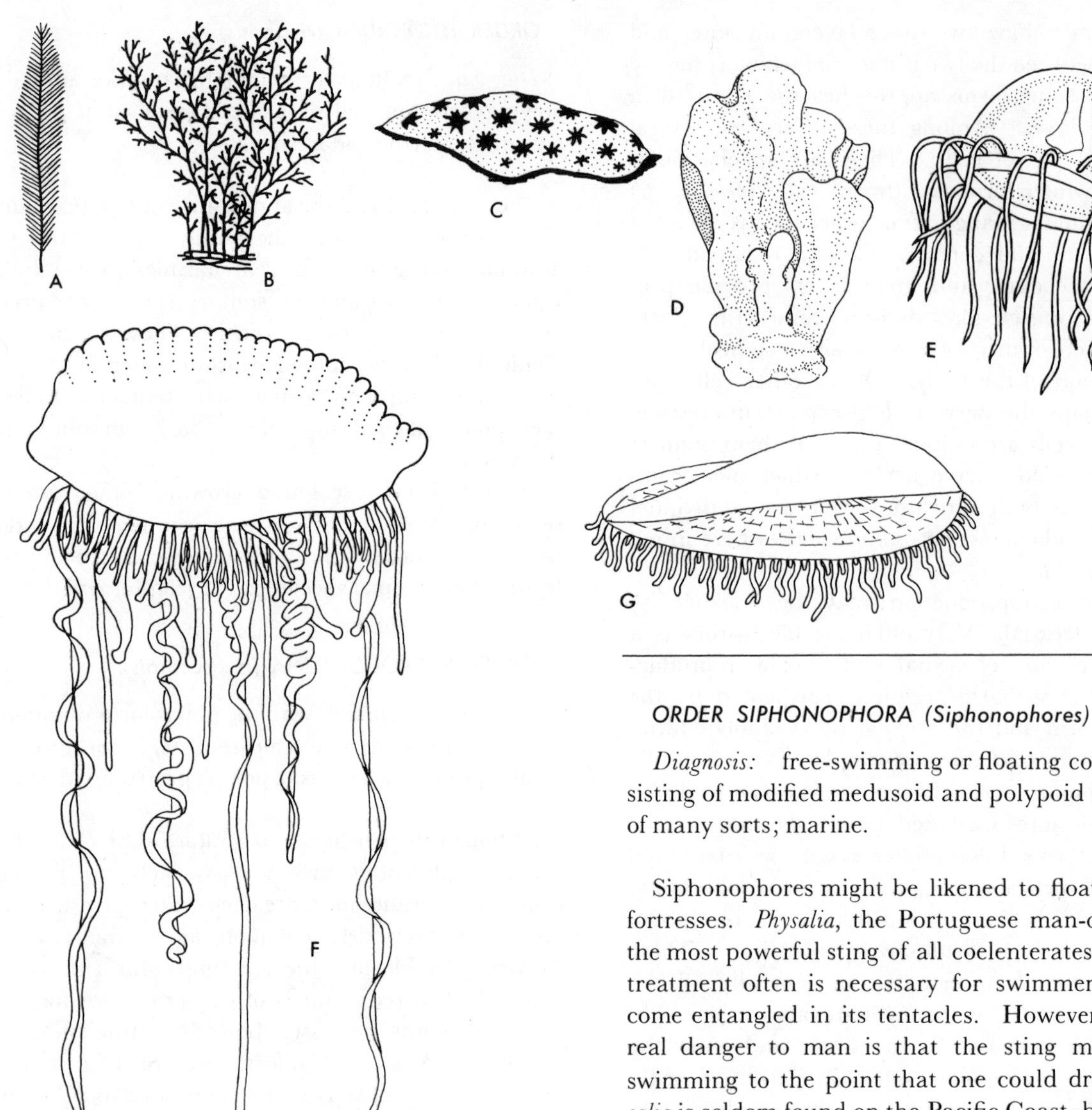

Figure 12.6 Hydrozoan types. Order Hydroidea: A, *Plumularia*, a colonial hydroid or sea feather; B, *Obelia*, a colonial hydroid. Order Hydrocoralina: C, *Stylantheca*, a hydrocoral; D, *Millepora*, a hydrocoral (an enlargement would resemble *Stylantheca*). Order Trachylina: E, *Gonionemus*, an hydromedusan. Order Siphonophora: F, *Physalia*, the Portuguese man-of-war; G, *Velella*, the purple sailor.

find a ½ to ¾ inch species that is made conspicuous by its reddish-brown sex organs; the "bell" and numerous tentacles tend to be invisible when the animal is in the water.

ORDER SIPHONOPHORA (Siphonophores)

Diagnosis: free-swimming or floating colonies consisting of modified medusoid and polypoid individuals of many sorts; marine.

Siphonophores might be likened to floating, living fortresses. *Physalia*, the Portuguese man-of-war, has the most powerful sting of all coelenterates. Hospital treatment often is necessary for swimmers who become entangled in its tentacles. However, the only real danger to man is that the sting might affect swimming to the point that one could drown. *Physalia* is seldom found on the Pacific Coast, but is fairly regularly encountered along the Gulf of Mexico and sometimes farther north along the Atlantic Coast. The common Pacific Coast species is *Velella lata*, the purple sailor. This floating species sometimes is cast upon California beaches in great numbers. In many areas it is improperly called the Portuguese man-of-war. On some purple sailors one might find attached gooseneck barnacles.

CLASS SCYPHOZOA (Jellyfishes)

Diagnosis: solitary umbrella- or bell-like animals, polyp form reduced or absent; medusae without a "shelf" (velum); material between inner and outer tissue layers very thick and jelly-like; medusa margin regularly with eight notches that contain sense organs; strictly marine; all large medusae belong to this class (Figure 12.7).

ORDER STAUROMEDUSAE (Sessile Jellyfishes)

Diagnosis: attached, upside down, usually to kelp or eelgrass; attachment is not permanent, and animals can crawl along the substrate; top of umbrella is drawn out into an attachment stalk; common species are about an inch or more in diameter and are most likely found on eelgrass in quiet waters such as bays.

ORDER CUBOMEDUSAE (Jellyfishes)

Diagnosis: free-swimming; umbrella cubical, with margin bent inward and with four, or four groups of, tentacles; United States species are found along Atlantic shores; mostly in subtropical to tropical waters; tend to be fish predators.

ORDER CORONATAE (Jellyfishes)

Diagnosis: free-swimming, umbrella margin scalloped and separated from umbrella proper by a circular furrow; mostly deep-water forms.

ORDER DISCOMEDUSAE (Jellyfishes)

Diagnosis: free-swimming; four corners of mouth prolonged into grooved oral arms, oral arms single (four) or double (eight); tentacles none to many; encountered mostly in coastal waters.

The true jellyfish are free-living and free-floating animals. They can swim in a slow jerky manner by sudden contractions of the umbrella or bell. Jellyfish feed in much the same way as do other coelenterates. Prey running into the tentacles is stung and moved to the mouth by the tentacles. Some jellyfish feed from the bottom. This bottom feeding is accomplished by the animal's lying upside down and drawing prey to the mouth by means of a current created by pulsating the bell. Other jellyfish assume an expanded, upside down position and slowly sink, capturing their prey on the way down.

These animals are most likely to be seen from a boat. Some larger species that may be observed are solid-colored yellow, orange, or brown; or pinkish or purplish with dark purple or purplish-black stripes. The smaller forms, about fist size or smaller, tend to be transparent; however, pigment usually makes the sex organs visible.

CLASS ANTHOZOA

Diagnosis: solitary or colonial; strictly polyps, no medusae known; polyps with vertical membranes partitioning the gastrovascular cavity; strictly marine (Figure 12.7).

Subclass ALCYONARIA

Diagnosis: with eight, branched tentacles; colonial; with an internal skeleton.

ORDER STOLONIFERA (Stolon Corals)

Diagnosis: polyps originate separately from a common, flattened, creeping tube (stolon) or mat; skeleton of spines occurring separately or fused into tubes; mostly in deeper water, intertidal species form low, encrusting, spreading growth on rocks, shells, or other hard substrates; polyps usually contracted to small pinkish mounds so the tentacles are usually not visible; coral base and ribbon-like stolons help separate these animals from simple ascidians (Chordata) in identification.

ORDER TELESTACEA (False Stolon Corals)

Diagnosis: colonial, of simple or branched stem bearing lateral polyps; each colony stem grows erect from a somewhat stem-like creeping base; internal skeletal parts united or not.

ORDER ALCYONACEA (Soft Corals)

Diagnosis: lower polyp parts fused into a fleshy mass, but some polyps reach the colony base; skeletal parts neither united nor axial; mostly a warm-water group.

ORDER GORGONACEA (Horny Corals)

Diagnosis: colony plant-like, originating from a single base; supported by a central coral skeleton, horn-like material, or both; polyps originate from

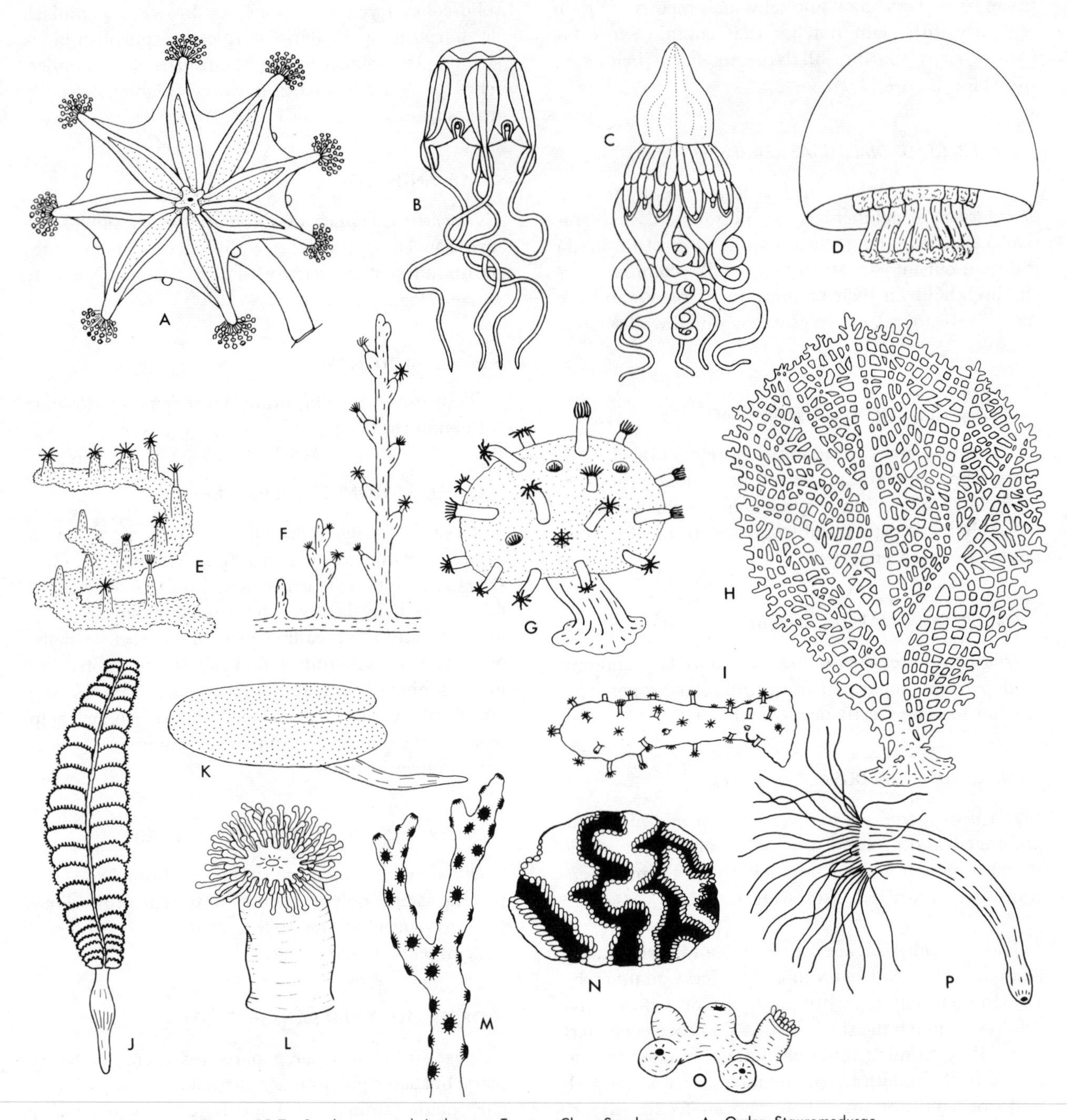

Figure 12.7 Scyphozoan and Anthozoan Types. Class Scyphozoa: A, Order Stauromedusae, *Haliclystus*, an attached jellyfish; B, Order Cubomedusae, *Charybdaea*, a jellyfish; C, Order Coronatae, *Periphylla*, a jellyfish; D, Order Discomedusae, *Stomolophus*, a jellyfish. Class Anthozoa: E, Order Stolonifera, *Clavularia;* F, Order Telestacea, *Telesto;* G, Order Alcyonacea, *Anthomastus;* H, Order Gorgonacea, *Gorgon;* I, Order Gorgonacea, *Euplexaura;* J, Order Pennatulacea, *Ptilostarcus*, a sea pen; K, Order Pennatulacea, *Renilla*, a sea pansy; L, Order Actinaria, *Corynactis;* M, Order Madreporaria, *Oculina;* N, Order Madreporaria, *Meandrinia*, O, Order Zoanthidea, *Epizoanthus* (grows on animals); P, Order Ceriantharia, *Cerianthus*. (Modified from various sources.)

each side of the skeleton, but no polyp reaches the colony base; often called sea fans, sea feathers, or sea whips according to extent of colony branching; found mostly in tropical and subtropical waters, but one type occurs at Newport Bay, California.

ORDER PENNATULACEA (Sea Pens)

Diagnosis: colony feather-like, fleshy, with leaf-like polyps borne on each side of a very long, stem-like polyp, the stalk; stalk usually embedded in sand or mud; skeleton of separate spines, occur on soft bottoms, mostly in warm waters; frequently found in shallow water in bays where they can sometimes be seen from a boat; some deep-water species have truly remarkable powers of expansion and contraction, the extremes showing a change on the order of three times the body length; includes the bay-inhabiting sea pansy (*Renilla*) of warm Pacific waters up to southern California, a purple animal in which the polyps grow from a single leaf-like structure above the stalk.

Subclass ZOANTHARIA

Diagnosis: tentacles of various numbers, but never eight; solitary or colonial; with or without a skeleton.

ORDER ACTINARIA (Sea Anemones)

Diagnosis: solitary but some closely grouped; no skeleton; polyp columnar, base usually attached to substrate by a suction disc, but not fixed to substrate; those lacking a suction disc have a pointed, rounded or bulb-like base.

The sea anemones are perhaps the best known of our intertidal coelenterates. Many people have sat on a tidepool rock to discover to their sorrow that what seemed to be solid rock was covered by very wet anemones. Many will remember having either poked them to watch the slow contraction of the body or dropped a rock on the mouth of an anemone to watch the rock being taken in and, later, rejected as food. These animals are very interesting from many respects. For example, their digestive juices are among the most effective in the animal kingdom. Also, some are the easiest tidepool animals to keep alive in captivity. One kind of anemone was kept alive in a quart jar for over thirty years. The remarkable thing about this situation is that the water was rarely changed more often than once a week.

ORDER MADREPORARIA (Stony Corals)

Diagnosis: mostly colonial; skeleton present; polyps small in cups of coral skeleton; mostly in warm, shallow waters; main contributors to coral reefs.

These true corals are well known for their reef-building habits. Stony corals are found in warm, shallow waters of the world. Many United States species occur, but the only semblance of coral reefs are formed off Florida coasts. Both solitary and colonial species are known along the Pacific Coast, but even the colonial species have fairly distinct, more or less isolated individuals with no real tendency toward reef-building.

ORDER ZOANTHIDEA (False Sea Anemones)

Diagnosis: mostly colonial, with polyps united by basal stolons; solitary forms have a stalked or wedge-shaped base; neither skeletons nor basal suction discs; many grow upon invertebrates.

ORDER CERIANTHARIA (Tube Anemones)

Diagnosis: solitary; polyps long, slender, and anemone-like but never with a basal suction disc; mostly burrowing forms in sand or mud; usually only the tentacles and mouth are visible on the surface, even when the animals are not disturbed; construct black, often slimy, parchment-like tubes up to 6 or more feet long.

CTENOPHORA (Comb Jellies)

Diagnosis: symmetry biradial, body more or less spherical, the general appearance causing the common name "sea walnuts," but some are flat and belt-like in appearance (Venus's girdles); tissue grade of organization, but muscles, digestive structures, and a sensory body on top indicate more complex organization than in coelenterates; jellyfish-like and semitransparent but have eight external rows of comb plates and no stinging cells; body topped by a sense organ and with mouth at the opposite end; strictly free-swimming and marine (Figure 12.8).

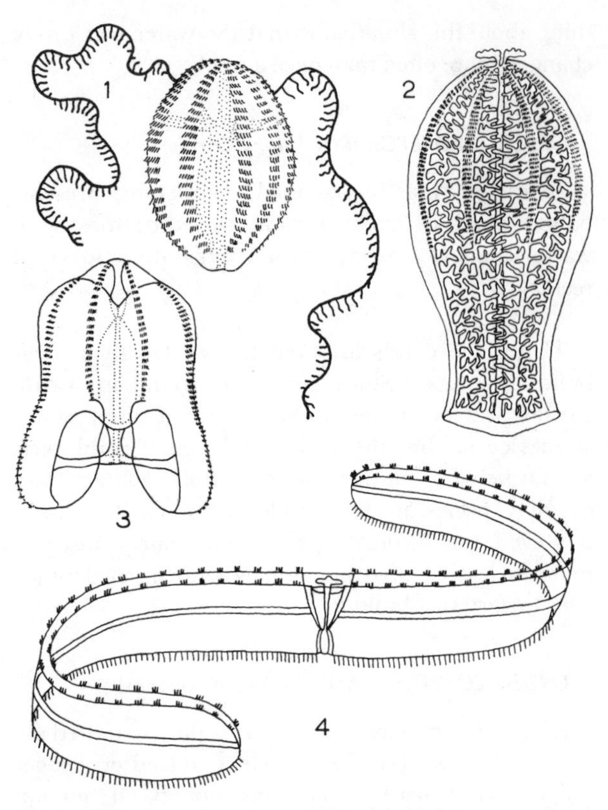

Figure 12.8 Ctenophore types: 1, *Pleurobrachia* (about natural size); 2, *Beroe* (about usual size, but grows to 8 inches in length); 3, *Bolinopus* (to about 2 inches long), a lobed and flattened genus; 4, *Cestum*, Venus's girdle (usually about 6 inches long, but grows to 3 feet). (Modified from various sources.)

Comb jellies may be confused with jellyfish, but the above distinctions should be sufficient for diagnosis.

The comb jellies have the tissue basis of organization seen in the coelenterates, but with modifications and complications. The ctenophores resemble coelenterates in the general appearance of their digestive structure and jelly-like middle layer, and in the lack of organ systems. They differ from the coelenterates in lacking stinging and related cells (nematocysts); in showing only one generation; and in having muscle-like fibers in the middle layer, a specialized sensory body, and a different type of larvae. Despite these differences, it seems likely that the comb jellies were derived from an ancestral hydromedusan.

The name of this phylum comes from eight longitudinal rows of comb plates which are modified cilia (see Ciliophora, p. 135) and are used like cilia for locomotion. Beneath each comb-plate row is a nerve-like cord integrated into a general nerve net similar to that of coelenterates. The ctenophores foreshadow organ system organization by possessing reproductive ducts through which eggs or sperm are shed.

Two anal pores on the top surface, which is opposite the mouth, as well as other features make most ctenophores biradial in their symmetry. A few species are creeping and bilateral, the general body shape being ribbon-like. Earlier workers considered these animals to be similar to the ancestors of the Platyhelminthes, but now this is not considered likely. As was indicated previously, it is now usually believed that the hydromedusans most closely resemble the Eumetazoan ancestor.

ACOELOMATA: PLATYHELMINTHES AND NEMERTEA

All of the remaining phyla in the animal kingdom possess organs that in turn are grouped into organ systems. However, not all organisms have the same number of organ systems. In general, the so-called lower phyla have fewer and simpler organ systems than the so-called higher phyla. In a sense it is inaccurate to speak of "lower" and "higher" phyla because both groups accomplish life processes successfully, and no one knows which group does so better. As a schematic device, however, such a distinction helps in charting the probable path of organic evolution and points up the fact that increased structural complexity was a major characteristic in the development of animal diversity.

The tendency for greater complexity can be traced from a hypothetical stem jellyfish to development of animals above the level of tissue organization. This tracing also serves to clarify some misconceptions that may have arisen from previous discussion of evolution.

Early evolution from stem jellyfish to flatworms is believed to have been through an early hydromedusan larva, not the adult jellyfish stage. (This creates no particular problem. In certain living animals the larva may reproduce; it may even be sexually mature and reproduce sexually. In such cases adults may or may not occur.) This step is thought to be from coelenterate larva to a stem, or ancestral, free-living flatworm. Although such a step might seem to be quite great as far as structural change is concerned, it is not. Even certain living larvae of the free-living flatworms are very similar to the modern coelenterate (especially hydromedusan) larval stages. Moreover, in some respects it is as difficult to establish the ancestry of all modern flatworms from an ancestral flatworm.

The ribbonworms are also believed to be offshoots of an ancestral free-living flatworm—one that was structurally more complex than the ancestor of all flatworms, however.

It is further assumed that ribbonworms have not given rise to anything other than more complex ribbonworms. In this respect they might, now at least, be considered evolutionary "dead ends," as could the mesozoans, sponges, and comb jellies. On the other hand, the mere fact that these phyla have not been successful in producing new phyla is no reason to consider them dead ends. All have evolved considerably, even if they did no more than retain their phylum identities. Although none seems to have produced a new phylum and no animal phyla likely arose after Cambrian times, it is not necessarily impossible for acoelomates (those phyla with no body cavity) to evolve further in the future. It must be remembered that one of the main characteristics of the planet Earth is change—change in land forms, climates, and animal habitats. Along with these environmental changes, organisms either change or perish. And the fossil record indicates that many more animals perished than were fortunate enough to acquire chance hereditary changes that enabled them to survive. For these reasons, we can consider no living phylum an evolutionary dead end. If such had ever been the case, the phylum would no longer be here.

PLATYHELMINTHES (Flatworms)

Diagnosis: symmetry bilateral; body unsegmented, soft and usually much flattened from top to bottom; worm-like; no body cavity, anus, circulatory, respiratory, or skeletal systems; includes the free-living flatworms of fresh and salt water and moist terrestrial environments, and the parasitic tapeworms and flukes.

The flatworms are the first phylum to be discussed whose activity is based on the possession of organs arranged in organ systems. However, in many respects a tissue-organ structure may better summarize their organization. The appearance of organs is associated with the presence in developmental stages of three germ layers, or embryonic cell groups, from which the adult organism ultimately forms. These germ layers are the outer ectoderm which forms the skin and nervous system, the inner endoderm which forms the lining of the alimentary canal and associated organs, and the middle mesoderm which forms muscular, connective, and circulatory tissues. In tissue-grade animals, coelenterates and ctenophores, the cells in the "jelly" between the outer and inner layers probably never form a complete layer, hence there is no third germ layer. The ctenophores may possess the third, or mesodermal, layer but their development is sufficiently confusing to leave the number of germ layers present in doubt.

The Platyhelminthes possess three germ layers, no body cavity, and are bilaterally symmetrical. Circulation and digestion are carried on by a gastrovascular cavity similar to that found in the Radiata, the coelenterates and ctenophores. The muscular system in flatworms is composed of two muscle layers in the body wall. Longitudinal nerve fibers with cross-connections form a so-called "ladder type" of nervous system. The animals usually are hermaphroditic (both sexes combined in one animal), with both sexual and asexual means of reproduction.

CLASS TURBELLARIA (Free-living Flatworms)

Diagnosis: regularly free-living; most under 1/5 inch in length but free-living carnivores reach 20 inches; also commensals or parasites; body undivided; covered by epidermis with cilia, no cuticle or suckers; mouth near middle of the undersurface; mostly hermaphroditic, with direct development of the adult form from the egg; also asexual by constriction across the worm's body (Figure 12.9).

The free-living flatworms inhabit fresh or salt water, and even moist terrestrial situations. Some few live either within or upon other animals. Many are brilliantly colored; in some a yellow or green color is due to the protistans or algae living in the tissues of the worm. The life history is usually somewhat simple. The fertilized egg gives rise to an immature form which transforms by simple growth and differentiation to an adult. Asexual reproduction by fragmentation and regeneration of each fragment is known in many species. Although, regeneration is highly developed and can play a part in reproduc-

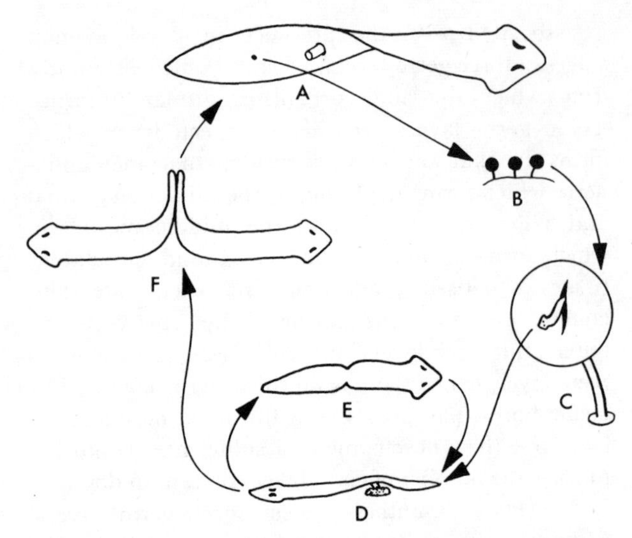

Figure 12.9 Life cycle of a free-living flatworm, *Euplanaria (Dugesia)*: A, mature adult laying egg-filled cocoons in fresh-water habitat; B, cocoons upon an object; C, immature flatworm emerging from a cocoon; D, adult feeding; E, asexual cycle in which an adult constricts transversely into two parts, each part regenerating into an adult; F, mating of two hermaphroditic adults (internal cross-fertilization occurs).

tion, it is essentially a process of healing rather than of reproduction.

CLASS TREMATODA (Flukes)

Diagnosis: strictly parasitic; body undivided, covered by a protective layer, a cuticle, one or more suckers, but no epidermis or cilia; mouth typically anterior; mostly hermaphroditic, with sexual reproduction; development direct (from egg to minute adult form) in external parasites, normally indirect in internal parasites and includes changes in hosts (Figure 12.10).

The flukes all live in or on other animals. A few of them cause no apparent harm; all others are true parasites. Associated with their mode of life are various modifications of the basic structure and life history. The mouth is anterior and leads into the "throat" which gives rise to an intestine composed of two arms and many side branches; the extent of the digestive system greatly increases the intake of nutrients. At least one attachment organ, a ventral sucker is present. The external ciliated epidermis characteristic of free-living forms is replaced by a protective, noncellular cuticle. Especially striking are the enlargement of sexual organs and the complex life cycle.

In the life cycle of *Fasciola hepatica*, the sheep liver fluke, fertilized eggs leave the sheep in excrement. If the eggs then reach water, they hatch into a ciliated larva. The larva must enter a particular kind of snail host to survive. It might be added here that almost without exception snails are necessary intermediate hosts for flukes. In boring into the snail's tissues, the ciliated larva loses its ciliated epidermis and transforms into a sac-like stage. Within the sac balls of cells accumulate and differentiate into many individuals of the third immature stage. These third-stage immatures are set free into the snail's tissues. By the same processes and within each third stage, fourth-stage immatures form. The fourth stages leave the snail and encyst on grass. When the grass is eaten, the cysts open in the intestine and young flukes emerge. Boring out through the intestinal wall of the susceptible animal, the flukes reach the body cavity and migrate to the liver, where they bore into this structure and take up their final position in the bile ducts.

From the above discussion we can see that para-

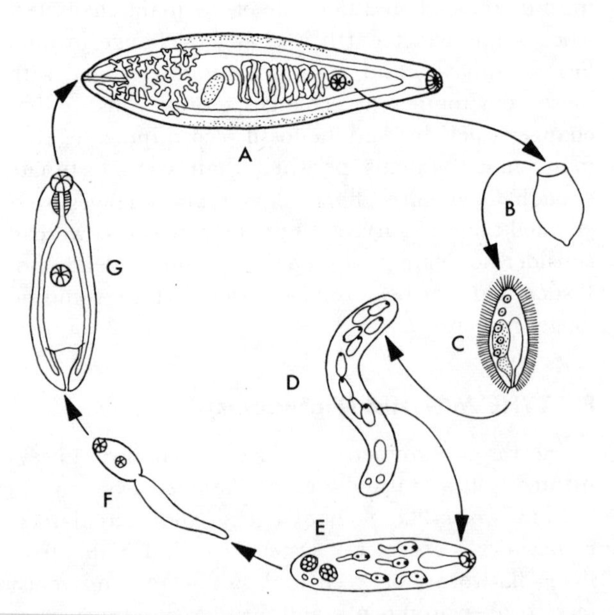

Figure 12.10 Life cycle of a human liver fluke, *Opisthorchis sinensis*: A, mature hermaphroditic adult in human liver bile ducts; B, egg case, which contains a ciliated larva when it leaves the human digestive tract; C, ciliated larva, or miracidium, which enters an aquatic snail; D, sporocyst, which develops from a miracidium (note that sporocyst contains many of the next stage); E, redia (like sporocysts contains the next stage); F, cercaria, which leaves the snail and swims to and enters a fish's tissues; G, metacercaria, the encysted stage within the fish. When man (especially in Asia) eats raw or poorly cooked fish, the adult emerges and takes up its habitat in the human bile duct.

sites are not really simple creatures. The impression of simplicity is often obtained when too much stress is placed upon structures that often are absent in parasites. However, as with flukes, parasites may have a high degree of specialization of certain structures, and often a very complex life cycle as well.

CLASS CESTODA (Tapeworms)

Diagnosis: strictly parasitic; body divided into proglottids which are not true segments, covered by a cuticle, but no epidermis or cilia; attachment often involves suckers, but also involves adhesive grooves or hooks; no digestive tract in the adult; mostly hermaphroditic and self-fertilizing; internal parasites with indirect development including changes of hosts; adults are vertebrate intestinal parasites (Figure 12.11).

Tapeworms were among the first animal parasites noted by man. Like the flukes, all members of this class live with other organisms; what is more, all are parasites. Tapeworms have lost all trace of a digestive tract, but they have gained certain unique adaptations. For example, feeding is accomplished solely by absorption through the body wall. The anterior end, the "head," fastens to the gut wall of the host by means of suckers and quite often an accessory armature of hooks. Behind this "head," or *scolex*, and its *neck* is a long body of many pseudosegments, or *proglottids*. The body is called the *strobila.* Least developed pseudosegments are nearest the "head," and sexually mature ones are at the posterior end. Pseudosegments bud off at the neck as relatively undifferentiated masses of tissue. As these masses are pushed back by the development of others, reproductive structures form within each proglottid, fertilization occurs, and most posterior pseudosegments are practically nothing but egg sacs. The pork tapeworm, *Taenia solium,* is a good example of the life cycle. Ripe pseudosegments, those containing fertile eggs, break off from the posterior end of the worm and pass out with the excrement. The eggs may be freed then or in the intestine of a pig eating contaminated food. In the pig's intestine, a unique larva emerges and with its six hooks bores through the intestinal wall of the pig to a blood vessel. At an appropriate place the worm bores through the blood vessel wall and emerges into muscle tissue. Here it encysts and, growing within its protective layer, produces a miniature "head" inverted within a capsule. This stage is called a bladder worm. When the pig is slaughtered for meat, this bladder worm remains alive for some time and survives if the cooking is not thorough enough. Emerging then in a human's intestine, the "head" is extruded, attaches to the intestinal wall and the parasite begins feeding and growing. As far as man is concerned, this organism is more dangerous as a larva than as an adult. If man eats food contaminated with tapeworm eggs, the burrowing of the larva and its subsequent growth may cause great damage and death. The effects of the adult on man are relatively minor.

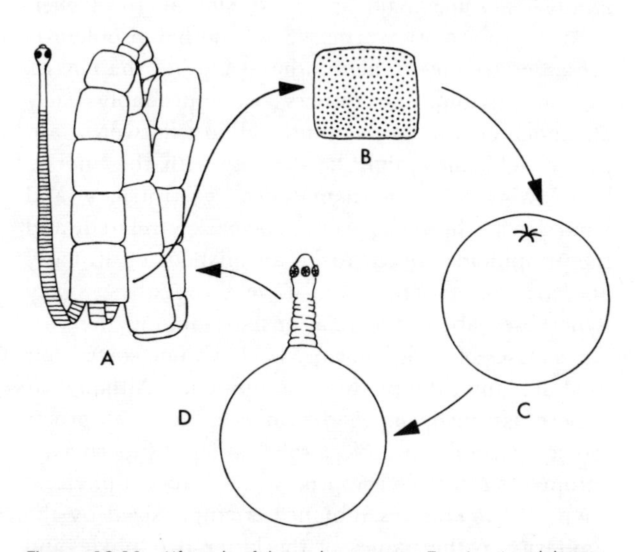

Figure 12.11 Life cycle of the pork tapeworm, *Taenia:* A, adult tapeworm in human intestine; B, mature egg sac (proglottid) breaks off end of tapeworm, leaves the human body, and is eaten by a pig; C, bladderworm stage resides in pig muscle after egg hatches, and hatchling migrates to the muscle; D, bladderworm evaginates its head when it reaches a human intestine. Survival of this human invading stage is dependent upon pork's being incompletely cooked. Under such conditions, the head of the bladderworm grows the segments to form the "tape." The farther the segments are from the head, the closer the egg sacs are to maturity.

NEMERTEA (= NEMERTINEA; RHYNCHOCOELA) (Ribbonworms)

Diagnosis: symmetry bilateral; body unsegmented, slender, soft, and highly contractile, wormlike; no body cavity, but with anus, circulatory system, and snout, or proboscis, having a tubular cavity above the digestive system; above the mouth the soft proboscis may extend far out or be completely withdrawn like the inverted finger of a glove, leaving only

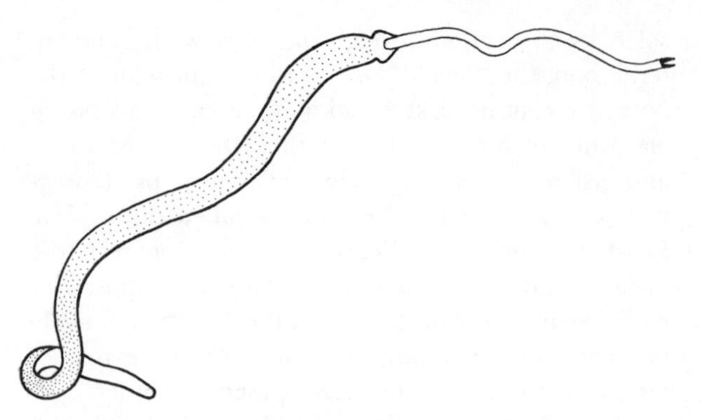

Figure 12.12 A ribbonworm, *Amphiphorus,* with proboscis everted (proboscis usually is retracted).

a pore to hint its presence; 0.2 inch to over 80 feet long; variously red, brown, yellow, green, or white; some are solidly colored, and others are striped or cross-banded; almost all are marine, a very few are fresh water or terrestrial; some are parasitic (Figure 12.12).

The ribbonworms and flatworms are the only multicellular animals of the grade Bilateria (i.e., bilaterally symmetrical animals) that do not possess a body cavity. However, the ribbonworms show much more structural complexity than the flatworms. For example, ribbonworms have a complete digestive system composed of mouth, alimentary canal, and anus; a circulatory system; and an eversible proboscis that can be retracted into a tubular cavity.

Ribbonworms are carnivorous, usually free-living, marine, shallow-water bottom dwellers. They are most common in temperate ocean regions under objects, among seaweeds, or in mud, sand, or gravel. Some construct tubes which are stabilized by a mucous lining that is secreted and applied by the worm. These and certain others are burrowing forms. A very few species are commensals (in sponges, bivalve mollusks, and tunicates) or parasites (in crabs).

The sexes are separate. Development of fertilized eggs takes two possible paths in these animals. In some, development is direct, the egg hatching into a miniature adult which simply grows to the adult size. The other path involves the egg's hatching into a free-swimming larva that is reminiscent of a football helmet. This larva later metamorphoses, or changes form, to the adult worm. Such sexual reproduction may involve the female's retaining the fertilized egg within her body and the young being born alive. However, asexual reproduction takes place in some species. During the warm parts of the year these species regularly fragment, each piece regenerating into an adult.

PSEUDOCOELOMATA: ACANTHOCEPHALA, ASCHELMINTHES, AND ENTOPROCTA

The spiny-headed worms, cavity worms, and entoproct "moss animals" are the only Bilateria with a pseudocoel, or false body cavity. These three phyla are believed to be closely related to flatworms and ribbonworms because of various similarities (e.g., a ladder-type nervous system) among the five phyla and because it is not a great step from the lack of a body cavity to the presence of a pseudocoel.

The three phyla probably evolved from somewhat advanced early flatworms. However, the spiny-headed worms present some problem in this interpretation because, in spite of the fact that their developmental stages resemble those of tapeworms, adult Acanthocephala are most similar to Aschelminthes, the cavity worms. Still another problem is presented by the Aschelminthes. One of the classes of that phylum, the rotifers, were probably early offshoots of the aschelminth almost-flatworm ancestor. This also might be the case with the "horse-hair" worms. The nematodes, gastrotrichs and kinorhynchs, however, seem to be closely related; and the priapuloids appear to be an offshoot of an early ancestral kinorynch. Even if we accept these shaky hypotheses about the relationships among the various classes of cavity worms, we have not solved our final difficulty, the phylum Entoprocta. Although it is here assumed, on good evidence, that entoprocts evolved from an ancestral rotifer, superficially entoprocts resemble ectoprocts (a schizocoel phylum, see p. 213). This resemblance is emphasized by the similarity in the names of the latter two phyla and their both being called "moss animals." However, this similarity seems to be more like that between a butterfly and a bird than an indication of truly close relationship. Entoprocts and ectoprocts have too many fundamental developmental and adult structural differences for there to be much likelihood of their close common ancestry.

ACANTHOCEPHALA (Spiny-headed Worms)

Diagnosis: symmetry bilateral; body unsegmented; body cavity a pseudocoel; all are parasites, larvae in arthropods and adults in the intestines of vertebrates; an anterior, cylindrical snout, or proboscis, can be withdrawn into a sheath; proboscis with hooks or spines; body usually elongate, somewhat flattened, and rough in life (rounded and smoother in preserved specimens); 0.06 to 26 inches long (Figure 12.13).

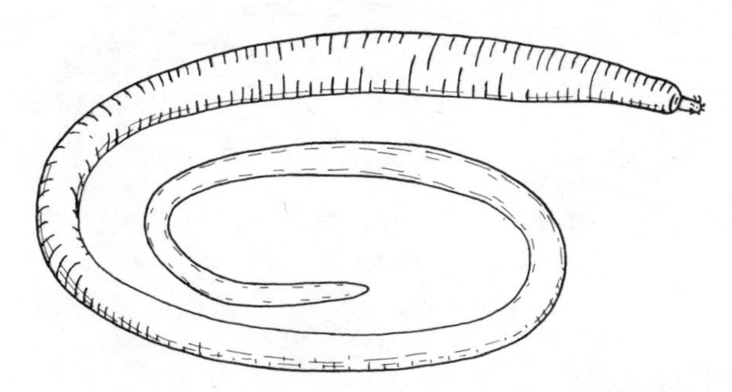

Figure 12.13 A spiny-headed worm, *Macracanthorhynchus*, that parasitizes pigs.

The spiny-headed worms do not actually have heads. Their name is derived from the proboscis armed with hooks or spines. The proboscis can be either withdrawn into the body or extended to the outside, but it is not turned inside out upon being withdrawn as is the case with ribbonworms.

Spiny-headed worms most closely resemble the roundworms; however, acanthocephalans differ in the presence of a proboscis and circular muscles, in the modifications of excretory and reproductive organs, and in the absence of a digestive tract.

The life cycle shows some complexities but the basic pattern is rather simple. The mature adults are parasites in the digestive tracts of various land, marine, and fresh-water vertebrates. Fertilization of eggs is internal and the eggs develop into a larva within the female. The larva must then leave its parent and the vertebrate host to find a suitable arthropod host, usually an insect, isopod, or amphipod. For the life cycle to be completed the intermediate arthropod host must be eaten by the host of the adult worm. Modifications of this basic plan can involve hermaphroditic adults, extrusion of eggs rather than larvae from the vertebrate host; and more than one intermediate host.

ASCHELMINTHES (Cavity Worms)

Diagnosis: symmetry bilateral; body unsegmented, worm-like; body cavity a pseudocoel, digestive tract lacking a muscular wall but terminating in an anus well behind the mouth; includes several groups of mostly slender, small to microscopic species that usually feed upon microscopic life; readily visible species are earthworm-like, but smooth and without an external ringed or segmented appearance (Figure 12.14).

The cavity worms are, at best, a loosely related taxon of pseudocoelomate, bilateral animals. Many investigators consider this to be a polyphyletic group, or not a true phylum because not all forms can be traced back to a common ancestor that gave rise *only* to Aschelminthes. However, all are pseudocoelomate, mostly worm-like, bilateral animals with an unsegmented body clothed with a cuticle. The gut is straight or curved, lacks a definite muscular wall except in the Priapuloidea, but ends in an anus posterior to the mouth and usually at or near the posterior end.

Only the roundworms and horsehair worms are likely to be seen with the unaided eye.

CLASS ROTATORIA (Rotifers or Wheel Animalcules)

Diagnosis: minute to microscopic; body somewhat cylindrical with an anterior group of cilia ("wheel organ") and posterior forked "foot"; most are free-living, with some fixed in protective tubes, a few parasites; mostly marine, a few freshwater species.

Although the largest rotifers barely reach 1/10 inch long, most are predators and usually upon protists. In predation they generally trap their prey with the wheel organ; movement of the cilia upon this organ is the means by which most rotifers draw prey into their mouths.

Rotifera are remarkable in that many species apparently lack males. Most reproduce parthenogenetically, but in some a situation reminiscent of sex determination in bees is found—fertilized eggs develop into females and unfertilized eggs into males. In species where both sexes are known, the males and females usually are distinctly different in appearance.

CLASS NEMATOMORPHA (Horsehair Worms)

Diagnosis: about 0.1 to 40 inches long; long and slender with a uniformly cylindrical body, a bluntly

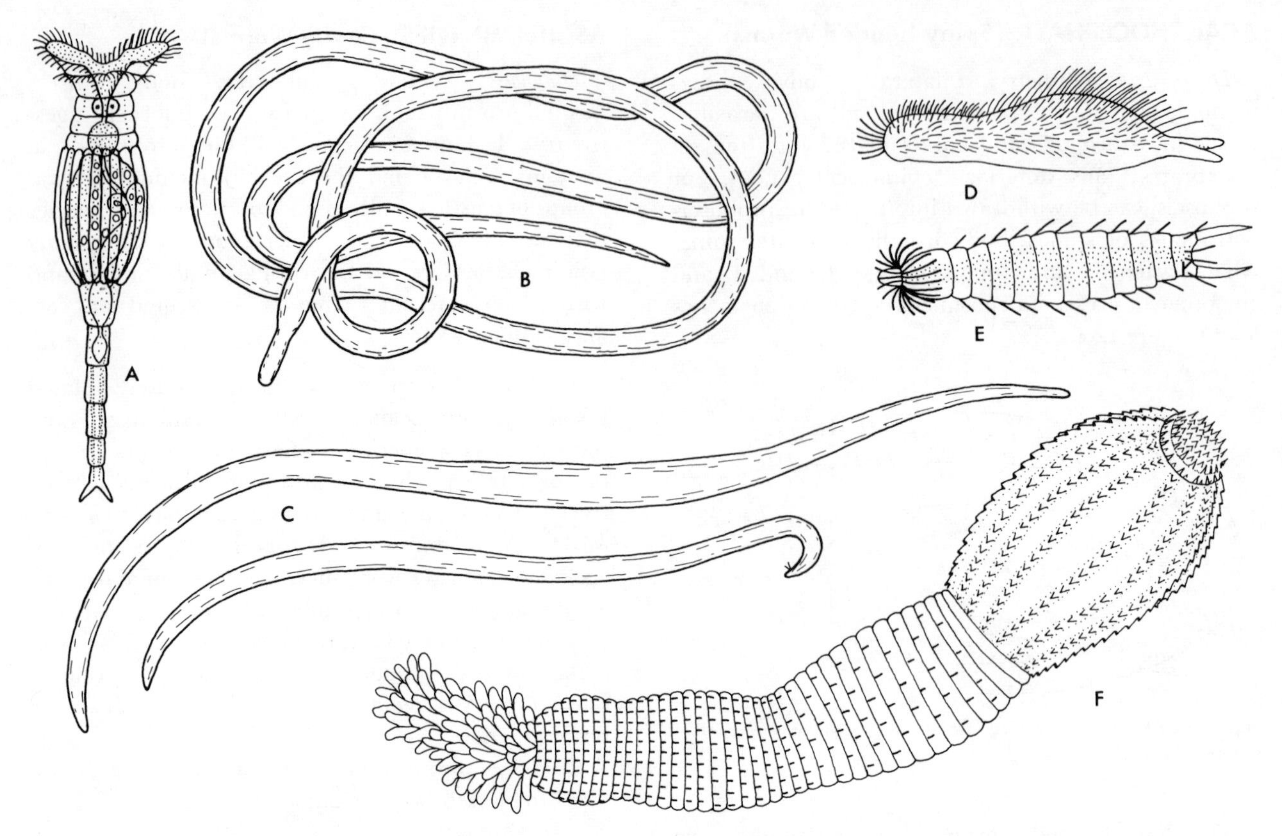

Figure 12.14 Cavity worm types: A, a rotifer, *Philodina;* B, a horsehair worm, *Gordius;* C, a roundworm, *Ascaris,* female above and male below; D, a fork-tailed worm, *Chaetonotus;* E, a spiny-crowned worm, *Echinoderes;* F, a club worm, *Priapulus.*

rounded anterior end, and slightly tapered posterior end; external resistant surface opaque and often colored; adults in fresh water, often ponds, rain puddles, or drinking troughs; larvae are insect parasites.

Because the adults superficially resemble the tail hairs of horses, a superstition, and hence the common name of the class, resulted. Some people actually believe that these worms are horsehairs that have come to life, probably because the adult worms were often found in drinking troughs used by horses. The actual story might not seem much less remarkable. The female worm deposits strings of eggs on objects and each egg hatches into a microscopic larva which is thought to enter an aquatic larvae of its host or to encyst upon vegetation. In the latter possibility, if the cyst is eaten by certain insects, usually grasshoppers or crickets, the larva emerges from the cyst and transforms to an adult; no matter how the larval worm may enter an insect, the larval worm then becomes an adult horsehair worm. Finally, if the insect falls into water, the adult horsehair worm emerges. These "ifs" may seem unlikely to occur, but they do. In fact, the completion of life cycles of most parasites is based on many unlikely "ifs" that do occur because great numbers of eggs and larvae are produced by the adults. Of thousands of eggs or larvae, only one may complete its life cycle.

CLASS NEMATODA (Roundworms)

Diagnosis: minute to over a yard long, most small or minute; unsegmented roundworms with slender, cylindrical bodies that often taper toward both ends (not bluntly rounded anteriorly); covered by a resistant cuticle; probably second to the insects in numbers (a few zoologists consider them more numerous); many are free-living in the soil or water, others are plant and animal parasites.

Roundworms invade all habitats from the hot deserts to the Arctic Seas, and other organisms, plant or animal, including fellow nematodes. Members of this group, more than those of any other group of animals, possess an amazing homogeneity of structure and, also, some common aspects of life history. Using *Ascaris* as an example for structural features, we note first that there is a very heavy, quite impervious, elastic, nonliving *cuticle* surrounding the animal. Beneath this is a single cell layer of *epidermis* which is organized in the adult into a condition in which cell membranes disappear and individual cells are no longer discernable. Within the epidermis is a single layer of huge, *longitudinal muscle cells*, which stretch the whole length of the body. Next, there is a cavity, the *pseudocoel*, filled with fluid. Within the cavity, the *alimentary canal* stretches from the *mouth* at the anterior end to the *anus* at the posterior end. Also lying free in the cavity are the *sex organs* which communicate to the exterior by a separate pore in the female, or by the anus in the male. The *excretory system* consists of two cells, whose main mass is centrally located; each cell is connected to a different longitudinal *excretory canal*. Only half of this system may be present in other forms. The *nervous system* is of the ladder type, as in the Platyhelminthes, having many trunks connecting anteriorly to a ring around the food pipe, or esophagus. This nerve system is unusual in that the two main trunks are dorsal and ventral rather than both being lateral or ventral. Also unusual, is the manner in which innervation of structures is accomplished. Instead of the nerve fibers branching on the surface of the structure supplied, fibers actually enter the innervated cells, running, for example, the whole length of the huge muscle cells.

The origin and function of the pseudocoel are of interest. The pseudocoel is not a primary cavity, but arises secondarily. The entire space is at first filled with cells. Some of these cells break down and others become circulatory cells or muscle cells, leaving a space. Thus, the cavity is bounded on one side by endodermal derivatives, the gut, and on the other by mesodermal derivatives, the muscle cells. The true body cavity, or *coelom*, which is found in entirely different phyla, is completely lined by mesoderm.

Functionally, the pseudocoel with cuticle and muscle cells is important in locomotion. The pseudocoel is filled with fluid under tension, retained by the elastic cuticle. All muscle fibers are longitudinal and can act only to shorten the animal if all fibers contract, or bend it to one side or the other if they contract on one side. Motion is accomplished by a series of looping actions like a flat spring, the muscles contract on one side and are then sprung back because of the compression of the body fluid by the cuticle.

Medically, one of our most important nematodes is the hookworm, *Necator americanus*. The adults live attached to the human intestinal wall, sucking blood. The eggs pass out in the excrement, and in the proper soil, develop to encysted larva. Later they emerge and become active again. The larvae are so sensitive that the change in temperature when a barefoot person steps on them causes them immediately to burrow into the skin. Reaching a blood vessel, the larvae are carried eventually to the lung, where they break out into the air space, migrate up and are swallowed, eventually reaching the intestine.

CLASS GASTROTRICHA (Fork-tailed Worms)

Diagnosis: all microscopic; ciliate, protozoan-like, but the posterior end is forked and the arched top surface (the back or dorsum) has many spines; found in fresh and salt water; development direct; fresh water species are parthenogenetic females; marine species hermaphroditic (have both male and female sex organs).

CLASS KINORHYNCHA (Spiny-crowned Worms)

Diagnosis: 0.04 to 0.2 inch long; body of 13 or 14 rings, two rings form the head which is spine encircled and has a short, retractile proboscis terminated by the mouth; the trunk rings bear lateral spines; the tail region may bear long spines; exclusively marine, known to occur in mud or sand and on algae; sexes separate, development with several larval stages and changes in form to adult stage.

CLASS PRIAPULOIDEA (Club Worms)

Diagnosis: up to 3 inches long; only three known species; cylindrical, clublike, yellow or brown, wormlike creatures; superficially resemble Sipunculoidea or Echiuroidea, but priapuloids have rows of spines or papillae on the anterior retractile proboscis and usually one or two posterior processes with gill-like outgrowths; marine burrowers in bottom muck of colder to arctic seas; sexes separate, development essentially direct but involving a larval stage.

ENTOPROCTA (Moss Animals)

Diagnosis: symmetry bilateral; body unsegmented; pseudocoelomates with a looped digestive tract; stalked, attached animals with a circlet of cilated tentacles around the mouth (lophophore); solitary or colonial with individuals not more than 0.2 inch in length and colonies of some size; superficial resemblance to coelenterates (hydroids) and seaweeds, but are rough to the touch; closer resemblance to Ectoprocta and formerly considered part of that phylum, but only the individual Entoprocta stalks can move independently; mostly marine, one conspicuous fresh-water species in the eastern and central United States (Figure 12.15).

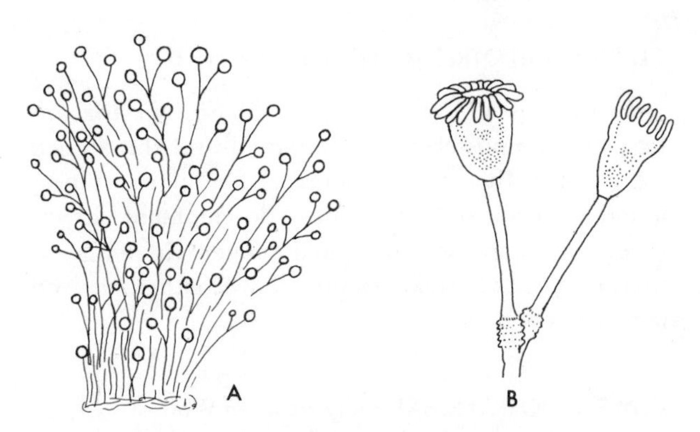

Figure 12.15 *Barentsia*, an entoproct moss animal: A, natural size of colony; B, magnified individuals; note the straight stalks that are independently movable (absent in Ectoprocta).

Although entoproct moss animals possess a lophophore, they are not part of that group (see p. 213). This is the case because Lophophorata is merely a term of convenience to designate a particular group of animals with a true body cavity. It has already been emphasized that entoprocts do not possess a coelom, but rather, that they have a pseudocoel.

The name Entoprocta points out another difference between *ento*procts and *ecto*procts. The entoprocts have the anus *inside* the lophophore and the ectoprocts have theirs *outside* the lophophore.

Entoprocts are either biparental or have both sex organs in one individual (hermaphroditic). After fertilization, the egg develops into a motile larva which transforms to the adult form. This larva, like that of many other phyla, is the only means by which the animals are disseminated; the adults are strictly sedentary creatures found growing on other animals or objects in water.

SELECTED READINGS

Barnes, R. D., 1963. *Invertebrate Zoology*. W. B. Saunders Co., Philadelphia.

Buchsbaum, R., 1948. *Animals without Backbones*. rev. ed. The University of Chicago Press, Chicago.

——— and L. J. Milne, 1960. *The Lower Animals*. Doubleday & Co., Garden City, N.Y.

Edmondson, W. T., ed., 1959. *Ward and Whipple's Fresh-water Biology*. 2nd ed. John Wiley & Sons, New York.

Hyman, L. H., 1940. *The Invertebrates*. Vol. 1: *Protozoa through Ctenophora*. McGraw-Hill Book Co., New York.

———, 1951. *The Invertebrates*. Vol. 2: *Platyhelminthes and Rhynchocoela*. McGraw-Hill Book Co., New York.

———, 1951. *The Invertebrates*. Vol. 3: *Aschelminthes and Entoprocta*. McGraw-Hill Book Co., New York.

Johnson, M. E., and H. J. Snook, 1927. *Seashore Animals of the Pacific Coast*. The Macmillan Co., New York.

MacGinitie, G. E., and N. MacGinitie, 1949. *Natural History of Marine Animals*. McGraw-Hill Book Co., New York.

Miner, R. W., 1950. *Field Book of Seashore Life*. G. P. Putnam's Sons, New York.

Palmer, E. L., 1949. *Fieldbook of Natural History*. McGraw-Hill Book Co., New York.

Pennak, R. W., 1959. *Fresh-water Invertebrates of the United States*. The Ronald Press Co., New York.

Ricketts, E. F., and J. Calvin (edited by J. W. Hedgpeth), 1952. *Between Pacific Tides*. 3rd ed. Stanford University Press, Stanford, Calif.

Tinbergen, N., 1953. *Social Behavior in Animals: With Special Reference to Vertebrates*. John Wiley & Sons, New York.

Vessel, M. F., and E. J. Harrington, 1961. *Common Native Animals*. Chandler Publ. Co., San Francisco, Calif.

13 ECTOPROCTA THROUGH ECHIUROIDEA

Unsegmented Schizocoels

The next eight "higher" phyla in the animal kingdom are the schizocoels. The schizocoels (Gr. *schizo*, cleave + *koilos*, hollow) are characterized by a true body cavity, the *coelom*, of a type formed by a cleavage, or split, in the middle germ layer, the *mesoderm*. The marine members of these phyla share a particular kind of larval stage, the *trochophore*. Actually larvae of these phyla show some variation and some are referred to by different names; therefore, it would be more accurate to say they share a "trochophore-like" larval stage. The schizocoelous phyla are grouped into the Lophophorata (Ectoprocta, Phoronida, and Brachiopoda) and the Schizocoela (unsegmented Sipunculoidea, Mollusca, and Echiuroidea plus segmented Annelida and Arthropoda). All of these phyla are believed to have developed from an ancestral trochophore that was, in turn, derived from an ancestral ciliated flatworm.

LOPHOPHORATA: ECTOPROCTA, PHORONIDA, AND BRACHIOPODA

The phyla Ectoprocta, Phoronida, and Brachiopoda probably followed similar lines of evolution. This similarity is implied by their all having a tentacle-like structure, the *lophophore*, surrounding their mouths. The lophophore is mainly a device for creating a current that directs microscopic food to the animal's mouth. This tentacle-like structure is the basis for the three phyla being called the Lophophorata, but rotifers, pterobranchs and certain other animals have a similar structure also called a lophophore.

ECTOPROCTA (Moss Animals)

Diagnosis: symmetry bilateral; body unsegmented; schizocoelomates with a lophophore; colonial, some as tufts or branches less than ¼-inch high, others resembling colonial hydroids and corals or seaweeds; a few are mat-like and some form thin crusts on rocks, seaweeds, shells, or other objects; difficult to observe, because most are small and inconspicuous, but some attain considerable size; most colonies are attached, but some are free floating; a few are not colonial but will not be seen; few are truly moss-like; fresh-water forms are mostly jelly-like or gelatinous; mostly marine, one fresh-water order (Figure 13.1).

The ectoprocts and entoprocts are called "moss animals," a common name referring to their similarity in external form and reflecting early confusion about the true relationships of the two groups. This confusion should not exist because, despite superficial similarities, ectoprocts are schizocoelomates and entoprocts are pseudocoelomates. Schizocoelomates possess a true body cavity, the coelom, and

TAXONOMIC SUMMARY

Kingdom Animalia (L. *animalis*, animate)—animals
Subkingdom Eumetazoa (Gr. *eu-*, true + *meta*, among + *zoon*, animal)—eumetazoans
Grade Bilateria (L. *bi-*, two + *lateralis*, side)

Eucoelomata (Gr. *eu-*, true + *koilos*, hollow)
- Lophophorata (Gr. *lophos*, the crest + *phoros*, bearing)
  - Phylum Ectoprocta (Gr. *ectos*, outside + *proktos*, anus)—ectoprocts or moss animals
  - Phylum Phoronida (Gr. *phoros* + *nid*, nest)—horseshoe worms
  - Phylum Brachiopoda (Gr. *brachion*, arm + *podos*, foot)—lamp shells
- Schizocoela (Gr. *schizo*, cleave + *koilos*)
- Phylum Sipunculoidea (L. *sipunculus*, a little siphon + *-oideus*, form or type of)—peanut worms
- Phylum Mollusca (L. *molluscus*, soft)—mollusks
  - Class Amphineura (Gr. *amphi*, both + *neuron*, nerve)—chitons or sea cradles
  - Class Scaphopoda (Gr. *skapha*, boat + *podos*, foot)—tusk shells
  - Class Gastropoda (Gr. *gaster*, belly + *podos*)—univalves
  - Class Pelecypoda (Gr. *pelekus*, hatchet + *podos*)—bivalves
  - Class Cephalopoda (Gr. *kephale*, head + *podos*)—nautili, squids, and octopuses
- Phylum Echiuroidea (Gr. *echis*, serpent + *oura*, tail + *-oideus*)—innkeepers and allies

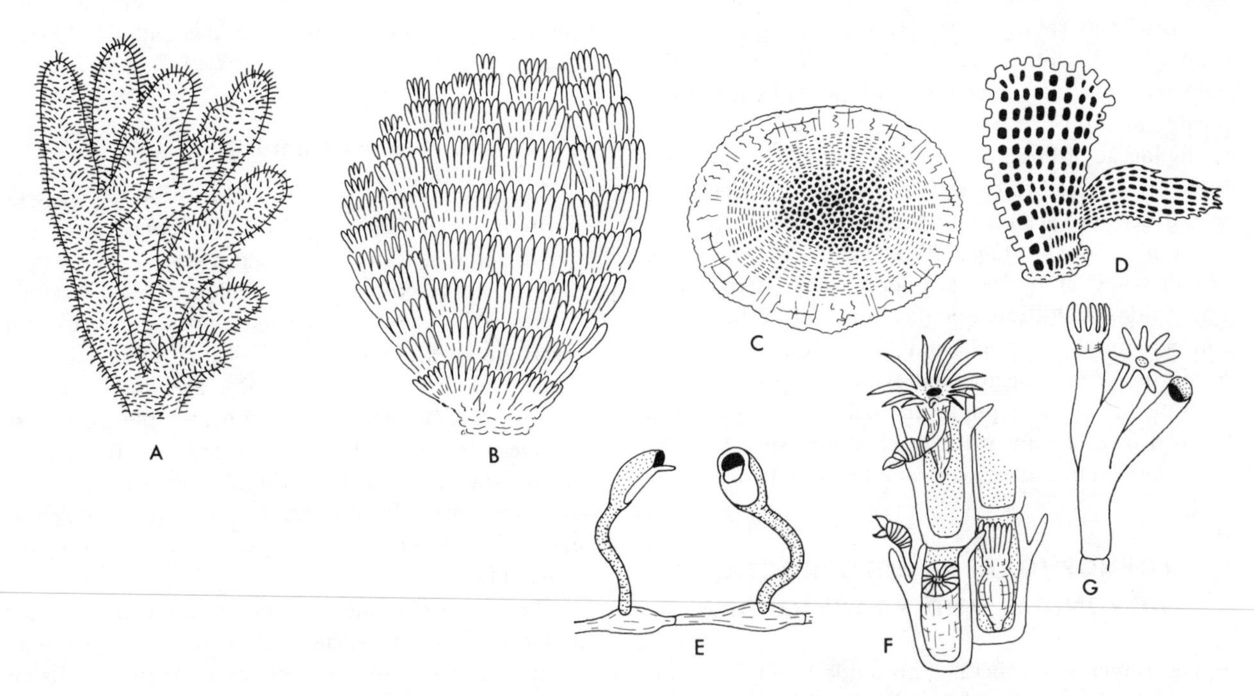

Figure 13.1 Ectoprocta types: A, *Flustrella*, an erect, soft colony covered with horny spines; B, *Bugula*, an erect, "moss" type; C, *Lichenopora*, a sea lichen, thin and encrusting; D, *Phidolopora*, sea lace, an erect animal growing from a calcareous base; E, *Aeta*, a colonial animal with creeping and partially adherent branches (individuals are solitary within the expanded part of each flexible tube, (x 15); F, *Bugula*, a section of a colony to show organization of individuals, x 25; G, *Crisia*, an encrusting or erect mass of tubes, a segment of a colony, x 15.

pseudocoelomates do not. The coelom is considered a true body cavity because it is completely lined by cells derived from embryonic mesoderm.

Almost all ectoprocts are attached, as colonies, on objects in shallow water. These moss animals are usually hermaphroditic, individuals containing both male and female sex organs, but some are male or female. The fertilized egg develops into a motile larva which soon attaches to a suitable substrate. The larva then transforms to an adult which asexually buds into a colony. Fresh-water species produce an internal asexual bud which is released upon death of the adult colony; the bud will grow into a colony only if environmental conditions are suitable for adult growth and survival. The internal bud is thus the ectoproct's means of surviving freezing or drying of their fresh-water habitat. For example, drying of a pond kills the adults and releases the internal buds; if and when rains replace the pond waters, each bud grows into an adult colony.

PHORONIDA (Horseshoe Worms)

Diagnosis: symmetry bilateral; unsegmented; schizocoelomates with a lophophore; red, orange, or green animals from under 0.1 inch to 15 inches long (tubes to 18 inches); live in self-secreted, leathery, membranous, or calcareous tubes containing cemented sand grains, shells, and other materials; superficially resemble some of the annelids (feather worms), but the "fan" (lophophore) is usually a double spiral of horseshoe shape, and the body is smooth and unsegmented; all are sedentary and marine (Figure 13.2).

The phoronids are tube-dwelling, worm-like animals, of shallow marine waters. They use their lophophores to filter microscopic organisms from the water, the microorganisms being trapped upon a sticky mucous secretion. Frequently they can be observed in the shallow waters of bays during low tides, but only the lophophore tentacles will be extended from within the tube—the characteristic feeding position.

Adults are hermaphroditic. Like most marine animals, they shed sperm and eggs into the sea water, the site of fertilization. The fertilized egg, or zygote, develops into a motile trochophore-like larve that may wander some distance. Soon the larva becomes sedentary and assumes the adult form.

BRACHIOPODA (Lamp Shells)

Diagnosis: symmetry bilateral; unsegmented; schizocoelomates with a lophophore; bear a superficial resemblance to bivalve mollusks in having an external shell of two valves, but these are top (dorsal) and bottom (ventral) rather than right and left; a flexible attachment stalk emerges through a hole in the ventral valve near the hinge (no such structure in bivalve mollusks); also possess internal skeletons, something very rare in bivalves; sexes separate, re-

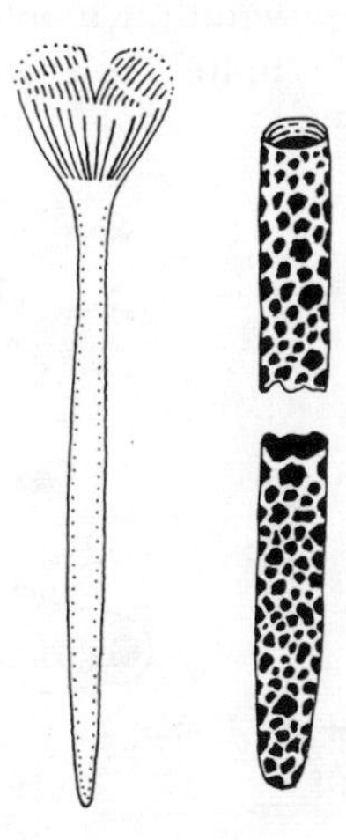

Figure 13.2 *Phoronis,* a horseshoe worm. The tube, a structure often formed of sand, silt, or other debris plus body secretions, is about twice the length of the worm.

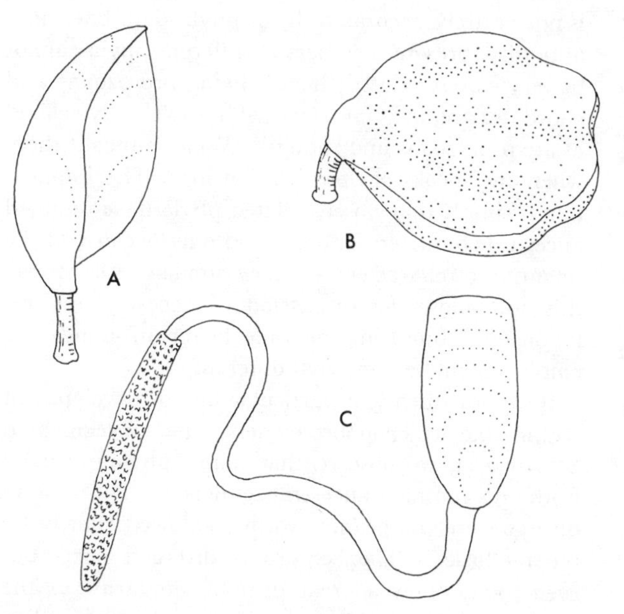

Figure 13.3 Lamp shell types: A, *Magellania;* B, *Terebratalia;* C, *Lingula* with tube found at its burrow bottom. The open part of the shell is at or facing the mouth of the burrow.

production resulting in a trochophore-like larva which attaches to some solid substrate and develops into the adult form.

The lamp shells receive their common name because many resemble old Roman oil lamps. All living species are solitary, usually attached, marine animals. Most are shallow-water forms, but a few are known from very deep water. They can sometimes be found in the lower tide levels under or on protected areas of rocks. One living genus, *Lingula*, has existed since the Ordovician period, some half-billion years ago, and is probably the oldest living genus of animal.

UNSEGMENTED SCHIZOCOELA: SIPUNCULOIDEA, MOLLUSCA, AND ECHIUROIDEA

It was mentioned previously that not all trochophores are exactly the same. They vary between the different phyla and in the individual species within phyla.

By now it should be obvious that the ancestry of all phyla goes back into antiquity. In fact, there is adequate fossil evidence for the statement that all phyla had become phyla more than one-half billion years ago! Therefore, when it is said that a certain phylum is "closely related" to another, the statement is not entirely accurate. If all phyla date back into antiquity, present members of different phyla cannot be very closely related; hence, living protozoans and chordates are, in a time sense, about as closely related as are protozoans and sponges. What is meant then, when one speaks of close relationship? The implication is simply that closely related phyla have retained ancestral characters for eons, and only because of the retention of characters are now similar. Of course, this still allows for discussion of ancestry and relationships, but with the time factor in mind, the emphasis will be somewhat different.

If we now turn to a particular line of development within the trochophore-owners, the unsegmented Schizocoela, we observe that many phyla diverged from one common ancestral tendency. The first to diverge were the peanut worms, followed shortly by the mollusks. The echiuroids diverged next, but even today show a great deal of similarity to the segmented worms. Final segregation along this "line of development" resulted in modern segmented worms (Annelida) and joint-legged animals (Arthropoda).

The peanut worms, mollusks, echiuroids, segmented worms, and joint-legged animals constitute the schizocoelous animals without a lophophore. These schizocoels can be further subdivided into those without true segmentation (sipunculoids, mollusks, and echiuroids) and those with true segmentation (annelids and arthropods). However, the peanut worms and echiuroids are very closely related to the annelids. Both taxa are sometimes classified as part of the Phylum Annelida. In fact, *all* schizocoelous phyla often are grouped in a Superphylum Annelida.

SIPUNCULOIDEA (Peanut Worms)

Diagnosis: symmetry bilateral; unsegmented; schizocoelous; cylindrical; yellowish, grayish, or brownish animals up to a foot long; superficially resemble priapuloids or echiuroids, but anterior retractile portion is terminated by tentacles, has fine and chitinous papillae, and is not a true snout or proboscis; anterior region withdraws inward as does the finger of a glove; called "peanut worms" because of the superficial, peanut-like appearance of the animals when their anterior portions are pulled into their bodies; marine in sand, mud, empty shells, crevices in rocks, etc. (Figure 13.4).

Extended peanut worms resemble an elongated flask. The opening of the "flask" contains short, hollow, fringed, ciliated tentacles which are used to capture microscopic food. The "flask neck" bears fine, hard objects. When the animal contracts, the head and neck are withdrawn into the body. The body proper, the "bulb," is covered by a slightly roughened cuticle.

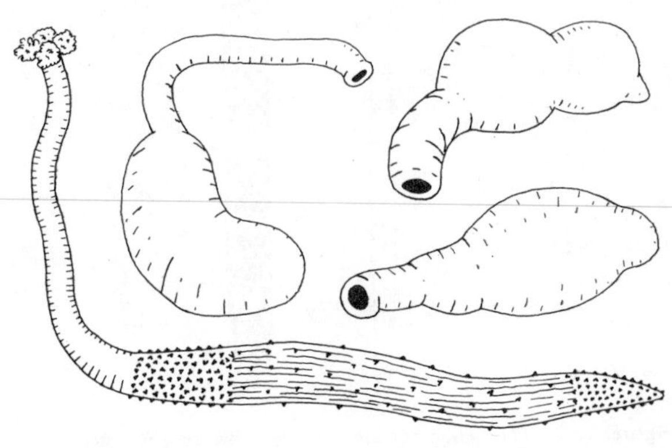

Figure 13.4 Various attitudes of *Phascolosoma*, a peanut worm.

Peanut worms are exclusively marine creatures that can be found from intertidal areas to extreme depths of about 3 miles. Intertidally, they usually are found in sand or mud, within rock cavities, among kelp holdfasts, or beneath rocks. These trochophore-owners possess separate sexes.

MOLLUSCA (Mollusks)

Diagnosis: symmetry bilateral; unsegmented, except in one order of odd chitons (representatives known from about 2-mile depths off the west coast of Mexico); of diverse forms, amphineurans or chitons are of elliptical outline with a large, flat, ventral foot and a shell of eight, overlapping, dorsal valves or plates that may be covered by the skin, the gastropods are generally snail- or slug-like (shell of one piece or absent), the scaphopods are snail-like but have a tubular shell open at both ends, the pelecypods are clam-like (shell of 2 parts or valves) and the cephalopods are the squids and octopuses (shell internal); mollusks are fresh-water, marine, terrestrial, and parasitic.

Unfortunately for the beginning student, the mollusks have evolved in so many diverse ways that there is no specific, generalized form to be used as a model. However, one can consider the different groups and hypothesize as to the nature of the ancestral type. Originally, the mollusks probably were bottom-dwelling, bilateral, worm-like forms. They likely crawled upon their bellies by means of a fleshy, muscular projection, the *foot.* The front end possessed a slightly differentiated head with various sense organs, a concentration of nerve cell bodies (a ganglion), and a mouth. Such an animal may have become almost too large to sprawl out over the bottom and may have been in danger of extinction. Fortunate chance changes in its heredity could have caused a piling of some of the animal's structures on its back. A second type of hereditary change, favoring those organisms that possessed it, may have caused the organisms to secrete a shell over their dorsal mass or hump. This layer which became capable of secreting a shell is assumed to be a skin fold now known as the *mantle.* Additional hereditary change perhaps caused the mantle to give rise to a pair of *gill structures* which hung in a posterior *cavity* between the hump and shell. Possibly this ancestor had further protection by being able to pull its body into the shell. Zoologists are even less sure of its internal anatomy. As a trochophore animal, one can suggest that it had *ventral nerve cords* connecting to a "*brain*" by a nerve *ring* around the food pipe, or esophagus. It seems fair to assume that a particular kind of excretory organ, *nephridium,* and an *incomplete blood system* (i.e., one in which the blood is not completely enclosed in blood vessels) leading to a *hemocoel* (a body cavity in which blood flows) mainly in the foot, were present. There probably was a true body cavity, the *coelom,* formed entirely within the mesoderm as that layer grew and extended in larval life. In present-day mollusks the coelom is restricted to a small heart cavity (from which the adult excretory organs drain wastes), to the kidney, and to the sex organ cavity. As for the *radula,* the distinctive rasping structure of most mollusks that is used in food getting, zoologists cannot say whether or not this was primitive, since one whole class lacks it.

CLASS AMPHINEURA (Chitons, or Sea Cradles)

Diagnosis: bilaterally symmetrical and unsegmented except for one order; body elongate, with a reduced head, radula, enlarged and flat ventral foot (sometimes absent), and shell of eight dorsal parts (valves) (Figure 13.5).

The chitons, also called sea cradles and coat-of-mail shells, generally feed upon marine algae. The different chiton species usually have specialized habitats. Some are found only under rocks of tide pools. One or more common species may be found in depressions in intertidal rocks. Others live on the surface of rocks exposed to the open ocean. A few are found in open tide pools, and some are subtidal.

Many chitons have a daytime retreat to which they return after nightly feedings. Most use their radula to scrape a film of microscopic plants, diatoms and algae, from rocks. Others feed on seaweed debris.

The sexes are separate. Typically, eggs are laid in jelly masses or strings, but some chitons lay single eggs. The eggs hatch to a free-swimming, trochophore-like larval stage. The free-swimming stage is lost when the larva settles to the bottom. Then follows a series of changes in form (metamorphoses) terminating in the adult. Some species lack the free-swimming stage and the developing young live under the mantle edge of the mother, perhaps for protection.

After chitons die, their plates, so-called "butterfly shells," wash up on the beach. These items of curiosity often are the closest contact many people have

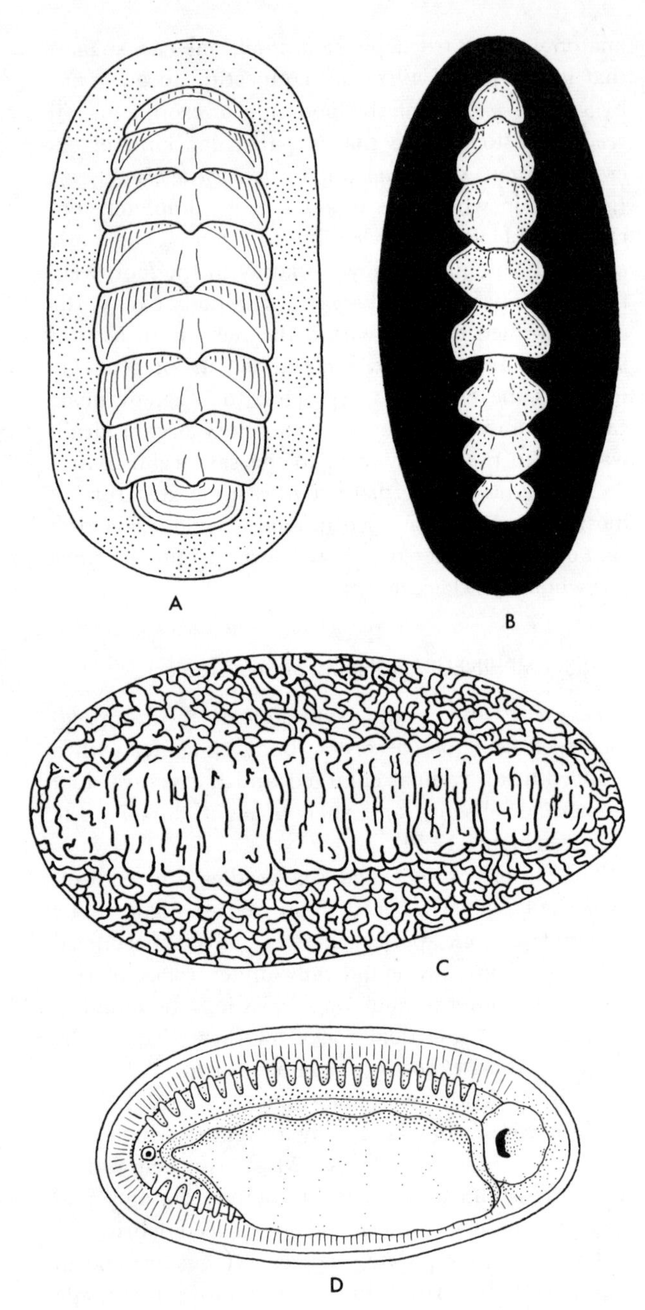

Figure 13.5 Class Amphineura, chiton types: A, *Ischnochiton*, representing chitons with freely visible valves; B, *Katherina*, with a black leathery tunic partially covering its valves; C, *Amicuta* (= *Cryptochiton*), with valves indicated but completely covered by its tunic, up to 1 foot long; D, undersurface of a chiton, with part of the foot curled away to show the head and mouth (right) and the gills running along the grooved margin.

with this group. Occasionally one finds costume jewelry made from chiton plates, but chitons are used much less for this purpose than are other mollusks.

CLASS SCAPHOPODA (Tusk Shells)

Diagnosis: bilaterally symmetrical and unsegmented; body elongate and enclosed in an undivided shell that is open at both ends, with a head area of sensory processes, radula, and reduced conical foot (Figure 13.6).

The tusk or tooth shells apparently feed upon small marine plants and animals. Around the mouth are delicate tentacles; these are sensory and are used to capture food. In a few forms, food is obtained by directing the sea water to the mouth where organisms are filtered and taken into the digestive tract. These are bottom dwellers that usually are partially buried in sand or mud. Most are deep-water forms, but a few are found just below the lowest tide level.

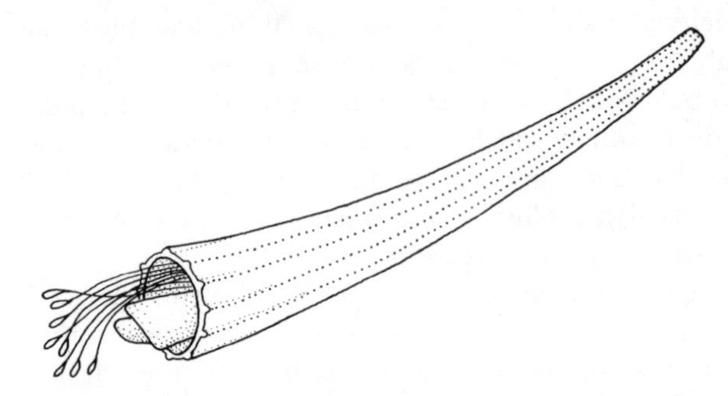

Figure 13.6 *Dentalium*, a tooth or tusk shell; not shown is the additional opening at the apex of the shell; Class Scaphopoda.

The sexes in Scaphopoda are separate. The life history following the laying of single eggs is similar to that of chitons.

American Indians prized a particular tooth shell, *Dentalium*, as money or wampum. Although the Indians obtained some shells that were washed into shore, their primary means of obtaining tooth shells was by dredging with long rakes from canoes.

CLASS GASTROPODA (Univalves)

Diagnosis: body typically asymmetrical, unsegmented; head well developed, with sense organs; radula and a flat, enlarged ventral foot are present; shell undivided, typically external, internal or absent in some (Figure 13.7).

The gastropods are fresh-water, land, and marine mollusks that possess a radula. Although the radula is a feeding organ, the food habits of gastropods are variable. Most fresh-water snails are vegetarians, feeding on algal scum on submerged objects, but

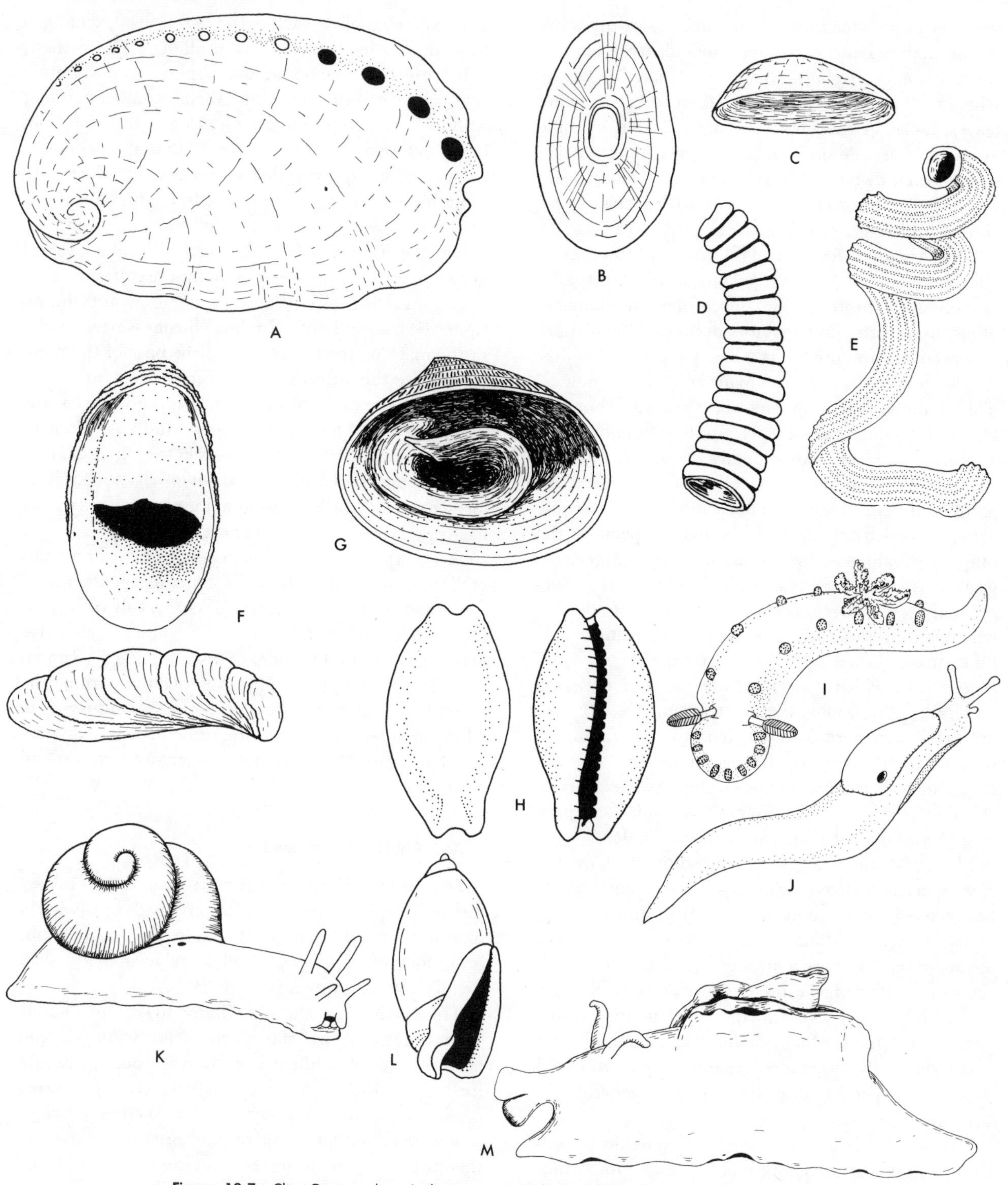

Figure 13.7 Class Gastropoda, univalve types: A, *Haliotis* shell from above, abalone, marine; B, *Megathura* shell from above, keyhole limpet, marine; C, *Acmaea* shell from the side and below, limpet, marine; D, *Caecum* shell, pouch snail or shell, marine; E, *Aletes* shell, tube snail or worm shell, marine; F, *Crepidula* shell from below and to the side, slipper shell, marine; G, *Crucibulum* shell from below and to the side, cup-and-saucer shell, marine; H, *Cypraea* shell from above and below, cowry, marine; I, *Triopha*, a sea slug; J, *Limax*, a land slug; K, *Helix*, a land snail; L, *Olivella* shell, a marine snail, also called olive shell; M, *Aplysia*, a sea hare.

some feed upon dead plants and animals or upon living animals. Land gastropods include two groups, the snails and the slugs. Most snails inhabit forests where they are sheltered under fallen trees, decaying leaves, rocks, or the soil. The natural food of these animals is vegetation, but some prey upon earthworms, their own eggs, and each other. Among those that are herbivorous, certain snail species cause considerable damage to crops and garden plants.

Slugs are more active at night and tend to be more closely associated with man's homes than are snails; hence, slugs probably do more garden damage. Slugs, like snails, prefer plants as food, but also act as scavengers and predators. Few people realize that slugs can hang by a thread made from dried mucus. This reminds one of spiders and their silk, but unlike spiders, slugs cannot travel up their thread.

Marine gastropods are of many kinds, but most resemble snails or slugs. Ocean univalves feed on many different things. The scum of microscopic algae is used by many rock dwellers, especially the limpets. Abalone and sea hares feed upon larger seaweeds, as do a very few snails and limpets. Surprisingly few marine gastropods feed upon detritis which is rich in decaying and living organisms. The tube snail, *Aletes*, secretes a triangular sheet of mucus with which it nets minute life and decaying material. The moon snails and murexes are two groups of carnivorous snails that use the radula to bore through the shells of other mollusks. The sea slugs have specialized meat diets, some species showing preference for sponges, hydroids, sea pansies, bryozoans, ascidians, and other animals.

Most gastropods are hermaphroditic, and in marine species a free-swimming larval stage occurs between egg and adult form. The slipper-shells, *Crepidula*, cup-and-saucer shells, *Crucibulum;* and certain other taxa have a strange life history in which adult life is started as a male, the male later changes to a sexless individual, and the latter in turn transforms to a female. In most limpets, abalones, and many snails the sexes are separate. In land and fresh-water species adult development generally is direct from an egg.

Gastropods are among the more economically important animals. Abalones are a most important source of gastropod food for humans in the United States, and other univalves are consumed elsewhere in the world. Univalve shells have been and are the counterpart of money in many parts of the world. For example, olive shells, *Olivella*, were exchanged as wampum by Pacific Coast Indians. These shells still are very common in many places, so common that anyone familiar with their numbers might wonder what kept all Pacific Coast Indians from being millionaires. The answer is that the economic principles of supply and demand was in effect. Although a few strings of olive shells might buy a wife inland it probably cost a sack full for a like purchase along the Coast. Hence, units of value varied geographically, but two common measurements of wampum strings were thumb tip to elbow and thumb tip to the base of hand. Indian "businessmen" had a tattoo mark on the thumb side at the base of the hand to indicate the latter-mentioned measurement. Abalone also were items of wampum. In addition, it was not uncommon for Pacific Coast Indians to place small abalone shells in the eye-sockets of their dead.

Gastropod shells were used for other purposes in former times. It is hard to imagine that knowledge of gastropods could make a people a world power, but such was the case with the Phoenecians. The cities of Tyre and Sidon became banking centers and crossroads of the ancient world as a result of Tyrian purple dye extracted from murex snails. This dye was used for the clothing of royalty, idols, Roman senators, and others of high position from the fifteenth century B.C. to the seventh century A.D. Many of our snails possess the same or a similar purple dye, especially certain of our marine snails and sea hares.

CLASS PELECYPODA (Bivalves)

Diagnosis: bilaterally symmetrical and unsegmented; body without a distinct head but with a mouth bounded by flaps (labial palps); radula absent; foot often large, usually wedge-shaped; shell divided into two valves (Figure 13.8).

The bivalves are clam-like individuals and include such organisms as clams, mussels, scallops, and oysters. Most of them are marine, but there are fresh-water forms. Most pelecypods feed by filtering organisms from the water. They secrete a sticky mucus over the gills and minute organisms stick to this mucus. The water current necessary to bring food to the gills is created by the beating of cilia. The cilia also serve to direct the mucous-trapped food to the mouth. The most surprising exception to the general feeding habit is found in the wood-eating

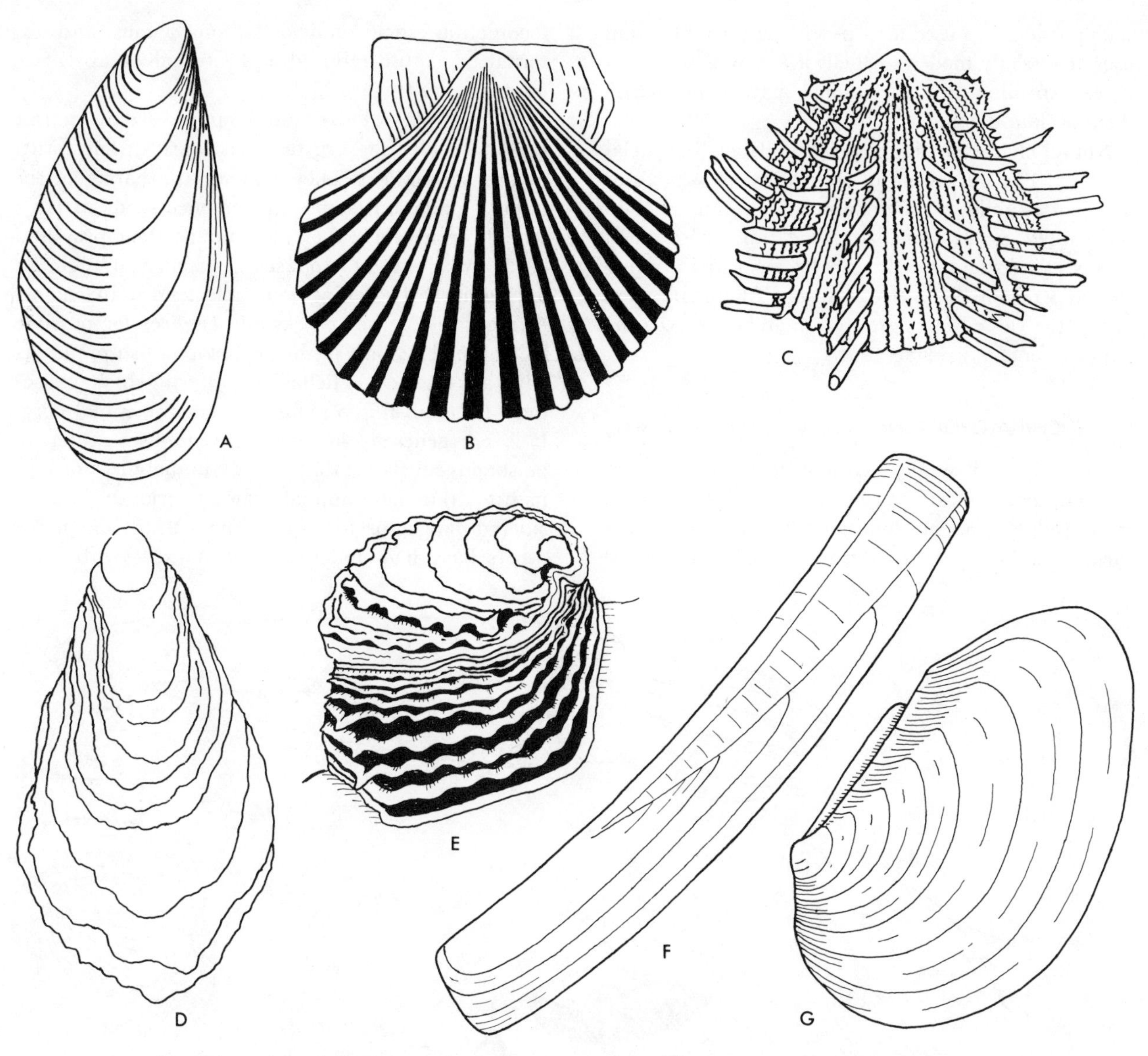

Figure 13.8 Class Pelecypoda, bivalve types: A, *Mytilus,* a mussel, marine; B, *Pecten,* a scallop, marine; C, *Spondylus,* a thorny oyster, marine; D, *Ostrea,* an oyster, marine; E, *Chama,* jewel box or rock oyster, marine; F, *Ensis,* a jacknife clam, marine; G, *Anodonta,* a fresh-water clam.

shipworms. These bivalves, when burrowing in wood, swallow and digest the fine wood particles. Most pelecypods live in sandy mud, but others are found in sand, clay, and burrowing in rocks or wood. They are found from intertidal to deep water.

In almost all pelecypods the sexes are separate and the egg hatches into a free-swimming larva which eventually transforms into a miniature adult. Some marine bivalves have brood pouches in which the egg is retained until hatching, but most shed their eggs into the water for fertilization. Fresh-water animals' larvae differ from the marine larvae by being fish parasites prior to becoming adults.

Man has relied upon clams, oysters, and the like for thousands of years. Coastal midden heaps of ancient men contain many bivalve shells, indicating that primitive man used them for food. The shells were also used for ornaments, as they are today to form jewelry. Pearls are formed by secretion of a calcareous substance around irritating sand grains. Circular portions of many shells (mother of pearl) were strung by American Indians for wampum; today such portions are used for "pearl" buttons. Certain uses are strictly modern. Shells are now a source of lime. An important recreational activity in coastal areas is clam-digging.

Not all characteristics of pelecypods are beneficial to man. The burrowing of shipworms in wharf pilings causes millions of dollars damage annually in the United States alone. At one time these wood borers caused fatalities at sea because their boring caused wooden boats to collapse. All in all, even today, the value of this group to man far exceeds the damage some individuals cause.

CLASS CEPHALOPODA (Nautili, Squids, and Octopuses)

Diagnosis: bilaterally symmetrical and unsegmented; body mostly a well-developed head with eyes; radula present; foot modified into tentacles (arms); siphon present and used for jet-propelled locomotion; shell undivided, conspicuous and external in nautili, reduced and internal or absent in other species (Figure 13.9).

The nautili, squids, and octopuses are all marine predators of fish, crustaceans, worms, and other mollusks. Little is known about the habits of the larger squids, but some smaller ones swim in large schools, from which they may pursue their prey and kill it by a bite. Octopuses are active at night or during the early evening hours and tend to live alone. At night they search cracks and crevices for possible food animals. Some of the cephalopod fish predators have an instinctive behavior pattern which causes them to bite fish in a manner to cut the spinal cord. It is not generally known that octopuses secrete a poisonous substance that quickly immobilizes or kills its prey, but these animals cannot seriously be considered dangerous to man. The author and many others have had underwater encounters with large

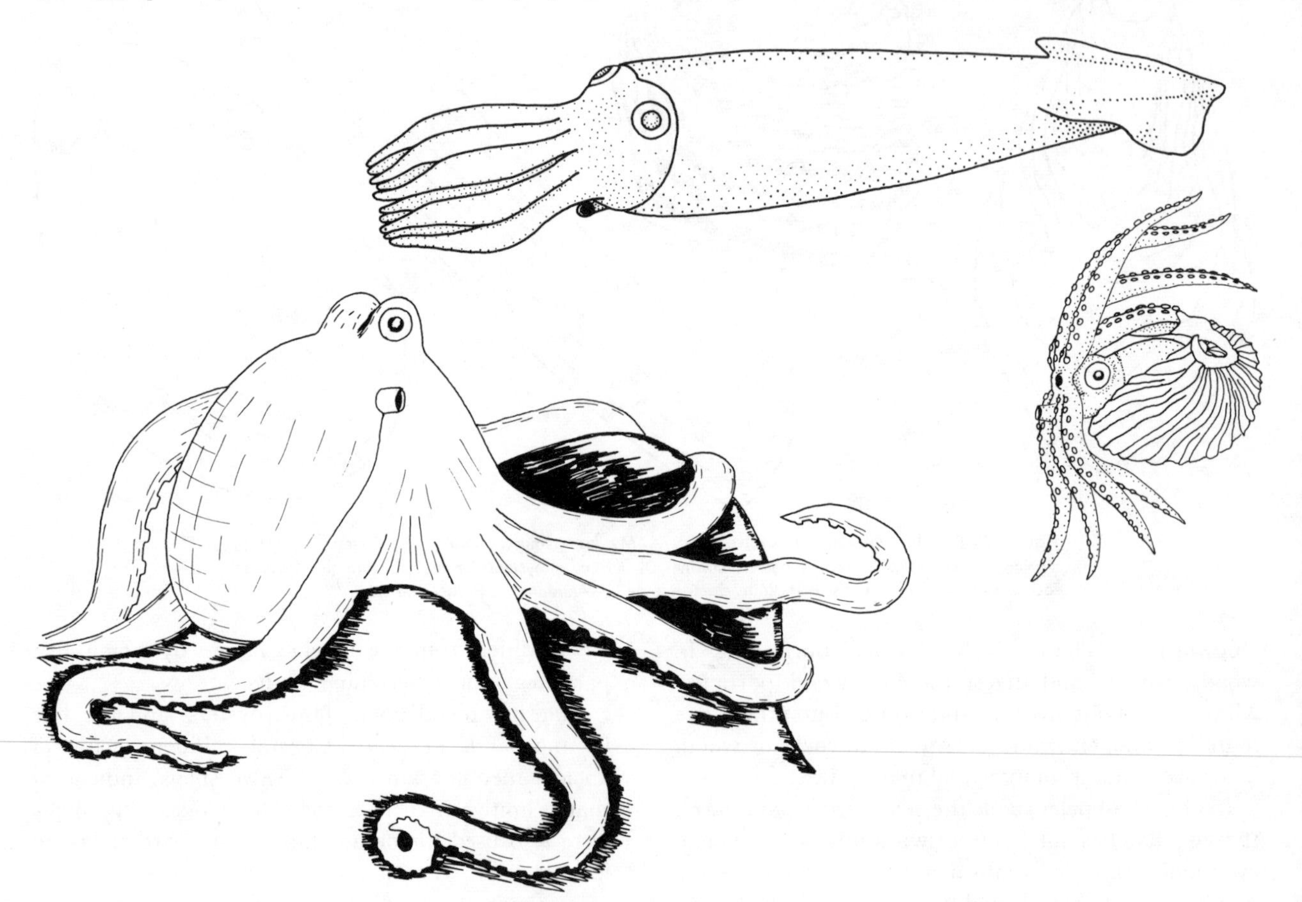

Figure 13.9 Class Cephalopoda, cephalopod types: above, *Loligo,* a squid, marine; right, *Argonauta,* a paper nautilus carrying its shell, marine; below, *Octopus,* octopus or devilfish, marine.

octopuses. All reliable witnesses indicate that no matter what size the octopus, it always tried to leave when encountered by man. The fear and tales of dangerous encounters appear to have come from sailors who enjoy terrifying land-lubbers. Giant squids, the largest known invertebrates, reaching a body-tentacle length of over 50 feet, could definitely be dangerous to humans; but they are deep sea forms. The tales of giant squids attacking and destroying boats are probably additional sea yarns for the land-locked individuals' benefit.

Except for two or three examples, the sexes of cephalopods are separate. Females seem to be four to seven times as numerous as the males in the different species. There is no free-swimming larval stage as found in other mollusks. The egg hatches into a miniature adult. Octopuses care for and protect the developing eggs, and it seems necessary for the female to wash or clean the eggs during development to prevent their loss from bacterial infection. The parent appears to remain with the eggs during the entire period of development, the adult never leaving even to feed. In most cephalopods the male is characterized by one flattened arm which is further modified for the transfer of sperm to the female.

Cephalopods have long been used by man as a source of food. Prejudice now causes many people not to eat octopuses, which are every bit as tasty as many "acceptable" mollusks. Cuttlebone for the birdcage is a representation of the cephalopod internal shell. The shells of nautili, mostly South Pacific animals not found in United States waters, are sought for their ornamental value. There is little about the group that one could possibly construe as being detrimental to man.

ECHIUROIDEA (Innkeepers and allies)

Diagnosis: symmetry bilateral; unsegmented; schizocoelous; gray, reddish, or yellowish, cylindrical creatures from 1 to 18 inches long; superficially resemble priapuloids, aschelminths, and sipunculoids, but the anterior proboscis is either spoon-like or thread-like and long; the proboscis is contractile, but cannot be withdrawn into the body; marine burrowers; sexes separate, trochophore producers (Figure 13.10).

These worms live in mud or sand in shallow coastal waters. Perhaps the most interesting of them is the innkeeper (*Urechis*). This intertidal California species constructs a U-shaped burrow in which it traps microscopic food by pumping water through the mucous funnel it secretes in its burrow. This innkeeper usually has a segmented worm, a crab, and a small fish as tenants in its burrow. The tenants apparently either live on the scraps that the innkeeper misses, or perhaps steal food from the innkeeper.

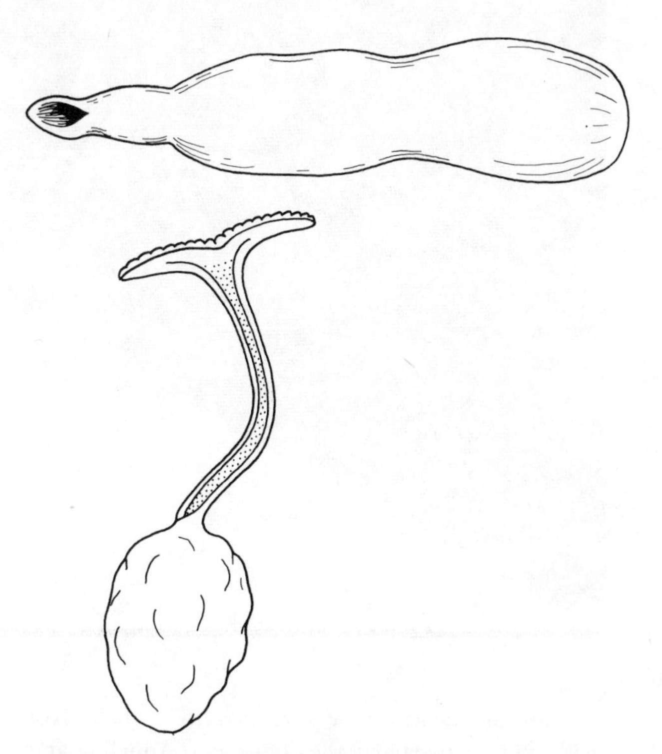

Figure 13.10 Echiuroid types: above, *Urechis*, the innkeeper, marine; below, *Bonellia*, a marine genus in which a sexless stage becomes a parasitic male if it contacts a female, or becomes a female if no male is found.

SELECTED READINGS*

Abbott, R. T., 1954. *American Seashells.* D. Van Nostrand Co., Princeton, N. J.

Hyman, L. H., 1959. *The Invertebrates.* Vol. 5: *Smaller Coelomate Groups*, McGraw-Hill Book Co., New York.

Morris, P. A., 1951. *A Field Guide to the Shells of our Atlantic and Gulf Coasts.* Houghton Mifflin Co., Boston.

———. 1952. *A Field Guide to the Shells of the Pacific Coast and Hawaii.* Houghton Mifflin Co., Boston.

Morton, J. E., 1958. *Mollusks.* Hutchinson University Library, London.

Pilsbry, H. A., 1939–1946. *Land Mollusca of North America.* 2 vols., each in 2 parts. Acad Nat. Sci., Philadelphia.

*See also p. 212.

14 ANNELIDA AND ARTHROPODA

Segmented Schizocoels

Is an earthworm closely related to a fly? Not really, but the two phyla they represent, Annelida and Arthropoda, are, as phyla go, closely related. Both phyla have true segmentation. Also, many anthropods, except for their legs, are worm-like. This is especially true of certain insect larvae, for example, the familiar caterpillars of butterflies and moths.

The final development of a group of ancestral Schizocoela, prior to its later evolution into distinct annelids and arthropods was true segmentation. Moreover, true segmentation is typical of only three animal phyla: the annelids, the arthropods, and the chordates. However, chordate segmentation was independently acquired because it evolved in animals that already were definite eucoelomates.

SEGMENTED, WORM-LIKE SCHIZOCOELA: ANNELIDA

We shall now discuss the adaptations of another worm-like group, the annelids, that enabled them to attain greater size and complexity. Again, these are bilateral Eumetazoa that develop from three germ layers. The true body cavity, or *coelom,* is the only body cavity. It occupies a large part of the body space. Since it is a cavity in the mesoderm, all organs are surrounded by mesoderm and none lie free in the cavity. These animals have solved the problem of growth by means of true *segmentation,* or *metamerism.* The body is essentially a series of like boxes, called *somites,* with partitions between them. Within these somites, various organs are repeated serially—the nephridia-type excretory organs, nerve ganglia, and locomotor organs consisting basically of stiff bristles, or *setae.* The digestive tract is not segmental and shows clearly defined regions for crushing the food; for storing it; for digesting, absorbing, and egesting it. Needless to say, the digestive tract is complete. The circulatory system is also complete, the blood being entirely contained within blood vessels, and respiration occurs through the body wall or specialized folds of its surface. The pumping vessel is dorsal and a main collecting vessel is ventral. The dorsal vessel serves the function of a true heart in that it is a pump with valves. The so-called "hearts," which connect dorsal and ventral vessels, act as a pressure-regulating mechanism, receiving blood in spurts from the dorsal vessel, and then contracting to force the blood under a steady pressure into the ventral vessel. The blood is red, owing to the presence of hemoglobin, but the pigments are usually dissolved in the plasma and the circulatory cells are colorless. The ladder type of nervous system is composed of a pair of head ganglia ("brain") and connectives to a solid, double, mid-ventral nerve cord extending the length of the body. The nerve cord has a ganglion and pairs of lateral nerves in each segment. Reproduction may be

TAXONOMIC SUMMARY

Kingdom Animalia (L. *animalis*, animate) animals
Subkingdom Eumetazoa (Gr. *eu-*, true + *meta*, among + *zoon*, animal)—eumetazoans
Grade Bilateria (L. *bi-*, two + *lateralis*, side)
Eucoelomata (Gr. *eu-*, true + *koilos*, hollow)
Schizocoela (Gr. *schizo*, cleave + *koilos*)

Phylum Annelida (L. *annelus*, little ring)—segmented worms
Class Polychaeta (Gr. *poly*, many + *chaite*, hair)—marine segmented worms
Class Oligochaeta (Gr. *oligos*, few + *chaite*)—earthworms and allies
Class Hirudinea (L. *hirudo*, leech)—leeches
Phylum Arthropoda (Gr. *arthron*, joint + *podos*, foot)—joint-legged animals
Subphylum Onychopora (Gr. *onychus*, claw + *phoros*, bearing)—joint-legged worms
†Subphylum Trilobita (Gr. *trias*, three + *lobos*, lobe)—trilobites
Subphylum Chelicerata (Gr. *chele*, claw + *keraos*, horny)—chelicerates
Class Merostomata (Gr. *meros*, thigh + *stoma*, mouth)—merostomates
†Subclass Eurypterida (Gr. *eurys*, broad + *pteryx*, wing)—sea scorpions
Subclass Xiphosura (Gr. *xiphos*, sword + *oura*, tail)—horseshoe crabs
Class Pycnogonida (Gr. *pyknos*, compact + *gonos*, gonad)—sea spiders
Class Arachnida (Gr. *arachne*, spider)—arachnids
Order Scorpionida (Gr. *skorpion*, scorpion)—scorpions
Order Pseudoscorpionida (Gr. *pseudes*, false + *skorpion*)—pseudoscorpions
Order Phalangida (Gr. *phalangion*, a spider)—harvestmen or daddy longlegs
Order Acarina (Gr. *akari*, a mite)—mites and ticks
Order Solpugida (L. *solpuga*, poisonous ant or spider)—sun spiders or wind scorpions
Order Pedipalpi (L. *pes*, foot + *palpus*, feeler)—whip scorpions
Order Palpigrada (L. *palpus* + *gradior*, to walk)—micro whip scorpions
Order Araneae (L. *aranea*, a spider)—spiders
Subphylum Pentastomida (Gr. *penta*, five + *stoma*)—tongue worms
Subphylum Tardigrada (L. *tardus*, slow + *gradior*)—water bears
Subphylum Mandibulata (L. *mandibula*, jaw)—mandibulates
Class Crustacea (L. *crusta*, shell)—crustaceans
Subclass Branchiopoda (Gr. *branchia*, gills + *podos*, foot)—branchiopods
Order Anostraca (Gr. *an-* without + *ostrakon*, shell)—anostracans
Order Notostraca (Gr. *noton*, back + *ostrakon*)—tadpole shrimps
Order Conchostraca (Gr. *konche*, sheel + *ostrakon*)—claw or clam shrimps
Order Cladocera (Gr. *klados*, a branch + *keras*, horns)—water fleas
Subclass Ostracoda (Gr. *ostrakon*)—ostracods
Subclass Copepoda (Gr. *kope*, handle or oar + *podos*)—copepods
Subclass Cirripedia (L. *cirrus*, curl + *podos*)—barnacles
Subclass Malacostraca (Gr. *malakos*, soft + *ostrakon*)—malacostracans
Order Isopoda (Gr. *isos*, equal + *podos*)—isopods
Order Amphipoda (Gr. *amphi*, apart + *podos*)—scuds
Order Stomatopoda (Gr. *stomatos*, mouth + *podos*)—mantis shrimps
Order Decapoda (Gr. *deka*, ten + *podos*)—decapods
Class Diplopoda (Gr. *diploos*, double + *podos*)—millipedes
Class Chilopoda (Gr. *cheilos*, margin + *podos*)—centipedes
Class Pauropoda (Gr. *pauros*, small + *podos*)—pauropods
Class Symphyla (Gr. *syn*, together + *phylon*, tribe)—garden centipedes
Class Insecta (L. *insectus*, divided)—insects

†Extinct.

Subclass Apterygota (Gr. *a-*, not + *pterygotos*, winged)
Order Protura (Gr. *proto*, first + *oura*, tail)—telsontails
Order Thysanura (Gr. *thysanos*, tassel + *oura*)—bristletails
Order Collembola (Gr. *kolla*, glue + *bole*, dart)—springtails
Subclass Pterygota (Gr. *pterygotos*, winged)
Division Exopterygota (Gr. *exo*, outside + *pterygotos*)
Order Orthoptera (Gr. *orthos*, straight + *pteron*, wing)—grasshoppers, crickets, roaches, walking sticks, mantids and allies
Order Dermaptera (Gr. *derma*, skin + *pteron*)—earwigs
Order Plecoptera (Gr. *pleko*, fold + *pteron*)—stoneflies
Order Isoptera (Gr. *isos*, equal + *pteron*)—termites
Order Embioptera (Gr. *embios*, lively + *pteron*)—web-spinners
Order Corrodentia (L. *corrodens*, gnawing)—book lice
Order Mallophaga (Gr. *mallos*, wool + *phago*, to eat)—biting lice
Order Anopleura (Gr. *anoplos*, unarmed + *oura*, tail)—sucking lice
Order Thysanoptera (Gr. *thysanos*, tassel + *pteron*)—thrips
Order Hemiptera (Gr. *hemi*, half + *pteron*)—bugs
Order Homoptera (Gr. *homos*, same + *pteron*)—cicadas, hoppers, scale insects and allies
Order Ephemeroptera (Gr. *ephemeros*, lasting but a day + *pteron*)—mayflies
Order Odonata (Gr. *odontos*, tooth)—damselflies and dragonflies
Division Endopterygota (Gr. *endon*, inside + *pterygotos*)
Order Neuroptera (Gr. *neuron*, nerve + *pteron*)—nerve-winged insects
Order Mecoptera (Gr. *mekos*, length + *pteron*)—scorpion flies
Order Trichoptera (Gr. *thrix*, hair + *pteron*)—caddisflies
Order Lepidoptera (Gr. *lepis*, scale + *pteron*)—butterflies, skippers and moths
Order Coleoptera (Gr. *koleos*, sheath + *pteron*)—beetles
Order Strepsiptera (Gr. *strepsis*, a turning + *pteron*)—strepsipterans
Order Hymenoptera (Gr. *hymen*, membrane + *pteron*)—sawflies, horntails, bees, ants and wasps
Order Diptera (Gr. *di-*, two + *pteron*)—flies
Order Siphonaptera (Gr. *siphon*, siphon + *a*, without + *pteron*)—fleas

asexual by budding, or sexual. Some animals are either male or female, others are hermaphroditic.

ANNELIDA (Segmented Worms)

Diagnosis: symmetry bilateral; segmented both externally and internally, body composed of many essentially similar and ring-like segments; appendages unjointed, minute, and rod-like (setae), but absent in leaches; schizocoelous; fresh-water, marine, damp soil, and parasitic.

CLASS POLYCHAETA (Marine Segmented Worms)

Diagnosis: Locomotion, respiration, and current-production by lateral, vaguely leaf-like structures (parapodia) having many bristles (setae); head distinct, with eyes, tentacles, and palps; body without a clitellum (a "collar" covering body segments); sexes regularly separate; also includes a group of primitive or degenerate worms (sometimes called the Class Archiannelida), without parapodia or setae and with only internal segmentation (Figure 14.1).

Polychaetes are an abundant group found in practically every habitat in the ocean. About five kinds are found in fresh water or inland in the United States. Two are strictly eastern, two are found near San Francisco, and one in the Salton Sea in Southern California. Many are tube dwellers which secrete tubes of calcium carbonate, leathery mucus, and cemented sand grains, shells, or debris. Some live in burrows; others are free-living. Still others have unusual habitats such as burrows in shells, eelgrass roots, kelp holdfasts, or on special animals.

The common names of polychaetes can be associated with their feeding structures (Figure 14.1). Such common names are used because indentification of families and orders is a beastly job. First, are

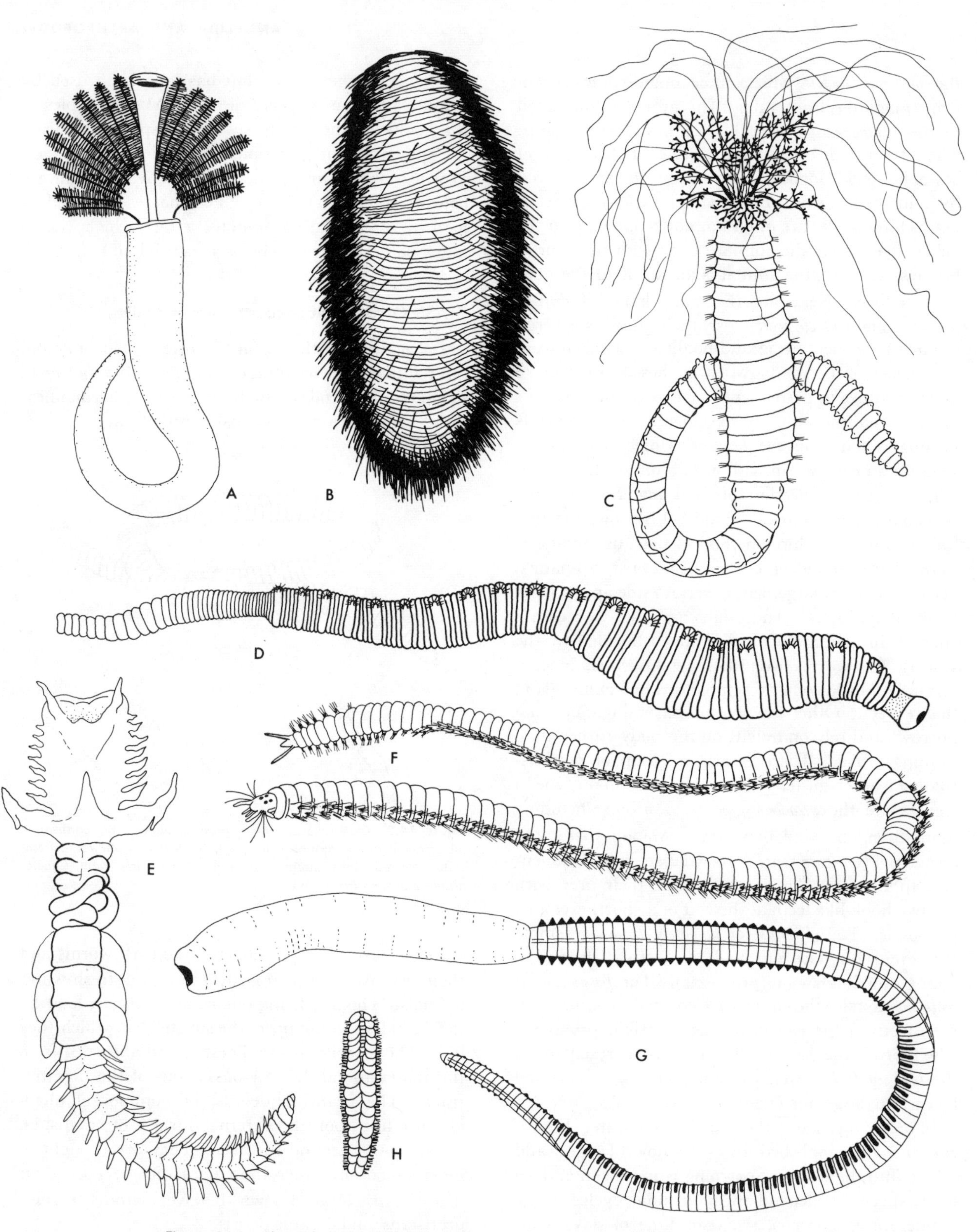

Figure 14.1 Class Polychaeta: A, *Serpula*, a feather-duster worm, a marine tube dweller; B, *Aphrodite*, a sea mouse, marine; C, *Thelepus*, a tentacle worm, a marine tube dweller; D, *Arenicola*, a lugworm, a marine burrower; E, *Chaetopterus*, a fanworm, a marine tube dweller; F, *Nereis*, a clamworm, a marine predator; G, *Glycera*, a proboscis worm, a marine form often found among kelp holdfasts; H, *Halosydna*, a scale worm, a marine form often found in holes or on other animals.

the *plankton feeders* which filter microscopic organisms (plankton) from water. This group is dominated by the "*feather-duster worms*" which have feathery gills. Then, there is *Aphrodite*, the *sea mouse*. This is an oval animal about 3 inches long whose sides are covered by irridescent, flexible bristles. The colorful bristles of this filter feeder are often not noticed, owing to the debris that covers the animal. Even with its colorful bristles, however, the animal is an insult to the goddess of love. Next, are the many kinds of *detritus feeders*. The *tentacle worms* use their mucous-covered tentacles to collect living and nonliving material from the surface of the mud. Most of these worms make leathery tubes in permanent burrows in mud flats or on the ocean bottom. A second method of detritus feeding is found in the *lugworm* which vaguely resembles an earthworm with a bulb on the front end. There is some selection of food materials by the mucous-covered bulb as the animal burrows through sand or mud. A third method of detritus feeding is most characteristic of certain *fan worms*, so-named because of the enlargement of certain side appendages at about midbody. These fans are used to create a current through a mucous bag that is formed by the worms. Fan worms live in U-shaped burrows in sand or mud and somewhat resemble certain echiuroids in this respect. Other fan worms have single-opening burrows and rely on mucus on the body rather than forming a bag. There is also a group of detritus-feeding feather-duster worms. The third main type of feeders are the *predaceous worms*, a group including more than one kind of worm. Among these, the *nereids*, or *clam-worms*, are somewhat snake-like in general appearance. These worms seize their prey with the two hook-like teeth at the end of a short, eversible proboscis. The *glycerids*, or *proboscis worms*, resemble the nereids but have four hook-like teeth at the end of a long eversible snout (proboscis). The *polynoids*, or *scale worms*, have the entire back covered by scales and have teeth at the end of a long eversible proboscis. The fourth, and last, feeding type is represented by the *seaweed feeders*. This feeding type is represented by certain, large burrowing nereids.

In most polychaetes the sexes are separate. Fertilization is accomplished by spawning of eggs and sperm into the water. Spawning is in unison and, in many species, is dependent upon lunar cycles, tides, temperature, season of the year, time of day, light, and calmness of the water. Asexual reproduction in the form of budding is known.

This is another group that has long been used by primitive man as a source of food. Many peoples of the Pacific Islands gather worms, especially during the spawning congregations of some worm species. Worms taken during the reproductive season are considered especially tasty. Polychaetes are used as food by many marine animals, a fact which causes many of these worms to be used as fish bait by man.

CLASS OLIGOCHAETA (Earthworm and allies)

Diagnosis: bristles (setae) involved in locomotion, but relatively few in number; no parapodia and head much reduced; collar (clitellum) present; hermaphroditic, eggs often in cocoons; without larval stages (Figure 14.2).

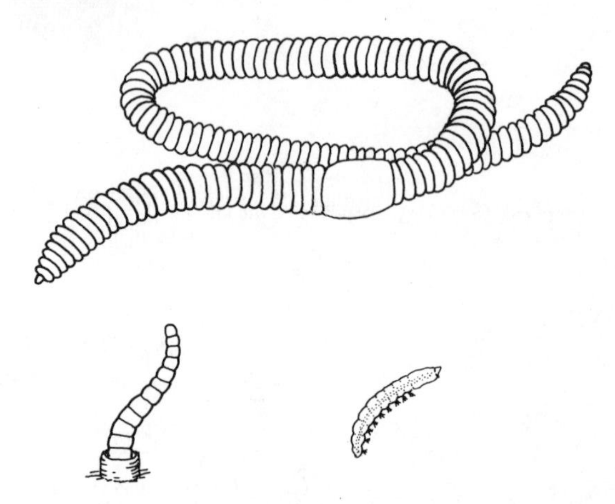

Figure 14.2 Class Oligochaeta: above, *Lumbricus*, an earthworm, subterranean and terrestrial; below, left, *Tubifex*, a bristleworm, fresh-water with reddish tail vibrating from mud tube; below, right, *Chaetogaster*, a bristleworm, fresh water.

In contrast to the polychaetes, the earthworms and their relatives are primarily land and fresh-water animals. The free-living oligochaetes obtain food by taking in large amounts of the substrate in which they live. The food items are digested and absorbed from this material and the rest passes out of the digestive tract. The branchiobdellids, or commensal oligochaetes, live upon the external surface of crayfishes, usually on or around the gills. They are thought to be commensal, rather than parasitic, because their digestive tracts are known to have diatoms, certain protistans, and organic debris.

Oligochaetes are mostly hermaphroditic, but cross-fertilization is the usual case. Asexual reproduction by budding occurs in a few oligochaetes, as it does in a few polychaetes.

Primitive peoples have used and still use oligochaetes as food. They also are widely used as fish bait. Perhaps, their greatest benefit to man is the making of burrows in the soil. This earthworm activity allows greater aeration of the soil and also contributes to soil formation because the earthworms cast wastes upon the ground surface.

CLASS HIRUDINEA (Leeches)

Diagnosis: without bristles (setae), parapodia, or collar (clitellum), and head much reduced; anterior and posterior suckers present and used for attachment; hermaphroditic, producing eggs in cocoons but no larval stage; many are external, blood-sucking parasites (Figure 14.3).

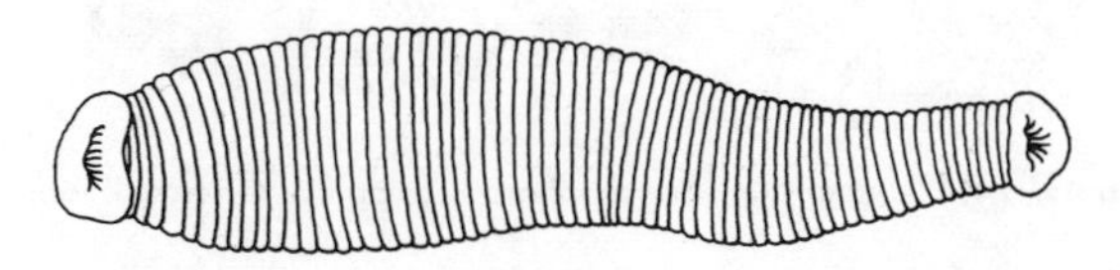

Figure 14.3 Class Hirudinea, *Macrobdella*, the common bloodsucker or American leech, fresh-water.

Most leeches are found in fresh water, but a few live upon marine fishes and some in moist places on land. Fresh-water species are most numerous in warm, protected shallows where there is little water movement and plants, rocks, and debris offer concealment. Because they require attachment surfaces, they are seldom found on mud or clay bottoms. Leeches are either scavengers, predators, or parasites. The scavengers rely mostly on animal remains; the predators most commonly eat small worms, insects, and mollusks; and the parasites are most common on crustaceans and vertebrates.

Leeches are hermaphroditic, but cross-fertilization is the practice. Most eggs are protected by a cocoon that is placed in water or in earth. In some species, the eggs are laid on rocks. Some carry their developing eggs on the underside of their bodies.

Leeches are food for various aquatic animals, especially fishes; hence, they are another source of fish bait. In our part of the world they are little more than a nuisance to swimmers, but some of the land leeches of Asia and the East Indies can cause severe injury to man. Most famous of the leeches is *Hirudo medicinalis*, the medicinal leech. This animal once was used in the practice of blood-letting. Today these leeches are sometimes used to treat "black eyes."

SEGMENTED, JOINT-LEGGED SCHIZOCOELA: ARTHROPODA

The primary difference between segmented worms and joint-legged animals is indicated by the common name of the arthropods. Annelids have no jointed legs and arthropods do. However, their similarity is shown by a living "missing link," *Peripatis* (Subphylum Onychophora), the joint-legged worm. Now, you should realize that the idea of a "missing link" breeds a great deal of misunderstanding. How might one describe the annelid-arthropod characters in *Peripatus*, when *Peripatus* probably originated as a species much later than the time of annelid or arthropod origin?

ARTHROPODA (Joint-legged Animals)

Diagnosis: symmetry bilateral; segmentation visible externally in varying degrees; appendages are jointed; schizocoelous; possess a hard, external skeleton, containing a chemical compound called chitin; probably more numerous than all other life combined; marine, fresh-water, terrestrial, aerial, and parasitic.

To discuss the arthropods in a few pages is akin to writing an encyclopedia on the head of a pin. The joint-legged animals are the largest and most diverse of all animal phyla. In fact, one single class, the Insecta, includes more than half of the known species in the animal kingdom. If any animal group today rules the earth, the arthropods must be acclaimed as masters. Let us then inspect these terrible conquerors to discover whence they came and what they are.

We may consider arthropods as basically annelid-like animals grown up in their evolutionary potentialities. Recall some of the features of annelid structure: segmentation, or metamerism, in which most segments are alike; a well-developed, segmental, ladder-type nervous system; simple, bristle-like locomotor appendages, the setae. Add to these the principle of cephalization, and evolution is well on the way to the arthropods. Cephalization is the evolutionary tendency in freely moving animals toward concentration of feeding structures, special senses, and nervous coordination centers in the anterior end—or, more simply, head formation. In their evolution from an annelid-like ancestor, the arthropods have developed cephalization to a marked degree. That is, they have good heads with all the appurtenances thereof: brain, eyes, chemical sense organs, and tactile organs. They have gone even farther in their differentiation by attaining a separation of their bodies into regions and their appendages into complex structures. Thus, not only are the head's segments and its appendages modified for feeding and sensory function, but the rest of the body is usually laid off in definite regions with definite functions. The evolutionary modification of appendages is in large measure tied in with this regional modification. Segmentation of this type, with widely varying body segments, is unlike that of the annelids whose body segments are essentially alike.

Head formation and specialized segmentation were not the only changes on the way from ancestor to arthropod. The coelom, or true body cavity, of ancestral arthropods exists today in early development but is later lost except for small cavities in the excretory and reproductive organs. The major body cavity in the modern adult is a spacious *hemocoel.* This cavity is created by the breaking down and migration of cells in the endoderm, resulting in the cavity's being lined by derivatives of all three germ layers. The blood (hemolymph) of this cavity is circulated by a dorsal pumping organ which may be a long tube or a compact heart. In living forms the entire body is encased in a protective external skeleton (exoskeleton) composed of nonliving material, chitin, secreted by the epidermis. The abdominal exoskeleton is usually segmented in agreement with the body wall segmentation. In the thoracic region segmentation is not defined so clearly. In the head segmentation can be traced only through study of embryonic development. Also, it is assumed that segmentation of the exoskeleton of appendages has evolved with the limbs; otherwise, arthropods would be encased in rigid boxes, incapable of complex function and limited in movement. Despite the great differences among specialized limbs, they may be reduced to a basic ancestral type. The ancestral arthropod limb is assumed to have been made up of three parts: at the base, a *protopodite,* from this, an inner *endopodite* and an outer *exopodite.* Modifications of the separate parts, along with their segmentation, lead to the diversity of appendages seen in the arthropods.

Subphylum ONYCHOPHORA (Joint-legged Worms)

Diagnosis: found in West Indies, Mexico, Central America, and Southern Hemisphere; about 70 species; of interest because of their "missing-link" features between Annelida and Arthropoda; vaguely caterpillar-like, a head with a pair of eyes, two "feelers" (antennae), and mouth bounded on each side by a blunt projection (oral papilla), without a shell; resemble annelids in having nephrida for excretion; body externally unsegmented, with poorly developed, barely jointed legs; respiration by air tubes (tracheae) as in many land arthropods; sexes are separate, the young being born alive (Figure 14.4).

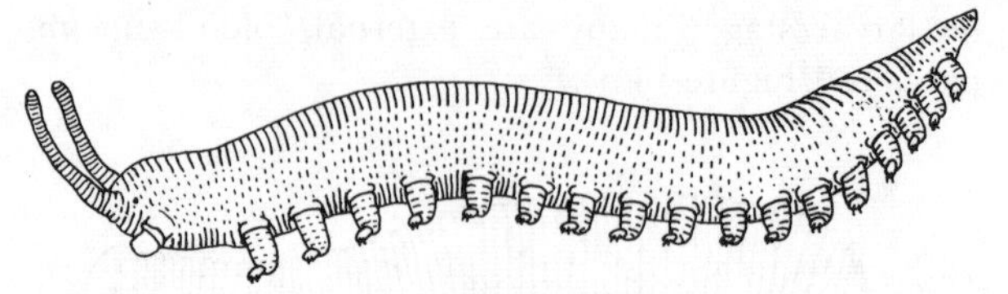

Figure 14.4 Subphylum Onychophora, *Peripatus,* terrestrial, about natural size.

Subphylum TRILOBITA (Trilobites)

Diagnosis: all extinct, Cambrian to Permian; hardly like any living creatures, perhaps vaguely sowbug-like; body covered by a shell and divided by two lengthwise dorsal furrows into three lobes; head, thorax, and abdomen distinct; body could be rolled up as in certain pillbugs; head with one pair of antennae and two eyes; appendages simple (Figure 14.5).

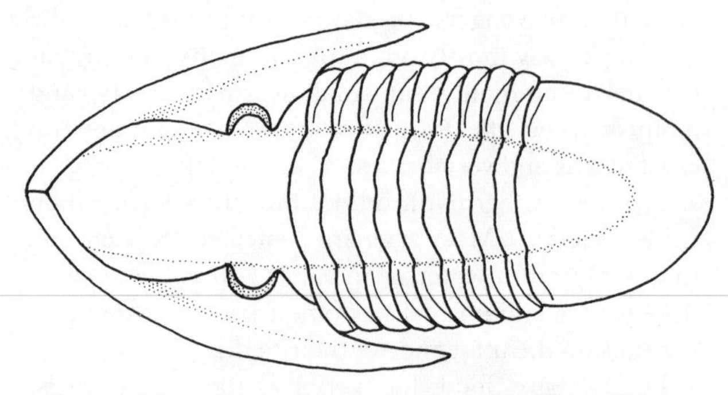

Figure 14.5 Subphylum Trilobita, *Isotelus,* an Ordovician trilobite.

Subphylum CHELICERATA (Chelicerates)

Diagnosis: body usually of two parts, cephalothorax (head + thorax) and abdomen, in Acarina (mites and ticks) cephalothorax and abdomen are fused together; cephalothorax has first pair of appendages with claws (chelicerae), one pair of projecting appendages (pedipalps), and four pairs of legs, but no antennae; cephalothorax and abdomen typically without obvious external segmentation.

CLASS MEROSTOMATA (Merostomates)

Diagnosis: lateral eyes two, each composed of many individual perception units grouped into a compound eye; body covered by a shell (including an extensive, solid anterior portion, the carapace), abdominal appendages bearing specialized respiratory structures (gills), abdomen terminated by an elongate, dagger-like structure; only Chelicerata with abdominal legs, five or six pairs.

Subclass EURYPTERIDA (Sea Scorpions)

Diagnosis: all extinct, Ordovician to Pennsylvanian; only vaguely scorpion-like, mostly small marine predators, but one to 7 feet long, the largest known fossil arthropod; external skeleton (carapace) covering cephalothorax but not expanded (Figure 14.6).

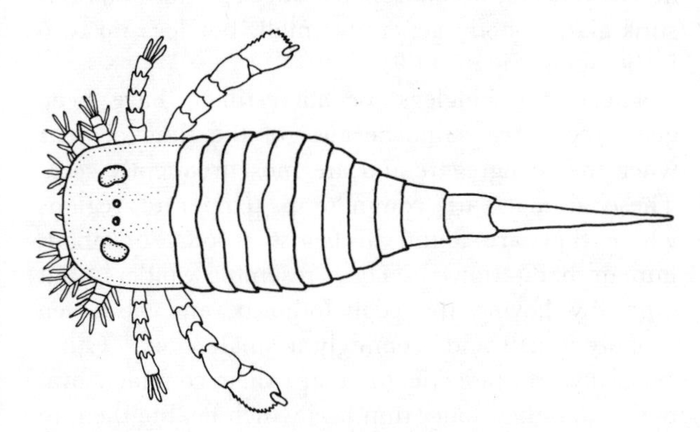

Figure 14.6 Subclass Eurypterida, *Eurypterus*, a Silurian sea scorpion.

Subclass XIPHOSURA (King, or Horseshoe, Crabs)

Diagnosis: mostly extinct, Cambrian to Recent; cephalothorax covered by an arched, expanded carapace of horseshoe outline; *Limulus* to 20 inches long (Figure 14.7).

Only about five species of the genus *Limulus*, the king or horseshoe crabs, are now living, inhabiting the Atlantic Coast from Maine to Florida, the West Indies, and the eastern shores of Asia. These species

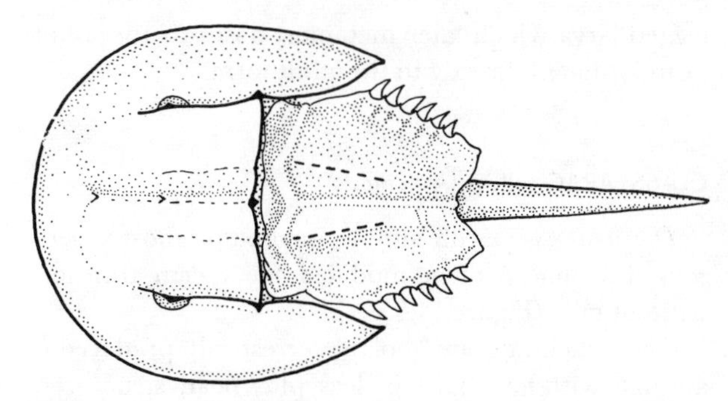

Figure 14.7 Subclass Xiphosurida, *Limulus*, a horseshoe or king crab, marine, grow to 18 inches long.

are very similar in appearance, all giving the impression of something out of the remote past. Their appearance is not deceptive, because they are close copies of horseshoe crabs that lived almost a half billion years ago. Therefore, the present horseshoe crabs truly are living fossils.

CLASS PYCNOGONIDA (Sea Spiders)

Diagnosis: mostly minute, but to about 20 inches; vaguely spider-like; four simple eyes; walking legs usually eight (also 10 or 12); without respiratory or excretory systems (Figure 14.8).

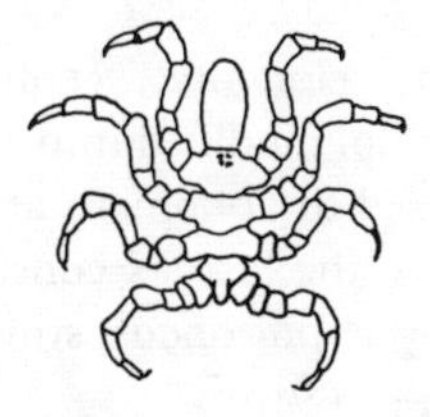

Figure 14.8 Class Pycnogonida, *Pycnogonum*, a sea spider, mostly minute to small.

The sea spiders are a secretive and semisedentary group of marine animals. Pycnogonids are infrequently seen, because their color matches their surroundings and their habit of feigning death when disturbed makes them inconspicuous. Most of their activity is confined to crawling slowly over seaweeds and attached animals. Although sea spiders are most frequently encountered on hydroids they are also found on anemones, algae, or under rocks, as well as in the ocean depths.

The sexes are usually separate, and the male carries the eggs until they hatch. Depending on the particular species, the eggs either hatch to a four-legged larva which later metamorphoses to the adult form, or hatch directly to the adult form.

CLASS ARACHNIDA (Arachnids)

Diagnosis: eyes all simple; pedipalpi mostly sensory, but male's often modified for sperm transfer; without gills (Figure 14.9).

The arachnids are mostly terrestrial, predaceous animals with four pairs of legs plus head structures, the pedipalpi, which often are sensory in nature. The body is of two parts, except in one group, the mites. The two body parts are the cephalothorax, a uniting of head and thorax, and the abdomen. There are no antennae ("feelers") or true jaws, and the eyes are all simple. Respiration is by book lungs or tracheae. Book lungs are so named because of their construction, resembling leaves of a book. Tracheae are air-tube systems whereby gases are conducted directly between the atmosphere and the cells of the animal. The sexes usually are separate, the males often being smaller than the females. Most lay eggs; there is no metamorphosis except for some slight change in form in the Acarina.

ORDER SCORPIONIDA (Scorpions)

Diagnosis: body elongate; cephalothorax relatively small, pedipalpi modified into pincers; cephalothorax broadly fused to abdomen; abdomen elongate and of 12 segments, the last six constricted (the tail) and terminated by a poisonous stinger; 1 to a few inches long (Figure 14.9).

A scorpion's tail typically is curled over the back and the stinger is thus directed forward in a position of attack or defense. Pincers, modified pedipalpi, usually are used to grasp anything that is to be stung. Although two Arizona species are often considered more poisonous than a black widow spider, most scorpions are not more dangerous than a wasp. The popular belief that they commit suicide by stinging themselves is as untrue as the belief that snakes swallow their young to protect them. Scorpions produce living young, which stay a week or more upon their mother's back. During this period, which is ended by the first molt, the young do not feed.

Scorpions inhabit warm, dry regions where they are active mostly at night, preying upon insects, spiders, and other scorpions. During the day they hide in burrows or under objects on the ground.

ORDER PSEUDOSCORPIONIDA (Pseudoscorpions)

Diagnosis: scorpion-like, but with abdomen of 11 segments that are not modified into a whip-like tail, abdomen not terminated by a stinger; minute, up to ¼ inch long; produce poison (Figure 14.9).

Although they bear no abdominal stinger, these animals do possess poison glands in the pincers. The poison probably is used to subdue the mites, psocids, springtails, and other tiny animals they eat. They share the ability of spiders to spin silk, spinning nests during periods of helplessness, such as molting. They live under objects on the ground; under tree bark; in bee, termite, or ant nests; and in human dwellings. Many are cave dwellers. Others can be found under rocks along upper beaches, and some are even intertidal. Pseudoscorpions are noted for their habit of attaching to and being transported by flying insects such as flies or beetles.

ORDER PHALANGIDA (= OPILIONES) (Harvestmen or Daddy Longlegs)

Diagnosis: somewhat spider-like; body oval, cephalothorax broadly joined to abdomen; abdomen with some indication of segmentation; pedipalpi not modified as pincers; nonpoisonous, but cephalothorax has stink glands; body generally small, but legs up to 6 inches long (Figure 14.9).

The daddy longlegs, or harvestmen, have been given the latter name because of the time of year when they congregate and are most frequently seen. These animals are common in temperate regions where they are found in fields, woods, or about human habitations. They resemble spiders, but differ by having the cephalothorax and abdomen broadly joined and seemingly a single unit. Other generally nonspider features are their compact, oval bodies and their long, thin legs which enable them to move rapidly.

Harvestmen are primarily scavengers, but they do prey upon small insects and suck juices from the soft parts of plants. Those that act as predators kill their prey be physical force alone; they lack poison glands. However, phalangids do possess glands that produce a malodorous secretion. These stink glands are presumed to be protective, acting to repel predators.

ORDER ACARINA (= ACARI) (Mites and Ticks)

Diagnosis: body oval, cephalothorax broadly joined to abdomen; without visible segmentation;

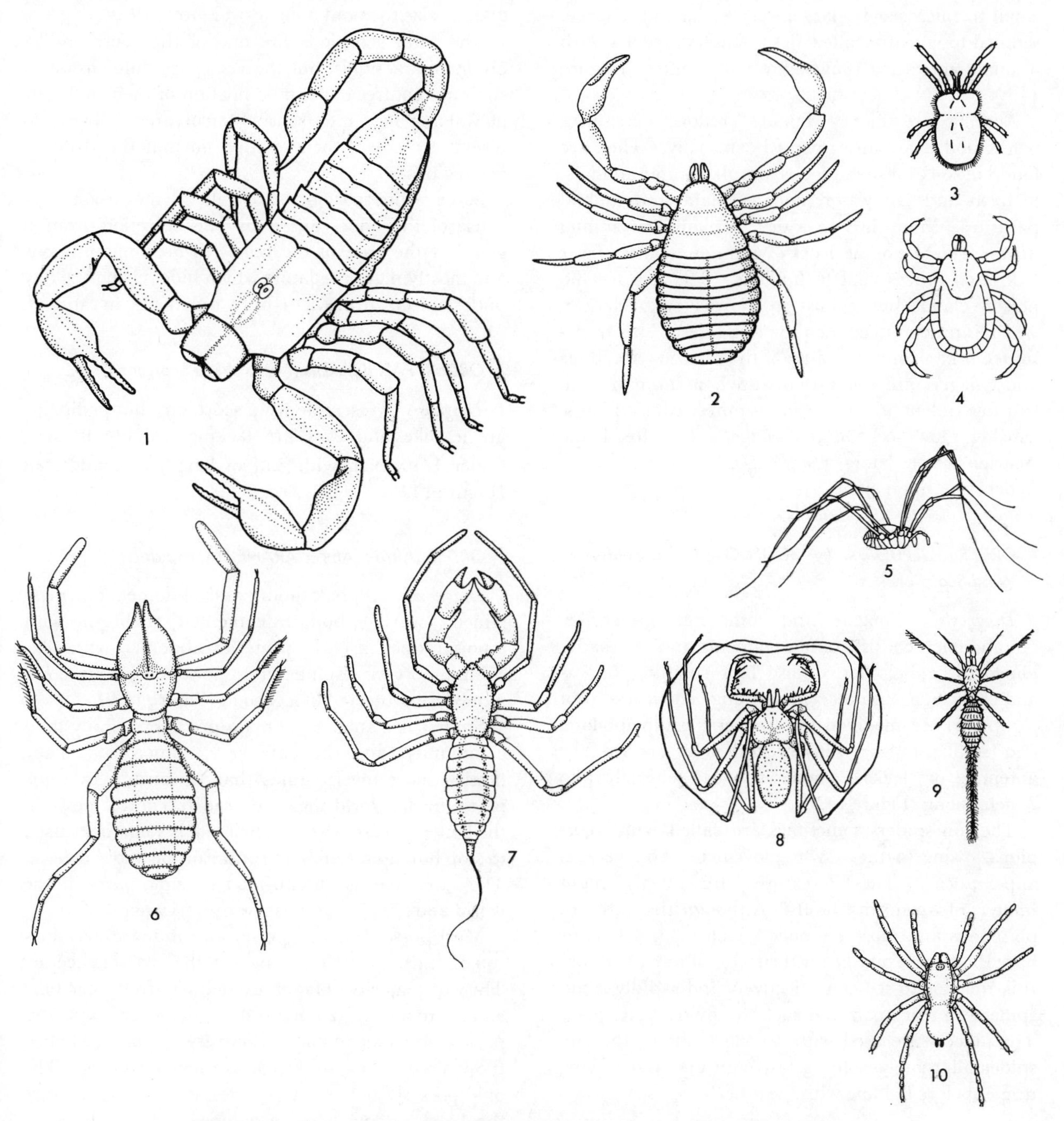

Figure 14.9 Class Arachnida. Order Scorpionida: 1, *Centrurus*, a scorpion. Order Pseudoscorpionida: 2, *Apocheiridium*, a pseudoscropion (x 5). Order Acarina: 3, *Eutrombicula*, a chigger mite (x 5); 4, *Dermacentor*, a tick. Order Phalangida: 5, *Phalangium*, a harvestman. Order Solpugida: 6, *Eremobates*, a wind scorpion. Order Pedipalpi: 7, *Mastigoproctus*, a whip scorpion (to 4 inches long); 8, *Charinus*, a vinegaroon. Order Palpigrada: 9, *Koenenia*, a micro whip scorpion. Order Araneida: 10, *Bothriocyrtum*, a trapdoor spider, a member of the suborder of bird spiders.

variable modifications of pedipalpi; nonpoisonous; small to microscopic; larger species having a large, toothed tongue are called ticks; smaller species with a small untoothed tongue are called mites (Figure 14.9).

Acarina are mostly minute, reddish creatures whose bodies are unsegmented externally. They are found in soil and stored foods, on plants and animals, in fresh and salt water, and as plant and animal parasites. Many live on a diet of plant and animal juices. The bite of the Rocky Mountain spotted fever tick often proves fatal to humans. The tick has no poison glands but is host to a virus or bacterium which is transmitted when the tick bites. This transmitted organism is the cause of the disease. Redbugs and chiggers are mites that attach to human skin, causing violent itching. Some mites attack plants, causing much economic damage. The free-living Acarina are predators or scavengers; they tend to live in debris or upon plants.

ORDER SOLPUGIDA (= SOLIFUGAE) (Sun Spiders or Wind Scorpions)

Diagnosis: Elongate and somewhat spider-like, but abdomen consists of ten segments and is broadly joined to cephalothorax; also lack spinning organs and chelicerae with a terminal fang; chelicerae (not pedipalpi) are modified into pincers; pedipelpi long and leg-like, but are sensory and held forward like antennae, or "feelers;" nonpoisonous; generally 1 to 2 inches long (Figure 14.9).

The sun spiders sometimes are called wind scorpions, owing to their swift movements and general appearance. These creatures are mostly night hunters of warm, dry lands. Although they are not poisonous and most are only 1 inch long, solpugids have the largest pincers for their size of any arachnid. It is amazing to see how effectively and rapidly a sun spider can tear apart and suck the fluids of its prey. The pincers are used with sawing motions, the sun spider alternately holding fast with one and driving deeper before holding with the other.

ORDER PEDIPALPI (Whip Scorpions)

Diagnosis: scorpion-like, with abdomen of twelve segments but not terminated by a stinger; end of abdomen with or without a whip-like structure; unique in having first pair of walking legs modified as sensory feelers; nonpoisonous, but some have stink glands; size to about 5 inches (Figure 14.9).

The whip scorpions are one of the scorpion-like orders of arachnids, but the Pedipalpi differ from all similar creatures in the modification of their first pair of walking legs into sensory structures. They do resemble many of their relatives in that they inhabit dry regions.

Some whip scorpions are called vinegaroons because of the odor caused by the secretion from a gland at the base of the tail. All are nonpoisonous and mostly night predators which hide during the day under objects, in crevices, or by burrowing in sand.

ORDER PALPIGRADA (Micro Whip Scorpions)

Diagnosis: resemble whip scorpions, but pedipalps are leg-like and eyes are lacking; minute in size, under 1/10 inch, with half of length a slender tail (Figure 14.9).

ORDER ARANEAE (= ARANEIDA) (Spiders)

Diagnosis: cephalothorax and abdomen narrowly joined ("waist"), both unsegmented; chelicerae with a poison duct in claw; posterior abdomen with silk-spinning organs (spinnerets); poisonous; eggs commonly are protected in a cocoon (Figure 14.9).

Spiders are among the main predators of any land community, and they are very numerous. They destroy more invertebrates than do birds. In some places in the world they are used to control pests in the home and elsewhere. Their silk is sometimes used to stop human bleeding in rural Europe and America. They are used as human food in some parts of the world and are bird and fish food everywhere.

Most possess enough poison to subdue prey. Poison is injected by the fangs of the two chelicerae. The vast majority of fangs are neither strong nor long enough to penetrate human skin; moreover few spider poisons are toxic to man. Contrary to popular belief, the United States tarantulas are nonpoisonous. The only possibly dangerous species in our country are the black widow and, to a lesser extent, the gray widow. Both produce a nerve poison, but neither are likely to bite, even if handled. The black widow will often cause grave illness, but its bite is rarely fatal.

Spiders feed primarily on insects and other spiders. Some American tarantulas, or bird spiders, are known to have eaten small birds, mammals, fish, and snakes, but these are tropical members of the group and probably were not eating their regular food. Spiders have specialized feeding behavior in that they are structurally limited to liquids. Within the poison injected into their prey are digestive juices. The spider feeds by sucking body juices and digested material. Spiders can go long periods without food; some have been known to have gone without food for as long as eighteen months.

Spiders have different means of obtaining their prey. The wandering spiders seek the animal and pounce upon it. The ambushing spiders hide and capture passing insects. The web-building spiders form nets and wait for them to snare their prey. Some spiders live in the webs of other spiders and feed upon smaller prey neglected by the web maker.

The webs of spiders are quite distinctive and can be used to identify the spiders making them. Irregular webs are mazes of threads extending in all directions and are characteristic of the black widow and other comb-footed spiders. Sheet webs are closely woven sheets in a single plane with threads in all directions in that plane and are made by the sheet web weavers. Funnel webs, made by funnel web spiders, are sheet-like in structure; but have a funnel extending from one side to the spider's retreat. The orb weavers make the most complex type, the orb web. The orb weaver framework consists of lines radiating in a single plane from the center. Sticky trapping silk spirals from the center and is attached to the framework. The spirals may be complete, incomplete, or sparse. The orb web may also be modified by being pulled into a dome-shaped structure. Some have a trapline from the center to a retreat. The triangular web is a pie-cut portion, a triangle, of an orb web constructed by certain orb weavers. Irregular webs with hackled bands, flat and more or less ribbon-like combinations of threads, are made by many cribellate spiders. The cribellum is a spinning device modified from part of the spinnerets. The sheet and irregular net webs are combinations of the two types and are constructed by some spiders. The orb and irregular net is another combination formed by some orb weavers, the labyrinth spiders.

Most spiders construct some type of nest. On the ground spiders may construct tunnels and turrets, a tunnel with a trap door, a silk-lined tunnel ("purse") with a silk surface extension, or a simple silk retreat. Some web makers have no nest; some make a silk retreat near the web; others fold or roll leaves and line the enclosed space; and many use a portion of the web, a crevice, or other natural retreat.

Female spiders lay one or two to a few thousand eggs. These are usually protected by an egg case that will identify its maker. Development in the egg sac is usually for a short period of time. In most species the female dies right after laying the eggs, but in some the females live and stay with the egg sac to protect the developing young. Certain spiders carry the egg sac around with them.

Once hatched, some spiderlings leave the area by ballooning. The young climb upward from the site of the egg sac. From a high perch they let out long strands of silk which soon catch the wind and so carry the spiderlings away. The spiderlings usually travel under 200 feet altitude but they have been found 200 miles from land. In this means of distributing the species, which is not limited to spiderlings, individuals may land and balloon many times. During the hatching period when much ballooning is taking place, the landing of many individuals can cause a large accumulation of silk, producing the so-called "gossamer showers."

Subphylum PENTASTOMIDA (= LINGUATULIDA) (Tongue Worms)

Diagnosis: worm-like, unsegmented parasites, but body constricted into rings that appear like segments; cephalothorax short, without appendages except for two pairs of ventral hooks on either side of the mouth; arthropod characters shown by body covering (chitinous cuticle), muscles, and nerve cord; without jointed legs or circulatory, respiratory, and excretory organs; vertebrate respiratory parasites; sexes separate, some with complex life histories and larval stages involving a change of animal hosts; an example of the fact that parasitic forms of any phylum usually are difficult to classify from gross anatomy, because adaptations often entail the loss of body parts (Figure 14.10).

Subphylum TARDIGRADA (Water Bears)

Diagnosis: unsegmented and worm-like, but with four pairs of short and thick, unjointed legs terminated by claws, last pair of legs are at end of body; without antennae, circulatory or respiratory organs; body covered by a cuticle that lacks chitin; sexes separate; eggs laid or shed with molding of old cuti-

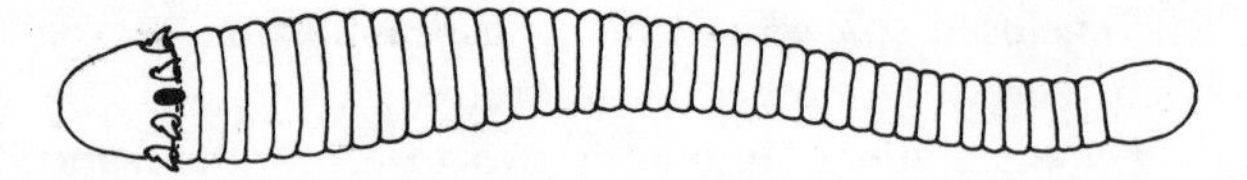

Figure 14.10 Subphylum Pentastomida, *Porocephalus*, a tongue worm.

cle; larval stages usually present, but normally are much like the adults in appearance (Figure 14.11).

The Tardigrada might not even be arthropods. They are included here because they show some resemblance to the Onychophora. Other than that, they really have few characteristics that might suggest a joint-legged animal.

Water bears probably will not be encountered by the reader. Although they are found in the ocean, in fresh water, and in damp terrestrial habitats, they grow no longer than 1/25-inch. However, they possess one amazing capability—they have a remarkable ability to withstand dessication. They can survive after long periods in a shriveled, dried, apparently lifeless state.

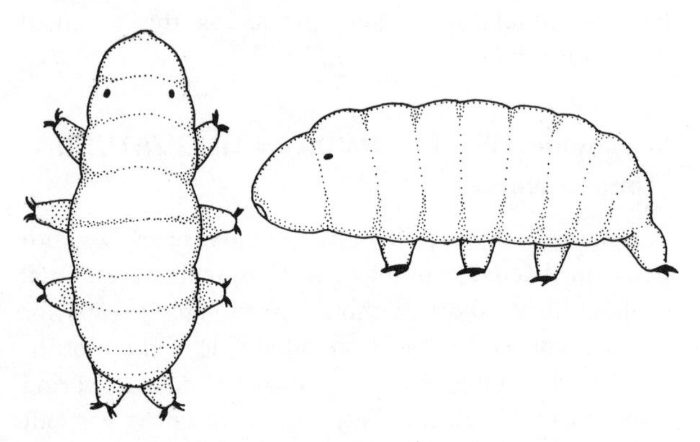

Figure 14.11 Subphylum Tardigrada, *Macrobiotus*, a water bear (× 50).

Subphylum MANDIBULATA (= ANTENNATA)

Diagnosis: body consists of head plus trunk or plus thorax and abdomen; head with one or two pairs of antennae (first two appendage pairs), one pair of mandibles (jaws, the third pair of appendages), one or more maxillae pairs, and three or more pairs of walking legs; sexes usually separate; eggs are laid or kept by the female until hatching; larval stages typically present.

CLASS CRUSTACEA (Crustaceans)

Diagnosis: head with two pairs of antennae, and two pairs of maxillae; body typically with a shell; shell usually with a single, extensive anterior portion, the carapace; exoskeleton, or shell, hard as a result of calcareous deposits; appendages often with two, sometimes pincer-like, terminal segments modified for walking, swimming, capturing food, respiration, and reproduction; sexes usually separate; eggs mostly carried by female; development typically with larval stages; mostly aquatic.

The crustaceans include quite different-looking creatures. The modification of the first two pairs of appendages as antennae serves to identify most of them. This class contains the marine crabs, lobsters, shrimps and barnacles, and a few land forms, for instance the sowbugs.

Many of the crabs, shrimps, and lobsters are utilized as human food. Others are an indirect source of our food, because many of the game and commercial fish eat crustaceans. The barnacles are often a nuisance because they grow on wharf pilings and boat bottoms. Other crustaceans are grown in aquaria as a ready source of fish food or for purely aesthetic reasons. Some parasites of man must spend part of their life in crustaceans. Sowbugs sometimes cause considerable damage to cultivated plants. And a wood-boring isopod can cause considerable damage to wharf pilings.

Crustacean sexes are usually separate. In nearly all there are means for an adult to carry the eggs. These structures include egg sacs, brood pouches, and specializations of the abdominal appendages. As many as six larval stages are found. The number and modifications of larval stages are characteristic for each group of crustaceans.

Subclass BRANCHIOPODA (Branchiopods)

Diagnosis: free-living; thoracic appendages leaf-like, four or more pairs, and with marginal gills; no abdominal appendages; reproduction from unfertilized eggs is typical; mostly fresh-water; include the following orders (Figure 14.12):

ORDER ANOSTRACA (Anostracans)

Diagnosis: include brine shrimp of saline and fairy shrimp of fresh waters; eyes stalked; no carapace.

ORDER NOTOSTRACA (Tadpole Shrimps)

Diagnosis: eyes sessile; carapace a broad and low oval shield, somewhat king crab-like; tail with terminal, jointed, forked, whip-like appendages.

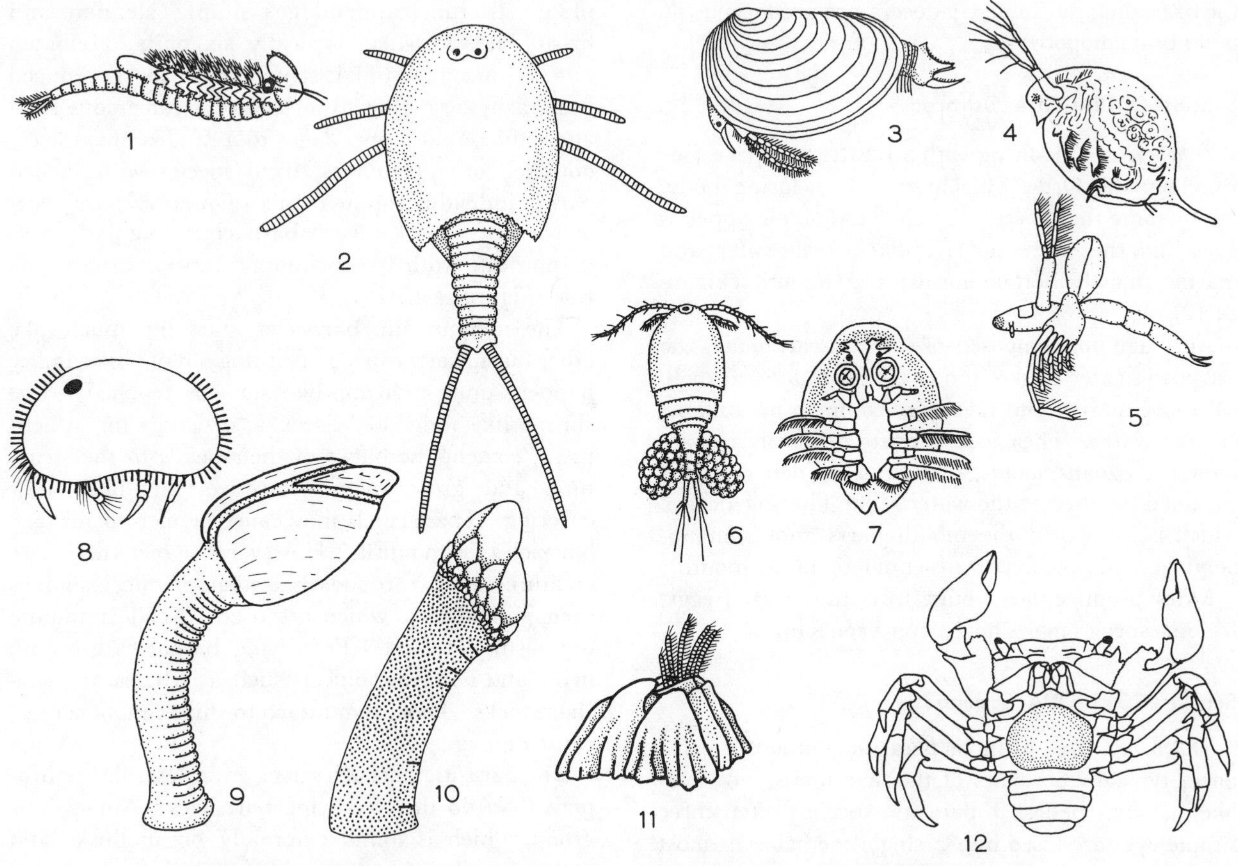

Figure 14.12 Class Crustacea. Subclass Branchiopoda: 1, Order Anostraca, *Eubranchipus*, a fairy shrimp (× 3), fresh water, in typical upside-down swimming position (the closely related brine shrimps of saline waters look similar); 2, Order Notostraca, *Apus*, a tadpole shrimp (× 1), fresh water; 3, Order Conchostraca, *Estheria*, a clam or claw shrimp (× 3) with its head at maximum extent, fresh water; 4, Order Cladocera, *Daphnia*, a water flea (× 15), fresh water; 5, Order Cladocera, *Leptodora*, a water flea (× 3), fresh water.
Subclass Copepoda: 6, *Cyclops*, a water hopper (× 25), fresh water; 7, *Argulus*, a fish louse (× 15), parasitic. Subclass Ostracoda: 8, *Cyridopsis*, an ostracod (× 20), fresh water. Subclass Cirripedia: 9, *Lepas*, a gooseneck barnacle (× 1), marine; 10, *Mitella*, a gooseneck barnacle (small specimen), marine; 11, *Balanus*, an acorn barnacle (small specimen), marine; 12, *Sacculina*, a parasitic barnacle on a very small crab, the bulbous (stippled) mass is the only external indication of the parasite (× 1/3). (Modified from various sources.)

ORDER CONCHOSTRACA (Claw or Clam Shrimps)

Diagnosis: eyes sessile; carapace bivalved, clamshell-like, enclosing the compressed body; tail often with terminal claws.

ORDER CLADOCERA (Water Fleas)

Diagnosis: eyes sessile; carapace resembles that of Conchostraca, and is often bivalved, but never encloses head; tail often with terminal claws; minute to microscopic.

All branchiopods, except for a few marine cladocerans, are found in fresh water; however, brine shrimp occur in saline lakes. Many branchiopods have a peculiar life cycle in which young of the summertime hatch from unfertilized eggs and the overwintering eggs are fertilized.

Branchiopod feeding is accomplished by movement of the bristle-covered legs. Leg bristles accumulate protozoans, rotifers, and detritus which are moved to the mouth along a groove on the underside of the animals. Besides this basic diet Notostraca are also known to feed upon the remains of larger animals such as earthworms, mollusks, and frog tadpoles. Anostraca and Conchostraca seem to be restricted to the basic diet, but some Cladocera are predaceous on other branchiopods.

Subclass OSTRACODA (Ostracods)

Diagnosis: free-living with a bivalve carapace (see Brachiopoda, Order Conchostraca) enclosing body, but no more than three pairs of true thoracic appendages and these are not leaf-like; fresh-water and marine, mostly bottom forms; size minute (Figure 14.12).

Although not composed of calcium carbonate, the ostracod's external skeleton is similar to a clam shell. Most are marine, but many are common inhabitants of fresh water. Their food consists primarily of bacteria, protozoans, molds, algae, and fine debris, and is obtained by filtering the water. The filtering device, which is formed by the mouth parts and front appendages, allows direct transfer of food to the mouth.

Many produce their young from unfertilized eggs. In some species males have never been found.

Subclass COPEPODA (Copepods)

Diagnosis: free-living or parasitic, without a carapace; typically six pairs of thoracic limbs, not leaf-like, but may be less in parasitic species; often three simple eyes are fused into a single medial eye; most are minute or microscopic; fresh-water and marine, free-living to parasitic (Figure 14.12).

Free-living copepods often are club- or pear-shaped, but the parasitic species are quite different and variable in appearance. Some of the parasites are difficult to identify as arthropods, much less copepods. Many of the parasites infest fish and are called fish lice.

The mouth parts of copepods are specialized for raking, seizing, and scraping food from a surface, or for filtering minute organisms from water. This generally limits food items to protists and to organic debris.

Sexual reproduction is characteristic of this group. After the eggs are fertilized they are retained by the female, being kept on the abdomen in one or two egg sacs.

Subclass CIRRIPEDIA (Barnacles)

Diagnosis: adults attached or parasitic; carapace of attached species becomes part of a body enclosing mantle, usually a fleshly mantle with calcareous plates; thoracic appendages simple, slender, and bristly, not leaf-like, typically six pairs; abdomen much reduced, vestigial; structures variously reduced in parasites, ranging from lack of a calcareous shell and reduction of appendages to a sac-like mass without shell or appendages; fixed species with shelled part of individual upon a stalk (gooseneck barnacles) or without a stalk (acorn barnacles); regularly hermaphroditic with free-swimming larvae; strictly marine (Figure 14.12).

The nonparasitic barnacles start life much like other marine arthropods. Nothing out of the ordinary happens until a shrimp-like stage is reached. The shrimp-like individuals seek a structure for attachment, cement the backs of their heads to the structure, and grow their protective shell-like outer covering. These shells may cause laymen to mistake barnacles for mollusks. However, the fact that these creatures are arthropods is evident if one examines their jointed legs, which are used to collect minute organisms for food. Free-living barnacles grow on living and nonliving objects such as whales and seashore rocks. Those that attach to ships can, of course, cause damage.

The parasitic barnacles look even less like arthropods than do the free-living barnacles. Among this group, which is found externally on mollusks and crabs, are adults of species that are little more than a sac-like reproductive organ. The reason zoologists know that these animals are barnacles is that the larval stages are similar to those of other barnacle larvae.

Subclass MALACOSTRACA (Malacostracans)

Diagnosis: free-living to parasitic; body typically of 19 segments, 5 head, 8 thorax (regularly covered by a carapace), 6 (rarely 7) abdomen with appendages (except on rare seventh segment); mostly marine, also freshwater, terrestrial, and parasitic (Figures 14.13 and 14.14).

This subclass includes the better known crustaceans. Although the Subclass Malacostraca contains about twelve orders, only four are treated here. Members of the other orders that might be found will most likely be vaguely shrimp-like, hence for practical purposes might be called "shrimps." The four orders to be treated are the Isopoda, Amphipoda, Stomatopoda, and Decapoda. They can be distinguished as follows:

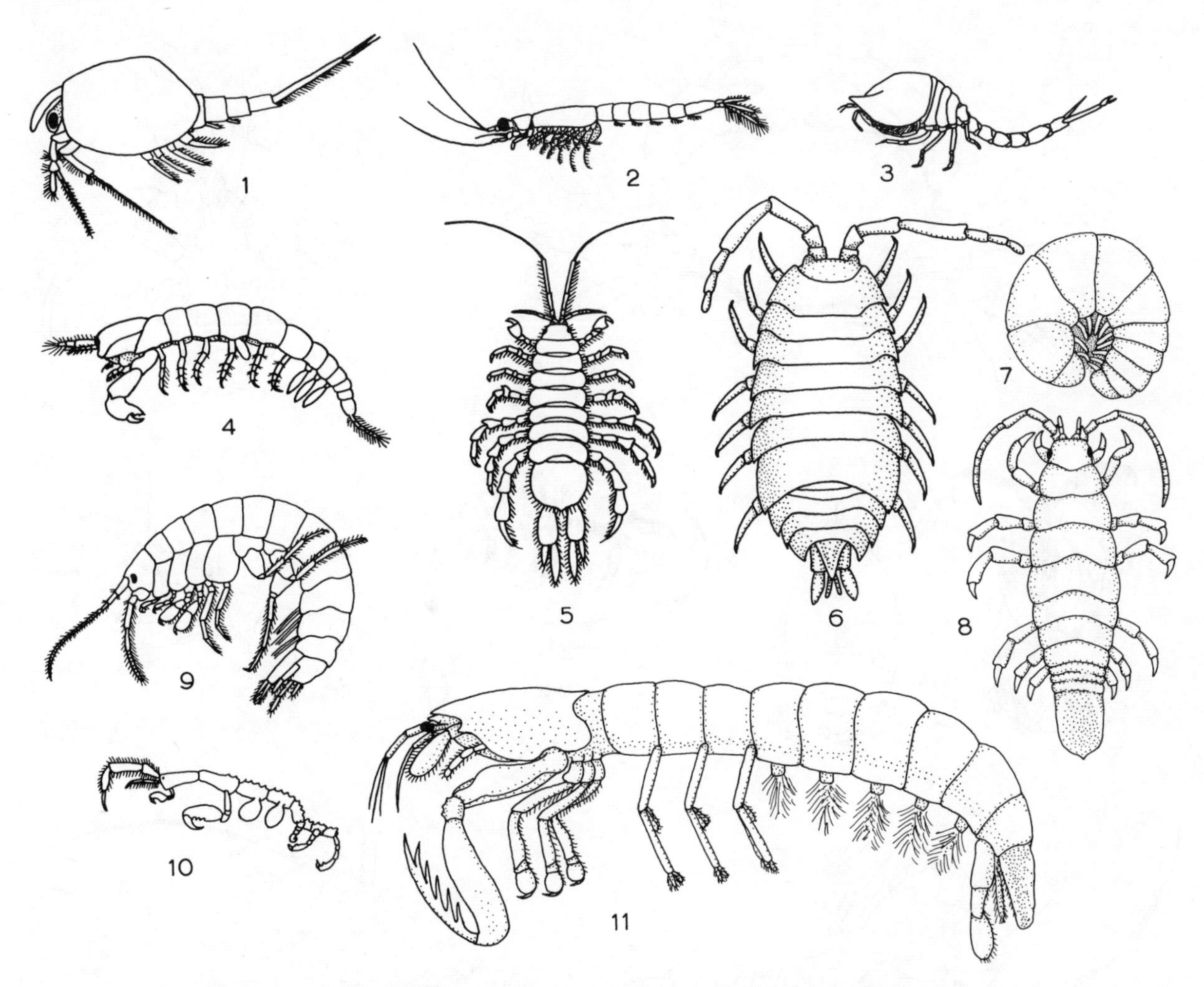

Figure 14.13 Class Crustacea. Subclass Malacostraca. Order Nebaliaceae: 1, *Epinebalia*, a primitive shrimp (× 5), marine. Order Mysidacea: 2, *Mysis*, an opossum shrimp (× 10), marine; note the brood pouch under the thorax. Order Cumacea: 3, *Diastylis* (× 5), marine. Order Tanaidacea, 4, *Tanais* (× 5), marine; note the incubation pouch at the base of the fifth leg. Order Isopoda: 5, *Asellus*, a fresh-water sowbug (× 2); 6, *Oniscus*, a sowbug (× 2), terrestrial; 7, *Armadillium*, a pillbug (× 2), terrestrial; note the resemblance to a sowbug; 8, *Idothea*, a kelp sowbug (× 1), marine. Order Amphipoda: 9, *Gammarus*, a scud (× 2), fresh water; 10, *Caprella* (× 2), marine. Order Stomatopoda: 11, *Squilla*, a mantis shrimp (× 2), marine.

ORDER ISOPODA (Isopods)

Diagnosis: no carapace; body usually dorsoventrally flattened; at least last six pair of thoracic legs very much alike, at least first pair often modified and involved with mandibles; abdomen short, partly to completely fused; marine, fresh-water, terrestrial, many fish and crustacean parasites; all might be called sowbugs, but variously named pill bugs, wood lice, etc. (Figure 14.13).

The isopods are another structurally variable group. The free-living species are mostly scavengers that eat dead and injured animals and green and decaying plants. The common garden sowbugs can cause considerable damage to cultivated plants. Some can roll up into a ball and are called pill bugs.

Again, the parasitic species are difficult to recognize as Arthropoda. The parasites range from those that are of typical isopod appearance to those that are little more than a sac of eggs.

ORDER AMPHIPODA (Scuds)

Diagnosis: no carapace; body usually laterally compressed; last six pairs of thoracic legs not of the

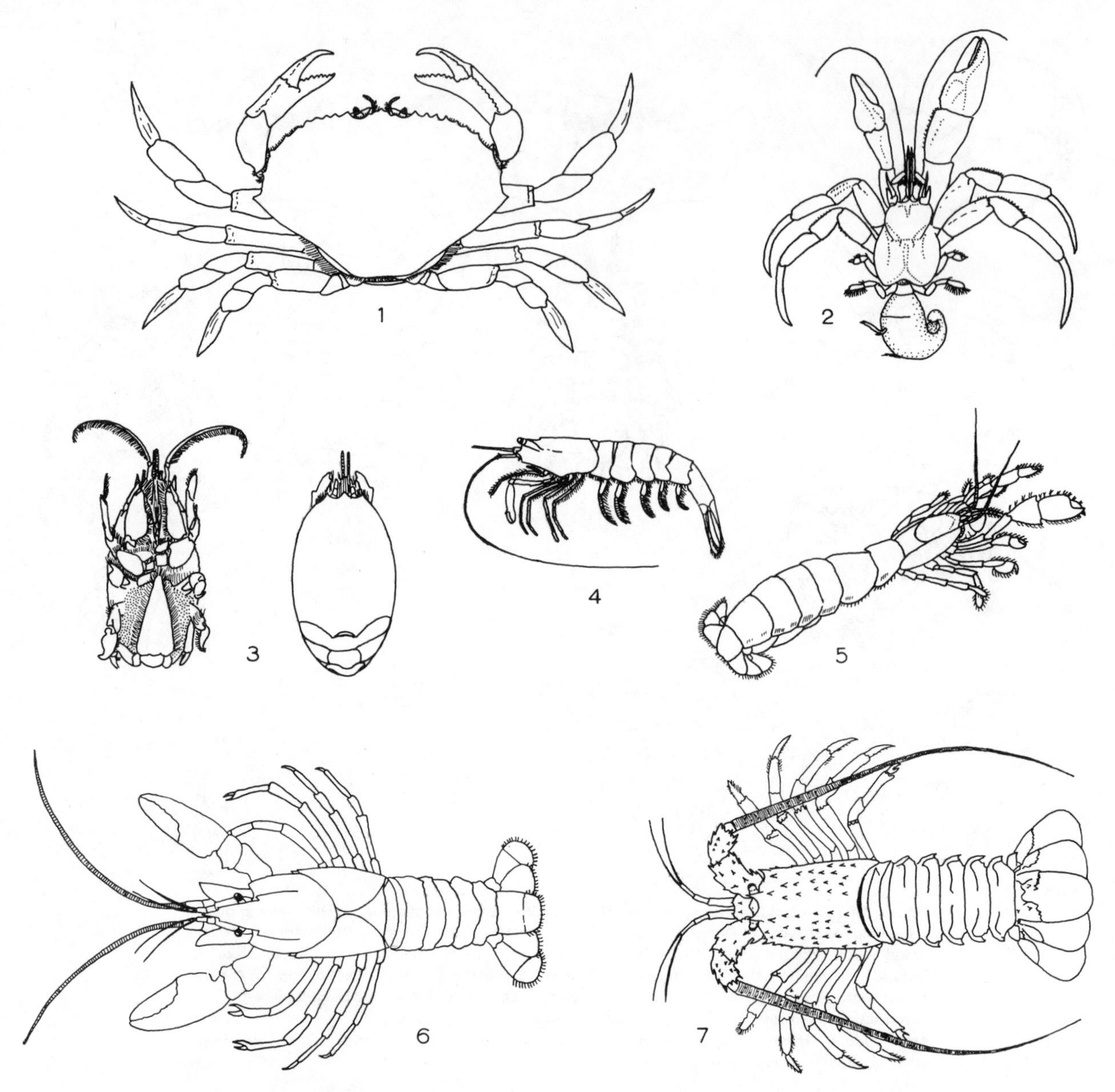

Figure 14.14 Class Crustacea. Subclass Malacostraca. Order Decapoda: 1, *Cancer*, a crab (× 1/4), marine; 2, *Pagurus*, a hermit crab (× 1/2), marine; 3, *Emerita*, a sand crab, to the left a small female carrying eggs under her reflexed abdominal plate, to the right a top view, marine; 4, *Crago*, a shrimp (× 1), marine; 5, *Callianassa*, a ghost shrimp (× 1/2), marine; 6, *Astacus*, a crayfish (× 1/2), fresh water; 7, *Panulirus*, a spiny lobster (to about 2 feet long), marine; *Homarus*, the Atlantic lobster has larger pincers and resembles a crayfish. (Mostly redrawn from Schmitt.)

same general structure; abdomen bent ventrally between third and fourth segments; mostly marine and some along the shore; also fresh-water (Figure 14.13).

Amphipods, sometimes called scuds or sideswimmers, bear a superficial resemblance to isopods; however, a good many can be identified because they are flattened laterally. However, the differences in leg and abdominal structures are a better basis for separating the two groups. Like free-living isopods, scuds carry their eggs in brood pouches under the abdomen until the larvae hatch.

Scuds are known for their voracious appetites.

Most are scavengers upon all kinds of plant and animal matter. Some are predaceous, feeding upon microscopic organisms.

ORDER STOMATOPODA (Mantis Shrimps)

Diagnosis: carapace present, but not covering the last four thoracic segments; second thoracic limbs jacknife-like and large, but first five pair of thoracic limbs are of similar structure; last three thoracic limb pairs not so modified; abdomen typically wider and longer than cephalothorax; strictly marine, burrowers in sand or mud or inhabitors of crevices (Figure 14.13).

The mantis shrimps are remarkable for their jacknife-like second thoracic limb, which is similar to the jacknife claw of the praying mantis (Class Insecta). Either "mantis" or "mantid" designates both groups. In some mantis shrimps the jacknife blade is sharp; in others the blade is comb-like. The blade is very effective in capturing or killing prey; some mantis shrimps attack animals of like size and cut the prey in two.

As with most crustaceans, mantis shrimp sexes are separate. The eggs are attached to the abdominal appendages of the female until the larvae hatch.

ORDER DECAPODA (Decapods)

Diagnosis: carapace covering the entire thorax; first three pairs of thoracic limbs more or less modified as structures associated with the mouth; the last five pairs are walking legs; abdomen of variable length but generally not wider than cephalothorax; mostly marine, some fresh-water, a few terrestrial (Figure 14.14).

The decapods contain a vast array of structural types and all of the crustaceans normally used as food by man. If we do not worry too much about taxonomic relationships, we can identify decapods as crabs, shrimps, crayfish, and lobsters. Crabs generally have a much reduced abdomen that is folded under and upon the thorax; however, hermit crabs have a large, soft, twisted abdomen that is usually protected, because hermit crabs live in and carry about empty snail shells. All crabs are marine.

Shrimps, like crayfish and lobsters, have the abdomen longer than the cephalothorax, straight, and not folded under and upon the thorax. Shrimps are fresh water and marine, crayfish strictly fresh water, and lobsters strictly marine. Fresh-water shrimps are distinguished from crayfish by having laterally compressed rather than rounded bodies and by having the last three pairs of thoracic legs without pincers rather than only the last two pairs. Of the three pairs of thoracic legs having pincers in crayfish, the first pair often are quite large by comparison. Marine shrimps, even the larger species called prawns, usually can be distinguished from lobsters by size alone. Also, the much larger lobsters have a rounded body rather than the shrimp-like compressed body.

CLASS DIPLOPODA (Millipedes)

Diagnosis: head with one pair of antennae and one pair of maxillae; body long, usually cylindrical; thorax of four segments, the first legless, the rest with one pair of legs; abdominal segments variable in number (each actually two segments), nine or more, usually numerous, two pairs of legs per segment; sexes separate, eggs laid; young with six body segments and three pairs of legs; up to ten molts to the adult form (Figure 14.15).

Millipedes, or thousand-legged worms, are entirely terrestrial, being found in dark, moist places under objects upon the ground. Contrary to the belief of some, they are nonpoisonous and harmless to man. Although not aggresive, if disturbed they frequently will roll up in a spiral and exude an offensive, probably protective, odor from their stink glands. These

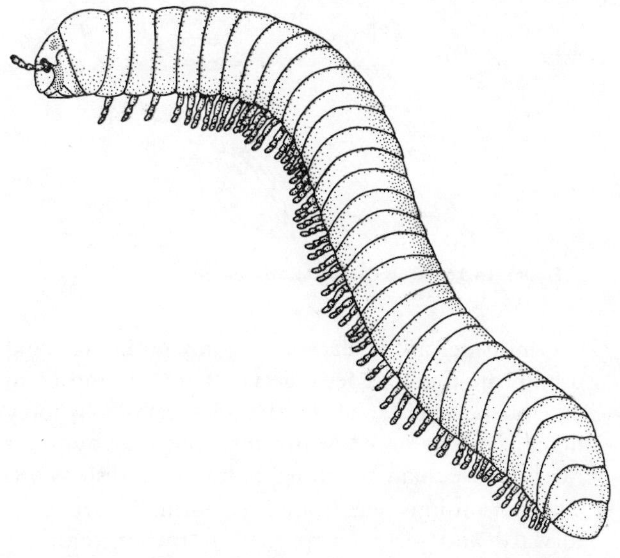

Figure 14.15 Class Diplopoda, *Spirobolus*, a millipede (× 1).

retiring animals usually are scavengers. Although they tend to feed upon decaying plant material, they can become garden pests when feeding on growing plants.

Sometimes the Diplopoda, Chilopoda, Pauropoda, and Symphyla are grouped in a single class Myriapoda. However, most students of arthropods no longer consider them a natural group.

CLASS CHILOPODA (Centipedes)

Diagnosis: head with one pair of antennae and two pairs of maxillae; body long, dorsoventrally flattened; body segments 15 to 181, each with a pair of legs; first pair of legs modified, hook-like, and with a poision duct leading to terminal fang, sexes separate, eggs laid or young born alive; young resemble adults (Figure 14.16).

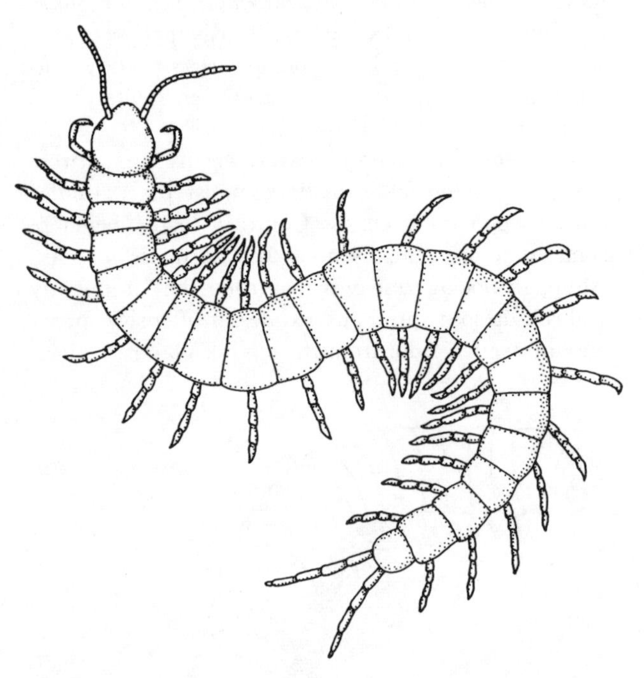

Figure 14.16 Class Chilopoda, *Scolopendra*, a centipede (× 1).

Centipedes are predaceous, mainly on insects, and usually are found under objects on the ground or in other dark, moist places. Large species may prey upon lizards or mice. Many are venomous, but bites rarely cause man anything more than discomfort. The poison-injecting front legs normally are bent forward and serve for predation rather than for walking.

CLASS PAUROPODA (Pauropods)

Diagnosis: head with one pair of three-branched antennae, and one pair of maxillae; body elongate, cylindrical, but minute, length 1/50 to 1/12 inch; body of 11 (sometimes 12) segments and with 9 (sometimes 10) pairs of legs; eyeless, whitish forms that resemble millipedes; reproduction with four larval stages and metamorphosis; terrestrial, in damp places under objects on ground surface, or in the soil; believed to feed upon fungi (Figure 14.17).

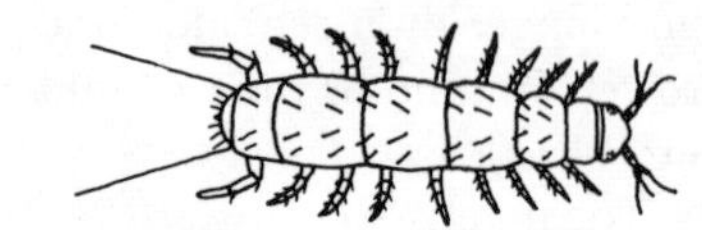

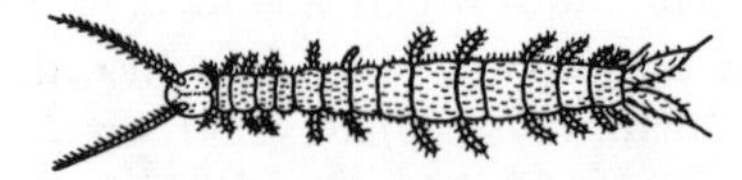

Figure 14.17 Class Pauropoda, *Pauropus* (× 30), and Class Symphyla, *Scutigerella*, a garden centipede (× 6), below left.

CLASS SYMPHYLA (Garden Centipedes)

Diagnosis: head with one pair of antennae, and two pairs of maxillae; body elongate, cylindrical, 1/25 to 1/3 inch long; body of 15 to 22 segments and with 10 to 12 pairs of legs; eyeless and centipede-like, but centipedes have at least 15 pairs of legs; larva with six or seven pairs of legs, metamorphosis to the adult; active, whitish, terrestrial animals of damp places containing humus; feed upon vegetable matter in the soil, sometimes damage cultivated plants or field crops (Figure 14.17).

CLASS INSECTA (Insects)

Diagnosis: body with head, thorax, and abdomen distinct; head with one pair of antennae and mouth parts variously modified for chewing, sucking, or lapping; thorax of three segments, typically with two pairs of wings (also one pair or none) and three pairs of legs; abdomen usually 11 segments, but variable, without legs; reproduction generally with separate sexes (also parthenogenesis), eggs laid (also retained by female), and usually some form of metamorphosis (development also direct); widespread and very numerous in all habitats, but only a few are marine.

Insects are arthropods with one pair of antennae, three pairs of legs and three body regions—head, thorax, and abdomen. Simple eyes and compound eyes are present in the group. The compound eyes are of interest in that each eye receives a portion of the image and any slight movement will cause the insect to be instantly aware of it.

The adaptations of insects are numerous and a few will be mentioned. Mouth parts are varied, often in relation to specific food items. Feeding habits are extremely varied, but some type of holozoic nutrition is the rule. The *ovipositor*, an egg-laying apparatus, is modified into a sting in bees, wasps, and some ants. This structure is 4 inches long in some wasps and can penetrate wood. Needless to say, the sting is limited to the females. Much behavior is instinct, a complex sequence of invariable automatic responses to a stimulus. The social insects, ants, bees, wasps, and termites, have complex societies with workers, kings, queens, and soldiers. Defense mechanisms are varied. Most insects depend upon speed to escape harm; others "play dead." The bite of many insects, sting of wasps and bees, and sting "hairs" of some caterpillars are effective deterrents to predators. Chemical secretions help still others; some bugs and other insects produce foul odors, bombardier beetles produce a "smoke screen," and ants secrete an irritating liquid. Many insects blend with their background or resemble plants or nonliving things in their environment. Some resemble ants, wasps, or spiders and supposedly gain some protection from such mimicry.

Insects in general are considered harmful, because of wood borers, termites, fleas, mosquitoes, weevils, scale insects, and the like, but their overall benefit greatly surpasses their harm. They provide food for many animals. They pollinate many plants that could not exist without them. Bees produce honey and wax; scale insects, shellac; and gall insects, tannic acid. The edible crimson pigment, cochineal, is produced by a Mexican scale insect. The silkworm is the source of raw silk. Burrowing insects aerate the soil. Most scavengers are beneficial. Some predaceous insects feed almost entirely upon harmful insects. Finally, certain insects are used for scientific research that is directly or indirectly beneficial to man. For example, much knowledge of heredity came from studying the fruit fly, *Drosophila*.

The insects have amazing reproductive powers, laying from a few dozen to many thousand eggs. Most insects lay eggs, but in some the eggs are retained and hatch in the female's body. Most eggs must be fertilized, but in some insects this may not be necessary, males are unknown. In aphids and gall wasps fertilized and nonfertilized eggs alternate seasonally. In a few insects larvae produce other larvae. In the honey bee sex is determined by fertilization, fertilized eggs producing females. In some insects a single egg develops into many individuals; perhaps more than a thousand. Eggs are laid singly or clustered and in a site that is usually protective or offers food to the young. Hatching takes from a few hours to many months. Escape of young from the egg is accomplished either by chewing mouth parts; by a temporary, sharp head process; or by internal pressure due to movement or air inflation of the insect.

Growth is accompanied by many molts, each involving replacement of the external skeleton and linings of the tracheae, foregut, and hindgut. Replacing structures are formed prior to each molt and are larger than molted parts because the insect inflates before the new structures harden. Most insects have four to eight molts, but some have over twenty. Bristletails molt after becoming adults, but most adult insects neither molt nor increase in size. The developmental form between molts is called an *instar*. The first instar is between hatching and the first molt, and so on. In most insects the different instars are distinct. In some, the young and adults are alike. This latter condition is called *direct development* (Figure 14.18). Other insects show some to many changes, that is, metamorphosis.

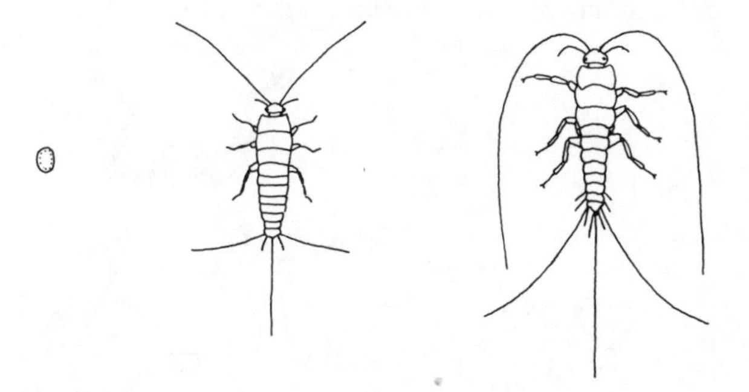

Figure 14.18 Direct development in an insect, a silverfish (Thysanura). From left to right, egg, immature, and adult.

Metamorphosis is of two main types, simple or gradual which normally has no resting or pupa stage, and complete or complex which does have a pupa stage. In forms having *simple metamorphosis* the hatchlings resemble the adults and are called *nymphs* (Figure 14.19). The principal changes from nymph to adult are in size, body proportions, formation of

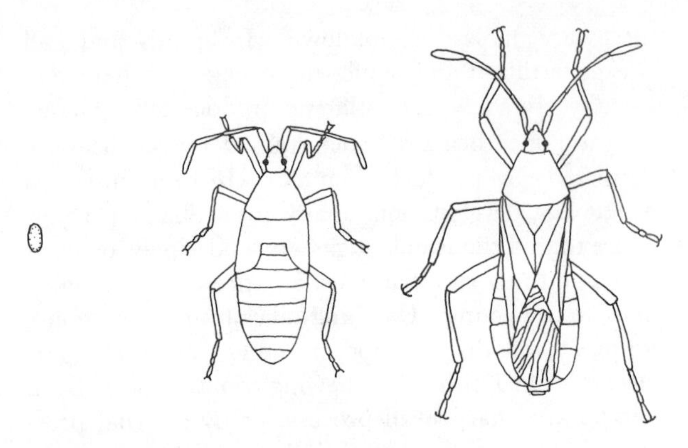

Figure 14.19 Simple metamorphosis in an insect, a squash bug (Hemiptera). From left to right, egg, nymph, and adult.

simple eyes, and increased wing size. In forms having *complete metamorphosis* (Figure 14.20) the immature and adults are usually quite different and, unlike those with simple metamorphosis, often live in different habitats and have different habits. The early instars are worm-like and are called *larvae*. The different larval instars are usually similar in form, their main change being increase in size. Transformation to *pupa* occurs after the last larval molt. The pupa is usually inactive, does not feed, and is often covered by a cocoon (many insects overwinter as pupae). The final molt produces the adult. Finally, there is a type of complete metamorphosis called hypermetamorphosis in parasitic insects. Here the different larval instars are unlike in appearance.

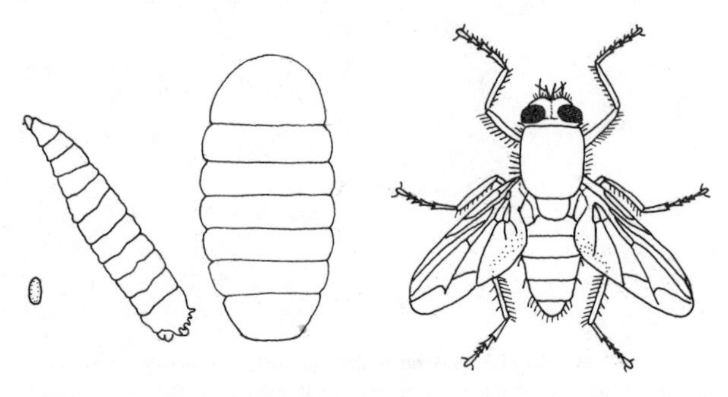

Figure 14.20 Complex metamorphosis in an insect, a fly (Diptera). From left to right, egg, larva, pupa, and adult.

Subclass APTERYGOTA

Diagnosis: primitive; wingless and not derived from winged ancestors; little or no metamorphosis; underside of abdomen with bristle-like appendages (Figure 14.21).

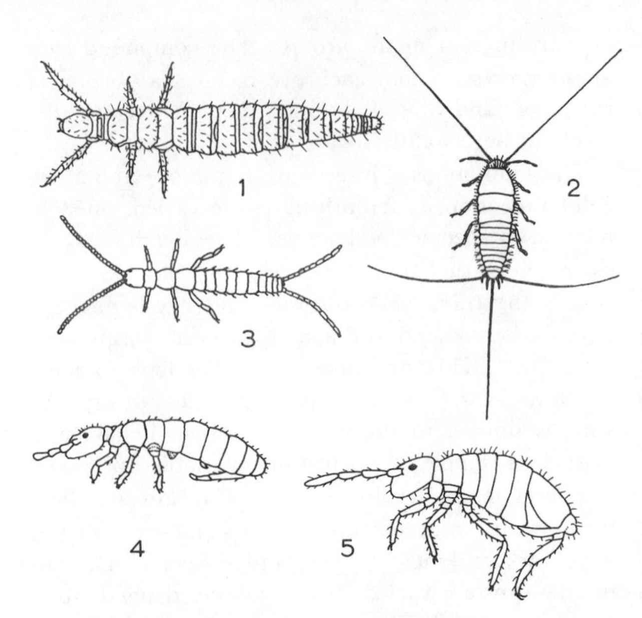

Figure 14.21 Subclass Apterygota. Order Protura: 1, *Eosentomon* (× 30). Order Thysanura: 2, *Thermobia*, the fire brat (× 1); 3, *Campodea* (× 3). Order Collembola: 4, *Isotoma* (× 6); 5, *Entomobrya* (× 10). (After various sources.)

ORDER PROTURA (Telsontails)

Diagnosis: uncommon; considered most primitive; minute, to 1/15 inch long; without eyes, wings, or antennae; development direct; scavengers in moist places, under and among surface objects and in soil (Figure 14.21).

ORDER THYSANURA (Bristletails)

Diagnosis: mostly under 3/5 inch to two inches, wingless, with two or three bristles on end of abdomen; development direct; scavengers, causing damage to books, clothing, and foods; in human dwellings, grassy and wooded areas, and damp places under objects (Figure 14.21).

ORDER COLLEMBOLA (Springtails)

Diagnosis: mostly minute, to about 1/3 inch; wingless, with a unique springing organ on ventral abdomen; jump to more than 15 times their length; development direct; scavengers or herbivores; in decaying matter under damp objects, sometimes on fresh-water surface or along seashore; usually appear in great numbers during the winter breeding season; may congregate on sidewalks, lawns, pools, or even snow; sometimes damage plants; include the remarkable ice-inhabiting snow and glacier fleas.

Subclass PTERYGOTA: Division Exopterygota

Diagnosis: winged or from winged ancestors; no ventral, abdominal, bristle-like appendages; division Exopterygota metamorphosis; gradual, young stages are nymphs and have compound eyes; wings develop externally.

ORDER ORTHOPTERA (Grasshoppers, Crickets, Roaches, Walking Sticks, Mantids, and allies)

Diagnosis: medium size to fairly large; front wings thickened, hind wings folded like a fan; chewing mouth parts; males of jumping forms "sing" by rubbing wings or hind legs against wings; widespread, mostly scavengers and predators; include some of the most destructive insects, crickets and grasshoppers destroy crops, roaches destroy clothing and leave a disagreeable odor, walking sticks rarely harm plants, mantids are mostly valuable predators of harmful insects (Figure 14.22).

ORDER DERMAPTERA (Earwigs)

Diagnosis: small to medium size, about 1/6 to 1 inch; front wings short and leathery, hind wings long and membranous; chewing mouth parts; abdomen terminated by pincers; often common in garbage and damp places, mostly scavengers but also predators and herbivores; mostly active at night and hide in

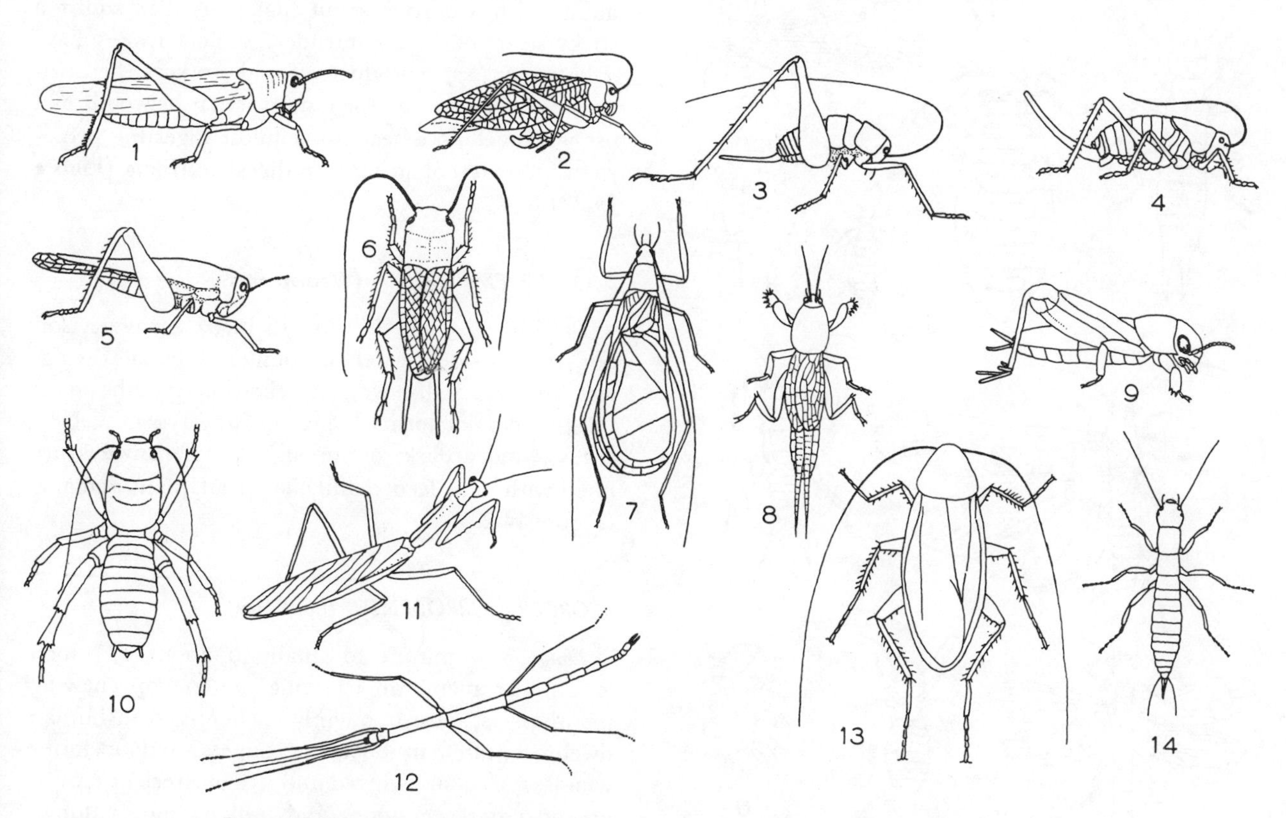

Figure 14.22 Order Orthoptera: 1, Acrididae, short-horned grasshopper or locust (× ½); 2, Tettigoniidae, a katydid (× ½); 3, Gryllacrididae, a camel or cave cricket (× 1); 4, Tettigoniidae, a shield-backed grasshopper (× ½); 5, Tetrigidae, a pygmy or grouse locust (× 2); 6, Gryllidae, a field cricket (× 1); 7, Gryllidae, a tree cricket (× 1½); 8, Gryllotalpidae, a mole cricket (× 1); 9, Tridactylidae, a pygmy sand or mole cricket (× 7); 10, Gryllacrididae, a sand or Jerusalem cricket (locally known as a potato "bug" or child of the earth, to about 3 inches long); 11, Mantoidea, a mantid or praying mantis (to 4 inches long); 12, Phasmatidae, a walking stick or stick insect (to about 3 inches long); 13, Blattidae, a roach or cockroach (to about 2 inches long); 14, Grylloblattidae, a grylloblattid (× 1). (After various sources.)

cracks and crevices or under objects during the day; often plant pests and harmful (Figure 14.23).

ORDER PLECOPTERA (Stoneflies)

Diagnosis: medium size to over two inches long; four wings membranous, held pleated and flat on back when at rest; chewing mouth parts, but often none in adults; nymphs in fresh water, often under rocks; adults poor flyers; nymphs and adults often herbivorous, sometimes insect predators, but some adults are short-lived and never feed; nymphs widely preyed upon by aquatic predators; nymphs desirable as bait for fresh-water fishing (Figure 14.23).

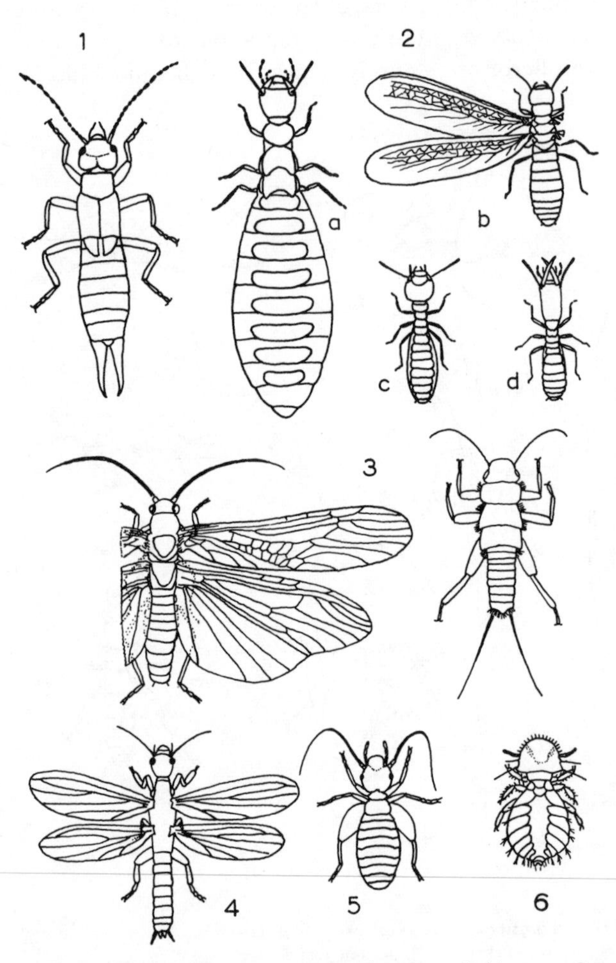

Figure 14.23 Dermaptera, Isoptera, Plecoptera, Embioptera, Corrodentia and Mallophaga: 1, Dermaptera, an earwig (to about 1 inch long); 2, Isoptera, termites (large specimens: *a*, supplementary queen; *b*, king; *c*, worker; *d*, soldier); 3, Plecoptera, stone flies (adult to the left and aquatic nymph to the right, × 2); 4, Embioptera, a web spinner (× 3½); 5, Corrodentia, a book louse (× 7); 6, Mallophaga, a biting louse (× 3). (After various sources.)

ORDER ISOPTERA (Termites or "White Ants")

Diagnosis: small to medium size; body soft, generally white or whitish; reproductive castes with four similar, narrow wings, chewing mouth parts; social insects (also ants, wasps, and bees) characterized by a caste system; four castes, *reproductives* (kings and queens) have fully developed wings (shed after mating), compound eyes, and usually pigmentation; *supplementary reproductives* also reproduce but have shorter wings, usually smaller eyes, and less pigmentation than reproductives; *workers* which are sterile males and females and nymphs are wingless, usually lack compound eyes, and are pale in color; *soldiers* are sterile males and females with greatly enlarged heads and mouth parts; sometimes there are two additional castes, *adults*, which are similar to workers in appearance but can reproduce, and *nasuti*, which are sterile adults with a narrow snout that is used to squirt a sticky secretion at an intruder; some termites have only two castes, reproductives and workers; herbivorous, well known for their destruction of wood; can use wood cellulose because cellulose-digesting protozoans are present in termite digestive tracts (Figure 14.23).

ORDER EMBIOPTERA (Web-spinners)

Diagnosis: small (1/6 to 1/3 inch), elongate, soft but straight-sided; rarely encountered; females wingless, males usually winged; chewing mouth parts; mostly colonial forms living in runways in debris, cracks, under bark, or among plants; runways are lined with silk; feed mainly on dead plant remains (Figure 14.23).

ORDER CORRODENTIA (Book Lice)

Diagnosis: minute to small, to about 1/4 inch long; four membranous wings or none; chewing mouth parts; most frequently encountered in human dwellings, often in books or papers; indoor forms wingless; most are winged and live on trees or shrubs or under bark or stones and feed on molds, fungi, pollen, cereals, and dead organisms (Figure 14.23).

ORDER MALLOPHAGA (Biting Lice)

Diagnosis: small to minute, to about 1/4 inch long; wingless; chewing mouth parts; external parasites of birds and mammals, feeding upon hair, feathers, and skin, not known to infest man (Figure 14.23).

ORDER ANOPLEURA (Sucking Lice)

Diagnosis: small, to about about 1/4 inch long; wingless, body flat, mouth parts piercing and sucking; eyes reduced or none; no true metamorphosis; external parasites on mammal blood and transmit various diseases including typhus and trench fevers; includes the human louse, or "cootie" (Figure 14.24).

Figure 14.24 Anopleura, a sucking louse (× 5), to the left; and Thysanopetera, a thrip (× 6), to the right. (After various sources.)

ORDER THYSANOPTERA (Thrips)

Diagnosis: minute to small (to 1/5 inch) and slender; wings four, alike and heavily fringed by hairs or wingless; mouth parts conical, rasping and sucking; commonly parthenogenetic; mainly plant feeders, destroying many plants by feeding or introducing disease; some predaceous on small arthropods, a few attack man (Figure 14.24).

ORDER HEMIPTERA (Bugs)

Diagnosis: mostly large; wingless or four wings, front wings thick with horny bases and otherwise membranous, crossed at rest; hind wings membranous and folding under forewings; mouth parts piercing and sucking; a large group of common fresh-water and terrestrial insects; some are beneficial predators on harmful insects, some are definitely harmful; some are blood-sucking, carrying diseases of man and other animals; many suck plant juices, thereby reducing plant vigor and introducing disease (Figure 14.25).

ORDER HOMOPTERA (Cicadas, Hoppers, Scale Insects, etc.)

Diagnosis: mostly small; cicadas to about two inches long; wingless or four wings, membranous and of like texture throughout, roofed over abdomen at rest; mouth parts piercing and sucking; herbivorous; many are serious pests and a few transmit diseases (Figure 14.26).

ORDER EPHEMEROPTERA (Mayflies)

Diagnosis: one inch long; four membranous wings, front wings much larger, all held up at rest; chewing mouth parts, but much reduced; up to 21 molts and three years as fresh-water nymphs, a few hours or days as an adult; nymph herbivorous, adults do not feed; prey of aquatic insects and vertebrates, hence fishing "flies" or lures are patterned after mayflies (Figure 14.27).

ORDER ODONATA (Damselflies and Dragonflies)

Diagnosis: large, to over three inches long; four wings, transparent and membranous, held vertically (damselflies) or laterally (dragonflies) at rest; chewing mouth parts, tooth-like; nymphs aquatic, feeding on mosquito larvae to small fish; adults terrestrial, feeding on other insects (Figure 14.27).

Subclass PTERYGOTA: Division Endopterygota

Diagnosis: Division Endopterygota metamorphosis complete, young stages are larvae without compound eyes; wings develop internally.

ORDER NEUROPTERA (Nerve-winged Insects)

Diagnosis: small to large, to about three inches long but most shorter; four wings, alike and membranous, with many cross veins, roof the abdomen at rest; chewing mouth parts; fresh-water or terrestrial; both larvae and adults are insect predators; also preyed upon, especially by fish, hence a group copied as fishing "flies" (Figure 14.28).

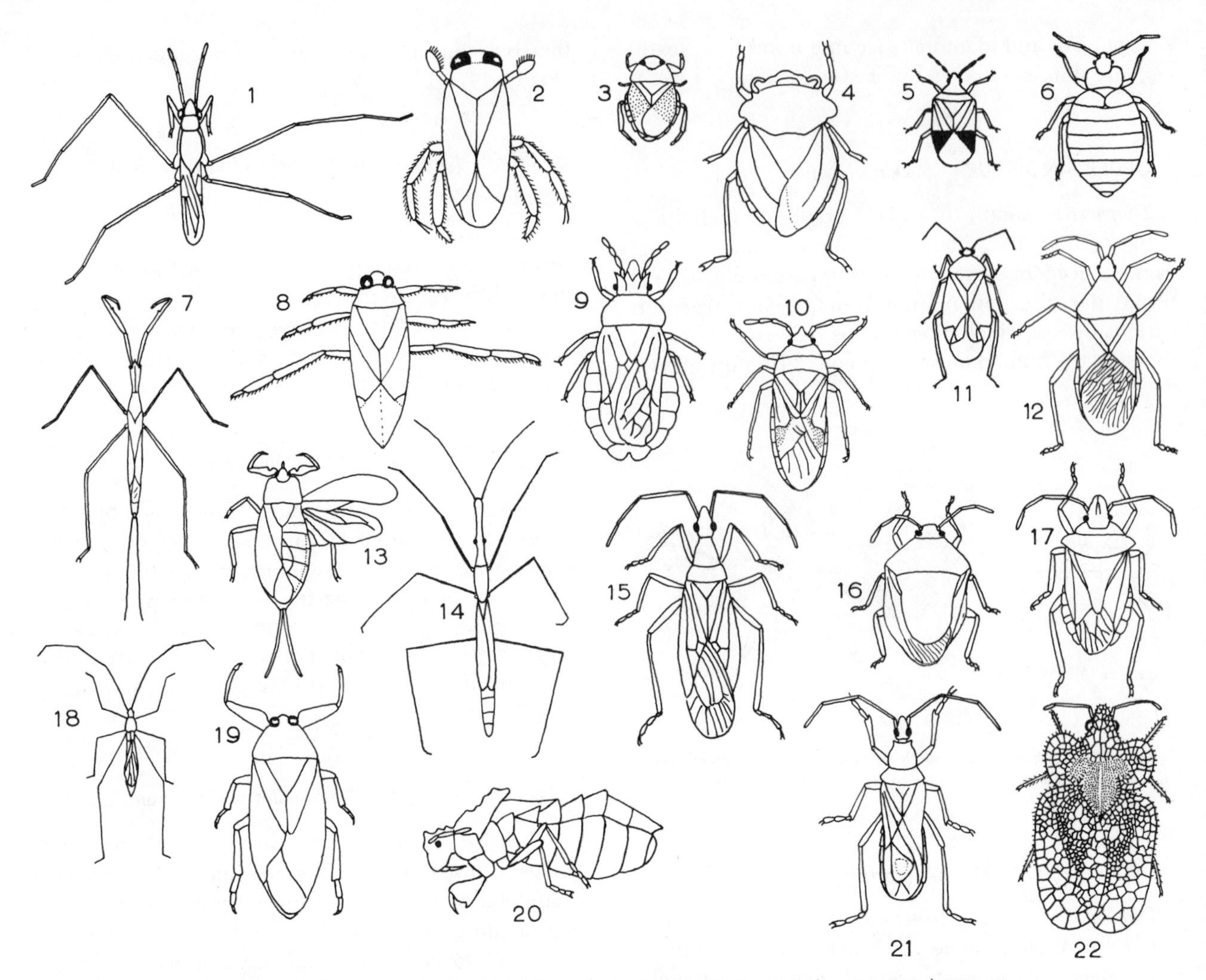

Figure 14.25 Hemiptera: 1, Gerridae, a water strider (× 2); 2, Corixidae, a water boatman (× 3); 3, Naucoridae, a creeping water bug (× 1); 4, Gelastocoridae, a toad bug (× 3); 5, Anthocoridae, a flower bug (× 7); 6, Cimicidae, a bedbug (× 6); 7, Nepidae, a water scorpion (× ½); 8, Notonectidae, a back swimmer (× 3); 9, Aradidae, a flat or fungus bug (× 3); 10, Lygaeidae, a cinch bug (× 1); 11, Miridae, a leaf bug (× 2); 12, Coreidae, a squash bug (× 1½); 13, Nepidae, a water scorpion (× 1); 14, Hydrometridae, a water measurer or marsh treader (× 2½); 15, Nabidae, a damsel bug (× 4); 16, Scutelleridae, a shield bug (× 3); 17, Pentatomidae, a stink bug (× 2); 18, Neididae, a stilt bug (× 1½); 19, Belostomatidae, a giant water bug (× ½); 20, Phymatidae, an ambush bug (× 3); 21, Reduviidae, an assassin bug (× 1½); 22, Tingididae, a lace bug (× 7). (After various sources.)

ORDER MECOPTERA (Scorpion Flies)

Diagnosis: small to large, most to one inch long; four slender, membranous, many-veined wings, roof abdomen at rest; chewing mouth parts on a downward-extending beak; some males curve the abdomen end upward, scorpion-like; inhabit plants and are scavengers, herbivores, or carnivores; some are found in snow (Figure 14.28).

ORDER TRICHOPTERA (Caddisflies)

Diagnosis: small to moderate, to one inch long; four membranous, mostly longitudinally veined wings, roof abdomen at rest; body and wings haired, sometimes scale-like; mouth parts vestigial; larvae fresh-water, often in rapid water, usually casemaking and clinging to underside of rocks; case of sand, debris, or plant matter; larvae are scavengers or

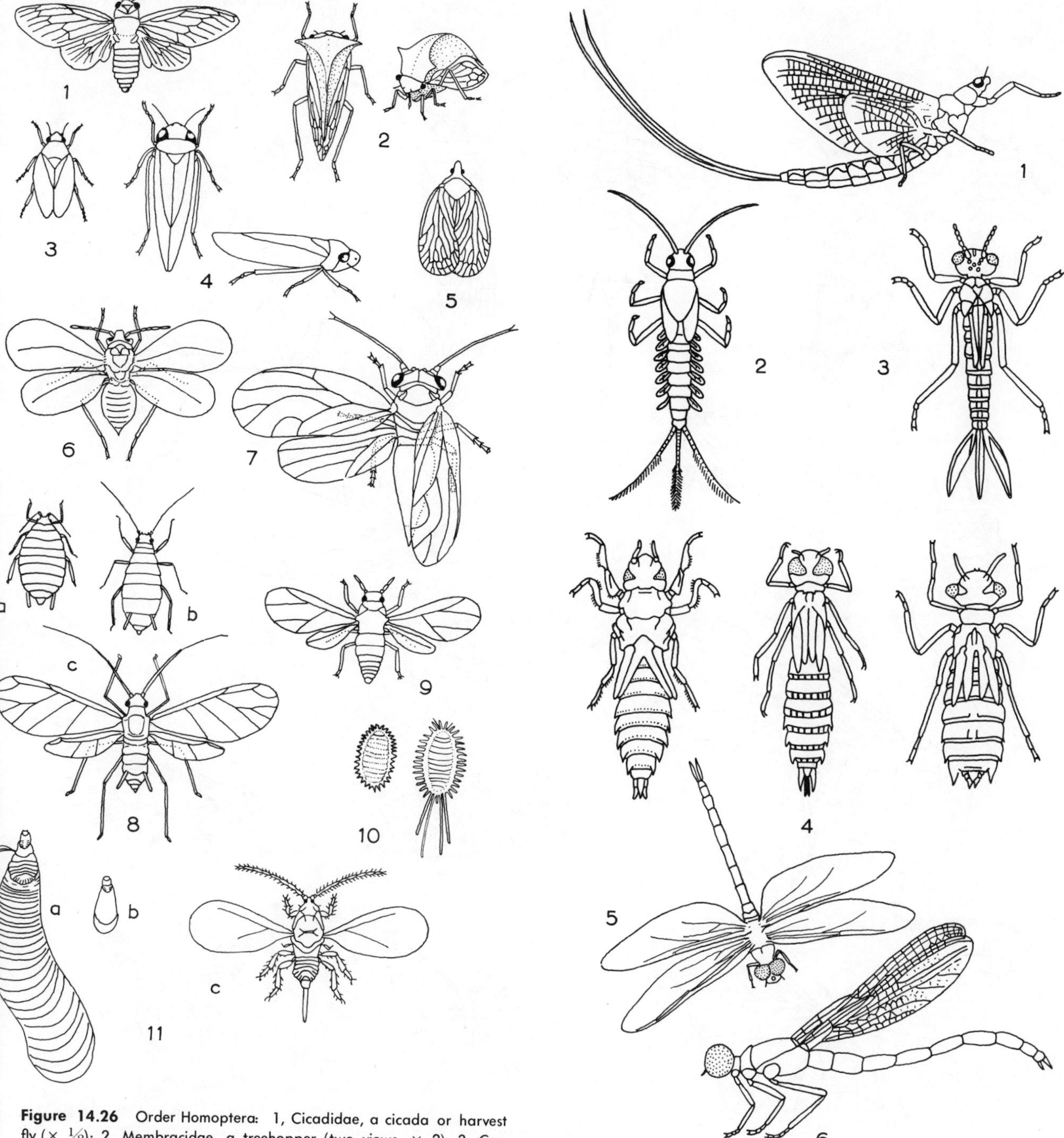

Figure 14.26 Order Homoptera: 1, Cicadidae, a cicada or harvest fly (× ½); 2, Membracidae, a treehopper (two views, × 2); 3, Cercopidae, a froghopper or spittlebug (× 1); 4, Cicadellidae, a leafhopper (top and side views, × 2); 5, Fulgoridae, a planthopper or lanternfly (× 2); 6, Aleyrodidae, a whitefly (× 5); 7, Psyllidae, a jumping plant louse or flea louse (× 5); 8, Aphididae, a plant louse (*a* and *b* are different kinds of females, *c* is a winged adult; × 3); 9, Phylloxeridae, a plant louse (× 3; note wing venation; wingless forms resemble aphids); 10, Coccidae, mealybugs (× 3, males become winged and resemble scale insects); 11, Coccidae, scale insects (× 5), (*a*), wingless female, (*b*) wingless male, and (*c*) winged male; the scale shapes vary a great deal among species and often entirely cover the insect. (After various sources.)

Figure 14.27 Ephemeroptera and Odonata. Ephemeroptera: 1, mayfly (× 2), a two-tailed adult that develops from two-tailed aquatic nymphs; 2, aquatic nymph (× 2), of the three-tailed type that metamorphoses to a three-tailed adult. Odonata: 3, damselfly aquatic nymph (× 1½); 4, three kinds of dragonfly aquatic nymphs (× 1½); 5, dragonfly (× ½); 6, damselfly (× 2). (After various sources.)

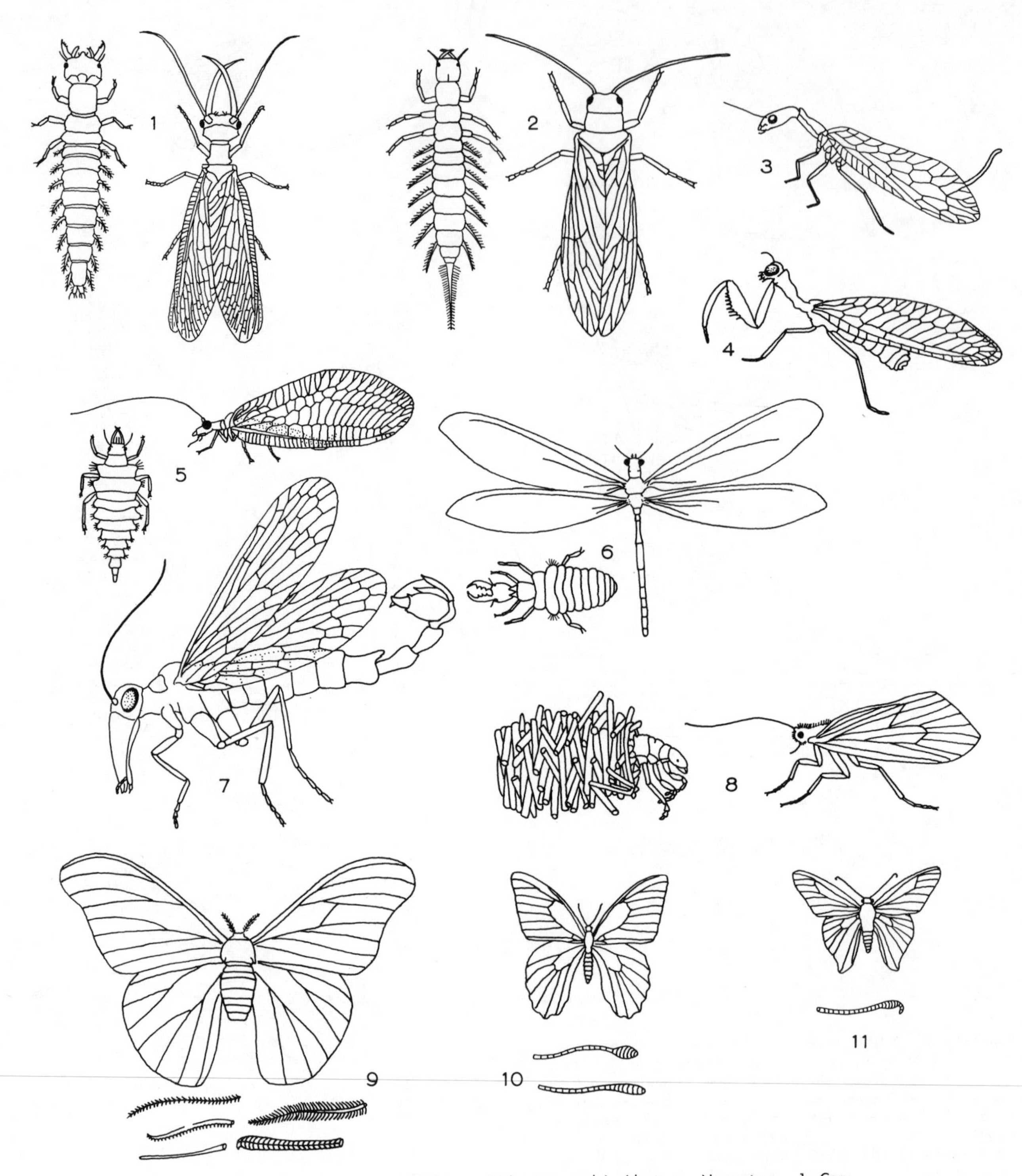

Figure 14.28 Neuroptera, Mecoptera, Trichoptera, and Lepidoptera. Neuroptera: 1, Corydalidae, dobson fly larva and adult (× ½); 2, Sialidae, alderfly, larva and adult (× 1½); 3, Raphidiidae, a snakefly (× 1); 4, Mantispidae, a mantidfly or rear-horse (× 1); 5, Chrysopidae, larva and adult lacewing (× 2½); 6, Myrmeleontidae, larva and adult ant lion (× 1). Mecoptera: 7, scorpion fly (× 4). Trichoptera: 8, caddisfly larva in case (case depends on available materials) and adult (× 1). Lepidoptera: 9, moth and moth antennae types; 10, butterfly and antennae types; 11, skipper and enlarged antenna. (After various sources.)

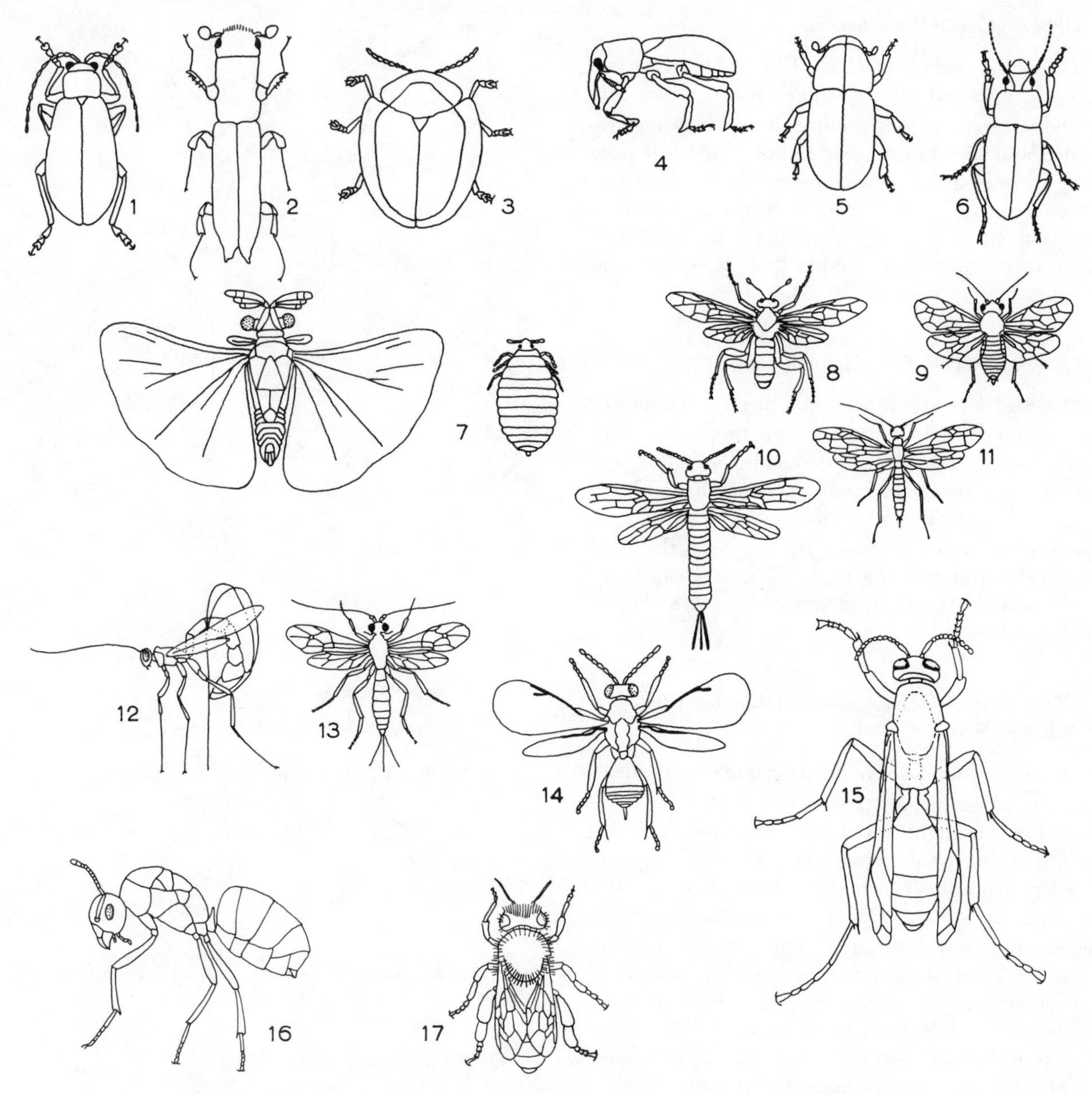

Figure 14.29 Coleoptera, Strepsiptera, and Hymenoptera. Coleoptera: 1-6, some beetle types. Strepsiptera: 7, winged male and wingless female strepsipterons (× 6). Hymenoptera: 8 and 9, sawflies (× ½); 10, a horntail (× ½); 11, a stem sawfly (× 1); 12 and 13, ichneumon wasps (× 1); 14, a calcid wasp (× 8); 15, a wasp (× 2); 16, an ant (× 2); 17, a bee (× 1). (After various sources.)

predators; adults are poor fliers, usually close to streams; feed upon liquids (Figure 14.28).

ORDER LEPIDOPTERA (Butterflies, Skippers, and Moths)

Diagnosis: minute to very large; four membranous wings (rarely none), covered with overlapping scales, held horizontally to vertically at rest; larval mouthparts chewing, adult sucking; larvae are wormlike caterpillars, with two silk glands on mouth part for spinning pupal stage cocoon; larvae herbivorous, often destructive to plants, or scavengers that may harm clothing and stored grain; adults valuable pollinators of plants (Figure 14.28).

ORDER COLEOPTERA (Beetles)

Diagnosis: minute to large, United States species to two inches long; front wings veinless, thick and leathery, meeting along midline; hind wings sparsely veined and membranous, fold under front wings at rest; some wingless; chewing mouth parts, sometimes on an elongate snout; larvae worm-like, pupa rarely in a cocoon; very numerous, widespread, and with great variation in food habits; both beneficial and detrimental forms (Figure 14.29).

ORDER STREPSIPTERA (Strepsipterans)

Diagnosis: relatively few and rarely encountered species; mostly minute; males with tiny front wings and fan-shaped hind wings; females wingless and without eyes or antennae; chewing mouth parts; extremely complex life cycle; females and larvae entirely parasitic on other insects, hosts showing distorted abdomens and perhaps protruding strepsipteran; males sometimes free-living and under rocks (Figure 14.29).

ORDER HYMENOPTERA (Sawflies, Horntails, Bees, Ants, and Wasps)

Diagnosis: small to moderately large; four membranous wings, or none, wings on each side interlocked during flight, variously held at rest; chewing mouth parts, or chewing-lapping; egg-laying apparatus (ovipositor) of female modified for sawing, piercing, or stinging; larvae worm-like, sometimes legless; pupae typically in cocoons; very numerous, include all social insects (bees, wasps, and ants) except termites; widespread, in various habitats; feeding habits variable; perhaps most beneficial order of insects, includes many insect parasites and predators, plant pollinators, and the honey bee (Figure 14.29).

ORDER DIPTERA (Flies)

Diagnosis: mostly small, minute to moderate sized; two membranous wings or none; hind wings represented by short knobbed structures; piercing-sucking or sponging mouth parts, often drawn out; larvae worm-like, called maggots; very numerous and widespread; many pests and truly dangerous species, larvae often ruin meat, mosquitoes carry malaria and other diseases; some are scavengers, others are insect predators (Figure 14.30).

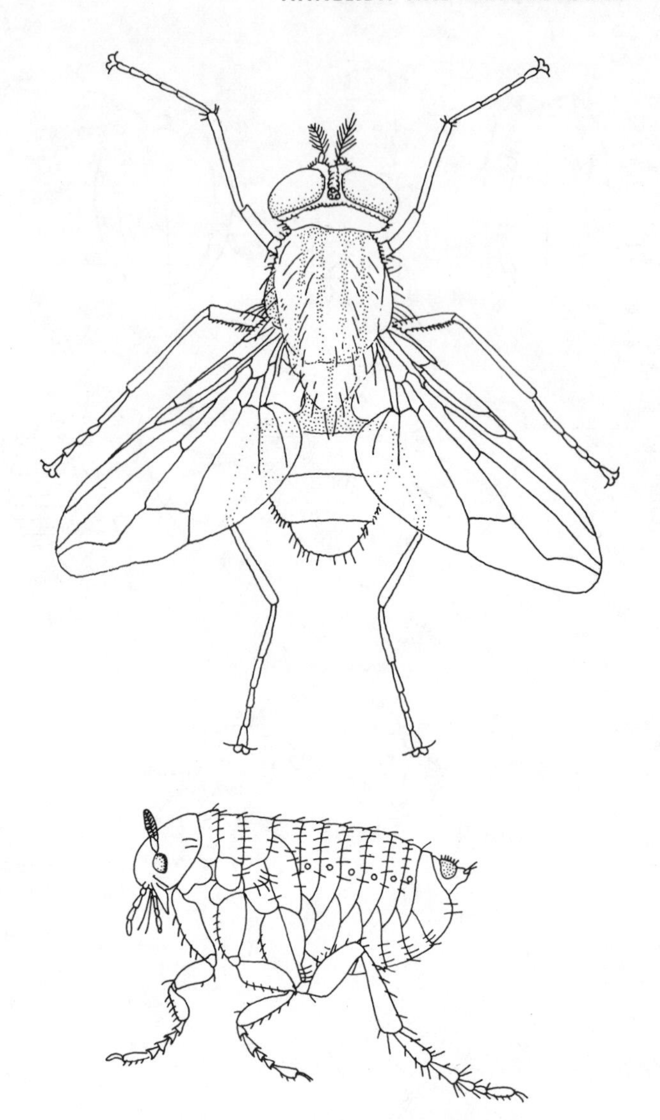

Figure 14.30 Diptera, a fly (above, × 4), and Siphonaptera, a flea (below, × 17). (After various sources.)

ORDER SIPHONAPTERA (Fleas)

Diagnosis: minute; wingless; sucking mouth parts; bodies laterally compressed, legs specialized for jumping; larvae minute, legless; adults periodic external parasites of birds and mammals; transmit such truly dangerous diseases as bubonic plague and typhus fever (Figure 14.30).

SELECTED READINGS*

Borror, D. J., and D. M. Delong, 1954. *Introduction to the Study of Insects.* Rinehart and Co., New York.

*See also p. 212.

Cloudsley-Thompson, J. L., 1958. *Spiders, Scorpions, Centipedes and Mites.* Permagon Press, New York.

Gertsch, W. J., 1949. *American Spiders.* D. Van Nostrand Co., Princeton, N. J.

Green, J., 1961. *A Biology of Crustacea.* Quadrangle Books, Chicago.

Klotts, A. B., and E. B. Klotts, 1959. *Living Insects of the World.* Doubleday & Co., Garden City, N. Y.

Mann, K. H., 1962. *Leeches (Hirudinea), Their Structure, Physiology, Ecology and Embryology.* Permagon Press, New York.

Schmitt, W. L., 1910. *Crustaceans.* Smithsonian Series. Series Publishers, New York.

Vessel, M. F., and E. J. Harrington, 1961. *Common Native Animals.* Chandler Publ. Co., San Francisco, Calif.

Waterman, T. H., ed., 1960. *The Physiology of Crustacea.* Vol 1: *Metabolism and Growth.* Academic Press, New York.

———. 1961. *The Physiology of Crustacea.* Vol. 2: *Sense Organs, Integration and Behavior,* Academic Press, New York.

15 CHAETOGNATHA THROUGH LOWER CHORDATA

Invertebrate Eucoelomates

The remaining phyla in the animal kingdom are called the Enterocoela (Gk. *enteron*, intestine + *koilos*, hollow) because their coeloms form from pouches that grow from the embryonic gut. Recall that in the schizocoels the true body cavity develops from a split in the mesoderm. The enterocoels include the Echinodermata, Chaetognatha, Hemichordata, Pogonophora, and Chordata.

RADIAL ENTEROCOELA: ECHINODERMATA

Having discussed the annelid-arthropod line, we now turn to another such evolutionary group, the echinoderm–chordate line. It was not implied in the earlier discussion that the arthropod arose from the annelid, but rather from an annelid-like ancestor which gave rise to both annelids and arthropods. In the same way, echinoderms, hemichordates, and chordates probably arose from a common ancestor that was not a member of any of these groups. The relationship of the three phyla is best seen in larval forms. Almost identical larvae occur in echinoderms and hemichordates, and it is a short step from hemichordate to tunicate larvae. Echinoderm–hemichordate similarity is so marked that it fooled the zoologist who first discovered a hemichordate larva; he called it a starfish larva.

The positions of chaetognaths and pogonophores are less definite, but each group likely is a member of the echinoderm–chordate line.

ECHINODERMATA (Spiny-skinned Animals)

Diagnosis: symmetry radial or biradial, a few bilateral; unsegmented; enterocoelous; includes the starfishes, brittle stars, sea urchins, sand dollars, sea lilies, and sea cucumbers; all marine.

It seems that the echinoderms must have evolved through a hypothetical, free-swimming larva-type of ancestor known as the *dipleurula*. Superficially this larval stage resembled the trochophore; however, both its mesoderm and coelom arose in a manner different from that occurring in the trochophore. In fact, the dipleurula probably looked and developed much like living echinoderm larvae, but the dipleurula could not have been exactly like any living echinoderm larva.

In surveying the hypothetical dipleurula, we must examine certain features. It most likely had bilateral symmetry, yet modern adult echinoderms are mostly radially symmetrical. This implies that there must be a metamorphosis in the development of living echinoderm adults from their larvae.

Perhaps this need for change can better be explained by a second hypothetical stage in echinoderm evolution, the *pentactula*. Supposedly derived from the

TAXONOMIC SUMMARY

Kingdom Animalia (L. *animalis*, animate)—animals
Subkingdom Eumetazoa (Gr. *eu*–, true + *meta*, among + *zoon*, animal)—eumetazoans
Grade Bilateria (L. *bi*-, two + *lateralis*, side)
Eucoelomata (Gr. *eu*- + *koilos*, hollow)

Enterocoela (Gr. *enteron*, gut + *koilos*)
- Phylum Echinodermata (Gr. *echinos*, spiny + *derma*, skin)—spiny-skinned animals
  - Subphylum Pelmatozoa (Gr. *pelmatos*, stalk + *zoon*)—pelmatozoans
    - Class Crinoidea (Gr. *crinon*, lily + *oideos*, form or type of)—sea lilies and feather stars
  - Subphylum Eleutherozoa (Gr. *eleutheros*, free + *zoon*)—eleutherozoans
    - Class Holothuroidea (Gr. *holothurion*, sea cucumber + *oideos*)—sea cucumbers
    - Class Echinoidea (Gr. *echinos* + *oideos*)—sea and heart urchins, sand dollars
    - Class Asteroidea (Gr. *aster*, star + *oideos*)—sea stars or starfish
    - Class Ophiuroidea (Gr. *ophis*, snake + *oura*, tail + *oideos*)—brittle and basket stars
- Phylum Chaetognatha (Gr. *chaeton*, bristle + *gnathos*, jaw)—arrow worms
- Phylum Hemichordata (Gr. *hemi*, half + *chorde*, string)—hemichordates
  - Class Enteropneusta (Gr. *enteron*, gut + *pneustos*, breathed)—acorn worms
  - Class Pterobranchia (Gr. *pteron*, feather + *branchion*, gill)—pterobranchs
  - Class Planctosphaeroidea (Gr. *planktos*, wandering + *sphaira*, ball + *oideos*)—planctosphaeroids
- Phylum Pogonophora (Gr. *pogon*, beard + *phoros*, bearing)—beard worms
- Phylum Chordata (Gr. *chorde*)—chordates
  - Subphylum Tunicata (L. *tunicatus*, clothed with a tunic)—tunicates
    - Class Larvaceae (L. *larva*, immature animal undergoing metamorphosis)—larvaceans
    - Class Thaliacea (Gr. *thalia*, abundance)—chain or pelagic tunicates
    - Class Ascidiaceae (Gr. *askidion*, a little leather bag)—ascidians
  - Subphylum Cephalochordata (Gr. *kephale*, head + *chorde*)—lancets

dipleurula, and perhaps its adult stage, the pentactula may have had the five tentacles that provide the basis of the five-rayed, or -armed, construction of this phylum and of an ancestral feeding habit that used the arms. Also, it is assumed that the tentacles gave rise to the echinoderm water-vascular system.

In the development of pentactula from the dipleurula, which probably was not an echinoderm and may have been the ancestor of the echinoderm-chordate line, there probably was first a bilateral pentactula stage. The bilateral pentactula perhaps already had tentacles and some development of the water-vascular system. Then, torsion, or twisting of the body mass would have had to occur for a radially symmetrical pentactula stage to result. From such a radial animal further evolution of the echinoderms would have been fairly easy.

We can learn more about echinoderms by studying the crinoids (sea lilies and feather stars), the most primitive living class. At the time of metamorphosis of crinoids and asteroids (starfish), the larva develops an attachment apparatus from the portion anterior to the mouth and becomes fixed to some object. The strictly fossil classes and their contemporary sea lilies seem to have had only attached organisms, suggesting that the earliest echinoderms were stalked, attached creatures. This idea is given a bit more weight by the fact that some living crinoids (feather stars) must first lose their attachment before becoming free-swimming organisms.

Another point of interest is the present developmental change from bilateral larva to the radial adult. Radial structure is typical of attached or floating forms. The coelenterates are, perhaps, the best example of this. The floating or attached radial organism does not seek its food but allows the environment to come to it. Therefore, we may again take radial symmetry as evidence of an attached echinoderm ancestor.

Summing up, we might hypothesize a basically bilateral type which became attached to the substrate; certain of the fossil attached forms, which no longer exist, do show bilateral symmetry. In the evolution of attachment, radial symmetry evolved as an adaptation to sedentary life. Later, most modern echinoderms lost their stalks and again became free, but retained their radial symmetry. Today, most modern echinoderms are still radially symmetrical, but there are sea cucumbers and sand dollars, which, in taking up a crawling life, seem to be selecting for a secondary bilateral symmetry.

The Phylum Echinodermata possesses several unusual features. The water-vascular system is found only in echinoderms. Basically, it consists of a ring anteriorly about the digestive tract and a vessel for each of the animal's arms or rays. In most echinoderms the water-vascular system is used in locomotion with the tube feet. Changes in water pressure in areas associated with tube feet cause movement of the tube feet. The skeleton is truly internal (endoskeleton) like our own. As in other coelomate animals, the gonads of echinoderms arise from the lining of the coelom, but in echinoderms the relationship is different. In other coelomates, the eggs at least are shed into the coelomic cavity before leaving the body. Here, the sex cells traverse ducts directly to the exterior without entering the coelom. Fertilization occurs free in the water. In general, the sexes are separate. The so-called blood system of echinoderms is also very strange. There is no pumping organ and the vessels are filled with a jelly-like material. Wandering amoeba-like cells of various kinds move through this blood system and out into the tissues. Some of these cells pick up insoluble wastes, wander through the body wall to the exterior, and there dump the wastes. Respiration and excretion are generally accomplished by means of thin-walled, coelomic extensions that can be projected through the body wall. Gas exchange takes place by diffusion from sea water to the coelomic fluid inside. The sea cucumbers have a special "breathing" mechanism, the respiratory tree.

Subphylum PELMATOZOA (Pelmatozoans)

Diagnosis: attached during part or all of life by the end opposite the mouth, attachment either direct or by a stalk; both mouth and anus are on the upper surface; body in a cup-like skeleton (calyx); five classes, four entirely extinct (Heterostelea, Cystidea, Blastoidea, and Erisasteroidea); Cambrian to Recent.

CLASS CRINOIDEA (Sea Lilies and Feather Stars)

Diagnosis: calyx symmetrical; arms five, branching at base; tube feet lack suckers, tentacle-like, food-collecting (Figure 15.1).

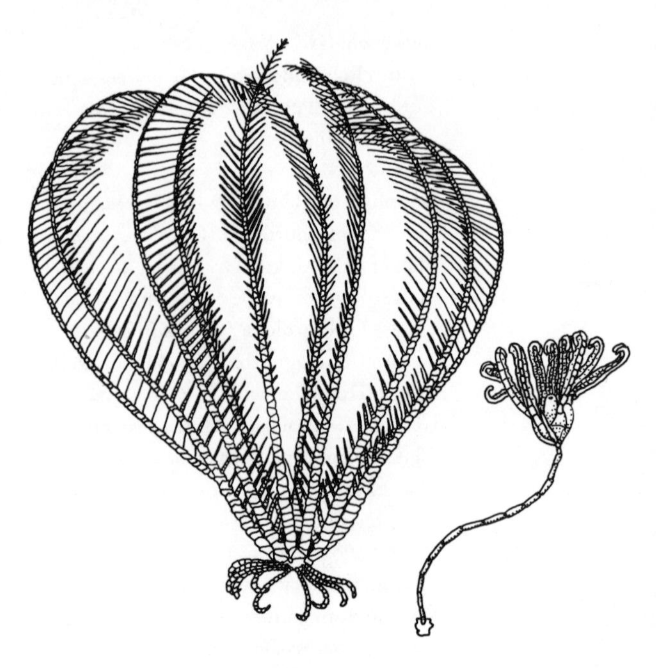

Figure 15-1. *Antedon,* a feather star: left, a free-living adult; lower right, an attached larva, which resembles the approximately 80 species of adult sea lilies. (Redrawn from Clark.)

The crinoids, known as sea lilies (attached) or feather stars (free-living), are an abundant group of mostly deep-sea animals. Most, if not all, are filter feeders of microscopic organisms; some may be detritus feeders. The young adult grows attached by a stalk to the substrate. Sea lilies remain attached throughout life, while feather stars break loose from the stalk, retaining a portion of the stalk and attachment organs. The latter group can creep along the substrate or swim by movement of the arms. This ability to move gives the feather stars an advantage if local environments become unfavorable, but a disadvantage if ocean conditions move them from a favorable habitat.

Subphylum ELEUTHEROZOA (Eleutherozoans)

Diagnosis: free-living, stalk-less; anus, if present, on side opposite mouth; structure regularly five-armed, or -rayed; five classes, only one entirely extinct (Ophiocistioidea); Cambrian to Recent.

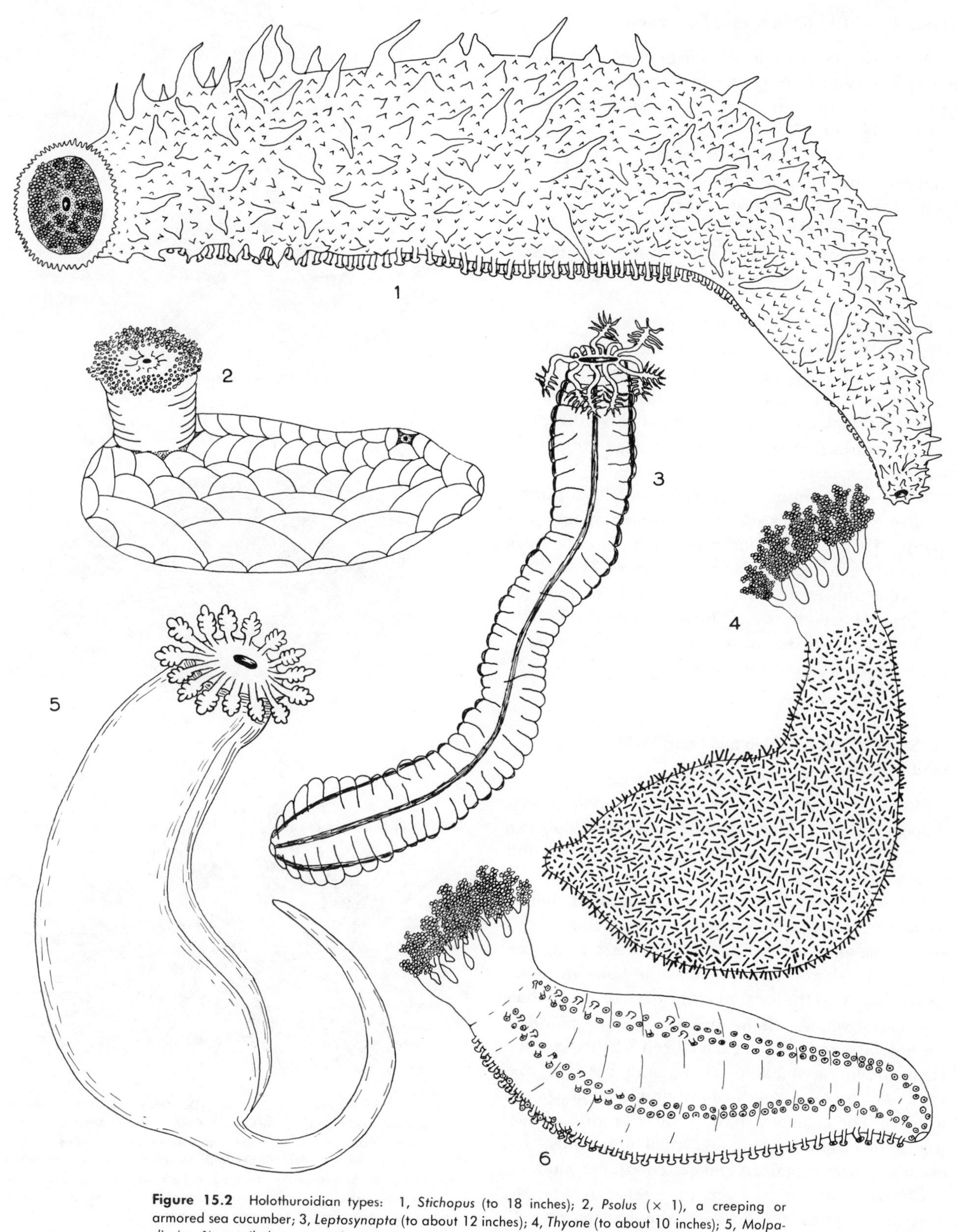

Figure 15.2 Holothuroidian types: 1, *Stichopus* (to 18 inches); 2, *Psolus* (× 1), a creeping or armored sea cucumber; 3, *Leptosynapta* (to about 12 inches); 4, *Thyone* (to about 10 inches); 5, *Molpadia* (× 1), a tailed sea cucumber; 6, *Cucumaria* (to about 10 inches). (Modified from various sources.)

CLASS HOLOTHUROIDEA (Sea Cucumbers)

Diagnosis: body elongate, soft or five-sided, without spines, sometimes worm-like, generally cucumber-like; mouth surrounded by tentacles; arms absent (Figure 15-2).

Sea cucumbers live on or under rocks and in or on sand and mud. Plankton are trapped by the mucous-covered tentacles, or bottom debris is taken into the body where the organic matter in the debris is used as food. Some have a posterior group of mucous-covered tubes that are thrust out to entrap food or entangle an enemy.

Partial self-destruction frequently is the result when the animals are irritated. Some may break off parts of their bodies by violent contractions; others may rupture the body wall, causing organs to be ejected; and some may cast out digestive and respiratory structures through the anal opening. After such behavior, the castoff parts are regenerated.

The sexes are usually separate, with fertilization occurring in sea water after the spawning of eggs and sperm. It is common for many to retain the eggs within or upon the body in brood pouches.

Sea cucumbers are of little direct use to man in our country. However, in the Orient and South Pacific, the boiled and dried meat is considered a delicacy and is called *bêche-de-mer* or *trepang*.

CLASS ECHINOIDEA (Sea and Heart Urchins, Sand Dollars)

Diagnosis: body globular (sea urchins), heart-shaped (heart urchins), or disc-like (sand dollars), covered by movable spines; no tentacles around mouth; arms absent (Figure 15.3).

The sea urchins, heart urchins, and sand dollars (sometimes called cake urchins) like all echinoderms are marine animals. Sea urchins are most often seen along rocky shores, where they live in holes in rocks. Others occur on the ocean floor in bays or other shallow coastal waters. Sometimes they can be found in the holdfasts of kelps that have been washed ashore. Heart urchins are inhabitants of muddy bottoms, and sand dollars of the sand of bays and shallow coastal waters. The echinoids have a variable diet of seaweeds, dead animal remains, small organisms, and organic matter contained in ingested sand or mud.

Characteristically, the sexes are separate and the eggs and sperms are spawned simultaneously. In

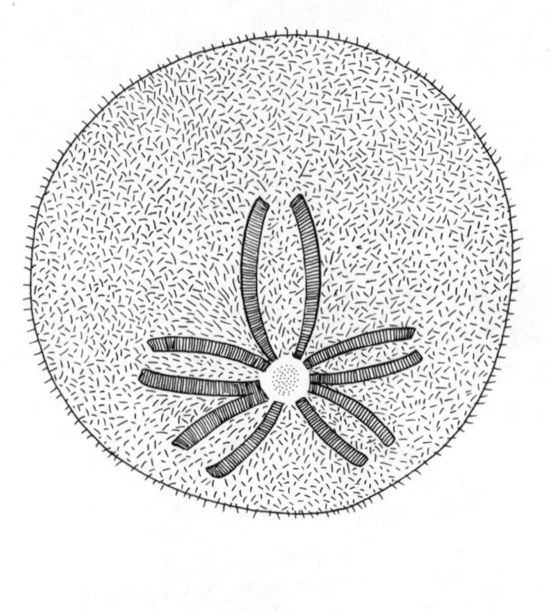

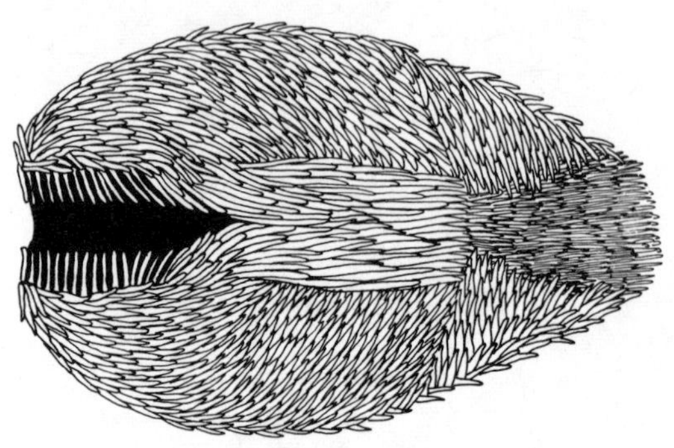

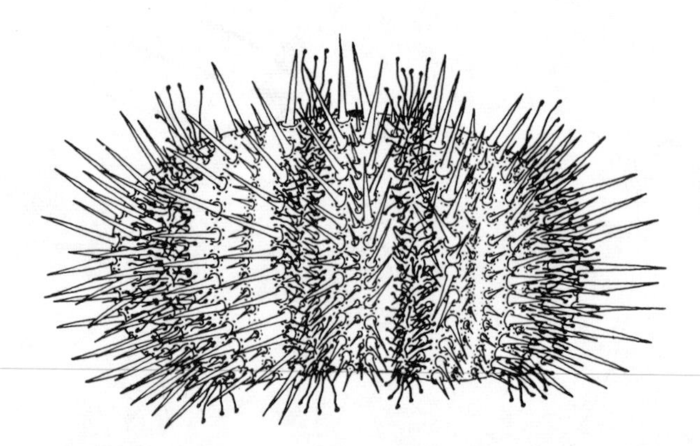

Figure 15.3 Echinoid types: above, *Dendraster,* a sand dollar (a moderately small specimen); thicker, but similar, species often are called sea biscuits; those species with holes near the margin are called keyhole sand dollars, and similar species with marginal notches are called notched sand dollars; center, *Lovenia,* a heart urchin (× 1); bottom, *Strongylocentrotus,* a sea urchin (small specimen); other sea urchins vary in body size and in spine number and spine proportions.

those spawning, development of the fertilized egg usually produces a free-swimming larva that eventually metamorphoses to the adult form. A few, chiefly polar or deep sea species, keep the young in brood pouches until the adult form is attained.

This group of echinoderms, like most other echinoderm classes, is of little direct use to man in the United States. Raw or cooked urchin gonads are eaten regularly by people of South America and the Mediterranean. The American Indian once recognized the tastiness of the same glands.

CLASS ASTEROIDEA (Sea Stars or Starfish)

Diagnosis: body star-shaped; generally five or multiples of five "arms;" underside of each arm (mouth or oral surface) with a deep, longitudinal groove containing tube feet (Figure 15.4).

The starfish are usually seen attached to rocks, but they are also found on sandy and muddy bottoms of bays, estuaries, and the deep ocean. Most starfish are carnivorous, preying primarily on shellfish such as clams, scallops, oysters, and mussels. Starfish are able to exert considerable pressure on a bivalve shell in attempting to open it. Opening such shells is either accomplished directly by the starfish's arms or aided by a poisonous, digestive secretion. The starfish then turns the front part of its digestive tract inside out so its stomach can envelop and digest the soft parts of the bivalve. When the nutrients have been extracted, the starfish's digestive tract returns to normal. One can see that the part of the digestive tract beyond the stomach is unused. Other starfish tend to eat anything that is at hand, the only criterion seeming to be that the material is organic; the predator starfish are partly scavengers.

These echinoderms are also typically bisexual. Both free-swimming and brooding larval stages are found in starfish, as well as in the other classes. In some starfish sexuality is similar to that in certain

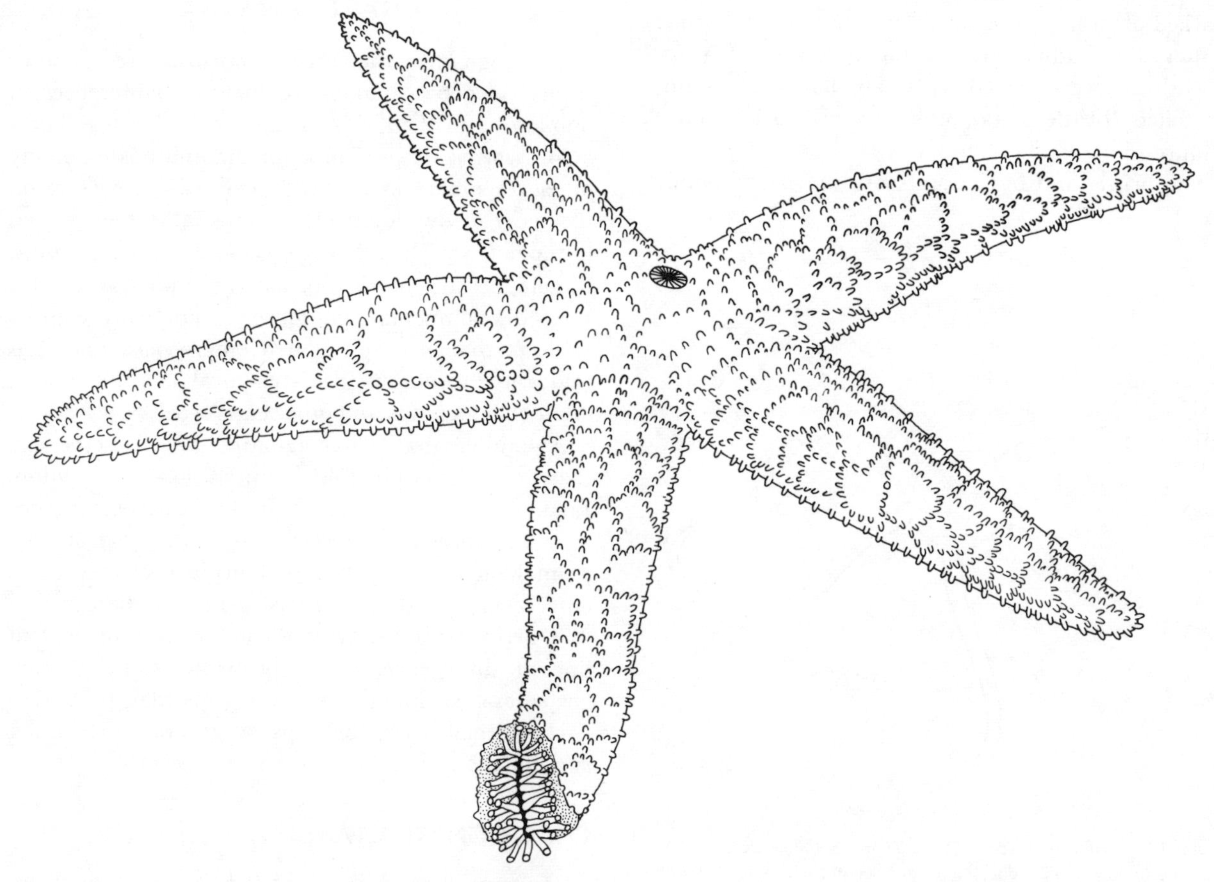

Figure 15.4 *Pisaster,* a starfish (about average adult size); other starfish range from much smaller to many feet across and display great variation in number of "arms."

univalve mollusks. These starfish start life as males, but later become females.

Starfish present little meat that could be used for food, hence even primitive people seldom eat them. Perhaps their closest relationship with modern man lies in the damage they cause in oyster beds. Oyster-bed owners not familiar with the regenerative powers of starfish have had real problems with these oyster predators. Bed owners have gathered the starfish in the beds, chopped the starfish in two, and cast the remains back into the oyster beds. Rather than destroying the starfish, this practice results in twice as many, because each part regenerates the missing portions and becomes a complete starfish. Now, most oystermen either collect and boil the starfish, or kill them by sprinkling lime on the beds during low tide.

CLASS OPHIUROIDEA (Brittle and Basket Stars)

Diagnosis: body star-shaped, but arms sharply marked off from a central disc; generally five arms; without longitudinal grooves on underside of arms, or with grooves covered by small plates; arms unbranched (brittle stars) or branched (basket stars) (Figure 15.5).

The brittle and basket stars are the most mobile echinoderms. Most can be found in fairly shallow water, especially in cracks or crevices or under objects in tidepools. The one great problem in collecting these animals is to obtain them with their arms intact. Their practice of casting off parts or all of one or more arms is defensive in that a predator is likely to be attracted by the wiggling dismembered portion of the animal. Castoff parts are regenerated.

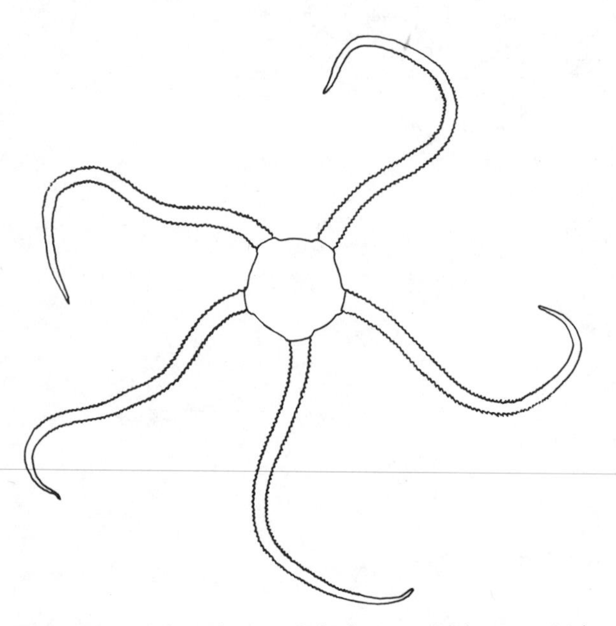

Figure 15.5 Ophiuroid type: *Ophioderma*, a brittle star. Brittle stars vary greatly in size, disc shape, arm length, and extent of arm spines. Basket stars are similar to brittle stars, but basket stars have the five arms much branched.

The greater mobility of these echinoderms is also reflected by some ophiuroids being able to swim. They use their arms much as a human swimmer does. Their food consists of a variety of small, marine animals, especially crustaceans and mollusks, and some feed on bottom debris. These stars in turn are eaten by fishes.

The sexes are usually separate, and fertilization of the eggs either results in a free-swimming larval stage or in development in parental brood pouches.

QUESTIONABLE ENTEROCOELA: CHAETOGNATHA

Chaetognaths, the arrow worms, are another subject of debate among zoologists. Differences of opinion as to their classification exist because adult arrow worms are pseudocoelomate and possess many other resemblances to cavity worms. However, on the basis of development, chaetognaths seem allied to the enterocoelous phyla. This alliance, is at best, remote, because arrow worms do not possess a larva, their developmental enterocoel is not truly comparable to that of unquestioned enterocoels, and it is impossible to obtain true structural identity among adult chaetognaths and other enterocoels.

Assuming that Chaetognatha are Enterocoela, there are three possible affinities for the phylum. First, arrow worms may represent early divergence from the ancestral enterocoel or from some archaic animal on the supposed path from coelenterate to enterocoel. That hypothesis is favored here. Second, arrow worms may be a completely independent line of divergence, again probably starting from coelenterates. Finally, arrow worms may be an entirely special case, perhaps a group representing simplification from more complex ancestors.

CHAETOGNATHA (Arrow Worms)

Diagnosis: symmetry bilateral; unsegmented; pseudocoelomate as adults; $\frac{4}{5}$ inch to $2\frac{4}{5}$ inches long;

transparent, torpedo-shaped forms; heads with characteristic bristles surrounding the mouth; body tube-like with lateral fins and tail terminated by a caudal fin; free-swimming marine forms (Figure 15.6).

About thirty species are known. They feed upon microscopic organisms and live in the open ocean. Because of their habitat, one is not likely to encounter them. Even if one were at sea, they would be hard to find. They have a habit of being at depths of several hundred feet during the day; however, at night they do come to the surface.

Arrow worms are hermaphroditic, but cross-fertilization is the rule. Apparently true larval stages do not occur; the eggs develop into a worm-like nonswimming creature that looks much like the adult.

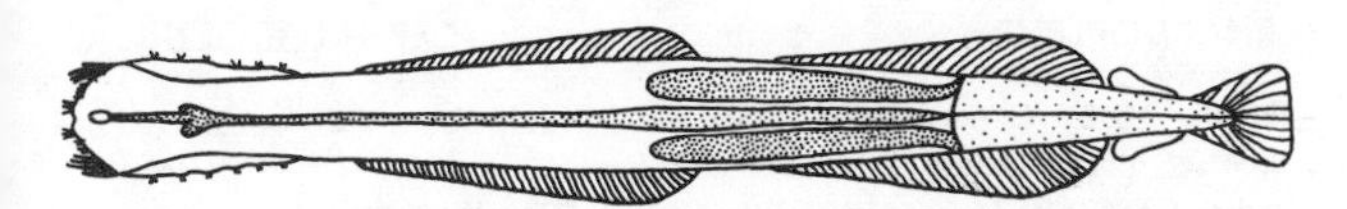

Figure 15.6 *Sagitta*, an arrow worm (adults mostly 12 to 25 mm. long, but range from 5 to 140 mm. long). (Redrawn from *The Encyclopedia of the Biological Sciences*, Peter Gray, ed. Reinhold Publishing Corp., New York, 1961.)

BILATERAL, NONCHORDATE ENTEROCOELA: HEMICHORDATA AND POGONOPHORA

The echinoderms, hemichordates, and chordates are considered to be closely related. In fact, hemichordates are seemingly sufficiently allied for some zoologists to treat them as a subphylum or class of the Chordata. Also, many zoologists unite the phyla Echinodermata, Hemichordata, and Chordata in a Superphylum Echinodermata. The Chaetognatha may also belong to this major taxon.

The Superphylum Echinodermata may encompass another group, the Pogonophora (beard worms). This taxonomic arrangement is made because beard worms seem closely related to hemichordates, either by having evolved from definite hemichordates or, more likely, having shared an ancestor that could be considered neither hemichordate nor beard worm. These assumptions are based on the many apparent fundamental similarities in structure. However, there are difficulties in joining the two phyla. Beard worms have neither gill slits nor a digestive tract. These missing structures and the fact that beard worms lack a larval stage make it difficult to establish any relationship beyond reasonable doubt.

HEMICHORDATA (Hemichordates)

Diagnosis: symmetry bilateral; unsegmented, with evidence of incipient segmentation; enterocoelous; worm-like or vase-like; body of three regions, proboscis, collar, and trunk; chordate-like in the possession of gill slits and a dorsal hollow nerve cord in the collar (but also a longer ventral one), but without a particular supporting rod (notochord) beneath the dorsal nerve cord; have a similar appearing rod (in the posterior proboscis), as an anterior outpocketing of the mouth cavity rather than the primitive gut proper as in the notochord; all marine.

CLASS ENTEROPNEUSTA (Acorn Worms)

Diagnosis: body worm-like, without a stalk, 1 to 100 inches long, mostly 5 to 25 inches long, fleshy and contractile; proboscis (prostome) cylindrical but drawn to a blunt point, short or long, somewhat tongue- or acorn-like; collar cylindrical, usually as wide as long; trunk elongate, with numerous paired gill slits entering pharynx; digestive tract straight; solitary, mostly intertidal animals that either form burrows or live under rocks, in rock cavities, or among algae, but also at some depth; filter feed by burrowing with mouth open; when water, sand, mud, and organic matter reach pharynx, water is expelled; after organic matter is digested and assimilated, sand, mud and undigested organic matter is expelled through the anus; sexes separate; a larva resembling that of certain echinoderms may be produced (Figure 15.7).

CLASS PTEROBRANCHIA (Pterobranchs)

Diagnosis: body vase-like, with a stalk, to $\frac{1}{5}$ inch long; proboscis shield-shaped; collar cylindrical, usually short, bearing 1 or more pairs of tentacles (lophophore); trunk relatively short, with one or no pairs of gills; digestive tract U-shaped with anus near mouth; sedentary, solitary, and tubeless or aggregated or colonial and forming tubes that are permanently fixed to substrate; found from shallow seas to deeps; filter feeders using lophophore; hermaphroditic or with separate sexes; larval stages known in

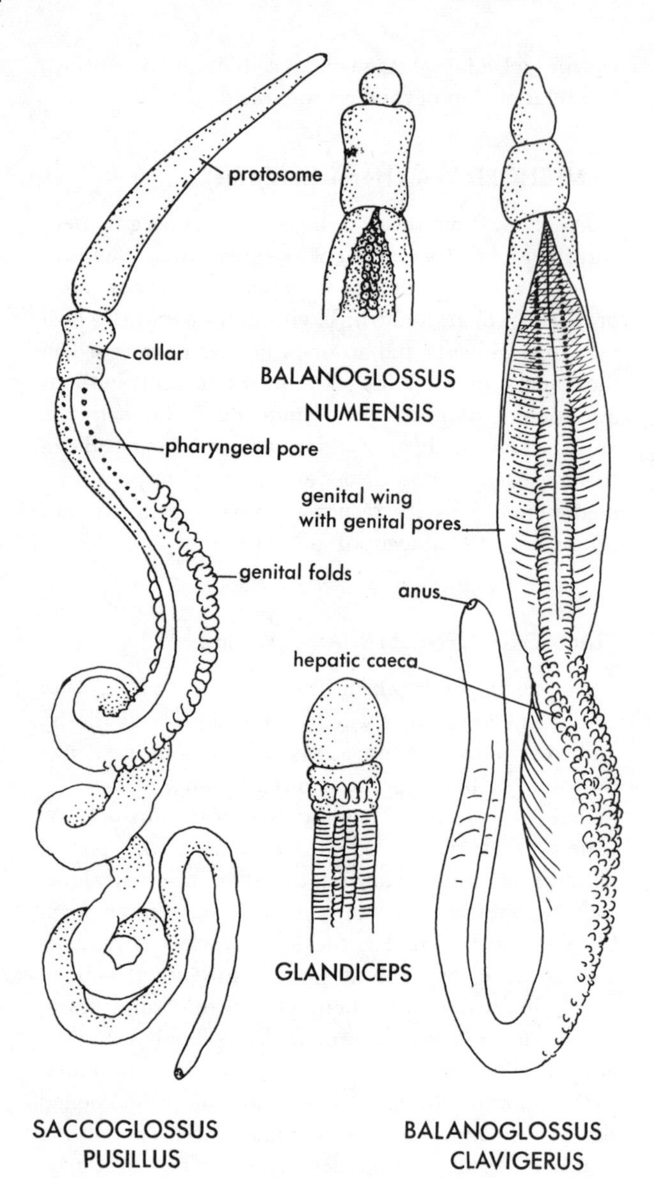

Figure 15.7 External appearance of several acorn worms. (From Malcolm Jollie, *Chordate Morphology*, Reinhold Publishing Corp., New York, 1962. After Dawydoff.)

some; some reproduce asexually by budding (Figure 15.8).

CLASS PLANCTOSPHAEROIDEA (Planctosphaeroids)

Diagnosis: represented by a few extremely rare transparent, spherical larvae; larvae of hemichordate type, but unlike those of the other two classes; found among marine plankton.

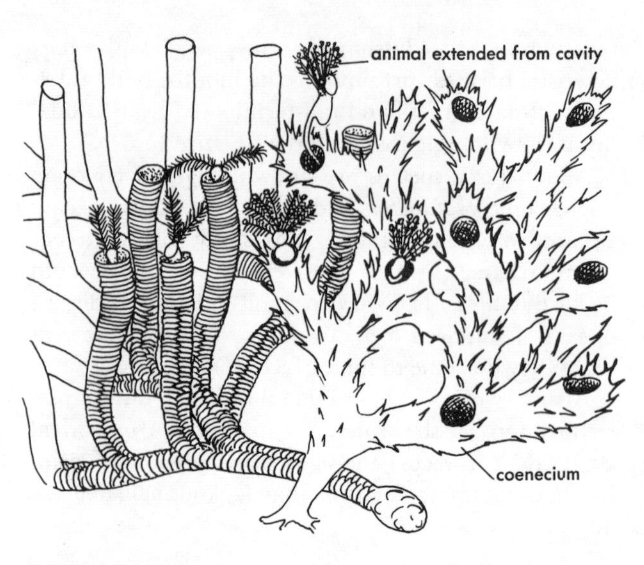

Figure 15.8 General appearance of two colonial pterobranchs and their secreted, common, external skeleton or coenecium. (From Malcolm Jollie, *Chordate Morphology*, Reinhold Publishing Corp., New York, 1962.)

POGONOPHORA (Beard Worms)

Diagnosis: symmetry bilateral; unsegmented; enterocoelous; round, worm-like tube dwellers; 4 to 14 inches long; three body regions consisting of one to many frilled tentacles on the anterior region, a weakly defined collar, and a trunk; no digestive system or gill slits; strictly marine, most very deep but some in shallower water (Figure 15.9).

The beard worms were first collected by the Dutch ship *Siboga* during its 1899–1900 expedition in the vicinity of Indonesia. For many years these worms were considered to be strange members of various phyla. In 1955, A. V. Ivanov, a Russian, finally established our present understanding of the phylum.

These mostly extremely deep-sea forms are believed to capture food with their tentacles and digest

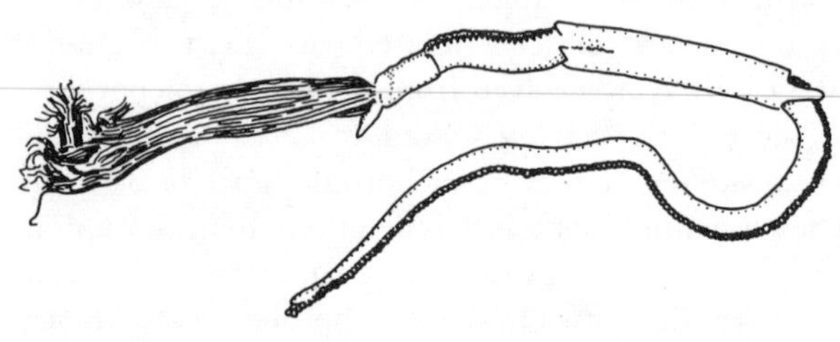

Figure 15.9 *Lamellisabella*, a beard worm. (Redrawn from Ivanov.)

it while it is held by the tentacles—they have no digestive tract. Of course, very little is really known about these animals, because they must be brought up from the depths before they can be studied. Because embryos are found in the tubes that the adults seem to form, it is believed that there is no larval stage and that the tube acts as a brood site for the developing individual.

CHORDATE ENTEROCOELA: CHORDATA

Perhaps the last animal phylum to evolve was the Chordata. In spite of our personal interest, because we are chordates, these animals are not necessarily the most successful ones upon earth. You may recall that we cannot make positive statements, because we are unable really to measure success. If we use such criteria as numbers of individuals or species and amount of the world occupied, the arthropods are the most successful group.

In the remainder of this chapter we shall examine the general nature of chordates and the kinds of chordates without backbones, a group often called the "Lower Chordates."

CHORDATA (Chordates)

Diagnosis: symmetry bilateral; segmented, but may not be visible externally; enterocoelous; includes the tunicates, lancets, and vertebrates; tunicates may be blubbery, club-shaped, or globular; all possess a sac-like covering or tunic; include sea squirts, which may be recognized by their habit of expelling water when touched, and which range from transparent to opaque and brilliantly colored; lancets' bodies are fish-like, but possess neither scales nor other complexities of vertebrates; marine, freshwater, and terrestrial; none are strictly parasitic.

Perhaps the subphyla of chordates bear less resemblance to one another as adults than do the members of any other phylum. It was already stated that they are considered more closely related to the echinoderms and hemichordates than to any other phylum. But, why are they a single phylum? The chordates are distinct in possessing *gill slits;* a *notochord*, a long, flexible, rod-like structure from head to tail along the back; and a *dorsal hollow nerve cord* along the back and above the notochord.

The chordate ancestor can be reconstructed from our knowledge of the invertebrate chordates. Perhaps it was most like the living tunicates, in contrast to other living forms, but it was much less specialized. The evidence suggests that the ancestor was sedentary and possessed an elaborate gill structure for food gathering, an alimentary canal, and reproductive organs, all enclosed in a soft body. For distribution of offspring, there may have developed, as in tunicate larvae, a propulsive tail with notochord and swimming muscles. From this hypothetical larva, fossils and developmental patterns show a small step to the living chordates.

Subphylum TUNICATA (= UROCHORDATA) (Tunicates)

Diagnosis: larvae minute, free-swimming and tadpole-like, with notochord and nerve cord; gills generally involved in filter feeding; adults sessile; adult body irregular, tubular to somewhat spherical, generally blubbery to club-like, covered by a transparent to opaque tunic, without notochord or nerve cord; strictly marine (Figure 15.10).

CLASS LARVACEAE (Larvaceans or Tadpole Tunicates)

Diagnosis: minute to $\frac{1}{8}$ inch, transparent, tadpole-like tunicates of persistent larval form, free-swimming marine plankton that have a jelly-like tunic they may leave to secrete a new one; microscopic food is filtered by tunic structures, the necessary water current for filtering being produced by moving the tail; usually hermaphroditic, but with cross-fertilization, individuals first functioning as males and then as females; open ocean forms.

CLASS THALIACEA (Chain or Pelagic Tunicates)

Diagnosis: small to 4 inches, colonies much longer; body cask-like or spindle-like with anterior and posterior openings, ringed by muscles that may provide contractions necessary for jet-propelled swimming, others transported only by currents; solitary or colonial, colonial forms generally arranged as chains of individuals; tunic permanent, adults without a tail; filter feeders on microscopic life; hermaphroditic, usually with different generations, hermaphroditic adult by sexual means produces a

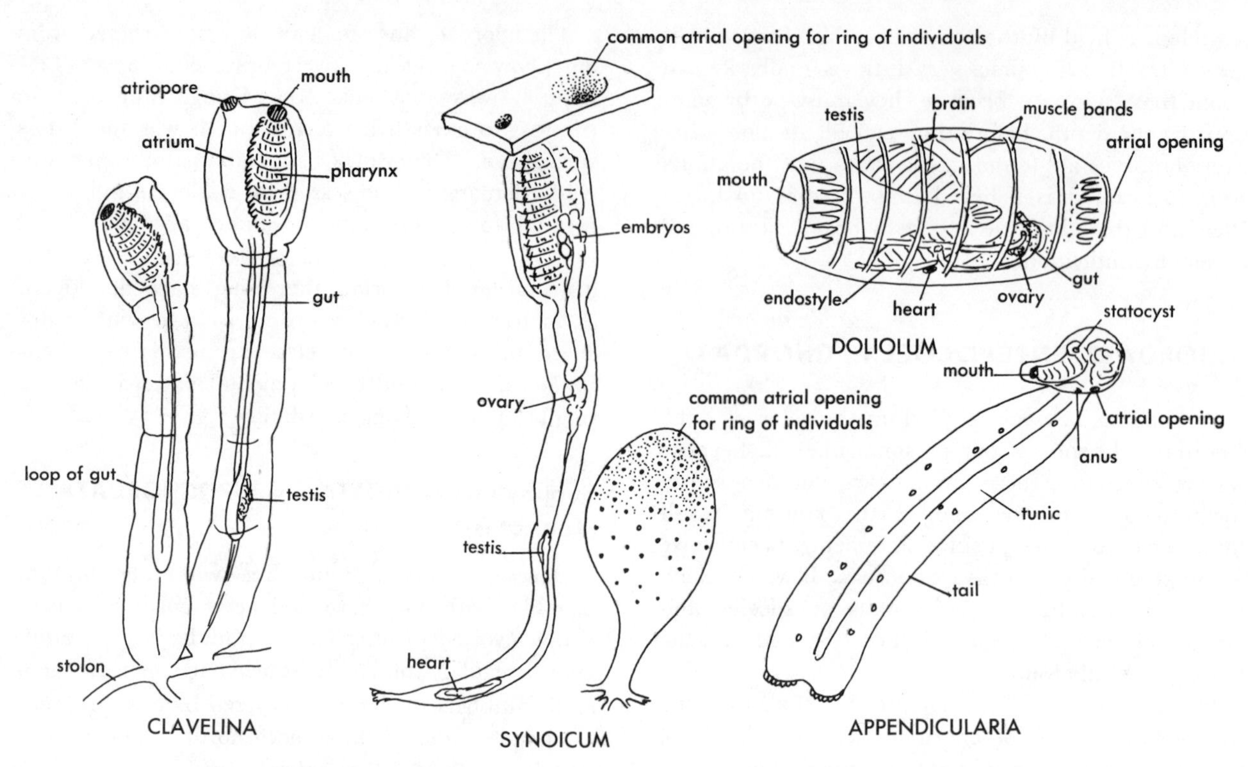

Figure 15.10 The basic kinds of tunicates: *Clavelina,* a colonial ascidian, a sea club; *Synoicum,* a compound ascidian, sea blubber (enlarged individual to the left, small colony to the right); *Doliolum* and *Appendicularia,* pelagic tunicates. (From Malcolm Jollie, *Chordate Morphology,* Reinhold Publishing Corp., New York, 1962.)

somewhat similar appearing "nurse stage" adult which by asexual budding produces hermaphroditic adults; nurse stage bears a chain of budding sexual adults; open ocean forms (Figure 15.10).

CLASS ASCIDIACEAE (Ascidians)

Diagnosis: variable in size and shape, individual, colonial, or compound, usually fixed to substrate; tunic usually gelatinous, sometimes of cellulose; compound type distinguished from other types by many individuals being in a single tunic; compound ascidians in a common gelatinous material; masses varying from thin flat sheets to groups of stalked, tall, irregular lobes, lobes sometimes tongue-like, club-like, or hand-like, are called sea blubber or sea pork; solitary and colonial types have somewhat similar-appearing individuals; colonies with individuals connected by bases of the tunics or stem-

Figure 15.11 Lancets, *Branchiostoma,* swimming (when disturbed) and feeding. An invalid scientific name, *Amphioxis,* often is used as a common name. (From Malcolm Jollie, *Chordate Morphology,* Reinhold Publishing Corp., New York, 1962. After Newman.)

like structures; if solitary forms or colonies are stalked, individuals usually are opaque, tough, and club-like (called sea clubs); if not stalked, individuals usually are semitransparent, fragile-appearing, and sac-like (called sea squirts); sea clubs and sea squirts frequently and abruptly eject water when disturbed; ascidians are hermaphroditic filter feeders; colonial and compound forms result from asexual budding; inhabit shallow water in rocky tide pools to deeps.

Subphylum CEPHALOCHORDATA (Lancets)

Diagnosis: mostly $\frac{1}{5}$ inch to 4 inches long, slender, simple structured and finless, but fish-like; adult with all chordate characters; gills generally involved in filter feeding; sexes separate, reproduction strictly sexual; shallow water, marine sand dwellers, but some are intertidal, at low tide, lancets may jump out and back into sand when disturbed (Figure 15.11).

SELECTED READINGS*

Bather, F. A., 1900. The Echinoderms. In *A Treatise on Zoology* (R. Lankester, ed.) Vol. 3, A & C Black, London.

Clark, A. H., 1915–1950. *A Monograph of the Existing Crinoids.* Bull. 82, U. S. Nat. Mus., Washington, D. C.

Fisher, W. K., 1911–1930. *Asteroidea of the North Pacific and Adjacent Waters.* Part 1: Phanerozonia and Spinulosa (1911). Parts 2 and 3: Eorcipulata (1928 and 1930). Bull. 76(1–3), U. S. Nat. Mus., Washington, D. C.

Hyman, L. H., 1955. *The Invertebrates.* Vol. 4: *Echinodermata.* McGraw-Hill Book Co., New York.

———. 1959. *The Invertebrates.* Vol. 5: *Smaller Coelomate Groups.* McGraw-Hill Book Co., New York.

*See also p. 212.

16 SUBPHYLUM VERTEBRATA

Higher Chordates

Vertebrates are chordates. Therefore, considering them in a separate chapter isolates them from other members of their phylum, the Chordata. Perhaps it is difficult to accept the close relationship between vertebrates and such things as sea blubber. How can animals with backbones and some semblance of a skull—fishes, amphibians, reptiles, birds, and mammals—be related to the chordates mentioned in the preceding chapter? The answer already was given: all possess a notochord, dorsal hollow nerve cord, and gill slits during some stage of their life cycles.

Before considering the individual groups, let us trace the probable ancestry of all of them.

VERTEBRATE AFFINITIES: SUBPHYLUM VERTEBRATA

We will start our discussion by reviewing the echinoderm–chordate line (Figure 16.1). Again, although qualifying words or phrases are not always used, phylogeny is probable but often hypothetical. Recall that the ancestor of this line likely was a stalked, attached organism that had a dipleurula larval stage. This ancestor perhaps gave rise to the echinoderms. After a time, chance hereditary changes probably modified both larval and adult echinoderm stages; the adult, although still attached, was a gill filter-feeder rather than an arm-feeder like the original adult ancestor. This hypothetical gill feeding, "second step" ancestor was an infinitesimal step below the hermichordate and tunicate ancestor. The actual tunicate ancestors, larval and adult, are believed to have been quite similar to certain modern tunicates. This assumed larva was essentially a tunicate and gave rise to an advanced chordate without a sessile adult stage; again, a small amount of change would have been involved. The advanced chordate probably was a direct step to the cephalochordates and also to primitive filter-feeding vertebrates. From these primitive vertebrates, in short order, there arose the ancestral jawless Cyclostomata, a group that exists today in the form of hagfishes and lampreys. The cyclostomes contained the now extinct order of archaic, jawless, armored ostracoderms (Figure 16.2), from which, in turn, evolved another extinct group, a class of jawed, armored placoderms (Figure 16.3). It is believed that placoderms evolved into two main lines, one leading to the cartilaginous fishes, Chondrichthyes (Figure 16.4), and the other to the bony fishes, Osteichthyes. The ancestral bony fishes (Figure 16.5) were the source of two living subclasses, the ray-finned Actinopterygii (Figure 16.6) and the lobe-finned Choanichthyes (Figure 16.7). The latter group still has two living orders, the lungfishes and the lobe-finned fishes. Ancestral lobe-fins most likely were also ancestors of land animals in the form of amphibians. Some of the earliest amphibians

TAXONOMIC SUMMARY

Kingdom Animalia (L. *animalis*, animate)—animals
Subkingdom Eumetazoa (Gr. *eu*, true + *meta*, among + *zoon*, animal)—eumetazoans

Phylum Chordata (Gr. *chorde*, string)—chordates
Subphylum Vertebrata (L. *vertebratus*, backbone)—vertebrates
Superclass Pisces (L. *piscis*, fish)—fishes
Class Cyclostomata (Gr. *cyklos*, circular + *stomatos*, mouth)—cyclostomes
Order Petromyzontoidea (Gr. *petros*, stone + *myzon*, suck + *oideos*, form or type of)—lampreys
Order Myxinoidea (Gr. *myxa*, slime + *oideos*)—hagfishes or slime eels
†Class Placodermi (Gr. *plakos*, flat round plate + *derma*, skin)—placoderms
Class Chondrichthyes (Gr. *chondros*, cartilage + *ichthys*, fish)—cartilaginous fishes
Order Holocephali (Gr. *holos*, entire + *kephale*, head)—chimaeras
Order Selachii (Gr. *selachos*, a cartilaginous fish)—sharks and rays
Suborder Batoidea (Gr. *batos*, a ray + *oideos*)—rays
Suborder Squaloideas (L. *squalus*, a marine fish + *oideus*)—sharks
Class Osteichthyes (Gr. *osteon*, bone + *ichthyes*)—bony fishes
Subclass Choanichthyes (Gr. *choana*, funnel + *ichthyes*)—choanate fishes
Order Crossopterygii (Gr. *crossoi*, a fringe + *pteryx*, fin)—lobe-finned fishes
Order Dipnoi (Gr. *di-*, two + *pnoe*, breath)—lungfishes
Subclass Actinopterygii (Gr. *actis*, ray + *pteryx*)—ray-finned fishes
Superorder Chondrostei (Gr. *chondros*, + *osteon*, bone)—primitive ray-finned fishes
Superorder Holostei (Gr. *holos*, + *osteon*)—intermediate ray-finned fishes
Superorder Teleostei (Gr. *teleos*, complete + *osteon*)—modern fishes
Superclass Tetrapoda (Gr. *tetra*, four + *podos*, foot)—land vertebrates
Class Amphibia (Gr. *amphi*, both or double + *bios*, life)—amphibians
Order Gymnophiona (Gr. *gymnos*, naked + *ophioneos*, snake-like)—caecilians
Order Trachystomata (Gr. *trachys*, rough + *stomatos*)—sirens
Order Caudata (L. *caudatus*, having a tail)—salamanders
Order Salientia (L. *saliens*, jumping)—frogs and toads
Class Reptilia (L. *repere*, to creep)—reptiles
Order Testudinata (L. *testudinatus*, turtle)—turtles
Order Rhynchocephalia (Gr. *rhynchos*, snout + *kephale*)—tuatara
Order Squamata (L. *squamatus*, scaly)
Suborder Sauria (Gr. *sauros*, lizard)—lizards
Suborder Serpentes (L. *serpens*, serpent)—snakes
Order Crocodilia (L. *crocodilius*, crocodile)—crocodilians
Class Aves (L. *avis*, bird)—birds
Subclass Archaeornithes (Gr. *archios*, ancient + *ornithos*, bird)—lizard birds
Subclass Neornithes (Gr. *neos*, new + *ornithos*)—true birds
Class Mammalia (L. *mamma*, breast)—mammals
Subclass Prototheria (Gr. *proto*, first + *ther*, wild beast)—egg-laying mammals
Subclass Theria (Gr. *ther*)—viviparous mammals
Infraclass Metatheria (Gr. *meta*, after + *ther*)—marsupials
Infraclass Eutheria (Gr. *eu*, true + *ther*)—placental mammals

(Figure 16.8), vaguely salamander-like in appearance, were the ancestors of reptiles. Among the earliest groups of reptiles were the so-called "stem reptiles." These "stem reptiles" gave rise to the great diversity of animals that typified the 300-million-year Age of Reptiles which ended about 70 million years ago.

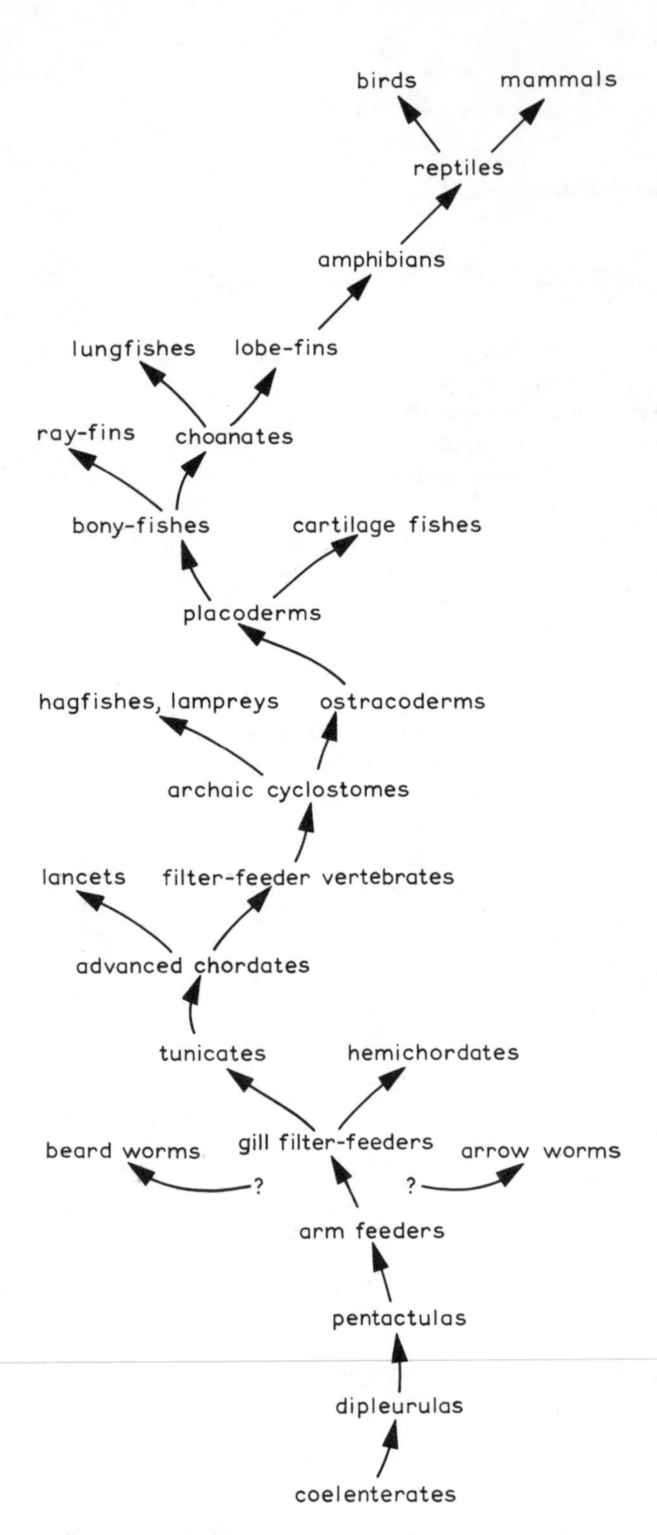

Figure 16.1 The family tree of the Chordata as related to probable evolution of an echinoderm–chordate line.

Some of these stem reptiles also evolved into the "ruling reptiles," which included dinosaurs, and into the birds and the mammals.

Subphylum VERTEBRATA (Vertebrates)

Diagnosis: small to huge animals with a backbone, or vertebral column; chordate characters in developmental or larval stages, present or absent in adults.

FISHES: SUPERCLASS PISCES

Vertebrates often are separated into two subclasses, fishes and land vertebrates. Such a separation is for convenience, rather than to show relationships. Recall that the ancestral vertebrates did not give rise to fishes and land vertebrates; the land vertebrates evolved from lobe-finned fishes.

Superclass PISCES (Fishes)

Diagnosis: aquatic vertebrates (some are periodically terrestrial); body generally laterally compressed and streamlined, specialized to offer little resistance to water; usually with two sets of paired fins (the evolutionary counterpart of legs) and often with additional unpaired fins; generally with both a body covering of scales and respiration involving gills; with neither a neck region nor a specialized movable joint between the head and the rest of the body.

CLASS CYCLOSTOMATA (Cyclostomes)

Diagnosis: body elongate, cylindrical, to about 3 feet, without scales; skeleton of gristle (cartilage); median fins on tail and part of body; appendages absent; jaws absent; gills in pouches with external slits, 6 to 14 pairs; fresh-water and marine (Figure 16.9).

ORDER PETROMYZONTOIDEA (Lampreys)

Diagnosis: mouth ventral, surrounded by a sucking funnel-like structure; eyes not covered by skin; seven pairs of gill pouches and seven pairs of external openings start close behind each visible eye; dorsal fin divided; sexes separate, eggs small, larval stage present and of long duration; fresh-water and marine.

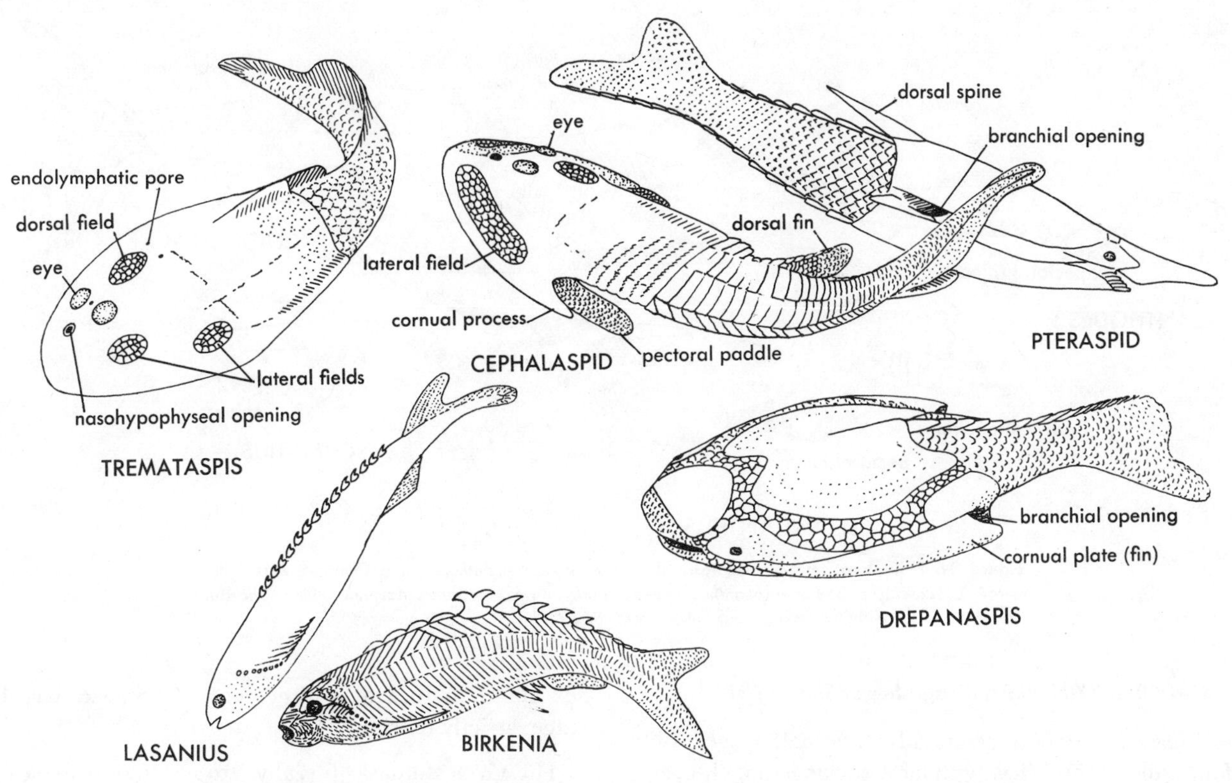

Figure 16.2 Restorations of some ancient ostracoderms and their relatives. (From *Chordate Morphology* by Malcolm Jollie. N. Y.: Reinhold Publishing Corp., 1962.)

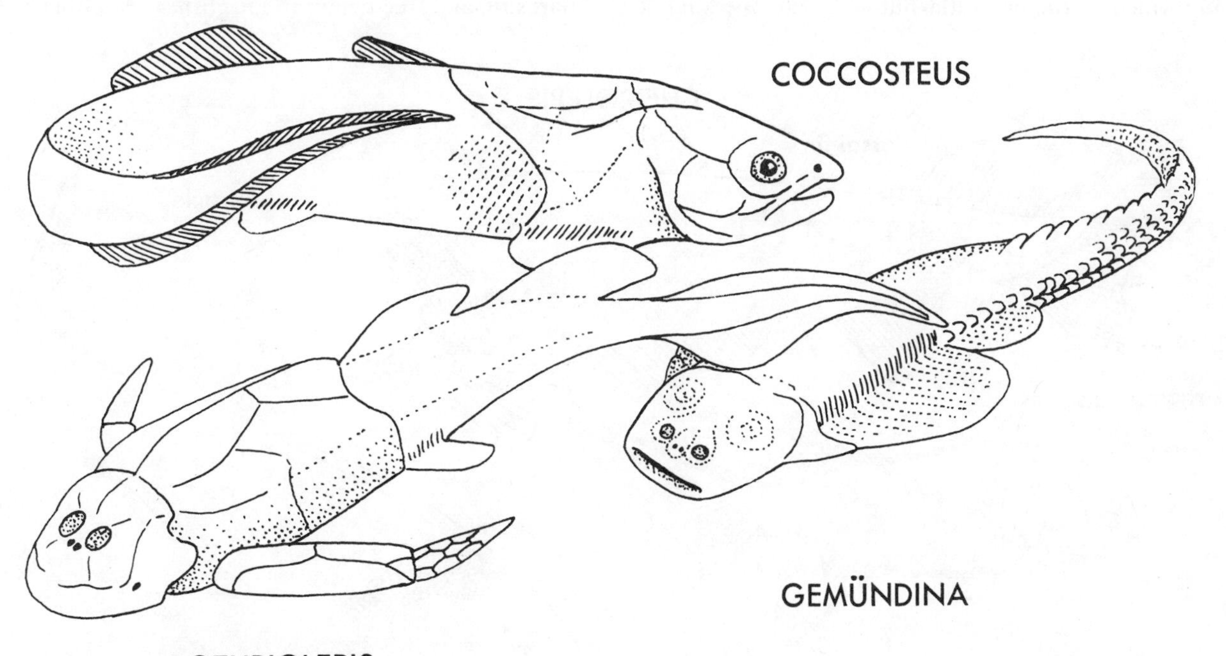

Figure 16.3 Restorations of some fossil placoderms. (From Malcolm Jollie, *Chordate Morphology*, Reinhold Publishing Corp., New York, 1962.)

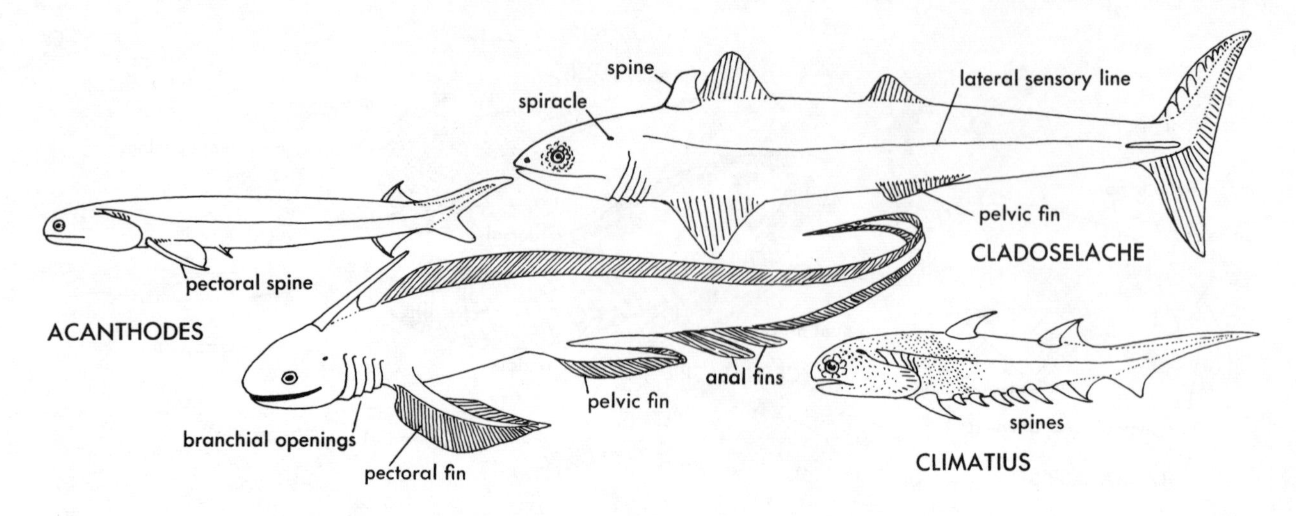

Figure 16.4 Restorations of some fossil shark-like fishes. *Acanthodes* and *Climatus* were Placodermi; *Cladoselache* and *Pleurocanthus* were Chondrichthyes. (From Malcolm Jollie, *Chordate Morphology*, Reinhold Publishing Corp., New York, 1962.)

ORDER MYXINOIDEA (Hagfishes or Slime Eels)

Diagnosis: mouth essentially terminal, ringed by four pairs of tentacles, without a sucking funnel, eyes covered by skin; 10 to 14 pairs of gill pouches opening some distance behind each covered eye; dorsal fin undivided; hermaphroditic, but with only one kind of sex gland mature at a time, eggs large, no larval stage; strictly marine.

The Cyclostomata, literally "round mouths," are jawless fishes that now are represented by two orders, the lampreys and the hagfishes. The lampreys are parasitic and free-living; the hagfishes are either fish

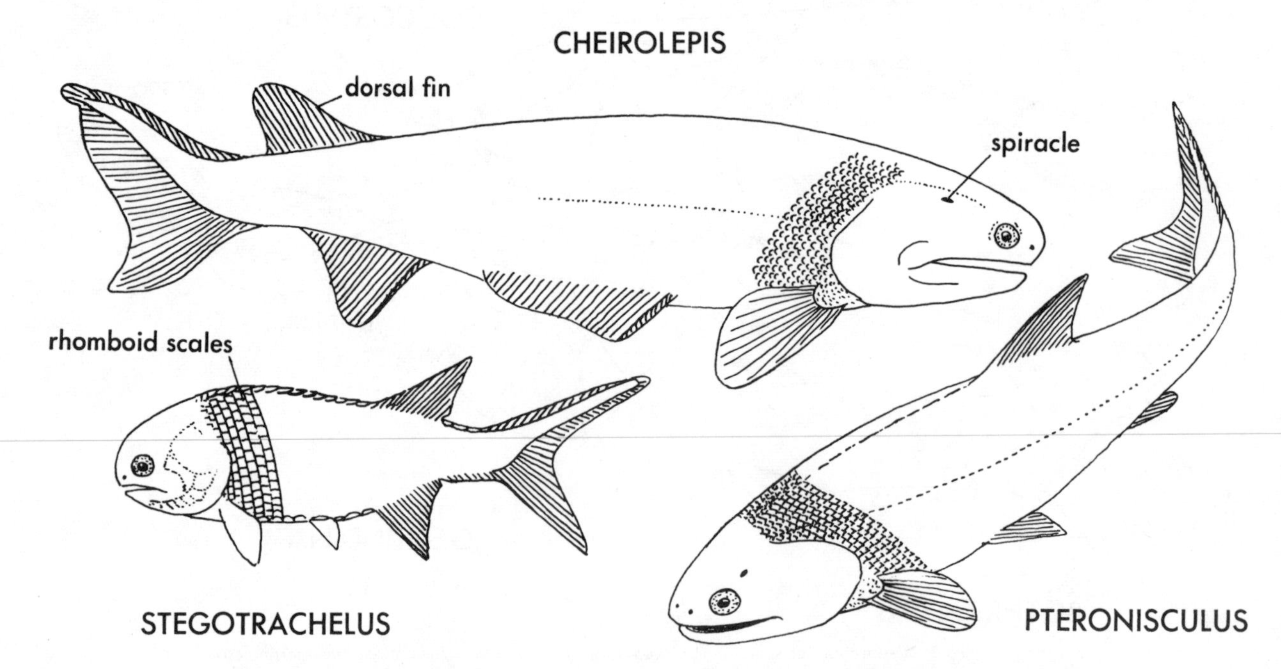

Figure 16.5 Restorations of some fossil, primitive Actinopterygii, Superorder Chondrostei. (From Malcolm Jollie, *Chordate Morphology*, Reinhold Publishing Corp., New York, 1962.)

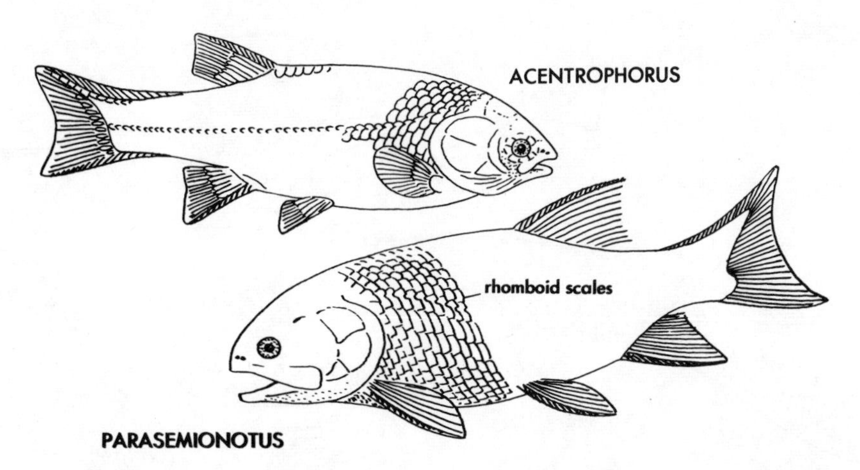

Figure 16.6 Restoration of some fossil Actinopterygii: *Acentrophorus,* Superorder Chondrostei; *Parasemionotus,* Superorder Holostei. (From Malcolm Jollie, *Chordate Morphology,* Reinhold Publishing Corp., New York, 1962.)

predators or scavengers on dead fish. Lampreys are found in both salt and fresh water, but hagfishes are strictly marine. Many species throughout the entire class have both a well-developed, rasp-like tongue, which is used to burrow into the true fishes they attack, and a sucker-like mouth, which is used to attach to fishes and other objects. These two structures are best developed in two of the feeding types—the parasitic forms that use mouth and tongue to gain nutrients from the body fluids of their hosts, and the predaceous species that literally rasp and eat their way through their prey.

Reproduction is interesting in both orders. The hagfishes lay large (to slightly over an inch in diameter) shell-covered eggs on objects in the sea and miniature adults hatch from the eggs. The young hagfishes first develop into males and later the males transform into females. On the other hand, both marine and fresh-water lampreys lay their eggs in fresh water, all lampreys migrating to their breeding grounds. To reach the clear-water breeding grounds, lampreys may attach to a fish or boat going in the right direction. Upon reaching the breeding site, they construct a small hollow to receive the large number of eggs—some lamprey females lay about a quarter of a million eggs. Perhaps this great expenditure of energy is the reason why all adults die after spawning. After the eggs develop awhile, they hatch into lancet-

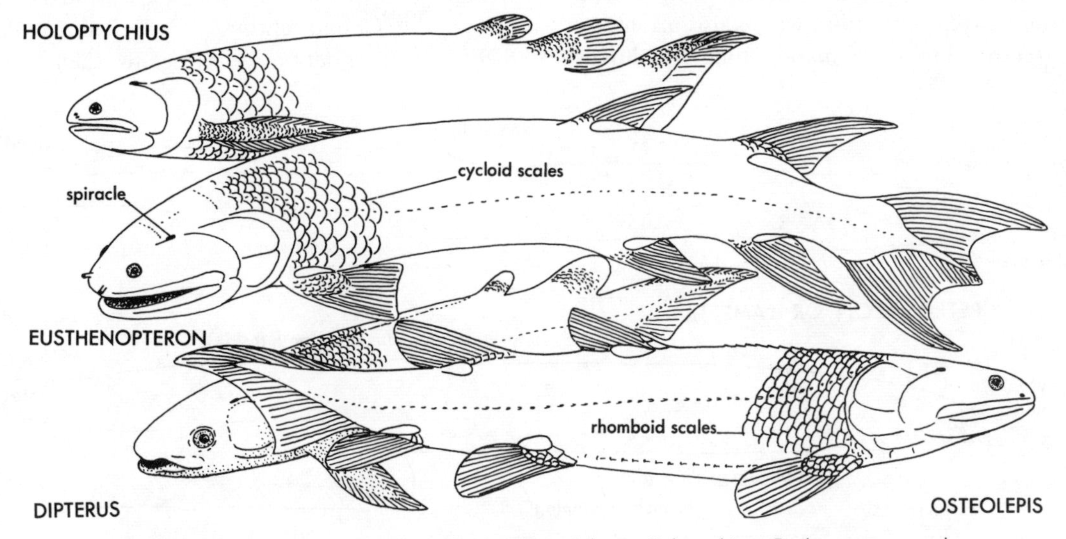

Figure 16.7 Restoration of some fossil Choanichthyes: *Holoptychius, Eusthenopteron,* and *Osteolepis,* order Crossopterygii; *Dipterus,* Order Dipnoi. (From Malcolm Jollie, *Chordate Morphology,* Reinhold Publishing Corp., New York, 1962.)

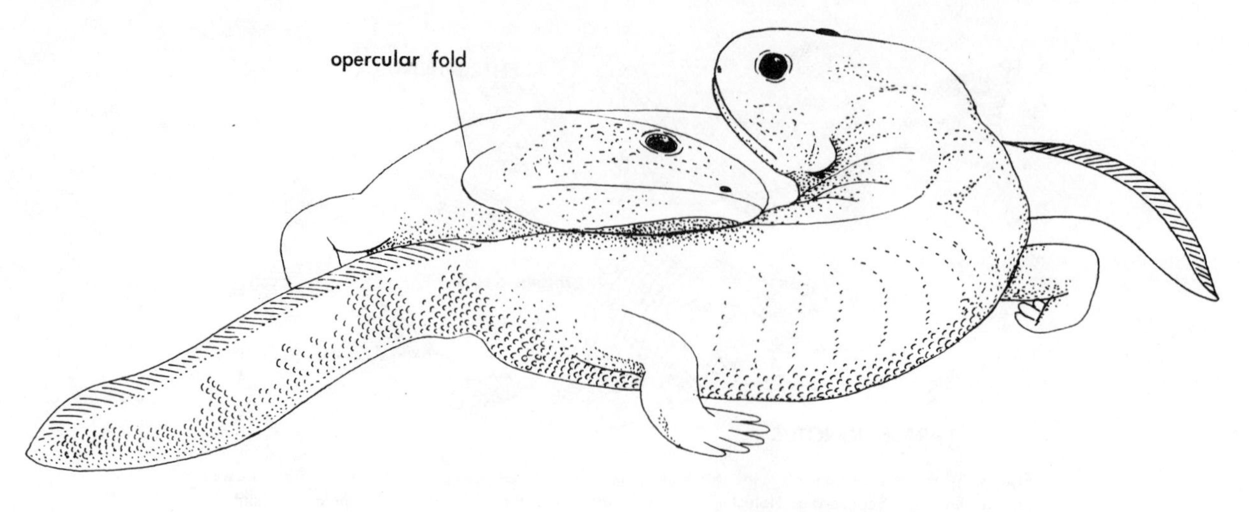

Figure 16.8 Restoration of *Icthyostega*, a Devonian stem amphibian. (From Malcolm Jollie, *Chordate Morphology*, Reinhold Publishing Corp., New York, 1962.)

like larvae that spend several years partly buried in the stream bottom, a place suitable for their filter-feeding habits. Two possibilities occur at the time of larval metamorphosis: some become predaceous or parasitic adults that pursue an active life for some time; others become adults that neither feed nor grow, but after a few months reproduce and die.

CLASS CHONDRICHTHYES (Cartilaginous Fishes)

Diagnosis: streamlined, cylindrical to flattened, perhaps to 50 feet long; skin tough and covered with minute, unique (placoid) scales which also are modified into teeth; skin with many slime or mucus glands; skeleton of gristle or cartilage; tail and two median dorsal fins present; appendages present, paired front or pectoral and paired rear or pelvic fins; jaws and fin rays present; five to seven pairs of gills and gill slits (usually exposed); sexes separate, fertilization internal, eggs laid or held and young born alive; development direct, so no larval stage; United States species mostly marine (Figure 16.10).

The Chondrichthyes include two living orders, the chimeras (sometimes also called ratfishes or ghost fishes) with no recognized suborders, and the selachians with two suborders, the sharks and rays. As a group the Chondrichthyes are called cartilaginous fishes, a designation referring to their gristle or

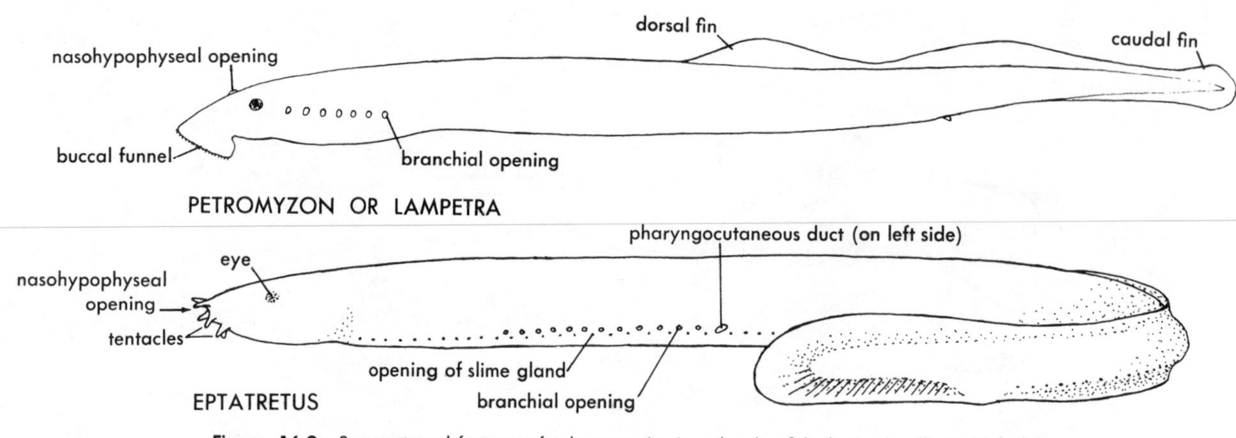

Figure 16.9 Some external features of a lamprey (top) and a hagfish (bottom). (From Malcolm Jollie, *Chordate Morphology*, Reinhold Publishing Corp., New York, 1962.)

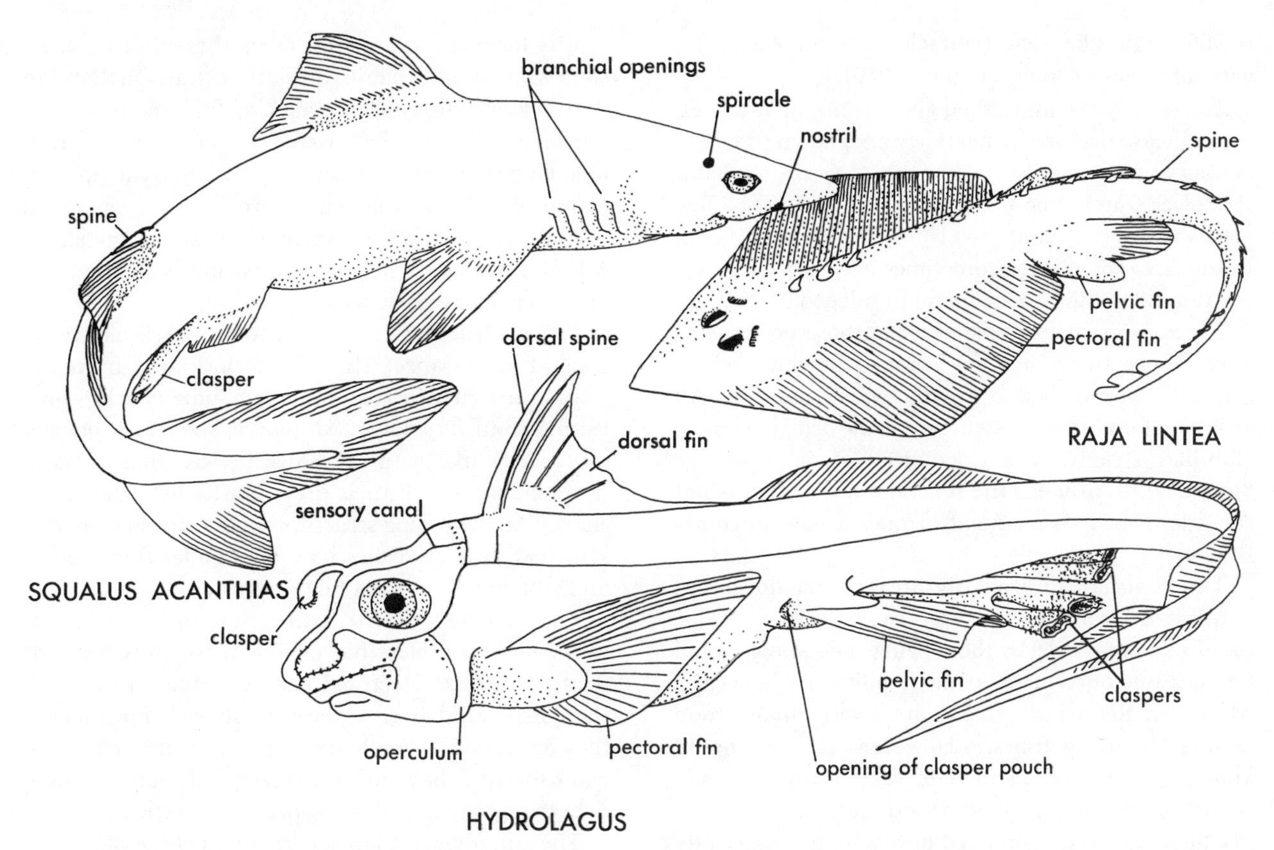

Figure 16.10 External features of the cartilaginous fishes: a shark, a ray, and a chimaeran. (From Malcolm Jollie, *Chordate Morphology*, Reinhold Publishing Corp., New York, 1962.)

cartilaginous skeleton. This skeleton distinguishes these fishes from the true fishes, which possess a bony skeleton.

Sometimes the chimaeras and a fossil order are joined in a Subclass Holocephali and the selachians and fossil orders are placed in a Subclass Elasmobranchii (Gr. *elasmos*, thin plate + *branchia*, gills). When Holocephali is considered a subclass, chimaeras are placed in an Order Chimaerae (Gr. *chimaira*, a she-goat or mythical fire-spouting monster).

Reproduction throughout the class involves internal fertilization; the males have accessory structures, the claspers, on the pelvic fins for this purpose. Shortly after fertilization female chimeras and some female sharks and rays lay "mermaids' purses," each purse consisting of an egg in a horny capsule that is distinctive in the various species. These purses usually are attached to objects; some egg capsules have "tendrils" that attach to such things as seaweeds. In spite of these attachment devices, the egg cases are sometimes found in tidepools and along the seashore.

Because fertilization is internal in the Chondrichthyes, it is only one step to the female's retaining the eggs until hatching. This is the case with most sharks and rays; hence, these cartilaginous fishes bear living young. Whether eggs are laid or not, in most cases a miniature shark or ray hatches without ever having received nourishment from its mother, nourishment being derived solely from the egg. However, in a few sharks that bear their young alive the developing individual does obtain sustenance from its mother. Contrary to popular belief, the mammals are not unique in nourishing their embryos; such conditions are also known in amphibians and reptiles, and even invertebrates.

ORDER HOLOCEPHALI (Chimaeras)

Diagnosis: gill slits covered by a membranous structure (operculum); hence one external opening leads into the four internal gill slits; grotesque form; each jaw with teeth modified into a plate; without a modified gill-like cleft (spiracle) behind each eye; without scales in adults (Figure 16.10).

The chimaeras, also called ghost fishes or ratfishes, typically are deep-sea fishes; they are known to live at depths of over a mile. Although they also inhabit shallower waters, the Pacific Coast is one of the few places where they occur just below the intertidal level. In this area, chimaeras sometimes are trapped by retreating tides and may be found in tidepools.

These are scaleless "fishes" of grotesque appearance, hence their common name, chimaera, which originally was applied to a mythological monster. An additional unattractive structure is the heavily spined, club-like, strictly male organ that stems from the "forehead." Although the function of this club is not really known, it is assumed to play a part in courtship.

The Holocephali probably are an archaic group, perhaps a group on its way to extinction. This premise is supported by there being nine known fossil families but only three living families in the order. Moreover, the living ratfishes are a very small group among the living fishes. However, as one should know by now, certain taxa of very small size may persist for geologically long periods of time.

Chimaeras feed upon hard invertebrates, especially shellfish, and their mouths are specialized for this purpose. Both upper and lower teeth are fused into solid plates, and the upper plate is fused to the skull. This arrangement provides a strong vise-like structure that is marvelously suited for its purpose.

ORDER SELACHII (Sharks and Rays)

Diagnosis: gills in five to seven separate clefts visible along each side of pharynx; form torpedo-like or flattened; jaws with individual placoid scales modified into teeth; spiracle and scales present in adults (Figure 16.10).

Suborder BATOIDEA (Rays)

Diagnosis: gill slits on underside of body; body generally flattened; front (pectoral) fins enlarged, attached along each side of head and body.

The Suborder Batoidea includes animals called skates and rays. In general, skates have longer, thicker tails, and the pectoral fins and front part of the body are not expanded to the point that a circular disc is formed. All members of the suborder have somewhat similar habits in that most are shallow- to deep-water bottom feeders on shellfish; mollusks and crustaceans are crushed by the numerous, small, flattened teeth. Swimming is accomplished by a rippling action of the "wings" which are broadly expanded pectoral fins, each fin attaching to almost an entire side of the body. Therefore, the primary adaptations are to a bottom existence.

The sawfish is a ray that is more shark-like in its general appearance. It receives its name from the "saw" (a structure also found in some sharks) projecting from its snout. Moreover, sawfishes possess other shark-like features. Sawfishes use their saws to dismember and kill their prey, mostly fish; they have shark-like swimming structures and swim like sharks. However, true sawfishes have gills under their bodies and still on the pectoral fins.

The torpedo, or electric, rays have modifications of the "wing" muscles that enable these muscles suddenly to release electrical energy. When disturbed, these fish can deliver a powerful shock. Fortunately they are found at moderate depths, so only commercial fishermen have much contact with them. These fishermen have a healthy respect for electric rays.

The stingrays are fairly common inshore along the coast. Not uncommonly, stingrays inflict painful, slow-healing wounds on swimmers and people clamming in coastal waters. These wounds are inflicted by the "stinger," a spine on the tail. The materials injected by the stinger, whether they be formed by the animal or acquired from its environment, are considered poisonous. Unfortunately, there is no known remedy to counteract the injected poisons.

The manta or devil rays are very large. The record California specimen, a female, was 18 feet wide and weighed 2310 pounds. In southern waters they are known to reach about 22 feet in width and about 3000 pounds in weight. Fortunately they have neither the equipment nor the habits to mistake man for food—these animals use their gill apparatus to filter tiny, free-swimming life. However, one habit tends to cause consternation among humans in small boats. Characteristically, these giants make spectacular leaps out of the water, falling back with crashes like gunshots.

The skates are the quiet, serene members of this suborder, but they follow the general habits already outlined for the entire group. They are not known to harm man in any direct way.

Suborder SQUALOIDEA (Sharks)

Diagnosis: gill slits on side of body; body generally torpedo-shaped; pectoral fins not enlarged.

Although some sharks resemble rays in appearance and habits, most can be considered the wolves of the sea. Prior to the recent and perhaps only temporary warming of eastern Pacific Ocean waters, there was little, if any, danger to Americans from sharks. This fact is emphasized by a 1950 publication, "California Sharks and Rays," of the California Bureau of Marine Fisheries. At that time, the possibly dangerous sharks occasionally were sighted out at sea; there was only one coastal California record, in Morro Bay, of the most dangerous man-eater, the great white shark. Since that time, there have been many incidences of humans being either killed or dismembered, as well as records of close calls, along the California Coast. Now (1963), the shark danger still may be greater along our Pacific shores than along our Atlantic and Gulf coasts; however, fewer attacks in California waters have occurred in the last two years. This lessened danger also seems to be related to a most recent decrease in temperature from the high of a few years ago.

Sharks are predators of the marine world. In the main they feed upon various kinds of fishes. To accomplish this they use many rows of small to large, very sharp teeth. Perhaps the most spectacular aspect of their feeding is the so-called "feeding frenzy." If considerable prey is available, a single shark may chop and tear the prey. This releases blood into the water and draws other sharks. Apparently if there is enough prey and if sufficient blood is released, the sharks will go into a frenzy, ripping and tearing one another as well as the prey animals. Reports of such frenzies by human observers frequently describe a "boiling of blood red water" and sometimes the sharks biting or crashing into the boats of the observers.

The closest association between small sharks and man probably involves the nuisance value and damage brought about by the animals' getting caught in fish nets. The larger sharks are dangerous to swimmers and small boats. However, the largest sharks, such as the whale shark and basking shark, would not attempt to eat humans. Their teeth are very small and probably incapable of cutting food; feeding is accomplished by filtering microorganisms with the modified gills. Although these giants of 30 or more feet could cause considerable damage if they charged swimmers, they are not likely to do so. They tend to stay a little distance offshore and are somewhat sluggish, seemingly unaffected by the close proximity of boats or swimmers.

CLASS OSTEICHTHYES (Bony Fishes)

Diagnosis: common fishes; skin with bony scales of three types (sometimes absent) and with slime or mucus glands; skeleton of bone; fins of variable distribution, but both paired front (pectoral) and rear (pelvic) and unpaired medial fins usually are present; jaws and fin rays present; gills supported by bony arches and covered by a bony flap (operculum); sexes separate, fertilization usually external but may be internal and eggs hatch internally; larva is often present and unlike the adults in form; fresh-water and marine (Figures 16.11 through 16.15).

The bony fishes, also called true fishes, are not "modern" because they possess a bony skeleton. Bone is a very ancient character in vertebrates. This is the case in spite of there being no bone in living jawless fishes, a condition that can be associated with their tendency towards a parasitic way of life. In this respect, it is very probable that ancient jawless fishes had not only a bony skeleton, but also jaws and fins.

Another "strange" characteristic of true bony fishes is the ancestral position of the air, or swim, bladder and the lung. The lung was the ancestral feature and was readily available for the offshoot of land vertebrates. Through modification of the lung, the air bladder developed. Modern fishes, having an air bladder, use this structure as a hydrostatic organ to regulate their depth in water. An increase in air content causes the fish to rise and a decrease causes the fish to descend.

Subclass CHOANICHTHYES (Choanate Fishes)

Diagnosis: primitively torpedo-shaped and tapering at both ends, living forms slender to thick; nostrils (choanae) connect to the mouth cavity; paired fins with a median lobe; apparently not now found in North America; fresh-water or marine; all living fossils.

ORDER CROSSOPTERYGII (Lobe-finned Fishes)

Diagnosis: heavy bodied; marine (Figure 16.11).

Until very recently the lobe-finned fishes were of little interest except to students of animal relation-

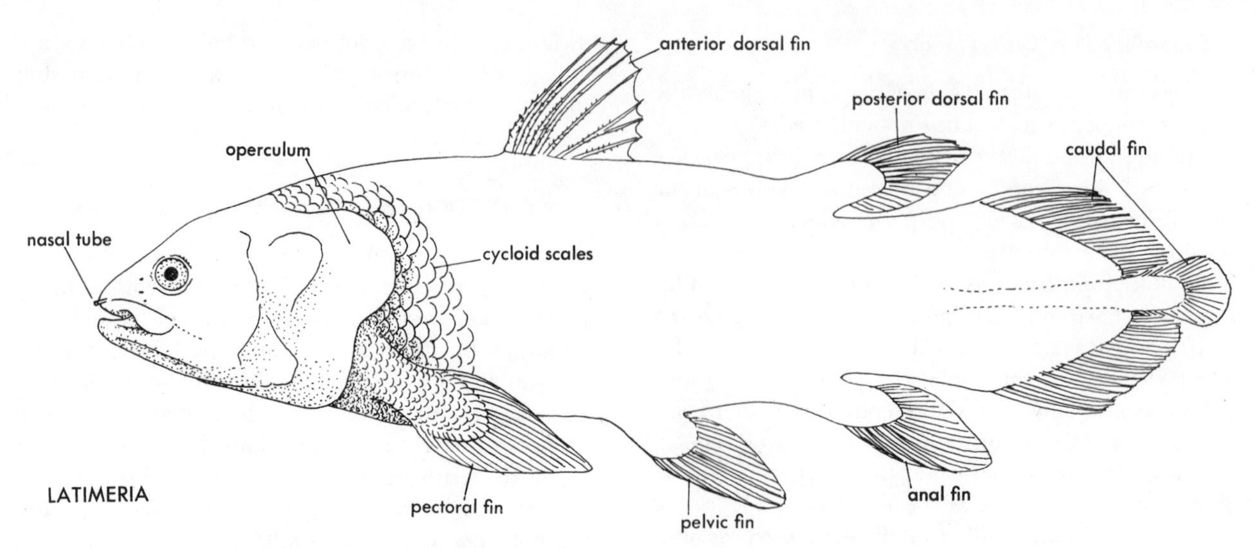

Figure 16.11 The living fossil *Latimeria*, a marine crossopterygian. (From Malcolm Jollie, *Chordate Morphology*, Reinhold Publishing Corp., New York, 1962.)

ships. Their zoological interest stems from a general belief that they were the ancestors of land vertebrates. This premise is made because of the very short developmental step necessary from their skeleton to that of a limbed, land vertebrate. The "step" is outlined in some detail in the fossil record, strongly indicating a gradual transition from fresh-water lobe-fins to fresh-water amphibians.

Although there are frequent reports of weird creatures in the sea and such reports usually can be discounted, in 1939 a commercial fisherman captured a living lobe-fin off East London, South Africa. Up to that time zoologists were sure that lobe-fins had been extinct for about 70 million years. Since World War II additional specimens have been collected. At the present time the fish is known to inhabit deep waters in the vicinity of the Comoro Islands, north of Madagascar.

Finding this animal was truly remarkable. Who was to expect a deep-sea representative of an ancient fresh-water group? Also, who was to expect a living animal very similar to its ancient ancestor? The living animal would not have been out of place if it had been found with its fossil relatives.

ORDER DIPNOI (Lungfishes)

Diagnosis: slender-bodied; fresh-water.

Three living genera and five species now represent the lungfishes. These five Dipnoi might be considered "living fossils" because they are not very different from their ancestors which were early offshoots from the ancestral lobe-fins. Of the living lungfish genera, *Neoceratodus* (one species) is found in the rivers of interior Queensland, Australia, *Protopterus* (three species) in the upper Nile River Basin of Africa, and *Lepidosiren* (one species) in the swampy region of the Paraguay River and adjacent Gran Chaco River in South America (Figure 16.12).

The early development of lungs in bony fishes is of interest. These structures evolved in fresh-water forms and probably resulted from selection of chance hereditary changes in areas of periodic stagnation or drying of fresh water. The selection for lungs, then, was first associated with periods during which many fresh-water species had difficulty in surviving in their fresh-water environment. Under such conditions, lungs would allow survival. The effectiveness of lungs can be seen in modern species. Lungs enable the Australian species to survive in the stagnant waters of drying pools; however, if ponds dry completely the animals die. The other two living genera can survive the complete drying of ponds. As their ponds dry, they burrow into the bottom mud, and, as the mud dries hard, the fish assume a coma-like, dormant state until the rains restore their ponds. This behavior is known to have been an ancestral condition, because fossil lungfish burrows with the fish remains in them have been found.

Subclass ACTINOPTERYGII (Ray-finned Fishes)

Diagnosis: includes all North American bony fishes; nostrils do not connect to the mouth cavity;

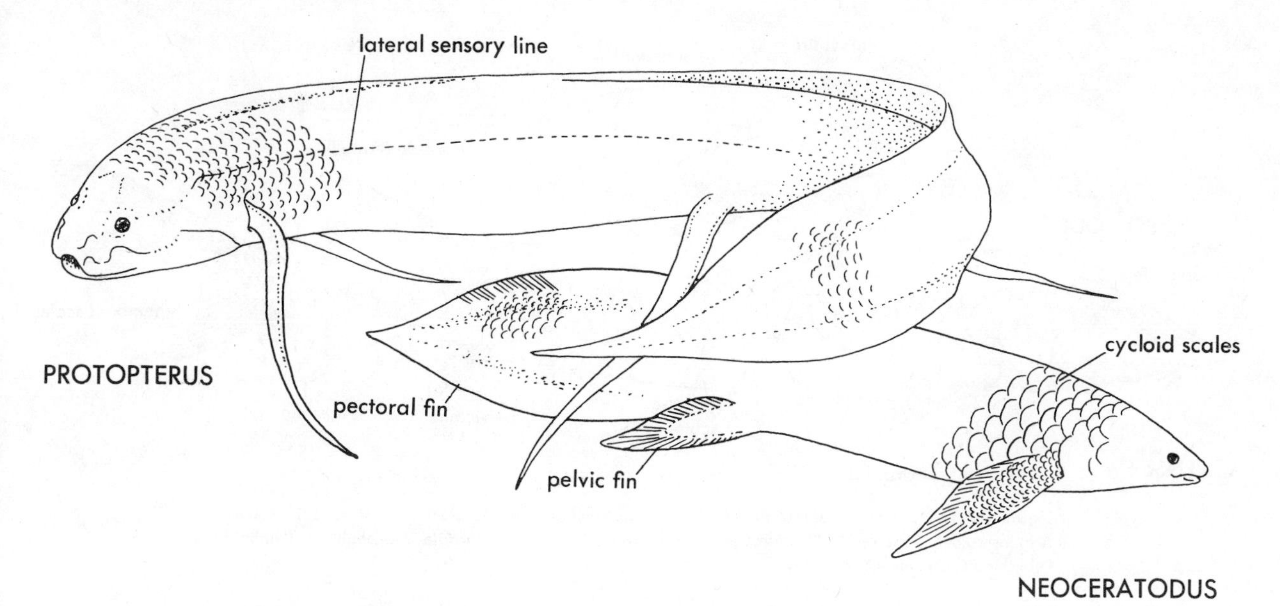

Figure 16.12 General appearance of two of the living lungfishes. (From Malcolm Jollie, *Chordate Morphology*, Reinhold Publishing Corp., New York, 1962.)

paired fins with bony rays, but without basal lobe portion; fresh-water or marine; three superorders, all represented in North America (Figures 16.13, 16.14 and 16.15).

Superorder Chondrostei (Primitive Ray-finned Fishes)

Diagnosis: North American species: backbone deflected upward into upper lobe of tail; tail fin strongly bilobed, the upper lobe usually larger than the lower; body species without scales or with longitudinal rows of bony plates; skeleton mostly cartilaginous; fresh-water and marine.

The primitive ray-finned fishes have an example of the ancestral lunged condition in the living African bichirs. These animals, including about ten species of true bichirs and a so-called reed fish, also display the ancestral covering of thick and shiny bony scales (Figure 16.13).

The two North American types are the paddlefish, or spoonbill, of the Mississippi and the more widely distributed sturgeons (Figure 16.14). Most of our

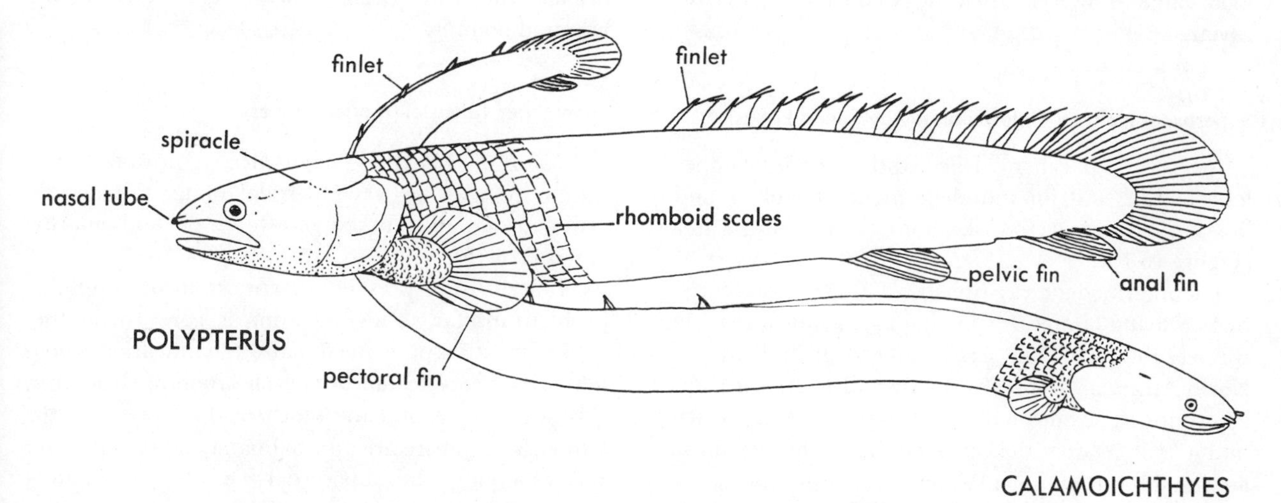

Figure 16.13 The two living genera of African chondrostians, a bichir (*Polypterus*) and reed fish (*Chalamoichthyes*), Order Polypterini, Superorder Chondrostei. (From Malcolm Jollie, *Chordate Morphology*, Reinhold Publishing Corp., New York, 1962.)

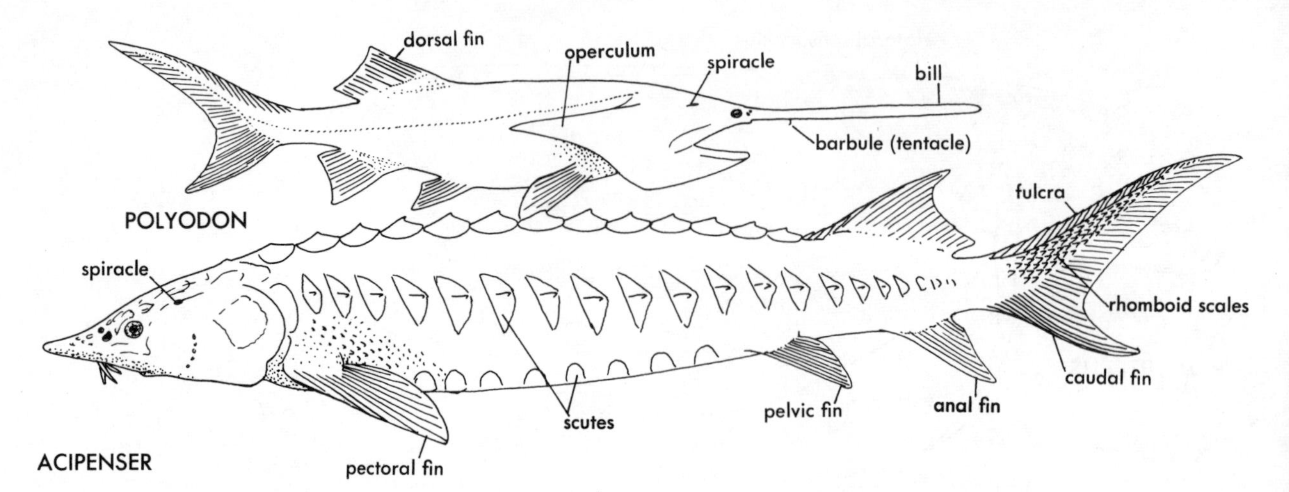

Figure 16.14 External features of *Polyodon,* a paddlefish, and *Accipenser,* a sturgeon. Order Acipenseroidei, Superorder Chondrostei. (From Malcolm Jollie, *Chordate Morphology,* Reinhold Publishing Corp., New York, 1962.)

sturgeons are fresh-water species, but there is a marine form in the Atlantic.

Paddlefish can usually be recognized by their paddle-shaped snouts and their almost complete lack of scales. They attain a length of 6 feet and feed upon small bottom invertebrates which are strained by the gill apparatus.

Sturgeons are shark-like in form but are unique in having five rows of bony plates along the body. They reach a length of about 10 feet. Their diet is varied; food items include aquatic plants, invertebrates, and smaller fishes. Despite their size and palatability, sturgeons often are considered of little food value; however, their eggs are the source of caviar.

Superorder Holostei (Intermediate Ray-finned Fishes)

Diagnosis: backbone deflected upward into upper lobe of tail; tail fin rounded; mouth terminal and bearing strong teeth; skeleton bony; fresh-water (Figure 16.15).

The intermediate ray-finned fishes are represented by two living families. One family includes a single species, the bowfin or fresh-water dogfish found in North America from Texas east and southern Canada south. The bowfin does not have its snout drawn into a beak as does the other family. The bowfin is an inhabitant of quiet waters, generally living in weeds and mud of lakes, rivers, and swamps. It is well known for its nest-building habits and ability to survive in small amounts of water. This animal is a voracious, pugnacious carnivore that feeds upon mollusks, crustaceans, insects, and other fish.

The other family is represented by a single genus, containing about eight species of beaked fish, the gars. Gars are found east of the Rockies in the greater Mississippi drainage, but are also found in the West Indies and well down into Central America. Gars are long, slender fishes that are protected by a heavy covering of overlapping plates and by long, thin teeth. In general, they are fish predators that quietly stalk their prey and swallow it whole. The fact that they stalk their prey may seem surprising, because they have been known to grow to over one hundred pounds.

Superorder Teleostei (Modern Fishes)

Diagnosis: backbone not deflected upward, fuses into a more or less symmetrical plate; tail usually symmetrical and forked; fresh-water and marine (Figure 16.15).

Modern fishes present an almost insurmountable problem insofar as identification is concerned. Because any attempt at meaningful identification would necessitate very technical consideration of structures, this taxon is beyond the scope of this book. In the United States there are approximately 600 fresh-water species alone. The Superorder Teleostei, containing over 20,000 species, includes the fishes most familiar to us. For example, teleosts include herring, salmon,

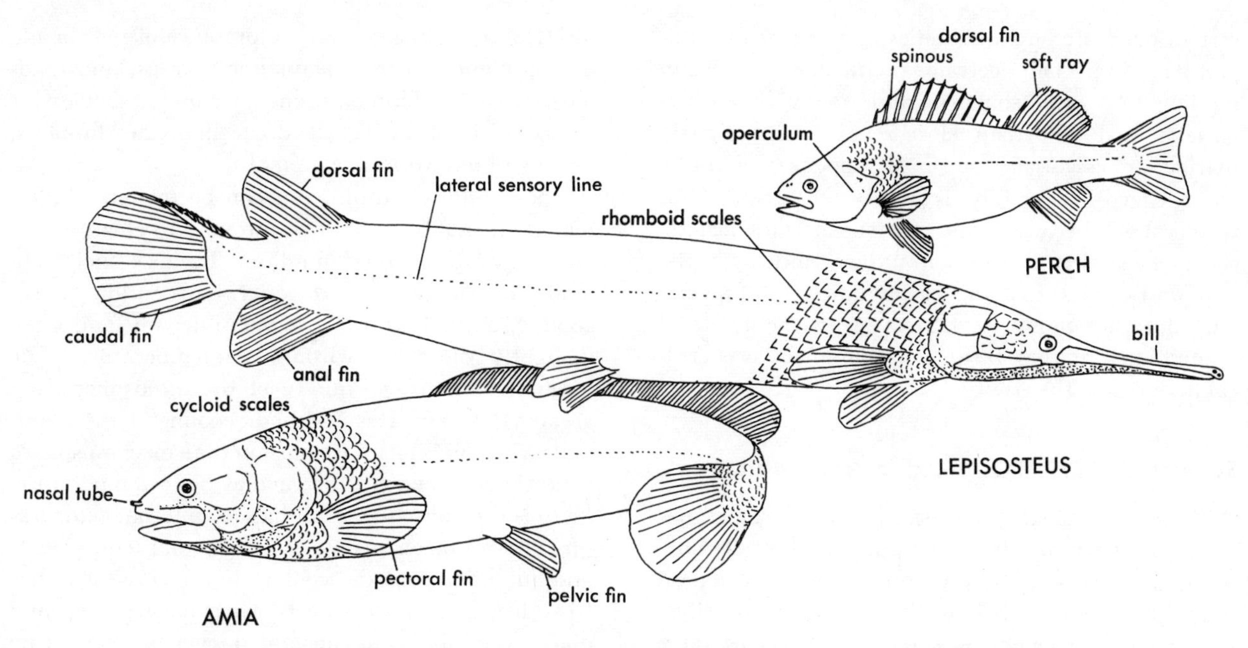

Figure 16.15 Holostean (*Amia*, a bowfin, and *Lepisosteus*, a gar) and teleostean fishes. (From Malcolm Jollie, *Chordate Morphology*, Reinhold Publishing Corp., New York, 1962.)

trout, flying fish, eel, codfish, catfish, minnow, perch, mackerel, flounder, and the "weird" deep sea fishes. They are animals that can be found in almost any fresh or salt waters of the world at almost any depths. Because of their number and diversity of aquatic habitats, they might be called the rulers of earth's waters.

We shall content ourselves with a brief and very general mention of their life cycle. Most fishes gather in breeding swarms, and sperm and eggs are shed simultaneously. Characteristically, many eggs are laid. The eggs hatch into a larva that is barely reminiscent of the adult, and after a variable period the larva assumes the adult form.

Some modern fishes display interesting modifications of the general reproductive pattern. Female surfperches retain the eggs within their bodies and bear the young alive, a phenomenon also found in the guppies and their allies. Although many teleosts merely shed their eggs in water, some build nests. The sticklebacks, for example, have elaborate courtships, build nests of varying complexity, and often remain to protect the nest and eggs.

The salmon are of particular interest because many spend most of their lives in the sea, but at the time of breeding return to their "hatching stream." In the headwaters of these streams a simple nest is scooped out of the bottom of the stream, the female lays her eggs in the nest, and the male fertilizes the eggs. In the Atlantic salmon most males die shortly after fertilizing the eggs, although many of the seemingly exhausted females drift down the breeding stream, regain the ocean, and survive. Both sexes of Pacific salmon die after reproducing.

A truly remarkable breeding pattern is found in the fresh-water eels. The American eel breeds in the vicinity of Bermuda, and the eggs develop into larvae which take one year to reach the United States. After metamorphosis, the young eels migrate up our eastern fresh-water streams. However, the really remarkable eel is the European form. It breeds in much the same area as ours but the young take two years to reach the European coast. However, approximately another year is taken before the completion of metamorphosis and reentry into the fresh-water streams.

LAND VERTEBRATES: SUPERCLASS TETRAPODA

Although most of Tetrapoda occur on land and are four-legged, we are hard pressed to provide a common name that truly describes all of them. "Land vertebrates" presents difficulties because many amphibians (especially certain salamanders), certain reptiles (the sea snakes), and many mammals (whales, seals and their close relatives) are strictly marine or essentially so. "Tetrapods," literally, "four-legged," probably is no better than "land vertebrates," because some (the snakes) are legless; some (the sirens) have only front legs; and some (the seals and whales) have the legs modified into flippers. Therefore, for those not familiar with the limits of amphibians, reptiles, birds, and mammals, it is critical to diagnose the group.

Superclass TETRAPODA (Land Vertebrates)

Diagnosis: mostly terrestrial, but sometimes aquatic, vertebrates; body streamlined generally only in aquatic species; usually with two sets of paired limbs, but often with one pair, none, or modified limbs; when the body is covered with scales there are no gills; specialized, generally mobile, neck bones and a neck region usually present; distinct joint between head and neck (or neck bones).

The above diagnosis gives a general description of usual features, but is so interlaced with exceptions or things difficult to determine as to be exasperating to the reader. Unfortunately, any characters that are truly diagnostic are difficult to observe and, as a rule, require the study of internal features. Therefore, for full appreciation of the limits of the Tetrapoda one must make such studies or become familiar with a number of representative species.

CLASS AMPHIBIA (= BATRACHIA) (Amphibians)

Diagnosis: skin moist and glandular, without scales; usually two pairs of legs, without paired fins; paired nostrils lead to the mouth; respiration by gills, mouth, throat, lungs and/or skin; sexes separate, eggs with jelly envelopes, laid in water or moist places (rarely retained), larvae usually aquatic (often metamorphose within the egg when eggs are laid on land); adults restricted to moist places, often aquatic; larvae herbivorous or carnivorous, adults typically carnivorous.

This class includes four living orders, the salamanders, the sirens, the frogs and toads, and the tropical caecilians. The amphibians, literally meaning "dual or double life," are named for the tendency of a great many to spend their developmental stages in water and their adult life on land. Typically, they have a moist, slimy skin owing to the presence of mucus and poison glands. Most salamanders, frogs, and toads have two pairs of limbs; sirens have only a single pair of limbs, the front legs; and caecilians are limbless, usually blind, worm-like animals.

The habitat of amphibians can be related to their moist skin and body temperature and to environmental temperature and humidity. Because their skin tends to lose water and water evaporation causes cooling, amphibian body temperature on land often is slightly below the environmental temperature. The lower the relative humidity of the atmosphere, the greater the water loss and body cooling of these animals. Amphibians have no internal mechanisms to control body temperature; actual body temperature, then, is the consequence of lack of internal temperature control mechanisms, environmental temperature and humidity, and the cooling due to loss of water. In addition, the loss of water when they are on land places amphibians in constant danger of death from drying. The above conditions indicate the reason why the best land habitat for amphibians is a moist, humid area. Moreover, owing to their dependence upon environmental temperature, amphibians usually are not found in perpetually cold or hot areas. In addition, because their skins are permeable to water, there are no marine amphibians. In spite of these various limitations on habitat, especially those of temperature and water, amphibians are fairly wide ranging, being found in moist areas from the deserts (including Death Valley) to the proximity of glaciers.

Because of environmental limitations and the fact that amphibians cannot move great distances, it might seem that only a few habitats would be suitable for them throughout a year. However, there are various ways in which these animals can exist in places that seem to be unfavorable. Since they need not spend their entire annual cycle on the surface of the land, some can retreat to water during the dry season. However, most go underground to a depth having relatively constant conditions of temperature and moisture throughout the year. Also, many amphibians go into coma-like states (summer aestivation and winter hibernation) that reduce their physical requirements (e.g., for food). Other amphibians avoid unfavorable environments by burrowing into the mud bottoms of ponds and streams or by moving into springs, caves, or deep cracks in rocks. The duration of their subsurface existence depends upon local conditions such as temperature and amount of moisture present.

Owing to climatic conditions, North America's amphibian activity varies throughout the year. The activity peaks in the spring (the breeding season), becomes low in the summer, rises in the fall, and drops again in the winter.

These seemingly unimportant animals like almost any group of animals are a major environmental force in their habitats. They are mainly carnivorous, feeding upon various smaller animals; in turn, they are eaten by certain fishes, snakes, birds, mammals, and invertebrates. They contribute to soil formation by burrowing into and aerating the soil and by adding humus to developing soil. Their eggs provide habitats for certain green flagellates and hosts for certain parasitic fungi. Their bodies (mainly through moisture loss and body mass) influence environmental temperature, moisture, light, and wind in restricted areas.

Very few amphibians have specialized food habits; their food habits are generalized and resemble those of many other animals. Amphibian diet is dependent mostly upon the size of the animal and its method of getting food, the habitat in which it lives and hunts for its prey, and the relative abundance and size of food organisms available when the amphibian feeds. Within these very general and minor limitations, there are seasonal and age changes in food intake. Seasonal changes are associated with seasonal abundance of prey and seasonal movements of amphibians and prey from habitat to habitat. Age, or life cycle, changes in food are typical, even when larval and adult food habits are much the same. Such changes normally occur as a result of differences in size among the various age groups. In addition, these different age feeding habits must be considered of some survival value, because the different age groups within a species show little competition for the same food. In conclusion, amphibian food habits are very generalized, but show sufficient differences among age groups to be of benefit to individual species.

Amphibian food is located by fairly simple sensory mechanisms. In aquatic forms, sight, chemical reception, touch, and vibration reception are the primary mechanisms. Aquatic individuals use these senses to seek or become alert when waiting for possible prey. Land forms tend to use vision, smell, and "hearing" to locate and then to seek or await possible prey.

Upon locating food, amphibians take their prey in different ways. Aquatic amphibians use their teeth to seize their prey or merely engulf the prey with water and swallow the prey after expelling the water. Those amphibians using their teeth may simply swallow prey, first crushing it with the teeth; with larger prey, the amphibians may first dismember it by shaking, rotating it and their own bodies, or by pressing the prey against the substrate. Terrestrial amphibians with small tongues may use much the same methods as aquatic forms. However, those land species with large, fleshy tongues flick out their tongues and capture their prey with a sticky mucus secretion on the tongue. Smaller food is merely swallowed, but larger food is crushed with the teeth, torn with the aid of the feet, or pressed against the substrate. Land amphibians either stalk their potential food or wait for it to come within reach.

ORDER GYMNOPHIONA (= APODA) (Caecilians)

Diagnosis: worm-like, without legs or leg girdles, tail short to absent; skin smooth and moist, glands including some that eject an irritant; skin transversely folded, some species have scales embedded in the skin at the base of the folds; tropical, invertebrate predators, and moist ground burrowers; reproduction typically with internal fertilization, eggs laid near water or retained, larva aquatic or developing in egg (Figure 16.16).

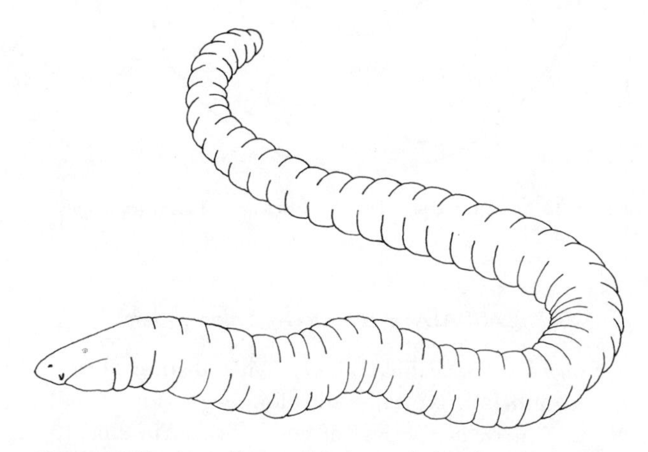

Figure 16.16 A caecilian or "blind worm," *Caecilia* (to about 18 inches long).

ORDER TRACHYSTOMATA (Sirens)

Diagnosis: eel- or snake-like, body with distinct head, trunk, and tail, all with two anterior legs only; skin smooth and moist, without scales; fertilization probably external; eggs laid in water; larvae aquatic and resemble adults; three species strictly aquatic and limited to Atlantic Coastal Plain, southeastern states, Mississippi drainage, and northeastern Mexico (Figure 16.17).

The sirens normally are included within the Order Caudata. However, there is sufficient anatomical and paleontological evidence to suggest their independence from salamanders and perhaps to assume they are more closely related to caecilians.

Figure 16.17 *Siren*, one of the two living genera of sirens (to about 3 feet long).

ORDER CAUDATA (= URODELA) (Salamanders)

Diagnosis: lizard-like, body with distinct head, trunk, and tail, typically with four legs, (four in all North American species) of equal size; skin smooth and moist, without scales; fertilization external or internal; eggs laid in water, on land, rarely retained; larva resembles adult, often aquatic, many larvae develop within eggs laid on land and a very few larva are developed in the female (Figure 16.18).

Salamanders have many other names regularly applied to them. For example, certain aquatic forms are called hellbenders, congo eels, or newts (or water-dogs). However, we shall use "salamander" to apply to all Caudata.

The word "salamander" dates back to mythology, referring to a mythical animal having the power to endure fire without harm. These amphibians probably were associated with this myth because on occasion they crawl out of logs placed into fires. In general appearance, they resemble lizards; however, salamanders have a smooth, moist skin rather than a dry, scaly one. Most of these amphibians are retiring in their habits in that they do not attempt to "fight off" predators. Some rely upon poisonous skin secretions to discourage predators. Another has poison glands in its tail, and will swing its tail in the direction of disturbance. If strongly pressed, this animal sheds its tail, a behavior similar to that of many lizards. A few salamanders sometimes bite potential predators and humans handling them, but the Pacific giant salamander is the only formidable "fighter" in North America. The latter species may also bite humans and is known to have killed a garter snake.

Salamanders are carnivorous throughout their life history. The primitive pattern of life history involves courtship and egg-laying in water, the hatching of gilled larvae that are otherwise much like the adults, and metamorphosis to the adult form. The adults may be terrestrial, only coming back to ponds during the spring breeding season, or may be gilled and never leave the water. However, most salamanders (mostly in one family that lacks both lungs and gills) do not have an aquatic stage. These terrestrial lungless salamanders (lung function is taken over by the mouth, throat, and parts of the skin) lay their eggs in moist, usually hidden, spots on land. Their eggs develop into a larval stage which transforms to the adult before hatching. A very few land salamanders bear their young alive, the mother giving nourishment to the developing young.

ORDER SALIENTIA (= ANURA) (Frogs and Toads)

Diagnosis: head broadly joined to body, without neck or tail; four legs, hind legs longer for leaping; skin smooth to warty, moist, without scales; fertilization usually external, eggs usually deposited in water and hatch to a tadpole larva (polliwog), adults aquatic or terrestrial; eggs may be carried by males in variously distributed brood pouches (Figure 16.19).

The Anura or Salientia are called frogs or toads. These common names have no meaning insofar as re-

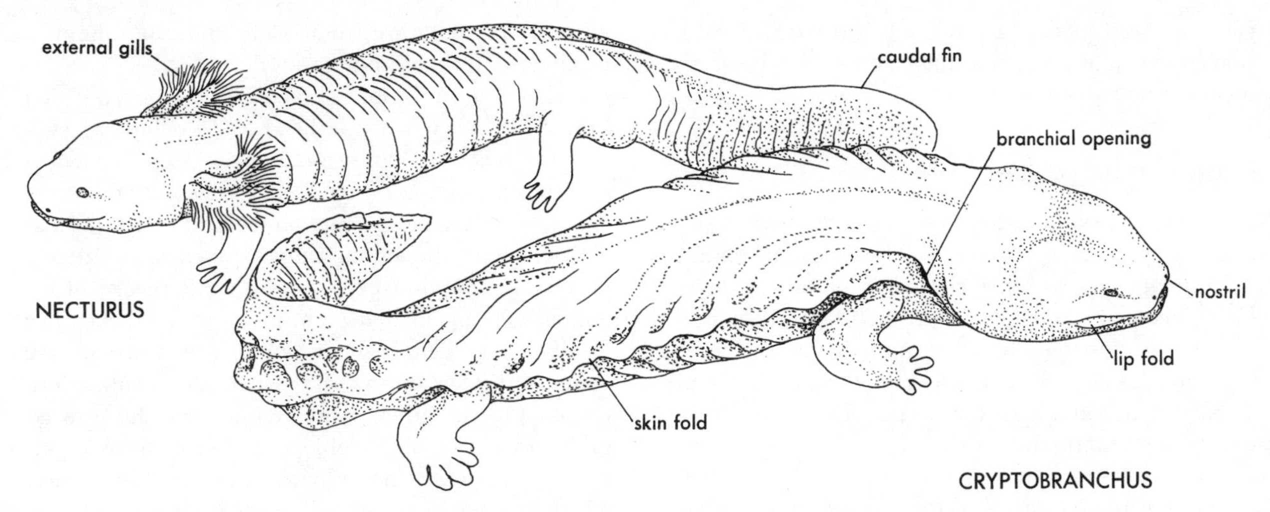

Figure 16.18 Two aquatic salamanders, *Necturus,* the mudpuppy, and *Cryptobranchus,* the hellbender. (From Malcolm Jollie, *Chordate Morphology,* Reinhold Publishing Corp., New York, 1962.)

lationships are concerned, because frogs and toads occur in the same genus. In general, frogs are aquatic forms having smoother skins, slimmer bodies, and longer hind legs than terrestrial toads.

Anura protective devices against enemies are similar to those of salamanders in that they are primarily defensive rather than offensive. When cornered, frogs and toads usually bloat and assume a squatting position tight to the substrate, or rely upon skin poisons to discourage predators. American frogs tend to be restricted to such habits. However, there are African frogs with poison and fangs to discourage predators and perhaps kill some food.

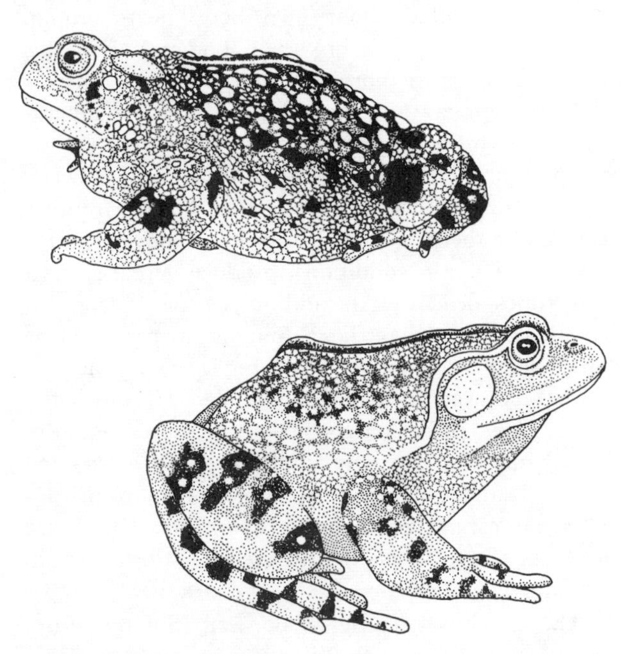

Figure 16.19 A toad, *Bufo* (to 7 inches long), and a frog, *Rana* (to 8 inches long). (After Dickerson.)

The sexes of our adult anurans can usually be determined by various external sexual differences. Only the male tailed-frog has a tail, an organ for internal fertilization. In most anurans only the breeding males have horny pads on the thumbs, fingers, and/or forearms. In many toads and tree frogs the breeding males have a darkening of the throat.

North American species lay their eggs in water. Adult toads and many frogs migrate from land during rains to their aquatic breeding habitats. The time of pond entrance is a noisy period (in many species the males croak or produce other breeding calls that attract the females), because hundreds of individuals congregate at localized breeding sites. In many species, the males clasp the females and sperm is shed simultaneously with the eggs. The egg hatches into a tadpole, a vaguely fish-like, highly aquatic larval stage. The tadpoles, or polliwogs, in contrast to the adults are usually plant feeders, but many are scavengers, and spadefoot toad larvae are carnivorous. Tadpole life extends from two weeks in some spadefoots and other toads to two years in some frogs. Metamorphosis involves marked changes: the tail and gills are lost, and the gill slits close; the digestive tract is shortened; the eyes are shifted in position; the jaws and skin are modified; and the forelimbs appear. In general, these changes are related to the transformation from aquatic, plant-eating habits to terrestrial, meat-eating habits.

CLASS REPTILIA (Reptiles)

Diagnosis: skin not moist and glandular, but dry and horny, usually covered with scales or plates; usually four legs with five-clawed toes, but legs may be reduced or absent, without paired fins; paired nostrils lead to mouth; respiration by lungs; sexes separate, eggs laid or retained in the female; no larval stage; greatest abundance in warm areas, terrestrial, fresh-water and marine.

The reptiles include four living orders: the turtles, the snakes and lizards, the crocodilians, and a single species, the tuatara. Their bodies are covered with dry, cornified skin. In many forms, scales or scutes cover the body. They are the first vertebrates so far mentioned that produce a land type of egg. These eggs are large, contain much yolk, and are protected by leathery or calcareous shells. The eggs usually are laid, but some snake and lizard females retain the eggs within their bodies until hatching.

Unlike amphibians, reptiles can live and be active in dry places, because their more impervious skin retards water loss. In reptiles, the greatest environmental restriction is temperature. Although their body heat is obtained from the sun, body temperature is a somewhat complex organismal-environmental relationship. Body temperature is not the same as that of the environment. Within limits, an active reptile approaches a constant body temperature, which implies some internal temperature regulation. Temperature is regulated as follows:

When a reptile's body temperature is below optimum, the animal basks in the sun. This practice brings its temperature up to the optimum, or normal activity range. Attaining this temperature is expedited in some species by their being dark colored when their temperature is below optimum range and lighter colored when it reaches this range. This helps them, because a dark surface absorbs more sunlight and heat than does a light surface. The normal activity range consists of temperatures best suited to life activities such as feeding and reproduction. To maintain this range and not rise to a semilethal, or even killing, body temperature, the reptiles alternate their activity between cooling shade and warming sunshine. When retreat to shade is insufficient to keep the temperature from rising above optimum, a reptile usually goes underground.

Related to duration of activity is the so-called "third eye" on top of the head and behind the eyes of many species. This structure might be likened to an exposure timing device, because even if an animal can still maintain a temperature within its normal activity range, the animal moves underground after a particular period of exposure. In this regard, if an animal gets insufficient exposure during the earlier part of a day because of extreme temperature, it may come out later in the day when the temperature drops. On the other hand, reptiles may have to go underground or under objects because the environment does not provide sufficient heat for their activity. They then come out when the environment provides sufficient heat to arouse them from their retreat.

The above emphasis of a normal activity range shows that the cold-blooded, variable-temperatured reptiles show some similarity to the so-called warm-blooded, or constant-temperatured birds and mammals. Reptiles' normal activity range, usually within 80 to 108° F., is comparable to the temperature range actually displayed by many birds and mammals. The latter, then, are not really much different from reptiles. The main difference between the two groups is that reptiles are dependent upon their external environment for a source of body heat and birds and mammals produce their own body heat through chemical activities within their bodies. For this reason, reptiles are more accurately called ectotherms (outside temperature) or heliotherms (sun temperature) and birds and mammals, endotherms (inside temperature). One additional difference between ectotherms and endotherms is that healthy reptiles can have either very low or very high body temperatures, but both conditions produce lethargy and sometimes death. An additional consequence of ectothermism is that these animals do not need as much food as endotherms. This gives reptiles an advantage over birds and mammals. However, the endotherms, because their normal body temperature allows immediate activity at all times, can more often react to danger or any other aspect of their environment almost instantaneously. (Further details are given in the discussion of vertebrate dormancy in Chapter 17.)

The activity of reptiles is not very different from that of amphibians. Reptiles display approximately the same annual activity cycle. The main functions performed during the year are reproduction, feeding, obtaining moisture, basking, and escaping harm. Spring is the peak of activity and is the breeding season in most species. This spring peak is gradually reduced to the minimal activity of summer. In the summer the reptiles may go into a coma-like aestivation or become crepuscular or nocturnal rather than diurnal. Activity then rises in the fall and once again is reduced in the winter. In the latter period some reptiles go into a coma-like hibernation. These activities are generally associated with temperature and moisture rather than light.

Reptiles are more independent of their environment than are amphibians. Although reptiles depend upon the environment as a heat source, they are more independent of this heat. For example, in the same habitat and at the same time different species may maintain different normal activity temperature ranges. Reptiles show much greater tolerance to low humidity and saline waters. Some reptiles actually live in the ocean. Notable are the poisonous sea snake and certain turtles which are almost completely marine, but some lizards and crocodilians are often found in marine shore waters.

Reptiles also show greater diversity in protective methods against their enemies. Most reptiles can leave an area of danger faster than amphibians can; some reptiles have protective armor (turtles), head spines (horned lizards), shed their tail (lizards), have offensive weapons (especially venomous snakes), or are protectively colored to blend into their background (many species). Amphibians tend to have these protective devices to a lesser degree.

ORDER TESTUDINATA (= CHELONIA) (Turtles)

Diagnosis: body oval, generally within a bony shell; shell of rounded dorsal carapace and flat ventral plastron; jaws with horny sheaths, without teeth; anus a longitudinal slit; sexes separate, eggs buried by female; terrestrial, fresh-water, and marine (Figure 16.20).

All Testudinata may be called turtles; however, the name "tortoise" is sometimes reserved for land species and "terrapin" for certain edible fresh-water species.

Turtles have been turtles since the Triassic, about 200 million years ago. There are now about three hundred species widely distributed over the warmer parts of the earth. Although there are fresh-water

Figure 16.20 *Clemmys*, a fresh-water turtle. (After Van Denburgh.)

and marine species, all turtles lay their eggs on land in an underground cavity that is excavated by the female's hind legs. Turtles usually have external sexual differences, the male usually having a longer tail and the anal (actually cloacal) opening farther out on the tail. Males also tend to have the underpart of their shells concave.

Turtles tend to be unspecialized in food habits, eating either plant or animal food. In general, they obtain their animal prey either by waiting for it to come along, or by stalking it and lunging at it. Although turtles lack teeth, they have rather sharp, horny jaws that cut cleanly like scissors. Small food items may be engulfed whole but usually are grabbed by the jaws and cut and torn while being held by the turtle's front feet. Large prey must be eaten piecemeal.

Aquatic species usually pull their prey underwater before eating it. One aquatic species has remarkable feeding specialization. The alligator snapping turtle of the lower Mississippi Valley and Gulf Coast has a worm-like tongue. This turtle opens its mouth while underwater and wiggles its tongue. The tongue lures fish, and when a fish comes the turtle snaps its mouth closed.

ORDER RHYNCHOCEPHALIA (Tuatara)

Diagnosis: one living species, lizard-like; jaws with teeth; anus a transverse slit; unique skeletal characteristics; sexes separate, female lays eggs; alternate habitats (see Figure 16.21).

The only living species is the lizard-like tuatara of New Zealand. It alternates its activities among land,

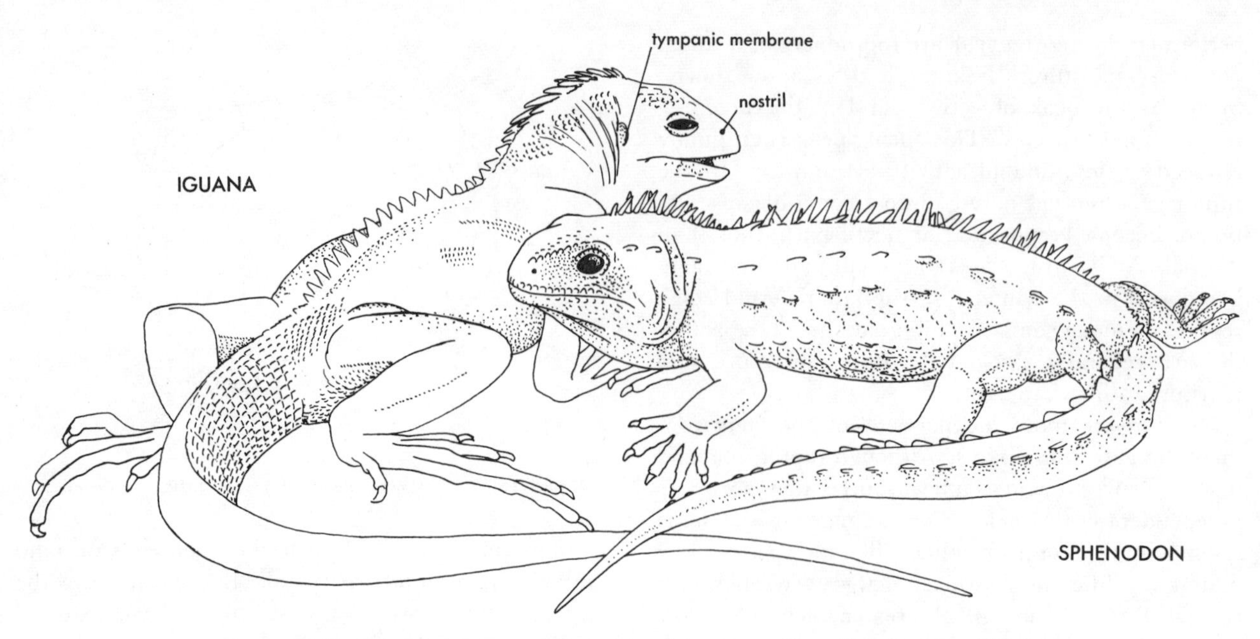

Figure 16.21 A lizard, *Iguana,* and the tuatara, *Sphenodon.* (From Malcolm Jollie, *Chordate Morphology,* Reinhold Publishing Corp., New York, 1962.)

burrows, and water where it feeds upon fishes, insects, and worms. Although the tuatara lays eggs like other reptiles, the eggs take a long time (about thirteen months) to hatch. The tuatara is called a "living fossil" because the only other known members of the order are fossils from Permian to Eocene, about 250 to 40 million years ago.

ORDER SQUAMATA (Lizards and Snakes)

Diagnosis: skin of horny scales or plates, outer layer periodically shed; jaws with teeth; anus a transverse slit; sexes separate, both suborders lay eggs or female retains them; terrestrial, fresh-water, or marine.

Although the combination of lizards and snakes into a single order might be surprising, it is standard practice because none of the so-called differences between lizards and snakes are completely reliable. There are many snake-like lizards and some snakes that bear vestiges of legs. Also, there are some Squamata families that cannot be assigned definitely either to the snakes or to the lizards.

Suborder SAURIA (= LACERTILIA) (Lizards)

Diagnosis: body usually slender and four-legged; point of lower jar bone usually fused; eyelids usually present; tongue usually unforked; North American species either with four legs or with movable eyelids (Figure 16.21).

Most of the lizards of North America lay eggs, but in some the eggs are retained within the female's body and the young born alive. Bearing of live young is characteristic of some alligator, scaly, horned, and night lizards, as well as the California legless lizard.

Lizards capture their prey with the teeth or flick it into the mouth with the tongue. They rarely swallow the food whole; they crush small prey and shake or tear large prey before swallowing. Some lizards are very adept at "lapping up" insects.

The only poisonous lizards are the beaded lizards, the Gila monster and the Mexican beaded lizard. Venom is produced by a lower jaw gland and secreted at the base of several lower jaw teeth between the teeth and lips. The teeth are a crude venom-injecting apparatus, but they can inflict serious and sometimes fatal bites to man. The venom-producing structure is thought to be a carryover from an ancestral structure, because the teeth of poisonous lizards are entirely adequate for most defensive purposes and for eating. The poisonous lizards feed upon bird eggs and fledglings, nestling mammals, and other small lizards.

The only beaded lizard found in the United States, the Gila monster, ranges from northern Mexico across Arizona, and barely enters Nevada, Utah, and

New Mexico. Although it lives close to the Colorado River, its presence has never been authenticated in California. This large, heavy-bodied, seemingly sluggish lizard can, as some humans have discovered to their sorrow, move very rapidly. It would be difficult to touch an aroused Gila monster without being bitten. In nature they are usually active at night and at dusk, moving about with a slow, awkward gait. They are powerful diggers who can construct their own daytime retreats and can dig 3- to 5-inch deep holes in damp sand to lay and cover their eggs.

The Gila monster is the only protected venomous animal. An Arizona law protects both it and horned lizards from being sold, given, offered for sale, or exchanged, except by written permission of the Arizona Game and Fish Commission.

Suborder SERPENTES (= OPHIDIA) (Snakes)

Diagnosis: body elongate, legless; lower jaw bones unfused anteriorly, joined by ligaments; eyelids absent; tongue usually forked; United States species with only claw-like vestiges of hind limbs (Figure 16.22).

Most snakes, like most lizards, lay eggs. However boas, pit vipers (including rattlesnakes), garter snakes, water snakes, and certain others bear their young alive. Some snakes brood their eggs.

Nonvenomous snakes use their long, slender incurved teeth to grab their prey. Small prey is frequently grabbed and swallowed alive and is killed by the powerful digestive juices. Larger prey is killed by suffocation or constriction before being swallowed. The whipsnakes and racers seize and suffocate their prey by pushing it against the ground or some convenient object, sometimes the snake's own body. The kingsnakes are examples of snakes that constrict their prey, a process also causing the prey to die of suffocation.

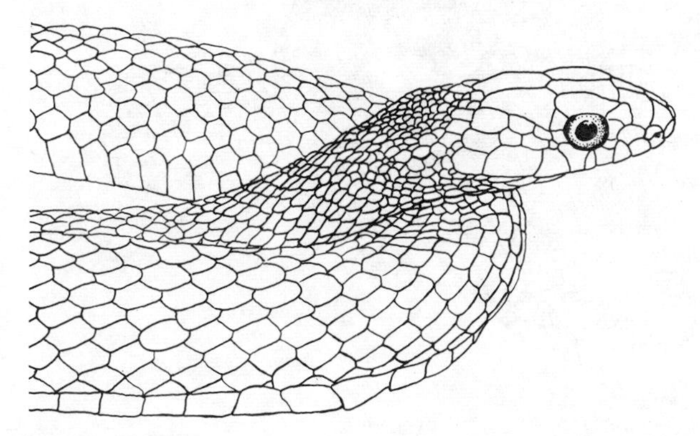

Figure 16.22 The head and part of the body of a snake, *Masticophis*. (After Ruthven.)

Venomous snakes secrete a poison that paralyzes or kills and starts digestion of the prey. There are two main types of poisonous snakes, those with fangs in the front and those with fangs in the rear of the mouth. The front-fanged snakes in turn have two groups, those with fixed and those with movable fangs. In the movable-fang snakes, pit and Old World vipers, the fangs are on a movable bone at the front of the upper jaw. This apparatus allows the fangs to be larger than those of fixed-fang snakes, because they can be folded against the roof of the mouth when not in use. The fixed-fang snakes, including the cobras and their relatives, have immovable, shorter fangs. In the front-fanged snakes each venom gland is connected by a duct to a hollow fang and there is a series of replacement fangs behind each functional fang; the fangs are replaced periodically. The rear-fang snakes have two or three pairs of rear teeth enlarged and grooved along the front or side. These "fangs" are frequently separated by a gap from the other teeth. The poison flows down the grooves into the victim, a relatively inefficient process. Frequently, rear-fang snakes must chew their victim to get the venom into it.

Snake venom is a mixture of digestive juices and poisonous proteins that can be classified as either nerve- or blood-affecting. Venomous snakes usually have both types, but a preponderance of one or the other. The nerve-affecting venom is most efficient on "cold-blooded" animals; the blood-affecting, on "warm-blooded" animals.

The lower jaw in most snakes is specialized to swallow prey without the necessity for chewing. The jaw is loosely attached to the skull. Also, the jaw consists of two bones connected at the "chin" by muscle, elastic tissue, and skin. These specializations allow a snake to make an extreme gape with the mouth, and the teeth are specialized so that the snake can pull its way over its prey. Swallowing is facilitated by the inward curving of the teeth, which prevents prey from escaping outward, and independent movement of each side of the jaw, allowing one side to obtain a forward "grab" while the other side holds fast.

There are four types of poisonous snakes in the United States. The cobra family is represented by two species of coral snakes. The pit viper family is represented by the cottonmouth or water moccasin, the copperhead, and about fifteen species of rattlesnakes. The pit vipers are named for a remarkable sensory structure they possess. This structure, the pit, is found between the nostril and eye and is larger than the nostril. It is a heat and infrared light receptor, that locates prey by detecting temperature differences as small as 1°F between the snake's body and surroundings.

There should be no doubt about the danger of rattlesnake bites. People die every year in the United States from such bites. However, certain rattlesnakes probably secrete insufficient venom for their bites to prove fatal, and proper treatment of any bite almost always prevents death. Because proper treatment is necessary, anyone likely to contact these animals should be familiar with *correct* treatment. The best source of such information can be found in a monumental work, Laurence M. Klauber's "Rattlesnakes, their habits, life histories, and influence on mankind," a 1956 publication of the University of California Press. Finally, do not have the false sense of security that rattlesnakes do not bite before they rattle. Many an individual has stepped on either a sleeping or cold rattlesnake and some of these individuals were bitten without the snake's ever having rattled. Also, many people have observed rattlesnakes watching them and later got these snakes to strike at a stick, all without the snake's rattling.

ORDER CROCODILIA (= LORICATA) (Crocodilians)

Diagnosis: lizard-like; jaws with teeth; anus a longitudinal slit; sexes separate, eggs laid; freshwater, somewhat terrestrial, semimarine (Figure 16.23).

Crocodilians are now represented by over twenty species in three families, the crocodiles, the alligators and caimans, and the gavials. Although the young crocodilians might be confused with some lizards, there is a simple way to distinguish between the two groups. Crocodilians have the anus in the form of a longitudinal slit; lizards, in a transverse slit. Among the largest crocodilians now living are the two United States forms, the American alligator which once was sufficiently undisturbed by man to grow to a length of about 20 feet, and the American crocodile which once grew to about 23 feet. Few of these animals now grow more than 10 feet long in the United States. How-

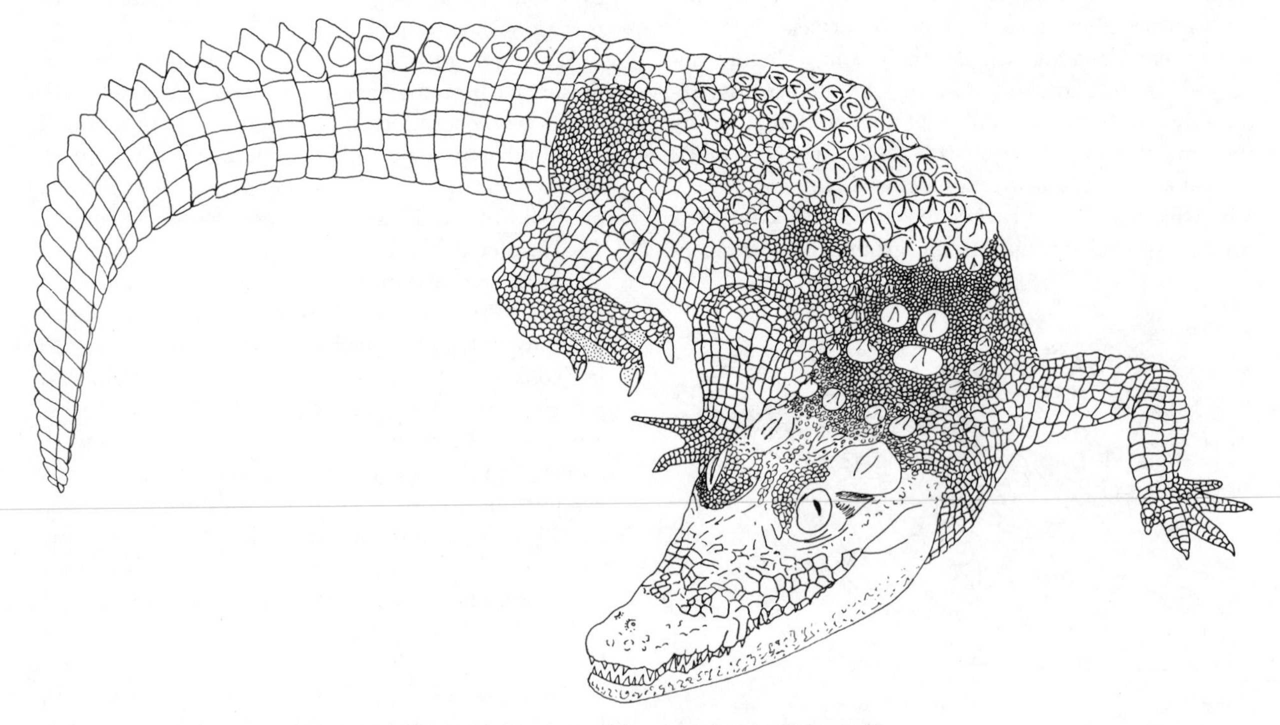

Figure 16.23 A crocodilian, *Crocodylus* (to 23 feet long).

ever, the crocodile still attains a fair size in the West Indies, Columbia, and Central America.

Crocodilians generally lay their eggs in piles of gathered vegetation. The decaying of the plants is believed to produce sufficient heat to "incubate" the eggs.

These animals are alert predators that tend to stalk their prey. Food is quickly seized by the peg-like teeth. Small prey is crushed and swallowed; larger prey often is drowned and torn by the spinning of crocodilians, and then is gulped down in sizeable chunks. Such predaceous capabilities are a danger to man. Some crocodilians use their tails to fell large prey (this has happened to man) and knock the prey into its jaws.

The crocodilians date back to the Triassic Age, 225 million years age, and are closely related to dinosaurs. The word "dinosaur" is applied to some of the orders of the Subclass Archosauria, or "ruling reptiles," and the Order Crocodilia is part of that subclass of the Class Reptilia.

CLASS AVES (Birds)

Diagnosis: skin not moist and glandular (except on the tail, which has an oil or preening gland), dry, with both scales and feathers; four limbs, front pair modified as wings that usually enable flight, hindlimbs variously modified for support or swimming; mouth modified as a beak; paired nostrils lead to mouth; respiration by lungs; body temperature internally regulated; sexes separate, eggs laid typically in some sort of constructed nest, no larval stage; terrestrial, marine, and fresh-water.

Subclass ARCHAEORNITHES (Lizard Birds)

Diagnosis: includes *Archaeopteryx*, the Jurassic toothed bird that clearly shows the reptilian ancestry of birds.

Subclass NEORNITHES (True Birds)

Diagnosis: includes all modern birds and some extinct, tooth-bearing forms; modern birds divided into two taxa; walking or flightless birds include ostriches, cassowarys, emus, elephant birds (extinct for several centuries), moas (extinct for several centuries), kiwis, rheas and tinamous (flying forms); most walking birds are African, South American, or Australian; remaining birds constitute modern birds (Figure 16.24).

Enumeration of the many living orders and any other identification of birds is beyond the scope of

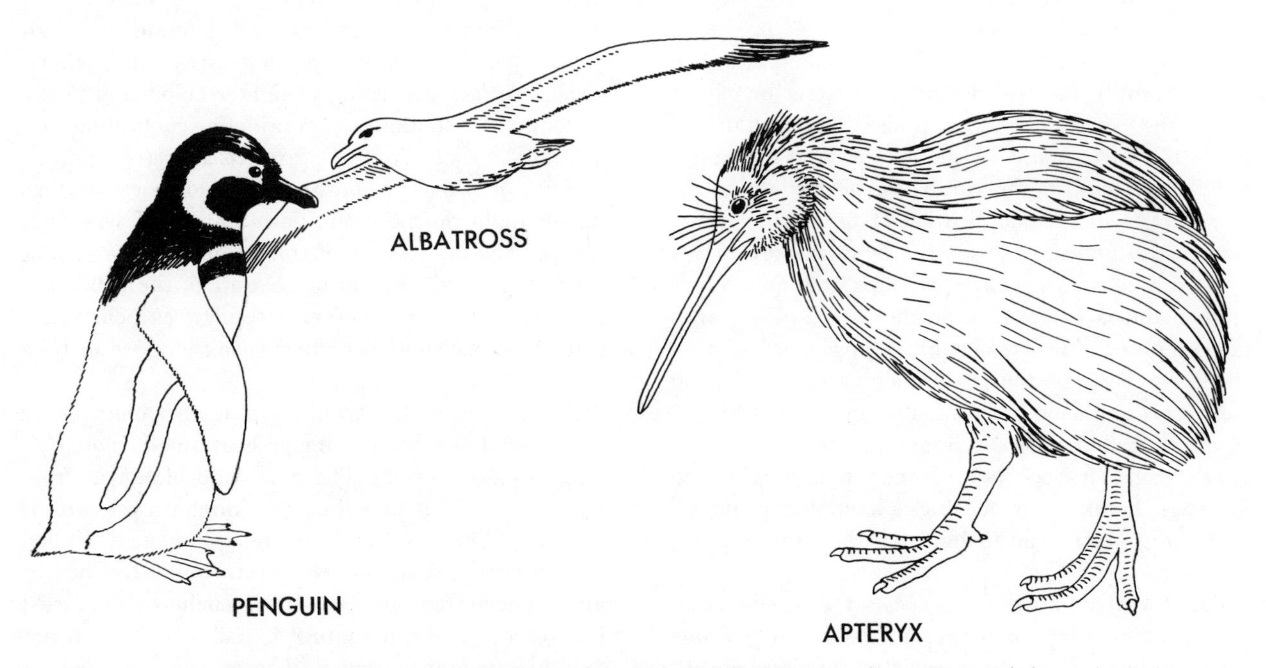

Figure 16.24 Some variation extremes of the birds, including *Apteryx*, a kiwi. (From Malcolm Jollie, *Chordate Morphology*, Reinhold Publishing Corp., New York, 1962.)

this book. Any adequate consideration of identification must treat species. For this purpose, there are many field books or guides. The present discussion is limited to certain aspects of the biology of birds.

RELATIONSHIPS

Perhaps the most obvious and definitely the most distinctive external characteristic of birds is the body covering of feathers. Feathers are modified reptilian scales. Therefore, the development of feathers and the presence of scales on the legs and feet indicate the close relationship between birds and reptiles. In fact, in one way of looking at relationships, birds are more closely related to crocodilians than crocodilians are to other living reptiles.

EXTERNAL FEATURES

Feathers are an obvious external adaptation to flight. These structures are extremely light and strong, their weight does not detract greatly from the ability to fly, and feather strength is necessary for flight. Other external structures show various modifications for ways of life other than flight. For example, bills are adapted for such things as eating seeds, spearing fish, tearing prey, obtaining flower nectar, catching fish and insects, and boring into wood. Also, feet are modified for such things as perching, walking, wading, swimming, and tearing prey. However, we shall confine our discussion to feathers.

A typical feather consists of two main parts, the *shaft* ("stem") and two flexible *vanes* (one on either side of the "shaft). The shaft is also composed of two parts, the lower *calamus* without vanes and the upper *rachis* that supports the vanes. Some birds have an *aftershaft*, or smaller duplication of the main feather structure attached to the shaft. The vane also has two parts, an *outer vane* which overlaps the next outer feather and is narrower than the *inner vane*. Vanes are composed of progressive branchings starting from the shaft. *Barbs* are the first branching of a vane from the rachis and each barb is like a tiny feather due to branches called *barbules*. Some barbules have their lower edges frayed into slender filaments called *barbicles*. Finally, some barbicles have slender hooks, or *hamuli*, which tend to hold together and support the vanes.

Adult feathers are of four types. The *contour* feathers form the outline or contour of the bird and include the flight feathers. *Down* feathers are hidden beneath the contour feathers and have no hamuli. *Filoplumes* are hair-like feathers. *Powder-down* feathers are modified down that grows throughout life but in which the barbs degenerate into a fine powder. Powder-down is found only in a few groups of birds such as herons and bitterns. These various feather types are distributed in one of two ways. The flightless birds, such as ostriches, rheas, emus, and penguins, have the feathers uniformly distributed over the body. However, most birds have feather tracts and areas where there are no contour feathers.

Plumage coloration is due either to the presence of chemical colors in the feathers or to the structure of the feathers. The main chemicals are carotenoids, producing red, orange, and yellow, and melanin, producing black, gray, brown, and reddish-yellow. Feather structure results in white, where all light of all wave lengths of the visible spectrum is reflected; blue, where blue light is reflected as a result of barb structure; green, where the cuticle enclosing the barbs is transparent yellow and blue light is reflected through the cuticle; and irridescent colors, where light is reflected either through broadened and twisted, overlapping barbules containing rod-shaped melanin granules, or through feathers having spherical melanin granules.

No matter how color is produced it is assumed to serve one of four purposes. Three types are considered protective because they may "hide" the animals from potential predators. *Cryptic coloration* blends the bird into its background and is found in marsh birds, sparrows, ground nesting birds, and others. *Counter shading*, consisting of lighter coloration below to counteract shadows, is considered concealing and is found in shorebirds. *Deflective coloration* is found in various birds having conspicuous colors or markings during flight but no such "flash markings" when not flying. The fourth type of coloration, *epigamic*, is not easily explained. Epigamic coloration, the brilliantly colored feathers of one sex, is sometimes believed to bring the sexes together during courtship or to be a means of sex recognition.

Birds go through a sequence of feather changes, or *molts*. After the adult plumage is attained, molts fall into an annual cycle. The molts and plumages from hatching to adult and the adult annual cycle are as follows: The first, or hatching, plumage is called *natal down*. This completely covers young hatched at an advanced stage of development such as shorebirds; it is scarce on the immature hatchlings, such as are found in songbird species. The *postnatal molt* pushes natal down to the tips of developing *juvenile plumage*. Juvenile plumage first appears as stiff quills that soon rupture to unfold the juvenile feathers. The *post-juvenile molt* of July to September removes the juvenile feathers. Most birds complete this molt prior to migration; however, the wing and tail feathers of juveniles are often retained, allowing the distinguishing of young from adults. The areas of post juvenile molt are replaced by the *first winter plumage*. These feathers generally are like those of the adult except for slight differences in color pattern due to retained juvenile feathers. The *prenuptial molt* removes the winter plumage in late winter or early spring and allows the *nuptial* or *breeding plumage* to develop. Few birds have a complete molt to produce the breeding plumage. Next is the *postnuptial* or *annual molt* in July, August, or September in which all feathers are replaced. The flight feathers usually are shed one at a time in sequence at this time; however, certain birds (e.g., rails, coots, and some ducks), shed all the flight feathers at the same time and are flightless for a period.

INTERNAL FEATURES

Birds also display various internal adaptations for flight. This is especially apparent in their metabolism and their skeletal, muscular, and respiratory systems. The tremendous energy necessary for flight is reflected in the high metabolism, indicated by a high heart rate (300 in the chicken and 400 to 600 in the chickadee—1000 when frightened) and by a high body temperature. Although body temperature fluctuates about eight degrees in birds, bird temperatures in general are between 100 and 112°F. The skeletal system is very light, being built upon the hollow-girder principal. Lightness also is accomplished by the reduction and fusion of many parts. For example, the tail is reduced to a rudimentary structure, and the "hip" and leg bones are reduced and fused. However, strength is aided by processes on the ribs which cause the ribs partly to overlap one another, forming a total structure much like a rigid box. Their muscular system shows its greatest flight adaptations in the very large flight muscles. Finally, the respiratory system has many air sacs filling spaces in the body. These air sacs act both to keep the birds' temperature from rising too high and to maintain lightness of the body.

BODY TEMPERATURE AND DORMANCY

Birds and mammals are the only endotherms, or animals whose internal body processes produce their body heat. Also, these processes are regulated so that body temperature is fairly constant. Only reptiles among ectotherms, the vast majority of animals that obtain their body heat from the sun, approximate regulated body temperatures. However, reptilian regulation occurs only when the animals are active.

Torpid or coma-like states are well known in many mammals and other animals. However, until fairly recently not much was known about these states in birds. Coma-like states are now known to occur in some goatsuckers, hummingbirds, and swifts. In some of these birds, body temperature and other functions are depressed as much as in truly dormant mammals. So far this true dormancy in birds seems to be limited to the winter; hence, the phenomenon is hibernation (in summer, states of dormancy are called aestivation).

MIGRATION

Migration is a very complex phenomenon and even now is only beginning to be understood. Part of the difficulty might occur because various factors affect migration, and migration may not be a single phenomenon. To appreciate this fact, one must examine some of the conflicting patterns within migrating species. First, not all birds migrate north and south. Moreover, some birds migrate when temperature is mild and food is ample, whereas others migrate under opposite conditions. Some birds seem to migrate as a result of seasonal alteration of rainfall and drought; others seem to migrate in association with day length; the migration of still others simply does not seem to be related to much of anything. In addition, only a portion of some species migrate, and other species migrate irregularly or not at all. In spite of all these difficulties to understanding, if there is a single stimulus to migration, it is believed to be involved with the attainment of a particular functional state of the body, a state that might involve the activity of the pituitary gland in the brain.

Some more specific characteristics of bird migration may be mentioned. There are five main migration routes in the United States, more or less indicated by the long migrators. The distance of migration varies a great deal; some birds show very localized seasonal movements from place to place, while the Arctic tern travels 11,000 miles. Some migration is merely up and down mountains. In general, migration is a hazardous phenomenon; in times of inclement weather many birds may perish. (Further details are given in the discussion of migration in Chapter 18.)

NESTING

Most birds construct some sort of nest. The nest may be only a few twigs placed upon a particular site or it may be a very complex structure. However, some birds make no preparation whatsoever for the laying of their eggs. Nest building might be a joint effort of both sexes, a phenomenon where one sex supplies materials and the other constructs, or a single effort of one of the sexes. In the various possibilities of nest building either the male or female might take on any of the tasks; in some birds the male is the only sex involved in nest building and incubation of eggs.

Although many birds tend to nest away from other birds, most show interesting associations with other animals. Birds may nest in colonies of their own kind or mixed colonies with other species. Some mixed colonies do not seem to provide obvious benefits; however, instances where small birds nest very close to hawks and owls seem to be "protective" for the smaller birds. In addition, there are often invertebrates, usually insects, inhabiting birds nests. Some of these invertebrates are parasites on the nestlings or adults and others are nest-cleaning forms that remove debris from the birds' nests.

Although birds lay eggs, not all birds lay eggs in their own nests. Some birds, notably cowbirds and cuckoos, lay their eggs in the nests of other species of birds. In these "parasitic" birds the young tend to hatch and develop quite rapidly, factors that usually result in death to the offspring of the parasitized parents.

The young of birds are of two types, advanced or immature. The fairly advanced, feathered young hatch in a state that enables them to care for themselves. There is little if any posthatching care of such birds by their parents. Immature hatchlings lack feathers, have their eyes closed, and are almost completely dependent upon parental care. Advanced young birds include the ostrich and its allies, tinamous, fowls, gulls, shorebirds, cranes, ducks, geese, grebes, and loons. The immature condition is characteristic of penguins, cormorants, petrels, albatrosses, herons, storks, pigeons, owls, hawks, parrots, swifts, woodpeckers, and perching birds, including the sparrows and their allies.

TERRITORY

Many birds establish territories, areas actively defended against their own kind and, frequently, other animals. Territories are of two kinds, breeding and nonbreeding. Breeding territories may be for mating purposes only, but may also be for nesting and/or feeding. Nonbreeding territories are used for feeding, wintering, and/or roosting. Territories are usually established by the males and involve pursuit, plumage display, and fighting behavior toward outsiders. Singing is the proclamation and warning of territory. Females may or may not aid in defending a territory; however, females are almost always less active than males in expressing territorial behavior. Territorial behavior is a strong instinct; moreover, it is for the purpose of defending an area and not such things as protecting a nest, eggs, young, and/or a mate. Of course, this behavior does lead to such protection, as well as being a means of instigating a sexual bond, of limiting the bird population of an area, and of guaranteeing cover, nesting materials, and food for the birds of a given locality.

SONG

Various functions might be attributed to bird song. It seems to proclaim territory and warn against intrusion, act as a means of sex identification, and perhaps release excess energy. Most females do not produce true songs. Songs are simple to complex, usually entirely vocal, and few males cannot sing. The duration of individual songs is associated with the annual cycle. Full song comes with the establishment of territories, decreases or ceases during mating, resumes during nest-building, egg-laying, and incubation, wanes with caring of the young, and usually stops unless a second brood is reared. Most singing is from a conspicuous perch and mostly away from the nest. A singing male can be a very busy bird; one patient observer counted the 2305 songs of a male song sparrow in one day. However, songs usually are not equally rendered throughout the day; there are early morning and, to a lesser extent, evening peaks. Young males start singing relatively soon, within a month after hatching in some species. Experiments have shown that the basic song is inherited but its perfection is learned from the adults; experimental birds can be taught some different or modified songs.

CLASS MAMMALIA (Mammals)

Diagnosis: skin dry, more-or-less covered with hair, glandular; typically four limbs, variously adapted for walking, burrowing, climbing, flying, or swimming; whales and manatees lack hind limbs; paired or single nostrils lead to mouth; respiration by lungs; body temperature internally regulated; sexes separate, almost always an embryonic stage nourished by mother, females with milk-producing mammary glands for suckling young.

Subclass PROTOTHERIA (Egg-laying Mammals)

Diagnosis: specialized but primitive egg-laying mammals (egg-laying probably was not present in earliest mammals); possess many features of their reptilian ancestors; egg heavily yolked, with a flexible shell, and early development reptile-like; teeth only in young, adults with a horny beak but without an external ear pinna; mammary glands without nipples; includes one species of platypus and four species of spiny anteaters, or echidnas, in two genera; the five species constitute the single Order Monotremata (Figure 16.25).

The *platypus* grows to 2 feet long. Head flattened, with a sensitive, rubbery, duck-like bill; body chunky; tail flattened, beaver-like; feet webbed, with heavy claws; hair dense and velvety; semiaquatic; underwater predator on invertebrates, prey masticated with horny tooth plates; construct burrows in stream or lake banks, females construct longer burrows (up to 60 feet) with a side nesting chamber; females lay and incubate one to three eggs, which hatch in 7 to 10 days; young nurse by lapping milk from mother's hair; young enter water in about 4 months; found in eastern Australia.

The *echidnas* grow to about 20 inches long. Body rounded; head with an elongate, cylindrical beak; tongue can be extended to lap up insects, jaw with horny ridges to grind insects against ridged palate; tail a stump; legs short, three to five toes are clawed; hair coarse, some modified as spines; terrestrial insect predators; do not burrow; female lays one egg, carried in a pouch that is present during breeding season (pouch not the same as that of marsupials); young remain in pouch for a few weeks; young nurse by lapping milk from mother's hair; found in Australia, Tasmania, and New Guinea.

Subclass THERIA (Viviparous Mammals)

Diagnosis: females bear living young.

Infraclass Metatheria (Marsupials)

Diagnosis: females usually with an abdominal pouch (marsupium) or folds surrounding nipples; embryos usually develop without a placenta; newborn are premature "embryos" that crawl to pouch, attach to a nipple, and stay until fully developed; after devel-

Figure 16.25 The two living genera of monotremes, *Ornithorhynchus,* the platypus, and *Tachyglossus,* the spiny anteater. (From Malcolm Jollie, *Chordate Morphology,* Reinhold Publishing Corp., New York, 1962.)

Figure 16.26 A marsupial and a placental mammal. (From Malcolm Jollie, *Chordate Morphology*, Reinhold Publishing Corp., New York, 1962.)

opment, young may use pouch as a shelter; mostly Australian, also South American and the possum in North America (Figure 16.26).

Infraclass Eutheria (Placentals)

Diagnosis: without a pouch; embryos become well developed in association with a placenta; newborn often helpless, but are not embryonic; include all aerial, aquatic, and terrestrial mammals other than monotremes and marsupials.

We now turn to the final class of animal kingdom. The mammals are familiar to us because both man and many of his domestic animals—cats, dogs, cattle, sheep, goats, horses, and others—are members of this class. Again, discussion is limited to certain aspects of biology.

Mammals are a very successful group of animals. Moreover, they seem to be more independent of their environment than are most other animals. Mammals have an essentially constant body temperature that is maintained within a few degrees by internal body mechanisms (endothermism) which are found in no other animals except the birds. Few mammals are strictly diurnal or nocturnal; however, the brightest and darkest periods of the day tend to be times of inactivity. Among animals, mammal activities seem to be most controlled by their inner workings, or physiology, rather than by their environment.

MOVEMENTS

Mammals display nomadism, emigration, and migration; and most mammals have well-developed homing abilities. The homing sense may or may not play a part in the three kinds of movements. Even among the nomads, e.g., wolves, the seemingly aimless wandering is not strictly so, but is in relation to a defined route.

Emigrants on the other hand do not seem to use any "homing" sense. The desertion of its home by part or all of a species is at least partly due to overpopulation. Although United States mammals such as the eastern gray squirrel, snowshoe hare, beaver, pika, and woodrat, are known to emigrate, the most striking example is found in the mouse-like lemmings of the birch-willow habitat near the timberline of the high Norwegian mountains. These animals live on succulent grasses and roots and normally bear one or two litters of four or five young each year. Periodically, there is an enormous increase of reproductive potential; three or four litters are produced in the summer, the first litter is bearing young by August, and there are up to eleven young per litter. In addition to this high reproductive rate, the young show exceptional vitality and can ward off disease in a remarkable manner. Needless to say, these conditions lead to overpopulation and lack of food for the expanded population. The vast majority of the population then emigrates downhill, seemingly letting nothing stop them. Many perish from drowning when attempting to swim lakes, from predation, from disease, and other causes. The last lemming population remnants may reach the sea, swim out, and soon drown.

Migration, a homing behavior, does not present so confusing a picture. It is the seasonal regular departure from and return to a region. This phenomenon is most marked in birds, but is also found in some mammals, amphibians, fish, and invertebrates. The incentives for many migrations seem to be to obtain food and water, to avoid unfavorable climate, and to reach the breeding grounds. In considering a few mammalian examples, one sees that migration can be extremely localized or can involve great distances.

The California gray whale spends early winter to late spring along the California coast where the young are born. All whales then move northward to congregate in the Arctic Ocean and Okhotsk Sea. Later, cool weather and reproduction cause their return to the California coast.

All fur seals except the old bulls winter as far south as California—the old bulls winter either south of the Aleutian Islands or in the Gulf of Alaska. As the breeding season approaches, the old males move to the Pribilof Islands breeding grounds, where the bulls obtain a territory and await the females. Shortly thereafter the females complete their 3000 mile trip to the Pribilofs and within a few hours or days their pups are born. The females then are impregnated and spend much of their time in the sea, returning every two days to nurse their pups. During the entire three-month period until early August, the breeding males do not feed; they are too busy defending their harem and breeding ground against the "stag line" of nonbreeding males. In early August the males return to their wintering grounds, but the females remain until early November when their young of that year can accompany them to the female wintering grounds.

The hoofed animals display less remarkable migrations. The caribou show a circular counterclockwise movement in the winter and strike north in the summer. Their movement is then somewhat erratic before they return to the wintering grounds. Elk and our deer summer in high mountain valleys and usually move in the winter to the climatically less severe lowland areas where food is more abundant. Even the bison showed a migration pattern, one seemingly related to available food.

Local migrations are shown by the Norway, or brown, rat and certain meadow mice. Some brown rats spend the spring breeding period in fields, meadows, or ditches and with the coming of winter move into human habitations. Meadow mice spend the rainy season in fields and the summer drought period in meadows and other damp places.

In addition to the above conspicuous movements, there are occasional periodic movements on the part of many mammals. Most of these movements can be related to reproduction, climate, overpopulation, and/or available food.

ADAPTATIONS

Mammals have many adaptations to their environment. Many of these adaptations are independent of ancestry or relationship of the animals involved; these features are a response to ecological factors. For example, in Australia, the marsupials, pouched mammals, have structures similar to those of our placental mammals. Adaptations of Australian marsupials are indicated by carnivorous, herbivorous, burrowing, jumping, and gliding forms. Also, two distantly related groups comprise the whales. In spite of similar adaptations in form, due to their environment, the toothed and baleen whales are believed to have separate origins. Therefore, in the following discussion of mammalian ways of life neither ancestry nor relationships are considered.

Aquatic mammals have certain features that are related to their mode of life. Heat loss is reduced either by a heavy layer of fat called blubber, or a heavy coat of fur. Swimming modifications are related to the form of the animals. The fish-like whales use body and tail undulations and the limbed mammals usually depend on the limbs. Most truly aquatic animals have a streamlined, often fish-like, shape. Also, in direct proportion to the aquatic nature of certain animals, there is a reduction of hair, increase in blubber, and increase in size.

Extreme aquatic specialization is seen in whales, which like all aquatic mammals have a land mammal ancestry. Whales have near perfect adaptation to a watery environment. They are streamlined; the neck is shortened; the hindlimbs absent, forelimbs paddle-like, external structures are reduced or absent; the tail is a propulsion organ; the single nostril is high on the head and has a valve to prevent water intake; eyes are adapted for under water; a special group of organs detect and recognize distant objects the animals can neither see nor hear; teeth are specialized for grasping or filtering; the air sacs of the lungs have muscles to prevent lung collapse under great outside pressure; and the blubber is a very thick layer.

Arboreal mammals have a way of life that allows them to escape many possible predators and to use another source of food. However, modifications for tree life are not as marked as those for aquatic life. In fact, many mammalian orders have arboreal representatives. The best-adapted species are not found in the United States; they are tropical animals. The New World monkeys have delicate hands, long limbs, and a long, prehensile tail that makes them very successful in trees. Another tree-adapted group, the sloths, have long toenails that are used to suspend the animals upside down from tree limbs. Sloth fur grows toward the backbone so it hangs toward the ground when the animals are hung upside down. Also, these animals often have camouflage in the form of green and blue-green algae growing on their fur.

No United States mammal is more than partly arboreal. The tree squirrel, for example, has only hand-like feet with long and flexible toes and sharp, strong claws, and a long bushy tail that is useful in breaking falls. Our flying squirrels have the same adaptations plus two folds of skin (from forelimbs to hindlimbs) that enables them to glide for some distance. In flying squirrels the tail is effective as a rudder during the gliding process.

Burrowing mammals show a range of modifications for their way of life. Animals such as ground squirrels, kangaroo rats, and prairie dogs are only partly modified. However, moles and gophers are examples of almost strictly burrowing, or fossorial, mammals. Their eyes are reduced, as are the external ears, but the senses of smell and touch are magnified. In addition, the limbs are short and strong and the claws are strengthened for digging.

Arctic animals acquire dense coats and thick fat or even blubber. In many the color matches seasonal changes in environment—many hares, weasels, foxes, and other animals are dark in the summer and white in the winter. Also, the external parts such as the ears and tail often become smaller, thereby presenting less surface area to give off heat. Finally, arctic mammals like reindeer and musk-oxen crowd together to conserve heat during periods of extreme cold. The exhaled air of these animals often creates clouds that can be seen from some distance.

Many desert mammals have specializations that aid water conservation. Although all animals have the ability to obtain water from even dry food, a process associated with body metabolism, some desert mammals have this highly developed. For example, kangaroo rats in the wild probably do not drink water. Many desert animals avoid the heat by burrowing, being nocturnal, and aestivating during the hottest and driest part of the year. Many desert species are seed gatherers and have cheek pouches to aid in this purpose. Finally, these animals tend to be jumping types, perhaps an aid to escape from predators in a fairly open situation.

SELECTED READINGS

VERTEBRATES, GENERAL

Blair, W. F. et al., 1957. *Vertebrates of the United States.* McGraw-Hill Book Co., New York.

Orr, Robert T., 1961. *Vertebrate Biology.* W. B. Saunders Co., Philadelphia.

Vessel, M. F., and E. J. Harrington, 1961. *Common Native Animals.* Chandler Publ. Co., San Francisco, Calif.

Young, J. Z., 1950. *The Life of Vertebrates.* Oxford University Press, New York.

FISHES

Axelrod, H. R., and L. P. Schults, 1955. *Handbook of Tropical Aquarium Fishes.* McGraw-Hill Book Co., New York.

Barnhart, P. S., 1936. *Marine Fishes of Southern California.* University of California Press, Berkeley, Calif.

Beebe, W., and J. Tee-Van, 1933. *Field Book of the Shore Fishes of Bermuda.* J. P. Putnam's Sons, New York.

Breeder, C. M., Jr., 1929. *Field Book of Marine Fishes of the Atlantic Coast.* J. P. Putnam's Sons, New York.

Clements, W. A. and G. V. Wilby, 1961. *Fishes of the Pacific Coast of Canada.* 2nd ed. Bull. Fish. Res. Bd. Canada, no. 68.

Coates, C. W. and J. Atz, 1954. Fishes of the World. In *The Animal Kingdom,* Vol. 3, bk. 4). Greystone, New York.

Eddy, S., 1957. *How to Know the Freshwater Fishes.* Wm. C. Brown Co., Dubuque, Iowa.

Herald, E. S., 1962. *Living Fishes of the World.* Doubleday & Co., Garden City, N.Y.

Hubbs, C. L., and K. F. Lagler, 1958. *Fishes of the Great Lakes Region.* 2nd ed. Cranbrook Inst. Science, Bloomfield Hills, Mich.

Innes, W. T., 1956. *Exotic Aquarium Fishes.* 19th ed. Innes Publ. Co., Philadelphia.

Lagler, K. F., J. E. Bardach and R. R. Miller, 1962. *Ichthyology, The Study of Fishes.* John Wiley & Sons, New York.

La Gorce, J. O., 1952. *The Book of Fishes.* National Geographic Society, Washington, D. C.

Lamonte, F., 1945. *North American Game Fishes.* Doubleday & Co., Garden City, N. Y.

Norman, J. R., 1947. *A History of Fishes.* 3rd ed. Ernest Benn, Ltd., London.

Schrenkeisen, R., 1938. *Field Book of Freshwater Fishes of North America.* G. P. Putnam's Sons, New York.

Schults, L. P., and E. M. Stern, 1948. *The Way of Fishes.* D. Van Nostrand Co., Princeton, N. J.

REPTILES AND AMPHIBIANS

Bellairs, A. d'A., 1957. *Reptiles.* Hutchinson's University Library, London.

Bishop, S. C., 1943. *Handbook of Salamanders.* Comstock Publ. Co., New York.

Carr, A., 1952. *Handbook of Turtles.* Comstock Publ. Co., New York.

Cochran, Doris M., 1962. *Living Amphibians of the World.* Doubleday & Co., Garden City, N. Y.

Conant, R., 1958. *A Field Guide to Amphibians and Reptiles.* Houghton Mifflin Co., Boston.

Goin, C. J., and O. B. Goin, 1962. *Introduction to Herpetology.* W. H. Freeman Co., San Francisco, Calif.

Mertens, R., 1960. *The World of Amphibians and Reptiles.* McGraw-Hill Book Co., New York.

Noble, G. K., 1931. *Biology of the Amphibia.* McGraw-Hill Book Co., New York.

Oliver, J. A., 1955. *The Natural History of North American Amphibians and Reptiles.* D. Van Nostrand Co., Princeton, N. J.

Pope, C. H., 1946. *Turtles of the United States and Canada.* Alfred A. Knopf, New York.

———. 1956. *The Reptile World.* Alfred A. Knopf, New York.

Schmidt, K. P., and D. D. Davis, 1941. *Fieldbook of Snakes of the United States and Canada.* J. P. Putnam's Sons, New York.

Schmidt, K. P., and R. F. Inger, 1957. *Living Reptiles of the World.* Doubleday & Co., Garden City, N.Y.

Smith, H. M., 1946. *Handbook of Lizards.* Comstock Publ. Co., New York.

Stebbins, R. C., 1954. *Amphibians and Reptiles of Western North America.* McGraw-Hill Book Co., New York.

Wright, A. H. and A. A. Wright, 1949. *Handbook of Frogs and Toads of the United States and Canada.* 3rd ed. Comstock Publ. Co., Ithaca, N. Y.

———. 1957. *Handbook of Snakes of the United States and Canada.* 2 of 3 vols. published. Cornell University Press, Ithaca, N. Y.

BIRDS

Berger, A. J., 1961. *Bird Study.* John Wiley & Sons, New York.

Gilliard, E. T., 1958. *Living Birds of the World.* Doubleday & Co., Garden City, N. Y.

Headstrom, R., 1949. *Bird's Nests: A Field Guide.* Ives Washburn, New York.

Hickey, J. J., 1948. *A Guide to Bird Watching.* Oxford University Press, New York.

Hoffman, R., 1927. *Birds of the Pacific States.* Houghton Mifflin Co., Boston.

Peterson, R. T., 1947. *A Field Guide to the Birds.* 2nd ed. Houghton Mifflin Co., Boston.

———. *A Field Guide to Western Birds.* 2nd ed. Houghton Mifflin Co., Boston.

Smith, S., 1945. *How to Study Birds.* Collins, London.

Van Tyne, J., and A. J. Berger, 1959. *Fundamentals of Ornithology.* John Wiley & Sons, New York.

Wallace, G. J., 1955. *An Introduction to Ornithology.* The Macmillan Co., New York.

Welty, J. C., 1962. *The Life of Birds.* W. B. Saunders Co., Philadelphia.

Wing, L. W., 1956. *Natural History of Birds.* The Ronald Press, New York.

MAMMALS

Anthony, H. E., 1928. *Field Book of North American Mammals.* J. P. Putnam's Sons, New York.

Booth, Ernest, S., 1950. *How to Know the Mammals.* Wm. C. Brown Co., Dubuque, Iowa.

Bourliere, F., 1954. *The Natural History of Mammals.* Alfred A. Knopf, New York.

Burt, W. H., and R. P. Grossenheider, 1952. *A Field Guide to the Mammals.* Houghton Mifflin Co., Boston.

Cahalane, V. H., 1947. *Mammals of North America.* The Macmillan Co., New York.

Davis, D. E., and F. B. Golley, 1963. *Principles in Mammalogy*, Reinhold Publ. Corp., New York.

Glass, B. P., 1951. *A Key to the Skulls of North American Mammals.* Burgess Publ. Co., Minneapolis, Minn.

Hall, E. R., and K. R. Kelson, 1959. *The Mammals of North America.* 2 vols. The Ronald Press, New York.

Hamilton, W. J., Jr., 1939. *American Mammals.* McGraw-Hill Book Co., New York.

———. 1943. *The Mammals of Eastern United States.* Comstock Publ. Co., New York.

Moore, C. B., 1953. *Ways of Mammals in Fact and Fancy.* The Ronald Press, New York.

Murie, O. J., 1954. *A Field Guide to Animal Tracks.* Houghton Mifflin Co., Boston.

Nelson, E. W., 1930. *Wild Animals of North America.* National Geographic Society, Washington, D. C.

Palmer, E. L., 1957. *Palmer's Fieldbook of Mammals.* Dutton, New York.

Palmer, R. S., 1954. *The Mammal Guide.* Doubleday & Co., Garden City, N. Y.

Sanderson, I. T., 1955. *Living Mammals of the World.* Doubleday & Co., Garden City, N. Y.

Seton, E. T., 1929. *Lives of Game Animals.* Doubleday & Co., Garden City, N. Y.

17 ECOLOGICAL FACTORS

The Environment

Are organisms slaves of their environment? In the sense that all living creatures require specific things of their surroundings and cannot withstand others, the answer is yes. Each of the physical and biological conditions of the environment is an ecological factor and has some influence upon life.

Physical factors of the environment include general climate, temperature, water, light, atmosphere, soil, fire, and topography. General climate is the most inclusive factor; it is probably the most important in determining the range of organisms. The other physical factors affect the local distribution of plants and animals. Of these latter factors, temperature and water are the most important for plants, because both are so closely affected by other physical factors that they often act as "measuring sticks" of their environment.

Biological (biotic) factors are the consequences of life activities. The biotic environment, then, is the influence of organisms on other living things. Naturally some of these factors are direct and of intimate nature; others are indirect. No matter how close or remote the relationships among the organisms of an area, each species is influenced by the other life around it.

In the present chapter many ecological factors, physical and biological phenomena, are discussed individually. However, it must be realized that any organism is subject to and responds to *all* environmental features simultaneously. Also, an environment is a synergistic phenomenon. A habitat is more than the mere sum of its parts. The parts acting together produce a dynamic total situation. Following the treatment of ecological factors are brief statements on ecological variation and ecological success.

LIMITING FACTORS

It is well known that humans like certain situations and dislike others. Of the conditions man dislikes, some are unpleasant, others are harmful, and many are lethal. The reactions of other organisms are much the same; however, each species responds in a particular manner to a given environment. These differential responses are indicated by the fact that some creatures may live in many unlike places and under a variety of conditions, whereas others have a limited habitat. This is not due to chance, but to unlike reactions to present and/or past ecological factors. The environmental factor or factors that cause such restriction of functions and partly determine the distribution of a species are called *limiting factors*.

TOLERANCE

Limiting factors exist when the basic conditions needed for growth and reproduction are absent. For an organism to be in a particular area, its *critical minimum* requirements for each factor must be present. This minimum, the *threshold*, is the lowest limit of a factor that produces or allows a visible effect in an organism, or is the amount of a factor that causes a minimum *rate* of response. Above the critical minimum, rate regularly increases with increase in the factor. However, any factor can become greater than a plant or animal can withstand, or can go beyond the *critical maximum*. Therefore, any species displays minimum and maximum *limits of tolerance*, including a range of conditions that are not limiting, for each environmental feature (Figure 17.1). Anything above or below these limits is lethal.

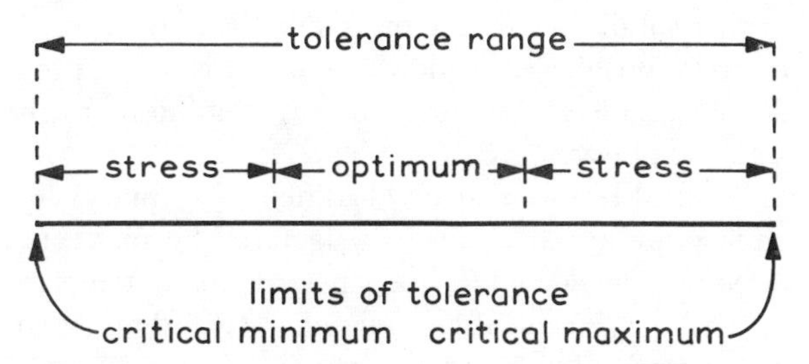

Figure 17.1 Features in an organism's tolerance to a single ecological factor.

Certain generalizations can be made about tolerance. First, it varies among species and within a single species. Within a species tolerance usually changes seasonally, geographically, and individually, and is allied to unique appearing or functioning seasonal, geographical, and individual variants within a species. Second, a species may have broad limits of tolerance for one factor and very narrow limits for another. Third, when a species is living near the critical limit for one factor, the limits of tolerance for other factors may be narrowed. An example of this would be a plant requiring more moisture than normal because of excessive heat.

Fourth, within limits of tolerance there is a narrow *optimum range* of conditions for an individual organism. Such optimum conditions may be necessary for specific life processes, for example, reproduction, to take place. Somewhere below the optimum range is the critical minimum, and somewhere above is the critical maximum. Between each critical level and the optimum range is a zone of physiological stress, upper and lower conditions of imperfect functional relation to an ecological factor.

Fifth, organisms are frequently found living outside the optimum range (but within their limits of tolerance) of one or more ecological factors. Sixth, environmental features tend to be most limiting during the period of reproduction, because early stages of the life cycle usually have less tolerance than do adults.

Finally, individual aspects of an organism's tolerance to environmental factors are generally hereditary. Therefore, tolerance is subject to mutation, natural selection, and evolution. Moreover, organisms eventually must mutate to survive ever-present geological and ecological changes. Any mutation, beneficial or detrimental, naturally is acquired by chance, and beneficial mutations become mandatory when environmental changes take organisms beyond the limits of tolerance of any part of their hereditary complex. Life cannot be static; it must evolve or perish.

ECOLOGICAL AMPLITUDE

The hereditary complex, or gene pool, that enables the particular reactions of an organism to its environment is expressed as an over-all *tolerance range* to all factors, called *ecological amplitude*. However, the gene pool is not uniformly distributed throughout a species; variation is the rule. Therefore, different gene combinations exist and frequently each leads to a unique ecological amplitude. Some of these individual gene pools are strongly associated with particular ecological conditions.

The nature of gene pools is seen in a species having an ecological amplitude that would permit its existence in unoccupied but readily available localities. The organism's ecological amplitude is a set of adaptations to its environment. These adaptations display unlike potentials for survival and success during the various stages of the life cycle, so adults might prosper in a habitat where other stages might not (Figure 17.2). However, the usual reason why a plant or animal does not occur where it could otherwise is *competition*. Because of organisms already in an area, certain other species in spite of their favorable ecological amplitudes are unable to occupy the locality. For this reason ecological amplitude does not include the hereditary bases that influence competition.

The above discussion indicates that ecological amplitude varies throughout the life cycle. In addition, the environment varies. Yet ecological amplitude is tolerance to all environmental fluctuations, except competition, a species encounters. Therefore, any stage of a species' life history may be subjected either to periods of optimum conditions and ready adjustment to the environment or of unfavorable conditions and bare adjustment. Bare adjustment most likely is related to periods of environmental extremes, circumstances that are usually limiting. For this reason environmental extremes are generally more important than average conditions. However, one cannot extend this concept to imply that optimum environmental conditions automatically mean great success for a species. Although optimum conditions *might* allow maximum vigor, numbers, and development, this is not necessarily the case. Again, competition with some other species in an otherwise "best" habitat can come into play and hinder the organisms.

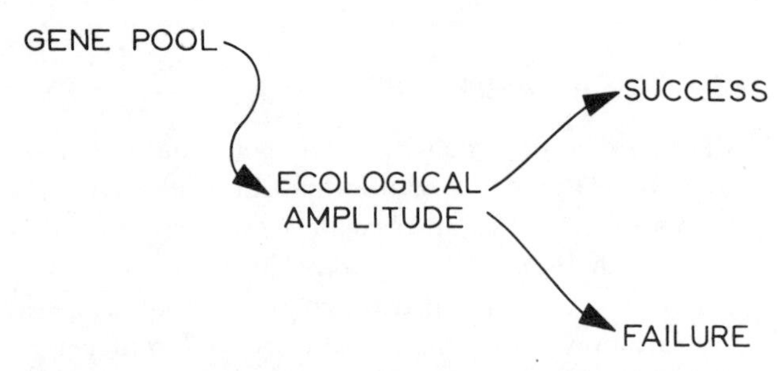

Figure 17.2 Features in the tolerance of a single gene pool (species or population of a species) to its total environment. The gene pool is the basis of an ecological amplitude, or over all tolerance to the environmental complex. The effects of age of individuals, season of the year, fluctuations in habitat, and so on, upon the ecological amplitude determine success or failure.

It should not be surprising that different gene pools can lead to the organism variations that characterize various phenomena. This can be appreciated in reference to altitudinal and latitudinal zonation of life. Both kinds of distribution reflect the zonation of many ecological factors, principally temperature and moisture. Therefore, when a variety of ecological amplitudes (actually, kinds of organisms) react to environmental zonation, the outcome is a zonation of the organisms. Moreover, many other zonations represent the same kind of phenomena. For example, there are distributions brought about by zonation of soil salts near the ocean or salt lakes, and those from the annual progression of climatic conditions. The progress of climate can be likened to zonation, because each segment of the year is associated with unique phases of each organism's life history.

ECOLOGICAL FACTORS

Plants often are used as examples in discussion of ecological factors, because they usually reflect their environment more closely than do animals. In addition, the reactions of organisms to land conditions are more complex, but often more precise, than are reactions to water habitats.

Ecological factors were said to fall into two categories, physical and biotic. The physical factors are climate, soil, and topography. Climate, the most inclusive category, includes general climate, temperature, water, light, and atmosphere. Soil and topography each have unique features but cannot be segregated into distinctive subunits. Biotic factors are further subdivided on the basis of kinds of interorganism relationships. An additional factor is fire, a product of climate or of biotic factors (including man); its action is physical.

Physical factors can be classified as primary, secondary, or tertiary. Primary factors, the only ones directly influencing life, are general climate, temperature, water (specifically, availability, including standing water and humidity), light, atmospheric gases, some actions of wind, and nutrients (generally only soil minerals for plants). Secondary factors are precipitation, atmospheric wind, and soil structure (especially texture), all features directly affecting the primary factors and only indirectly affecting organisms. The only tertiary physical factor is topography. Land forms directly affect only secondary factors.

Biotic factors are not always primary, secondary, or more remote, because each factor has varying effects upon different organisms. Only in reference to a particular organism at a particular time is a biotic factor primary, secondary, or less direct (Table 17.1).

Climate is the most important ecological factor. This is true because, even where local minute variations must be appraised, climate includes most of the primary ecological factors of plants. In addition, climate is an important animal control, acting either as a direct check or as an indirect one through plants. Therefore, plants, at least, exist only where climate is suitable, and animals never are really independent of climate. On the other hand, local fluctuations in individual climatic factors, soil, topography, and biotic features are important. Any of these single factors can prove limiting locally to a plant or animal. For this reason, *all* ecological factors must be examined.

TABLE 17.1 RELATIONSHIPS AMONG ECOLOGICAL FACTORS AND ORGANISMS

Tertiary Factors →	Secondary Factors →	Primary Factors →	Life
Topography		General climate	
Latitude		Temperature	The various factors
Relief	Precipitation	Water	affect ecological
Distribution		Light	amplitude or are
		Air	the sources of
	Wind	Wind	particular needs
	Soil structure	Nutrients	
Biotic factors	Biotic factors	Biotic factors	

Discussion of ecological factors, owing to their interrelations, requires some repetition. However, this may be welcome because even a superficial treatment of factors is somewhat complex.

MICROHABITAT

Further discussions of physical and biotic factors may lead to the implication that an individual environment is a large area of ecological homogeneity. Nothing could be further from what exists in nature, because factors work in combination to produce very minute as well as fairly large distinctive units. The minute areas, or *microhabitats* are likely to be overlooked. For example, the fact might be disregarded that different sides of a fallen tree or of a leaf have unlike microenvironments and organisms.

Although the large, more conventional habitats emphasize the importance of horizontal distribution of environmental factors, one kind of microhabitat, *layers*, stresses the vertical zonation of factors. These microhabitats portray the ecological uniqueness of trees, shrubs, herbs, mosses, leaf litter, and tiers of the soil. Often a surface microhabitat is much different from one underground. For example, when the substrate is covered with snow and few organisms are active upon the surface, the organisms underground in their insulated, warmer microhabitat may be quite active.

The presence or absence of individual microhabitats is likely to be very important in animal occurrence. An animal may be most closely associated not with a plant community or any major portion of a habitat, but with being under objects, in moist situations, in sandy soil, on a particular species of plant, or even on a limited part of a single plant species. Such places usually are not studied in detail; however, the serious student must locate these microhabitats. The only way that it can be done is to make careful records of the exact place in which an animal is found. This place also must be described according to the details of the ecological factors that are present.

An appreciation of many possible microhabitats in any locality is gained even by a superficial examination of a conventional habitat. (The word "habitat" is all inclusive; microhabitats and conventional habitats are both habitats). For example, in a woodland one can usually find trees, shrubs, herbs, mosses, climbers, epiphytes, saprophytes, and parasites. Each of these plant layers possesses different species and ecological factors, and even different parts of a single layer contain unlike microhabitats. The parts of a tree provide variations in environment, hence many habitats, for organisms. If the bark of a tree is studied, the outer surface, cracks, and bark interior are the more obvious sites of unique microhabitats and species.

Certain microhabitats might be overlooked. In a woodland one can usually find logs, boards, and/or rocks upon the ground. Different organisms are found under or within these objects. Also, it frequently is profitable to examine any litter that may be under these objects. In addition, the ground beneath most woodlands is covered by decaying plant remains that are forming humus. Decaying organic remains of different thickness, moisture content, and stage of decomposition generally support unlike organisms, and often there is a layering of different species within a single layer of thick humus. Finally, unlike conditions are found in both soil variations and layers within any soil.

GENERAL CLIMATE

Present climatic classifications are based upon fairly exact measurements of temperature and moisture. These classifications consider average values, seasonal distribution, and effectiveness. For example, temperature monthly averages of mean, minima, and maxima, plus indirect temperature estimates by recording the average growing season are utilized. Comparable data for precipitation are used. All these criteria for climates are of prime importance to life. Each criterion is reflected by particular limits of tolerance and, for this reason, can be a limiting factor.

Although climate is operating upon all aspects of an environment, its main ecological act is to help delimit the ranges of many species and of the mature soil types. This is the case in both tropical and temperate regions. However, in tropical regions there may be no seasonal climatic differences and in temperate regions there may be marked seasonal changes. In the temperate zone most animal adaptations related to seasonal changes appear most closely associated with temperature changes, and not with both temperature and moisture as in plants. However, in spite of these close relationships, the climatic adaptations of organisms probably are related to all physical conditions producing climate. In fact, organisms are influenced by all features of their environment and usually react to the complete environment rather than to any single factor.

In spite of being closely correlated with organism distribution, general climate is less important at the local level. Locally, the individual factors of temperature, moisture, light, wind, soil, and other organisms —usually in combination, but also singly—are most important in determining the presence or absence of a species. Here also, freak weather conditions, including storms, can have severe consequences for plants and animals.

CLIMATIC RHYTHMS

The rhythms or trends of climate are of six types: equable, tropical wet-and-dry, Mediterranean, continental, polar, and desert. Normally, each rhythm conforms to a major type of climate.

Equable rhythms usually have little seasonal climatic difference. Even the maximum possible seasonal changes are insignificant, so the most typical equable trends are near the equator in tropical climates where the predominant vegetation is rainforest. As one might expect, existing climatic fluctuations cause, at most, only minor responses among the organisms.

Tropical wet-and-dry rhythms display seasonal changes in temperature and precipitation. The temperature cycle is associated with, and is mostly the consequence of, the precipitation cycle. Temperature extremes occur during the dry season. Under such rhythm, rainforests are first replaced by deciduous plants (typical rainforests have evergreens); if climate is less equable, an open type of vegetation, called *savanna*, grows. The savanna plants are woody, generally deciduous, and sometimes quite specialized for arid conditions; however, these adaptations are responses to progressively less equable trends. Therefore, in these tropical rhythms the most equable environments contain a deciduous, or monsoon, rainforest and progressively less equable trends are inhabited by a variety of savannas.

Other rhythms are fairly distinctive, closely related to climate, and more familiar to North Americans. The *Mediterranean rhythms* have evergreen woody plants, such as the chaparral of western North America. The *continental rhythms* have three main types of vegetation. In areas where rainfall is heavy and is distributed with a summer maximum and where the winter is cold but of moderate length and conditions, the vegetation is a deciduous forest. Such a forest covers much of the eastern United States. In colder areas, such as the Great Lakes and northeastern United States, the vegetation is a needle-leaf forest. Finally, in drier areas, steppe or grassland like that of the Great Plains prevails. The *polar rhythms* have a stunted woody and herbaceous vegetation called tundra. The *desert rhythms* have a sparse coverage of specialized woody and herbaceous plants.

Although each rhythm is most easily recognized by its plants, there is also a definite association between climatic trends and animals. Whether this animal association actually reflects rhythm or vegetation, or perhaps both, is difficult to ascertain. Perhaps the various influences upon animals contain examples of strict rhythm control, of vegetation control, of rhythm -vegetation control, and probably even some independence from these factors.

PLANT LIFE FORMS

Various schemes summarize the over-all responses of plants, through adaptations, to ecological conditions. Because climate is all important in the control of plant distribution, these schemes can be related to climate. One of the earliest and still very useful schemes is Raunkiaer's method of classifying plants by their *life form* and of compiling the life forms of a locale's plants into a *biological spectrum.* A spectrum is a percentage analysis of an area's plants classified according to the position of their regenerating parts. Regenerating parts (usually buds) are those portions of plants from which new growth originates after the dormant period. The dormant period exhibits the death and loss of certain aerial parts of many species.

Life form spectra have little direct bearing upon the taxonomy and phylogeny of plants. For example, certain mosses, ferns, and flowering plants are within a single life form class, and individual higher taxa are scattered throughout many classes. This should be expected, because plants within any major taxon usually are adapted to unlike environments. Broad ecological occurrence is manifested especially by the flowering plants.

On the basis of the position of the regenerating parts, five major life form classes often are used (Figure 17.3). (Neither the full number of categories, nor the subunits originally proposed by Raunkiaer are usually used at the present time.) *Phanaerophytes* (*PH*) are trees and shrubs; *chamaephytes* (*CH*) are aerial plants, generally herbs and smaller shrubs; *hemicryptophytes* (*H*) die back to and regenerate from the surface of the ground; *geophytes* (*G*) have their regenerating structures below ground level; and *therophytes* (*Th*) are annuals.

Raunkiaer formulated the concept of the biological spectrum to show the over-all adaptations of plants to local conditions. He determined the percentage occurrence of each life form for particular areas of the world and the world average for plants in general. His and other samplings of the flora of certain parts of the world indicate the prevalence of phanerophytes in the moist warm tropics, of hemicryptophytes in moist temperate areas, and of therophytes in dry regions. Moreover, Raunkiaer concluded that local

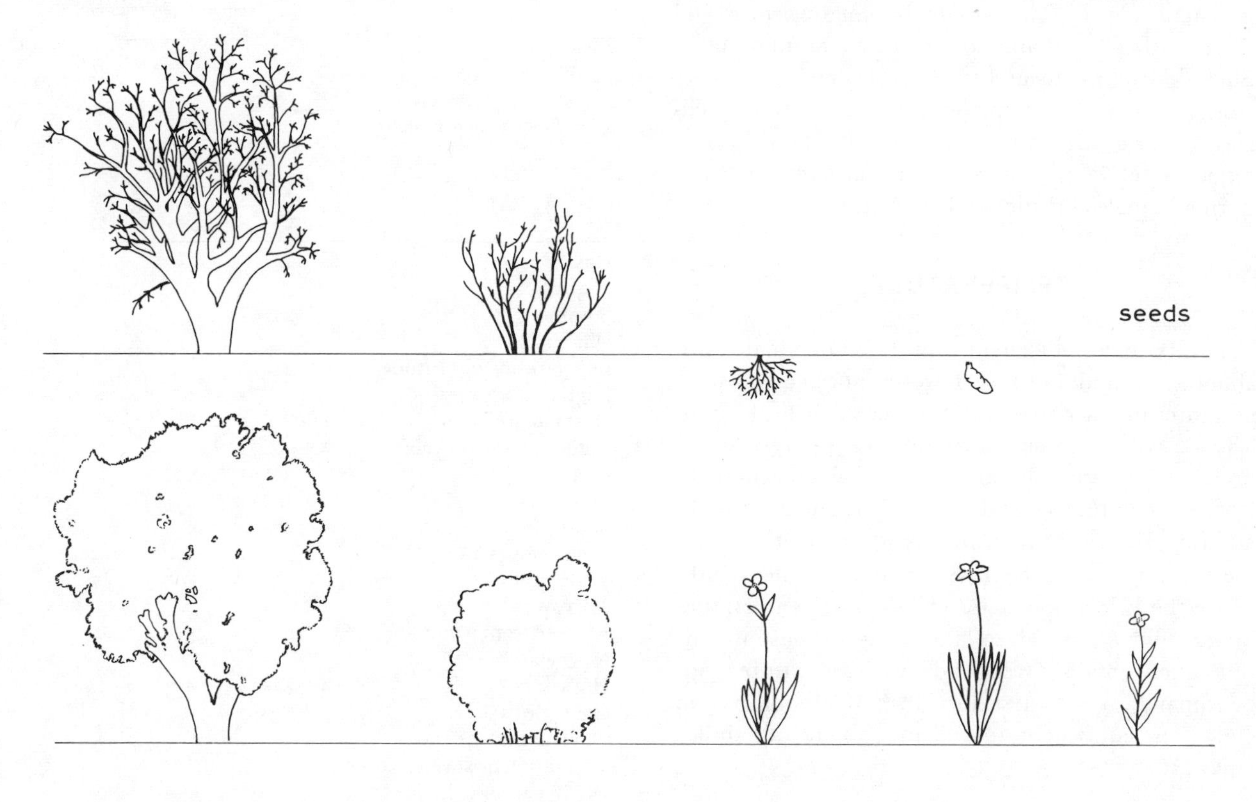

Figure 17.3 Raunkaier's plant life forms. Examples of the major life forms and their appearance during unfavorable (above) and favorable (below) seasons.

areas had to be interpreted in reference to departures from the world norm. The world norm, then, would be the spectrum of any locality where chance alone was operating to determine the species present, or where there was little ecological restriction of the flora.

CLISERAL MOVEMENTS

The more important climatic aspects as related to vegetation, heat, and moisture, are not static. Climate displayed very remarkable changes in the past and fluctuations are taking place today. As a reflection of these climatic variations, vegetation has been and is evolving. Although evolution of plant species is of primary importance, another significant consequence of climatic change is the *movement* of vegetation. In the northern hemisphere, with cooling there is a general southward displacement of vegetation; with warming, there is a general northward one (Figures 19.12 through 19.20). At the present time, there is a tendency for climates to become warmer and drier, with a resultant northward plant movement. Such shifts of plants and their associated animals are *cliseral movements*, a term that refers to changing climate (hence vegetation) in local situations. The sequence of communities at a particular locality during a single climatic trend constitute a *clisere*.

TEMPERATURE

The extremes of air temperature on our planet are about −95° and 140°F. However, surface soil temperatures in deserts are said to exceed 200°F. Even in a single locality temperature displays many associations. There are daily and seasonal fluctuations related to the presence and angle of the sun's rays. In addition, the closer a locality is to one of the poles, the greater is the solar rays' angle from the zenith, hence the colder the daily or seasonal temperature range. Finally, at a given latitude an increase in altitude often entails a reduction in temperature—approximately a 3°F. loss for every 1000-foot rise in elevation, equivalent to moving about 600 miles poleward.

TEMPERATURE VARIATIONS

In addition to daily and seasonal temperature variations, temperature is related to many physical and biological factors in local areas (Table 17.2). First, dark-colored surfaces absorb more heat than do light-colored ones, because light surfaces reflect more radiation. Second, coarse soils acquire heat more rapidly than do fine soils, because fine soils are wetter and water warms more slowly than do other soil materials. Third, temperature extremes usually are less in areas covered by plants than in open areas. In the daytime plants interrupt solar radiation and reduce insolation; at night plant cover inhibits the loss of surface heat. Seasonally, plant cover tends to keep winter temperature minima higher and summer maximum lower and to retard spring warming and winter cooling of the underlying soil.

Fourth, surface cover such as snow or organic matter usually is more effective than plant cover alone in preventing temperature extremes.

TABLE 17.2 SOME TEMPERATURE–ENVIRONMENT RELATIONSHIPS

Environmental Features	Temperature Conditions					
	High	Low	Great variation	Slight variation	High day/low night	Low day/high night[a]
Day	x					
Night		x				
Summer	x					
Winter		x				
Low latitude or altitude	x			x		
High latitude or altitude		x	x		x	
Dark-colored objects	x		x			
Light-colored objects		x				
Coarse soils	x		x		x	
Fine soils		x		x		x
South slopes	x		x			
North slopes		x		x		
Wide valleys	x		x		x	
Narrow valleys		x		x		x
Remote from water	x		x		x	
Near water		x		x		x
Hot winds	x					
Cold winds		x				
Open areas			x		x	
Vegetation or surface cover				x		x
Dry, clear, or calm air					x	
Moist, dusty, cloudy, or foggy						x

[a]Actually, day temperatures normally are higher than night temperatures. This temperature condition is recognized because it contrasts with temperature conditions of adjacent environmental types.

Fifth, the angle of the sun's rays affects the temperature of different mountain slopes. For example, the southern slope of a mountain receives more direct solar rays, hence more heat, than does the northern slope. Also, west slopes obtain more heat than east slopes and both get more than north slopes.

Sixth, soil surface temperatures usually are higher during the day and lower at night than air or subsurface soil temperatures. This relationship is more pronounced at higher altitudes.

Seventh, at a given latitude air temperatures usually become lower with altitude, approximately 3°F. for every 1000 feet.

Eighth, wide valleys usually are hotter and drier than narrow valleys. Narrow valleys are more protected from insolation and are more subject to cold air drainage into them from higher areas.

Ninth, at a given latitude higher and larger mountains generally are warmer at a particular altitude than are smaller mountains at the same altitude.

Tenth, because water reduces temperature extremes, the closer an area is to a body of water the more stable and less extreme are its temperatures. This is the basis for classifying the interior areas with marked temperature extremes as having continental climates and coastal areas with stable temperatures as having oceanic climates.

Eleventh, the temperature of ocean currents usually reduces the temperature extremes of nearby land. Even cold, fast-flowing streams from mountains cool otherwise desert areas some distance from the stream.

Twelfth, direction of air movement often modifies temperature. Winds from the ocean stabilize temperatures for some distance if their movement is uninterrupted. Winds from mountains into lowlands tend to be cooler than those from low elevations. Winds from polar areas are mostly colder than those from tropical areas.

Finally, foggy or cloudy areas often are cooler than clear areas; however, foggy regions often maintain heat when clear areas become cooler.

To summarize, environmental temperature is generally warmer during the day, in summer, near the equator, on plains, on dark-colored objects, in coarse soil, on south-facing slopes, in wide valleys, at sites remote from water, during warm winds, and in places having a sparse ground cover of plants or other insulating objects. Temperature is generally cooler at night, in winter, near the poles, on mountains, on light-colored objects, in fine soils, on north-facing slopes, in narrow valleys, at sites near water, during cool winds, and in places having a dense ground cover. Temperature is variable from time to time and is higher in the day and lower at night in wide valleys, places remote from water, open areas, and sites featuring dry, clear or calm air. Finally, temperature stability with warmer nights and cooler days is found in narrow valleys, locales near large bodies of water, areas of fine soils, sites having dense plant or other surface cover, and places with moist, dusty, cloudy or foggy air.

TEMPERATURE INVERSION

Another local temperature phenomenon, called temperature inversion, causes higher elevations to have a warmer temperature than the surrounding lowlands. Inversion usually takes place at night and is associated with several weather conditions that stimulate the cooling of surface air. Such things as long nights, clear skies, dry air, calm air, and snow cover cause lowlands to lose their heat faster than do the nearby elevations, and the lowlands become colder than the uplands.

Temperature inversion also can be fortified or caused by heavier, colder, higher air draining down into lowlands and upthrusting the lower, warmer air to higher elevations. No matter which of these two mechanisms brings about inversion, the resulting warmer upper slopes may have distinctly different vegetation, perhaps even with less resistance to cold than plants in the lowlands.

ORGANISM REACTIONS

Because different species of organisms react differently to the temperature spectrum on earth, temperature has a pronounced role in determining which habitats are usable by individual species. The temperature range at a given site might be the single feature (limiting factor) that prevents a species' being there.

Most plants and animals are in various degrees dependent upon their external environment, particularly the sun, for a direct source of heat. The general exceptions are the birds and mammals, which have internal mechanisms (endothermism) to control and regulate their body heat. Endothermism generally allows these two groups to exist in both colder and warmer places than other organisms can. Also, this internal control enables individual birds and mammals to remain active within greater temperature extremes that can other organisms. Most other groups can carry on their life processes only between 35° and 110° F.; temperatures above or below this range prevent reproduction and, if they depart too far, cause death. However, this does not mean that life other than birds or mammals cannot exist at extreme temperatures. Subarctic coniferous forests are found where −80° F. has been recorded and certain buttercups and other plants can germinate under and grow through snow. Temperatures above the general range are found in deserts where the vegetation is heated to over 130° F. and in hot springs where a few blue-green algae and bacteria are known to survive in situations over 190° F.

The temperature tolerance of plants varies in different climatic regions. Tropical plants have a relatively narrow range in which life processes prosper, and slight deviations from this range are likely to be fatal. On the other hand, temperate zone plants have a wider range of temperature tolerance. They carry on their functions over a broad range and can withstand greater deviations from their optimum ranges than can tropicals. Even within the temperate zone there is variation in plant temperature tolerance. The greatest tolerance is found in desert plants and is necessitated by the desert environment. For example, in an area of Death Valley, California, a temperature range of over 100° F. was recorded in less than twenty-four hours. Plant adaptations to cold climates will be discussed in the section on alpine plants, in reference to wind as an atmospheric factor.

In animals definite temperature reactions take place. There are comalike states, winter hibernation and summer aestivation, which enable survival during unfavorable extremes in temperature. Also, in desert situations animals often retreat to burrows during a hot day but are active on the surface at night. Other animal–temperature relations include animals' changing their habits and body structures, conditions associated with annual temperature fluctuations.

In marine organisms, temperature appears to be a prominent factor in the determination of geographic distribution. Also of importance and associated with temperature is salinity. This may be surprising, because ocean currents allow only very small temperature and salinity changes to exist. In spite of this, temperatures are related to the geographic limits of many Pacific Coast marine species at Cape Flattery, Washington; Point Conception, California; and San Diego, California. However, these "barriers" seem to be losing much of their effectiveness at the present time, a situation that is allied to a general warming of eastern Pacific Ocean waters. Owing to the warming, there is now a northward shifting of many Pacific Ocean animals, including the northward movement of sharks dangerous to man.

VERTEBRATE DORMANCY

Dormancy is characteristic of many plants and animals; however, further mention of the subject here is limited to vertebrates.

Because many people are somewhat familiar with the concept of hibernation, dormancy is frequently believed to be an adaptation to temperature alone. However, as more is learned about dormancy, it appears to be a general response to various unfavorable environmental conditions of a temporary nature. For example, it can be associated with reduced food, high temperature, low temperature, and reduced moisture. Therefore, dormancy probably is a response that conserves body materials, especially water and sources of energy. The conservation of materials comes from considerable slowing down of body processes as the animal assumes a comalike state, or torpor. The effects of the comalike state are pronounced in endothermic birds and mammals which have the greatest regulation and stability of their life processes. Some endotherms enter a relatively complete comalike state. In these species dormancy results in reduction of body temperature to essentially that of the surroundings, in drastic lowering of breathing and heart rates, and in a general slowing of life processes. One might say that life processes are reduced to a point that approaches the bare minimum rate for survival.

Degree of dormancy varies among vertebrates, especially the endotherms. In some, reduction of life processes is so slight that it is hardly proper to call the phenomenon dormancy. This is the case with bears. Although breathing rate might be greatly reduced in some bears, heart rate and body temperature generally are normal. In addition, the animals do not become torpid; disturbances are likely to awaken them. For practical purposes, bear reactions are only a very deep sleep.

Dormancy frequently is seasonal. When dormancy is mentioned, one is likely to limit his thoughts to winter hibernation. However, dormancy frequently occurs in the summer (aestivation). Also, it need not be limited to winter or summer or to a regular cycle of annual repetition. Unfavorable conditions, regardless of annual cycle, can cause dormancy; so if ecological factors fluctuate from year to year, an animal might aestivate and hibernate in one year, not become dormant in another, or might even become dormant without strict summer or winter association in yet another year.

Dormancy can be restricted to brief periods of a single day. A daily cycle of dormancy and activity is common in ectotherms of localities having daily fluctuations of temperature. Even in birds and mammals, especially bats, daily dormancy cycles are known. In these endotherms, the intensity of dormancy is associated directly with the amount of temperature reduction. Such daily cycles are called *diurnation*.

Clarification of the term *endotherm* is now possible. Strictly speaking, the term should be limited to those organisms whose body temperature is controlled by internal body functions. Automatically this limits attention to the birds and mammals, because no other living creatures contain the specific controls that diagnose true endothermism. However, birds and mammals that become dormant no longer control their body temperature. In many respects, when torpid, these "endotherms" are not different from ectotherms. For this reason, there is a trend to provide special recognition to the shifting from one mechanism to another by applying the name *heterotherm* to those endotherms that become truly dormant.

Organisms usually become dormant in places having fairly uniform environments. Apparently the factors that stimulate dormancy also cause an animal to seek shelter. Good shelters are environments in which temperature and other ecological factors do not reach extremes that would be fatal to the dormant animals. This requirement allows for a good deal of variety in the actual sites of successful dormancy. Almost any possible underground or underwater retreat that can be reached is used. Even above-ground places like log interiors and rock or debris piles are inhabited.

WATER

Organisms need water. Meeting this requirement can be a problem, even in aquatic environments if they have fluctuating water levels, little incoming water, or a high salt content. Fluctuating waters often have much alluvium and debris during the wet season and a low oxygen and food supply. They may even become dry during the dry season. This prevents the survival of many creatures, but certain taxa (especially algae and protozoans) are fairly successful by being active during the wet season and dormant during the dry season. However, even these creatures must have incoming water to replenish such necessities as food and oxygen and to prevent waters from becoming salty. Salinity is an absolute barrier to most life, whether the saltiness is in the ocean or in saline or alkaline lakes on land, because the water is not readily separated from the salt.

WATER NEEDS AND TRANSPIRATION

In any land habitat insufficient water can eliminate certain creatures from the area. This is most readily appreciated in reference to a vascular plant process called *transpiration*, a function involving almost constant movement of water through active plants and consisting of water being absorbed by the roots, transported via vessels into the leaves, and lost (transpired) from the leaf surfaces. In general, transpiration rate is directly related to temperature. Most plants transpire large amounts of water, a reason why plant cover tends to restrict temperature extremes. Among the plants having a high transpiration rate are corn and alfalfa. Both transpire many times their dry weight each day—corn about six to nine times and alfalfa about thirty-six to fifty-six. These rates are much greater than known rates of desert plants which lose only 1/100,000 to 1/175,000 as much water.

Transpiration appears to be an adaptation that cools a plant. If this is true, transpiration is analogous to animal perspiration, both functions acting to reduce body temperature.

AVAILABLE MOISTURE

The moisture in a given habitat comes from many sources, primarily the different forms of precipitation. However, the actual amount of water that is available to an organism also is dependent upon humidity, temperature, wind, sunshine, and other factors within an environment (Figure 17.4). These factors are more specifically related to available moisture through their influence upon evaporation and transpiration rates. Lower humidity and

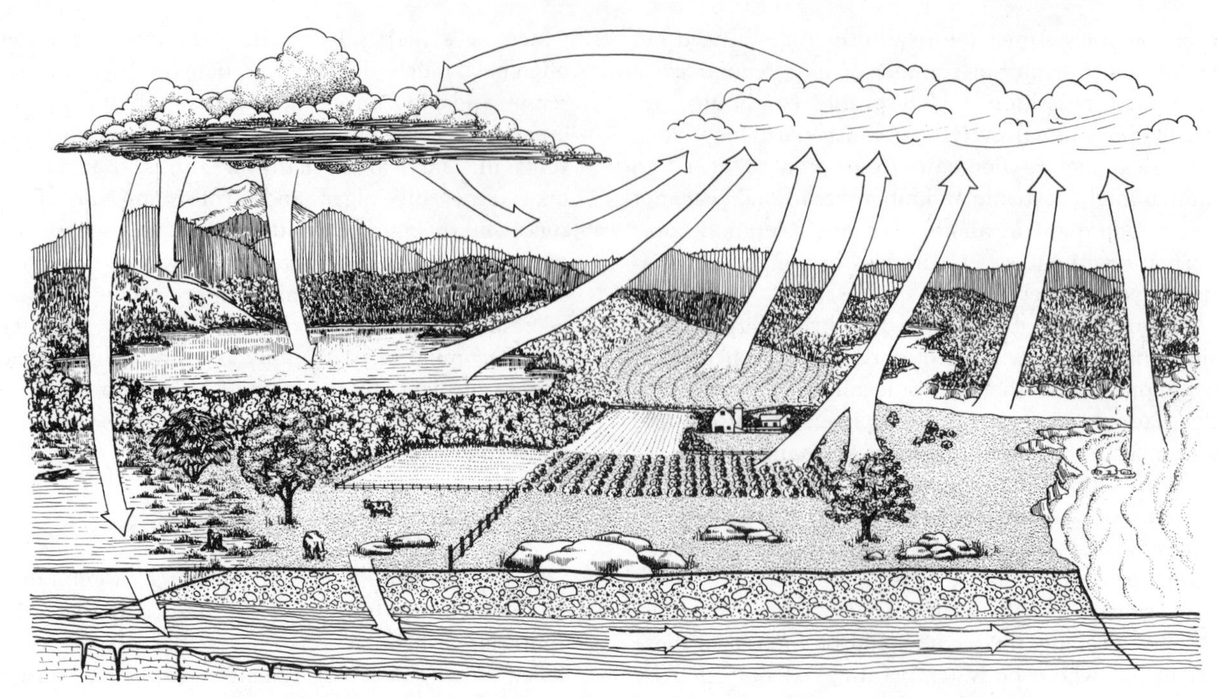

Figure 17.4 The hydrologic cycle, emphasizing the more common relationships between water and an environment. The water available to organisms in a given habitat is not simply the sum of precipitation and condensation. From this sum water is lost to life by evaporation into the air, interception by plants, runoff to other areas, adsorption or being bound to the soil, and percolation to depths beyond those penetrated by life. (From George K. Reid, *Ecology of Inland Waters and Estuaries,* Reinhold Publishing Corp., New York, 1961.)

greater temperature, wind velocity, and solar radiation all increase water loss, and thus decrease the amount of available moisture. Also of primary importance in water availability is soil porosity. This is the case because precipitation is the basic source of soil moisture, which in turn is the main source of plant moisture, and the physical nature of the soil determines what water is available to plants. The water-holding capacity and drainage of the soil are instrumental in how much moisture is held in soil spaces and how much is available to plants. This interrelation of various factors acting on available moisture is another example of the complete interdependence of physical factors in a habitat.

In spite of the importance of interrelations of available moisture factors, rainfall alone can be used to indicate the type of habitat in an area. Deserts regularly exist wherever the rainfall is 10 or less inches per year, because there is insufficient moisture for most plants during all parts of the year. Grasslands, savannas, and open woodlands are found where the rainfall is 10 to 30 inches per year. Dry forests are in places of 30 to 50 inches of rainfall. Wet forests are in areas with over 50 inches of rainfall.

PLANT DORMANCY

Contrary to popular belief, plant dormancy is related most closely to available water and only secondarily to temperature. Dormancy occurs mostly during the dry season. However, in forest areas plants may be dormant during the winter, for even if water is available temperature may be sufficiently low to retard plant functions, including the takeup of water.

Dormancy adaptations are pronounced in deciduous plants. The loss of deciduous leaves, which because of their functions make tremendous demands for moisture, preserves water supplies in nondeciduous structures. When leaves are removed the plant is mobilized for extreme conditions of the environment, conditions that owing to plant dormancy are mostly avoided.

Most deciduous plants make ready for the next

growing season before entering dormancy. For example, at the base of most twigs resistant buds are formed. These buds contain embryo leaves, stored food, and cells capable of rapid growth, all enclosed in a protective envelope of bud scales, modified leaves.

PLANT–WATER RELATIONS

The structures of plants may reflect their water relations in many ways; however, most if not all of these reflections also might be adaptations to temperature and other environmental factors. In habitats having contrasting dry and wet seasons the perennial plants often are deciduous; the deciduous period, that of leaf loss and general dormancy, is in the dry season. In contrast, the wet season is one of leaf development, growth, reproduction, and general functional activities of the plant.

The associations between plants and available moisture are so important that many types of plants are recognized on this basis. The three primary types are *hydrophytes* (water plants), *mesophytes* (moist plants) and *xerophytes* (dry plants) (Figure 17.5). Hydrophytes have very high to maximum available water, their substrate is either water or is covered by water, and they usually are found in moist habitats. The primary characteristic of these plants is their ability to survive under the minimal oxygen conditions of water. Structurally, the main macroscopic modifications are smaller root systems (if roots are present) and the tendency for underwater vegetative structures to differ from surface or above-water structures.

There are five subtypes of hydrophytes. *Floating hydrophytes*, such as duckweed (*Lemna*) and mosquito fern (*Azola*), contact only air and water. *Suspended*

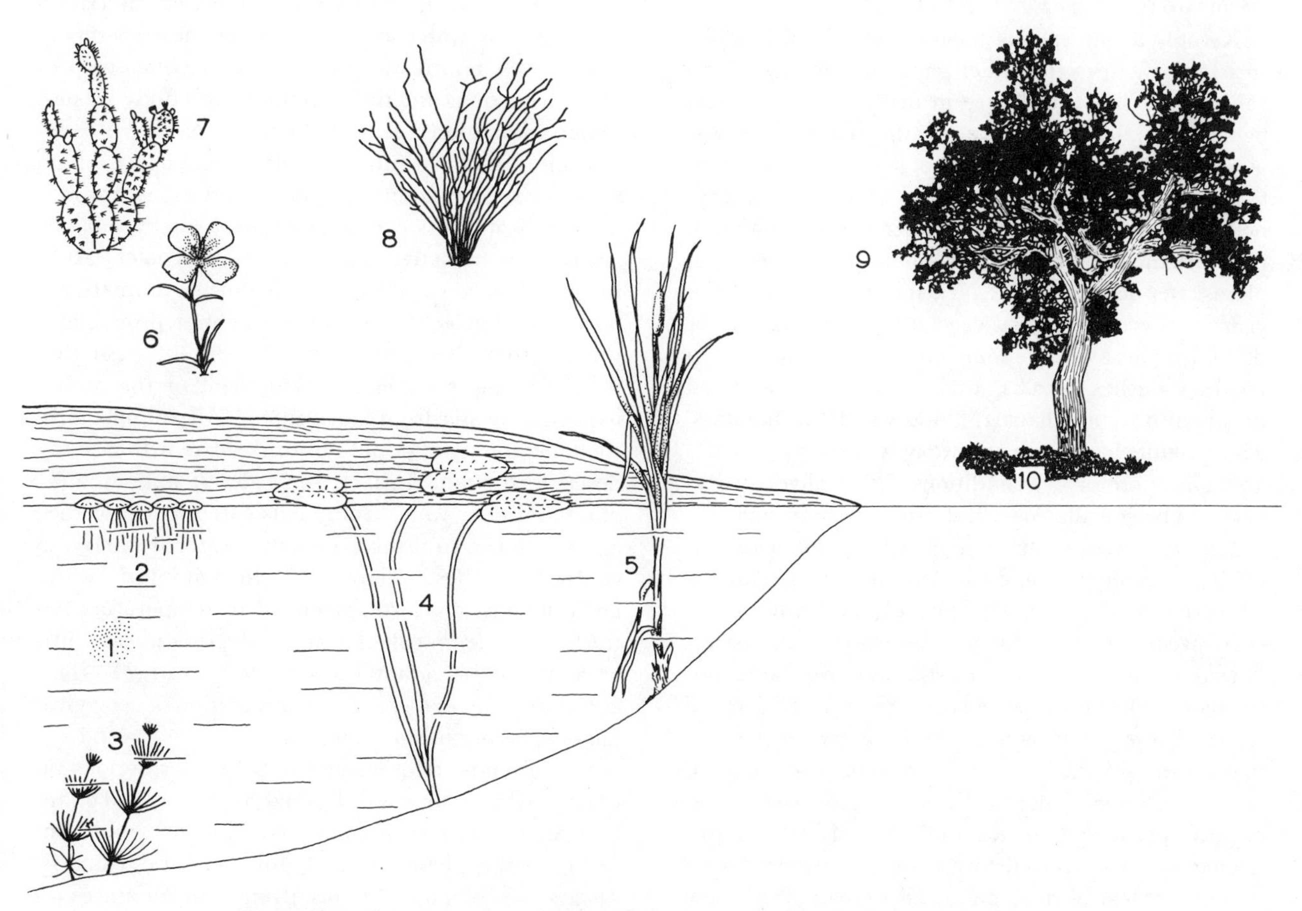

Figure 17.5 Plant–water relationships as indicated by hydrophytes, mesophytes, and xerophytes. Hydrophytes: 1. suspended; 2. floating; 3. submerged; 4. floating-leaved anchored; 5. emergent anchored. Xerophytes: 6. ephemeral annual; 7. succulent perennial; 8. nonsucculent perennial. Mesophytes: 9. sun plant; 10, shade plants.

hydrophytes, various plant plankton, only contact water. *Submerged anchored hydrophytes*, typified by many pondweeds (*Potamogeton*) and stonewort (*Chara*), are attached to the substrate but covered by water. *Floating-leaved anchored hydrophytes*, like the water lily (*Nymphaea*), have only the upper surfaces of their leaves contacting air. *Emergent anchored hydrophytes*, such as bullrush (*Scirpus*) and cattail (*Typha*), have a larger proportion of the vegetative structures above water.

Mesophytes have medium available water because they are found in moist soils and climates. They cannot inhabit situations that have either a great deal of water or very little water. For this reason they are not found in water, wet soil, or dry environments. These plants have no structural specialization for their way of life and have low to high water loss, depending on environmental conditions. Mesophytes are of two types, *sun plants* and *shade plants*.

Xerophytes are plants having low available moisture because the soil is either physically or physiologically dry. They usually are in dry climates but can be in any climate type. As a rule they have a low rate of water loss. Physical dryness of soil is related either to a rock, gravel, or sand matrix, or to climate dryness. The dry climates have desert plants that lack moisture much of the year; grassland plants (prairies, plains, steppes, etc.) that lack moisture some of the year; and certain woody vegetation that has low or discontinuous available moisture. Woody vegetation includes bushes, shrubs, and small trees, grouped mostly into scrub, chaparral, and woodland habitats, whose plants have thick and waxy leaves—apparently an adaptation for dry conditions. Physiological dryness will be considered with the discussion of soils.

Xerophytes are of three main types: ephemeral annuals, succulents, and nonsucculent perennials. *Ephemeral annuals* complete their life cycles in a very short period of time. Only a few weeks may be required for germination, growth, and reproduction; the more unfavorable periods are spent in the form of seeds. These plants tend to avoid the dry season, but many can withstand strong atmospheric drought if their soils remain moist. *Succulents* have tissues and organs specialized to accumulate and store water during wet periods and to release this water during drought. Most of these plants also function at a low rate of transpiration and have shallow root systems, an adaptation to gather moisture from light rains. *Nonsucculent perennials* might be called the only true xerophytes. Unlike the ephemeral annuals and succulents, these perennials have specializations that react against dryness rather than avoiding it. Perhaps most surprising is that many of these plants can endure permanent wilting. Although the woody forms can tolerate only short perids, some herbaceous plants can tolerate years of permanent wilting. Other nonsucculent adaptations are extensive root systems, rapid growth of roots in young plants, reduced transpiration, and smaller leaves. However, both succulents and nonsucculents often are small and greatly spaced.

ANIMAL–WATER RELATIONS

Most animals contain 70 to 90 per cent water by body weight, and none are likely to survive the loss of one third of their body water. This is probably the reason why various adaptations are related directly to possible body water loss. Certain of these modifications merely retard water loss; examples include protective coverings and the secretion of dry body wastes. Other adaptations, actually behavior patterns, cause the animal to avoid situations that would exact a high water loss. For example, when desert areas are hottest and water loss would be greatest, many animals aestivate or are active at night when it is cooler. Also, many of the aestivating and nocturnal animals are burrowing forms, the burrowing habitat providing a retreat from the great heat of the sun. Another specialization is extreme development of the ability to produce water from foods eaten. All animals form such metabolic water but not to the extent that many desert forms can. In fact, some desert animals may obtain all their water from foods eaten, because they are not known to drink even when water is offered in captivity. These adaptations to minimum water environments are also correlated to temperature extremes, hence so-called water adaptations are just as likely to be adaptations to temperature. This correlation again displays the integration of ecological factors and organism responses.

Overabundance of water can be just as serious an environmental stress as limited moisture. To appreciate the problems of excess water one must understand the phenomena of diffusion and osmosis. *Diffusion* is of common occurrence in mixtures of different kinds of gases or different kinds of liquids. It is the tendency for each component of a mixture to move from any area of higher concentration to any other areas of lower concentration until an over-all uniform concentration of every substance exists throughout the mixture. *Osmosis* might best be understood if one imagines sugar, a solute, dissolved in water a solvent. If such a mixture is placed in a particular kind of membranous bag and the bag in turn is placed in pure water, the process of diffusion will take place. The pure water (the area of highest concentration of water) will move into the sugar solution (the area of lowest concentration of water) through the membranous bag. Notice that the bag prevents sugar diffusion into pure water; only the solvent does the moving. Osmosis, then, is diffusion of a solvent through a differentially permeable membrane from a region of higher concentration of the solvent to a region of lower concentration of the solvent.

Now consider an animal in fresh water. You should know that an animal's body fluids are salty and that most animals have only about 70 per cent of their weight in water. In this situation water is the solvent and salt the solute. With this in mind, it is obvious that the water is of lower concentration in the animal's body than in fresh water. Therefore, fresh-water animals should swell and finally burst from the continuous intake of water. Fresh-water fishes are good examples of why no such explosion occurs. Nothing prevents the water intake, but the excess water is removed by a continuous secretion of urine. However, this creates another problem. Most animal urine contains salts, so if fishes were to continuously lose salts in large quantities, their life processes would not continue properly and death soon would occur. Therefore, fish adaptations that absorb salt from the urine are essential and do exist. In addition, most fresh-water fishes have specialized gills that extract salts from the surrounding water, even though these salts are in weak concentrations.

Marine fishes provide good examples of water relationships in the ocean. Their bodies contain a higher concentration of water than does the sea, so marine fishes should lose their body waters to the lesser salt concentration in their surroundings. Fishes do lose water and for this very reason! However, adaptation again makes the difference. These animals drink large quantities of salt water, much of the salt being excreted by the gills, and they form very little urine.

Both marine and fresh-water areas provide a myriad of conditions for life. A brief introduction to intertidal and fresh-water habitats will illustrate some of these conditions. In addition to examination of ecological factors, some mention will be made of general trends of *biotic succession*, the sequence of life from its first invasion of an environment through subsequent changes and to final conditions of stability (*climax*).

INTERTIDAL ENVIRONMENT

The ocean is a much less severe habitat than the land. This can be appreciated if one compares marine and terrestrial environments in relation to usual animal responses. The environmental differences may best be illustrated through comparisons of ectotherms, especially those whose body temperatures closely approximate that of their environment. The marine animals reflect ocean conditions by having a more constant and generally lower body temperature. Because of their low temperature, these marine creatures have a slower living rate and are less active; and because of relatively constant ocean temperatures, they have no need for special mechanisms to escape heat extremes. In addition, marine life leads a less rigorous existence than terrestrial life because water and food are more plentiful. Even reproduction requires less energy in the ocean. For example, most eggs neither need cases (drying is impossible) nor yolk (microscopic food is available to the larvae). Also, water buoyancy enables slower movement with less energy than is needed for land movement; however, fast movement requires more energy in water than on land. Finally, even pressure is of little concern. Slow movements from the depths to the surface are possible.

The large brown algae called *kelp* are examples of the relative ease of marine existence. Such large algae presumably do not grow on land partly because they lack the necessary supportive tissues for erect growth; any large land plant lacking sufficient supportive tissues would be reduced to an entangled mass that would have difficulty accomplishing its life processes. Also, kelp require no specialized structures such as roots, stems, and leaves. Although kelp have specialized anchoring devices called *holdfasts*, the entire algal structure tends to carry on the various life processes. Owing to this lack of special areas such as those for food making, large marine algae need not have veins to transport materials from one part of the plant to another. In short, one can say that kelp, like marine animals, need not be specialized as land organisms are.

MARINE FACTORS

Certain ecological factors often have more influence on sea rather than land creatures. Ocean currents change water temperatures and salinity, distribute plant and animal nutrients, and disperse the larvae of sedentary animals. Tides seem to have no effect upon open sea organisms, but are associated with the various adaptations of intertidal animals (those between highest and lowest tide levels) to temperature and salinity changes and drying. The greater the surf action, the more plants and animals found with specialized attachment devices. Salinity tends to be a very stable thing except when associated with other factors. Although some animals, especially bay, estuary, and tidepool species, can withstand gradual salinity changes, only a few can survive rapid, great changes in salinity.

In intertidal areas many marine organisms are at different and characteristic depths along the shore. The most important local factors thought to bring about this intertidal distribution of plants and animals are wave shock, substrate, and exposure. Wave shock naturally varies from harbor swells to waves of large proportions (20 feet or more). The primary types of substrate are sand, mud, and large to gigantic boulders, or even rocks integrated into their geological formation.

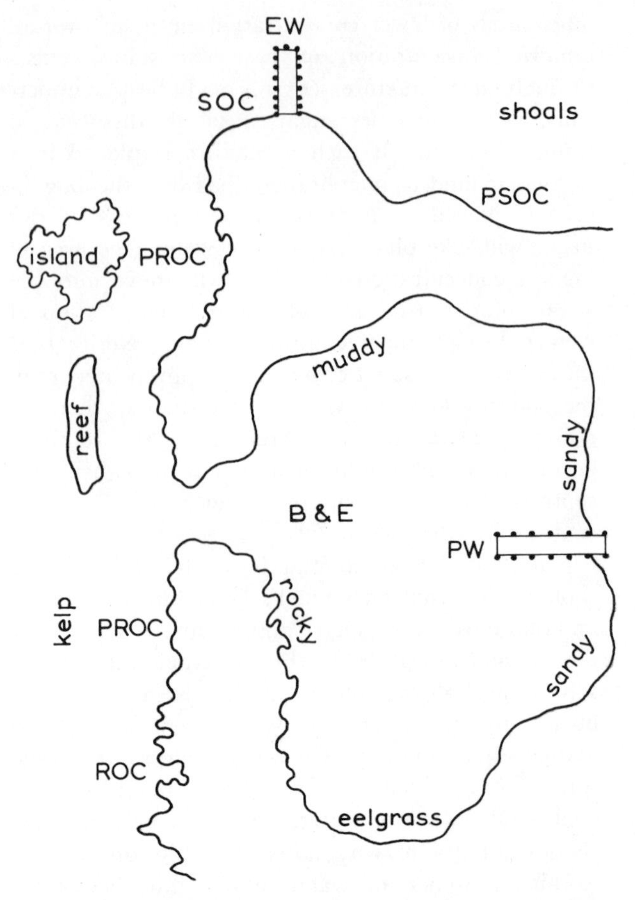

Figure 17.6 Intertidal habitats: SOC, sandy outer coast; ROC, rocky outer coast; PSOC, protected sandy outer coast; PROC, protected rocky outer coast; EW, exposed wharf; PW, protected wharf; B & E, bay and estuary with subdivisions of mudflats, sandflats, eelgrass, and rocky shores.

INTERTIDAL HABITATS

The major intertidal habitats, diagnosed primarily by amount of wave shock, are Protected Outer Coast, Open Coast, Bay and Estuary, and Wharf Piling. The subdivisions of these habitats are based upon exposure and substrate.

On the basis of wave shock alone, the following intertidal habitats can be recognized (Figure 17.6):

Protected Outer Coast. This habitat includes semi-sheltered coasts, open bays, and other areas protected from the full force of ocean waves. Protected areas can exist as a result of offshore reefs, kelp beds, islands, or even gradual sloping shore bottoms. There are two subdivisions of this habitat, Rocky Shores and Sandy Beaches. These particular Rocky Shores maintain more life than any other intertidal habitat. Every available place is likely to be used by organisms. Common animals are crabs, chitons, brittle stars, and sea anemones. Protected Outer Coast Sandy Beaches have fewer organisms than any other intertidal habitat. Part of this is the result of the limited extent of this habitat. The main organisms found are scuds and segmented worms.

Open Coast. This completely unprotected habitat has fewer organisms than the Protected Outer Coast. Open Coast species either require or tolerate the most violent surf action. The subdivisions found in the Protected Outer Coast are found here as well. Along Rocky Shores are animals with remarkable resistance to wave shock and capabilities of attachment. The most characteristic animals are goose-necked barnacles and mussels. The Sandy Beaches have certain crabs, and clams. All of these animals burrow, probably to resist wave action.

Bay and Estuary. In this habitat there is almost complete protection from surf, but life in these waters is subject to greater temperature and salinity variations than in any other intertidal habitat. However, many of the animals are in other ocean habitats, especially deep water. Four subdivisions are generally recognized: Rocky Shores with jingle shells (clams) and slipper shells; Sand Flats with sand dollars, heart urchins, and snails; Eelgrass (not seaweed but a vascular plant) with snails, hydroids, and sessile jellyfish; and Mud Flats with various snails, sea pens, ghost shrimps, and clams.

Wharf Piling. Here are found an assemblage of animals often found elsewhere. Animals are hydroids, crabs, sea anemones, sea blubber, boring snails, and mussels.

INTERTIDAL ZONATION AND TIDAL EXPOSURE

Normally the intertidal habitats are subdivided into four zones that reflect tidal exposure. Zone I, the Uppermost Beach or Spray Zone, extends from the highest reach of spray and storm waves to about average level of all high tides. Zone II, the High Tide Region or Upper Horizon, extends from the average high tide line to about the average level of the higher of the two daily low tides. Zone III, the Mid-tide Region or Middle Horizon, extends from the average higher low tide line to the average lower low tide line. Zone IV, the Low Tide Region or Lower Horizon, extends from the average lower low tide level to the lowest low tide level.

Fortunately the tidal definitions of exposure zones need not always be applied in the field. In rocky areas, and especially along the Pacific Coast, living creatures tend to indicate the zonation (Figure 17.7); elsewhere, the zones often are obscure.

The following characteristic organisms regularly are sufficient to diagnose particular rocky-area zones:

Zone I is mostly bare rock but contains scattered green algae (Chlorophyta), lichens, limpets, and periwinkles (snails, Gastropoda), and acorn barnacles (Cirripedia).

Zone II often has a type of green algae called sea lettuce, various branching brown algae (Phaeophyta) called rockweeds, a new and diverse group of limpets and snails (Gastropoda), more acorn barnacles but often added to the species in Zone I, various crabs (Decapoda), colonial hydroids (Hydrozoa), and marine worms (Polychaeta).

Zone III has many kinds of seaweeds; the greater diversity alone often is sufficient to separate this zone from Zone II. Here, often, are silky, tufted types of green algae, additional kinds of brown algae, and the

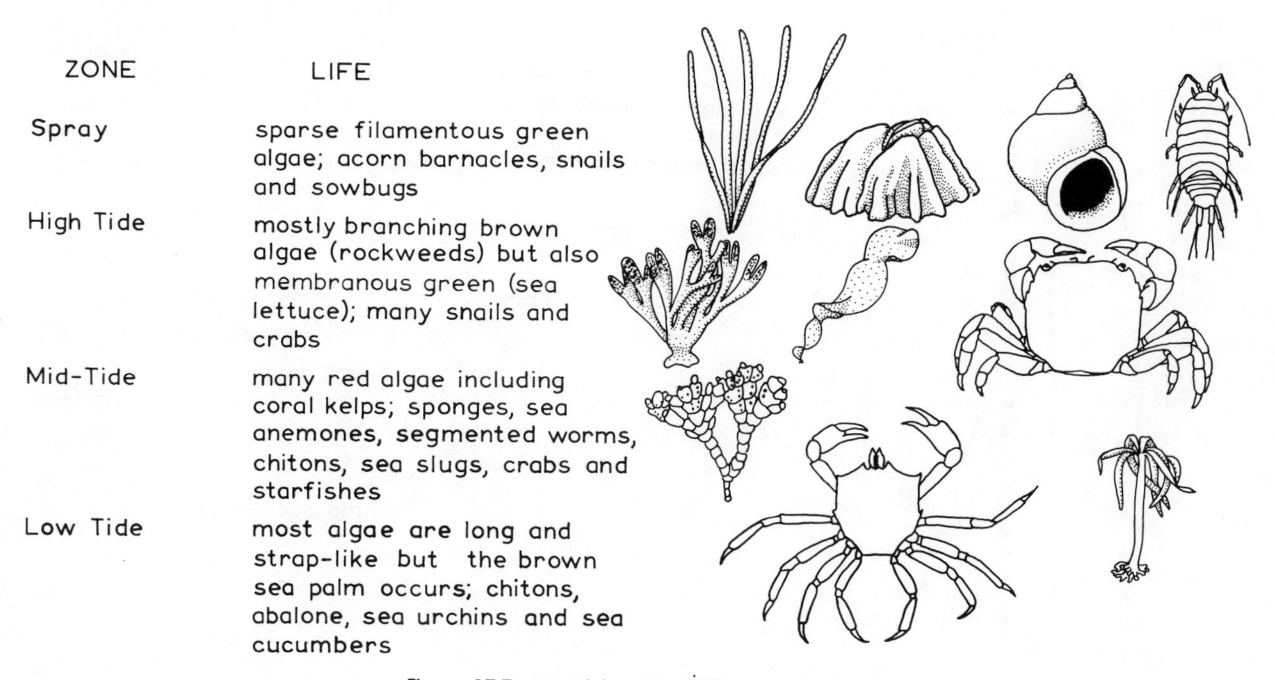

Figure 17.7 Intertidal zonation of life on a rocky shore.

first significant numbers of red algae (Rhodophyta). Among the red algae are various coral-like and feather-like forms. In addition, animals are more numerous and more varied.

Zone IV usually displays the greatest diversity and numbers of plants and animals. The more conspicuous algae are laminarians, a group of brown algae diagnosed by their long, straplike blades.

SUCCESSION

Although the details of the process of transition through various unstable communities to a stable community, or climax, at a particular place is to be delayed, some consideration of the phenomenon is of help here.

Intertidal areas are not stable. They can be transformed, owing to deposition, to fresh-water sites or to land (Figure 17.8). (See Figure 4.17 and related discussion, pp 54–55. In the transformation to fresh-water sites the first step is the development of quiet waters and a salt marsh, a situation already prevalent in quiet marine waters. The transformation from saline marsh could be directly to a land habitat, but in the change to a fresh-water area, it involves sedimentation leading to greater elevation of the bottom to a point where marine waters no longer invade the area. Further steps to a land habitat might be inferred from the discussion of fresh-water succession (pp. 318–322).

Intertidal succession to land might be assumed to start with the Zone IV condition and, again as a result of sedimentation, the site proceed to Zone I. From Zone I, further development probably approximates normal land succession from bare rock, a subject to be delayed until the general topic of succession (Chapter 19). However, in sandy areas near the ocean (*strands*) certain unique stages might be

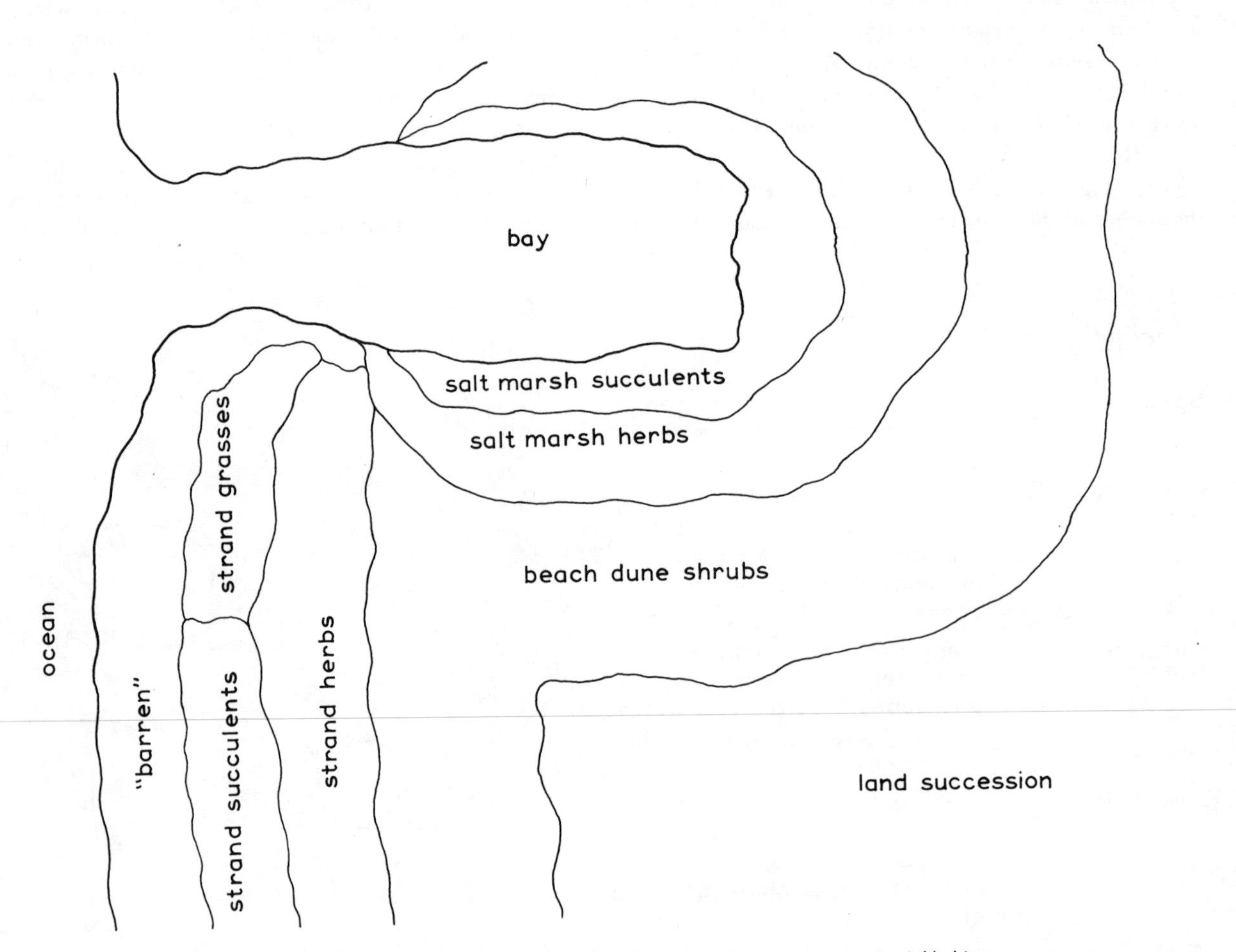

Figure 17.8 Plant succession near the ocean; possible sequences from marine to terrestrial habitats.

present. Strands are considered desert conditions because there is a general lack of available moisture; the moisture that is abundant is salty and not usable to plants other than the strand-adapted, salt-tolerant species.

Immediately adjacent to the ocean there often is a sand area devoid of plants and having a rather limited number of animals, often a restricted variety of arthropods.

The first site containing plants has the most severe maritime influence. In some cases certain grasses occur, but in many the plants are almost exclusively succulents. These plants and the few animals with them (again, mostly arthropods) are subject not only to salt spray but to high winds which both dry and sand blast the life and move the sand substrate. Such groups of plants and animals, and any other herbaceous communities that may follow, even though slightly more remote from the ocean, are often called *coastal strand communities*.

Although herbaceous habitats may form several coastal strand communities, the next stage (or stages) of apparent real differences consists of shrubs. These *beach-dune communities* may be closest to the sea if the beaches are protected from maritime winds; however, where there is little protection, shrubs gradually replace the coastal strand herbs.

Further sequences of communities frequently fit into land succession normal for the particular area. In some cases the next stage may be an herb community; in others, a shrub or tree community.

FRESH-WATER ENVIRONMENT

Factors of most importance in fresh-water habitats are temperature, suspended materials, current velocity, oxygen–carbon dioxide concentration, and salt content. Although *temperature* fluctuation in water is much less than that on land, temperature frequently is a primary limiting factor because the tolerance of aquatic life tends to be very low; many aquatic plants and animals can exist only within very narrow ranges of temperature. *Suspended materials* are related directly to light penetration. Those waters with a great deal of suspended materials allow a minimum of light penetration and may well have few organisms. The *velocity* of currents typically is directly associated with the distribution of most organisms and the adaptations of certain animals. Animals inhabiting rapidly moving waters may possess various features to prevent removal from their environment. Among these specializations are body shape (e.g., flattened or streamlined) and attachment devices (e.g., sticky, hooks, or growth to the substrate). Insufficient *oxygen* frequently acts as a limiting factor. The oxygen concentration in any particular body of water often is highest at low temperatures and salinities, and wind and water movements are important in determining the rate of oxygen intake by water. The *salt content* of water influences organisms. Most life can exist only within a relatively narrow range of water salinity. If there is too much salt in the water, many species lose their own body water; if there is too little, they may take on too much water and burst. Either effect usually leads to death.

Fresh-water environments are of two types, *standing* and *moving waters*. Standing waters tend to fill in as a result of physical and biological developments (succession) in a sequence of habitats. A possible sequence is lake, pond, marsh, and swamp. Moving waters usually show the result of physical development from fast- to slow-moving water. This sequence normally entails progression from brook to river, with further history following that given in previous discussion of life cycles of streams (pp. 42–44).

The ecology of lakes requires classification of biological and physical subunits and then classification of lakes themselves. The biological subunits are treated as organism types and the physical subunits as light zones and temperature layering.

ORGANISM TYPES IN STANDING WATERS

Fresh-water creatures usually are segregated according to their general shape and appearance, or life form, into *benthos*, *periphyton*, *plankton*, *nekton*, and *neuston*. Benthos are bottom creatures that are either resting upon, attached to, or living within the underlying strata. Periphyton are attached to any surface rising above the bottom. Plankton are floating species whose movements are most dependent upon water currents. They are either nonmotile or very weakly motile, and are normally microscopic or submicroscopic. Nekton are active swimmers that are independent of water currents; usually they are macroscopic. Neuston are all surface organisms.

Benthos occur in a variety of bottom situations. In general, dark and sandy bottoms have fewer species (except for clams) than other areas. Typical benthic life includes bacteria (Schizophyta), protozoans except sporozoans (Protozoa), fresh-water sponges (Porifera), free-living flatworms (Turbellaria), ribbonworms (Nemertea), roundworms (Nematoda), rotifers (Rotatoria), gastrotrichs (Gastrotricha), moss animals (Ectoprocta), snails (Gastropoda), clams (Pelecypoda), earthworm relatives (Oligochaeta), leeches (Hirudinea), water bears (Tardigrada), mites (Acarina), fly and other insect larvae (Insecta), water fleas (Cladocera), ostracods (Ostracoda), copepods (Copepoda), and scuds, crayfish, and other malacostracans (Malacostraca).

Periphyton might be eliminated as a category of fresh-water organism types. In many cases this group consists of the overflow from benthic life. However, there often is some tendency for encrusting forms such as sponges and colonial ectoprocts to reach their greatest concentration here.

Free-floating life, plankton, may contain the greatest concentration of plants, the suspended hydrophytes, in any body of water. In fact, plankton may contain the greatest mass of life in an aquatic habitat; however, much of the life is microscopic or nearly so. Among the most conspicuous fresh-water organisms are blue-green algae (Cyanophyta), green algae (Chlorophyta), and diatoms (Chrysophyta). Bacteria and true fungi often are numerous. Planktonic protists and animals are represented by the protozoans except sporozoa, reproductive structures of sponges (gemmules), rare hydromedusae or hydroid jellyfish (Trachylina), rotifers, gastrotrichs, reproductive structures of bryozoans (statoblasts), mites, fly larvae, water fleas, ostracods, and copepods.

Nekton are most obviously fish and shrimp. However, members of all the previous groups may swim in a body of water. In addition, certain terrestrial or aquatic margin species occasionally become part of the nekton or other groups already mentioned. These latter animals include salamanders, frogs, snakes, turtles, loons, mergansers, pelicans, cormorants, terns, gulls, ospreys, bald eagles, swallows, other so-called marsh birds, muskrat, mink, and otter.

Some neuston previously were mentioned, the floating hydrophytes.

LIGHT ZONES

Light penetration is used to designate certain habitats within standing waters (Figure 17.9). The

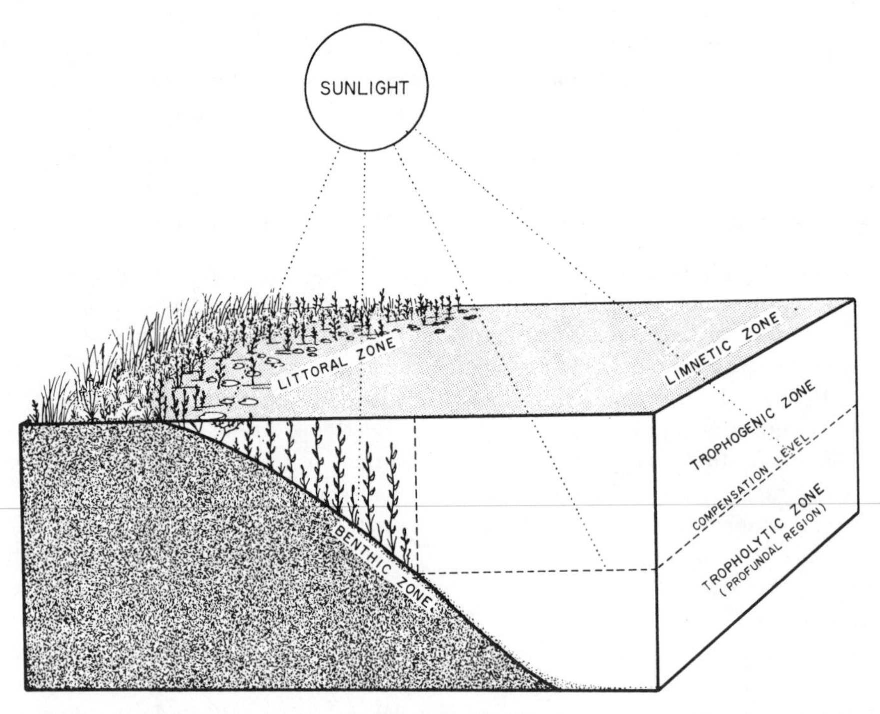

Figure 17.9 The major horizontal and vertical life zones of a lake. (From George K. Reid, *Ecology of Inland Waters and Estuaries*, Reinhold Publishing Corp., New York, 1961)

littoral zone is that part of standing water where light reaches the bottom. The *limnetic zone* is the illuminated water above areas of ineffective light penetration. The *profundal zone* is the region of ineffective light penetration. The *benthic zone* is the bottom.

TEMPERATURE LAYERING

In deep standing waters (for practical purposes, lakes) three characteristic temperature layers are developed in the summer and the winter and lost in the fall and the spring (Figure 17.10). These three layers are from top to bottom the epilimnion, thermocline, and hypolimnion. Often the *epilimnion* is an area of warm water, the *hypolimnion* of cold water, and the *thermocline* of rapid temperature change between the other two areas.

The annual cycle of lake waters that show temperature layering regularly displays the following general pattern (Figure 17-11):

In the spring the waters of the entire lake assume the same temperature, and wind is the most important force creating a circular path of movement from top to bottom, the so-called *spring overturn.* As summer temperatures rise, the surface waters become warmer than the bottom waters and a thermocline forms between the two. This stratification can lead to hypolimnion oxygen depletion if the lake is shallow and the hypolimnion is small, or if the hypolimnion is below the depth of effective light penetration.

With the approach of fall, epilimnion temperature gradually drops to that of the hypolimnion and the

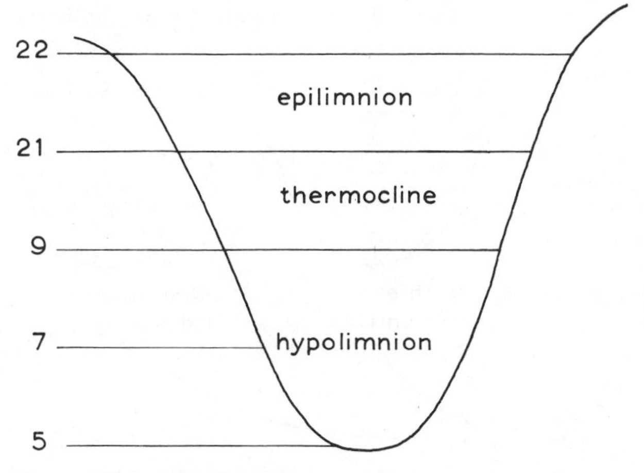

Figure 17.10 Thermal stratification in lakes. Temperatures (°C.) are given for 5-meter intervals.

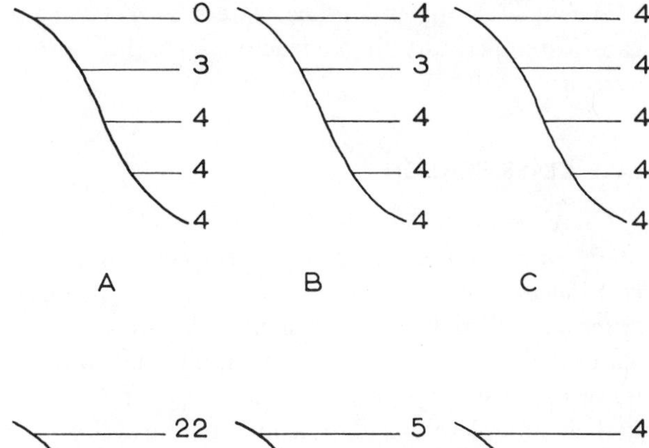

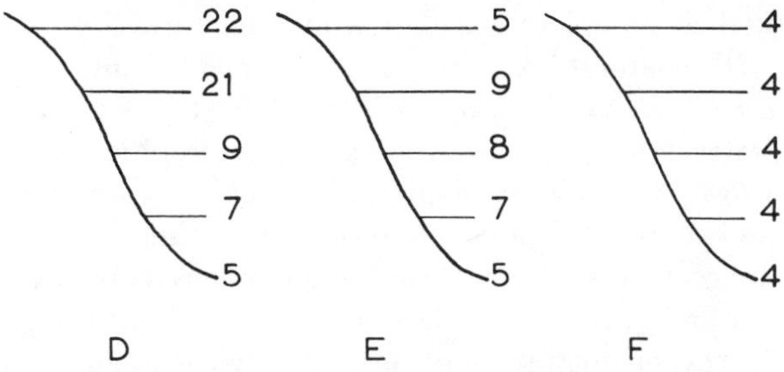

Figure 17.11 The annual temperature cycle in most deep-water lakes of temperate climates. (Temperature in degrees centigrade is given at the surface and at depths of 5, 10, 15, and 20 meters.) A, the condition of winter with a surface ice cover and lower stagnation; B, the time of early spring when the surface waters are warmer than those a few meters down; C, spring overturn; the entire lake waters are 4°C. so winds cause waters to overturn; D, summer stratification, the same conditions shown in Figure 17.10, produced by surface warming; E, fall cooling again causes surface waters to become cooler than intermediate waters; F, fall overturn, like spring overturn, occurs when the entire body of water is 4°C.

fall overturn results. Further temperature drop takes place but there is little change in condition until 4° C., the point of greatest water density. As the cooling surface waters reach 4° C, they sink; cooling and sinking finally causes the entire lake to obtain a temperature of 4° C. When surface waters fall below this temperature they become lighter and remain floating upon the denser, deeper, 4° C. water. The consequence again is stratification, but the warmer waters are now in the hypolimnion and the surface of the epilimnion usually freezes. This stratification tends to cause little oxygen depletion in the lake, for the cold reduces the biological activities and oxygen needs of its organisms. Actually, because they are cold the waters may contain more oxygen than at any other time of the year. The one general exception to this is when deep ice or snow sufficiently retards light penetration to prevent photosynthesis and to kill many plants and, therefore, animals.

Spring warming of surface waters to 4° C again causes temperature homogeneity and the spring overturn.

LAKE CLASSIFICATION

Large bodies of standing water are classified in many ways. One of the frequently seen, simplified classifications uses *artificial* vs. *natural* as the primary criterion of segregation. Artificial lakes have many features that are unique to the individual waters; however, most are poor habitats for organisms, owing to their water level fluctuation and high turbidity.

The natural lakes are further subdivided into *clear water lakes* and *impure water lakes*. The two clear water types are oligotrophic and eutrophic lakes. *Oligotrophic lakes* (little-producing) usually are deep and contain hypolimnion oxygen at all times. These are geologically young lakes whose materials produce few organisms. However, oligotrophic lakes through succession mature into eutrophic (good-producing) lakes. *Eutrophic lakes* have conditions that support many organisms. These lakes are usually shallow. However, because their hypolimnions are relatively small (they represent a later stage than an oligotrophic lake, a stage in both a geomorphic and biotic succession cycle reached after considerable sedimentation and resultant filling), summer oxygen depletion occurs at the bottom and many organisms die to contribute to the organic richness of these waters (Figure 17.12).

Impure water lakes are of many types. Their classification is not as logical as that of clear waters, because the impure types normally do not represent a geomorphic or biotic succession sequence.

The main impure types are *dystrophic* (bad-producing), *volcanic*, *alkali*, and *salt*. Dystrophic are acid lakes containing a particular chemical compound, humic acid. The primary example is the bog lake. When such lakes become filled with peat moss they are called a peat bog or, sometimes, a moor. Volcanic lakes are either acidic or alkaline, depending on the nature of the surrounding igneous rocks. Alkali lakes and salt lakes are found mostly in desert areas. The former result from waters draining igneous areas; the latter, from waters draining sedimentary areas (Figure 17.12).

Certain additional information about the kinds of natural lakes is required if each kind is to be examined in detail.

Clear Water Habitats. These habitats fall into two main groupings, life cycle and successional. The life cycle group is related to the geomorphic cycle of a lake. Youth is indicated by the *oligotrophic lake* whose subhabitats are largely limited to the life forms previously mentioned. Early maturity, the *eutrophic lake*, has greater numbers and diversity of organisms. In addition, benthic aquatic vegetation becomes dense and the substrate mucky or muddy. If this vegetation is strictly herbaceous, the habitat is a *marsh;* if it contains trees, a *swamp*. Later geomorphic maturity is first indicated by the *pond* stage and then the *temporary pond* stage. Finally, old age occurs when the area dries completely and becomes part of the *land*.

Within these geomorphic stages there usually is a shoreward zonation of benthic life into progressively later successional stages. These stages may be considered individual habitats. In actual practice, one should first classify clear water habitats on the basis

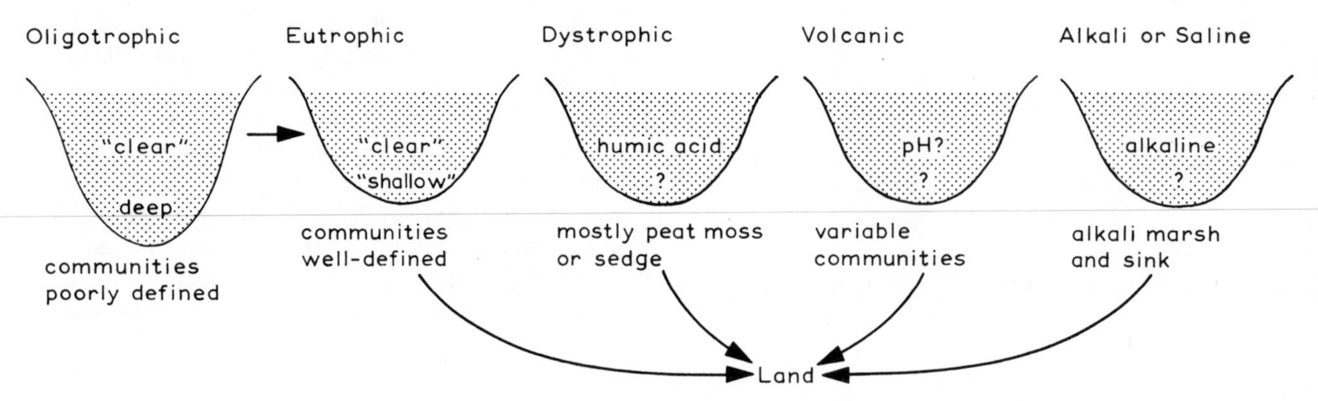

Figure 17.12 Characteristics of natural fresh-water lakes and some indication of their path of development to a land habitat.

of geomorphic stage, then on the basis of life forms within the lake, and finally, on the basis of benthos subdivision into developmental stages from open water to shore.

The variety of successional habitats, according to their progress in succession, are *submerged stage, floating-leaved stage, emergent stage, saturated soil stage, moist soil stage,* and *climax*. This classification of hydrophytes is slightly different from that to be given later for water habitat, or hydrarch, succession where the general similarities between kinds of succession are stressed. In further discussion the saturated soil and moist soil stages are not emphasized.

Impure Water Habitats. Impure water habitats show a great deal of local variation and little relationship to one another. *Dystrophic lakes* have many successional habitats that might be termed *open water, moss stage, peat bog, bog swamp,* and *bog forest* stage. *Volcanic lakes*, owing to the diversity of their waters, can have many habitats. These habitats can be named according to the appearance of the plants or any other convenient aspect of the waters. *Alkali lakes* may have little or no life in the waters. However, the margin regularly has an alkali marsh and adjacent land usually has scrub vegetation in the form of an alkali sink community. *Saline lakes* may contain little more life than brine shrimp (Anostraca). However, the margins generally have the same sort of communities as those found around alkali lakes.

MOVING WATERS

Most of the factors operating in standing water are also important in running water. However, temperature layering is insignificant in most streams. Of greater importance is the rate of water flow; many animal adaptations are directly related to this.

Stream classification is based upon geological age. However, within young, mature, and old streams is a diversity of habitats. Unfortunately these habitats cannot be segrated in any simple, meaningful manner. This is the case because a multitude of ecological factors produce complex environments that are not easily categorized. For example, falls, rapids, and plunging pools of one young stream might possess entirely different organisms, however in another young stream these situations might display no such distinction.

This does not mean that stream habitats defy segregation. One can study physical factors of areas having unique organisms and seek environmental correlations. Perhaps the habitats can be named according to these unique situations. In addition, quieter waters of streams normally display the water-to-land sequence of stages that are found in standing waters. As in standing waters, these stages of succession are unstable and developmental (seral), each being replaced by another stage until the stable climax is reached.

FRESH-WATER COMMUNITIES

Oligotrophic Lakes. These young, "little-producing," clear water lakes have a poor definition of successional stages. For practical purposes, any clear water lake having neither clearly defined open water; submerged, floating-leaved, and emergent stages; nor life in the form of neuston, plankton, nekton, periphyton, and benthos is an oligotrophic lake. However, such lakes may have well-developed saturated soil and moist soil stages as described under eutrophic lakes.

Eutrophic Lakes. These "good-producing" lakes are geologically mature and have a great diversity of life. Also, zonation of life is clearly marked, the stages being indicative of the hydrarch succession that will eventually fill these bodies of water. From first (at or near deepest water) to last (a land habitat), the stages are (Figure 17.13):

Open Water Stage. In open water there are many plants and animals, occurring as neuston, plankton, nekton, and benthos. A fifth category, periphyton, can also be recognized.

Submerged Stage. This community may be influenced by the presence of neuston, plankton, nekton, and benthos similar to those in the open water stage. However, most typical of the submerged-stage organisms are submerged anchored hydrophytes, plants with thin, dissected, and/or linear leaves. Typical plants of this habitat are pondweeds (*Potamogeton*) and stonewort (*Chara*). The maximum depth of this stage is limited by sunlight penetration and the minimum depth is limited by invasion of the next stage.

Floating-leaved Stage. Although organisms inhabiting the four microhabitats are present, most characteristic here are the floating-leaved anchored hydrophytes. These plants often have leaves of two types. Their underwater leaves are similar to those of submerged anchored hydrophytes but the floating

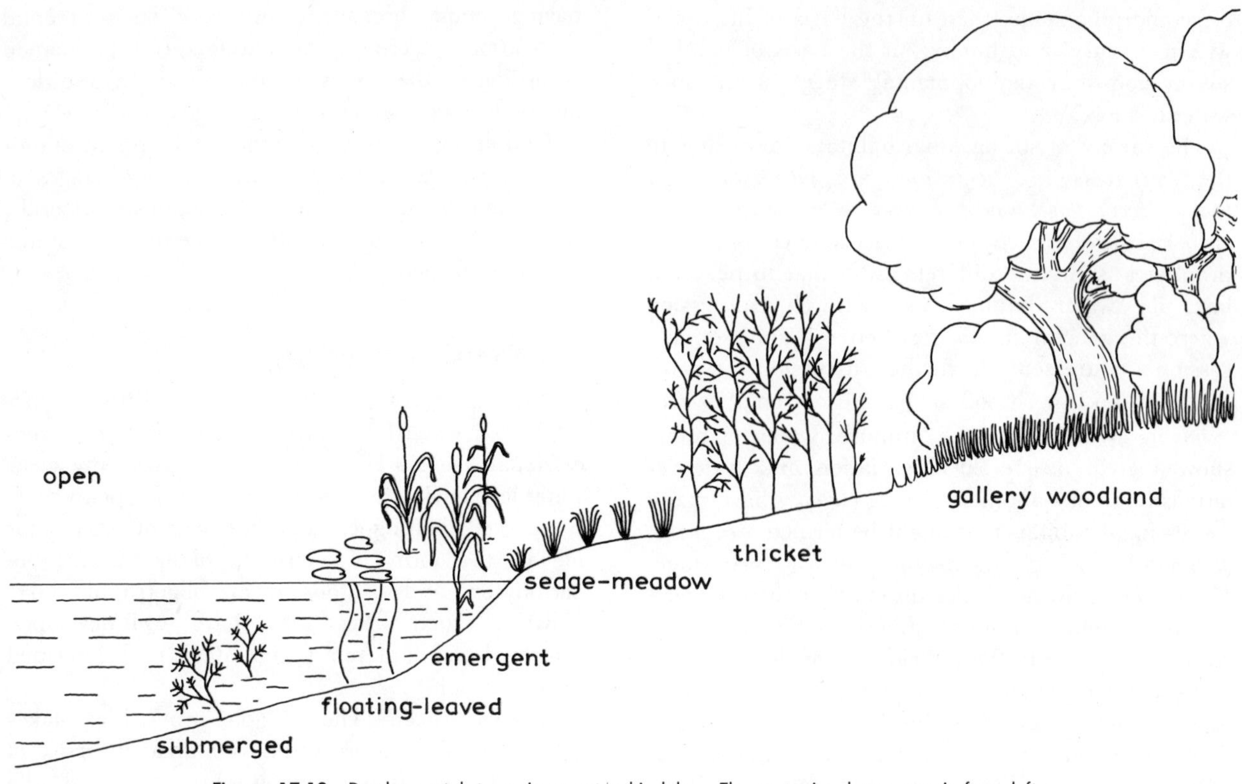

Figure 17.13 Developmental stages in an eutrophic lake. The successional sequence is from left to right.

leaves are usually neither thin, dissected, nor linear. Common plants include certain pondweeds (*Potamogeton*), water lilies (*Nymphaea*), and water buttercup (*Ranunculus aquatilis*).

Emergent Stage. This stage features emergent anchored hydrophytes. Because of its vegetation, the stage also is called a tule, reed, or cattail marsh. Characteristic species are bullrush or tule (*Scirpus*), reed (*Phragmites*), and cattail (*Typha*).

Saturated Soil Stages. The area from within the edge of a body of water out to the end of the land zone of soil saturation might have three communities; however, only one or two of these stages may be present in a given area. Only two are always associated with saturated soil. They are presented in their usual order of succession.

Sedge-meadow stage: The herbaceous vegetation of this area also makes it a marsh. Predominant plants include sedges (*Carex*), rushes (*Juncus*), spike rushes (*Eleocharis*), and smart weeds (*Polygonum*). The roots and rhizomes of these plants form a dense, tough, sodlike mat. Within this mat are many organisms found nowhere else in the area. Also, this stage frequently has an understory herb and perhaps other layers of plants and animals.

Thicket stage: Saturated to moist soils in relatively drier surroundings often have shrub vegetation along the margin of the body of water. The shrubs are variable from place to place. However, willows (*Salix*) are present in most localities having this swamp community.

Moist Soil Stages. The moist soil stages are distinct shore situations. Although brushland and fringing woodland stages are included, the brushland is of quite restricted occurrence.

Brushland stage: Bushes, low shrubs, and stunted trees forming more or less closed communities on the borders of arctic and alpine vegetation or along cold streams or lakes are called brushlands. Water usually is abundant; however, low absorption and high water loss present conditions unfavorable to forest development, yet more favorable than in colder areas where excessive dryness or snow fields prevent growth of trees. The stage could just as well be treated as a saturated soil stage, because it is found in both saturated and moister soils next to bodies of water.

Fringing woodland stage: This moist soil community takes a variety of forms depending on local climate and topography. If the stage has restricted available water there may be only a few species of shrubs and/or trees present; these plants are in the form of a woodland. However, if available moisture is high the stage may assume the appearance of a dense forest. In a lush situation, the following species of plants may be found; a tree layer or layers composed of maple (*Acer*), elm (*Ulmus*), ash (*Fraxinus*), sycamore (*Platanus*), and cottonwood (*Populus*); and a shrub layer composed of alder (*Alnus*), willow (*Salix*), and dogwood (*Cornus*). In addition, there may be well-developed herb, moss, epiphytic, saprophytic, and parasitic life.

Another tree often found with the above group is oak (*Quercus*). In many cases the oak merely contributes to a woodland-to-forest situation in conjunction with the other trees and the shrubs. However, in some cases the entry of oaks constitutes a more advanced stage in succession. Even though this is the case, the other species normally remain a part of the habitat.

Dystrophic Lakes. "Bad-producing" lakes typically contain acid-producing vegetation, usually sphagnum moss (*Sphagnum*) but sometimes other vegetation, e.g., sedges (*Carex*). The stages are only vaguely similar to those found in an eutrophic lake; the lake usually can be diagnosed on the basis of moss or acidity of the waters (Figure 17.14).

Open Water Stage. Very few organisms are present. The stage often has only a few species when adjacent stages are composed of acid-producing plants.

Moss Stage. The innermost stage may consist of floating moss; however, there may be a series of stages comparable to the submerged-to-emergent stages as they are found in oligotrophic lakes. These oligotrophic-like stages would then supplant the moss stage; however, the subsequent communities would be the next two listed.

Bog Stage. This community is similar to the sedge meadow stage of oligotrophic lakes in that the vegetation forms a dense, sodlike mat. However, the species compositions of the two are very different, and the bog stage usually extends much farther out over the water.

Shrub Stage. The dystrophic shrub community

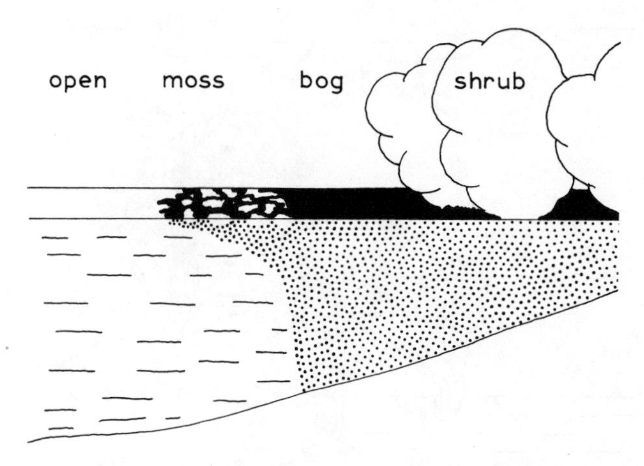

Figure 17.14 Developmental stages in a dystrophic lake.

normally consists of a unique assemblage of vegetation. In sphagnum bogs, cranberries (*Vaccinium*) and Labrador tea (*Ledum*) often are quite common. However, sphagnum bogs and their allied vegetation are uncommon in subtropical and more arid areas. In these latter areas, dystrophic lakes typically are not as acid and the shrub stage vegetation tends to consist of the hardier, acid-resistant, semiaquatic plants.

Saturated and Moist Soil Stages. These communities are much the same as those found around eutrophic lakes.

Volcanic Lakes. These bodies of water are diagnosed on the basis of their stages, substrate, or pH (acid, neutral, or alkaline). Ecologically they can be similar to oligotrophic, eutrophic, or dystrophic lakes. For practical purposes, it probably is best to consider them as such.

Alkali and Saline Lakes. Although these lakes are chemically different, they present a similar ecological situation. One can determine whether a particular lake is saline or alkaline; however, further treatment of subunits is very similar.

Functionally, these lakes are dry habitats, very little water being available to plants not adapted to the habitat. Three developmental stages usually are recognized (Figure 17.15).

Open Water Stage. Surprisingly, perhaps, many creatures often are in the open water, as well as the margins, of these lakes. The species are mostly arthropods but are different from those in the open water stage of eutrophic lakes. Also, some neuston, plankton, nekton, and benthos normally are present.

Figure 17.15 Developmental stages in an alkali or saline lake.

Alkali Marsh Stage. The margins of these lakes often have two species of extremely tolerant plants, glasswort (*Salicornia*) and bush picklewood (*Allenrolfea*) plants also found in coastal salt marshes of the Pacific coast.

Alkali Sink Stage. This community might actually be a stable one (climax) and not developmental, because it is found in relatively uniform conditions of salinity or alkalinity either on the margin of alkali marshes or in the soils resulting from the drying of temporary lakes. Common plants are saltbushes (*Atriplex*) and greasewood (*Sarcobatus vermiculatus*).

Ponds and Temporary Ponds. These areas represent late stages in the geological and ecological succession of a lake. Therefore, they each contain, some to all of the stages presented under the discussion of eutrophic lakes.

Streams. Streams are classified according to geological age (young, mature, or old), and permanence (temporary or permanent). Size also could be indicated by referring to brooks, rivers, etc. Further subdivision could be made according to succession from open water (when present) to land. The stages found in a stream could be like those presented in the discussion of eutrophic lakes.

LIGHT

Solar radiation is essential for life as we know it, but light is not a simple or uncomplicated factor in an environment. It is indispensable for the basic food-making process of photosynthesis; at the same time, its direct rays are lethal to many organisms. Among plants, certain species require direct sunlight throughout their life, others only during germination; still others never can tolerate direct solar rays. Its general importance to animals is shown by the fact that most species have organs that perceive light, although these perceptions might be simply of light intensity rather than actual vision. However, the importance of vision for locating food is indicated by the fact that various organisms that might be preyed upon are camouflaged.

In spite of the critical nature of light, some organisms spend much (perhaps all) of their life in eternal darkness. Cave life is a prime example of this. However, there are only a few cave creatures—a few bacteria, fungi, and animals such as crickets, beetles, crayfish, fish, salamanders, and bats. Owing to a unique radar-like sense, bats apparently are the only animals that move freely into the extremely dark areas of caves and back out into the open. The permanent cave residents are remarkable for their general lack of pigmentation and absence of functional eyes. Apparently color is unnecessary to protect the animals from light and eyesight would be relatively useless in caves.

WAVELENGTH, INTENSITY, AND DURATION

The wavelength, intensity, and duration of light usually are aspects of greatest ecological significance. Wavelengths are critical to animals because only certain lengths are visible and many others are harmful radiations. Plants also are harmed by some invisible rays; however, parts of visible light are most efficient in stimulating photosynthesis. Ultraviolet wavelengths are instrumental in killing many germs and enabling many animals to form vitamin D. Also, infrared light is of primary importance in producing heat.

Light intensity has a great many ecological associations. For example, it is directly related to the amount of photosynthesis and transpiration in plants and to the structure and function of developing and adult plant organs. In the ocean and deep lakes intensity of light regulates the concentration of microscopic plankton near the surface. In dense forests there are shade plants that can survive only in the shade created by a tree canopy. These shade plants are specialized to carry on adequate photosynthesis under minimal conditions that would kill many other species.

Locally, light intensity can be reduced by many factors. Some of these were mentioned in relation to climate. The more important factors limiting light intensity are thicker air at low altitudes, greater moisture or clouds in the air, solar radiation coming at an angle through the atmosphere (therefore traveling through more atmosphere), radiation striking the substrate at an angle, greater depth of water, number and volume of particles in air or water, vegetation cover, and angle and direction of slope of the substrate. Because these factors can cause a variety of light intensities in a locale, unlike responses may be made by organisms living there.

The duration of light is often called an environmental clock because the length of night and day have remarkable associations with plant and animal activities. In plants, those species termed "long-day plants" bloom only after many days with more than twelve hours of sunlight; in "short-day plants" the period of light must be less than twelve hours (actually, the duration of darkness seems most important to these plants). In animals, length of day is associated with reproductive cycles, migrations, molts, and many other life functions.

PHOTOPERIODISM

The phenomenon whereby organism responses are related to light duration is called photoperiodism. In plants, photoperiodism is limited to arctic and temperate zone, long- and short-day species. The long-day plants include all species poleward of latitude 60° and some in the temperate zone. These plants flower in late spring and early summer, in contrast to short-day plants which flower in early spring or late summer. The short-day plants are found almost exclusively in the temperate zone.

Various plant and animal responses are related to photoperiodism. The more significant plant responses include length of life cycle, flowering, germination, size and structure of vegetative organs, degree of branching, lobing of leaves, pigmentation, formation of storage or fibrous roots, nutrient requirements, dormancy of deciduous plants, and susceptibility to parasitism and disease. Also, photoperiodism is significant in plant distribution. Its importance is best appreciated in terms of day length, because plants tend to require lengths of day corresponding to the locality in which they grow and the season in which they flower. Therefore, the fact that day length shows definite geographic relations causes light duration to be a very important factor in geographic distribution.

Neither light intensity nor wavelength are related to plant geography. These two factors display great local variation and are most important as contributors to local peculiarities in the distribution of individual plants and habitats.

ATMOSPHERE

The atmospheric gases directly influencing organisms are the 21 per cent oxygen and .03 per cent carbon dioxide. Both plants and animals utilize oxygen and release carbon dioxide in the function of respiration. However, plants consume more carbon dioxide than they release and expel more oxygen than they ever utilize in respiration. This condition exists because the daytime process of photosynthesis uses carbon dioxide and expels oxygen to a greater extent than the continuous process of respiration uses oxygen and expels carbon dioxide. Therefore, plants act to prevent potentially poisonous concentrations of carbon dioxide and provide oxygen for most other organisms.

Atmospheric gases enter and leave plants by openings in leaves, by openings in woody twigs, and by diffusion through rootlets (Figure 17.16). Waste gas is expelled only by leaves and twigs. This entire gaseous change is related to transpiration, because all gaseous exchanges necessitate wet cell surfaces and thus cause water loss to the plants.

Proper plant aeration is essential for normal growth and function, but aeration problems rarely

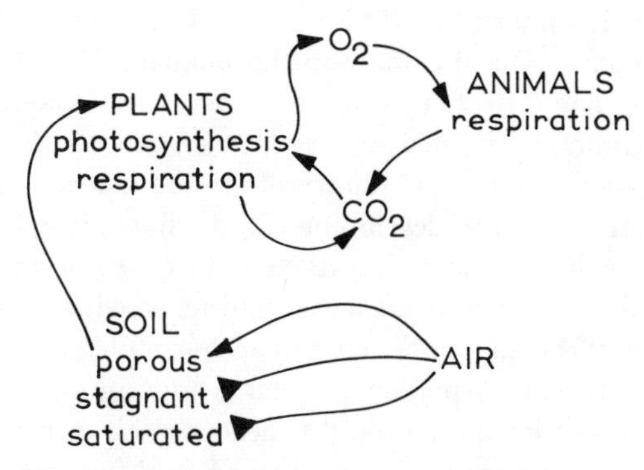

Figure 17.16 Oxygen–carbon dioxide relationships of plants, animals, and soil with air.

involve aerial parts of plants. Usual difficulty is with excess water causing air stagnation (carbon dioxide buildup and oxygen depletion) in the substrate. Excess water limits the availability of gases to plants and creates an environment that is suitable only to hydrophytes. Air stagnation is a normal tendency in many soils. However, air renewal can occur in several ways. For example, water infiltrating the soil will first replace stagnant air; when the moisture either evaporates, is used by plants, or percolates deeper, fresh air is drawn into the soil. Other means of air replacement in soil are provided by changes in wind velocity, air pressure, and temperature.

Soil air becomes stagnant when its oxygen is depleted or made less available by organism respiration, amount of pore space, size of pore space, and effectiveness of drainage. Respiration by soil organisms and plant roots uses oxygen and produces additional carbon dioxide. Amount of pore space should be directly related to amount of soil air; however, heavy soils which have about 60 per cent of their volume in pore space are more subject to stagnation than are light soils which have about 40 per cent pore space. This is so because heavy soils usually contain more water (thus, actually have less soil air and greater stagnation) and take longer to replace their gases. Pore size, on the other hand, is directly related to air replacement; coarse soils with larger pore spaces than finer soils replace air much more rapidly. Drainage is directly related to air replacement; the better the drainage of a soil, the more rapid the replacement.

WIND

The ecological influence of wind, direct and indirect, is important (Table 17.3). Indirectly, wind can modify a local climate to the point of forming a unique habitat. For example, a dry wind may remove much of the moisture and create a desert in an otherwise humid area. On the other hand, winds can be instrumental in developing clouds that are moved into localities where they then reduce temperature and water loss and create a moister environment. Direct effects of wind need not be harmful. For example, wind transports many plants and animals into new areas. For plants wind is necessary to transport the pollen and seeds of many species, and for animals wind moves the eggs and adults of many species.

The harmful consequences of wind are best seen in plants of coasts, high altitudes, or flat plains. Less harmful effects include such things as dessication, dwarfing, and deformation of plants. Most serious is breakage, abrasion, uprooting, and burying. A more complex situation is associated with movements of snow. Localized areas that are kept free of snow by wind often have plants different from those places free from modification or subject to accumulation of deep snow. Finally, coastal winds subject many strand plants to salt spray. Because the amount of salt spray is related directly to proximity to the ocean, plants nearest the sea frequently are limited to salt-tolerant types. However, these coastal strand types also are subject to uprooting and burying, perhaps the basis for the adaptations of extensive roots and capabilities for growing above burying sands.

ALPINE HABITATS

Wind is not the only powerful ecological factor in high mountains, nor is it necessarily the most important. However, in such places as alpine areas and deserts wind does reach its greatest importance as an ecological factor.

The nature of the atmosphere at high altitudes has great influence on the other ecological factors. Because of the altitude, the atmosphere is thin. This low air density means less oxygen per unit volume of air, one of the few stable alpine factors. Most alpine ecological factors display some of the most extreme fluctuations that can be found on earth. This especially is the case with temperature, wind, and water. The thin atmosphere allows much more intense solar radiation than is found in lowlands, so that daily temperatures may be very high and heat loss rapid at night.

Wind is important because its velocity is directly related to altitude: the greater the altitude, the greater the wind velocity. When wind velocity doubles, the force of the wind is quadrupled. Because gusts of wind at high altitudes approach 250 m.p.h., it is not surprising that wind frequently is a limiting factor in alpine areas. However, such wind velocities are not found in many mountains, since velocity is related to prevailing world winds. Only mountains located within zones of strong prevailing world winds can have gusts approaching the maximum figure—and, again, only certain areas within

TABLE 17.3 WIND EFFECTS ON THE ENVIRONMENT

Soil	Climate	Plants	Animals
Deflation (rocky)		Transportation	Transportation
Desiccation	Desiccation	Desiccation	Desiccation
Moistening	Moistening	Moistening	Moistening
	Zonation	Zonation	Zonation
		Dwarfing	Mechanical damage
		Deformation	
		Breakage	
		Abrasion	
		Uprooting	
		Burying	
			Behavioral changes

strong prevailing winds have the maximum velocities. These limited sites are related to geomorphic features that channel winds, causing considerable air to be forced through a narrow defile. Such natural, high-altitude wind tunnels may always have winds above 100 m.p.h.

Temperature and wind together contribute to a factor called *wind chill*. This is due to the well known fact that an actually higher air temperature associated with a strong wind can remove heat from an object much faster than a lower air temperature related to little or no wind. Therefore, because of high wind velocity in the area, the body temperature of alpine organisms can be sharply reduced, with lethal effects in many organisms.

Alpine water fluctuations are largely a consequence of topography. Precipitation can be extensive, but so is runoff. In addition to reflecting angle of slope, runoff is related to the soil, another factor of considerable alpine importance. The soil is generally thin, not having the characteristics that would tend to hold water. Also, the soil is such that it is subject to geological mass movements. Gravity, especially when supplemented by the lubricating action of water, causes all kinds of landslides and their side effects to prevail at high altitudes.

ALPINE PLANTS

Although high mountain plants vary in their adaptations, there is enough similarity among the species for generalizations to be made about the typical alpine plant (Figure 17.17). Most alpine plants are perennials. An examination of the structures and functions of well-adapted plants will show why annuals are unlikely to prove successful.

The typical alpine plant has many adaptations. The aerial parts are closely set in an over-all clumped cushion or tufted growth. This arrangement traps daytime heat and retards interior heat loss; at night interior temperatures may be 20 or more degrees higher than the outside air. The clump is broad but low owing to dwarfing, which locates the plant in an area of lesser wind velocity created by ground friction. However, the growth form is not due to inherent causes. The exposed uppermost plant parts are pruned by winter wind and subfreezing temperatures, and the untrimmed lower parts are protected by a blanket of snow that shields against the wind and prevents temperatures much below freezing. In addition, the aerial parts tend not to be woody, but rather to be extremely flexible, thus reducing the possibility of wind breakage.

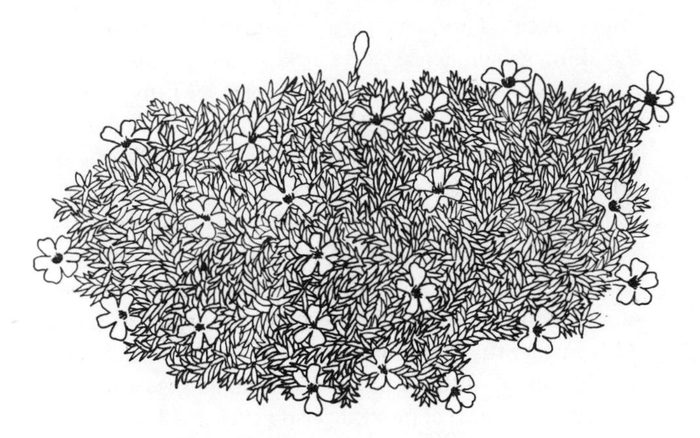

Figure 17.17 An alpine adapted plant.

Aerial leaves regularly possess certain specializations. The leaves are normally dark green (often very dark), a trait that enhances heat absorption. Such leaves typically are thick and waxy, thereby being specialized to resist evaporation. However, in certain plants the leaves have hairs that are white or approach that color. Although this might seem to cause undue heat reflection, again the color involves a means of retaining heat. The white color is only a surface coat upon many otherwise black hairs. Therefore, once heat is absorbed (even though somewhat inefficiently) the white outer coating reflects heat back into the hair of the plant. For this reason, as environmental temperatures are reduced from the extreme day highs, heat is retained in the plant.

The extensive root system serves two purposes. First, it is a means of reaching deep water during surface drought periods, especially in the relatively arid rain-shadow sides of mountain tops. Second, it serves the very necessary function of anchorage, the only deterrent to mass movements. However, since roots cannot control landslides, a further adaptation of plant aerial parts is significant. Alpine leaves and stems, more than those of plants in most other areas, act as if they are lubricated; landslides frequently pass over these plants without killing them.

Certain reproductive adaptations can be related to this environment. Although alpine plants are slow-growing and take a long time to flower, they produce many flowers and many seeds, thus increasing the probability of reproduction. Also, most alpine plants either are wind-pollinated or self-fertilized. The restriction of pollination by insects is understandable, because there are few flying insects in this windy habitat.

Some of the functional adaptations are of major importance. The plants are slow-growing because of the short growing season. Perhaps most remarkable are some of the adaptations to cold. Many alpine plants germinate and even flower below a snow cover. For this reason, plants function under conditions of little or no sunlight and of freezing temperature. Although the adaptations making this possible are little understood, some of the processes involved have been discovered. The plant fluids contain more nutrient materials than do typical plants elsewhere. This means that there is less water in tissues, hence less likelihood of freezing. Most amazing is the discovery that some plants flowering under a blanket of snow can produce some heat. Therefore, in some plants we find a condition analogous to the internal heat production of endothermic animals.

ALPINE ANIMALS

The ability to move enables many alpine animals to avoid the more rigorous periods of their environment. Such large mammals as elk, deer, bighorn sheep, and mountain lions move to lower altitudes during the winter. At lower altitudes food and shelter are more readily available; the elk, deer, and bighorn feed and live among thickets and the mountain lion preys upon these plant eaters.

In addition to migration, two other means are used by alpine animals to combat climatic extremes. Animals such as ground squirrels and marmots simply avoid the extremes. Before winter they eat large quantities of food and become exceedingly fat; with the coming of winter they hibernate. However, weasels, pikas, snowshoe hares, certain voles, and the mountain goat remain active throughout the winter. In all of these animals, activity is aided by the growth of a denser winter coat. In the pikas and voles, heat loss is minimized by the body's approaching spherical shape and extremities being much shortened. Also, pikas, voles, and weasels spend much or all of their time beneath the insulating blanket of snow. Of these mammals only weasels spend considerable time upon the surface.

During relatively favorable winter conditions, weasels and snowshoe hares become quite active, the weasels looking for prey and the hares for plants. Moreover, it may be assumed that both animals are subject to heavy predation because of their protective adaptation, a white winter coat. On the other hand, the weasel's coat may be an example of camouflage that helps in stalking prey. The completely white coat, except for blackish points on the extremities, allows an animal to blend with its white environment.

The North American mammal best adapted to alpine conditions is the mountain goat. Its coat is composed of long and short hairs that together provide water and wind resistance. Its hoofs are flexible, pincer-like structures with arched bottoms, features allowing great agility among precipitous cliffs. Therefore, it can obtain food in almost unbelievable places and readily avoid potential predators.

The commonest alpine invertebrates are insects. Alpine invertebrates as a group have few obvious adaptations for alpine life. They are no different from their lowland relatives in ability to withstand great extremes of temperature. Most invertebrates can withstand high mountain minimal temperatures without reaching the critical point at which their body fluids freeze. For example, some land snails can survive −184° F. if they are warmed gradually. However, some invertebrate adaptations can be related to high mountains. More of the alpine species are black, thereby absorbing the heat of the sun. Many of the flying insects have instincts causing them to fly close to the ground, thereby avoiding the upper zone of strong winds. Some insects are even wingless, in contrast to their lowland relatives.

Perhaps the most startling information about alpine life was the discovery of jumping spiders plus glacier fleas and related springtails at 22,000 feet and above. All of these animals are wingless and dark-bodied, the dark body every day absorbing the heat necessary to thaw the organisms out of the glacial ice. The jumping spiders feed upon the glacier fleas and springtails, the fleas and springtails feed upon fungi and decaying plants at lower elevations—but far above this level, well into glaciers where no plants are known, the animals feed upon windblown materials, mostly small insects and plant pollen.

SOIL

Soils normally support a vast number of organisms. The plants and animals usually have adaptations associated with certain features of their soil environment. For example, burrowing animals are frequently limited to specific soil conditions, especially textural, in direct relation to the animals' physical capabilities for burrowing. Plant correlations with their soil habitat are often more fundamental. Among the soil factors of greater importance to plants are soil texture, organic matter, moisture, pH, and salinity.

SOIL TEXTURE

Various generalizations are possible as to the relationships between plants and soil texture (Table 17.4). (1) Fine-textured silt and clay soils offer the greatest resistance to plant root penetration, and the coarser textured soils offer least resistance. (2) Water penetrates coarse soil readily and there is little runoff, but finer-textured soils retard water penetration and erode more readily owing to the greater runoff. In nature this may mean that two habitats having much the same precipitation have different plants. For example, a sandy site may have a forest which requires more available moisture, and a clayey area may have grassland. (3) Water moves more slowly through finer-textured soils. Because water moves rapidly through sandy soils, sandy soil plants often must have deeper roots. However, in sandy soils water may rise between the grains by capillary attraction, eliminating the need for deep-rooted plants. (4) Fine-textured soils tend to hold more water. This feature is an advantage of fine soils over coarse ones in places subject to drought periods. The actual holding of water is related directly to the surface area of soil particles, the combined area of spaces between particles, and the amount of water imbibed by individual particles. Since each of these physical features is best developed in fine soils, fine soils have greater water retention than coarse soils. (5) Fine soils usually are more fertile, because they are physically better suited for storing nutrients. (6) Coarser soils because of greater porosity have faster evaporation, better aeration, and closer agreement with atmospheric temperature changes than do finer soils. (7) Few soils are simply fine or coarse; rather, most are aggregates of finer particles among larger particles and display both the good and bad features of their particle sizes.

TABLE 17.4 ASSOCIATIONS BETWEEN SOIL TEXTURE AND PLANTS[a]

Soil Feature	Fine-textured Soils	Coarse-textured Soils
Root penetration	Poor	*Excellent
Water penetration	Poor	*Excellent
Erosion rate	High	*Low
Water movement	Slow	*Fast
Water retention	*High	Low
Fertility	*High	Low
Evaporation rate	*Low	High
Aeration	Low	*High
Temperature	*Stable	Reflects air

[a]The conditions generally more beneficial to plants are starred.

ORGANIC MATTER

Plants rely upon soil minerals as a source of nutrients; but usable inorganic sources of minerals are limited. Most minerals required by plants are derived from pre-existing organic matter, but most organic matter is far from usable. When an organism dies, it decays and becomes humus, but even this humus must be further simplified chemically before minerals can be extracted by most plants.

Soil humus has certain peculiarities that are mostly of benefiit to life. It is a source of food when transformed to minerals, but its potential nutrients are not limited to minerals. Various saprophytic plants and certain soil animals obtain nourishment directly from humus. Humus also has physical properties that cause it to hold both water and minerals in the soil and to yield these nutrients freely to plants. In addition, humus or organic matter in the uppermost layers of the soil insulates underground vegetative structures against temperature extremes, retards soil compaction by raindrops, and reduces soil erosion by runoff.

SOIL MOISTURE

The spaces between soil particles, 40–60 per cent of most soil volumes, contain soil moisture and gases, but the actual amount of water in a given soil is related to many factors. Basically, soil moisture reflects the amount of precipitation in a locality; however, equal amounts of precipitation over a widespread area do not necessarily result in homogeneous soil moisture. Possible variables modifying water content are evaporation rate before precipitation strikes the ground, vegetation "trapping" moisture prior to its infiltrating the soil, slope or frozen ground increasing runoff, greater soil porosity or dryness increasing intake, topographic depressions collecting water, and greater soil water evaporation because of coarse soil texture (all factors in the hydrologic cycle). In addition, water is lost by being chemically "tied" to soil compounds (adsorption) and by penetrating below the level where it is available to plants (percolation). These various relationships are summarized by an equation of water availability. The water available to a plant equals the total precipitation plus condensation of water minus that portion lost by air evaporation, interception, runoff, absorption, collection, soil evaporation, adsorption, and percolation. (Figure 17.4).

Soil moisture is the main source of plant water, the most critical need of these organisms. Plants require water to take in, transport, and expel materials and to carry on photosynthesis and transpiration. Also, plants must have moisture to maintain cell turgidity, because less than normal water causes wilting. If sufficient water is lost, permanent wilting and often death result.

SOIL REACTION

Soil reactions may be acid, neutral, or alkaline. Reactions are said to be acid when there are more hydrogen ions (acid producing) than hydroxyl ions (alkali producing) in a soil solution. The reaction is measured in terms of the negative logarithm of the concentration of hydrogen ions and is called the pH. All that must be known about this is that there are three possible reactions, acid, neutral, and alkaline, and that a pH of 7.0 is neutral, values below 7.0 are progressively more acid, and values above 7.0 are progressively more alkaline. The pH values for most soils range from 4.0 to 9.0 and the extremes of pH are 0 and 14.

Soil acids and alkalis form in many ways. Acids usually are derived from acidic igneous rocks, soil organisms, and many organic remains. Alkalis usually come from decomposition of limestone or basic igneous rocks and evaporation of water from drainage basins such as semidesert or desert lakes.

Soil reaction is related to the availability of soil minerals to plants. Most minerals are available at a pH of 6.5, a slightly acid condition. At a pH much below or above this figure some minerals may become poisonous; at a pH of 4.0, hydrogen ions and at a pH of 9.0, hydroxyl ions become injurious to plant tissues.

To summarize, slightly alkaline or acid conditions seem to have little effect on many animals and (probably) some plants. However, plants in general appear to be more restricted by the reaction of the soil in which they live. In both plants and animals there are species that can live in only a narrow range of alkali or acid near neutrality; but some species actually might prefer one of these media, and a few, such as tapeworms, can withstand wide ranges.

SALINITY

Certain plants, called salt plants, live naturally only in places too salty for most life. In some respects calling the plants of saline environments salt plants creates a misconception, because these organisms also are adapted to the poor aeration related to either excess moisture or salinity. Such saline habitats prevail along the ocean in coastal strands and salt marshes and inland around salt lakes or saline basins.

Inland saline habitats usually are limited to arid regions where rock weathering releases salts that are transported by water to collecting basins. In these lakes the water may or may not be seasonal, but whether they are permanent or temporary, the salinity of the waters is usually high. In salt flats there also may be a seasonal fluctuation in topsoil salts. The salts may leach downward during a wet period and rise again with evaporating water during the dry season; with either alternative, the vegetation is limited to salt plants.

Salt plants possess properties that enable them to exist in situations that are impossible for most plants, places with abundant water but too much salt. These environments are called physiologically dry because water is present, but not in a form that is usable by most plants. Yet salt plants survive by one or both of two general methods. The first method involves the actual intake of salt with the water and special glands that excrete excess salt from cell fluids. The other method is a complex chemical process.

Another and little understood specialization of salt plants is the succulent vegetative form. Most of these salt plants, whether they be coastal or inland (in fact, both areas often share the same species), have soft, thick tissues and organs that contain an abundance of water—in other words, a succulent structure. Although succulence does appear to be an adaptation to store water for use during the more adverse periods, this does not really explain why strictly maritime salt plants should be succulents. The latter are capable of extracting the water they need from high tidal ocean waters and would seem to require no water storage.

Salt plants tend to be shallow rooted. This is an advantage in that fresh water is made available when rain leaches salts below the roots. Shallow rooting also aids in aeration, because saline subsoils usually are waterlogged. Although salt plants are shallow rooted, they often are extensively rooted. This is especially the case in those species inhabiting windswept coastal strands where plant existence is somewhat dependent upon individual plants' "holding" the loose sands.

There often is some confusion between alkaline and saline areas, because the two habitats share a basic pH and the same or similar salt plants. However, saline sites are rich in free salts and usually have a pH below 8.5, whereas alkaline areas have few free salts and a pH often above 8.5. In spite of these ecological differences, the habitats are similar in vegetation because only salt plants are uninjured by either salt or alkali.

SOIL ANIMALS

The size of adult animals within the soil allows soil fauna to be summarized in four main groups. Each of these groups is distributed throughout the horizons of any particular soil and the organic layer above the soil (see Figure 5.1, p. 76). Therefore, fallen trees, isolated logs, and any plant or animal remains upon the soil are considered part of the medium of the soil animals.

Although soil animals vary a great deal, mostly in relation to the characteristics of each of the organic and soil horizons, the adult animals can be defined as follows:

largest animals, including small mammals, reptiles, amphibians, arthropods (millipedes, centipedes, and large spiders, scorpions, and insects), large earthworms, and large snails and slugs.

fairly large animals, including arthropods (garden centipedes, most millipedes and centipedes, ticks, most spiders and scorpions, harvestmen, sun spiders, and most large insects) and mollusks (most snails and slugs).

smallest macroscopic animals, typified by a vast array of small arthropods (pauropods, garden centipedes, mites, whip scorpions, larval insects, and the smallest spiders and insects) and many kinds of roundworms.

microscopic animals and *protozoans*, including arthropods (water bears), cavity worms (roundworms and wheel animalcules), the smallest free-living flatworms, and a great variety and number of protozoans.

The occurrence of individual species of animals appears to be less restricted by soil conditions than is the occurrence of plants. However, soil texture displays clear associations with certain animals. For example, legless lizards, horned lizards, and kangaroo rats may be geographically restricted more by soil texture than by any other ecological factor. Each group generally is confined to sandy or loamy soil. In addition, the amount of organic matter, moisture, salinity, and alkalinity or acidity in the soil affects the presence of many animals.

Soil organisms, both plant and animal, have some influence upon their environment. When death occurs, the organic remains contribute to soil humus. The burrowing of animals and growing of plant roots contribute to breaking up of soil particles and its parent material. In addition, such things as organic decay and waste contribute to chemical decomposition of soil. Among the animals, the most influential species include earthworms, ants, sowbugs, millipedes, and rodents; but such creatures as amphibians and reptiles also play a part. The influence of monerans and fungi was indicated in their taxonomic accounts.

FIRE

In spite of man's efforts, fire is likely to be a major ecological factor for some time. Even before the advent of man, wildfires were fairly common over much of the globe. The only fire-exempted localities are the very wet, very dry, and very cold regions.

There are three main kinds of wildfires. Crown fires extend from tree tops to ground surface and remove most of the vegetation. Surface fires remove only the herbaceous and other low plants; trees may not be affected too seriously. Ground fires cause the burning of organic material in the soil, but usually occur with other fire types. Because ground fires normally burn with one or both of the other two types, they are the most extensive and destructive of the wildfires. Both ground and crown fires are limiting factors for most creatures. Ground fires cause the most damage to life in restricted areas, and lead to entire habitats' taking the longest time to recover; but even crown fires often remove the characteristic vegetation of a locale and so necessitate some habitat recovery. Surface fires, too, cause removal of some species. Although surface fires might not affect the more fire-tolerant forms, they might cause a change in the plant assemblage and necessitate recovery.

Any fire is likely to alter an environment. An alteration may be minor and produce no visible change in the species composition of the area, but there is usually some visible fire injury to plants. These injuries may be little more than fire scars or a greater amount of parasitism on the species. More dramatic damage causes the removal of some to all of the species previously present. When only some species are removed, the surviving forms may assume an unnatural assemblage, or strange habitat. When all species are removed, abnormal developmental stages, or habitats, characterize recovery.

FIRE ADAPTATIONS

Certain plants possess structures and functions that enable them to persist in repeatedly burned areas (Figure 17.18). These many plant adaptations are found in all stages of the life cycle of plants, but few species have more than a few of the different specializations. Germination adaptations occur in the seeds of some shrubs, which sprout only after being burned, and the cones of some conifers, which shed their seeds

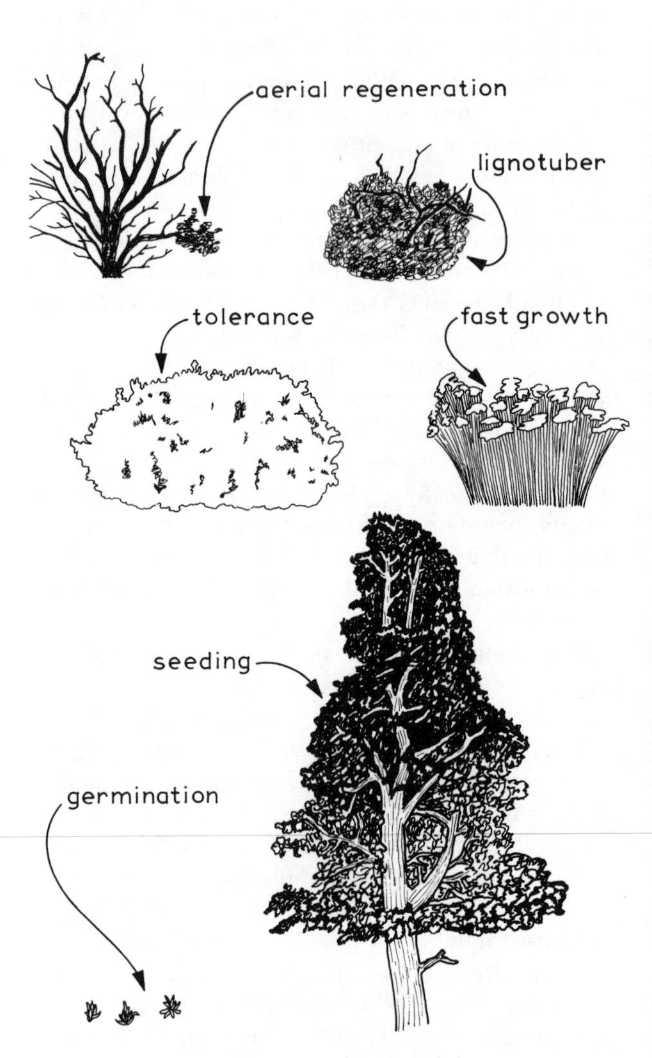

Figure 17.18 Some fire adapted plants.

only after fire. Many "fire plants" grow and become sexually mature very rapidly, enabling the life cycle to have a good chance of completion prior to another fire. Other growth adaptations are displayed by immature stages that have great fire tolerance. Adult modifications are of many kinds. Many species have fire-resistant leaves or bark. Others have means of rejuvenation after much of their aerial parts have been destroyed. For example, some plants have buds that regenerate from the remains of aerial parts; other plants have enlarged structures (near the ground surface but mostly or entirely below the surface), lignotubers, that sprout after all aerial parts are consumed.

CHAPARRAL

The western North American (especially Californian) shrub habitat called chaparral grows in semiarid areas having long, dry summers—conditions that are associated with frequent fires. The various species that compose this habitat display the gamut of fire adaptations. After a fire there is usually profuse germinating and sprouting of plants and the habitat returns to normal in about ten years. Because chaparral is subject to recurring fires, the average habitat is about twenty-five years old and few are more than fifty years old. However, even the specialized plants of this scrub cannot withstand too frequent fires. Recurring fires will cause the habitat to revert to bunch grass.

CONTROLLED BURNING

The value of man's use of fire to "improve" land is debatable. It is definitely known that burning can cause moderate to severe damage to a habitat, but so many ecological factors are involved that one cannot predict with any real accuracy the full consequences of burning a given landscape. In some instances burning would appear to benefit the land use of an area; however, the effects of this treatment are difficult to appraise because they are likely to be delayed. Any seeming benefit, even if pronounced, may be a temporary thing. Often after variable periods of time, the nutrients released by fire are removed; then, although some time may be required, soil depletion and consequent vegetation destruction allow the area to erode, perhaps even to a badland situation.

The possible effects of burning can be related to the cycle of development of habitats (succession). All that need be said here is that succession is a process characterized by soil improvement and that burning of a forest, woodland, or shrub habitat causes regression and sets soil and other environmental factors back to the point where herbs, usually certain grasses and forbs, can grow. This fire setback does not create the natural environment that supports a native herbaceous habitat because the soil is such that weedy herbs, actually less nutritious than the native ones, often prevail. Unfortunately, there is an all too common belief that some of these weeds, especially filarees (*Erodium* spp.) are ideal forage plants. However, in spite of any temporary good that comes from such plants, these weeds indicate a disturbed habitat that is more subject to erosion from natural causes or grazing activities than is native vegetation. Frequently such areas, whether they are the consequence of burning or overgrazing, are short-lived forage lands that soon become wastelands in a destroyed watershed.

The differences between a mature watershed and a cleared or overgrazed one can be extreme. When such drainage areas that contribute to the supply of a river or lake contain mature and stable (climax) vegetation, there are the best possible soil and vegetation conditions for water retention and for reduction of both runoff and erosion. Therefore, when land is either cleared or caused to have a different plant growth, the consequences usually are less water retention, greater runoff and erosion, and poorer soil. Although the mature vegetation uses much of the water that it and its soil trap, mature watersheds normally yield water over a much longer period and a more nearly constant rate than do disturbed watersheds. Even if streams in cleared or modified drain age areas are dammed, the water gain most likely is offset by the degradation of the watershed and the accumulation of erosion products in the dams.

TOPOGRAPHY

Physiography is related to some dramatic aspects of the distribution of plants and animals. Some of the physiographic effects can be very puzzling. For example, an area of higher elevation may have more luxuriant vegetation than a lower one, partly because of lower temperatures and greater precipitation. The lower temperatures cause near maximum conservation of the moisture that is available. On the other hand, mostly because of low temperature, or perhaps wind, the vegetation may be stunted and reduced in species and number. Also, there may be a general upslope transition of vegetation from arid to humid and finally alpine types, or there may be temperature inversion and contrasting belts of vegetation showing no such "normal" transitions. In addition, north-facing slopes usually have denser and taller plants than do south-facing slopes. Actually, there is often a progression of decreasing plant development from north to east, to west, and to south exposures, because sunlight causes the greatest drying on south and west slopes and precipitation comes from the north. The general exception to this slope orientation exists when the pattern of precipitation is different.

Increasing altitude can have consequences that are very similar to those of increasing latitude. Plants might be reduced in number of species and individuals and may be stunted. Trees might become shrubs or very poorly developed shrubs and little more than ground cover. Also, there might be changes in species of the same genus or races of the same species. When this situation involves species of the same genus, the species are called *substitution species*. In addition, there is a tendency for vegetation zonation, or the development of distinct altitudinal tiers of plant communities. A unique effect of altitude is the flag-like form of woody plants, especially trees (Figure 17.19). This deformation probably is related to many aspects of the tree limit environment but is most closely associated with wind.

Other topographic influences upon environment

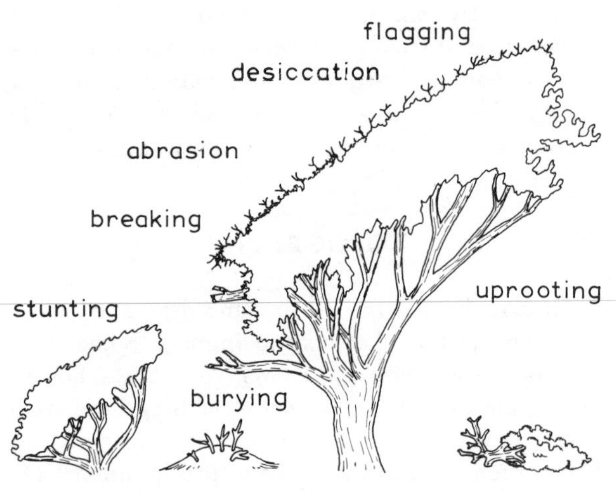

Figure 17.19 Wind effects upon plants.

were outlined previously. Of most importance are variations in soil depth, amount of precipitation, and velocity of winds. Soil depth is inversely related to the amount of slope; the greater the slope, the thinner the soil. Precipitation is low on the leeward side of mountains in the so-called rain shadow. Winds are greatest at the highest elevations and along ocean coasts.

Although there is a definite relationship between amount of slope and soil depth, flat lands have varied soil conditions. In considering the possible variations, the soil of most plains is used as the average type, or point of reference. Plateaus may possess thick soils that are excessively leached and have thick clay hardpans in the B layer. Poorly drained plains also have thick soils, but the main material that accumulates is humus. This accumulation is due to water saturation, a factor that inhibits organic decay because oxygen is not readily available.

VEGETATION ZONATION

The correlation between altitude and latitude can be appreciated further by examination of the distinct altitudinal bands of plant communities (Figure 17.20).

Lowlands have vegetations no different from that of the surrounding area, because this terrain is the prevalent one. A California example of such lowlands is the Foothill Woodland Community of the western foothills of the Sierras. The *Montane Zone* is cooler, cloudier, and more humid; but the growing season is shorter and less effective in stimulating plant growth. In the Sierras this zone is represented by the Montane Forest, usually in the form of a Yellow Pine Community. The *Subalpine Zone* is still cooler, but is typically more arid than the Montane Zone as a result of its clear, dry atmosphere. The increased aridity causes Subalpine trees to be smaller and less dense than Montane ones. The Subalpine Zone has its upper margin at the limit of trees where trees display decrease in numbers, stunting, and modification in shape. In the Sierras the Subalpine contains a Subalpine Forest Community. The *Alpine Zone* is colder yet. In spite of its frequent cloud cover, trees cannot survive here, but herbs or small, stunted shrubs can. The herbs regularly predominate and are of tufted and cushionlike form, so the over-all vegetation has the appearance of Tundra or modified grassland. In the Sierras this zone contains the Fell-fields Com-

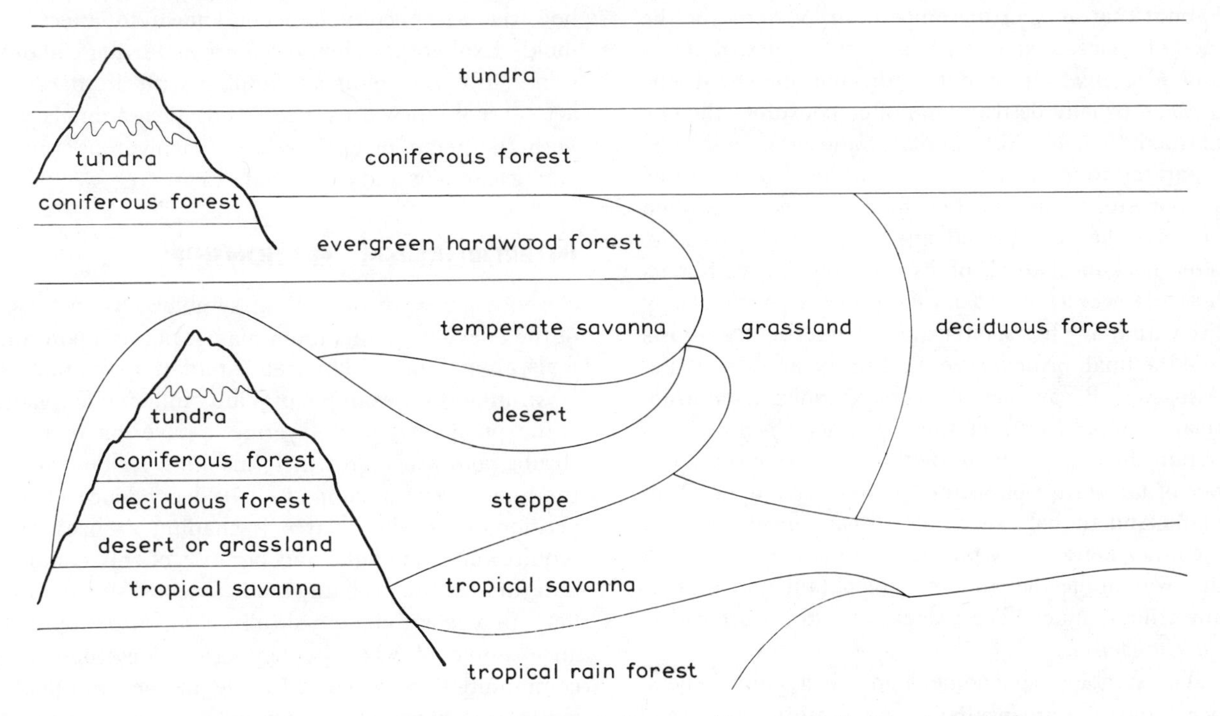

Figure 17.20 Vegetation zonation, implying both geographic and altitudinal trends in North America.

munity. Finally, the highest and coldest, or *Nival Zone*, is found. This is the area of perpetual ice or snow and is found only in the tallest mountains. Although the zone occurs in the uppermost elevations of the Sierras, such as Mount Lyell, the community does not receive formal designation. Perhaps its lack of a name stems from the paucity of plants and animals found there. The Sierran plants are mostly a few species of algae and the animals are a few invertebrates.

BIOTIC FACTORS

In most instances, the physical factors of an environment are the governing forces within a community. However, certain activities of living organisms have direct and to some extent governing effects upon other species and the environment. These biotic factors are created by relationships within and among species. The strongest forces exist when different species display close contact with one another, a phenomenon called *symbiosis*.

SYMBIOSIS

Symbiosis is a much abused term. It has been given many definitions, and many of them are still used; however, its original meaning is literally "living together" of unlike creatures. The original meaning is followed here, so the word will denote any close relationship among different species.

There are many possible reactions when two species are in intimate contact. The more important interrelationships are (1) *neutralism*, in which neither species is affected; (2) *mutualism*, in which both species are benefited and both require the relationship; (3) *cooperation*, in which both benefit but neither requires the relationship; (4) *competition*, in which both are harmed in the sense that each strives for the same materials, especially food and shelter; (5) *commensalism*, in which one is benefited and the other unaffected; (6) *amensalism*, in which one is harmed and the other unaffected; and (7) *exploitation*, in which one is harmed and the other benefited.

Further clarification of neutralism and exploitation is necessary. Neutralism is probably a rare phenomenon; rarely are two organisms found in the same habitat that are not in competition for some of the food or space. Exploitation is of two types, *predation* and *parasitism.* In predation the one benefited, the *predator,* usually destroys and often consumes the one harmed, the *prey.* Also, predator and prey tend to be separated from one another a good deal of the time. In parasitism the one benefited, the *parasite,* often destroys the one harmed, the *host,* but the parasite often lives most to all of its life upon or within its host. However, during its life cycle, a parasite may live with many hosts, often various intermediate hosts and the final, or definitive, host of the adult parasite. Also, not all parasites absolutely require a parasitic relationship. Many of these *facultative parasites* can obtain their nutrients in another way. A large number of facultative parasites live and feed upon dead plants and animals; such parasites are *saprophytic.* On the other hand, many parasites are so specialized to that way of life that they cannot obtain nutrients in any other manner. These dependent forms are called *obligate parasites.*

The symbiotic phenomena in which only benefit occurs are commensalism, cooperation, and mutualism. These are called positive interactions and are presented in their probable evolutionary sequence. Commensalism is the simplest and is especially common in the sea where many active organisms benefit from gaining shelter upon or within sedentary forms. Cooperation is a little more complex. An example occurs in the marine masking crab that benefits from the camouflage provided by creatures the crab tends upon its back. The creatures in turn gain from the crab's keeping them in well-oxygenated situations. The classical example of mutualism is found in certain extremely close associations of algae and fungi that are of mutual benefit. The algae form food and the fungi collect moisture. These organisms are so intimately related that they are recognized by a distinct name, *lichens.*

The harmful, or negative interactions, in their probable order of evolutionary origin are competition, amensalism, and exploitation. Competition may or may not be a serious factor in interspecific relationships, but it is of low symbiotic development because the individuals frequently have only moderate contact with one another. Amensalism usually features more contact and is more definite. An example is the relationship between the bread mold (*Penicillium*) and many bacteria, the mold secretes the drug penicillin which is well-known for its bacteria-killing properties; however, the bacteria are not known to affect the mold. Exploitation should require no further elaboration. Also, most of us are familiar with the parasitic activities of tapeworms, fleas, and other animals and with the relationships between carnivorous (meat-eating) animals and the prey they eat.

INTERORGANISM RELATIONSHIPS

Another way of describing symbiosis is in terms of the effects of plants upon plants, plants upon animals, animals upon plants, and animals upon animals.

An important example of plants influencing plants is the phenomenon of layering. Layering of trees, shrubs, and other growth forms in a single habitat can indicate either competition or dependence. Competition exists when a tree is shading a shrub that requires open sunlight and because of this competition (in this case probably really amensalism) the tree may, in a sense, kill the shrub. This also would be an example of why the temporary, developmental communities are replaced by one another and finally by the permanent, stable climax. On the other hand, a particular shrub may require some shading by trees. Because bright sunlight would kill the shrub, the shrub is a commensal upon the tree.

Three additional interplant relationships are found in special kinds of plants: saprophytes, epiphytes, and parasites. Saprophytes are those plants that break down the complex products of dead green plants. For example, many green plants form basic foods, carbohydrates, fats, and proteins, and living tissues, mostly proteins. Saprophytic bacteria decompose the basic foods and tissues into carbon dioxide, water, and certain nitrogen compounds (ammonia, nitrates, and nitrites). Epiphytes are plants that grow upon other plants, man-made objects, and even some animals. Among such plants are lichens, mosses, ferns, and orchids. When true epiphytes grow upon living creatures, the epiphytes are commensals. Parasites are distinguished from epiphytes because only parasites feed upon living creatures. Examples of plant parasites can be found throughout the phyla of the plant kingdom.

Plants in general have a pronounced influence upon animals. All animals rely upon plants as a basic source of food because only green plants can form food from inorganic materials. Many animals utilize plants as a means of shelter; some plants are animal parasites; other plants are carnivorous, mostly upon small insects; and animal distribution is related to the distribution of plant communities. According to distribution, some animals are found with a single plant species, vegetative form, or plant community; other animals are wide-ranging, occurring in many habitats and showing only a general alliance to plants.

Animals rarely dominate their environment. In fact, the usual role of animals in a habitat is that of a dependent. However, there are many circumstances in which animals partly modify or even alter their habitat. For example, grazing or browsing animals may overgraze or seriously affect vegetation, causing certain plants to be replaced by other species and thereby creating a new habitat. Effects similar to those from overgrazing can develop when animals feed upon seeds and seedlings. On the other hand, some animals activities are definitely beneficial to plants. For example, insects and birds are instrumental in pollination, and therefore reproduction, of many plants; other animals are very effective in spreading plant seeds.

Interrelations between animals assume complex patterns. The major types of interanimal activities were mentioned as symbiotic phenomena.

COMPETITION

Competition often is given a much broader interpretation than that described earlier. In the more inclusive sense, it involves direct and indirect relationships. Direct competition, also called *interference*, is competition much as was defined, referring to direct and antagonistic action by both of the competitors whether they be members of the same species fighting for food, shelter, or mates, or members of different species actively contending for some material. Indirect competition, or *amensalism*, occurs when one organism either monopolizes materials (e.g., food or shelter) required by another, or creates conditions (e.g., shade or toxicity) detrimental or lethal to another.

Both direct and indirect competition are closely related in their effects within a species (*intraspecific competition*) and between species (*interspecific competition*). For this reason, unless otherwise stated, further mention of competition refers to both competition and amensalism.

Antagonism among organisms need not be constant. It might occur only at certain times of the day or year, at certain stages of the life cycle, or in certain habitats. However, its consequences are fairly predictable. Within animal species it often is instrumental in creating social dominance, forming territories, and determining population size. Between species it also influences population size, but its main interspecific effects are to regulate the ecological role of species and the process of speciation.

ECOLOGICAL VARIATIONS

The ecological factors discussed in this chapter are in a sense individual physical or biological facets of any environment. Although *ecological variation*, especially that of a cyclic nature, can be treated as an environmental factor, such variation really is not an individual factor. Rather, variation is a synthesis of ecological phenomena of two kinds, daily and annual.

Daily variation, or *diurnation*, naturally is related to the presence and absence of the sun during a twenty-four hour cycle. However, the sun in providing a source of energy to any locale affects light, temperature, moisture, wind, and life itself. Therefore, the daily cycle of day and night, owing to progressive change in solar influence, exhibits somewhat regular changes in those factors affected by the sun.

Annual variation often is examined from three points of view: periodicity, phenology, and aspectation. *Periodicity* refers to the cyclic recurrence of particular life cycle phenomena, usually on an individual species basis. For example, basic heredity as modified by environment and annual changes in environment causes an annual cycle of germination, vegetative growth, flowering, and fruiting in flowering plants. The particular stage in a species' life cycle at a particular time of the year is its periodicity. *Phenology* is more of a calendar treatment of annual variation, referring to the date or season when a particular periodicity is expressed by a species or when a particular over-all community appears.

Aspectation pertains to the appearance of an entire community during different seasons. Also, aspectation is the seasonal rhythm or cycle of the presence and activities of conspicuous organisms within a community.

Aspectation is difficult to separate from a time table, or phenology. For this reason, aspectation normally includes the concept of phenology. In this sense aspectation encompasses the periodic or seasonal phenomena of plants, animals, and environment and the time of appearance of characteristic annual events in the life cycle of organisms under natural conditions of the related environmental cycle. All phases of aspectation are closely related to the sun-controlled climatic cycle; hence in any area possessing seasonal changes in climate there are seasonal changes in most to all ecological factors and in aspects.

DIURNATION

The majority of living creatures have some relationship to daily cycles of ecological activity. In animals, especially, such associations become pronounced because most animals are active only during certain portions of the daily cycle. On the basis of period of activity, animals active during the night are *nocturnal*, those active during daytime are *diurnal*, and those active during the late evening and early morning hours of limited light are *crepuscular*. Those animals not displaying such distinct relationships, the irregular species, are *arhythmic*. Arhythmic animals are in the minority, including mostly subterranean creatures, especially cave animals, and perhaps burrowing forms such as ants, termites, moles, and gophers.

Activity of the periodic animals is not uniform. In this respect, crepuscular animals with two periods of activity indicate the nature of diurnal and nocturnal animals. Diurnal animals display their greatest activity during the earlier daylight hours, but often have a secondary activity peak before dusk. Nocturnal animals, in similar manner, have their major activity during the first part of the night and often a secondary peak just before dawn.

ASPECTATION

The presence of four annual aspects, or seasons, is familiar to most people of temperate climates. In temperate and arctic climates ecological factors generally vary in such a way that winter (*hiemal aspect*), spring (*vernal aspect*), summer (*aestival aspect*), and autumn (*autumnal aspect*) can be recognized. On the other hand, in tropical rainforest climate there is very little seasonal variation, the climate being generally uniform throughout the year. However, in those tropical climates with a wet and dry climatic rhythm, there are at least two seasons and, therefore, two contrasting periods in the life of the area.

SEASONAL VARIATIONS

The four aspects are most contrasting in deciduous forests of temperate climates. Here, seasonal changes in available food and shelter are most pronounced and the consequences of such changes are easiest to observe. In addition, two or three subdivisions of the four aspects, called *sectors*, often are recognizable. Although most to all aspects and their sectors normally are present in temperate areas, they vary from year to year with regard to character and distinctiveness and to their time and duration. The particular nature of local expression and variation of aspectation is related to the weather conditions of a given year, to the latitude of the locale, and to the type of community.

Table 17.5 summarizes the general features that help define the aspects and their sectors in areas of temperate climate. Although it must be reemphasized that these data represent only trends, the tabulated material should be sufficient for determination of aspect and sector at any time if all aspects and their sectors are present. Not included in Table 17.5 are the relationships with environmental factor variations during the annual climatic cycles. The related factors include temperature, relative humidity, precipitation, light, and evaporation.

ECOLOGICAL SUCCESS

The success or failure of an individual species is the consequence of the reaction of ecological amplitude to the environment. This is no more than saying that an organism is as successful as its hereditary pattern allows it to be, but little more than this can be generalized. For success, ecological amplitude must permit the organism to become a part of its total environment and to obtain its requirements there. The full implication of what becoming part of a population, community, or ecosystem means can be appreciated after these levels of the life spectrum are studied. This "becoming a part" is a very intricate thing, requiring integration within processes and relationships of extremely complex and dynamic phenomena. The complex and rather tenuous nature of ecological success is indicated by the fact that many more species have become extinct than are living today. Therefore, success is dynamic rather than static. Degree of success fluctuates through time, and history records that it is most likely to change eventually to failure—that is, extinction.

TABLE 17.5 ECOLOGICAL SEASONS AND SOME PLANT AND ANIMAL ASSOCIATIONS[a]

Aspect	Sector	Duration	Plants	Invertebrates	Vertebrates
Hiemal	Hiemine	Nov.–Dec.	Lichens and mosses conspicuous; some mosses form capsules; herbs mostly dead; deciduous trees mostly bare	Most enter hibernation; active forms are mostly insects and small; some active insects "swarm"	Amphibians, reptiles, and some mammals entering hibernation; a few sluggish amphibians are found; last bird migration
	Hibernine	Dec.–Mar.	Most to all plants are dormant, especially flowering plants	Maximum hibernation, but some species are active	Maximum hibernation, except for some birds and mammals
	Emergine	Jan.–Apr.	Vegetative growth, swelling buds and sprouting foliage but no flowers	First hibernators emerge from dormancy	Hibernators emerge; some amphibians enter breeding ponds; migrant birds appear
Vernal	Prevernine	Mar.–May	First spring flowers appear	Most hibernators emerge and activity increases	Most amphibians enter ponds and lay eggs; resident birds and mammals begin reproductive activities
	Vernine	Apr.–June	Plants fully foliated; shade-tolerant species flower; maximum flowering	New forms become active; become abundant throughout habitat in tree, shrub, etc., layers.	Many amphibians become subterranean or terrestrial; reptile reproductive activities; peak of migrant bird entry; birds are nesting and mammals bearing young
Aestival	Cisaestine	May–Aug.	Fully foliated; reduced flowering, only summer-blooming species; period of maximum vegetative growth	Reduction of midday activity in diurnal forms	Last terrestrial amphibians aestivate; reptiles decrease during midday; bird nesting peak; diurnal mammals reduce midday activity
	Aestine	July–Aug.	Habitat dries; fruiting of some herbs; many wilt or dry; flowering very limited	Many aestivate; foliage insects reach peak	Reptiles and some mammals aestivate; birds become quiet and enter molt, some migrate south
Autumnal	Serotinine	Aug.–Oct.	Last fruits ripen; herb leaves become yellowed and ragged; blooming and fruiting of fall-flowering species	Many species disappear from the surface and higher layers	Renewed activity of some amphibians and reptiles; maximum southward bird migration; maximum mammal populations
	Autumnine	Oct.–Nov.	Deciduous leaves color and fall; herbs mostly dead; fungi form fruiting bodies	Insects and spiders move from plants to ground	Some amphibian and reptile activity when warm; birds mostly residents; mammals decrease

[a]After Macnab, J. A. 1958, Biotic Aspectation in the Coast Range Mountains of Northwest Oregon Ecological Monographs 28: 21–54.

The dynamic nature of success is revealed by living organisms. Living creatures are mostly evolved descendants of unsuccessful (extinct) species. Moreover, most living species are about a million years old; only a few really old species are known and none of these appear to date back as far as one-half billion years in the probably more than three billion years of life. Even if discussion is limited to the relatively recent emergence of the vast majority of present-day species, success is associated with change. Almost invariably the best-adapted ecological amplitudes of species persisted; and because environments fluctuated and the mechanisms of evolution operated during this time, ecological amplitudes also changed.

Success, then, is tenuous because environmental changes occur. When geological processes take place, many individual factors also change and create new problems for organisms in satisfaction of their basic requirements and integration into their environment. Fortunately for life, geological processes are slow enough so that many species can be successful, because evolutionary processes modify their ecological amplitudes while retaining their specific identities. However, success in another sense is not attained through retention of the old species, even with some change in its previous ecological amplitude. Rather, many species might gradually evolve with their environment and become new species. Therefore, the life of an ecosystem evolves through time and so does the nature of the ecosystem. Although evolution of species and ecosystems often occurs, success in the original sense takes place in those species that retain their identify because hereditary changes are not pronounced.

Ecological success is so complex that man's attempts to measure it are truly inadequate. Very little is known about why certain fossil species were successful for a time and then became extinct.

SELECTED READINGS

Daubenmire, R. F., 1959. *Plants and Environment.* 2d ed. John Wiley & Sons, New York.

Reid, George K., 1961. *Ecology of Inland Waters and Estuaries.* Reinhold Publishing Corp., New York.

Ricketts, Edward F., and Jack Calvin (edited by Joel Hedgpeth), 1952. *Between Pacific Tides.* Stanford University Press, Stanford, Calif.

GENERAL ECOLOGY REFERENCES

Allee, W. C., et al., 1949. *Principles of Animal Ecology.* W. B. Saunders Co., Philadelphia.

Benton, Allen H., and William E. Werner, Jr., 1958. *Principles of Field Biology and Ecology.* McGraw-Hill Book Co., New York.

Buchsbaum, Ralph, and Mildred Buchsbaum, 1957. *Basic Ecology.* The Boxwood Press, Pittsburgh, Pa.

Clarke, George L., 1954. *Elements of Ecology.* John Wiley & Sons, New York.

Elton, Charles, 1947. *Animal Ecology.* Sidgwick & Jackson Ltd., London.

Hesse, R., W. C. Allee, and K. P. Schmidt, 1951. *Ecological Animal Geography*, 2nd ed. John Wiley & Sons, New York.

Kendeigh, S. Charles, 1961. *Animal Ecology.* Prentice-Hall, Inc., Englewood Cliffs, N. J.

Moore, Hilary B., 1958. *Marine Ecology.* John Wiley & Sons, New York.

Odum, E. P., 1953. *Fundamentals of Ecology.* W. B. Saunders Co., Philadelphia.

———. 1963. *Ecology.* Modern Biology Series. Holt, Rinehart & Winston, New York.

Reid, George K., 1961. *Ecology of Inland Waters and Estuaries.* Reinhold Publishing Corp., New York.

Russell, Franklin, 1961. *Watchers at the Pond.* Alfred A. Knopf, New York.

Sears, Paul B., 1962. *Where There Is Life.* Dell Publishing Co., New York.

Storer, John H., 1953. *The Web of Life.* New American Library, New York.

Weaver, J. E., and F. E. Clements, 1938. *Plant Ecology.* McGraw-Hill Book Co., New York.

18 POPULATION ECOLOGY

Relations within a Species

Natural hermits cannot live; the single plant or animal is incapable of existing without other members of its kind. There is a fundamental and absolute minimum population size requirement for each species to live in each environment. Even if a habitat is favorable, a certain number of individuals must still be present before a species can survive. This minimum population possesses unique properties beyond those of any smaller group and constitutes the basic synergistic unit that determines the ecology of the species. In this ecology, or population dynamics, the reactions of individuals are relatively insignificant in the complex function of the whole, that is, the success or failure of one organism has little influence upon its population. On the other hand, the spatial relations and fluctuations of minimum or larger groups are primary in any aspect of population success (see Figure 18-2, a chapter summary). For this reason, population dynamics is a phenomenon of single species and their environment, or population ecology; however, though the species alone is emphasized, this ecology includes principles developed in the previous chapter.

POPULATION ORIGIN

Local populations constantly are being created and destroyed by constructive and destructive forces. These antagonistic processes are analagous to those of land forms. For populations, the constructive force is *biotic potential*, the ability to increase in numbers, and the destructive force is *environmental resistance*. Both are of primary importance in the origin, development, and extinction of populations. In fact, these antagonistic forces are fundamental to any aspect of population ecology.

The origin of populations is best understood in relation to geographic segments; however, groups of a single species originate in two related ways, by reproduction and movement. Reproduction starts a new population whenever a single member or smaller-than-minimum group of the same species gives rise to a minimum unit. Movement, both passive and active, also can produce populations. Passive movements are those in which organisms are transported by the environment. For example, the transportation of individual organisms by wind can provide the reproductive nucleus for part of a single species to form a new local aggregation. Active movements, those made by the organisms themselves, can begin a new species segment whenever one to a few members of the species are "drawn" into an area. Therefore, populations can form in any place already occupied by a subminimum species group by reproduction alone, or in new localities if transportation is followed by reproduction to minimum size.

POPULATION EXTINCTION

The exact causes of species extinction are poorly understood. However, if one ignores times when removal of life was relatively widespread, it seems that the two primary causes are change in heredity and change in environment. Hereditary shifts lead to extinction if there is a greater and greater increase in lethal and detrimental genes. There is a belief that gene mutations can lead to racial senility and explain the death of species that were inhabiting seemingly suitable environments. The second cause, variable environment, may provide ecological conditions under which a species no longer can perpetuate itself. These environmental fluctuations can be either catastrophic and sudden, as in volcanic eruptions and the hardly slower activities of man, or they can be gradual, as in slowly changing climates.

The most dramatic extinction is that beyond the population level, that affecting entire communities and even much of the life of the globe. Such devastation is recorded from the end of the Paleozoic and Mesozoic Eras. The possible details of these events are presented in the discussion of biogeographical dynamics in Chapter 19.

POPULATION FLUCTUATIONS

Populations are rarely static. Most have some seasonal, periodic, and/or noncyclic variations in numbers. The main factors causing these fluctuations are birth and death. The reproductive rate is related to the life history and habits of each species in its environment, and mortality rate is adjusted to each reproductive rate.

REPRODUCTIVE RATE

Reproductive rates are affected by the biotic potential as represented by types of reproduction, fecundity, fertility, and reproductive periodicity. They are affected by environmental resistance as represented by the complete environment, especially population density. Each of the four general types of reproduction has a different potential insofar as reproductive rates are concerned. *Sexual reproduction* provides organisms with great hereditary variation, a gene pool upon which selection can act to produce generations of individuals ever more well-suited to their environment. *Parthenogenesis*, virgin birth, allows rapid production of individuals that often are suited to their environment. *Self-fertilizing hermaphroditism* regularly results in a low reproductive rate when environmental changes occur, because the heredity of the offspring is like that of the parent and there is little opportunity for individual hereditary types to adjust to their changing habitat. *Asexual reproduction* influences reproductive rates much as does parthenogenesis, because genetically there is little difference between the two phenomena.

Fecundity and fertility are kindred functions. Fecundity is the rate of formation of the units of reproduction, usually eggs and sperm, and fertility is the rate of production of living offspring. There are both individual and species rates of fecundity and fertility. These different rates stem from variations in the ages at which young reach maturity and in the sizes of individuals at maturity. Within a species larger organisms regularly have more offspring than do smaller individuals. Other somewhat related variables are environmental, annual, and geographic effects upon the bearing of young. Although the latter three effects can be independent of one another, environmental factors normally have annual and geographic variations that act upon fertility. For example, in the "average" environment, with its seasonal diversity and geographically "unique" features, reproduction often is during a particular time of the year; in other geographic areas it may be at different times. Also, a single locale's ecological variations can implement reproduction. In one instance an early spring might advance the reproductive season; in another, unfavorable weather might either reduce the number of or even eliminate offspring.

Reproductive periodicity, the bearing of young at approximately the same time each year, was said to be modified by environmental factors. However, most organisms have a definite season within a year or definite number of years between reproductive periods. Whether offspring are produced one or more times a year or less frequently, reproduction in temperate and arctic plants and animals tends to be during the spring, the best time for the appearance of offspring. During the spring, the surrounding factors, especially food, water, and temperature, are most favorable for the young, which are more susceptible to environmental extremes than are the adults.

MORTALITY RATE

The frequency of death within a population really is not a single rate, because different segments of any species vary as to mortality rate. For example, adult males and females, different age groups of immature organisms, and embryonic stages have unlike potentials for death. Moreover, the deaths within any biologically meaningful grouping might have seasonal and other fluctuations. Therefore, "the mortality rate" of a population is an average of many individual, often variable and independent, mortality rates.

The causes of death can be stated simply as being heredity and/or environment, or a detailed listing can be made of genetic and ecological factors. The hereditary list would contain many traits that are either lethal or semilethal in one or more stages of a life history. The environmental causes, collectively being environmental resistance, are either physical or biotic. Physical causes would include such things as freak weather or fire. Biotic causes would include insufficient food, predators, parasites, disease, competition, overpopulation, and underpopulation.

POPULATION VARIATIONS

Species groups fluctuate in size. These variations, whether they cause permanent increase, permanent decrease, or cyclic changes in numbers, are further modified by movements into and out of a population, reproductive rate, and mortality rate. Moreover, movements, births, and deaths are so difficult for the naturalist to record that in many species little is known about the cause of population variations. Even if fluctuations in numbers of a group were restricted to the birth and death rates, the obstacles to research still would be great. However, discussion of what is known about these two rates will reveal some important features of populations.

The reproductive potential, a precise kind of birth rate, is the product of the number of breeding females, the average number of offspring, and the average number of litters. However, this ignores the fact that while the many older females are breeding, new females become sexually mature and contribute to an even greater reproductive potential. In terms of possible population increase, the rate would become greater geometrically through time. However, this potential for geometric increase is not realized in nature. The potential is checked by mortality rate, the ratio between the potential rate of increase and the actual population density. This check operates even when a new population is introduced into a favorable habitat. When a group originates, there is at first a rapid increase in its numbers; soon, however, there is a tendency towards equilibrium in which the biotic potential and mortality rate are the same. On the other hand, recall that in spite of any tendency toward equilibrium under a constant environment, ecological factors in nature vary so much that equilibrium is unlikely. Because environments have regular and noncyclic fluctuations, populations typically are either increasing or decreasing.

CAUSES OF POPULATION CYCLES

Reasons for permanent increase or permanent decrease in populations are often relatively simple to explain. Permanent increase frequently is related to some improvement in the environment. More specifically, one or more of the factors contributing to species mortality rate are either eliminated or reduced. Permanent decrease, up to and including extinction, would then be allied to increase in factors favoring a higher mortality rate.

The big mystery in population fluctuations is the cause of cyclic changes in numbers of individuals. Many plants and animals, but especially mammals, are known to display such variations. A large number of these cycles are joined to regular fluctuations in the physical environment; however, the cycles of certain rodents in particular are not closely related to these factors. Many attempts have been made to connect rodent population cycles with many factors. Early studies indicated that many climatic features—and even sunspots—might be relevant to population cycles, but the association of none of these factors is really close. Another explanation is that a rodent population decreases as a result of increase in predators and/or greater contacts among individual rodents, thus spreading disease. As a supplement to this hypothesis, after the rodent population is reduced, there is a natural tendency for increase because of the lag in increase of predators, parasites, and disease-causing organisms. However, this hypothesis does not explain why individuals during cyclic increase are more vigorous, why there is less susceptibility to disease, why litter sizes are larger than average, why more litters are produced per year, and why other phenomena generally elevate the biotic potential.

Some recent studies lead to a hypothesis that might well be the answer to the mystery of cycles. This is the only hypothesis that accounts for both increase in vigor and vitality during population growth and decrease during population decline. The hypothesis uses the physiology of stress. Stress is strain, pressure, urgency, effort, exertion—the many phases of environmental resistance. The physiology of stress encompasses an organism's functional reactions to stress. Unfortunately, the effects of stress upon internal functions are poorly known. However, there is evidence that many human disorders, such as colds, arthritis, and mental illness, are either a direct consequence of stress or an indirect one in which stress creates the susceptibility to these disorders. Therefore, it seems that when great stress occurs, man becomes less vigorous and has less vitality.

Assumptions about the physiology of stress can be applied to rodent cycles. The general hypothesis is as follows: When a population is small, there are less contacts among individuals. This would mean less competition, less strife for food, shelter, mates, and other life activities. The reduced competition would in essence mean less stress placed upon individuals of the species, so the individuals would display high vigor and vitality and there would be more young per litter and more litters per year. Naturally, if young also were subject to less stress, more of them would survive. This, then, might explain why cyclic populations periodically have an eruption in numbers. The next phase of the cycle would come from much greater stress resulting from the competition created by increased individuals in the population. With ever-increasing stress there would be a parallel reduction in vigor and vitality; and at the height of stress, there would be conditions already observed in nature. For example, litter size is smaller, fewer litters are born each year, all animals are more susceptible to parasites and disease, offspring reach adult size but are not sexually mature, and animals captured alive seem to die from "shock" alone.

CARRYING CAPACITY

The subject of population variations is conveniently summarized by the concept of *carrying capacity*, the maximum number of individuals in each population or the entire community that a particular geographic unit can support (Figure 18.1). The two major factors, biotic potential and environmental resistance, are the antagonistic forces that affect carrying capacity. To summarize, biotic potential is the innate tendency for organisms to increase, that is, all aspects of potential increase within the general framework of ecological amplitude. Environmental resistance is the biotic and physical complex of factors which curtail increase and place an absolute maximum of numbers (carrying capacity) for each population within an area.

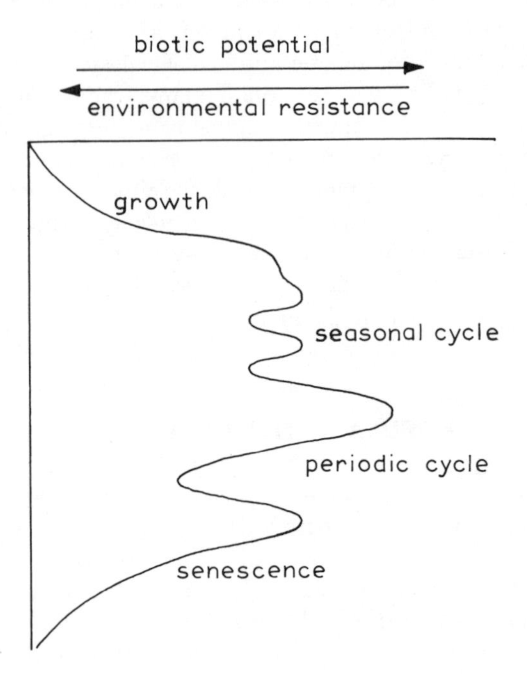

Figure 18.1 Population numbers under particular conditions, from origin and original population growth to cyclic behavior, senescence, and extinction. Minor fluctuations in numbers and seasonal fluctuations during the periodic cycle are not shown.

SPATIAL RELATIONS

Organisms require a definite amount of space in which to live. This need causes animals to display many reactions that are summarized in the concepts of home ranges, territories, migration, emigration, and immigration. A home range is the area occupied by an individual animal; a territory is the portion of the home range that is actively defended by the animal. Migration is the cyclic movement of populations between two or more places, emigration is the permanent exit from a locality, and immigration is the permanent entrance into a new area.

HOME RANGES AND TERRITORIES

These two spatial relationships are different degrees of the same phenomenon, the space occupied by an animal. The major difference between the two is in the matter of defense of the space; only territories are defended. A home range is the area covered by an animal in its normal activities. It possesses a degree of permanence and does not exist for completely nomadic species. Although most animals have some sort of home range, only a few actively defend an area and therefore have a territory. Territoriality is most common in vertebrates, especially birds and mammals, but is also fairly well developed in some fishes and reptiles. A few amphibians display rudimentary territorial behavior, and among invertebrates (especially certain insects, crustaceans, spiders, and mollusks) territoriality can be found in a number of groups.

Home ranges and territories also differ in that home ranges are used for all life processes whereas territories are frequently specialized, many different territories being defended for somewhat specific activities. For example, birds often have many seasonal territories. During the breeding season different species of birds may have either a single territory for mating, nesting, and feeding; one mating and nesting territory and one feeding territory; or three distinct territories—mating, nesting, and feeding. Also, during the nonbreeding season birds may have one or more territories for feeding, daytime roosting, nighttime roosting, and other functions.

Although individual home ranges and territories of members of the same species vary in shape, area, and location, the main function of both spatial relationships is protection. The establishment of either allows greater efficiency in the individual animal's food getting, escape from predators, and other critical processes. In some cases additional protection exists because the animals construct burrows or other shelters. Territories generally provide greater protection than do home ranges. For example, in birds territoriality reduces actual fighting for breeding sites; guarantees food, cover, and nesting materials; protects the nest, young, and mates; prevents overpopulation; and acts as a means of instigating the sexual bond. In addition, the effectiveness of both home ranges and territories is a function of population fluctuations. As populations increase in numbers both territories and home ranges are contracted toward a minimal size; and there often is a greater than normal number of individuals with no set home range or territory. These nomads wander through the unoccupied space that exists among territories. The consequences of overpopulation, then, are greater contact among individuals of restricted territories and/or nomads and greater stress, especially where territoriality is a strong instinctive behavior pattern.

MIGRATION

Interarea movements fall into three categories, metamorphic, daily, and annual. *Metamorphic migrations* must include the change of form from an immature stage to the adult. These movements commonly occur in many groups in which the adults are terrestrial, e.g., certain amphibians and insects, and the immature stages are aquatic. *Daily migrations* are interarea movements, often associated with the daily cycle of light and darkness. Oceanic and lake plankton, tidepool animals, and many land animals are in areas of semidarkness during daylight hours and are near the surface of water or active in the open during the night.

Annual migrations, often simply called "migrations," are movements between areas in which one journey is made during a certain portion of the year and the other during another portion. Such migrations tend to be further classified in reference to the amount or kind of space traversed, as *latitudinal* (north–south), *altitudinal* (in reference to mountains and valleys), and *local* (limited in distance and not necessarily associated with either latitude or altitude). However, migration still is a study of almost meaningless contrasts. Perhaps this confusion comes from attempts to explain all migration, even that within single groups of animals, in the same terms. When this is tried, each new hopeful explanation of cause and effect tends to be negated by further investigations of other members of the same large taxon.

VERTEBRATE VARIATIONS

The migration of birds presents the best example of the problems that arise in attempts to explain this phenomenon. No other taxon displays either such complexity or diversity in its interarea movements, or such pronounced behavior patterns by some species and almost complete reversal of these patterns by others. The following examples serve to describe bird migration and to emphasize the contrasts.

(1) Not all birds migrate north and south. Some travel east and west, others uphill and down; still others move in somewhat irregular circular routes. Moreover, some birds migrate in one direction while others, at the same time, travel in the opposite direction. (2) Some species or individuals within a species migrate during the day and others at night. The day type feed upon the wing and spend the night resting. Night types normally feed and rest during the day, but some forms also feed upon the wing. (3) Movement from an area frequently is associated with the environment's becoming unfavorable. However, some birds migrate when temperatures are mild, food and water are plentiful, and the environment appears favorable. (4) Some birds move in relation to seasonal alternation of rainfall and drought; the migration of others seems to be directly associated either with late spring to early summer increase in day length or with late fall to early winter decrease of day length. In many spring-to-summer, or breeding season, migrants day length increase is in direct proportion to gonadal development. In contrast to this are other birds which move to the nonbreeding range in association with increasing light. Also, birds that move across the equator may move in both directions in direct relation to a single aspect of day length, either increasing or decreasing. (5) In still other birds, interarea travels are allied to increasing day length and rising temperature; again, the opposite conditions also prevail. (6) Still other birds appear to move without any definite environmental associations. (7) There also is a tendency for more northern forms of our hemisphere to migrate more than do other groups of their own species. Such species are said to reflect differential distribution in which the more northern forms, when migrating southward, have to pass over suitable areas (already occupied by the more southern populations of their own species) to find an unoccupied favorable habitat. As a consequence, the northern forms travel much farther than do the southern ones. In fact, some of the southern populations might not migrate at all; rather, they may be permanent residents of a particular region.

Mammalian migration is most dramatic among the deer, marine mammals, and bats. Deer and elk regularly perform altitudinal migrations in which high areas are left when food is covered by snow and are reinhabited when suitable conditions return. Caribou display a like behavior, but in some cases they remain at high altitudes. During the winter, these animals move to windswept north slopes, places where snow is constantly blown away and does not cover the food. Many marine mammals among the whales, seals, and sea lions perform north–south travels in direct relation to seasonal warmth. Whether this is the result of seeking more favorable physical environments or more protected breeding sites, or perhaps even some other reason, is a matter of conjecture. Bats appear to migrate in direct relation to decreasing temperatures and/or food supply.

Many fishes and amphibians display migration relationships that frequently are associated with the breeding season. Fishes that enter fresh water from the ocean often use the new site as hatching waters. In these movements into fresh water, the first arrivals regularly occupy the first encountered favorable situations and later arrivals have to seek waters progressively farther from the ocean. This constitutes another example of the phenomenon of differential distribution. Amphibians, in addition to seeking breeding sites, frequently migrate to dormancy sites. This latter migration is often closely related to increasing temperature and decreasing humidity.

CHARACTERISTICS

General fascination with the subject of bird migration has led to studies of speed, height, distance, routes, and regularity of arrival. As one might expect from the previous discussion, there is a great deal of variation in each of these characteristics. The speed of migratory flight is not as fast as the fastest speeds recorded for the birds. Birds are known to have maximum flight speeds from less than 20 m.p.h. to over 100 m.p.h., but most migrants travel at speeds close to the lower figure. Altitude of flight varies from near ground level to about one mile. The distance traveled can be as little as a mile or so to about 11,000 miles in the Arctic tern. Routes are fairly specific for individual species; there are tendencies, but only tendencies, for certain major "flyways" to be used by migrating birds in general. In the United States, the major paths are called the Pacific, Central,

Mississippi, and Atlantic Flyways in reference to the general areas covered. However, the flyways are not clear cut; they sometimes cross and merge with one another. The regularity of migrant arrival has drawn much attention. Some birds appear to be quite predictable in this respect, because they generally arrive within a day of a particular average time; however, other species vary a few weeks in both departure and arrival dates.

DANGERS

Migration is one of the most hazardous activities of a species. Migrants are highly susceptible to predation. At no other time are they as likely to be so completely in the open and have as little access to protective retreats. In fact, certain predators appear to capitalize on this situation by traveling with the migrants or by shifting their prey species to the migrants in their area. Migrants are also susceptible to environmental extremes, especially freak weather changes. Nonseasonal storms can eliminate large numbers because the animals cannot find suitable shelter.

Birds have some unique difficulties. Night migrants not infrequently crash into man-made objects. For example, encounters with lighthouses have caused thousands of birds to be killed in a single night. Of the natural dangers, weather appears to be the greatest. Rain can watersoak wings and lead to drowning in the ocean. Snow or ice storms may bury thousands in a frozen substrate. Wind may blow them from their course, perhaps far to sea; and even if they survive the storm, the birds may be unable to return to land. Also, such windblown individuals might arrive in an unfavorable land environment and die because they can find neither suitable food nor shelter.

HOMING MECHANISM

Localities sought by migrants probably are not reached by a universal mechanism. This constitutes one of the few real facts in a set of phenomena that are barely beginning to be understood. A few examples will emphasize the state of present knowledge about how animals locate places they return to year after year.

Silver salmon (*Onchorhynchus kisutch*) migrate between their fresh-water hatching grounds and the ocean. The means of finding the ocean probably is a relatively simple mechanism, involving either passive reaction to the effects of downstream water flow or some orientation down a stream. Once the fish gets into the ocean it leaves the vicinity of the stream, but where it travels from there is virtually unknown. For this reason, there is no basis for theories as to how the site of the breeding stream is reached again. However, at the point of return, the sense of smell may be used to identify the proper stream.

The western North American newts, salamanders of the genus *Taricha*, may utilize two different ways to locate migration areas, one mechanism functioning in the breeding travel and the other in the landward one. The breeding ponds or streams are located from some distance by the sense of smell. However, some experimental individuals found their breeding stream three years after being placed three miles away and on the other side of mountains! It appears that the distance and topography involved in that investigation would have prevented identification by smell; and memory of the smell or appearance of landmarks also is not likely, because the animals were transported into what must have been an unknown area. In the opposite movement from breeding waters to underground retreats on land, the sense of sight is used to seek dark horizons. This behavior pattern causes the animals to locate protected substrates. The dark horizons are most likely to be produced by woods or similar habitats. On the other hand, light horizons generally are toward open areas, or places of greater temperature extremes and lower humidities than the dark habitats.

Memory, in conjunction with sight and smell, may be the mechanism of the deerlike mammals, but memory alone may serve migrating whales. Deer have interdigital and tarsal glands on their legs. The secretions of these glands may persist long enough to "mark" the migration trail for later smell perception, but sight recognition of familiar features of the migration trail might also be of help. Migrating whales often lift their heads in a manner that suggests they view the shoreline. For this reason, it is assumed that they use knowledge of shoreline topography to navigate to the breeding grounds.

Birds long have represented the great unknown of migration mechanisms. For some time, memory has been used to explain the method of species that follow well-marked physiographic features. These birds follow large rivers, mountain ranges, and valleys in a manner that can be likened to man's following a highway. However, this cannot explain how certain other species home. For example, the young that hatch during the breeding season might precede the adults to the nonbreeding grounds. Also, other species migrate high and at night, conditions under which land features are not likely to be used; and some species migrate over water, out of sight of the land.

Various attempts have been made to explain the mechanism of such homing. Most modern hypotheses of cause and effect are related to a peculiar fan-shaped structure, the *pecten*, within the eye of a bird. All that is definitely known about the structure is that it is present in the eye, an organ that must be involved in any mechanism of migration. However, the pecten also is present in some reptiles that hardly move at all. Although this might appear to constitute a problem in the hypothesis, it does not. There are various examples of like structures that have different functions in different organisms.

However, even if one assumes that the pecten does perceive the stimuli that enable navigation, the problems are just beginning. What is perceived? Here again, hypotheses vary because data on different birds indicate a number of possibilities. The better-documented conclusions imply orientation by stars, sun, and/or the earth's magnetic field. Another possibility, apparently less likely, is the use of the Coriolis force, the force of the earth's rotation which deflects northern hemisphere air masses to the right (clockwise) and southern hemisphere air masses to the left (counterclockwise).

Once again, even if one assumes that the pecten received stimuli from a particular set of navigational aids, how are these stimuli used in finding a migration area? In cases where young birds migrate with the adults, the answer might be learning. However, how can one explain the navigation of young birds that first migrate by themselves? The only possible answer at the present time is hereditary behavior pattern, or "instinct," perhaps a tidy way of clouding ignorance.

EMIGRATION AND IMMIGRATION

Emigration is associated with overpopulation, but there are cases of permanent departure without prior increase in numbers. Many of the latter emigrations are related to such things as reduced food supply or modified climate, but there are other seemingly unexplanable movements. No matter what the cause, home desertion often ends in death; however, in some species the movement assumes a semipermanent wandering state, or nomadism, and in others causes a permanent range extension. However, death is probable because the species is not likely to find an available suitable habitat. It is true that traveling animals might reach a locality already occupied by their species, but the new arrivals rarely can find room in which to live (immigrate), or can compete with their resident kinsmen.

POPULATION COMPOSITION

The components of groups up to and including a single species are determined mostly by reproductive and mortality rates, but also by movements of individuals into and out of an area. Moreover, seasonal and other periodic fluctuations in rates and/or movements cause the makeup of populations to be ever changing.

Of most importance in reproduction and mortality control of population structure is the length of life span. At one life-span extreme is the single age class found in ephemeral *annual* plants, species that locally are progressively germinating, growing, flowering, fruiting, shedding seeds, or dying, but usually never more than one of these functions is present at a given time. The next life-span step is the population of *biennial* plants with two age classes, the first-year and second-year forms. In animal populations the short-lived species may be as simple as biennials, or even annuals. For example, many invertebrates resemble annuals in that a single generation is hatched, reproduces, and dies each year.

More complex age classes are found in *perennial* plants and long-lived animals. When some members become reproductively mature each year, and especially over a period of each year, the makeup of the population contains many age classes of immatures and reproductives. In some cases, the complex organizations also have one or many age classes of postreproductives, as is the case in man.

Variations exist within, as well as among, species. Within species, changes in population structure may be found by comparing geographically isolated subdivisions. Such races probably vary because of unlike environments, mutations, and selections. However, unlike environments alone might favor unique compositions of age classes, and social behavior can modify the influence of any other factor.

DISTRIBUTION

The compositions and activities of populations are factors of distribution, but distribution itself is analyzed best in terms of geographic range and local occurrence of species. *Geographic range* is the political or over-all segment of the world that encompasses the distribution of a species, and includes many sites not actually containing the species. For this reason, *local occurrence*, any area in the geographic range that actually is occupied by the species, is recognized. The distinction between range and occurrence is important because the range of a species might cover a large political segment of the world, whereas local occurrences might be only islands within the geographic range.

GEOGRAPHIC RANGE

The limitations upon the range of any species are brought about by ecological factors. It is well known that environmental factors vary geographically and that organisms have definite environmental requirements. Therefore, depending upon the requirements, there are definite limits (barriers) to the extent and number of places in the world a species can inhabit.

Although geographic restrictions exist, an entire species often inhabits sites that many single, localized populations could not occupy. This is possible because local populations are not exactly the same, population composition altering geographically in the form of unlike gene combinations (gene pools). This local variation is within the framework of individual gene combination fluctuations and spatial relationships; however, each population deviates about particular average conditions, which are what change spatially. These geographic variations within a species are of many types. There might be local modifications of reproductive and mortality rates, hence spatial differences in population fluctuations. The proportions of the separate age classes also might conform to latitudinal or altitudinal environmental gradients. Finally, and probably of greatest significance, is the fact that local populations can be unlike structurally and functionally; this is the basis for calling each a geographic *race* or, if these races are sufficiently unique, a *subspecies* or *variety* of their species.

LOCAL OCCURRENCE

The basic spatial units of a species can be described in terms of density and spacing. Density is the number of individuals per unit area. Spacing considers whether the individuals form closely knit groups but with distinct isolation among groups (*clumping*); maintain maximum separation from one another (*even spacing*); or occur according to chance alone (*random distribution*). Although density and spacing when combined present a good picture of restricted ranges, these phenomena are subject to so much variation that they rarely can be measured. Frequently, different age classes and sexes have independent modifications in local spacing and density and in seasonal and other periodic fluctuations in numbers, spacing, and density.

Density and spacing are reflections of environmental conditions and species behavior. Different habitats place restrictions on species numbers per unit area and also cause clumping or even spacing rather than random patterns. Random patterns probably do not exist in nature. Nonrandom distributions are the rule because the environments tend toward one or the other of the organized patterns. In fact, a species that is locally random will seem to be in clumps if local distributions occur as widely separated habitat islands, or seem to be even spaced if their habitat islands are of uniform size and distance from one another.

Although species behavior must act within environmental restrictions, behavior also has a distinct influence upon density and spacing. The most important phases of behavior are means of offspring distribution and social relationships. The offspring of plants and animals may be very close to their parents or some distance away. In certain species an entire local area is composed of a single family group; in others, the young are farther from the parents and family groups do not form; spacing varies from still fairly close to the parents, or at least the female parent, to almost random over a wide geographic area. In essence, the distribution of many young may be a mechanical thing rather than a true behavior pattern. In most plants this is the case, because true behavior is restricted to animals with complex nervous systems. Animal behavior definitely can influence the ultimate distribution pattern of offspring. In many nonsocial animals the young are forced to leave the parental environment (emigrate) by the parents. For this reason, the distribution of animal offspring is molded by behavior patterns.

SOCIAL BEHAVIOR

One can now appreciate that the presence of a species in a given habitat is allied to social behavior, and true social behavior is limited to animals. If the relations of individuals within the same species are close, or social, the spatial unit is clumped. If individual associations within species are remote or antagonistic, that is, nonsocial, local occurrence is random or even spaced. Note that we are not using "social" in the restricted sense of social insects.

Certain terms are useful in reference to social behavior. A *social group* is any aggregation of two or more individuals of the same species. A *society* is a social group in which a cooperative relationship takes place, and a *nonsocial* population is a social group in which no cooperation exists. A *colony* is a nonmoving social group, and a *band* is a mobile one. The opposite of a social group is a *solitary organism.* Solitary individuals exist where members of the species are actively antagonistic to one another except during brief portions of the reproductive period.

NONSOCIAL POPULATIONS

Members of the same species can be together without benefit or cooperation among the individuals. In fact, nonsocial groups can display active competition. This normally is the case in germinating plants that are very close to one another because seeds are concentrated near the parent. Such germinating plants are in direct competition for the necessities of life, especially space. Also, animals of the same species frequently congregate without any active cooperation. Nonsocial animal populations may form at a common feeding or courting location and may or may not display active competition. For example, if food or mates are plentiful, competition might be insignificant; but if things that fulfill needs are restricted, competition may exist among parts or all members of the nonsocial group. Partial competition might take place when only a particular age class or one sex is involved, for example, in courtship where competition might be restricted to males, or in a feeding area where adults ignore one another but drive away or are cannibalistic upon the young.

SOCIETIES

Cooperative social groups can be simple to complex, temporary or permanent aggregations of a single species; only animals generally form true societies. Temporary societies originate during a particular part of a day or during a particular part of the year. Temporary daily societies are formed by many birds that spend the night in a common roost and feed together in a definite area. Such groups are true societies because mutual protection comes from the association. Seasonal cooperative groups join for such purposes as migration, reproduction, and local protection.

Permanent societies also are of many types. They might consist of a single *pair* of parents, a *harem*, a *family*, a *clan* derived from a single pair of ancestors, a *clone* derived asexually from a single parent, or a *caste* society. The true caste society represents the most complex system of social behavior and is limited to insects, mostly termites and ants but also certain wasps and bees. In the most complex caste societies there are kings, queens, potential kings and queens, food storers, workers, and soldiers; most groups are distinguishable on the basis of body form alone.

The degree of organization of a society is directly proportional to the degree of its leadership and division of labor. Almost any society displays some amount of internal leadership, also called *social dominance* or "pecking order." The latter term refers to early studies of leadership that were made on birds. In a simple society there usually is an order of dominance among the individuals of the society. For example, in chickens the order is expressed by pecking, which may be linear or circular. In linear dominance the number one leader dominates all others, the number two leader all except number one, and so on down to the individual that is dominated by all other members of the society. In circular dominance there may be no single leader; each individual of the society is in a single peck order that is independent of all others. Therefore, circular dominance can feature somewhat peculiar relationships. For ex-

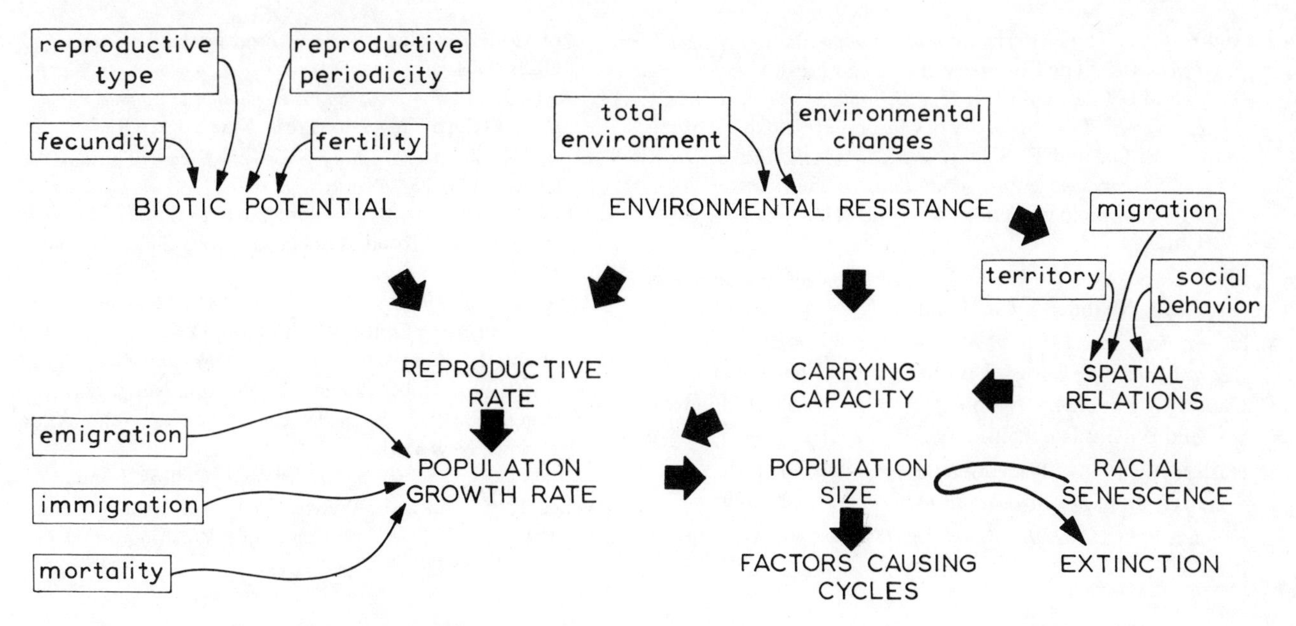

Figure 18.2 Interrelationships among factors contributing to population size—a summary of the more important phenomena of population dynamics.

ample, animal B might dominate animal C and be dominated by animal A, but animal C might dominate animal A.

Social division of labor is a phenomenon in which each individual of a society performs one of several possible separate functions. This social relationship is limited to colonial organisms and to complex societies. An example of colonial division of labor is found in certain coelenterates; the Portuguese man-of-war is a colony made up of reproductive, feeding, and protective individuals. Among complex societies the most intricate divisions of labor are in caste societies. For example, in termites each kind of individual not only performs a separate function but also is specialized structurally to perform these functions. Where caste societies have the most unique-looking types of individuals, there is also the most nearly absolute dominance by single individuals; the reproductives, especially the queen, dominate the activities of all other members of the caste society.

There are both advantages and disadvantages to social behavior. The advantages exist from individual effort's benefiting the entire group or the group's benefiting the individual. A society benefits when a single animal locates food and other necessities, or danger. Benefits from unified activity include cooperative defense and predation, greater likelihood of mating, and control of environmental extremes. An example of environmental control is found in bees which beat their wings to reduce temperature or group together to prevent the hive's freezing. The main disadvantages of social behavior are greater possibility of disease and parasitism transmission, of predator attraction, and of food depletion.

Societies contribute to all of the population phenomena discussed. Their relationship to the local occurrence of species is especially significant. Societies are by their very nature examples of clumping; however, individual societies might in turn be random, even spaced, or clumped. Also, mobile societies (bands) cause local spatial relationships to fluctuate; when societies are moving, it is possible for spacing to assume any of the three types at different times.

SELECTED READINGS*

Allee, W. C., 1931. *Animal Aggregations, a Study in General Sociology*. University of Chicago Press, Chicago.

———. 1951. *The Social Life of Animals*. Beacon Press. Boston.

*See also the General Ecology References, p. 338.

Andrewartha, H. G., 1961. *Introduction to the Study of Animal Populations*. The University of Chicago Press, Chicago.

———and L. C. Birch, 1954. *The Distribution and Abundance of Animals*. The University of Chicago Press, Chicago.

Dethier, V. G., and E. Stellar, 1961. *Animal Behavior: Its Evolutionary and Neurological Basis*. Foundations of Modern Biology Series. Prentice-Hall, Englewood Cliffs, N. J.

Elton, C. S., 1958. *The Ecology of Invasions by Animals and Plants*. Methuen & Co., London.

Frisch, Karl von, 1950. *Bees: Their Vision, Chemical Senses, and Language*. Cornell University Press, Ithaca, N.Y.

Gause, G. F., 1934. *The Struggle for Existence*. Williams and Wilkins Co., Baltimore.

Hasler, A., 1956. Perception of Pathways of Fishes in Migration. *Quarterly Review of Biology*, *31*: 200–209.

Klopfer, P. H., 1962. *Behavioral Aspects of Ecology*. Concepts of Modern Biology Series. Prentice-Hall, Englewood Cliffs, N. J.

Lack, D. L., 1954. *The Natural Regulation of Animal Populations*. Oxford University Press, New York.

Lorenz, K. Z., 1952. *King Solomon's Ring*. Thomas Y. Crowell Co., New York.

McCabe, T. T., and B. D. Blanchard, 1950. *Three Species of Peromyscus*. Rood Associates Publ., Santa Barbara, Calif.

Murie, Adolph, 1944. *The Wolves of Mount McKinley*. U. S. Govt. Printing Office, Washington, D. C.

Slobodkin, L. B., 1961. *Growth and Regulation of Animal Populations*. Holt, Rinehart & Winston, New York.

Tinbergen, N., 1953. *Social Behavior in Animals*. John Wiley & Sons, New York.

———. 1953. *The Herring Gull's World*. Collins, London.

Welles, R. E., and F. B. Welles, 1961. *The Bighorn of Death Valley*. U. S. Govt. Printing Office, Washington, D. C.

19 COMMUNITY ECOLOGY

Relations among Species

A community has already been defined as the sum total of the populations in a given area. One may think of a forest or other habitat with its many kinds of plants and animals as a community. Another way of thinking of this ecological unit is in terms of *functions;* by definition, the community must include all the functions of its many populations. This means that everything said about populations must apply to communities; however, as one might expect by now, a community is more complex than the sum of its parts.

THE NATURE OF THE COMMUNITY

Communities are so complex that their true nature probably is unappreciated. However, two concepts, superorganism and continuum, give some idea of their nature.

THE COMMUNITY, A SUPERORGANISM?

The community as a whole may be treated as an entity, a *superorganism* similar to a living organism or to many organisms, especially in terms of its functions. The similar functions include fluctuations, equilibrium, influence on environment, relations with others of its kind, life cycles, division of labor, organization, adaptations, regulation, and definite structure. In varying degrees these functions are the subject of this chapter. Some consideration of them now serves to illustrate the concept of a community as a superorganism.

Life cycles in the form of succession show that communities originate ("birth"), grow, mature, and die. Only stable, climax communities have a means of self-production and perpetuation, but a function analogous to reproduction exists where competition causes one community to replace another (succession). Also, division of labor is found in plants providing food through photosynthesis, in plants improving habitat conditions, and in all organisms having different functions, discrete, but working together in a dynamic equilibrium. Such segregated functions often are needed by, and thus benefit, the various specialized creatures. In addition, organisms providing necessary functions automatically assume a position of some permanence in the community. Since complex organization is the rule in communities, individual plants and animals must conform or be adapted to life within their locale. Adaptations in each population are such that the activities of species are integrated so that a local area's life is regulated by its internal units. This dynamic process of preventing extreme conditions resulting from overactivity of any species causes a trend toward community equilibrium. Finally, definite community structure exists in some appearance of uniformity, in the occupation of space, in the limits of a boundary, and in some permanence or durability through time.

THE COMMUNITY, A CONTINUUM?

Although many communities appear as distinct units, or *stands*, having precise boundaries, many merge gradually into others. This is a natural consequence of physical and biotic factors' following gradients; and because the important factors of temperature and moisture normally change through space, habitats may assume the appearance of a spectrum. There may be distinct communities, but one almost imperceptibly changes into another, resulting in an over-all arrangement called a *continuum*.

When a continuum exists any segregation of communities becomes somewhat arbitrary. For practical purposes, one approaches the problem by attempting to define pure entities and to treat the zone of transition between any two pure units as a special edge effect, called an *ecotone*. Because these edges have peculiar ecological properties that cause them to be very important habitats, they cannot be ignored. Although ecotones can be perplexing, especially when they are extremely broad, and one might wish he could avoid them because they hinder any tidy scheme of community classification, ecotones generally are no more difficult to recognize than so-called "pure" communities. Actually, communities in general probably are no more difficult—in some respects, they are easier—to classify than individual groups of organisms.

COMMUNITY VARIATIONS

Like populations, and because each is composed of many populations, communities display variations in their living components. For practical purposes, these variations can be classified as *temporal* or *spatial*.

Temporal and spatial variations are the consequence of chance, ecological amplitude, competition, and the environment. Moreover, each of these major factors leading to variation is subject to change and is intimately related to other factors; thus, temporal and spatial variations really are not distinct from one another.

SOURCES OF VARIATION

Although the sources of variation are chance, ecological amplitude, competition, and the environment, it is convenient to deal with these sources singly and collectively under certain topics (Figure 19.1). These topics are *activity*, *movement*, and *environmental gradients*. Other topics of importance—individual adaptation, evolution, extinction, chance, and geological changes, especially in reference to highways and environments—have already been treated thoroughly enough for present discussion. However, they will be reconsidered, along with the present subject, in relation to biogeographical dynamics (pp. 364–371).

ACTIVITY

Few plants or animals are active to the same extent or are present throughout every day and season of the year. In green plants there is a daily fluctuation cycle. During the day the plants carry on photosynthesis and respiration; at night, photosynthesis ceases and respiration continues. In animals the daily cycle usually consists of a period of sleep and one of activity. Actually four periods are recognized as possible: roughly, dawn hours, daylight hours, evening hours, and night hours. In relation to these periods certain animals are active while others are inactive.

Seasonal variations in activity normally have more influence upon community composition and structure than do daily cycles. In plants there are definite parts of the year for germination, vegetative growth, flowering, fruiting, and seed maturity. Many species flower during the spring, but the fact that others flower in the summer, fall, or even the winter causes conspicuous seasonal variations in community structure. Therefore, when viewed at any one time the many plant species display many to all possible phases of growth and reproduction. In animals, also, most to all stages of life cycles are represented by the various species independently, each may be carrying on courtship, bearing young, or functioning in some other process. In addition to active organisms, both plant and animal species often have an inactive period or periods of the year. Plant dormancy displays the loss of leaves and reduction of functions in perennial plants and the presence of

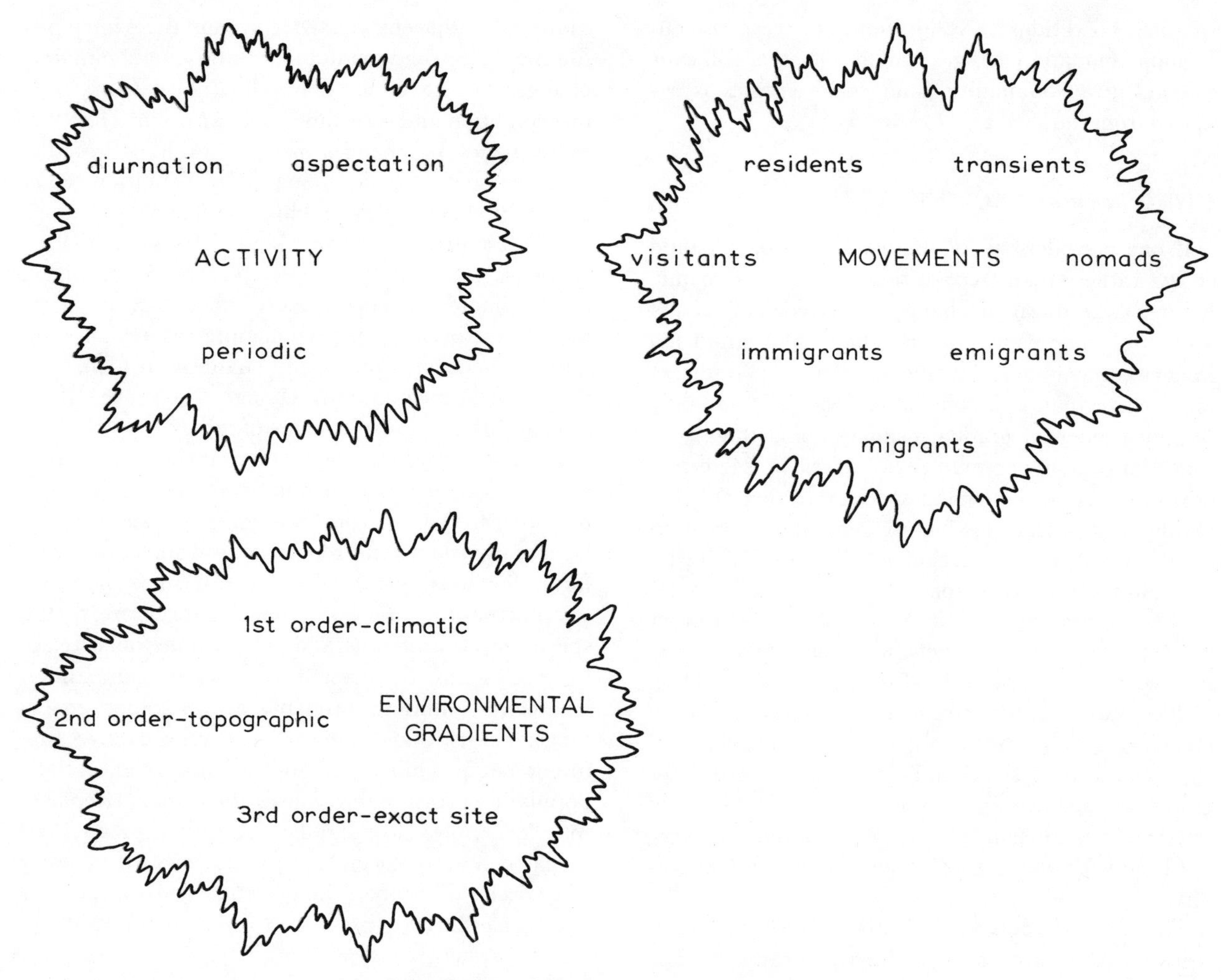

Figure 19.1 The sources of community variation.

only seeds in annual plants. In animal dormancy, inactivity is characterized by comalike states, especially summer aestivation or winter hibernation.

MOVEMENTS

Movements of all kinds can be used to classify the occurrence of individuals or populations within a community. *Nomads* are wanderers that are irregular occupants; *residents* are present at all times; *transients* are predictable seasonal migrants through the community; and *visitants* are seasonal occupants distinguished on the basis of their time of presence, usually summer or winter.

Travel, like activity, can be both daily and seasonal; and also like seasonal activity or dormancy, movement causes alteration of community composition and structure. Daily animal motility is within the home range, but can be vertical or horizontal. For example, vertical movements are common in the soil or in water, and horizontal ones are within or between surface communities. All of these journeys contribute to changes in spatial relations, and some contribute to changes in composition and structure of a community during any twenty-four hour cycle. Seasonal movements can be vertical or horizontal, local or distant. When they involve some distance, they may be permanent departures (*emigrations*) or involve later return (*migrations*).

Daily and seasonal movements are not the only possibilities. In addition, movements can be related to cyclic increase of a species or years of peculiar weather conditions. Relocations in response to periodic climatic changes might cause significant changes in a community if an entire species is removed from the locality.

ENVIRONMENTAL GRADIENTS

If one considers a community as a fixed, static entity rather than recognizing its true dynamic nature, large to small changes in ecological factors are better appreciated. Such changes or gradients in environments are the rule in nature. Gradients may be irregular or directional and each of these may display sudden or gradual changes. For these reasons, individual communities and their segments, down to parts of individual species, display either a regular distribution, owing to geographic zonation of gradients, or an irregular distribution, owing to a mosaic occurrence of gradients through space. However, gradients exist in a hierarchy. First-order gradients tend to reflect general climate and are expressed mostly as latitudinal or altitudinal zonation of life. Second-order gradients normally relate to local topography, being observed in somewhat restricted effects of slope and exposure. Third-order gradients exist within communities, and consist of restricted expression of life in relation to very localized variation in such things as soil or topography.

The various orders of gradients, and whether each is irregular or directional, sudden or gradual, leads to a basic framework of variation within any community. It is this basic framework that is modified by daily, seasonal, and periodic directional and cyclic changes. In addition, the changes—and hence, the framework—are either functions of or are further modified by activity, movements, extinction, and evolution.

NATURE OF VARIATIONS

Variations operate as an intricate complex that contributes to the dynamic nature of the community. However, as was mentioned, this complex may be examined from temporal and spatial points of view.

TEMPORAL CHANGES

Fluctuations in the composition and nature of life through time can be studied in the species, community or adjacent related communities (intercommunities). Species, community, and intercommunity changes can be either noncyclic (not starting from one condition and returning to it) or cyclic. Furthermore, noncyclic changes may prove either irregular or directional. Cyclic changes, by definition, complete a circle of events in which both start and finish are represented by the same kind of life (Table 19.1).

Species Changes. Species changes were discussed in the chapter on population ecology, but are mentioned here because they contribute to over-all community changes. Community changes, in turn, contribute to intercommunity changes—and even these are part of the grander scheme of things.

Noncyclic irregular changes may involve additions, subtractions, or replacements in a community. Additions can come from immigration, subtractions from emigrations, and replacement from substitution for individuals lost through death of a noncatastrophic nature. Because these changes are at the species level, additions and subtractions must relate to species already present in a given community. Therefore, additions probably are of minor importance, contributing nothing that reproductive rate might not produce; but subtractions might reflect population pressure that causes emigration. Replacement generally, is of significance because after individual death, replacement usually is by a member of a species other than the one that died—a member of a species already present in the community, however.

Noncyclic directional changes in individuals, or even entire species, can be due to any species' replacing another as a result of competition. When the change occurs within a species it might be due to chance or to natural selection of a better-adapted individual. When one species replaces another, it can be due to competition.

Cyclic changes in single creatures or entire species are shown in periodicity and phasic cycles. *Periodicity* was discussed in terms of the annual occurrence of particular stages in the life cycle of individuals or a species. *Phasic cycles* start with the death of a member of a species and end with the reestablishment of the same species (Figure 19.2). For example, an individual may die. Then, decomposers of various kinds may invade the organic remains and, during decomposition, other organisms may follow a sequence in invading the remains. Finally, bare ground is the consequence of complete decomposi-

TABLE 19.1 TEMPORAL CHANGES IN LIFE. THE PRIMARY SOURCES OF NONCYCLIC IRREGULAR, NONCYCLIC DIRECTIONAL, AND CYCLIC TEMPORAL CHANGES ARE INDICATED FOR SPECIES, FOR COMMUNITIES, AND FOR ADJACENT COMMUNITIES.

Type of Temporal Change	Species Sources	Community Sources	Intercommunity Sources
Noncyclic irregular	Nomadism Emigration Immigration Replacement (after death)	Speciation Extinction	Barrier changes
Noncyclic directional	Competition Chance Natural selection	Integrated evolution	Barrier changes Cliseral shifts Evolution Succession Regression
Cyclic	Arhythmic (phasic cycles) Seasonal cycle (periodicity) Migration	Cyclic environment (diurnation, aspectation, etc.)	Environment (causing community progression)

tion, the original remains and decomposers being eliminated; but prior to reinvasion by the original species, a sequence of intermediate creatures of different species may occur.

Phasic cycles often are more complex than implied by the outline above. Individual cycles within a community may display unique additions or deletions of stages from the "typical" cycle. Therefore, the phasic cycles of any community (there can be many, completely unrelated cycles) regularly create many patches of life throughout a community that are foreign to most of the community. The foreign nature of these patches can cause them to be confused with noncyclic directional intercommunity changes, such as succession, regression, cliseral shifts, and evolution of new communities.

Community Changes. These phenomena involve single groupings of similar life in a particular unit of space, the life constituting a stand.

Noncyclic changes include irregular ones due to speciation and extinction and directional ones due to evolution of the community as a whole. Actually, community evolution is on an individual species basis, involving individual perfection of adaptations

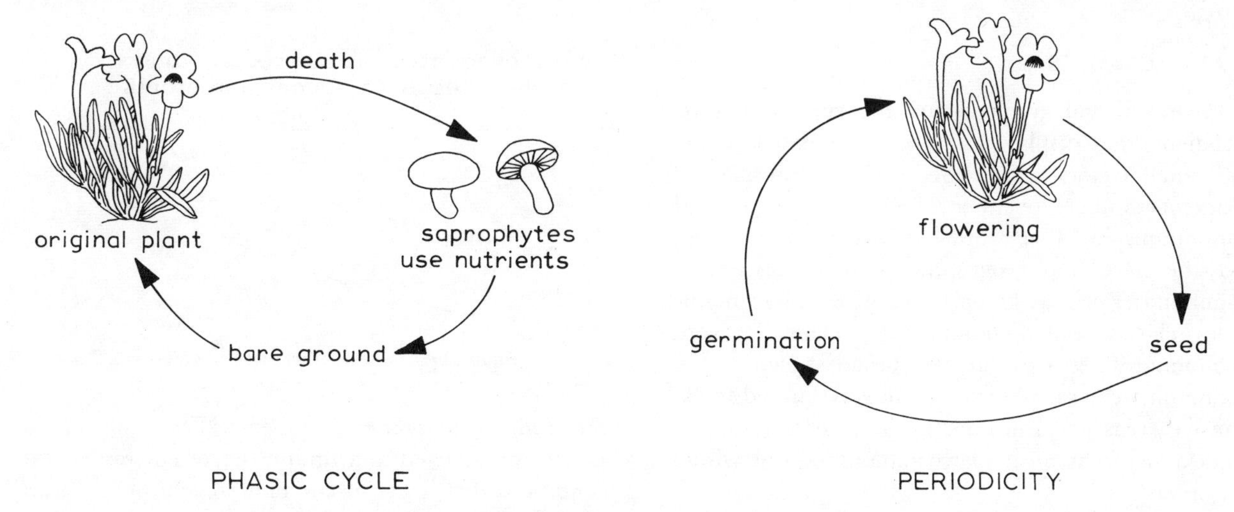

Figure 19.2 A phasic cycle in contrast to periodicity.

to the existing and evolving ecosystem. In general, direction is present in reference to a fairly prescribed "path" toward greater complexity in the community as a whole.

Cyclic changes were mentioned already as reflections of environmental cyclic changes (pp. 335–337). These community cycles are diurnation, aspectation, or any longer periodic cycle.

Intercommunity Changes. Intercommunity changes involve interworkings among adjacent stands; thus, they have a strong spatial emphasis.

Noncyclic irregular changes can be due to periodic opening and closing of barriers during geomorphic or climatic cycles, and lead to irregular additions, and perhaps subtractions, of species in the different communities involved. *Noncyclic directional changes* may be in the form of cliseral shifts, evolution of new communities from the mixing of the old, succession, and regression. Succession (progression in place to a community of stability) will soon be discussed in more detail. Regression is a partial reversal of normal succession, owing to such things as natural catastrophies, human influence, and overgrazing. It is treated under the topic of succession as secondary succession.

Cyclic changes are similar to regression, but are due to a normal progression from one to another community and then back to the first (Figure 19.3). For example, in certain marshes there is a progression to a marsh community that is destroyed by wind or other normal features of the environment and from this destruction there is development to a marsh community like the original one.

SPATIAL CHANGES

Environmental gradients are the rule in nature. Gradients may display close or remote association in individual factors. The effect of this interplay of gradients is to create either a regular or an irregular continuum; in other words, adjacent communities may be part of a geographic gradient of similar communities or may be part of a geographic mosaic of less closely related communities. Here, the word "community" is used in the broadest sense. A community can range in size from very limited to expansive areas and can even be large enough to include a hierarchy of smaller communities, one within the other.

Communities through space do not clearly reflect the gradients in their environment. No organism is so narrowly restricted to a unique set of environmental conditions that it can occur only at one point in an over-all environmental gradient. Rather, each spec-

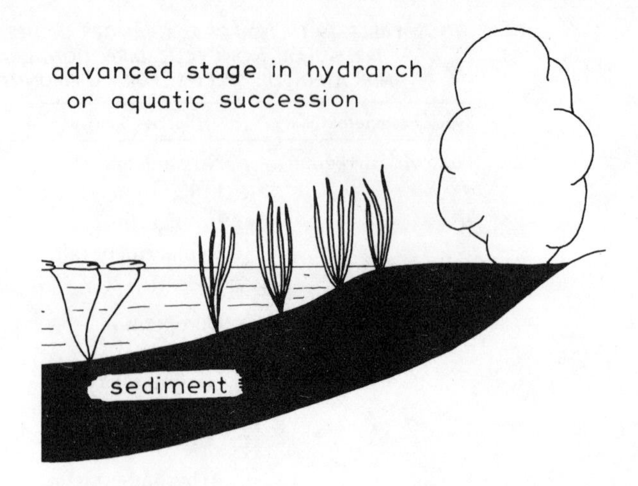

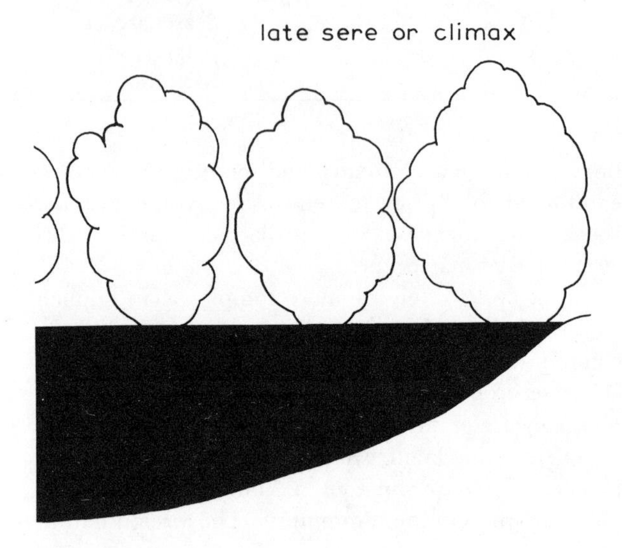

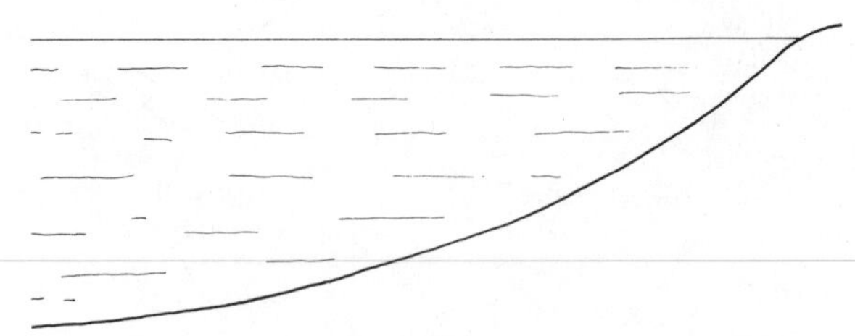

Figure 19.3 A cycle of community progression.

ies, and each individual within a species, possesses an ecological amplitude that determines its environmental distribution. However, ecological amplitudes vary, especially among different species. For this reason, one also finds particular environments in which species can exist together, and as one goes further from this environment, a gradual dropping out of one species after another.

The precise horizontal and vertical space inhabited by organisms to form a large, individual community is a function of many environmental factors. Each environmental factor normally encompasses a hierarchy of gradients in which each small gradient contributes to the nature of the next higher gradient. Each level of gradients, and especially the largest level, is characterized by either a continuous or discontinuous change in the particular factor. Therefore, organisms are subjected to both individual and collective ecological factors and the gradations of each and all. Certain individual factors or combinations of factors will prove limiting to each species; if further intolerable situations are present, the particular species cannot exist. On the other hand, where organisms occur, the species are in dynamic equilibrium with their physical environment and the other organisms composing their ecosystem. Owing to these various physical and biotic relationships, species and communities display less diversity than do their habitat and the environment in general.

So far we have assumed rather fixed environmental conditions, yet the complexity of even static habitats is difficult to comprehend. Soon, the topic of biogeographical dynamics will briefly outline what takes place when environments shift in relation to geomorphic cycles.

TENDENCY FOR EQUILIBRIUM

It is easy to overemphasize the changes and conditions for change that are present in any community. All communities normally progress to a condition of equilibrium under the set of environmental conditions present at a given time. Under uniform conditions (which probably do not exist in nature), change regularly is directional and toward greater complexity in the sequence of communities occupying a particular site. However, the more complex the replacing communities become, the greater is the tendency for equilibrium conditions to be approached. In fact, the basic workings of most habitats are likely to lead to eventual stability (see discussion of succession). This stability, or equilibrium, is not rigid or fixed; actually it is dynamic, like the swinging of a pendulum about a central point in its fluctuation.

Equilibrium is best conceived in terms of a *balance of nature*. Although individual populations, and even entire communities, fluctuate, there are mechanisms that regulate or control departure from average conditions (Figure 19.4). For example, if a species becomes overabundant it is more likely to be a source of food for more animals, to have increased parasitism and disease, and to enter into greater competition with its own kind. In other words, an overabundant species is reduced by *density-dependent factors* of its environment. On the other hand, a species with reduced numbers is affected only slightly by density-dependent factors and tends to increase in numbers.

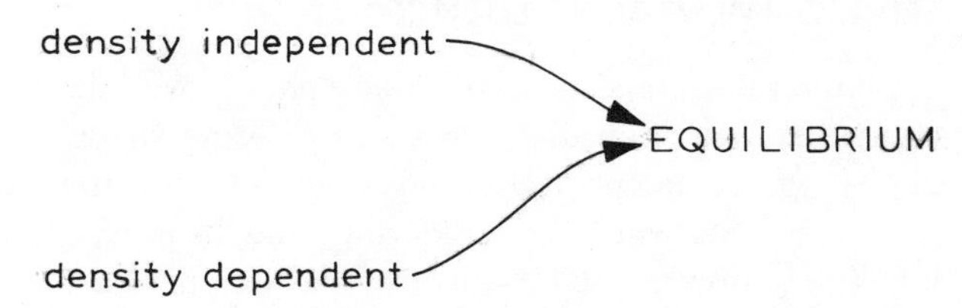

Figure 19.4 The two major groups of ecological factors contributing to community equilibrium.

Equilibrium is not simply the result of all ecological factors affecting species in direct relation to the number of individuals per unit area, because some factors are independent of species density. These latter ecological factors, which can include most physical aspects of an environment, are termed *density independent factors*.

COMMUNITY INFLUENCE

In addition to modifying one another, communities often modify their physical environment.

COMMUNITY INTERRELATIONS

The influence of one community upon another is directly related to the size and stability of each and to the distance between the communities. In general, the larger a community the more influence it is likely to have upon others. Proximity is important in interrelations because distance alone is an effective barrier to possible activities between communities, and stability is important because only a stable community (climax) can complete with another habitat and still maintain its identity. When two or more climaxes compete with one another, each retains its identity; however, when a climax competes with an unstable, or seral, community, the climax replaces the seral stage.

Community interrelations exist because of natural movements of materials between communities. For example, wind or water can move soil, organic debris, or organisms, and organisms can travel between communities. These movements are not uncommon; daily and seasonal movements of animals have already been mentioned. Therefore, some of the resources of one community can actually be used by another.

ENVIRONMENTAL INFLUENCE

Communities tend to have some control over the climate of their immediate area. In creating shade, plants reduce temperature and decrease moisture loss; in slowing wind, reduce drying; and in providing litter, prevent soil moisture and temperature extremes. Animals by reducing vegetation can reverse these plant effects. Plants have many other actions upon their environment. They can deplete the soil of its moisture and minerals; in turn, they are important agents of soil formation. Plants can change atmospheric composition by releasing more oxygen into the air during the day and more carbon dioxide at night; however, plants generally use more carbon dioxide during the day than they release during a twenty-four hour period. Vegetation also retards water runoff, and thus retards erosion of the soil in the community.

Animal influences normally are less striking, or at least usually less beneficial. Animals do aid in soil formation when burrowing species mix the soil; however, their most pronounced actions are destructive. For example, overgrazing can increase erosion, cause environmental change, and ultimately create drastic alteration in community composition.

STRATIFICATION

Stratification involves the influence of layering within a habitat. For example, a community may have tree, shrub, herbaceous, and moss layers. Each of these layers, like a rock layer, is called a *stratum;* collectively, the layers are *strata.* The phenomenon of vertical distribution is called *stratification.* Stratification occurs because a stand as a rule has vertical distribution of both its ecological factors and organisms, but only the layering of life is implied by the concept of stratification. Both plants and animals are stratified, both in water and on land. However, further discussion here is limited to land plants and the animals associated with this plant layering.

Classical segregation of layers is based on whether or not the plants contain chlorophyll (i.e., are or are not green) and on whether or not the plants have free support. The classification follows (Figure 19.5).

Green Plants: Mechanically Independent. This category includes *trees*, *shrubs*, *herbs*, and *mosses*.

Green Plants: Mechanically Dependent. *Climbers* are subdivided according to their attachment mechanisms. Twiners wrap around other plants because

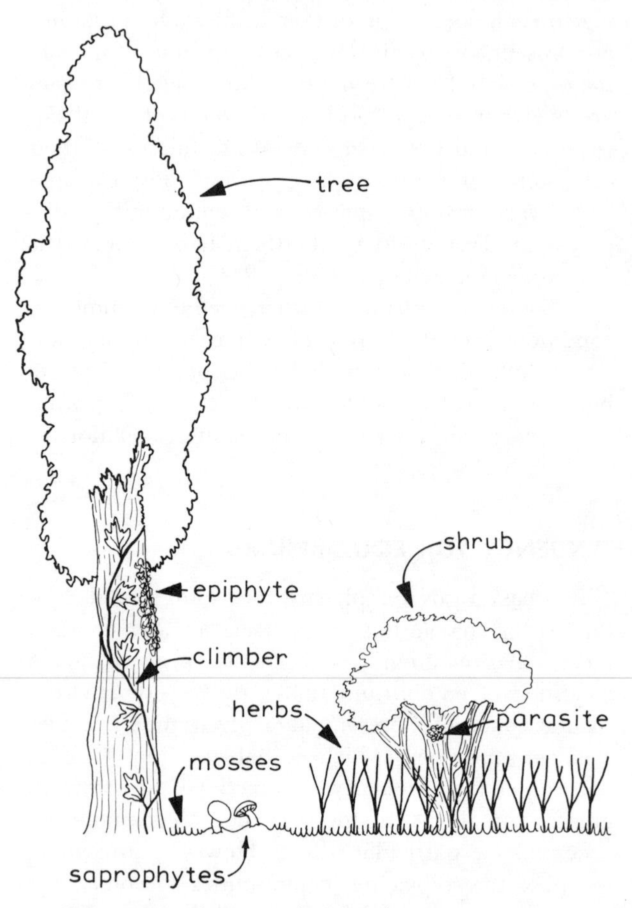

Figure 19.5 The strata or layers of plants in a community.

twining tips grow in a rotating movement. Tendril climbers have various structures modified into thin, elongate tendrils that encircle or in some way "grasp" any object they contact. Root climbers periodically grow roots that attach the plants in their upward growth. Leaners are almost capable of independent support, but gain their upward growth by leaning on nearby plants. Leaners have no specialized means of support to their upward growth. Climbers are also called *lianas*.

Epiphytes live upon other plants, but for support only.

Nongreen Plants. These plants, because they lack chlorophyll, do not carry on photosynthesis. Therefore, they are dependent upon other creatures for their food.

Saprophytes obtain their food from dead organic matter.

Parasites usually live upon and receive their food from living creatures.

A few to all of the above layers may be present in a given habitat. For example, a well-developed forest may have all strata present, but a grassland may have only an herb stratum. When many layers are present, each possesses unique environmental factors and each progressively lower stratum is composed of plants that are more independent mechanically as well as being shorter. In addition, each layer that is present has a few characteristic plants, the *dominant species;* however, the entire habitat tends to hinge upon the highest stratum. For example, if the highest dominant trees of a forest habitat are destroyed, many species of the lower strata will be lost; but lower strata might be removed without pronounced changes in the trees or any other unaffected layer.

Any type of habitat might show stratification. Shrub habitats often have many lower strata present. Even a herbaceous habitat can have two or more layers, each herb stratum created by many species of the same general height.

Significance. Progressively lower strata usually have less light, lower daytime temperatures, higher night temperatures, a moister atmosphere, and lower wind velocity; the taller plants have greater influence on the environment. In general, the lower the stratum the less the environmental extremes. Also, stratification frequently is an indication of the developmental status of a community. The climax, because of its stability, regularly has well-organized strata, with climax species adapted to the environment. In contrast, seral stages normally have poor strata formation; most of the plants must germinate and grow in more open situations, because shade is a limiting factor for them. In addition, each layer comprises a single unit of vegetation, or *layer society*.

SUCCESSIONAL STATUS

Succession is the somewhat orderly process of progressive replacement of organisms in a restricted area over a long period of time. This replacement is a continuous thing; the plants and animals of a community develop their environment to the point where new species can invade the area, replace the previous species, and develop a new community. Each of the communities on the way to a stable situation is called a *seral stage*. The first species or group of species invading an area constitute the *pioneer* or *primary seral stage*. From this, various *intermediate seral stages* are present on the way to the final stable habitat, the *climax*. A single successional sequence from pioneer stage through climax is a *sere*.

A climax might be somewhat difficult to diagnose in nature. However, any climax possesses a single characteristic which aids in its recognition. This characteristic, or phenomenon, is a state of dynamic equilibrium. Climax organisms generally modify neither one another nor their physical environment sufficiently to create surroundings more favorable for potential invading species or less favorable for the species already in the habitat. Therefore, the climax is a phenomenon in which environmental factors are relatively stable and species composition is relatively fixed.

DYNAMIC EQUILIBRIUM

This picture of balance in a climax can cause misunderstanding. In spite of the fact that a climax is a condition of equilibrium, it is not one of static equilibrium. Although species composition of the characteristic dominant species at least is somewhat fixed, some fluctuation in numbers and even spatial relations is not uncommon. This fluctuation partly exists because daily, seasonal, and annual variation in ecological factors is the rule, and factor variation causes some response by organisms. Therefore, any kind of equilibrium that is present within such variations must be a dynamic one. Also, the fact of dynamic equilibrium necessitates a synergistic response to the environment by the climax. Otherwise, the climax could not partially control its environment to the extent of preventing extremes in the physical environment from destroying some of its organisms. This is another way of stating that climaxes have some power to control their environments and seral stages do not.

OCCURRENCE

Succession is not a unique phenomenon that takes place in a single fragment of the biosphere. It is found in most, if not all, habitats. For example, succession is found among the microscopic animals in water. It can occur in as temporary a situation as a puddle of water. Also, a fallen tree may go through a sequence of seral stages that are associated with the progress of complete decay. Although such microsuccessions are of definite interest, they are beyond the scope of this book. Present treatment is limited to the two general patterns of large-scale land succession, that starting on a dry substrate and that starting in fresh water.

Succession starting in either dry or water areas can be of two types, primary or secondary. *Primary succession* starts on bare rocks or in water where vegetation has not grown before. *Secondary succession* is the consequence of disturbance of previous vegetation, seral or climax, and begins after such things as fire, abnormal weather, overgrazing, or cultivation.

Succession is an orderly phenomenon; however, one can predict the likely stages only in primary succession. For this reason, only primary succession from rock and from water will be examined in detail. Secondary succession resembles primary succession if the disturbance of previous organisms was not too great. On the other hand, severe disturbance might create a unique set of seral stages. This might even be true in the case of mild disturbance. For example, if some of the climax vegetation is removed from an area, secondary succession might consist of one or more peculiar seral stages in which both climax and seral plants are present.

COMMUNITIES AND SUCCESSION

A convenient classification of communities is made on the basis of successional status. *Seral communities* are those of a temporary nature that will be replaced by other communities. *Climax communities* are in a self-regenerating state of equilibrium and are not replaced by another community unless some outside disturbance affects their environments. Climax communities are also called *associations*.

Climaxes and the associations they represent can be of two major types (Figure 19.6). *Primary climaxes* are those that tend to reflect major environmental features. They include the *climatic climaxes* that are found on gentle topography and loamy soils; *edaphic climaxes* that are in unique soil conditions; *topographic climaxes* that are in slope, exposure, or some other unique landscape feature; and *topoedaphic climaxes* that are in places with unique interrelations of topography and soil.

The second major type of climaxes, *secondary climaxes* or *disclimaxes*, reflect disturbance. Disclimaxes include those produced by animals, *zootic climaxes*, and by fire, *fire climaxes*. Although all primary and secondary climaxes are recognized here as true climaxes, many ecologists treat only climatic climaxes as true climaxes.

CAUSES OF SUCCESSION

It might seem that most of the landscape should consist of climax communities. However, this is often far from the case. There are portions of the earth where most of the communities are stable and in equilibrium, but widespread areas are composed of seral stages alone. Various things contribute to the presence of seral stages. They may come from pronounced environmental changes that are sufficient either to remove a climax or to cause the old climax to be unstable. Possible sources of new environments can be geology, weather, or life itself. Geomorphic cycles, such as those involving glaciers, volcanoes, earthquakes, tidal waves, landslides, and shifting streambeds, can remove vast areas of climax. Weather catastrophies, such as floods, tornadoes, hurricanes, or rare extremes of temperature and moisture also can alter succession. Biotic factors, including great increases in plant-eating animals, overgrazing, and disease, can denude or modify a habitat. In addition, fire, no matter what its source, may be extremely destructive.

KINDS OF SUCCESSION

In *biotic succession*, the kind treated here, both plants and animals are related in *bioseres* (often

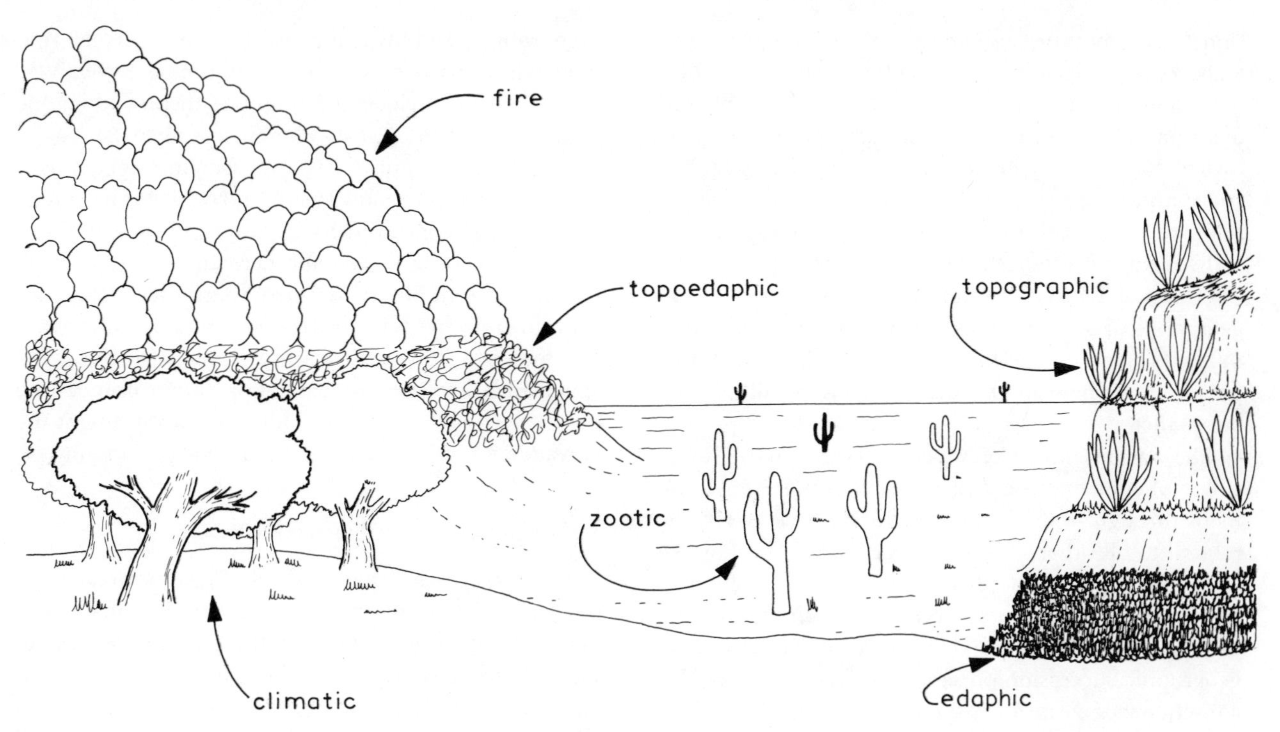

Figure 19.6 The kinds of climaxes.

simply termed *seres*). The other major successions are climatic, physiographic, geologic and biogeographic (Figure 19.7). *Climatic succession* entails a nongeographic temporal sequence of biotic communities (often climaxes), called *cliseres*, that reflect climatic change. The climax of climatic succession is a rather nebulous entity, but one might consider it to be the particular climatic climax during a stable period that might terminate a single climatic trend. *Physiographic succession* consists of *eoseres*, each a sequence of biotic communities reflecting a constructive or destructive phase of a geomorphic cycle. For practical purposes, there really is no eosere climax. However, if all elevating processes were to cease and erosion proceeded to its full extent, a stable state that might be called a climax would exist in the form of 12,000 feet of water covering a uniform ocean bottom. *Geologic succession* places emphasis on taxa rather than communities. Steps in this succession, *geoseres*, might be defined as the "ages" or dominance of particular major groups of organisms (e.g., Ages of Monera, Algae, Pteridophytes, Gymnosperms, Angiosperms, Invertebrates, Fishes, Amphibians, Reptiles, and Mammals). However, there can be confusion of geoseres when plants and animals are considered together because the "ages" of plants and animals overlap but do not necessarily coincide exactly with one another. Further confusion is possible because there really is no past geologic climax, nor is there likely to be a future one. For a geologic climax to exist, evolution must cease. Therefore, the only possible culmination with potential stability would be the cessation of life upon our planet. *Biogeographical succession* is similar to geologic succession, but places emphasis on the evolu-

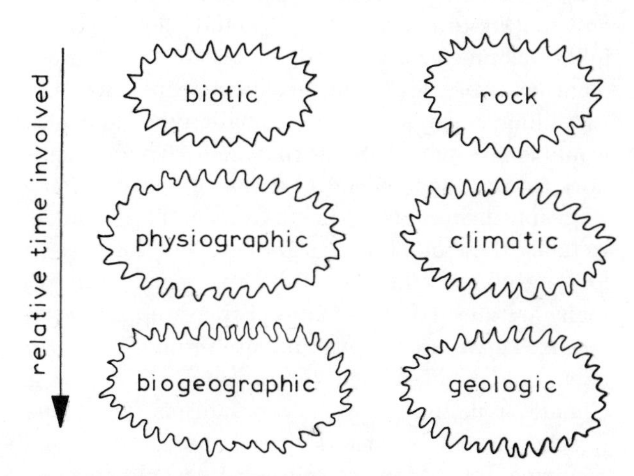

Figure 19.7 The kinds of succession. Rock succession is not mentioned in the text, but it implies changes and unique features in rocks and topography that lead to nonclimatic climaxes.

tion of communities rather than taxa. Biogeographical succession is very similar to biotic succession but is of much longer duration, treating the development of all past floras and faunas through space and time rather than biotic climaxes under a relatively stable space-and-time segment. It is particularly difficult to relate to a seral concept because a single biogeographical succession (*biogeographical sere*) encompasses the evolution of all past communities. Therefore, a biogeographical sere includes all of the complex communities between the first living organisms and the present biosphere in the development of all life on our planet.

The various kinds of succession are phases of a single phenomenon, changes of life and its environment through time. Moreover, each phase is closely related to all others. Biotic succession is of shortest duration. Biotic succession is related to climatic succession, and climatic succession might be due to physiographic changes. Finally, geologic and biogeographic succession present long-term views of the consequences of the other types of succession.

TERRESTRIAL SUCCESSION

In terrestrial environments, including both land and fresh water, the entire concept of biotic succession is most closely applied to plants. This is the consequence of plants' usually showing greater ecological restrictions than animals. The ecological relationships of animals usually can be associated with those of plants.

Climaxes on land are largely due to climate. However, if climate is the only criterion of the climax, only mature to old land forms would allow time for full development of soil and the rest of the environment necessary for a single climax in one locality. Limitation of climaxes to the climatic type alone also would ignore many habitats that are in dynamic equilibrium (the fundamental criterion of a climax) because of environmental factors other than climate. Actually these other factors are never the sole reason for any climax; the so-called nonclimatic climaxes really are affected by climate. For example, certain localized areas are in apparent equilibrium, but these communities differ from climax communities of the climatic type, in that their organisms are more closely affected by factors of soil, topography, and recurring fires. Many ecologists now would consider these localized communities to be climax (edaphic, topographic, and fire climaxes) because it seems that the environments of such communities are relatively fixed and the various communities display dynamic equilibrium in their particular environments.

In addition to primary and secondary climaxes, *climax patterns* are now being recognized in which vegetation is conceived as a pattern of populations, variously relating to one another, and corresponding to the pattern of environmental gradients (a continuum concept). Therefore, one should realize that a climax is a homogeneous thing only in a restricted space and that one climax habitat often grades into another climax. In fact, all vegetation might be considered part of a single, world-wide continuum.

SUCCESSION AND GEOMORPHOLOGY

Plant succession bears a relationship to geology and, in a broad sense, to the constructive phase of a geomorphic cycle. The destructive phase resemblance (regression) would be caused by fire, volcanism, disease, erosion, and any other phenomenon that can bring about biologically sterile or disturbed areas. On land the sterile areas can be of many types; however, the types approach two extremes, bare rock and water. Study of succession, starting from biologically sterile bare rock and water, will illustrate the various types of succession.

XERARCH SUCCESSION

Succession on land normally starting from bare rock is called xerarch succession. Many successional stages are possible (Figure 19.8). The primary stage usually consists of combinations of algae and fungi called lichens but may be blue-green algae. In sequence, the remaining possible stages usually are moss stage, herb stage, shrub stage, tree stage, and climax. However, many deviations from this sequence are possible. First, particular intermediate stages—the moss stage, for example—may be absent. Second, more than one stage of the same general type may occur. For example, more than one herb stage might exist. Third, terminal or near-terminal stages, especially the shrub and tree stages, do not necessarily precede the stage of climax. A shrub climax, for example, may form prior to the invasion of any tree stage. Fourth, there can be a reversal of stages on the way to the climax. Such a condition could come about in an area having a stream. For example, the

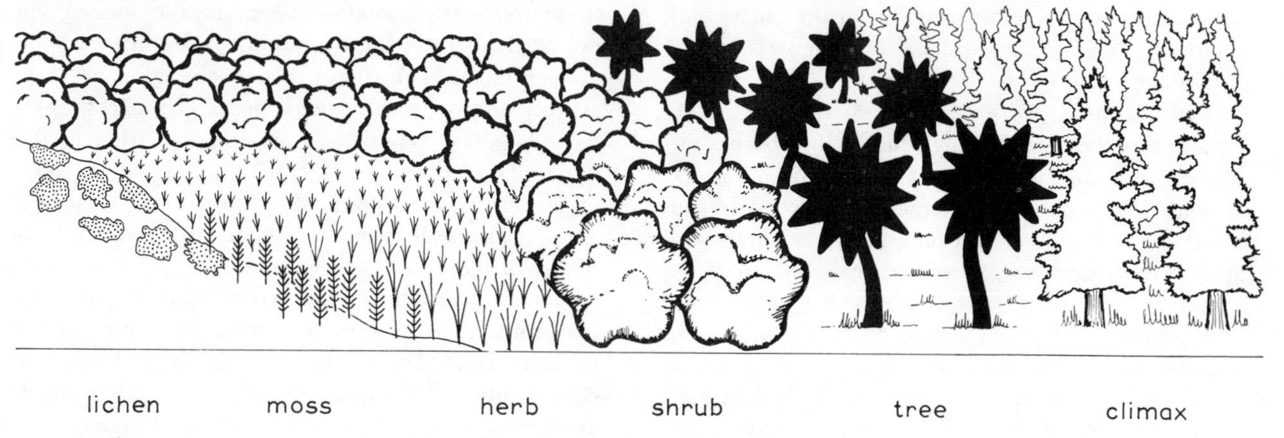

Figure 19.8 The typical stages of xerarch succession.

climax of the area might be grassland, but the streamside vegetation could be seral and a woodland. The climax, then, would come when the streamside woodland was transformed to a grassland. This complication of "normal" succession would take place because xerarch succession is modified by the presence of excess water. Fifth, stages in addition to those that might be considered typical can occur. For example, a spike moss (*Selaginella*) stage commonly follows a moss stage in central coastal California. Finally, certain species found in late seral stages may remain in the climax. For example, a seral shrub may enter the shrub layer in a woodland climax.

There are two main reasons why seral stages tend to proceed in an orderly change of vegetation forms. First, the sequences in seral stages are in direct relationship to plants' needing a better environment. By "better," it is meant that later stages require a more fully developed soil, more moisture, a reduction in temperature extremes, and a generally more stable environment. Second, an existing seral stage creates the better environment necessary for the next stage. This phenomenon might actually start prior to the invasion of a rock by the pioneer lichen stage. The various physical factors of erosion may have to modify a rock to some extent before lichens can invade. The lichens further erode the rock, primarily by acid production, and many of the eroded rock particles are held by the lichens. This accumulation of rock particles is the start of soil formation. After sufficient particles accumulate, the proper conditions of moisture and other factors exist for the invasion of mosses. The mosses further the process of soil formation and general modification of their own environment until herbs can invade and replace them. Further seral stages continue this process of creating conditions for the next stage to invade. Finally, a seral stage gives rise to the climax, the stage featuring dynamic equilibrium.

HYDRARCH SUCCESSION

Succession in water tends to follow a set sequence in standing waters. This sequence was diagramed in Figure 17.13 (see p. 320). The primary feature in this series of changes is alteration of an aquatic environment to a land one by the filling in of a body of water. This major tendency progresses in a gradient from the water to the land. Recall that the central and deepest part of the water may have a bottom free of vegetation. In suitable adjacent, shallower depths the primary seral stage is found. This submerged stage has plants with thin, dissected, and/or linear leaves, and these underwater plants are at depths that are mostly determined by available light. Closer to the shore are plants whose leaves float upon the water surface. This floating stage generally excludes further shoreward occurrence of the submerged stage by creating shade; however, floaters are attached to the bottom and so are excluded from the deeper waters inhabited by the submergents. The next seral stage, the emergent stage, is limited to shallower waters where such plants as cattails, sedges, rushes, and reeds crowd out the floaters. Emergents usually grow very close to one another, and for this reason they regularly hold a great deal of sediments. The sediments, in the form of silt and remains of dead emergents, accumulate to the point where an herb stage can invade. From this point, further succession might approximate xerarch succession beyond the herb stage.

Xerarch and hydrarch succession have many similarities, the most striking being that in both kinds of succession one stage creates the conditions necessary for the next. Also, whether primary succession starts upon a rock or within water, the later seral stages, from herb stage onward, can be much the same.

In moister and colder areas, hydrarch succession usually shows a notable deviation. Such environments might have one or more of the early hydrarch stages prior to an invasion of sphagnum moss (or perhaps some other aquatic plant), but even the primary stage might be sphagnum. However, when present this moss develops into a dense growth, called a peat bog, that can support the weight of a man. The peat bog stage often is invaded next by a shrub stage, but the invader sometimes is a tree stage. In the event of a shrub stage, a tree stage usually follows. Finally, the tree stage is followed by the climax (see Figure 17.14, p. 321).

BIOGEOGRAPHICAL DYNAMICS

The places occupied by populations and communities rarely are static or fixed, and even when they are, such conditions are temporary. Always there are tendencies toward range expansion or restriction. Expansion is the normal consequence of a reproductive rate that produces more individuals that can be supported by the carrying capacity of an ecosystem. The excess of individuals leads to population pressure, a form of struggle for existence. Population pressure, in turn, regularly leads to dispersal of the young. In many organisms, eggs or comparable stages are structurally adapted for passive dispersal, a form of emigration, to areas other than the site of birth. In other organisms, behavioral adaptations as related to population pressure appear to lead to emigration in the form of active dispersal of the young.

Area contraction is due to unfavorable environments. During unfavorable time periods, individual populations of a species are reduced in size. Faced with minimal environmental conditions and such things as catastrophies, remnants of decimated populations may emigrate to sites of optimum conditions that remain for the species. Moreover, while these unfavorable conditions remain, the species will not normally leave these optimum environments.

Such factors contribute to ever-changing areas, a subject summarized by the concept of biogeographical dynamics. However, fuller appreciation of the dynamics of distribution can be gained only when other factors are examined (Figure 19.9). For example, dispersal adaptations are the manner or means of increasing a species range. However, dispersal adaptations alone account neither for sizes of communities, for sites of community origin, for the types of communities, nor for the organization of communities. Understanding of such things necessitates reconsideration of such matters as highway vs. barriers, geomorphic cycles, ecological amplitude, interorganism relationships, and evolution. These operate and function in a process much the same as biotic succession. Here, the process is called biogeographical succession.

Each stage of biogeographical succession involves success and failure of organisms. Success demands passage through certain steps or stages. These steps are *population pressure* owing to an excess of individuals, *dispersal* (emigration) across highways to a particular area, and *ecesis*. (Ecesis really is three steps: first, becoming an occupant of an area; second, increasing population size; and third, becoming integrated with

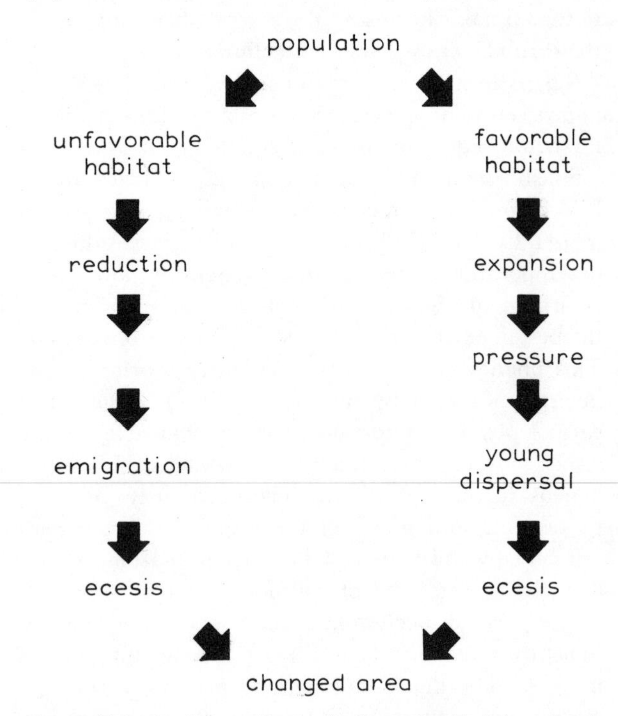

Figure 19.9 The factors affecting the biogeographical dynamics of a population.

the energy cycle of the invaded ecosystem.) However, this gives only a general and oversimplified idea of what must take place. In actual practice, success applies to those species that can respond synergistically to the total environment, physical and biotic, during each step necessary for success.

BIOGEOGRAPHICAL SUCCESSION

The distribution of individuals, species, and communities must be dealt with in terms of the dynamic relationships between the environment and organisms through time. These dynamics appear to proceed in an orderly sequence of events that can be termed a kind of succession. Although any segment of the over-all biogeographical succession varies according to the nature of a particular environment and its organisms, it is possible to assume certain general tendencies in the events of most restricted sequences. These restricted events, or biogeographical seral stages, here are arbitrarily termed *abiotic area* (any space without life), *primary biosere* (an unstable organism congregation lacking clear community organization), *consolidating biosere* (presence of a definite community organization but at the seral level), *biotic climax* (a climax community as considered in biotic succession), *biome* (a group of similar climaxes), *biome-class* (a group of similar biomes), and *biosphere* (the part of the earth containing life) (Figure 19.10). The biosphere will only be touched on in the following discussion.

In the discussion that follows a single successional sequence, or biosere, can be assumed. However, the sequence really involves a sequence of bioseres. For this reason the term "biosere" was and will be used somewhat loosely to recognize what might be called phases (each, part to more than a biosere) of the over-all biogeographical succession.

ABIOTIC AREA

For practical purposes, the areas now lacking life are hardly worth mentioning. Although there are places such as glaciers where kinds of species and numbers of individual creatures are very few, one can be excused if he says that the lower part of the atmosphere, the entire surface of the land, and the entire depths of the waters constitute the biosphere. Hence, the concept of an abiotic area or areas treats a rather nebulous condition. Areas lacking life existed in the past, in primeval seas prior to life and on the land prior to its invasion by marine organisms. Furthermore, after life invaded these places, for some time only certain locales had living creatures. Therefore, it appears that one of the trends of biogeography was gradual dispersal and population of the earth's land and water. However, this does not necessarily mean that now there are more species and numbers of organisms than ever before. In the past there were tremendous fluctuations in the density and diversity of life on earth, fluctuations affecting both local and world-wide aspects of biogeography.

The likelihood that most of the land and water have had life for many million (perhaps a few hundred million) years, necessitates some mental gymnastics in regard to recent abiotic areas. In other words, one often gains understanding by assuming abiosis in a situation where it really does not exist. For example, a vast area might be elevated and change from ocean bottom to land. When ocean, the area would contain many marine creatures; all during the process of becoming land, it would contain a sequence of other organisms. However, one might perform the mental gymnastics of ignoring the sequence of life between strictly marine and land creatures. If this is done, biogeography is more easily understood. Therefore, one might assume that any area that loses its old life and gains a new type of life was an abiotic area just prior to invasion by the new life.

Abiotic areas are the product of geomorphic change and of the main consequence of geomorphic change, climatic change. Such changes also modify the nature of past barriers and highways, thereby setting the scene for the invasion of new life. However, of primary importance is the nature and distribution of the created highways. Recall that highways can be broad, fairly long-lasting, connections between two favorable environments (corridors); narrower and less permanent than corridors and allowing only certain species to pass (filter bridges); or chance paths along which one to a very few species can pass (sweepstake routes). Each kind of highway has a part to play in populating an abiotic area.

When a particular site becomes open to life, immediately adjacent areas are connected by corridors; more remote areas are connected only by filter bridges; and most remote, perhaps only by sweepstake routes. Therefore, an abiotic area normally will acquire the majority of its life from adjacent communities via corridors, some of its life from more remote areas via filter bridges, and a very few (if any) species from the most remote areas via sweepstakes routes.

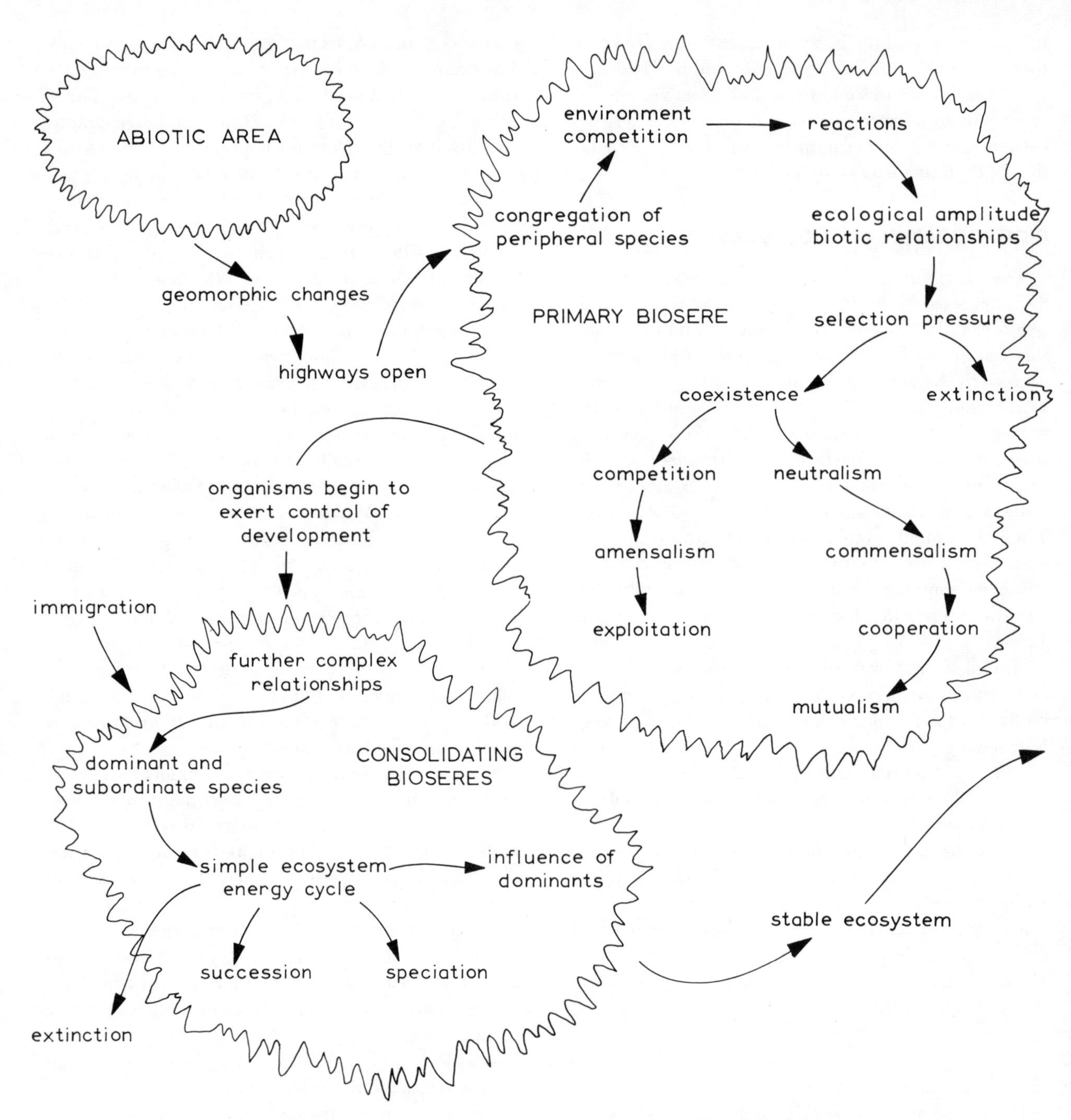

Figure 19.10 The stages and events in biogeographical succession.

PRIMARY BIOSERE

When an abiotic area opens to life, the consequence is an unstable assemblage of plants and animals, a primary biosere. To a great degree the ecological factors of the new area determine the form and species composition of the primary biosere and further seres. The species composition of the primary biosere may be unique and only remotely related to the areas previously inhabited by the various species. Also,

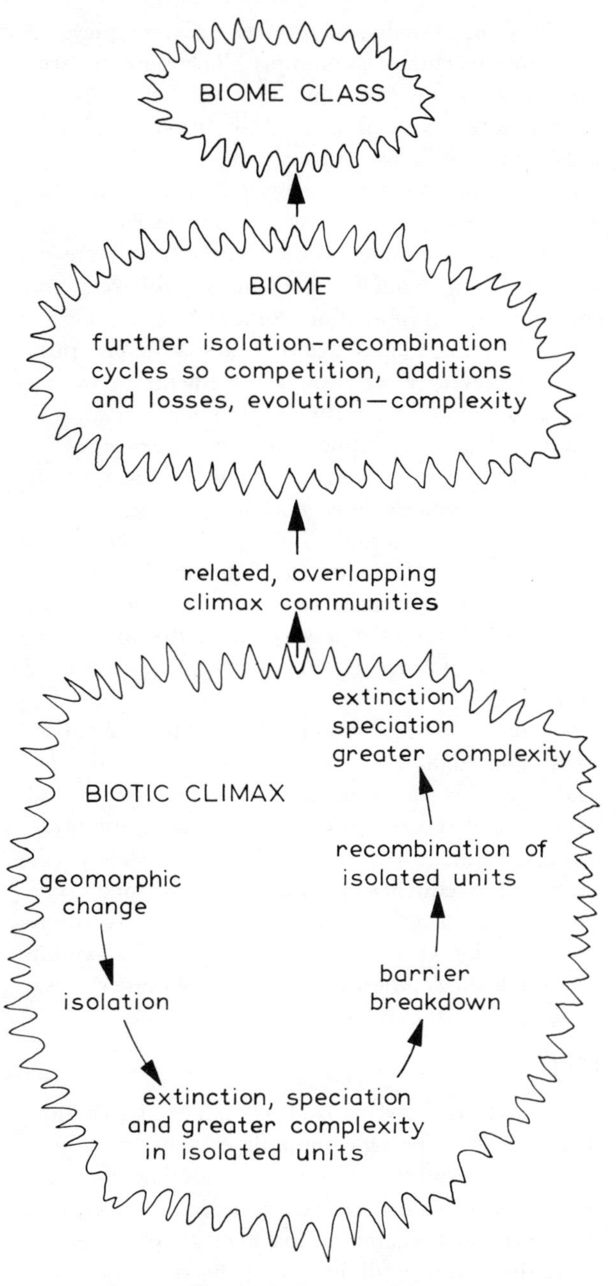

Figure 19.10 (continued)

there may be fewer species in the primary biosere than in any of its parent communities. This would be the consequence of selection pressure.

Within the new primary biosere, selection pressure is brought about by the competition of organisms and by the environment's affecting ecological amplitude. These biotic and environmental influences cause individual species either to become extinct in the area or to enter a state of coexistence with other species. The coexistence of surviving species is the basic step to further evolution in the primary biosere. Such further evolution is most pronounced in biotic relationships.

Perhaps the first evolved biotic relationships under coexistence are competition and something approaching commensalism that might be almost neutralism. Starting immediately, but continuing to evolve for a long time, some competition may evolve to amensalism and then some amensalism to exploitation. Also, some neutralism-commensalism may evolve into true commensalism and then some commensalism to cooperation. Perhaps later still, some cooperation may transform into mutualism. Along with the development of the negative interactions, especially exploitation, the exploited species may evolve protective devices. However, this evolution is not independent; all classes of interorganism relationships are and become further integrated into the synergistic dynamics of the evolving community in which they occur.

CONSOLIDATING BIOSERE

The consolidating biosere like the primary biosere, is a special case of biotic succession. Therefore, the consolidating biosere contains a sequence of seral stages in which organisms, especially plants, tend to control further development. Hence, this part of an over-all biosere is marked by further complexity of interspecific relationships and the presence and increasing complexity of a simple ecosystem energy cycle.

Of importance here and throughout further evolution is the presence of *dominant* and *subordinate* species. Dominants are plants most characteristic of a community, because only dominants are found throughout a community and cover or cast shade upon a relatively high percentage of a community's surface area. The dominents reflect the ecology of an area because they are best suited to cope with the physical environment and biotic relationships. Also, dominants regularly influence the rest of their community. Often, dominants function in critical parts of food relationships of the community, hence their ecological success can determine the success of most to all subordinate species. This possibility is further supported by the fact that dominants influence ecological factors, thereby partly affect the presence of other species. In some cases, loss of all dominant species would lead to extinction of the particular community. However, particular dominant species need not have such pronounced influence upon the subordinate species of their community.

Subordinate species respond only to a particular influence of dominants, an influence that can be maintained by a sequence of taxa. Therefore, if a sequence of dominants have the same growth form (trees, shrubs, etc.), all dominants might have the same general influence and not lead to changes, or even to much modification, of subdominants. Such a sequence of dominants usually occurs through time, and for this reason, subordinate species regularly are taxonomically independent of the dominants.

Returning specifically to the consolidating biosere, each successive stage within the consolidating part of the over-all biosere typically has more species, greater refinement in its evolved interorganism relationships, and therefore greater complexity than the previous stage. These trends are common in spite of the fact that species are lost to the community by extinction or emigration. Other species are added by immigration (either of preadapted species that finally find a highway through barriers, or of adjacent species that finally evolve the ecological amplitude required for entrance and a place in the ecosystem) and by speciation.

BIOTIC CLIMAX

The stage of biotic climax can be any of the primary or secondary climaxes of biotic succession, but must be the first climax originating in the abiotic area. Once equilibrium is reached, further complexity is possible if geomorphic changes occur. (Perhaps certain changes in ecology can occur without geomorphic change.) Again, this is especially true if the geomorphic changes bring about climatic changes. The consequence of change is isolation; the space of the old biotic area (now containing many individual stands of various seral stages and of the climax) is fragmented. When this fragmentation is caused by such things as arms of the ocean, glaciers, and mountain ranges, the geomorphic causes probably lead to independent environmental changes in the isolated segments of the old abiotic area. With the development of progressively unique environments in each segment, there is increased extinction and speciation, and growing complexity of ecological relationships. Finally, each isolated segment develops into a unique climax community. Therefore, isolation can lead to a situation somewhat similar to opening of an abiotic area—at least, a situation in which a unique biotic climax results.

At any time during the period of isolation geomorphic changes can cause the once-isolated communities to recombine. If the communities were not separated long enough to become very different from one another, recombination can lead to a melting pot in which a single climax community is the end product. However, when isolated segments were separated long enough for the development of a certain amount of diversification, the consequence of recombination is not a single melting pot. Rather, the result is an interlocking and overlapping of communities, both seral and climax, causing competition of dominants and leading to different, but related, new climaxes adjacent to one another. Such a complex of communities is a *biome*, and the process by which it was formed is called an *isolation–recombination cycle*.

So far in our discussion relationships have been oversimplified, and they will continue to be so. The reader must realize that the true complexity of biogeographical succession is being greatly minimized. Perhaps recalling the great differences in life of the past and the sequence of dominant taxa through time, and remembering that all this reflects isolation–recombination cycles is sufficient for understanding the significance and great complexity of these cycles.

BIOME

Biomes must be visualized as chance aggregations of similar, overlapping communities. The component communities and their biome *in toto* are imperceptibly but constantly changing—are typically in some phase of an isolation–recombination cycle, are subject to competition and the influence of the resulting dominant plants, are gaining and losing species, and are evolving and changing taxonomic composition through time. However, a biome also is composed of a single growth formation (e.g., forest) in which changes in dominants, no matter how different taxonomically, need not cause any real change in the influence of dominants on subordinate species or individual communities. Therefore, biomes are not taxonomic units. Rather, they are ecological units brought about by the influence of the physical environments and dominants. Hence, dominants can and have changed from one small taxon to another and eventually from one major taxon to another. For example, tropical rain forests have changed from the Mississippian lycopsid-sphenopsid-pteridosperm-dominated types, to fern-cycad-conifer types, and finally to the present flowering plant dominants. (Pteridosperms, or seed ferns, were fern-like plants that produced seeds.) However, with each replacement of type, there still is a tendency for the subordinate species or their evolved representatives to remain. For example, the tropics of today, areas probably most typical of ancient environments, are the usual habitats for living representatives of ancient plant groups such as psilopsids, lycopsids, sphenopsids, ferns, cycads, and primitive conifers. Therefore, when subordinate plants or animals evolve or disappear in direct relation to dominants it usually must be the result of some intimate biological relationship, rarely of chance alone.

Another way of looking at these observations is in relation to the persistence of the various units, communities (seral and climax), biomes, and biome-classes. Although biome-classes will not be considered until later, one can now point out that they are more persistent than biomes and biomes are likely to last longer than their communities. Particular communities may last millions of years; but because they are only a part of a biome, communities can be lost because any of the factors causing biomes to evolve also tend to destroy some of the components of a biome.

Persistence at the community level normally favors seral stages over climaxes. Seral stages are more flexible; they persist while climax stands are disturbed or destroyed. This is true even though seral stages regularly are grouped in an orderly sequence (succession) from the community first invading an area (primary seral stages) to the climax. Climaxes require more time to develop; they are a later stage in evolution, a stage most closely adapted to the existing environment. The differences between developmental stages and climaxes are emphasised at the species level. Seral species often occupy larger areas than do climax species. Although individual species may be seral in one biome and climax in another, typically, seral-restricted plants and their associated animals inhabit greater expanses of the world than do climax plants and their allied animals. As a consequence, seral stages generally occupy more different biomes than do climaxes. Again, this probably reflects less stringent ecological requirements on the part of seral species as compared with climax species. Hence, seral species might not be as specialized for success in restricted environments as are climax species.

Further differences between seral and climax stages are significant in biogeographical succession. The fact that seral stages normally are widely distributed throughout biomes, or even biome-classes, in a sense causes seral communities to be more important biogeographically. One consequence of their occupying greater space is an increase in probability that seral stages will be near a new highway. The opening of such highways causes them, to a greater extent than climaxes, to have remote, discontinuous distributions. Also, wide-ranging animals probably disperse through seral stages rather than climaxes. Another consequence of larger ranges leads to seral stages having greater potential for evolution. This potential comes from greater environmental diversity throughout their ranges and more opportunity for isolation of individual stands of the stages.

To summarize, the factors that produce biomes and biome-classes are complex. The factors do not form identical isolated subunits. However, biomes such as the Tundra can have a continuous distribution, and in such cases the various geographic segments of the biome are similar. It is only when discontinuities in a biome or biome-class exist that taxonomically unlike communities might develop. The degree of dissimilarity of isolated subunits, as in the Tropical Rain Forest, occurs in direct proportion to the amount of extinction, differential evolution, and differential immigration in the various segments. This means of causing dissimilarity of isolated segments is also the means for unique rates of change in different members of a single taxon. Moreover, it is this independent evolution within taxa that causes biomes not to change *in toto*, but to evolve gradually by replacement and evolution of individual large taxa. Therefore, biogeographical succession is the consequence of evolution of individual large taxa and not of biomes *per se;* for this reason biomes are organizations of unrelated taxa.

BIOME-CLASS

Further changes in a biome can come from replacement of one or more of the climax dominants. Although such substitution often does not alter the influence and basic nature of the biome, when the new dominants do alter biome influence, they may represent the evolution of a new climax community. The new climax often causes the previous climax to become a seral stage just prior to the new climax and also causes the original biome to be altered.

Perhaps maximum change in biomes is brought about by climatic change, which normally stems from geomorphic change. Shifts in climate tend either to separate species of a single biome into many biomes or to congregate species from adjacent biomes (isolation-recombination cycle) into new biomes. Both are eventualities, because the unlike ecological amplitude of different species can allow them to occur together in certain environments but not in others. Hence, a single biome as a result of climatic change can become fragmented into two or more distinct but closely related biomes, especially when the earth proceeds from geomorphic periods lacking climatic zonation to periods having climatic zonation. On the other hand, the opposite geomorphic cycle can lead to fusion of biomes, extinction and evolution of many species, and creation of a very complex biome or simple biome-class. However, the individual biome components of a biome-class probably differ from any preexisting biome, the unique physical and biotic factors leading to unique combinations of species into communities and, perhaps, to unique successional relationships among species.

Biome-classes, then, probably are due to no unique process. From the time of the primary biosere to the biome-class—and even to the biosphere, if one wishes to carry discussion that far—isolation-recombination cycles are sufficient to build one level of complexity into the next higher level; thus biomes become biome-classes, and biome-classes become related within a biosphere.

EXTINCTION AND ORIGIN

Biogeographical succession is probably intimately associated with the extinction of certain groups of organisms and the origin of new groups. Since Cambrian times, two remarkable periods of extinction and origin have occurred. The first of these was at the end of the Permian and the start of the Triassic, a time of the extinction of the archaic amphibians, the formation of many new reptile groups, and the origin of the mammals. The second period was at the end of the Cretaceous and start of the Paleocene, a time featuring the extinction of most reptiles and ancient mammals and the origin of modern reptiles and mammals. These two occasions mark the separation of Paleozoic, Mesozoic, and Cenozoic eras.

Extinction at both times probably was neither catastrophic nor devastating, as is often believed; each period of extinction and origin probably lasted ten million years or more. However, the tempo and rate of extinction were greater than usual. In animals it occurred generally at the ends of eras; in plants, decline or extinction of forms often was during eras. Also, quite logically, the origin of certain plant taxa preceded that of animals associated with them. For example, during the last of the Mesozoic Era, the Upper Cretaceous Period, flowering plants entered as dominant species; however, modern animals seem not to have reached their present role until the start of the Cenozoic Era.

Unfortunately, it is very difficult to provide a single reason for these between-era happenings. Among various possibilities are great geological activity, including vulcanism, diastrophism, and changing climates, ocean currents, or ocean levels. However, there is no geological evidence that catastrophies were extensive enough to have caused between-era changes in animals, but not in plants. For this reason, many paleontologists have sought biological reasons for extinction. Until fairly recently, the assumed biological causes were racial senescence and overspecialization. With moderately changing environments such features could cause extinction. However, once again, it does not appear that these biological phenomena singly, or even together, could explain what the fossil record portrays. Although certain groups that became extinct could be considered senescent or overspecialized, others appear to have been generalized, quite vigorous forms. Therefore, although catastrophies, senescence, and overspecialization might have *contributed* to widespread extinction, they do not provide an unequivocal explanation for the phenomena involved.

Recently, a new proposal was made. This hypothesis does not exclude previously suggested geological and biological causes for extinction; rather, these previous causes might have acted sufficiently to trigger the final, more dramatic phases of extinction of animals, explain the different response in plants, and also explain the conditions where chance mutation and selection of genes would produce remarkably new taxa in a very short period of time.

Think of these times prior to the ends of eras as periods of more than normal extremes of geomorphic change. Under extreme conditions dominant plant species, owing to their specialization, might become extinct. If dominants are lost in some seral stages as well as in climaxes, biomes and even biome-classes would be subject to chaotic relationships in their ecosystems. To support this view, it is known that present-day ecosystems are composed of many closely interdependent organisms. Moreover, if certain key organisms are removed from these ecosystems, it is known that the ecosystem might collapse. In a sense, this is no more complex than the disturbance of a single climax causing the area to revert to some seral stage. However, if physical and biological factors in the past eliminated key members of many seral and climax communities, there would be widespread extinction of organisms in many biomes.

The consequence of the collapse of ecosystems on this scale would be a rather chaotic recombination stage of survivors. The survivors would be hard pressed for survival, and thus would be subjected to conditions optimum for rapid evolution.

Carrying speculation further, the Lower Cretaceous opened with an expansion of the gymnosperms. However, by late Lower Cretaceous gymnosperms were definitely declining. The reason for this is pure speculation, but it might be that the Lower Cretaceous was the start of a change from a lack of climatic zonation to climatic zonation, or conditions similar to those prevailing today. Evidence indicates that there were progressive diversity, seasonal changes, and zonation of climate. Assuming this was true, a strong isolation-recombination cycle could start and end with the Upper Cretaceous dominance of flowering plants. Moreover, during most of this cycle, animals probably could exist in many areas where older conditions prevailed. This would be the case especially with animals associated with seral stages rather than climaxes. Finally, however, the end of the Upper Cretaceous, with its complete dominance of flowering plants, could prove too much for archaic animals to survive; hence, widespread extinction could take place and conditions be created for new animal evolution in the Paleocene.

This interpretation of extinction as the removal of key organisms resulting in the collapse of various ecosystems fits in with known physical and biological paleogeographical records. It does not hypothesize truly catastrophic geological changes—conditions that do not appear to be supported by present data about those eras.

HISTORICAL BIOGEOGRAPHY

The area occupied by a species or community is the function of interplay between organism and environment through time. The important species responses to environment through time are accomplished by adaptations that allow rapid dispersal and penetration of environments. These adaptations contribute to an over-all ecological amplitude that determines the success or failure of a species in expanding or maintaining its range and, more important, its very existence. An additional possibility of success, even greater success than that achieved previously, can come about through chance hereditary changes and selection of these changes, resulting in evolution of a new ecological amplitude that is either broader or better adapted to environmental conditions.

Previous discussion described how variations in ecological amplitude of single species and communities resulted in their establishment in particular habitats. Inferences about the origin and development of new areas could be made from those now existing. However, such minutae tend to be lost in an over-all view of the past history of organisms, especially in a synopsis of part of the past history of life on our planet. Such is the case in the discussion that follows. For this reason, the reader may want to review earlier chapters before continuing.

NORTH AMERICAN FLORAS AND LAND VERTEBRATES

One of the better examples of the past history of life is the Late Cretaceous to Recent record of the floras and land vertebrates of North America.

This historical discussion of plants involves *geofloras*. A geoflora is an extremely large unit of vegetation that usually can be diagnosed on the basis of the vegetation type or growth form that is present. Each geoflora is composed of many *elements*, each element often being roughly equivalent to a fairly large unit of vegetation. In addition, a geoflora is a historical unit, which means that both the individual species and the unit as a whole evolve through time. Therefore, a geoflora never is exactly the same thing thoughout time, it displays moderate to great changes in different geological periods.

The evolution of many geofloras through time results in new species, new communities, new community elements, and even new geofloras. This evolution can be extremely confusing unless one realizes that each of these ecological units through time is of changing size and is evolving in some areas and not in others. In addition, evolution can be extremely rapid in some localities and imperceptible in others. Because of these possibilities, a single element or even smaller unit could give rise to a geoflora in one part of its range and to additional elements in other parts, but still maintain its identity elsewhere.

In reading the following account, one must be prepared for change—change in the shape of the continents, in the topography of the land, in climate, in the distribution of geofloras, and change in smaller ecological units, down to and including the individual species.

A group of maps are provided to aid the reader in following the changes. These maps imply no more than general trends. They are far from being as accurate as maps of the present distribution of vegetation. At the present time there is insufficient information for such accuracy. However, the maps could be much more accurate on the basis of the information available. For example, no serious attempt was made to include the available information of discontinuous distributions or altitudinal distributions. Also, very crude approximations were made to select and simplify the limits of distribution of the various floras. The generalization of distribution is believed to serve best as an overview of what has happened.

GEOFLORAS AND ELEMENTS

The history of North American vegetation relates the evolution and dispersal of three major geofloras. Two of these major floras were present some 75 million years ago, and the other appeared shortly thereafter. Since the time of their origin each geoflora was subjected to great changes in composition and to major movements over vast areas of our continent. However, no geoflora has lost its essential identity as Neotropical-Tertiary, Arcto-Tertiary, or Madro-Tertiary.

Neotropical-Tertiary Geoflora. The Neotropical-Tertiary Geoflora has been the southernmost unit, mostly broad-leaved evergreen plants of subtropical to tropical climate. Although it ranged over wide areas of the United States and even up to Canada on occasion, at the present time it is mostly in the subtropical forests from southern Mexico to Panama and in eastern Asia, areas now having relatively uniform climate and over 80 inches of rainfall per year. In the United States, the only living remnants of the geoflora are in southern Florida. The geoflora includes such plants as cycads, palms, magnolias, figs, laurels, avocados, and cinnamon.

Arcto-Tertiary Geoflora. This, the northernmost of the three geofloras but a temperate climate flora, at first contained mostly temperate deciduous plants. However, some primarily nondeciduous present-day elements probably were derived from this geoflora. Possible derivative now include:

1. *Tundra*, the northernmost flora, ranging from Alaska, across the northern edge of the continent, and to Labrador, is a cold-climate element having lichens, mosses, grasses, sedges, other herbs, and a few shrubs.

2. *Taiga* is a savanna flora just south of the Tundra, extending across the continent from Alaska through Canada almost to the Great Lakes, and then on to Vermont. It is composed of scattered conifers, including black spruce, white spruce, hemlock, white pine, jack pine, balsam fir, and a few deciduous trees such as aspens and birches, among a ground cover of shrubs and lichens. This element often is not separated from the Northern Coniferous Forest, and probably it should not be.

3. *Boreal Forest*, a group of elements, is a dense forest of mostly conifers that range south of the Taiga approximately to the United States border in the east and down the mountain ranges of the west. Within this coniferous forest, four major subdivisions can be recognized. The *Northern Coniferous Forest* is little more than a consolidation of Taiga trees. The *Subalpine Forest* is a western mountain (Cascades, Sierras, and Rockies) counterpart of the Northern Coniferous Forest. The *Montane Forest*, also of the western mountains but just below the Subalpine Forest, is typified by yellow pine, lodgepole pine, firs, western larch, and some Douglas fir. The *Coast Forest* of the Pacific Coast, especially the Coast Ranges, from Alaska to central California contains Sitka spruce, western hemlock, Douglas fir, western white pine, redwood, western white cedar, arborvitae, and yellow pine.

4. *Deciduous Forest*, a temperate forest dominated by deciduous, broad-leaved trees and actually a group of elements, is south of the Boreal Forest in the eastern United States. It occupies all of the east except for Florida. Included in the Deciduous Forest is a somewhat aberrant, probably fire-maintained, subunit, the Southern Evergreen Forest. This evergreen forest inhabits the Atlantic Coastal Plain from Virginia to Texas except for southern Florida. Characteristic evergreen forest plants include live oak, bald cypress, long-leaf pine, magnolia, gums, and shortleaf pine.

5. *East Asian*, an additional fossil element, also was present. Despite its name, modern derivatives of the East Asian element are found in both Boreal and Deciduous forests in eastern Asia; in eastern Asia and eastern United States; or in eastern Asia, western United States, and eastern United States, typically in the form of deciduous trees. Strictly speaking, East Asiatic species now include the dawn redwood and the ginkgo, or maidenhair tree. Plants of eastern Asia and eastern North America include hornbeans, hickories, chestnuts, beeches, liquidambars, and elms. Those in eastern Asia and the western and eastern United States include maple, birch, dogwood, ash, Walnut, spruce, pine, plum, oak, rhododendron, rose, willow, and arborvitae.

Madro-Tertiary Geoflora. Named for the Sierra Madre Mountains area of northern Mexico where many relicts now live, this geoflora apparently evolved mostly from the Neotropical-Tertiary, but also from the Arcto-Tertiary, and assumed definite but poorly developed form by the Middle Eocene. Its vegetation was much different from that of the broad-leaved evergreen Neotropical-Tertiary or the hardwood deciduous and coniferous Arcto-Tertiary Geofloras. Rather, the plants were and are small-leaved, often deciduous and/or sclerophyllous (having leaves with very thick, often waxy-walled cells in the epidermis), drought-resistant plants. These adaptations imply an arid climate group of plants, but the flora now extends from warm temperate to dry tropical areas.

The Madro-Tertiary Geoflora now includes three elements of woodland, two elements of chaparral, and one of thorn scrub.

1. The *California Woodland Element* contains madrone, walnut, digger and pinyon pines, live oaks, Catalina ironwood, cottonwood, and bay. It can be further subdivided into the maritime climate Insular Woodland of the islands off the southern coast of California, the cold-winter Digger Pine Woodland of central coastal California, and the warmer climate Oak-Walnut Woodland of southern California mountains.

2. The *Sierra Madrean Woodland Element* includes madrone, juniper, avocado relatives, locust, cottonwood, soapberry, holly, and oak. It now survives in areas of summer rain from Arizona to west Texas and south into Mexico.

3. The *Conifer Woodland Element* has pinyon pine, juniper, service berry, plum, hard tack, cream bush, snowberry, and antelope bush. It is found in cold semiarid places from eastern California to the Rockies.

4. The *California Chaparral Element* of manzanita, ceanothus, hard tack, bush poppy, silk tassel bush, Christmas berry, plum, oak, coffeeberry, redberry, and lemonade berry and its relatives now dominates the California Chaparral.

5. The *Southwestern Chaparral Element* consists of much the same genera as California Chaparral, but different species now occur from Arizona and eastward and southward into Mexico in locales of summer rain.

6. The *Thorn Forest Element* was found in southern California during warmer periods. Now it forms the arid subtropical scrub vegetation of northeastern and northwestern Mexico.

Subtropical Scrub and Grassland Elements. The Subtropical Scrub is here treated for convenience as an element, but its element status is in question. It could have been only an early stage of the Grassland Element. It did consist of scrub and herbaceous vegetation, and probably originated in eastern Mexico and the Great Plains during the abrupt climatic change at the end of the Eocene and very beginning of the Oligocene. Throughout the Oligocene and into the Miocene it was the vegetation of our country's interior, probably a semiarid habitat. In any event, it was in the mid-continent during a period of cooling and drying. However, with further cooling and perhaps increased moisture, the scrub was replaced by, or evolved into, the grassland.

The Grassland Element is of major significance. This flora formed very rapidly after the Oligocene. By the Late Miocene it had become well developed and generally assumed its present distribution in the Great Plains. Its origin is rather indefinite, but it probably has components from both Arcto-Tertiary and Madro-Tertiary elements.

MESOZOIC PALEOGEOGRAPHY

It must be emphasized that the following account is based on biological and geological evidence at hand. Because such evidence is incomplete, many statements should be prefaced by qualifying phrases, but this is not done. Also, the evidence frequently allows for variation in interpretation of past events. The accounts here presented could definitely be altered by new fossil evidence.

At the end of the Paleozoic Era in the Permian Period volcanoes were prevalent in eastern Oregon and California and in western Idaho and Nevada. Some of this vulcanism took place under what then was part of the Pacific Ocean. Also in the Permian, the Appalachian Mountains started growth and probably soon rivaled the Alps in size; but toward the end of the Permian and start of the Mesozoic, growth ceased and erosion prevailed.

Further history of the Appalachians, and thus of significant eastern North American mountains, can be dispensed with briefly at this point. However, western mountains have a more complex history that will be treated in reference to the sequence of life.

The Mesozoic saw the culmination of the Appalachians as significant mountains (Figure 19.11). Early Triassic erosion was followed by late Triassic rejuvenation, and then by Jurassic peneplaination. This peneplaination prevailed into the Cenozoic when only a chain of 2,000- to 3000-foot mountain remnants remained to imply past grandeur. Later in the Cenozoic, the extensive region was elevated, but only about 100 feet, into a shallow fold. Finally, the Appalachians gradually were eroded to their present form. Therefore, only the earliest Cenozoic displayed topography sufficient to affect the distribution of flora and fauna.

A more complex Mesozoic picture existed in the west (Figure 19.11). The Triassic contained the forerunner of three important geological features that dominated the entire Mesozoic. These were the Pacific Coast Geosyncline in the extreme west, the Mesocordilleran Geanticline in the middle, and the Rocky Mountain Geosyncline at the eastern margin of this western region. The Mesocordilleran Geanticline existed roughly in the area of the present Rocky Mountains and was the major highland of the Mesozoic. To its west, the Pacific Coast Geosyncline was a major basin of deposition throughout the Mesozoic. However, the Pacific Basin progressively grew to its greatest extent in the Upper Triassic, declined in the Jurassic, and reached its last significant growth early in the Upper Cretaceous. The decline was the consequence of intermittent growth in the coastal mountains. The Rocky Mountain Geosyncline was a less important center of deposition until its start of growth in the Jurassic. This growth culminated in continental bifurcation in the Upper Cretaceous.

Mesozoic Life. The Mesozoic frequently is called the Age of Gymnosperms and Reptiles. Predominant plants were conifers, including many living genera, but ginkgos, ancient cycads, seed ferns, cycadeoids, and modern types of ferns were conspicuous. Later in the Mesozoic cycads and, for a while, members of the now extinct Caytoniales also were common. The forests probably had most of the groups named, but more arid slopes and plains might have featured ferns and cycadeoids.

The conspicuous reptiles of these times commonly are called dinosaurs. Earliest forms were of small to moderate size, but by the Jurassic some of the true giants were prevalent. The gamut of types truly ruled the world then. Oceans contained shark-like and many bizarre reptile types. Flying types occupied the air. The land contained a great variety of herbivorous and carnivorous species, including the largest land animals ever known. In addition, reptiles gave rise to the first known mammals of the Triassic and first known birds of the Jurassic. However, the end of the Mesozoic was the end for the old reptile line.

LATE CRETACEOUS TO RECENT

Part of the Mesozoic, the Upper Cretaceous, must be stressed for full appreciation of present life in North America. This is necessary because the major groups of modern plants already were present at that time. This emphasizes the fact that subdivisions of geological history are based primarily upon the animal record. Because plants appear to evolve before animals and provide the conditions necessary for adaptive radiation of animals, there is a logical basis for our starting with the last of the Mesozoic.

In the following account of the Late Cretaceous to Recent, much detail is omitted. The Neotropical-Tertiary Geoflora and Madro-Tertiary Geoflora are not treated below the geoflora leval. The Arcto-Tertiary is mostly discussed at the geoflora level. The Grassland Element is recognized from the time

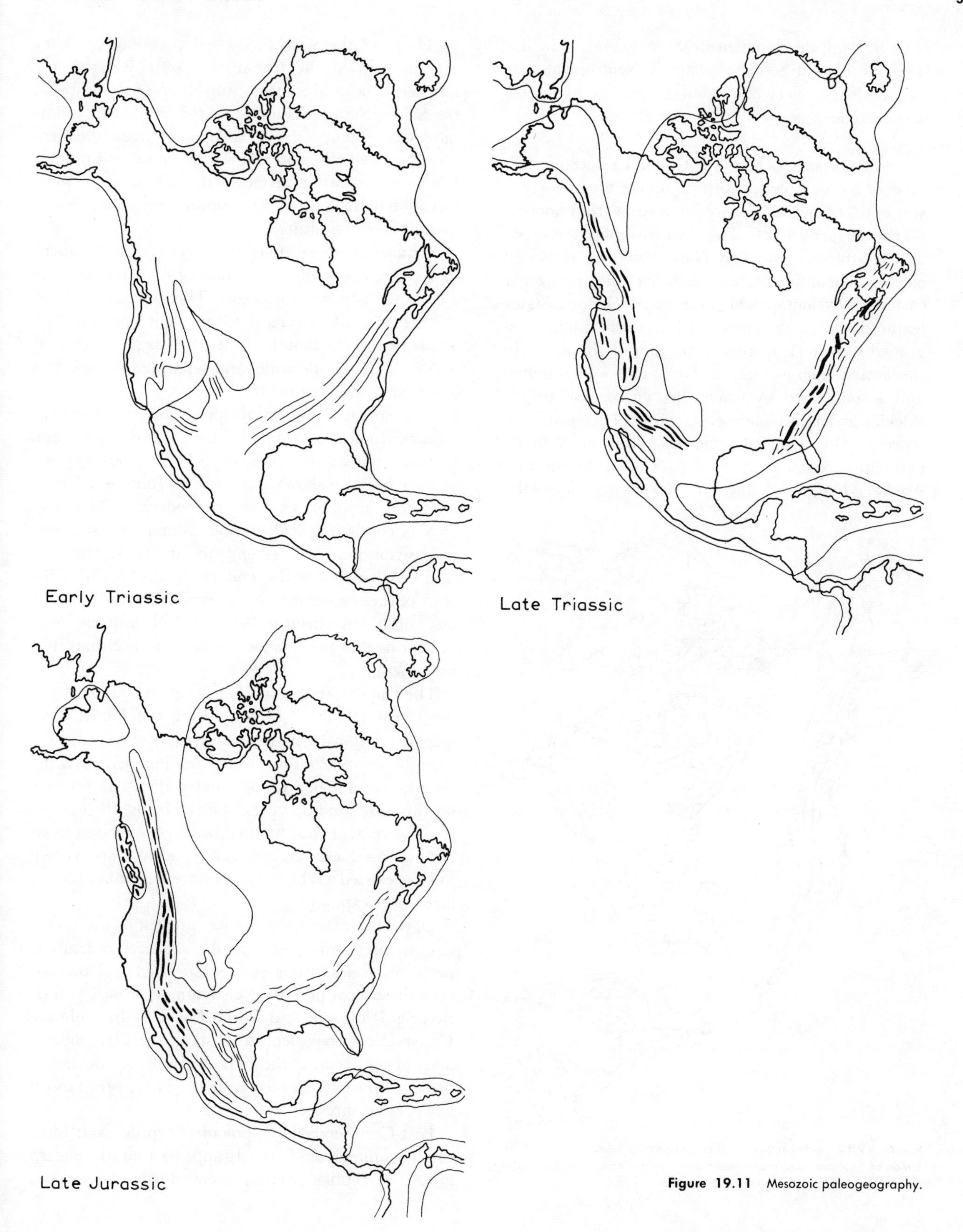

Figure 19.11 Mesozoic paleogeography.

of its first full development in the Miocene. Finally, The Subtropical Scrub, perhaps a Neotropical-Tertiary derivative, is mentioned in reference to its period of occurrence.

Late Cretaceous. The late Upper Cretaceous features of North America were so unlike modern landscapes that they might represent a scene from another planet (Figure 19.12). The land was more restricted and mostly very low, and North America consisted of two subcontinents, one western and the other eastern. Physiographically, the eastern United States featured the Appalachians, which were highly degraded but much more conspicuous than now. In the west submerged and lowland areas were uplifted and accompanied by vulcanism, giving rise to the Rockies and intermontane plateaus. This probably reflected early Upper Cretaceous intrusion of many batholiths from the tip of Baja California up into Alaska. In general, these batholiths still form the backbone of the western coastal mountains. They are involved in the Canadian Coast Ranges, the northern Rocky Mountains, the Klamath Mountains, the Sierra Nevada Mountains, the southern California Coast Ranges, the Transverse Ranges, the Penninsular Ranges, and Baja California mountains. When these batholiths formed, each led to some elevation of the land and mountain formation, mostly by folding and faulting.

Figure 19.12 Late Cretaceous paleogeography, including the distribution of geofloras and major mountains. Arcto-Tertiary to the North and Neotropical-Tertiary to the South.

Perhaps the most amazing aspect of North American geology was the separation of our continent by a continuous arm of the ocean. This gigantic channel, the Mesocordilleran Geosyncline, went from the Gulf of Mexico to the mouth of the Mackenzie River, was about 12° longitude wide, and separated the western and eastern subcontinents.

The climate was subtropical up to southern Alaska, tropical over most of the United States, and temperate probably to the North Pole. There appears to have been no significant climatic zonation; hence, elevations probably were low to moderate. The presence of corals, tropical marine animals whose limits of distribution now extend to an 18° C. barrier, fairly well indicates the end of the tropics and the start of the temperate zone. Fossils of Late Cretaceous corals have been found to 53° N. latitude, thus indicating that the seas were much warmer than they are now.

The Upper Cretaceous often is called "The Time of the Great Dying." Either during the Upper Cretaceous or toward its end most reptiles became extinct, hence some ten to twenty million years saw the removal of animals that dominated the earth for over one hundred million years. Of the birds, the earliest types were gone, but toothed birds plus certain modern types—ducks, grebes, and pelicans—are known to have existed. While reptiles were becoming scarce, birds were expanding.

Of the five mammalian orders present in the Lower Cretaceous, only the small, vaguely rodentlike, herbivorous multituberculates survived. However, even these most persistent of mammal groups (Jurassic origin) disappeared in the Eocene. In addition, Upper Cretaceous deposits display the first appearance of two orders, the first marsupials, much like present opossums, and the first insectivores, much like present shrews.

Post-Cretaceous development of reptiles and birds can be summarized here. It appears that all modern groups of reptiles were present during Cretaceous times. Perhaps most spectacular in the general trend of Cenozoic persistence of modern types of reptiles were strange distribution patterns that included far norther localities when the areas possessed warm climates. In addition, the Eocene featured a snake related to our boa constrictor that was 35 feet long, and the Pleistocene featured land turtles slightly larger than the present giants on the Galapagos Islands.

Cenozoic bird evolution has not been dramatic since the Eocene appearance of most modern bird orders. Somewhat remarkable in view of modern times was the Eocene start of large, flightless birds. The Eocene featured a form almost seven feet tall and the Miocene a form almost eight feet tall. However, the tallest bird was alive up to a few centuries ago in New Zealand. This ostrichlike bird was about ten feet tall. It was destroyed by man, the Maoris.

Paleocene and Eocene. The start of the Tertiary was a time of great geological change. The continents rose and mountains formed. North America assumed much of its present outline (Figure 19.13). The Appalachians were being degraded. The area from the Appalachians to the Rockies rose above sea level and probably was mostly a site subject to erosion and some uplift in the west. In the Rockies folding and faulting continued locally into the Eocene. In most places in California now having mountains the forces of mountain building, especially vulcanism, were active. Western areas of Washington and Oregon obtained vast flows of basalt, and parts of Wyoming had like flows of andesite. Also, the various basins in Wyoming, western Colorado, eastern Utah, northwestern New Mexico, and perhaps northeastern Arizona seem to have contained many very large lakes. However, these lakes probably were ineffective as major barriers and major molders of the evolution of further life.

In spite of these geological events, there appears to have been little latitudinal modification of previous climatic or geoflora conditions. Although latitudinal zonation remained much the same, the elevation of ancient Coast Ranges and Sierras produced a rain shadow, hence a drier climate in the region of the present southwestern deserts. This rain-shadow site became the place of Madro-Tertiary Geoflora origin and later development (Figure 19.14).

The geoflora elements of this time indicate that there were both horizontal and vertical variations in climate. Also, the Arcto-Tertiary of this early Tertiary had most of the present-day elements, but not with their present distribution. For example, the central part of our continent had dawn redwood, ginkgo, sycamore, alder, oak, chestnut, hazlenut, and poplar or cottonwood.

Figure 19.13 Paleocene to Early Eocene paleogeography, including the distribution of geofloras and major mountains. Symbols as in Figure 19.12, plus marsh along western Gulf Coast. Black areas indicate inland lakes.

The types of Paleocene and early Eocene mammals indicate that definite connection existed between North and South America. In the late Eocene this Panamanian land bridge was closed and seems to have remained closed, except as a sweepstake route, until the Pliocene. Also, early Eocene to Pliocene fauna indicate the necessity of movements between North America and Asia via a Bering land bridge. However, the Bering land bridge closed in middle Eocene, reopened in late Eocene, and stayed open, except for brief and minor disconnections, until the cycle of recurrent opening and closing during the Pleistocene.

The Paleocene was the dawn of most to all of the

Figure 19.14 Eocene paleogeography, including the distribution of geofloras which partially indicate the distribution of major mountains. Arcto-Tertiary to the North, Neotropical-Tertiary to the South, and Madro-Tertiary Geoflora in mid-western United States.

present orders of mammals. However, few species other than the persistent marsupials and insectivores, which reached their present insignificance in the Oligocene, would be familiar to us; all dominant forms were archaic types. The most numerous orders were the multituberculates, marsupials, insectivores, somewhat squirrel-like primates, creodont carnivores, archaic rodents, and two of the many orders of hoofed mammals. The dominant hoofed mammals were the slim and almost carnivore-appearing condylarths and amblypods; older groups like the creodonts were replaced by more modern representatives of the orders, so many new types appeared. Among the generally small hoofed types that dominated this time were "dawn horses," tapirlike animals, rhinoceroses, titanotheres, oreodons, and primitive camels. Many of these forms appear to have entered from Asia.

Oligocene. Geologically, erosion was the most important process in the Oligocene. Western mountains seem to have approached degradation to base level. However, this geological picture is difficult to reconcile with that of the climate and flora. A partial explanation might involve the continuation of Eocene vulcanism well into this period.

The short period of latest Eocene to earliest Oligocene seems to have had one of the greatest climatic changes of the Tertiary. Immediately there was much drying and cooling of climate and, as a result, marked southward movement, mixing, and evolution of floras. Moreover, this was just the start of a continuous cooling cycle that ended with the great ice ages of the Pleistocene. There were intervals of increased warmth, but the over-all trend was toward the Pleistocene and its ice ages.

The Middle to Upper Oligocene was the time when the western states were first invaded by the Arcto-Tertiary Geoflora, an invasion whose southern limit reached central Colorado (Figure 19.15). However,

Figure 19.15 Late Oligocene to Early Miocene paleogeography, including the distribution of geofloras. Symbols as in Figure 19.14 plus Subtropical Scrub in present Great Plains area.

the southern migration was not continuous over the United States.

Owing to these changed conditions, the Great Plains and lowlands of the eastern Rockies developed a unique climate and a unique grassland and shrub flora, the Subtropical Scrub Element. This element acted like an indented finger that separated the Arcto-Tertiary Geoflora distribution between middle Colorado and eastern Texas as far north as southern Canada. As a result of the scrub barrier, only western North America contained species whose closest living relatives now are found in eastern Asia. The barrier apparently prevented any of these species' getting into the eastern United States or Mexico. The effectiveness of the southern part of the barrier is indicated by the fact that prior to the barrier western North American species did enter Mexico. For example, the early Eocene floras of the Pacific States have their closest living relatives in the highlands of Mexico and Central America.

The majority of mammals, owing to late Eocene or early Oligocene events, were of modern types. The condylarths and amblypods were gone, the last creodonts and archaic primates soon disappeared, and marsupials and insectivores assumed their present subordinate role. Unfamiliar forms were mostly among the hoofed mammals. More advanced horses, rhinoceroses, oreodons, and huge titanotheres were dominant. However, bats maintained the modern form they gained in the Eocene, and modern carnivores and rodents truly dominated the scene.

Miocene. The Miocene marks the start of rapid growth of the western mountains. This mountain building, which became most pronounced in the late Pliocene, led to climates, and thus to floras and faunas, which progressively assumed a more complex pattern of distribution and more fixed zonation (Figure 19.16). The pattern and zonation intensified barriers and caused rapid differentiation and evolution of life. In addition, the entire period to latest Pliocene continued the general trend of cooling and drying.

Findings of geologists imply the following: The Rockies upwarped into a low fold hundreds of miles broad, a trend culminating in the Pliocene. Although the Sierras were the site of a broad plateau only 3000 feet above sea level (western Nevada was at about 2000 feet), folding and faulting prevailed in the Coast Ranges, adjacent ranges, and Puget Sound Basin. Elsewhere, faulting was the major force, generally contributing to elevation and vulcanism. Of great significance was the extensive volcanic activity of this time. Areas near the Pacific Ocean from Alaska down into California were extremely active. The Columbian Plateau of eastern Washington, eastern Oregon, and southern Idaho gained much of its present form except as it has been modified by erosion; so did the Cascade Range. Further activity took place in the Basin and Range province just to the south of the Columbia Plateau and in the Colorado Plateau province just to the southeast of the Basin and Ranges. This activity extended even into Mexico. In fact, most to all of the areas discussed had significant vulcanism well into the Pleistocene.

Figure 19.16 Miocene paleogeography, including the distribution of geofloras. Symbols as in Figure 19.14 plus grassland in present Great Plains area.

Although this period featured a mixed deciduous-coniferous forest in the northwestern states and Great Basin, a flora with modern remnants restricted to China and the Appalachians, the Middle Miocene was the start of grassland development. However, a full-fledged Grassland Element did not exist until the

Pliocene. Along with the development of grassland there were sharp changes in the nature of the mid-continental to Mexican border Subtropical Scrub Barrier. There is evidence that a highway opened near the Canadian border and allowed some mixture of eastern and western Arcto-Tertiary species.

Perhaps geomorphic processes largely influenced Madro-Tertiary evolution. Both Miocene and Pliocene geology featured vulcanism and increasing aridity in areas of Madro-Tertiary development. For example, it now appears that geology contributed to the frequent fires that selected fire-adapted plants now represented by Madro-Tertiary derived woodland trees and Chaparral shrubs.

By Upper Miocene times temperature averages were much like those of today. However, the summer maxima were not as high and the winter minima were not as low; therefore, the climate was much milder than it is now. Still this was real similarity to modern conditions, in that during the Upper Miocene there was a shift in the west from past climate of summer showers and winter rains to dry summers and a single winter rainy season.

The Miocene was the culmination of mammalian development in North America; more kinds existed than during any time of the Cenozoic. This development can be related to evolution in the grassland and movements from Asia. The carnivores included dogs, ancestral wolves, bearlike dogs, saber tooth and false saber tooth tigers, members of the weasel family, and primitive racoons. Modern types of rodents became more numerous. Rabbits and hares were present. Also, hoofed types became very numerous. Elephant relatives, which originated in Africa and traveled through Eurasia, entered North America. Bizarre types were represented by the common but no longer abundant oreodons and by giant, piglike creatures, all of which disappeared at the end of the period. Deerlike species, rhinoceroses, horses, tapirs, camels, peccaries, and antelope were present.

Pliocene. Although modern climatic features started in the Upper Miocene and were approximated more closely in the Lower Pliocene, truly modern climate did not prevail until the Upper Pliocene (Figure 19.17). Modern climate was preceded by fluctuation and progressively stricter zonation, trends caused mostly by the elevation of greater mountain masses (owing to general uplift of the western mountains) and the previously set pattern of distribution of these western masses. In addition, mountain building (especially the rise of the modern Sierras) caused an increase in climatic extremes that were associated with increases in temperature maxima and lowering of temperature minima. For these reasons, desert vegetation and communities evolved and the over-all nature and distribution of plants was much as it is now, though the continent was somewhat differently shaped. Only the more drought-resistant vegetation remained and the Grassland Element became fully established.

Figure 19.17 Pliocene paleogeography, including the distribution of geofloras. Symbols as in Figure 19.16.

Unfortunately, Pliocene mammalian fossils are rather scarce. Apparently previous North American groups became further modernized and many present genera and species were developed. Some hoofed animals declined (tapirs and camels) and others disappeared (oreodons and rhinoceroses), but still others remained abundant or even expanded their numbers (horses and antelope). Also, with the opening of the Panamanian land bridge South American marsupials, New World monkeys, primitive rodents, primitive hoofed mammals, and edentates entered

Central America. However, most of these mammals likely never moved north of the Tropics. Southern taxa that may have invaded the United States include opossums among the marsupials; the capybara and porcupine among the primitive rodents; and armadillos, glyptodonts, and ground sloths among the edentates.

The opening of the Panamanian land bridge allowed rapid and extensive invasion of South America by North American species. Consequently, many of the primitive types of South America became extinct and were replaced by northern taxa.

Pleistocene. The Pleistocene, a brief epoc of about one million years, was the time of great mixing of floras and faunas. The drasic oscillations of life brought about by the southward advances (Figure 19.18) and northward retreats (Figure 19.19) of glaciers caused widespread extinction and intermingling of species. For example, advances produced progressive local changes in floras from one extreme to another (cliseral shifts). At one time Florida had a Boreal Forest.

Figure 19.18 Pleistocene paleogeography and geofloras at the time of maximum glaciation. Symbols as in Figure 19.16. White areas of continent indicate ice-covered areas and black areas indicate lakes.

Figure 19.19 Pleistocene paleogeography and geofloras at a time of maximum warmth showing Greenland ice. Symbols as in Figure 19.16.

When glaciers retreated, southern species traveled northward. However, relicts often were left in certain southern and western localities. In addition, newly ice-freed areas often presented entirely new environments, characterized by restricted invasion, much evolution, and, later, new floral and faunal elements. Finally, the Grassland moved north and east, a movement that caused much mixing with other floras, especially the Deciduous Forest. Under such conditions there could be nothing but the remarkable instances of change in composition and evolution that are documented.

Southward movement of glaciers also had its effects. Some species were able to survive upon southern slopes. In many species, both those remaining and those moving, survival required the fortunate acquisition of hereditary changes. Some did evolve and persist in this manner; other did not and became extinct. Also during these glacier advances, the

Grassland moved to the southwest, again mixing with other floras. As a consequence, there were additions and subtractions of species in the Grassland. The additions came from hereditary changes in existing southwest species and hybridization between southwest and Grassland species, producing new species.

The North American Pliocene was very important in reference to modern mammals. At the close of the Pliocene there was little extinction compared to other times. However, the Pleistocene modified this picture considerably. Most forms either became extinct or had their ranges considerably restricted. Forms that became extinct included the large dire wolf, saber-tooth tiger, American lion, mammoth, Columbian elephant, imperial elephant, mastodon, tapirs, horses, camels, giant beaver, glyptodons, ground sloths, and many others. A great many of the living groups of hoofed mammals had close relatives that were lost.

The Pleistocene glaciers did not cover all of the northern United States. Sites in the Pacific and Atlantic coasts did remain free of ice. In fact, animal fossils indicate moderate persistance of an ice-free corridor along the Pacific Coast from the Pacific states to Alaska, across an open Bering land bridge, and down the coast of eastern Asia.

One of the places having pronounced Pleistocene effects was Europe. During the Ice Age, the flora and fauna of Europe became much reduced. The primary reason for this extinction is believed to have been the presence of east-west mountain chains (Pyranees, Alps, Balkans, Caucasus, and so on). These mountains were glaciated early and formed a substantial barrier to southern retreat of the more northern floras and faunas. It is known that certain animals and plants were trapped and killed in the ice retreat (e.g., hairy mammoths are found in Siberian glaciers of today). However, other organisms escaped from the north and found safety in India and Africa. For example, the Indian elephant probably evolved from hairy mammoths that found suitable habitats in India. Also, the deer are thought to have found refuge and been able to return to Europe. However, a good percentage of Indian mammals (south of the Himalayas) and African mammals (south of the deserts) are descendants of the old European stock.

The present fauna of northern Europe is composed mainly of species that could have come back from southern retreats, plus others that are invaders from the south. That portion derived from original stock apparently came from species that remained near the northern fringe of their southward-moving habitat and were able to return with the habitat to Europe. The animals that never returned went farther south, and instead of following the retreating ice northward evolved sufficiently to remain in their "new" environments. Moreover, these southern species remained south long enough to be trapped by unfavorable northern areas, such as the Sahara Desert.

The present European flora and fauna also include certain North American forms. These organisms were able to cross the then continuous land from North America to Asia, traverse Asia, and finally inhabit Europe. All of this took place during Pleistocene times.

Along with general reduction, present-day European flora and fauna display inconsistencies in distribution. This inconsistency is best observed in southern Europe where the plants form a unit called the Mediterranean Flora. This flora developed from Pleistocene species that found a refuge in the Balkan Peninsula. Very few of these Balkan plants re-entered northern Europe. In contrast to this simple explanation of over-all plant distribution, that of certain animals is puzzling. For example, the Barbary ape of Gibraltar (native there until recent extinction and more recent introduction) and the Atlas Mountains is not closely related to African apes. Its close relatives are in eastern Asia, so its present range involved distant immigration, perhaps with the creatures that came from North America across the Bering land bridge. However, this is but a single example of the fact that the origin of the European flora and fauna required both simple north–south movements with the ice and more complex east–west invasions.

The Pleistocene does not provide full explanation for the reduction of organisms in Europe. Another reason is the extensive cultivation and associated removal of primitive areas. In contrast to Europe, eastern Asia, even with its denser human population, still has more primitive areas. For example, India has a very large human population, but man is densely packed in various centers of habitation; between human habitats, there are many primitive areas. For this reason and human beliefs which largely prevent killing, animals such as tigers are able to survive in India. On the other hand, the present European primitive areas are so restricted and modified that they could not support such animals.

Recent. Since about ten thousand years ago there has been gradual warming of the continents. However, the peak of warming was about six thousand years ago. Since that time there has been a period of cooling. Now there appears to be another warming cycle, but as yet it is not as warm as it was six thousand years ago. Ignoring the fluctuations, the over-all warming since the last ice caused northward shifting of floras to present conditions, which approximate those of the latter part of the Pliocene (Figure 19.20).

INTERCONTINENTAL MOVEMENTS

The previous discussion of the origin of North American floras and mammals allows a simple explanation of intercontinental transfer of organisms by a land bridge, specifically an Asian-North American interchange across the Bering Sea area, or the Bering land bridge. Even when all discontinuous intercontinental distributions of closely related life are studied, land bridges can still explain the patterns of these distributions. Moreover, there would have been no need for a large number of land bridges. For example, observations of the patterns of discontinuous distributions might cause one to assume land bridges between Africa and South America, between South America and Australia, and between North America and Europe. However, none of these bridges seem to be necessary to explain the present.

Figure 19.20 Present geofloras. Symbols as in Figure 19.16.

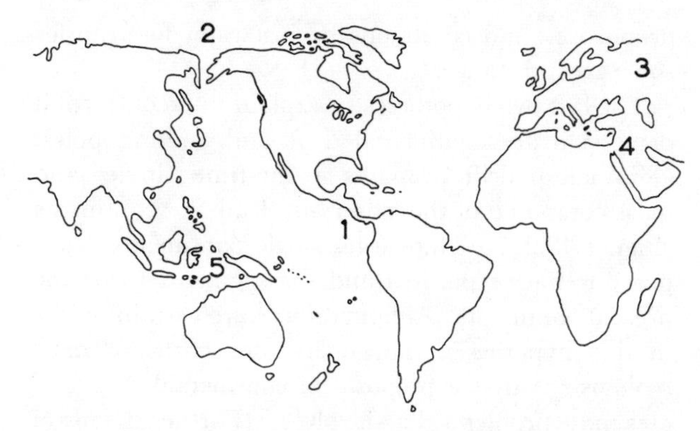

Figure 19.21 The distribution of the major land bridges: 1. Panama, 2. Bering, 3. Eurasian, 4. Afro-Eurasian, 5. Australasian.

If one assumes no more than the five geologically well-documented land bridges (Figure 19.21), plus knowledge of changing climates and floras, he can formulate a simple and plausible hypothesis of routes of dispersal to explain the present distribution of life on earth. The five land bridges are as follows: (1) The Panama land bridge, now open but normally a barrier during the Tertiary, is a north–south highway between the Americas. (2) The Bering land bridge is the only other American land bridge, but it now is in the rare state of closure, acting as a barrier to many species. (3) The Eurasian land bridge now is a gigantic interconnection between Europe and Asia. (4) The Afro-Eurasian land bridge even today is a fair highway between Africa and Eurasia. (5) The Australasian land bridge was an effective barrier throughout most of the Tertiary and still is.

Another plausible means of dispersal, if it is limited to hypotheses of short-distance intercontinental dispersal, is rafting. This hypothesis uses the known fact that major rivers tend to accumulate large amounts of debris. Upon such debris vegetation often grows, and because of this growth, the rafts tend to hold together when released into the ocean. On occasion such rafts are encountered at sea and their variety of life is surprising. For this reason, it is assumed that organisms can be rafted short distances to new land habitats. Perhaps, in very rare instances, rafts can assume huge proportions and conditions be just right for transfer some great distance.

The last two hypotheses to explain intercontinental dispersion are continental drift and shifting poles. Continental drift proposes a one-time single land mass composed of the materials of all the continents (Figure 19.22). This large, single continent is supposed to have separated and the segments to be the present continents. Although there are certain merits in this hypothesis, the general consensus of most biologists is that a proposal of continental drift creates more problems than it solves. (Further details of this hypothesis are given among the readings, especially Wulff.)

The hypothesis of shifting poles was used to explain what once appeared to be unbelievable, temperate floras at the poles. Present evidence implies fluctuations in past climates, hence denies the shifting poles hypothesis. Also, the geological record would indicate that the North Pole has not shifted since at least the Late Cretaceous. If such shifting occurred before the Cretaceous, it would not have been of primary importance in the present distribution of life.

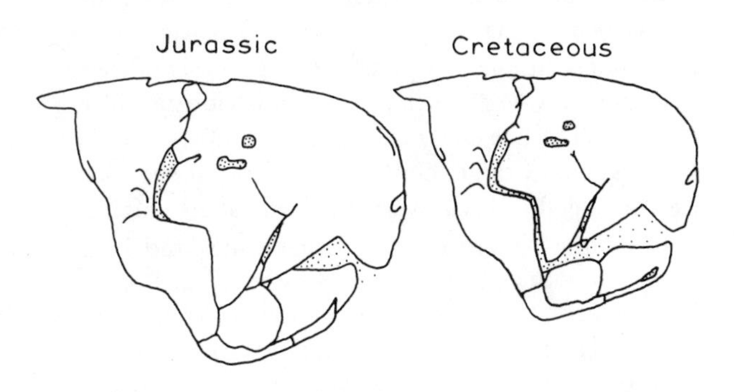

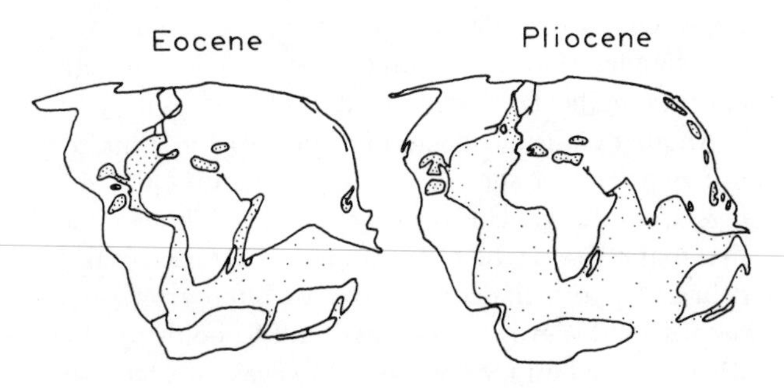

Figure 19.22 Stages in the hypothesis of continental drift: The initial stage supposedly was a single, huge land mass called Pangea and was found during the Paleozoic Era. The intermediate stage, conjectured for the Eocene, showed continental separations, the so-called jigsaw puzzle effect of the continents, and the presence of two major continents (a northern Laurasia and a southern Gonwanaland). The culminating stage, starting with conditions much like now, is proposed for the Pliocene. (After Wegner.)

DISTRIBUTION SCHEMES

How is one to summarize present-day distributions of organisms? If the species constituting each community had exactly the same ecological amplitude and distribution, and if neither of these were changing, a very simple mapping procedure could be applied to record the spatial relations of each kind of community. However, this simple situation does not prevail. Probably no two species have the same range. When this simple fact of biogeography is extended to the investigation of communities, it becomes extremely difficult to define exact limits, because communities tend to merge over fairly broad geographic areas. For this reason, even if one had information on the precise area of each species, no completely satisfactory summarization or scheme of distribution would be possible. However, distribution is even more complex: the ranges of species and communities are dynamic. Both individuals within communities and communities as a whole are continuously affected by their changing environment. As a consequence, areas are always being changed. Therefore, man's attempts to categorize them are found to suffer from inaccuracy.

Although completely accurate summaries of floras and faunas are impossible, distribution schemes can outline major trends in the spatial relations of life. Moreover, these major tendencies—if it is remembered that they are no more than tendencies—are a great aid to human understanding of the general groupings of life and of how such groupings in one area compare with and are related to other areas. For these reasons, some of the distribution schemes will be examined.

FAUNAL REGIONS

One of the first distribution schemes was proposed by P. L. Sclater in 1858. This scheme divided the world into *zoogeographic realms*. Because the scheme is a valuable general summary of animal distribution, it has received further study and modification up to the present time.

Six faunal realms, or regions, are recognized (Figure 19.23). Each realm is a major part of the earth, which had only minor internal barriers during the Tertiary but was isolated from other realms during some part of the Tertiary. However, this does not mean that each realm contains a completely unique fauna or flora. Only the *total* life of each realm distinguishes these major areas.

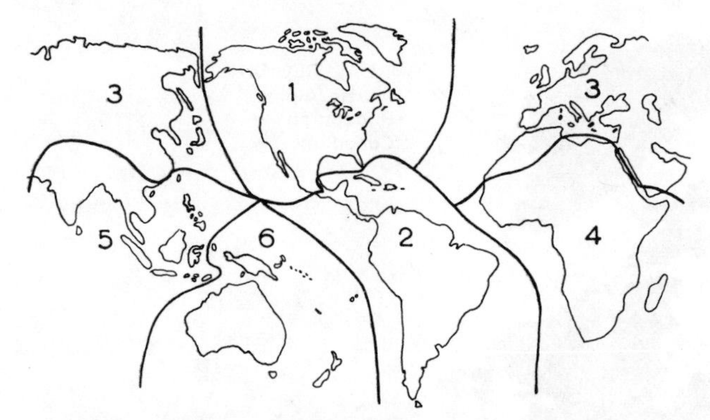

Figure 19.23 World Faunal Regions: 1. Nearctic, 2. Neotropical, 3. Palearctic, 4. Ethiopian, 5. Oriental, 6. Australian.

The six realms are: (1) *Nearctic,* including all of North America south to the limit of the interior uplands of Mexico; (2) *Neotropical,* including the rest of Mexico and extending southward to the southern limit of South America; (3) *Palearctic,* including all of northern Africa, Europe, and Asia roughly north of the Sahara Desert and Himalaya Mountains; (4) *Ethiopian,* including the rest of Africa and some of Arabia; (5) *Oriental,* including the southeastern tip of Arabia, southern Asia, and many islands from Asia toward Australia; and (6) *Australian,* including the rest of the islands to Australia, Australia, and New Zealand. In addition, the fauna of the islands in the Pacific Ocean, some of it unique, is sometimes used to classify another region, *Oceania.*

One cannot deny the value of realms as a point of reference. However, they are so generalized that one gains no appreciation of the details of each area. For example, the entire United States, including perpetual glaciers and some of the most arid places in the world, is in a single region, the Nearctic. This example represents the major criticism of the scheme, a criticism that lead to an early subdivision of faunal regions. In this subdivision, the Nearctic was segregated into a Canadian, or Cold, Subregion; a Western, or Arid, Subregion; and an Eastern, or Humid, Subregion. However, even these smaller units were too large to be of much use.

LIFE ZONES

Inadequacy of distribution schemes led to various, mostly superficial, attempts at meaningful schemes. The first good scheme was presented in detail by C. Hart Merriam in 1892. The scheme resulted from Merriam's study of the San Francisco Mountains of Arizona, an area with relatively clear zonation of plants and animals. From his studies, he concluded that temperature was the most important cause of the "life zones" and that northern limiting factors were different from southern ones. For the north, he used temperature to measure the length of the growing season, the sum of the days with temperatures above 6°C. (4°C. is now believed a better approximation) to determine limits; for the south, he used the average temperature during the six hottest weeks of the summer.

Merriam's data were the basis for designating three major *Regions,* the northern *Boreal,* the southern *Austral,* and the southern tip of Florida's *Tropical* (Figure 19.24). Within the Boreal and Austral regions, subdivisions called *Life Zones* were made; a Life Zone of transition between the Boreal and Austral Regions, the *Transition Zone,* was also recognized. Furthermore, Merriam knew that plants were the best indicators of his Life Zones, but he also listed mammal and bird indicators.

The Boreal Region contains three Life Zones. The *Arctic-Alpine Zone* is north of the limit of trees, or in the Tundra, and above timberline in the western mountains. Some of the indicator plants are dwarf willow, arctic poppy, saxifrages, and gentians; indicator animals are the arctic fox, arctic hare, lemming, snow bunting, snowy owl, and rosy finch. The *Hudsonian Zone,* named because the Hudson Bay area is typical, consists of the Taiga in Canada and the upper reaches of the Subalpine Forests in the western mountains. Indicator animals are the wolverine, woodland caribou, great gray owl, and pine grosbeak. The *Canadian Zone* includes the Northern Coniferous Forests in Canada and the lower reaches of the Subalpine Forests. Indicator animals are the varying hare, marten, lynx, spruce grouse, Canada jay, and white-throated sparrow. The Boreal Region, then, contains Tundra, Taiga, and most of the Boreal Forests.

The *Transition Zone* is a distributional wastebasket, a catch-all of Boreal-Austral overlaps. Being a wastebasket, it is difficult to characterize throughout North America. In the east, it includes areas of vegetational overlap (ecotones) between Boreal and Deciduous Forests; in the west, it includes the Montane and Coast Forests; and in both east and west, it includes certain other Boreal-Austral transitions. Generally recognized animal indicators are the Columbian ground squirrel, the sage grouse, and the sharp-tailed grouse.

The Austral Region has two Life Zones. The *Upper Austral Zone* contains two geographic subunits. The eastern, or *Carolinian Zone,* has its western margin

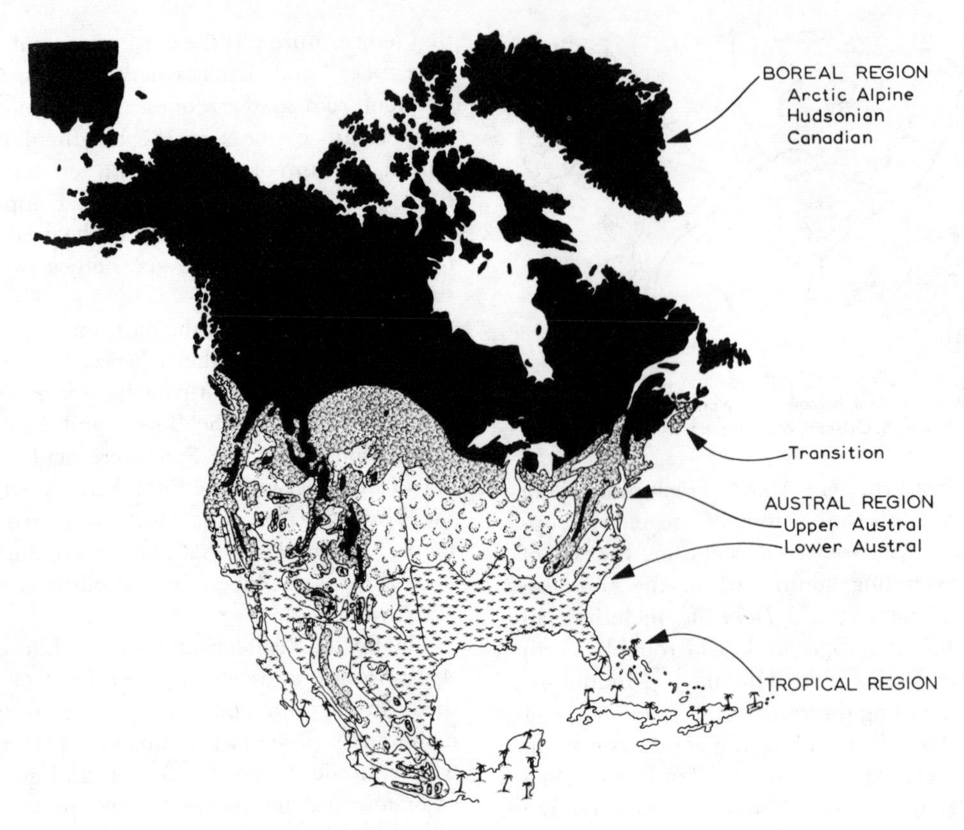

Figure 19.24 Merriam's Life Zones.

in the northeastern Great Plains Grassland and continues eastward into the Deciduous Forest. Common animals are the fox squirrel, prairie vole, eastern wood rat, many warblers, lark sparrow, cardinal, and Carolina wren. The western, or *Upper Sonoran Zone*, has areas of sagebrush, chaparral, and woodland characterized by the gray fox, ring-tailed cat, grasshopper mouse, valley quail, scrub jay, Bewick wren, plain titmouse, and bushtit. The *Lower Austral Zone* also has humid eastern and arid western subunits. The *Austroriparian Zone* is in the Southern Pine Forest of the Atlantic and Gulf Coastal Plains; it features the cotton rat, rice rat, boat-tailed grackle, chuck-will's widow, and Swainson's warbler. The *Lower Sonoran Zone* includes southwestern Desert Scrubs, kangaroo rats, pocket mice, desert quail, vermilion flycatcher, cactus wren, and the verdin.

In the small Tropical Region of southern Florida, the vegetation is typified by palms, orchids, mangroves, and many plants of climbing habit. The common animals are mostly birds, especially the great white heron, reddish egret, caracara, Everglade kite, white-crowned pigeon, and mangrove cuckoo.

CRITICISMS

Life Zones were defined solely on the basis of temperature. However, temperature is associated with many other ecological factors. For this reason, Life Zones can be said to approximate the effects of latitude, altitude, slope, slope exposure, prevailing winds and air currents, nearness to water and deserts, amount of water, type of substrate and rock outcrops as related to heat absorption and reflection, and size of mountains (small, isolated elevations show little zonation). Moreover, because temperature is a fair environmental indicator, Life Zones are related to the distribution of plants and, therefore, animals.

The Life Zone scheme once was the only available scheme. Certain newer ones exist and generally are used much more frequently by biogeographers. However, these newer concepts mostly supplement the ideas of Merriam. Most supplements—perhaps all of them—could have fitted within his Life Zone concept. In many respects, it is unfortunate that they were not. Perhaps most unfortunate is the possibility of Merriam's major contribution being overlooked. His Life

Zones were the first units that allowed some level of local recognition of areas, and the so-called refined schemes often provide no better understanding than does Merriam's scheme.

Present reduction in use of Life Zones came from the following criticisms of the concept: (1) It is inflexible, not allowing the use of additional larger or smaller categories. (2) It indicates that zonation is across the continent, whereas geological history and present organisms indicate a definite difference between the east and the west. (3) Basing the scheme strictly upon temperatures during the period of growth and reproduction allows for many possibilities for error. For example, other parts of the year can be just as important, and daily and seasonal extremes might be more important than the averages that were used. (4) Often there is no close correspondence between Life Zones as originally designated and the actual distribution of flora and fauna. (5) Few organisms appear to be confined to the Hudsonian Zone, which seems to be little more than a diluted Canadian Zone. (6) Finally, perhaps because of misinterpretation, it seems that there were distinct errors in temperature computations and hence in the final Life Zone map.

COMMUNITY TYPES

The "association types" of G. E. Nichols were present in 1923. At the present time reference is made to "community" or "vegetation types" rather than to association types because of possible confusion of meaning of the term "association." A community type is classified on the basis of the growth formation, or appearance, of a group of organisms. On this basis, forests, woodlands, marshes, deserts, and like habitats are recognized.

Although this scheme has great value in referring to a particular group of organisms, it is not used to imply distribution. For one thing, the scheme provides little chance for drawing lines between communities, because species are not considered. For example, one community type can consist of many different and remotely related communities, and the community type of a single community can be modified near the margin of its area.

Community types contain units designated on the basis of over-all adaptations (the growth formations). Therefore, if this scheme is applied to show over-all local responses between organisms and their environment, it can be of value. However, except for a broad interpretation of four Vegetation Types (Figure 19.25), most community types have received little use in modern treatments of distribution. Moreover, most of the community types probably will remain limited to the role of convenient summaries of the adaptations of organisms.

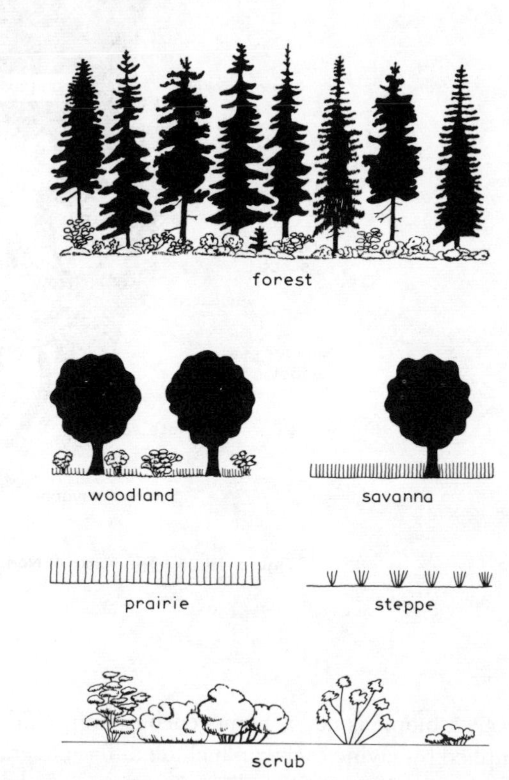

Figure 19.25 The major vegetation types: forest, woodland, grassland, and desert. In forests the trees form a closed canopy above the ground. As this canopy opens a woodland develops. The transition between a woodland and grassland is recognized as a savanna. Grasslands are of two types, prairies and really a grassland-desert transition of bunch grasses called steppes. Deserts generally have a more or less open shrub vegetation called scrub. A particular scrub vegetation called chaparral is found outside desert areas in western North America.

BIOMES

The biome consists of a single plant formation and its animals. It normally is composed of a broad geographic area having a single type of climate and the potential of a single climatic climax community (Figure 19.26). By implication it contains all seral stages leading to the climatic climax, all nonclimatic climaxes, and all seral stages leading to the nonclimatic climaxes in the area of a particular climatic type.

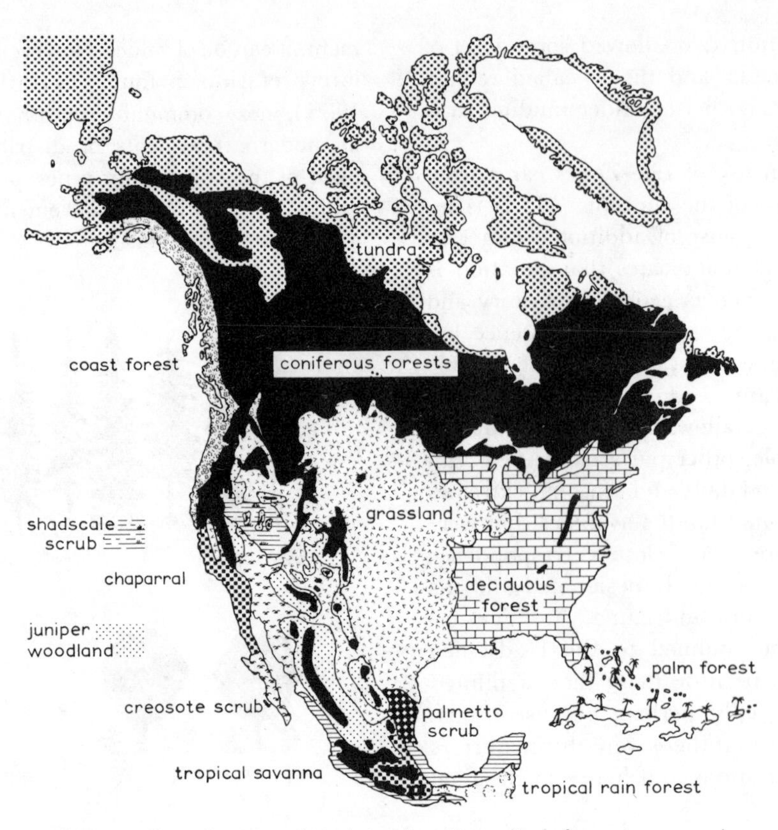

Figure 19.26 The Biomes of North America. (Generalized after various sources.)

However, a biome is not a homogeneous unit. This was implied by saying each can include different seral stages and nonclimatic climaxes. In addition, a biome can contain several closely related but slightly different climatic climaxes. This possibility stems from lack of homogeneity in a single climate type. Rather, each climate possesses some gradients in the various factors that distinguish it. For this reason, there may be strong, gradual, or abrupt, over-all gradients in the area of a single climate; and these climatic variations are the basis for more than a single climatic climax being present.

The biome scheme was formulated by Clements and Shelford in 1939. In the scheme plants are the dominant organisms and are called *dominants* in the sense of the present book. Animals are interpreted correctly as being secondary to the dominant plants, but animal importance in a community is recognized as *influents*. Although the diagnosis of biomes is made on the basis of the plant formation (a group of closely related climax plant communities), biomes can be further subdivided into associations, consociations, fasciations, and societies. However, the "association" of Clements and Shelford refers to a climatic climax; it is not any primary or secondary climax, as is the "association" in other parts of this text. In addition, overlaps (ecotones) between biomes are recognized.

Biomes are named in more than one way. Generally they are named on the basis of the plant formation alone, but names might indicate the type of vegetation and common animals. For example, the Great Plains Grassland might be called either the Grassland Biome, or the Grass-Bison-Pronghorn Biome.

The biome scheme is applicable to the entire surface of the earth. Because a biome is a plant formation (plus its animals) and many plant formations exist, there are more biomes than could possibly be considered in a brief outline of the subject.

CRITICISMS

The biome scheme has a sound basis and does provide a great deal of flexibility. However, its value as a means of classifying ecological communities suffers from the problems of such classification. This is true even if one ignores the fundamental things preventing complete accuracy in a distribution scheme. The state of ecological knowledge is such that few ecological units definitely are agreed upon by ecologists, so that no uniform basis for classifying vegetation exists. Primary difficulties arise from disagreement as to what constitutes a seral stage or a climax: some ecologists classify nonclimatic climaxes as seral stages; others classify them as climaxes. Also, the exact limits of individual seral stages or climaxes are not agreed upon.

Biomes are similar to community types in that both normally have organisms of a single adaptive type, or growth formation. Although community types are diagnosed strictly in this manner, many biomes can share a single growth formation and one biome can encompass many growth formations. Such complexity creates a problem in recognizing biomes and studying their interrelationships. If biomes always followed a definite distribution pattern in nature, the difficulties would be reduced. However, regular patterns are not common. Due to complex variation among environments, biomes might assume a mosaic of unrelated but adjacent formations. Therefore, there can be a problem in placing a particular climax in one or another biome.

Another criticism of the biome and many other schemes is that most to almost all organisms are ignored. To a certain extent, this criticism of the biome is reduced if the dominants of each seral stage and climax are discovered and named. However, even if dominants are known, knowledge is insufficient for explaining many relationships among communities. Such minimum information obscures the concept of a community as a sort of superorganism. Also, lack of data hides the fact that a community has a place or center of origin where it first became an entity, and that, through time, a community has established various relationships internally and with other communities.

Because the biome concept gives little idea of the evolution of areas, it is somewhat static. The biome scheme tends to hide the dynamic nature of areas where everything indicates change. There are seasonal changes in composition and progressive changes in the internal features and entire distribution of areas. Moreover, these changes can be traced back through geological history in a study of geoflora. Therefore, the contrast is startling when dynamic data are used to convey the idea of permanently fixed distributions of organisms.

BIOTIC PROVINCES

The scheme of biotic provinces in its most modern form was proposed for North America by L. R. Dice in 1943. A *biotic province* is an ecological unit that, except for islands, occupies a continuous geographic area (Figure 19.27). Each province covers a large, uninterrupted space having one or more ecological "associations." Each province supposedly is somewhat equivalent ecologically and is characterized by climate. However, a biotic province's greatest significance is as a primary center of possible evolution, each province somewhat conforming to the ranges of fairly distinctive variants of individual species. For

Figure 19.27 The Biotic Provinces of North America. Provinces are incidated but not named. (After various sources.)

this reason, biotic provinces are described as "units of evolution."

Biotic provinces can be defined only in general terms. They tend to be identified by their general environment in terms of climate, soil, and topography. However, each of these factors varies considerably within a province; the environment within a province can be more variable than the average difference between provinces. For this reason, the best diagnosis stresses their being units of evolution that approximate the natural areas (distributions or ranges) of flora and fauna. Biotic provinces are thus said to be centers of evolution and dispersal; each may have a unique race of one or more wide-ranging species.

Because of their close relationship, natural areas and biotic provinces have many of the same characteristics. Biotic province boundaries are defined by tangible or intangible barriers; however, the barriers never are absolute for all species within a single province. Many species have the limits of their distribution beyond those of the province, and some species have their margin of area within the confines of a province. Such range restrictions are associated with horizontal or altitudinal ecological differences.

Ecological differences within a province are the basis for forming lesser units. A *biotic district* is a horizontally distributed but ecologically unique province subunit. A *life belt* is the altitudinal equivalent of a biotic district.

CRITICISMS

This scheme represents areas of potential evolution, something not attempted by the previous schemes. For this reason, it is most used in studies of speciation. However, it does not provide a foolproof method for combining like organisms. Because different species have unlike ecological amplitudes, they display independent reactions to their environments that may lead to unique patterns of geographic variation. On the other hand, the scheme does provide a useful average distribution of potential units of evolution, or natural areas.

The biotic province also suffers from being a static presentation of dynamic phenomena. The scheme does not portray geographic changes in the areas of species. This is an especially serious shortcoming in a summary whose avowed purpose is to display the dynamic nature of evolution.

Although this is only secondarily an ecological scheme, it has received many criticisms on an ecological basis. The use of a strict geographic unit is criticized, because some provinces include unlike habitats and other provinces share much the same habitats and life. Also, some provinces are dominated by a single climatic climax, others by two or more climatic climaxes, and a few cut across climatic climaxes.

DYNAMIC FAUNAS

K. L. Gordon in 1947 presented a close approximation to a truly dynamic scheme of distributional analysis. The dynamic nature is shown by the fact that subunit mapping is not an important part of the scheme and that single localities, normally *stands*, are the usual unit of study. The study of such units allows comparison of close to remote areas and later investigations to appraise any changes in a stand. At the present time, detailed development of the scheme is limited to mammals.

The major subdivisions of dynamic faunas are of two types, faunal elements and faunas. A *faunal element* is a broad geographic area of origin and is roughly equivalent to a geoflora (Figure 19.28). The individual elements of the North American mammalian fauna are the South American, Tropical North American, Austral North American, Boreal North American, and Old World Elements. A *fauna* is a dynamic assemblage of animals, the members of which constantly shift their ranges in differing amounts according to ecological amplitude (especially in reference to mobility and adaptations) and to availability of their habitats. As one might expect, each fauna normally is associated with a certain type or types of vegetation that in turn reflect the sum of ecological factors (Figure 19.29).

The individual fauna is ecological in nature. The Boreal Faunas are the Tundran Fauna of Tundra relationship and the Coniferan Fauna of Boreal Forest relationship. The Austral Faunas are the Deciduan Fauna of Deciduous Forest affinity and the Sonoran Fauna of non-forest alliance. The Sonoran Fauna includes many different areas that are united because they are arid Austral. The only Tropical Fauna relates to the Tropical Forests and Savannas.

Each fauna is further considered in two ways: according to niche organization and/or as a center of evolutionary differentiation. Specific consideration depends on the particular use of the scheme; in many

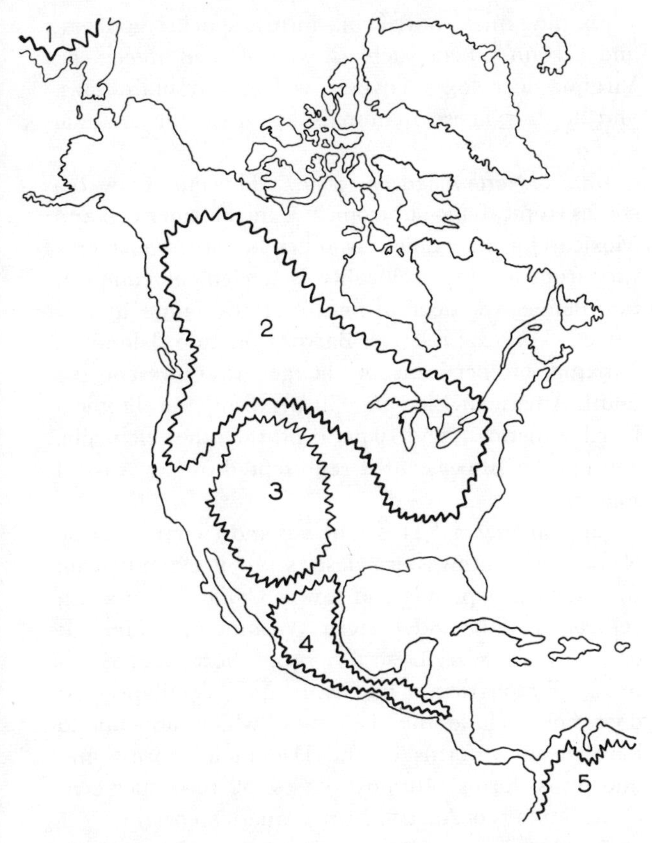

Figure 19.28 Mammalian Faunal Elements in references to their centers of origin: 1, Old World, 2, Boreal North American, 3, Austral North American, 4, Tropical North American, 5, South American.

instances both means of subdivision might be used. Niche organization can imply either a microhabitat (environmental niche) or food relationship (functional niche), and both kinds of niches are utilized.

FAUNAL ELEMENTS

The *South American Element* originated in South America during the Paleocene or Eocene to Pliocene ocean isolation of South America from North America. At the present time most of the North American emigrants of this element are in Central America and Mexico. The element includes anteaters, monkeys, a large and distinctive group of rodents (including cavies, capybaras, spiny rats, and porcupines), armadillos, and marsupials. Among this group, the armadillo is in the southern Gulf States, the opossum is widespread, and the porcupine is mostly in coniferous forests.

The *Tropical North American Element* originated and developed with the Neotropical-Tertiary Geoflora. Owing to changing climatic conditions and the opening of the Panamanian land bridge in the Pliocene, this element invaded South America and now is an important part of the fauna of that continent. It contains many tree squirrels, members of the New World rat and mouse family, members of the dog family, the ocelot, the jaguar, the coatimundi and other racoon relatives, peccaries, the American tapir, and New World deer.

The *Austral North American Element* has two subunits, one developed with the Deciduous Forest and the other with the Grassland and Southwestern Deserts flora. The Deciduous Forest unit has some shrews, the eastern mole, eastern chipmunk, eastern gray squirrel, and fox squirrel. The Grassland and Desert unit has ground squirrels, prairie dogs, pocket mice, kangaroo rats and mice, grasshopper mice, the badger, and the pronghorn antelope. This element

Figure 19.29 Mammalian Faunas: 1, Tundran, 2, Coniferan, 3, Sonoran, 4, Deciduan, 5, Tropical North American. The wide-ranging Afaunal group is not shown and the Grassland area that does not constitute a fauna is shown but not numbered.

also has wide-ranging species that are more or less common to the entire area, for example, cottontail rabbits, gophers, harvest mice, white-footed mice, gray foxes, racoons, skunks, and deer.

The *Boreal American Element* evolved with the Arcto-Tertiary Geoflora; for this reason it contains some species that now are panboreal, that is, distributed across the top of the world. Some of these panboreal forms are of definite Old World origin, but others appear to be of New World origin. In either event, the Bering land bridge allowed the present panboreal distribution. Panboreal forms are hares, beavers, lemmings, red-backed voles, pine mice, meadow mice, weasels, wolves, the arctic fox, and the red fox. New World forms are pigmy shrews, shrew moles, Brewer's moles, western moles, pine squirrels, flying squirrels, and lemming mice. Other genera definitely developed in the New World but later moved to the Old World and now inhabit both areas. These include western chipmunks, marmots, and jumping mice.

The *Old World Element* entered the New World during the Pleistocene by way of the Bering land bridge. In North America this element is mostly northern in distribution and includes the conies, bears, martens, wolverines, lynxes, elk, moose, caribou, bison, mountain sheep, mountain goats, and musk oxen.

FAUNAS

As one might expect, most areas of North America have some representatives of the various elements; however, there is a definite tendency for certain areas, or faunas to have more of one element than another. For example, the Tundran Fauna is almost entirely represented by Old World and Boreal Elements; the Tropical North American Fauna is almost devoid of these elements.

The faunas are geographic units and are static. Each is roughly equivalent to one or more biomes. However, because one can analyze the general nature of each locale of each fauna, the fauna is not as static as the biome. Analysis allows study of locale changes through time, perhaps even study of how a locale can change from one fauna to another.

Afaunal. Certain North American mammals that occupy a large part of our continent are hard to fit into a particular fauna. This group includes stream species—the otters, minks, and beavers; marsh forms—the muskrats; water border and wet meadow forms—jumping mice; burrowing forms—pocket gophers; and certain others such as white-footed mice, elk, Virginia deer, foxes, coyotes, wolves, mountain lions, and bears. These mammals comprise the Afaunal group.

Tropical North American Fauna. This fauna now occupies tropical and subtropical Central American and Mexican forests. Like any other fauna, its elements vary from locality to locality and element composition defines the general nature of the fauna at any place. For example, at Barro Colorado Island in Panama, 60 per cent of the genera represent the South American Element; 30 per cent, the Tropical North American; and 10 per cent, the other elements. Most of the 10 per cent is represented by the Austral Element.

Sonoran Fauna. This fauna is most characteristic of the arid southwestern deserts but it extends from the Mexican Uplands and Lower California to south central Canada and eastern Washington state. It occupies areas of Desert Scrub, Shortgrass, Sagebrush, Bunchgrass, Chaparral, and Woodland. It does not include the Tallgrass, which appears to have meadow forms of the Deciduous Forest and Shortgrass forms. In most places, 50 to 60 per cent of the fauna is of Austral North American origin.

Deciduan Fauna. These mammals are found in the eastern United States. Two subunits can be distinguished: the Deciduous Forest Association and Southern Pine Forest Association. Each faunal association has a definite and distinctive group of mammals. A "faunal association" is not the same as an "association."

Coniferan Fauna. Found in all Boreal areas except the Tundra, this is the fauna of the coniferous forests. It covers much of Canada, the western mountains, and the area adjacent to the Pacific Coast. This fauna is mostly of Old World and Boreal North American origin.

Tundran Fauna. The mammals of the far north are almost entirely of Old World and Boreal North American origin. Therefore, this fauna is the most homogeneous insofar as origin is concerned. By way of contrast, the Sonoran, Deciduan, and Coniferan tend to possess representatives from other elements.

DIFFERENTIATION AREAS

A subunit, the differentiation area, is an area set aside by barriers that isolate part of a fauna from its nearest relatives; it frequently contains endemics, that is, organisms found only in a restricted area. To obtain the information necessary to define differentiation areas one must study and compare many localities.

Differentiation areas regularly display *orders of differentiation.* First-order differentiation is represented by the oldest, or first, isolation of a segment of a species or a fauna. Also, it usually consists of the largest subdivision of a fauna or subunit of a fauna; progressive orders of differentiation in sequence consist of smaller subunits of a fauna. The last-order differentiation regularly contains the smallest area of a fauna. Second-order differentiation is within the area of first-order differentiation; third-order, within second, and so on (Figure 19.30). Last-order differentiation also represents the most recent area isolated within a particular area of first-order differentiation.

The Coniferan Fauna of the western mountains might serve to clarify these subunits. In the southern part of its range are two arms of distribution, one down the Rocky Mountain System and the other down the Sierra-Cascade System. These two areas represent first-order differentiation centers.

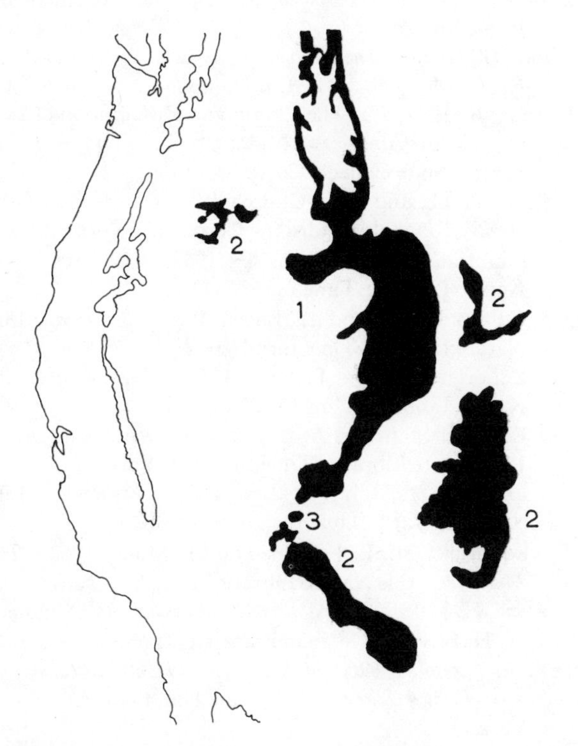

Figure 19.30 Differentiation areas as found in the western North American mountains. Gaps are indicated in the Rocky Mountains only if the gaps act as biological barriers to some mammals. Numbers designate the order of differentiation of the particular areas.

Second-order differentiation is found in many areas. For example, the mountains of northeastern Oregon are part of the Rocky Mountain System but are isolated from the System proper by the Snake River and a vegetation barrier of juniper. Also, in Wyoming, there is a gap isolating an eastern arm of the Rockies. A final gap of significance is in the south and isolates a southern segment of the Rockies. These three main barriers stop such mammals as the fisher, northern weasel, Columbian ground squirrel, northern flying squirrel, and wolverine. However, these barriers are not the only ones; minor gaps occur in Idaho, but they are poor secondary barriers.

Third-order differentiation is found in the Kaibab Plateau. This area is definitely isolated now by a dry sagebrush area, by the Grand Canyon on the south, and by lowlands to the north and northeast. This isolation plus gene mutation and selection led to an endemic, the Kaibab squirrel. The Kaibab squirrel is closely related to Abert's squirrel, a southern Rockies species that once was able to pass through the barrier to the Kaibab Plateau.

The possible origin of the Kaibab squirrel summarizes the nature of a third-order differentiation area. Apparently Abert's squirrel or its ancestor once ranged continuously into the Kaibab Plateau. Next, changing environmental conditions created an impenetrable barrier between the present area of Abert's squirrel and the Plateau. Finally, evolution of the Kaibab population produced a new species, the Kaibab squirrel.

The evolution of the Kaibab squirrel might be appreciated from the nature of the fauna of the Kaibab Plateau. There is a definite restriction of species as compared with the adjacent Rockies. There are no marten, lynx, golden-mantled squirrel, least chipmunk, spruce squirrel, Abert's squirrel, bushytail woodrat, or porcupine. Therefore, one might conclude that evolution of the Kaibab squirrel was necessary for its ancestor to survive in an area whose few species indicate its ecological severity.

NICHES

Niches are subunits diagnosed mostly on the basis of diet and means of locomotion. The main advantage of such a system is that it maintains the dynamic aspects of the scheme. Use of such things as habitats would immediately cause the scheme to become static. The diet subdivisions are *herbivores* with subunits of vegetation feeders and seed eaters, *insectivores* (insect eaters), *carnivores* (meat eaters), *piscivores* (fish eaters), and *omnivores* (variable plant and animal eaters), all functional niches. These functional niches are the primary units of subdivision. Secondary subdivision, based upon means of locomotion, is not necessary for understanding of the scheme.

A summary of number of species in particular niches in relation to faunas is given in Table 19.2.

TABLE 19.2 ANALYSIS OF NORTH AMERICAN FAUNAS BY NICHES (IN PER CENT)

	Tundran	Coniferan	Deciduan	Sonoran	Afaunal
Herbivores	59	61	68	81	27
Insectivores	18	25	30	13	40
Carnivores	18	8	—	3	3
Piscivores	—	2	—	—	7
Omnivores	6	4	2	3	23

Another rough approximation discloses that eighteen genera of North American mammals are Boreal, twenty-one are Afaunal, seven are Deciduan, and fifteen are Sonoran. In addition, nine genera are Boreal-Sonoran, five are Boreal-Deciduan, and six are Sonoran-Deciduan. In birds, approximately 74 genera are Boreal, 62 are Afaunal, 25 are Deciduan, and 63 are Sonoran. Also, 22 are Boreal-Sonoran, 18 are Boreal-Deciduan, and 56 are Sonoran-Deciduan. In reptiles, one is Boreal, five are Afaunal, 26 are Deciduan, and 31 are Sonoran. Interfaunal inhabitants are two Boreal-Sonoran, no Boreal-Deciduan, and 20 Sonoran-Deciduan. Finally, amphibians have five Boreal, six Afaunal, 16 Deciduan, three Sonoran, two Boreal-Sonoran, one Boreal-Deciduan, and five Sonoran-Deciduan.

SCHEME INTERRELATIONSHIPS

No distribution scheme is unique. Each scheme is related to others, and no scheme need necessarily be the only summarization that is of value. This is especially true of the biomes, biotic provinces, and dynamic fauna. Biomes stress climatic climaxes and their similarities of structure and form. Biotic provinces, focus upon potential centers of new evolutionary development. Dynamic fauna remove consideration from a static view by emphasizing the immediate consequence of past history of flora and fauna in terms of major units of evolution as defined through adaptations in climaxes and differentiation areas. Therefore, biomes and biotic provinces are extremely useful summarizations of present conditions in a static sense, and dynamic fauna are summarizations of what has happened and is happening through time.

SELECTED READINGS*

Andrewartha, H. G., and L. C. Birch, 1954. *The Distribution and Abundance of Animals.* The University of Chicago Press, Chicago.

Andrews, H. N., Jr., 1961. *Studies in Paleobotany.* John Wiley and Sons, New York.

Axelrod, D. I., 1959. Geological History. In *A California Flora* by Philip A. Munz. University of California Press, Berkeley.

Cain, S. A., 1944. *Foundations of Plant Geography.* Harper, New York.

Clements, F. E., and V. E. Shelford, 1939. *Bio-ecology.* John Wiley & Sons, New York.

Dansereau, Pierre, 1957. *Biogeography, an Ecological Perspective.* The Ronald Press, New York.

Darlington, P. J., Jr., 1957. *Zoogeography: The Geographical Distribution of Animals.* John Wiley & Sons, New York.

Dice, L. R., 1943. *The Biotic Provinces of North America.* University of Michigan Press, Ann Arbor.

———. 1949. *Natural Communities.* University of Michigan Press, Ann Arbor.

Elton, G., 1958. *The Ecology of Invasions by Animals and Plants.* Methuen & Co. Ltd., London.

Gordon, K. L., 1947. The Origin and Distribution of Living North American Mammals. In *Biogeography.* Oregon State College, Corvallis, Ore.

Hanson, H. C., and E. D. Churchill, 1961. *The Plant Community.* Reinhold Publishing Corp., New York.

Life Editorial Staff and A. Beiser, 1962. *The Earth.* Life Nature Library. Time Inc., New York.

Life Editorial Staff and L. Engel, 1961. *The Sea.* Life Nature Library. Time Inc., New York.

Life Editorial Staff and P. Farb, 1961. *The Forest.* Life Nature Library. Time Inc., New York.

Life Editorial Staff and A. S. Leopold, 1961. *The Desert.* Life Nature Library. Time Inc., New York.

Life Editorial Staff and W. Ley, 1962. *The Poles.* Life Nature Library. Time Inc., New York.

Life Editorial Staff, L. J. Milne and M. Milne, 1962. *The Mountains.* Life Nature Library. Time Inc., New York.

Oosting, H. J., 1956. *The Study of Plant Communities.* 2nd ed. W. H. Freeman Co., San Francisco, Calif.

Polunin, Nicholas, 1960. *Introduction to Plant Geography and Some Related Sciences.* McGraw-Hill Book Co., New York.

Wulff, E. V., 1942. *An Introduction to Historical Plant Geography.* 3rd ed., translated by E. Brissenden. Chronica Botanica Co., Waltham, Mass.

*See also the General Ecology References on p. 338.

20 ECOSYSTEM ECOLOGY

Environment-Community Interrelations

Each organism performs a particular function and occupies a particular situation in its environment. The term *niche* is used to indicate either phenomenon. However, the more complex of the two niches is the functional one. The place niche is the immediate physical and biological environment, the home range of an animal or the surroundings of a plant. The functional niche is the ecological role played by each creature in its community; it also refers to a particular community function that is performed by one or more species in their environment.

The fundamental workings of an ecosystem include the operation of functional niches and the transfer of energy that is a part of this operation. This basic energy comes from the sun as radiant energy, or light, and is used by plants to form food to support their life processes. In addition, these plants, including their stored foods, are ingested and transformed by animals to the simpler chemical compounds, that support animal life processes. This entire energy cycle, which encompasses organism nutrition and the transfer of certain nutrients through the ecosystem, includes most to all biogeochemical cycles that collectively may also be called a biogeochemical cycle.

ENERGY CYCLE

The transfer of energy in an ecosystem encompasses both the cycle of transfer and the functional niches found within the cycle. The cycle can be reduced to fundamental "steps" and nonessential "steps," and the functional niches can be treated in many ways (Figure 20.1).

FUNDAMENTAL STEPS

Essential components in the operation of an ecosystem energy cycle include the following:

(1) Production of radiant energy by the sun.

(2) Utilization of solar energy, carbon dioxide, water, and various minerals by photosynthetic plants to form organic materials, chemical compounds that contain carbon and are synthesized by life.

(3) Decomposition of dead photosynthetic plants to inorganic compounds by saprophytic bacteria.

(4) Transformation of inorganic compounds by chemosynthetic bacteria, the transformers, to compounds that can be used by photosynthetic plants.

Note: The essential components of an ecosystem usually are more than sunlight, carbon dioxide, water, minerals, and photosynthetic plants (steps 1 and 2), because most plants must get their mineral nutrients from steps three and four, from pre-existing organic compounds that are first decomposed and then transformed into minerals. (Note: many ecologists consider decomposition and transformation a single step.) This condition exists because most plants are unable to obtain minerals directly from

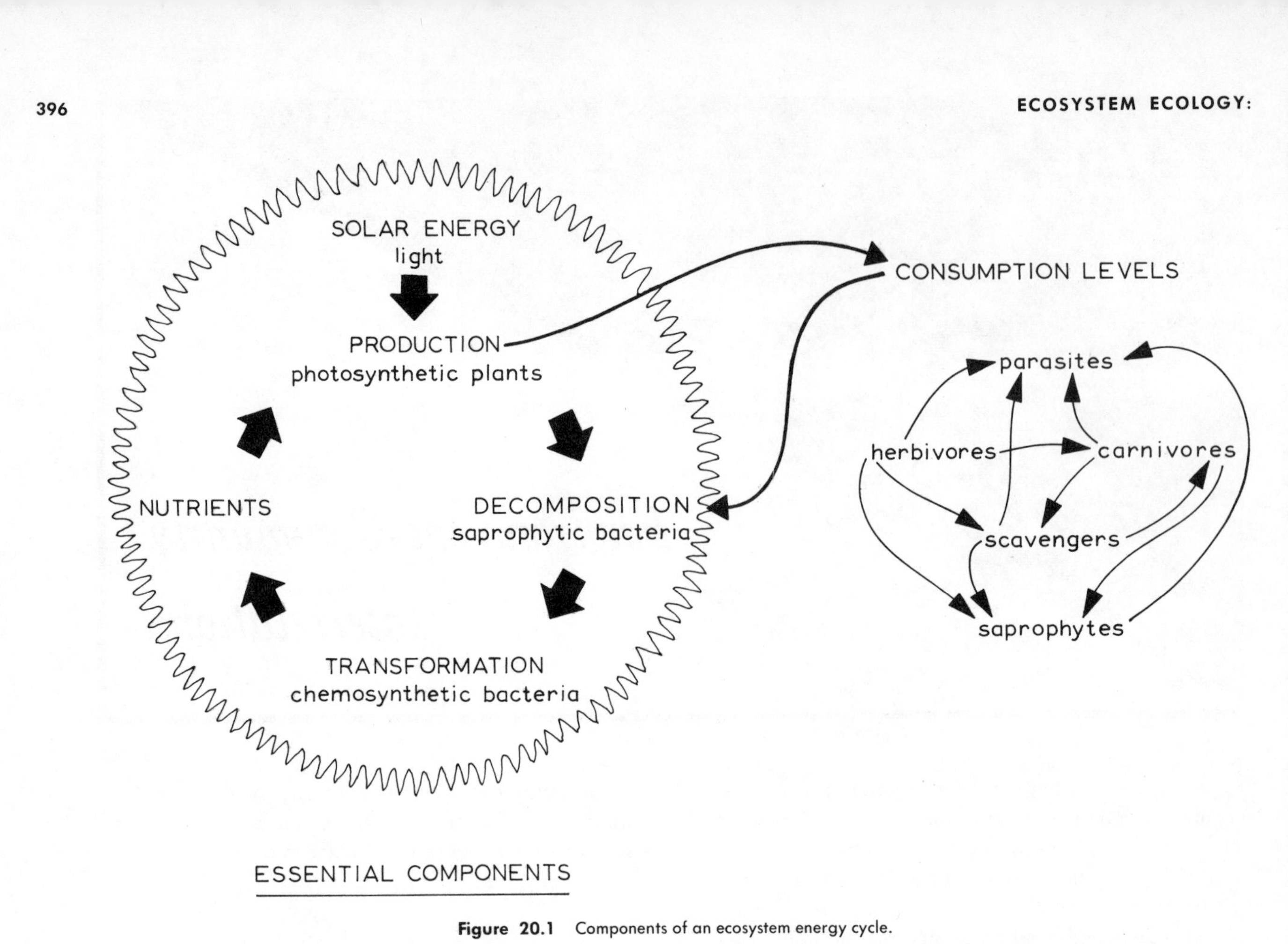

Figure 20.1 Components of an ecosystem energy cycle.

rocks. Therefore, steps three and four are essential to photosynthesis and more complex synthesis in step two.

NONESSENTIAL STEPS

Various other steps add to the complexity of the energy cycle; however, none of them are necessary for an ecosystem to operate. These steps are nonessential in the sense that life could go on without them.

The nonessential portion of the energy cycle is a complex rather than a series of steps. It is a complex because no direct, or step-by-step, relationship exists among the basic components of herbivores, carnivores, omnivores, parasites, scavengers, and saprophytes. It is true that herbivores are a logical next step in energy transfer from photosynthetic plants, and carnivores tend to rely mainly on herbivores for their food. However, omnivores use both plants and herbivores for food, thus sometimes acting as carnivores and at other times, as herbivores. Parasites, scavengers, and saprophytes gain nutrients from plants, herbivores, and carnivores. A more detailed presentation of the interrelationships among essential and nonessential "steps" is portrayed in Figure 20.1. Omnivores are not included as a separate component in the figure; they are indicated by the collective functions of herbivores and carnivores.

FUNCTIONAL NICHES

The discussion of steps in the energy cycle mentions the functional niches present in an ecosystem, and Figure 20.1 portrays these same niches. This illustration emphasizes two phases of function: production and consumption. Although there is a single level of production, that by green plants, green flagellates, blue-green algae, and certain bacteria, there are many possible levels of consumption. For example, because herbivores generally are the first, or direct, users of living plants, herbivores are *primary consumers;* because carnivores obtain produced food second hand when they eat herbivores, they are *secondary consumers*. In addition, a larger carnivore eating a smaller carnivore would be a *tertiary consumer.* This concept which segregates functional niches into producers, primary consumers, secondary consumers, and so on, is called the *food chain* (Figures 20.1 and 20.2). The chain implies a linear order of food consumption.

In nature the actual functional niches do not assume the straight-line relationship that is implied by a food chain. Rather, natural niche interrelationships, when diagramed in terms of what eats what, disclose a netlike pattern of energy transfer. The phenomenon represented by such a pattern is called a *food web* (Figure 20.2).

Functional niches are clarified by considering various *food pyramids*, especially the production, biomass, and numbers pyramids. These pyramids all stress the fact that the energy cycle in an ecosystem is not 100 per cent efficient. In other words, it takes more than one pound of plant materials to form one pound of herbivores, and more than one pound of herbivores to form one pound of carnivores. The various pyramid concepts disclose the inefficiency, or loss, in energy transfer in unlike ways. A *production pyramid* from base to apex represents a food chain. The base portrays the amount of organic materials, usually by weight, that are produced by the plants in a particular area. The level next above the base shows the amount of growth that takes place in the herbivores that consume the produced amount of plant materials. Progressively higher layers diagram the

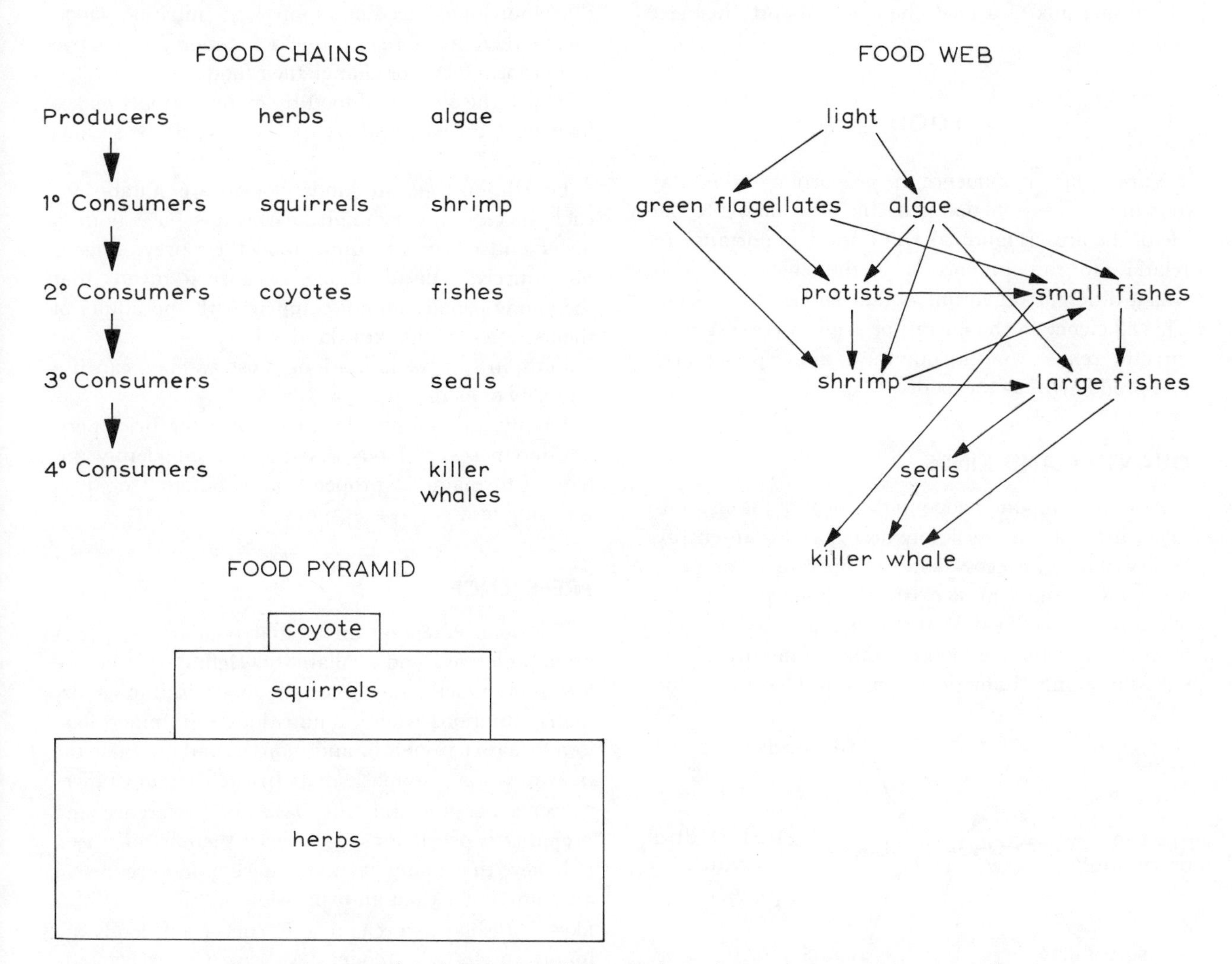

Figure 20.2 Food chain, food web, and food pyramid. Food pyramids may imply the amount of food formed, weight of life in a particular level of the energy cycle, or the number of individual organisms in each level of the energy cycle.

amount of growth as a result of consumption of the materials in the next lower layer. Each level of the pyramid shows neither numbers nor weight of the life represented, but rather depicts growth, or production, as a consequence of consuming the next lower level's production. A *biomass pyramid* has the same components with the same relative positions and implications as the production pyramid, but the graph indicates the weight of all living creatures in each step of the food pyramid. A *pyramid of numbers* also has the same food-chain basis, but displays the number or organisms in each link of the chain. Hence, the food-pyramid concept treats in different ways—either in terms of materials formed, weight of creatures, or number of individuals—the fact that it takes more life in one link of a food chain to support the next link.

FOOD

Various factors influence the proportion of the total food in an ecosystem that is usable or available to the life of the area (Figure 20.3). Of most importance in relation to this proportion is the efficiency with which different organisms obtain energy from food. This efficiency in the energy of a given ecosystem is directly related to the quantity, kind, preference, and productivity of the food.

QUANTITY AND KINDS

A certain amount of food in the form of plants, animals, and water is absolutely necessary for an energy cycle—hence, an ecosystem—to operate. Moreover, this total biomass must exist in definite proportions of unlike kinds of food. Without such a balance in the form of a functioning food pyramid, some organisms will starve and dramatic changes will occur in the composition of some of the populations within the ecosystem. Such imbalance probably is the basic cause of ecosystem collapse and of community extinction.

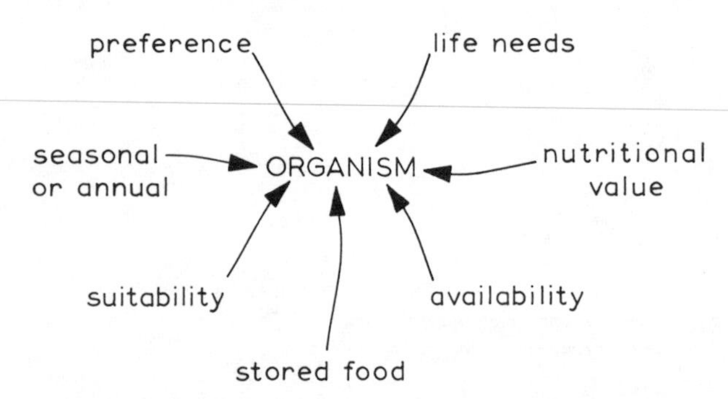

Figure 20.3 Factors determining the food available to an organism.

Certain factors, especially with reference to animals, affect the availability and balance of food. First, the already-mentioned possibilities of seasonal and annual variations in population numbers naturally cause fluctuation in the composition of an ecosystem. It is not likely that any species of animal can eat the same food throughout its lifetime. Rather, if animals are to survive, seasonal and often annual variations in food consumption must be common.

Second, the nutritional value of certain foods, especially plants, is known to vary. This may mean that individuals feeding upon less nutritious food must either eat more, assume a functionally inactive state (dormancy), or change their food habits.

Third, the storage of food by many animals makes food available when otherwise there would be serious famine.

Fourth, only certain kinds of food are suitable for each species. For example, carnivores have both a lower and upper size limit upon their prey. This is not entirely a disadvantage, because it means that the young usually do not compete with the adults of their species for the same kind of food.

Fifth, in spite of limitations most animals can use a variety of foods.

Finally, many animals can survive for brief periods on emergency foods that are not sufficiently nutritious to maintain proper health, but that do prevent starvation.

PREFERENCE

The food eaten by an animal regularly depends upon preference and availability. Definite preference for or prejudice against certain foods is implied by many situations where a nutritious but minor food item is easier to obtain and more abundant than the mainstay of an animal's diet. In such circumstances it seems possible that the basis for preference and prejudice is psychological. At least there is no reason to believe that many cases of choice of food represent anything other than an expression of "likes" or "dislikes." Insofar as preference is concerned, foods are highly preferred, moderately eaten, occasionally eaten, or refused; however, the easiest available foods still tend to be most used.

Closely allied with preference and availability in

determining food taken is the quantity of food required by an animal. Food needs naturally are extremely variable both among species and within a species. However, the main factors determining the amount of food needed are an animal's body surface area, body temperature, and degree of activity—"activity" implying not only amount of physical exertion but functional, or physiological, activity such as reproduction, which requires more energy than normal. Moreover, increase in any of these factors of need increases chemical reactions (specifically, metabolic processes) and requires more energy. Finally, in addition to the animal functional factors determining food needs, there is the already-mentioned factor of nutritional value of food.

PRODUCTIVITY

The amount of usable food produced by a given ecosystem is subject to many variables (Figure 20.4). Of course, the primary criterion of food availability is the amount of food produced. However, this does not determine how much food is utilized; some food is wasted. Various things cause the food consumption rate to fall short of the basic production rate. For example, some food usually is destroyed because animals trample the area. Also, waste may exist if more of a particular food is produced than there are animals to consume the "crop."

Total food availability determines the number of individuals of each species possible in a community. This possible composition of species is called the *carrying capacity* and is allied to its community. Carrying capacity can be related to a climax community. In a climax the area is in equilibrium because none of the species exceed the limits that would cause the carrying capacity of the entire community to be exceeded. In addition, carrying capacity is associated with certain possible effects of excessive grazing practices. Overgrazing occurs as soon as the carrying capacity is exceeded. Because food utilization is greater than productivity, the most desirable forage plants cannot reproduce, hence less nutritious (because they make less energy demands and store less energy) plants replace the original forage.

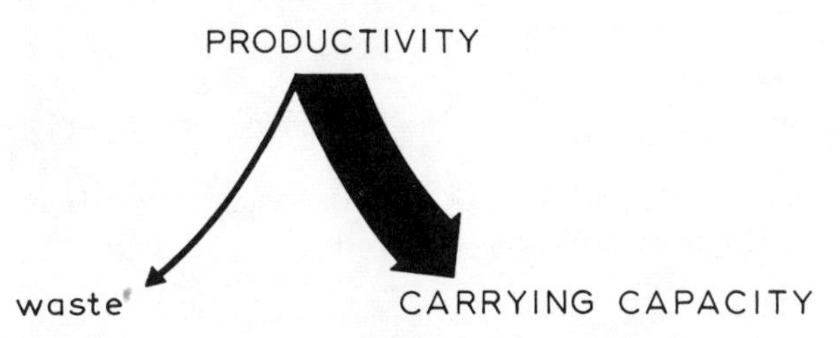

Figure 20.4 Relationship among productivity, waste, and carrying capacity in an ecosystem.

The above is a bare indication of the fact that available food determines the kinds and numbers of organisms present in any community, and that food is one of the most significant factors in determining the characteristics of a community.

BIOGEOCHEMICAL CYCLES

The energy cycle of an ecosystem is dependent upon the recirculation of all the essential elements of protoplasm, an all-inclusive biogeochemical cycle (Figure 20.5). However, this recirculation, or over-all biogeochemical cycle, consists of many smaller biogeochemical cycles, each related to the circulation of one or more protoplasmic elements. By definition, each restricted cycle must include the chemical processes of living creatures, which form organic compounds, and chemical processes of the inanimate world, which form inorganic compounds. These two kinds of compounds include the more than thirty elements that are essential in the formation of protoplasm. The elements needed in the largest quantities are hydrogen, oxygen, carbon, nitrogen, phosphorus, and sulfur. These commoner elements and some of the less common ones are circulated in the water, carbon, nitrogen, phosphorus, and sulfur cycles.

In a sense, the biogeochemical cycles collectively are identical with their local geomorphic cycles. Although the biogeochemical cycles emphasize only the chemical reactions of protoplasmic elements, these reactions are identical with the chemical processes in the geomorphic cycles. This is true because a geomorphic cycle includes life and its processes as well as physical features and their processes.

Although the individual biogeochemical cycles are part of a single, over-all cycle of nutrient circulation, a consideration of individual cycles stresses the varying efficiencies of the circulation of different elements. For example, the water, carbon, and nitrogen cycles are very efficient; in each, circulation tends to proceed regularly. However, in such cycles as those for phosphorus and sulfur there are steps in which materials might accumulate much more rapidly than they are released. When such accumulations exist there is an imbalance in the natural processes of the ecosystem. This imbalance necessarily brings about

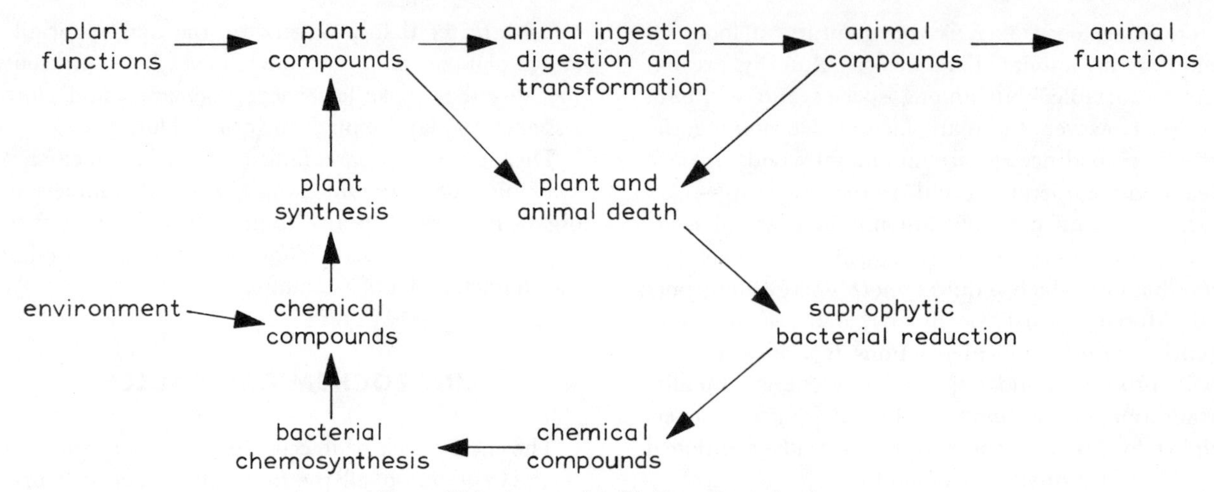

Figure 20.5 Processes found in biogeochemical cycles.

a change in the composition of the ecosystem that usually causes habitat destruction and leads to some form of secondary succession.

Ecosystem imbalance as a result of the accumulation of biogeochemical materials in particular parts of the cycle results from disturbance. For example, human exploitation removes materials from an ecosystem much faster than materials are replaced. This means that certain protoplasmic elements are not in sufficient supply to meet the nutritional demands of the energy cycle, and soon there will be a collapse of the ecosystem. Again, the consequences of this collapse is secondary succession, or regression to a community capable of entering a balanced energy cycle in the available environment.

GENERALIZED CYCLE

Any biogeochemical cycle involves the nourishment of the various organisms in an ecosystem. Basic to this nourishment is the production of food by green plants, green flagellates, blue-green algae, and certain bacteria. These organisms, mainly by photosynthesis but also by other complex synthesis, are producers of energy used by the organisms themselves, by animals, and by the parasites of both. Bacteria are of many nutrition types. Some autotrophic bacteria, those forming their own food from inorganic materials, are photosynthetic and fulfill the same functional niche as do other photosynthetic organisms; these bacteria are producers for the microscopic world. Other autotrophic bacteria are chemosynthetic, using oxygen in a process called oxidation to obtain nutrients and at the same time forming compounds either simpler or more complex than those they use. The other bacteria are heterotrophic saprophytes. By a process called reduction these saprophytes obtain nutrients and form simpler substances from these ingested materials. Therefore, bacteria have three important nutritional roles in an ecosystem. First, they act as producers, forming by photosynthesis and other syntheses the nutrients that are needed by microscopic primary consumers. Second, saprophytic forms act as primary consumers and decomposers (reducers) of dead and waste organic materials, freeing the materials for resynthesis. Third, chemosynthetic forms act as transformers of decomposed products by oxidizing these products into substances that are either further transformed by other chemosynthetic bacteria or are used directly by plants.

The final phase of any biogeochemical cycle is the contribution of materials from the physical environment. This environmental contribution comes mostly from the atmosphere; however, such geological processes as sedimentation and vulcanism are also important contributors.

SELECTED READINGS*

Dansereau, Pierre, 1957. *Biogeography, an Ecological Approach.*

Odum, E. P., 1963. *Ecology.* Modern Biology Series. Holt, Rinehart & Winston, New York.

*See also the General Ecology References on p. 338.

Concluding Statement

Throughout this book we have examined nature, using its organization as a basis for approaching and relating various phenomena. Summarization, perhaps conclusion, seems in order.

Organization was stressed in the brief mention of the universe and its subunits down to and including a star system. Also, specific organization of our star system, the solar system, introduced the main topic of this book, the planet earth. Organization of the earth led to discussion of air, sea, land, and life, and, again, orderliness was a primary concern in each. Finally, life was treated on the basis of the individual, population, community, and ecosystem. Yet, all these physical and biological phenomena comprise a single unit, the sum total of all forces in the universe, nature.

Let us attempt to summarize these forces. By now it should be obvious that nature displays organization. This was the basis of our segregation of topics. However, our segregation is not necessarily the only one that could be made. We as humans observe what to us appears as organization. Different individuals could well express this organization in different terms and different categories. Therefore, the groupings indicated in this book are the choice of the author, mostly because they present a useful framework for pedagogical purposes.

Certain other concepts, again not necessarily the only ones possible, may help in our final view of nature. These concepts are limitation, regulation, compensation, steady state, equilibrium, and synergism.

Limitation is a convenient way of expressing the role of the environment on particular organisms. The air, sea, land, and life limit any particular individual, population, community, or ecosystem upon which we focus our attention. We examined the role of limitation, limiting factors. Also, specific ecological factors, physical and biotic, were discussed in terms of how they limit life. Additional examples of life limitation were given in chapters on populations, communities, and ecosystems. In a sense, all ecological phenomena, directly or indirectly, contribute to limitation.

Regulation emphasizes the fact that limitation need not be harmful. The gamut of ecological relationships may harm individuals and often populations, communities, and ecosystems; however, many relationships contribute to ecological success because they regulate. A limiting factor may control organisms by restricting their numbers, hence preventing their needs from excluding the materials available in their environment. In other words, regulation causes organisms to be in balance with the energy cycle in their ecosystem. Moreover, this regulation is related to changes. For example, regulation is a major factor in dynamics, influence, succession, stratification, diurnation, aspectation, and many other temporal or spatial variations and gradients in populations, communities, and ecosystems. In a sense, evolution and all other factors involved in ecological success can be regulatory.

Compensation in the sense of balancing relationships can exist in the environment, individual, population, community, and ecosystem. The balances of ecological factors at each of many locales can be identical in the sense of all locales having the same climate, yet individual ecological factors can and often would vary among the locales. Biological compensation *per se* can be related to adaptation. In the main it would be related to newly created balances in environmental conditions, balances unlike the old ones. Specialization, hereditary adaptation, is in turn related to evolution. The normal means for balance through specialization would be gene mutations to provide the structures, functions, and behavior patterns required for continued success. Adjustment, so-called nonhereditary adaptation, would come from an organism's or larger group's acclimating to a new balance of environmental conditions.

Steady state or *stability* is allied to regulation and compensation. Moreover, degree of steady state is associated with life at the individual, population, and community level. Many attributes or features of life become less variable, perhaps we might say less complex, as one proceeds from individual to population to community. In addition, the interrelations of life and environment, the ecosystem, tends to be least variable in these certain attributes. Examples of such attributes include phenomena related to energy production and consumption because compensation and regulation act as checks and balances (steady state mechanisms). In the ecosystem these mechanisms normally allow less variation than at any other level of the life spectrum. Even the physical environment is affected. For example, atmospheric gases, endotherm temperature, population size and function, climax components, and ecosystem energy cycles tend to display, in sequence, progressively more regulation and compensation, hence greater efficiency of steady state mechanism and greater stability.

Equilibrium and *synergism* were discussed at length. Both were related to all aspects and levels of nature. Perhaps their most meaningful, definitely their most inclusive relationships, are with the universe as a whole.

Glossary

abdomen an animal's major body region occurring behind the thorax and containing the viscera.

abiotic devoid of life.

aboral opposite the mouth.

abrasion process or result of rubbing away by friction.

absolute humidity the grams of water vapor per cubic meter of air.

absorption the taking up of fluids or other substances as a sponge takes up water.

acellular without cells; pertaining to body organization in which the organism appears unicellular or its nuclei are not separated by cell membranes.

acid a substance that releases hydrogen ions in water; with a pH less than 7.

acoelomate without a body cavity; the basis for defining Acoelomata, animals without a body cavity but with organs and organ systems, the Platyhelminthes and Nemertea.

Actualistic Phase that portion of earth history having an over-all environment, especially an atmosphere, similar to that of the present; about the last two billion years.

adaptation the fitness of structure, function, or behavior of an organism or taxon for its environment; also, the process of becoming so fitted; specialization and adjustment.

adaptive radiation the evolution of several distinct organisms with unique adaptations from a single ancestor; an evolutionary process generally involved in the formation of large taxa.

adjustment an adaptation that is primarily due to an organism living within and being modified by an environment.

adsorption the adhesion of a very thin layer of gaseous, liquid, dissolved, or suspended substances to the surface of a solid.

advanced pertaining to a relatively recent or complex stage in the life cycle of an organism; generally implies complex, rather than simple, and specialized, rather than generalized, features; assumed to denote features developed during a period remote from the origin of life; not primitive.

aerobe an organism requiring oxygen for respiration.

aestival pertaining to the summer season.

aestivation summer dormancy in an organism

Age a geological time unit of variable meaning: (1) the precise time unit represented by a rock stage; (2) the loose time unit represented by a conspicuous group of organisms, e.g., Ages of Monera, Algae, Amphibians, etc.

air mass a large moving body of air, generally recognized by uniform conditions of temperature and moisture.

alkali a substance that releases more hydroxyl than hydrogen ions in water; with a pH more than 7.

alluvium materials carried or deposited by a stream.

alternate leaves or buds an arrangement in which either or both occur singly at a node.

alternation of generations the occurrence of two or more distinctive types of adult individuals during the life cycle of a single species, each adult being produced in a different manner; generally, an alternation of two unlike-appearing, sexual and asexual, generations.

amensalism symbiosis in which one organism is harmed and the other unaffected.

amitosis cell division involving direct division of a nucleus or nuclear material without the appearance of chromosomes.

amoeboid pertaining to the putting forth of protoplasmic extensions as does *Amoeba* (Sarcodina); often related to movement, as in *amoeboid movement*.

anaerobe an organism living in the absence of free oxygen and not using oxygen for respiration.

anatomy the study of life organization, particularly of visible structures.

andesite a fine-grained, intermediate-colored (often dark grayish); igneous rock rich in feldspar; generally any intermediate-colored lava.

angiosperm any flowering plant, Class Angiospermae.

annual an organism that completes its life cycle, from origin to death, in one year.

antenna a movable sense organ found in many arthropods and certain other animals.

anterior toward the front.

anticline an elongated, archlike fold in the land.

anticyclone a localized atmospheric pressure distribution or area in which pressure decreases and winds travel away from the center; a "High."

aphelion the point on a solar system body's orbit that is farthest from the sun; also applies to any body orbiting about another.

appendage any part of an organism that projects from the main body mass and has a free end; in animals, generally confined to movable parts.

arete a sharp, narrow, irregular ridge that separates two depressions carved by glaciers.

asexual without sexual processes.

aspect the appearance of a community at a given time.

aspectation pertaining to the changing appearance of life in a community from season to season.

association a climax community.

asteroid a small planet or planetlike body.

astronomy the study of the heavens.

atmosphere the gaseous envelope around a heavenly body.

atoll a circular coral reef enclosing a body of water called a lagoon.

atom the smallest complete unit of a chemical element.

autonomous (1) existing, reacting, or responding independently; spontaneous reaction; (2) pertaining to reacting or the reaction due to an internal stimulus.

autotroph an organism that manufactures its food from inorganic substances; an organism practicing chemosynthesis or photosynthesis.

autumnal pertaining to the fall season.

axil the upper angle between a plant's stem and leaf or branch.

bar in geology, an offshore wave- or current-formed embankment of more or less exposed materials.

barchane a crescent-shaped sand dune with the crescent pointing away from the wind.

barrier any physical or biological feature restricting the movement of an organism to a place outside its range.

basalt a fine-grained, dark, igneous rock composed of feldspar, pyroxene, and often olivine; generally any dark lava whose crystals are not visible to the unaided eye.

basic in chemistry, pertaining to an alkali or a chemical base.

batholith the largest masses of igneous rock, formed by magma flows deep underground; like a stock (q.v.), but over 40 square miles in surface area.

bay an inlet in the shore of an ocean or lake; the largest bays grade into gulfs.

beach the zone of unconsolidated rocks between the lowest tide level of the sea and vegetation or cliffs of the land; the seaward portion of a strand.

bedrock the essentially solid, undisturbed rock either at the surface or beneath soil, sand, or gravel.

bench in geology, a generally flat, horizontal, long and narrow surface that is bounded on one side by an ascending slope and on the other by a descending slope.

benthic pertaining to the bottom of a sea or lake.

benthos the life on the bottom of a sea or lake.

biennial an organism that completes its life cycle, from origin to death, in two years.

bilateral symmetry the arrangement of a structure, especially an animal's body, so its parts can be halved in only one plane if mirror image halves are to be formed.

Bilateria the mostly bilaterally symmetrical animals having an organ system basis of structure; animals other than Porifera, Mesozoa, Coelenterata, and Ctenophora.

biogeochemical cycle the continuous circulation of the chemical elements of protoplasm, as elements or in various compounds, between organisms and their environment; various subunits, also called cycles, may be recognized, e.g., the nitrogen, carbon, and water cycles.

biogeography the study of the distribution of organisms.

biological spectrum Raunkaier's means of characterizing the plants of an area according to the relative percentage of various life forms.

biology the study of living things.

biome a plant formation and its animals, monerans, and protistans.

biome-class a group of biomes diagnosed by plant formations of similar appearance; a formation-class, as deciduous forest, boreal forest, or rain forest plus its animals, monerans, and protistans.

biosphere the part of earth containing life; in reference to the life spectrum, may imply a single ecosystem involving all life on our planet.

Biotic District a continuous part of a Biotic Province distinguished by ecological differences of lesser importance than those separating biotic provinces.

biotic potential the maximum possible rate at which a species might reproduce itself in a particular environment; the inherent ability of a species to reproduce and survive in its environment.

Biotic Province a considerable geographic area characterized by the occurrence of one or more relatively important stands, climax or not.

biparental having two parents, usually one male and one female.

bipinnate leaves twice pinnate; pinnate subdivision of each leaf part that in turn is a unit of a pinnate arrangement.

biradial symmetry the arrangement of a structure, particularly an animal's body, that is partly radial and partly bilateral; a structure composed of two radially arranged parts oriented half on one side and half on the other side.

bisexual pertaining to an organism with both male and female sex organs; hermaphroditic.

bivalved pertaining to a shell of two parts, as in clams.

blade the usually flattened and expanded part of a leaf, modified leaf (e.g., a sepal or petal), or leaflike structure.

bog a wet, spongy substrate that yields under the foot and regularly is rich in decayed plant matter.

book lungs a respiratory organ consisting of a cavity having structures whose appearance and arrangement resemble the leaves of books and having an exit on the ventral body surface, as in spiders.

botany the study of plants.

bud (1) any structure or individual produced by budding; (2) a true bud is limited to an asexual reproductive cell produced by budding, e.g., a spore; (3) an embryonic vascular plant shoot or stem, areas of further plant growth; (4) a developing flower.

budding (1) asexual reproduction by the outgrowth of miniature individuals from their parents; (2) asexual production of multicellular structures that will in turn grow into an adult individual; (3) asexual production of a single cell, a true bud, that will grow into an adult individual; (4) a means of artificial plant propagation by man.

bunchgrass any grass forming a small cluster of elongate, flexible, and dense stems.

caldera a large excavation created by renewed volcanic activity leading to the collapse of the top of a volcano into molten magma, e.g., Crater Lake, Oregon.

calyptra the cap or sheath covering the capsule of a moss sporophyte.

calyx (1) the outermost whorl of modified leaves (sepals) in a flower; (2) the body disc of a sea lily or feather star.

capsule (1) in liverworts and mosses, the sporangium; (2) a sheath enclosing many organisms.

carapace an external skeletal shield covering part to all of the back of certain animals, especially turtles and some crustaceans.

carnivore (1) any organism that bulk feeds upon portions of or entire animals; a flesh or meat eater; (2) pertaining to the Carnivora, the mammalian order including, among others, cats, dogs, bears, racoons, skunks, seals.

carpel a leaf highly modified into the structural unit of a pistil, a flower organ; a simple pistil.

carrying capacity the maximum number of organisms, individuals and species, a particular locale will support through the most critical part, usually of a year; roughly, organisms resulting from biotic potential minus environmental resistance.

cartilage roughly, gristle; a stiff but often pliable skeletal tissue as in the human ear or tip of the nose.

caste society the most complex social organization of animals in which division of labor is accomplished by structurally and functionally unique individuals; found in termites, ants, bees, and wasps.

caudal pertaining to the tail or posterior part of the body.

Caytoniales fossil order (Upper Triassic to Lower Cretaceous) of the Class Cycadae; seeds enclosed in modified leaves (angiospermlike and thought by some to be ancestral to the flowering plants); generally trees or shrubs.

cell a small mass of protoplasm including and enclosed by a cell membrane and containing a central nucleus and surrounding cytoplasm; the structural and functional unit typical of plants and animals.

cell-like organism any organism whose entire body structure is comparable to the structure of a single cell; distinctive for monerans and protistans, but includes some primitive or degenerate true algae.

cellulose a complex carbohydrate found in the cell walls of most plants and in the body covering of some tunicates.

cephalization head formation, the tendency for centralization of sense organs and other structures in a head region.

cephalothorax the combination of head and thorax into a single major body region.

chaparral broadleaf evergreen or small, stiff, and waxy-leaved evergreen or deciduous plants, or the region having such plants; pertaining to a particular scrub region.

chelicerae the anterior pair of often pincerlike appendages diagnostic of the Subphylum Chelicerata.

chemosynthesis autotrophic nutrition of certain bacteria that obtain energy for the manufacture of organic matter from inorganic materials.

chitin a horny, organic material common in the external skeleton of arthropods, cuticle of certain other invertebrates, and cell wall of certain protistans.

chlorophyll a green organic pigment that is chemically similar to hemoglobin and is required in photosynthesis; a pigment in plants, blue-green algae, and certain flagellates (green flagellates).

chromosome the gene-containing, rodlike bodies that originate within a cell's nucleus and are found during meiosis and mitosis.

cilium a microscopic, hairlike structure attached to the surface of a cell-like organism or cell; a structure capable of vibration and acting as a source of unicellular locomotion; probably a modified, shortened flagellum.

cirque an amphitheater excavated in mountains as a result of frost or glacial action associated with a snow field.

class a taxon ranking above an order and below a phylum; also used as a category to classify many nonliving things.

cleavage (1) the early stages in an organisms's development, from a fertilized egg to many cells; (2) the splitting of rocks into thin parallel sheets, as in slate; (3) the splitting tendency, parallel to existing or possible crystal faces, of certain minerals that is related to the chemical structure of the crystal.

climate the average atmospheric conditions that usually characterizes a broad, geographic region; the average weather conditions, especially moisture, temperature, wind, pressure, and evaporation at a place over many years.

climatic rhythm the uniform climatic features, especially of temperature and moisture, typifying an area of uniform topography and coming from a single air mass or from definite seasonal occurrences of a sequence of air masses.

climatology the study of climate, contributing phenomena, and their causes.

climax any stable, self-perpetuation community, particularly one that culminates a sequence of seral stages, is in equilibrium with its environment, and will remain relatively unchanged so long as its environment remains unchanged.

clisere a sequence of climaxes occuring in a particular region through time in relation to changing climate; for practical purposes, a cliseral stage is any climax.

cloaca the common passageway at the posterior end of the body of certain animals (especially certain insects and many vertebrates) for digestive, excretory, and reproductive organs.

coastal plain any relatively flat land formed by uplift of the ocean floor; generally restricted to sites adjacent to the ocean.

cocoon any protective covering over any stage (egg through adult) in the life cycle of an animal; e.g., the cases covering the pupa of many insects.

coelom a body cavity lined by mesoderm; a true body cavity.

col a short, sharp-edged pass across an arete (q.v.).

colloid a fine-particled material in which each particle is larger than those in a true solution but smaller than those in coarse solutions; substances such as glue or gelatin in water.

colony generally denotes a social group; in many animals, involves interconnected individuals; more precisely, a nonmobile social group.

columella (1) the sterile central axis of a sporangium; in mosses it may act as a fluid-conducting tissue; (2) applied to the central axis of many organisms.

comet a heavenly body of relatively small mass, of generally irregular form, but often of denser central body and (when near the sun) very thin tail; a body orbiting about the sun.

commensalism symbiosis in which one organism benefits and the other neither benefits nor is harmed.

common ancestor a member (generally a population) of a taxon that was the immediate forefather (progenitor) of (and only of) all others in the taxon, or the members of a taxon that were the immediate and only forefathers of another taxon; the progenitor of a monophyletic taxon; some biologists accept as potential common ancestors taxa larger than a species.

community the organisms of any circumscribed area, usually of any logical spatial unit.

competition symbiosis among organisms (one or more species) occupying the same locale and requiring one or more of the same things from their habitat.

compound in chemistry, a combination of atoms or ions in definite proportions (by weight), independent of method of preparation.

compound leaf a leaf divided into two or more separate parts, each part being leaflike, a leaflet (q.v.).

compound organism a colony, particularly in certain ascidians, in which individuals share structures other than a common attachment stalk and occur in a common "body mass," thus being difficult to distinguish.

cone scale a modified leaf arranged with like structures on a modified branch to form a cone.

conformable bed rocks laid down in uninterrupted succession through time.

conjugation a multicellular organism mating process featuring temporary fusion of mating partners.

constructional land form any geological feature produced by uplift or vulcanism; sometimes includes products of deposition, such as deltas, and of organisms, such as coral.

consumer an organism that must obtain organic food, directly or indirectly, from plants or other producers.

continental shelf the gently sloping, shallowly submerged area of land fringing continents.

continental slope the steeply sloping submerged area of land between the continental shelf and the ocean floor.

continuum the distribution of populations along an environmental gradient that leads to overlapping populations and more complex overlapping communities.

convergence the evolution of similar structures by separate means in remotely related organisms.

cooperation symbiosis in which the different organisms benefit but, in contrast to mutualism, none of the organisms require the relationship to survive.

coral (1) the calcareous skeleton formed by certain coelenterates or the animals making these skeletons; (2) less frequently applied to calcareous deposits of any marine organism, especially certain Rhodophyta and Ectoprocta.

corridor a broad, continuous highway of long duration that allows extensive interchange of organisms between the connected areas, e.g., the present connection between Europe and Asia.

cortex the outer, generally living, layer of an organ.

cotyledon a seed leaf; one or more are developed by the sporophyte embryo of spermatophytes.

crepuscular pertaining to the dusk periods before sunrise and after sunset.

crystal a body formed of a single chemical element, a compound, or particular type of mixture that is organized into a definite pattern so that external surfaces (crystal faces) are flat and symmetrically arranged.

cuesta an elevation with one steep and an opposite gentle slope, the dip of the gentle slope sometimes is recognized as not surpassing 12 degrees; usually associated with fairly recent shorelines of emergence.

cuticle a noncellular, external, protective covering; especially found in plants and animals and formed by the epidermis.

Cycadeoidales fossil order (Permian to Middle Cretaceous of the Class Cycadae; mostly treelike and palmlike, seed-forming plants.

cyclone an atmospheric pressure distribution or area in which pressure decreases and winds travel toward the center; a "Low"; generally characterized by moderate to violent storms; hurricanes and typhoons are violent types, of tropical origin.

cyst a protective, resistant, and nonliving covering about certain dormant monerans, protozoans, some other small organisms, spores, and certain cells or groups of cells; usually associated with asexual reproduction.

cytology the study of cells, especially their structures and functions.

cytoplasm the portion of a cell surrounding the nucleus and within the cell membrane.

deciduous (1) to fall off, as leaves do in the autumn; (2) a tree or shrub of such habit.

decomposer an organism that breaks down organic molecules into smaller molecules or atoms.

decompound leaf one that is more than once divided; each of the leaflets that would be the consequence of a single compounding is in turn compounded at least once and like a leaflet has the appearance of a leaf.

degeneration evolutionary retrogression; the process of losing features that typify a more complex or higher body organization to assume a simpler or lower organization; typical of many parasites.

delta the essentially triangular, mostly alluvial, deposits at the mouth (end) of a stream.

dendritic much branched, as in a tree.

deposition the laying down, accumulating, or placing into position of thin sheets of sediments (beds), of materials in cracks (veins), or of irregular masses.

desert a generally rocky or sometimes sandy region where evaporation is greater than precipitation and vegetation is very sparse and often stunted.

desert pavement the close-fitting gravel-to-boulder substrate characterizing many deserts because wind removes sand and finer particles.

desert varnish a magnesium or iron oxide, brown to black, typically shiny, thin stain on the surface of many desert rocks; the varnish is polished by wind carried materials or by being moved over the substrate by wind.

destructional land form any geological feature produced by erosion; sometimes does not include land forms produced by the deposition of erosion products; may or may not include features formed by organisms.

detritis materials remaining after destruction of an object.

dew point the temperature at which air with a known moisture content will become saturated and with any further cooling will deposit dew.

diastrophism the processes whereby the earth's crust is deformed.

differentiation the developmental changes, generally from simpler structures and functions of early life cycle stages, to greater complexity in the adult; often implies the evolution of complex structures.

differentiation area a geographic site that, owing to particular features such as isolation and a unique environment, is the place for the evolution of one or more new species.

diffusion movement of particles, owing to the energy they contain, from sites of higher concentration to those of lower concentration that tends to equalize particle distribution throughout the system.

dike any mass of igneous rock formed by magma filling a crack in older rocks.

dip the angle a geological feature (usually a stratum or fault but also a vein, crack, or similar feature) makes with a horizontal plain (the earth's surface) as measured perpendicular to the strike of the geological feature; see Figure 4.23, p. 62.

dipleurula a hypothetical larval stage, presumed ancestral to echinoderms.

diplobiontic a life cycle in which diploid adults by meiosis give rise to spores that grow to sexual, haploid adults; the haploid adults produce the gametes for the zygote formations that lead to asexual, diploid adults.

diplohaplontic a life cycle with two kinds of adults, the diplobiontic life cycle.

diploid pertaining to two of each kind or two sets of chromosomes; twice the number typifying gametes or twice the haploid number.

diplontic a life cycle with all diploid adults, the gametes being the product of meiosis.

diplophase that part of a life cycle characterized by diploid nuclei.

disclimax any climax maintained by fire or animals.

dissolve to cause to pass into solution by separating a material into component parts.

diurnal pertaining to the daylight hours; neither crepuscular nor nocturnal.

diurnation the phenomenon of fluctuation in an organism's or population's activity or a community's composition within a 24-hour period.

dominant any of the commonest (in terms of *both* surface area covered and evenness of distribution) species of a community that receives the full impact of the environment and more or less alters it to affect the habitat of its associates; dominants generally are plants on land and in shallow water and are animals below 100 feet in water.

dormancy the apparently spontaneous arrested activity or development in any stage in the life history of an organism.

dorsal the back of an animal, upper surface of a plant, or comparable part of other organisms.

dorsoventral from back to belly or upper to lower surface.

drift rocks of any sort after they have been moved and deposited in another place by glaciers or streams; glacial drift is *till.*

drumlin a smooth, oval hill of glacial origin, generally of clay but also of particles up to gravel size.

dystrophic pertaining to bodies of water with fewer than normal organisms and often with brown, acid water; often associated with peat bogs.

earthquake an abrupt shock (snapping) or many vibrations (rolling) of the earth, probably due to disturbance of the equilibrium of rocks at or beneath the surface; perhaps due mostly to displacement along a fault.

ecesis the establishment of invading organisms within the ecosystem of an area.

ecliptic the great celestial circle upon the plane containing the sun and all points on the earth's path about the sun; roughly, the earth's orbital plane; hence, the apparent annual path of the sun through other stars.

ecological amplitude the inherent capability of an organism to tolerate a range of total environmental conditions, exclusive of competition with other organisms.

ecological factor any biological or physical feature in an organism's surroundings; anything contributing to an organism's environment.

ecology the study of the interrelationships between organisms and their total environment, physical and biological.

ecosystem a community and its physical environment, plus the dynamic relationships existing within and between the two components, all operating as an integrated unit.

ecotone a mixed community or transition area formed by the overlays of two adjacent communities and having characteristics of both components plus characteristics of its own.

ectoderm the outer layer of cells, perhaps tissue, of the gastrula or embryo stages of most animals; often applied to any tissue formed from this layer.

ectotherm any organism (but usually restricted to animals) whose primary source of body heat is the sun.

edaphic pertaining to soil.

eelgrass any marine member of the Zosteraceae, the pondweeds, a family of mostly fresh-water and strictly aquatic, perennial, herbaceous vascular plants.

egestion the process of discharging unusable and undigested materials from the digestive tract.

element (1) chemical, one of about 100 natural or man-made, distinct kinds of matter that singly or in combination, are the components of all substances; the smallest representative unit of an element is an atom; (2) biogeographical, the organisms typical or characteristic of a particular ecological unit; floral and faunal units can be recognized separately and can be of any size; one element might be part of a larger element.

embryo generally, any development stage starting from a fertilized egg; often restricted in plants to developmental stages within a seed and, in animals, to stages prior to birth or hatching.

embryo sac the female gametophyte of a flowering plant, a typically eight-celled structure found in the ovule, which in turn is in the ovary of a flower's pistil.

embryology the study of the formation and development of embryos.

emigration the desertion of its home by an organism.

encystment the formation by any life-cycle stage of a protective outer covering or cyst.

endemic a taxon of any size having a relatively restricted geographic distribution.

endoderm the innermost layer of cells (perhaps tissue) of the gastrula or any embryo stage of most animals; often applied to any tissue formed from this layer.

endodermis the single tissue layer of roots and some stems found between the outer cortex and the inner veins.

endoskeleton an internal framework or similar structure providing support from within an organism.

endosperm the triploid nutritive tissue surrounding a flowering plant embryo and within an ovule.

endotherm an organism that both produces and regulates its body heat by means of self-regulating body functions; specifically, birds and mammals.

enterocoel a coelom that originates by formation and separation of a series of pouches from the embryonic gut; the basis for defining the Enterocoela, the Echinodermata, Hemichordata, Pogonophora, Chordata, and (perhaps) Chaetognatha.

environmental resistance the restriction of the total environment upon biotic potential; a factor determining carrying capacity.

Eon any of the two or three most inclusive subdivisions of geological time; the more recent Phanerozoic Eon of about the last 600 million years is diagnosed by a relative abundance of fossils; the older Cryptozoic Eon is represented by few fossils; the time before the origin of life, the "Azoic Era," also may be recognized as a third Eon, the Azoic.

epidermis the outermost living layer that covers the surface of plants and animals with tissue or more complex structural organization.

epilimnion the wind-disturbed upper layer of a lake; waters above the thermocline in a temperature-layered lake.

epiphyte an organism that grows upon a plant but does not gain nutrients from the supporting plant.

Epoch a subdivision of a geological time period, representing a lesser and more localized break in the time sequence of the rocks; the time during which a rock series was formed.

Era any of the three major subdivision of Phanerozoic time recognized by characteristic and dominant life—the Cenozoic with modern mammals and flowering plants, the Mesozoic with reptiles and gymnosperms, and the Paleozoic with various invertebrates and, in part, pteriodophytes; the time of a major rock group.

erosion the process of wearing away and removal of earth's crustal materials by natural phenomena.

erratics drift, often limited to large rock particles.

esker a long, narrow, winding ridge of sand and gravel deposited by a stream within and, perhaps, in front of a glacier.

esophagus the food pipe; the part of the digestive tract between the pharynx and stomach

estuary an inlet of the ocean into a river mouth; especially likely in places recently submerged by the sea, that is, most places.

Eucoelomata organisms with a coelom; the Lophophorata, Schizocoela, and Enterocoela.

eutrophic pertaining to bodies of water rich in nutrients but perhaps seasonally poor in oxygen content; lakes having abundant life.

excretion any metabolic waste product that is cast out of an organism's body, the process of forming such materials.

evaporation the conversion of a liquid into a gas at temperatures below the boiling point, hence below-normal occurrence of the gaseous state.

evergreen any plant not losing all of its leaves as the end of the growing season.

evolution the process by which organisms change structurally, functionally, and behaviorally through time; in a broader sense, the change of living and nonliving things through time.

exoskeleton an external covering and/or supporting structure of an organism.

exploitation symbiosis in which one organism is harmed and the other benefits; predation and parasitism.

family (1) a taxon ranking between order and genus; a group of genera; (2) a major category in the classification of clouds or soils; in soils, a category below an order.

fascicle a small cluster or bundle; in plants often refers to leaf or flower arrangements.

fault a break in rocks of the earth's crust along which there has been and may be some horizontal to vertical movement parallel to the break surface.

fault line the portion of a fault seen on the surface of the earth's crust; often restricted to the straight or linear type.

fauna the animal life of a particular area at a particular time.

Faunal Region or Realm a major unit in classifying the distribution of animals on a world-wide basis.

fecundity in a strict sense, the capability or rate at which an organism produces reproductive units such as gametes or spores.

fertile pertaining to organisms or parts of organisms capable of carrying on reproduction.

fertility (1) in a strict biological sense, the capability or rate at which an organism produces living offspring; (2) the quality of a substrate in providing substances, generally nutritive, required by organisms.

fertilization the union of one gamete with another, usually sperm and egg; the essential feature of sexual reproduction.

filament any threadlike structure.

filter bridge a highway of temporary duration and limited size that restricts the numbers and kinds of organisms that can cross over it.

fiord usually, a glacial valley submerged by the sea.

fission (1) asexual reproduction of two daughter cells of equal size by a single cell; (2) usually, binary fission is the production of two daughter cells by mitosis and multiple fission is the production of many daughter cells by a sequence of mitoses, but amitosis (q.v.) may be involved.

flagellum any long, threadlike structure that is capable of vibration; a structure typifying the Phylum Flagellata.

flood plain a plain roughly centered on a stream and formed by erosion and deposition activities of the stream.

flora the plant life of a particular area at a particular time.

flower an organ system diagnosing the angiosperms that is composed of leaves modified into sepals, petals, stamens, and/or one or more pistils.

foehn a warm, dry, sometimes destructive, wind blowing down a mountain side.

food chain a graphic or conceptual representation of the dependence upon food of organisms being related to other organisms in a sequence, e.g., producers (plants), primary consumers (herbivores), and secondary consumers (carnivores).

food pyramid a graphic representation of a food chain showing that the greatest number, weight, or production is by producers at the base and that there is progressive marked reduction in successive consumers.

food web an illustration of all interconnecting food chains in a community.

foot in liverworts, mosses, and many vascular plants, the basal part of the developmental sporophyte, which attaches to and obtains nutrients from the gametophyte.

forb an herb other than a grass; sometimes restricted to herbs that are distinctly not grasslike.

forest a community having a dense growth of trees, usually over various shorter plants.

formation (1) in geology, the fundamental unit of rock classification; any group of similar rocks formed without interruption under similar conditions at approximately but not exactly the same time; formations need not be continuously distributed geographically; (2) in ecology, plant communities, seral or climax, occupying either a single or similar climatic regions; a very large unit of vegetation composed of similar-appearing communities in similar environments; a biome minus its animals.

fossil any evidence of past life, including remains of organisms that have just died and such things as tracks or burrows of dead organisms.

fragmentation asexual reproduction by the breaking of a multicellular organism into two or more segments, with most to all segments regenerating a new individual.

front any boundary between air masses of different temperatures.

fruit a plant structure consisting of one or more ripened ovaries and any enveloping parts that may be associated with them.

fruiting body any reproductive structure in plants.

gamete a mature reproductive (sex or germ) cell that is capable of uniting with another in sexual reproduction to form a zygote.

gametophore loosely, one of the two gametophyte stages in the life cycle of certain bryophytes; specifically, the second and true gametophyte stage because it bears the sex organs and produces gametes; the budding product of a protonema, the first gametophyte stage.

gametophyte specifically, the gamete-forming adult stage in the diplobiontic life cycle, in a loose sense, any gamete-forming plant.

ganglion a group of nerve cell bodies, generally set apart from other nerve cell bodies and acting as an independent source of nervous influence.

gas one of the three states of matter (solid, liquid, and gas); the state of matter that completely fills a container (theoretically, even one of infinite size) without regard to the amount of matter.

gastrovascular pertaining to or serving both digestive and circulatory functions.

gastrula an early stage in animal development in which surface cells migrate into the embryonic mass and internal cells become oriented into germ layers.

geanticline a gigantic and elongate arching fold of the earth's crust; a gigantic anticline.

gemma an asexual, multicellular outgrowth by budding of a parental body, as in liverworts, capable of developing into an individual like the parent.

gemmule generally considered a bud (but usually a group of cells formed inside a parental sponge) that is released upon decay of the parent, and grows into a new adult.

gene definable only in functional terms; the unit of heredity; the chromosomal site of a unit of genetic information.

gene pool the total genetic material (genes) of a species; any definable segment of a species or an individual.

generalized pertaining to any organism at an early stage (not a time concept) of evolutionary development; primitive; an organism lacking complex structures, functions, and/or behavior.

genetics the study of heredity.

genus (1) a taxon ranking above a species and below a family; composed of a closely related group of species or a species; (2) a category below a family in the classification of clouds and certain other things.

geoflora an extremely large unit of vegetation, diagnosed on the basis of growth form, that evolves but retains its identity through time; three were (and are) important in the development of North American vegetation.

geology the study of the history of the earth and its life as recorded in rocks.

geomorphic pertaining to the form of the earth.

geomorphology the study of the form and changes in form of the earth.

geosyncline a gigantic syncline, generally submerged and acting as a collecting basin, especially for sedimentary deposits.

germ cell a gamete.

germ layer any of the two or three basic cell layers (ectoderm, mesoderm, and endoderm) in the embryo of most animals (Subkingdom Eumetazoa).

germ plasm roughly, genes.

germination the beginning of growth of a plant spore, seed, or other reproductive structure.

gill an animal organ for underwater respiration.

gill pouch an outpocketing of the pharynx in all chordate embryos; the precursor of the gill slits of fishes and certain amphibians but only of temporary gill slits in other vertebrates.

gill slit an opening for the pharynx to the outside of the body, typical of chordate developmental stages and adult fish.

gland a cell, tissue, or organ of secretion or excretion.

gonad a reproductive organ (ovary, testis, or combination of the two), in which gametes are formed; generally limited to an animal sex organ.

graben a fault valley depressed between more or less parallel faults.

granite an igneous rock composed of a mass of visible, mainly interlocking crystals, mostly of feldspars and quartz.

grass any plant of the Family Poaceae (Subclass Monocotyledoneae); distinguished by sheating leaves, jointed stems, and fruit in the form of grain.

grassland loosely, any area containing mostly grasses; specifically, an extensive area of perennial grasses.

gravity that force of nature observed as a mutual attraction between bodies.

growth form the appearance or shape of an organism; less restrictive than life form.

growth formation the appearance of a community, e.g., forest, woodland, and scrub.

guard cells specialized plant epidermal cells surrounding and controlling the size of opening in a stoma.

gymnosperm a seed plant that bears naked seeds, those not enclosed in an ovary; once considered a natural group and taxon of plants.

habitat the natural dwelling place of an organism or group of organisms; sometimes applied to the physical and biological environment of such a place.

haplobiontic a life cycle having all adults either haploid or diploid; either a haplontic or diplontic life cycle.

haploid a single set of chromosomes (symbol n) as found in a mature gamete.

haplontic a life cycle with all haploid adults, the zygote undergoing meiosis.

haplophase that part of a life cycle in which adults and/or other stages have a single set of chromosomes.

hardwood (1) pertaining to the wood of a broad-leaved deciduous tree as opposed to a conifer; (2) pertaining to any tree with heavy, close-grained resistant wood.

heat that form of energy into which mechanical energy may be converted; when given to a body, raises its temperature; when removed from a body, lowers its temperature.

heliotherm an organism whose main source of body heat is the sun.

hemocoel a portion of a body cavity functioning as part of a circulatory system.

hemoglobin an iron-containing blood pigment that combines with and transports oxygen; a complex chemical compound resembling chlorophyll.

herb a plant whose aerial parts die back to the ground during the annual period of dormancy; any plant that is not woody; a grass or forb in contrast to a tree or shrub.

herbivore an organism that bulk feeds upon entire plants or parts of plants.

hermaphrodite a bisexual organism; an individual containing both male and female sex organs; also applied to individuals that have one sex organ at a particular time but, during their life cycle, first one then the other sex organ.

heterogamy union of unlike gametes (heterogametes), usually egg and sperm.

heterotherm an organism that is an endotherm except during dormancy, when it becomes a heliotherm.

heterotrophic pertaining to an organism that is unable to synthesize required organic compounds from purely inorganic substances, hence requires complex organic substances as food.

hibernal pertaining to the winter season.

hibernation winter dormancy, generally in an animal.

"High" an anticyclone

highway in biogeography, any physical or biological feature allowing the movement of an organism outside its area.

hogback any cuesta-like ridge formed by differential erosion upon rock layers having a dip surpassing 12 degrees.

holdfast the simpler-structured, but rootlike, basal attachment device of many algae, especially kelps.

holozoic pertaining to an organism that feeds upon bulk or solid food; nutrition characteristic of animals; generally pertains to a carnivore, herbivore, omnivore, or scavenger.

home range that portion of an animal's habitat traversed during its normal activities.

horst a fault mountain elevated between more or less parallel faults.

host an organism supplying such things as food and shelter to a parasite.

humidity the absolute humidity of air.

humus soil organic matter, dark in color and so decomposed as to provide no semblance of its original structure.

hurricane a severe cyclone of tropical origin.

hydrarch pertaining to a sere beginning in a site of abundant water.

hydraulicking erosion mechanism by water having great force.

hydrocarbon an organic compound composed only of carbon and hydrogen.

hydrologic pertaining to water; the hydrologic cycle includes the movement of water from the atmosphere by precipitation and back into the atmosphere, mostly by evaporation.

hydrophyte a plant growing partly to completely submerged in water and usually displaying specializations for its habitat.

hydrosphere the water upon the earth's surface.

hypha a threadlike structure basic to the body organization of many fungi.

hypolimnion in temperature-layered lake, the water at the bottom and below the thermocline.

hypothesis a tentative and reasonable explanation of observed phenomena; an intelligent guess adopted for the purpose of critical experimental testing to determine its validity.

igneous pertaining to fire or to rocks formed from the solidification of magma.

immigration the movement of an organism into a previously unoccupied area.

indusium a fern epidermal tissue often found covering a sorus (q.v.).

influent any organism, usually an animal, that is not a dominant but has important effects upon its physical and/or biological environment.

inorganic pertaining to matter formed by natural physical processes and not by an organism.

insolation energy received from the sun as by the earth.

instar any stage of an immature insect between any two successive molts, but excluding a pupa.

integument (1) any outer covering of an organism; (2) the outer covering of a plant ovule that develops into a seed coat; (3) generally restricted to living coverings.

internode any plant stem region between any two successive nodes; sometimes applied to jointlike parts in stemlike structures of animals.

intertidal the ocean zone from the highest level of land struck by spray of the highest high tide surf to the lowest point uncovered by the lowest low tide.

invertebrate any animal without a backbone (vertebral column).

ion an atom or group of atoms bearing positive or negative charge; one of the particles formed by ionization.

ionization the dissociation of a molecule into two or more charged particles (ions); the addition or substraction of charged particles from atoms.

isogamy fusion of gametes of like appearance, isogametes.

joint (1) in geology, an essentially flat break or separation between rocks along which there was little or no movement as in a fault; (2) in biology, the movable or immovable, junction between separate body parts.

kame a small hill deposited in front of a glacier by a stream leaving the interior of the glacier and entering a lake.

kelp loosely, any of the large marine algae, a seaweed; more specifically, any large, marine brown alga, a rockweed.

kettle hole a depression in a glaciated area believed to have formed by melting of a block of ice once covered by glacial debris.

kingdom the largest taxonomic subdivision of life; Monera, Protista, Plantae, or Animalia.

labial pertaining to the lip.

laccolith a dome mountain formed by underground injection of a lens-shaped body of igneous rock.

lanceolate shaped like a lancehead.

larva an immature, often wormlike, life cycle stage between embryo and adult stages in many organisms; generally, an immature organism that hatches from an egg, is active and mobile, is quite different from the adult in appearance, carries on most life processes of adults, but usually does not reproduce.

lateral pertaining to the side of a structure.

layer society a group of organisms within a particular layer of plants, e.g., trees, shrubs, or herbs.

leaflet any distinct unit in a compound leaf.

lichen an intimate grouping of a fungus and a green or blue-green alga into a single mass that functions in many respects like a single organism.

Life Belt an altitudinal subdivision of a Biotic Province, distinguished by ecological differences of lesser importance than those separating Biotic Provinces.

life cycle (1) the series of stages or phases in structure and mode of life of an organism from zygote to natural death; (2) any regular sequence of stages or phases of an inanimate feature from its origin to disappearance; (3) generally, life history.

life form the characteristic appearance of an organism or species at maturity.

life history pertaining to the record or history of a life cycle.

life spectrum the range in organization of living structures and organisms.

Life Zone a region characterized by distinctive plants and animals and the distribution scheme using such regions.

limestone a sedimentary rock composed mostly of calcium carbonate which yields lime (CaO) when burned.

limiting factor any physical or biological feature of the environment that restricts one or more functions (hence, distribution) of an organism.

limnetic pertaining to open water in a lake.

liquid the fluid state of matter in which shape is dependent upon shape of the container but volume is independent thereof.

lithosphere the solid rock of the earth, usually limited to the earth's crust.

littoral pertaining to water-covered areas near the shore; often defined in terms of depth of light penetration or wave or tide action.

lophophore a structure surrounding the mouth and bearing ciliated tentacles; found in certain aquatic invertebrates; although found elsewhere, it is the basis for defining the Lophophorata, the Ectoprocta, Phoronida, and Brachiopoda.

"Low" a cyclone.

macroscopic large enough to be seen with the naked eye.

magma the molten and gaseous material that is formed within the earth and cools to form igneous rock.

magnetosphere the radiation belt about the earth.

mandible a jaw; either jaw of an arthropod; the lower jaw of a vertebrate.

mantle (1) an animal's body fold, which encloses soft structures; in a mollusk it secretes the shell; (2) the middle layer of the earth between the surface crust and the central core.

marsh a semiaquatic habitat having emergent herbs.

mass movement any movement of earth materials by gravity, particularly a movement of the products of weathering.

massive rock or mineral without crystals; also a rock of homogeneous or irregular structure, without layering or capable of being separated into layers.

matterhorn any needlelike peak resulting from glacial activity.

maxilla in certain arthropods, mouthparts behind and lying partly upon the mandibles; in vertebrates, the large upper jaw bone.

medial toward the center, midline, or middle of an organism's body.

medusa the free-swimming, vaguely umbrellalike, adult stage in the life cycle of coelenterates; a jellyfish.

megaphyll a true leaf with many, often branching veins.

meiosis a process, occurring in various possible stages in the life cycles of different organisms, in which the number of each kind of chromosome is halved; the process compensating for chromosome doubling due to fertilization and zygote formation.

membrane any thin, pliable sheet or layer of cells, tissues, or secretions of cells or tissues.

meristem a group of cells or tissue that lack maturity and contribute to essentially continuous growth of an organism, typically a plant.

mesoderm the middle layer of cells, perhaps tissue, of the gastrula or other embryo stages of animals other than Porifera, Mesozoa, Coelenterata, and Ctenophora; often applied to any tissue formed from this layer.

mesophyte any plant adapted to habitats lacking extremes of moisture and drought.

metabolism the total chemical processes (mainly nutrition, formation of living substance, and energy production) in protoplasm; the site is in cells or cell-like organisms.

metamerism segmental repetition of body units (somites) of like basic structure and origin, as in annelids, arthropods, and chordates; true segmentation.

metamorphosis (1) in organisms, the marked change in body form, during development, from one stage of the life cycle to another; in insects, gradual or simple metamorphosis involving egg, nymph, and adult and complete or complex metamorphosis, egg, larva, pupa, and adult; (2) in rocks, the alteration of any existing rock to metamorphic rock.

Metazoa a descriptive term or taxon synonymous with animals as here defined.

meteorology the study of the atmosphere and its phenomena.

microhabitat a small habitat within a larger habitat, generally confined to a single object or part of an object, such as a fallen log or tree trunk.

microphyll a true leaf having one, generally unbranched, vein.

micropyle the opening in the integuments of a spermatophyte's ovule, allowing pollen tube entrance to the female gametophyte.

microscopic invisible or not clearly discernable by the unaided or naked eye.

midvein the central, usually largest, vein of a leaf.

migration not used here in the sense of any organism's movement; the periodic, annual, or daily movement of organisms between two areas.

mimicry the imitation of the structure or behavior of a comparatively protected species (the model) by a comparatively defenseless species (the mimic).

mineral refer to p. 68.

"missing link" an organism possessing features, usually structural, that cause it to appear intermediate between two other groups of organisms; usually applied to one or a few species that are sole representatives of a large taxon; an unfortunate connotation in that no species is strictly intermediate in all structures, functions, and behavior patterns between any two other species or higher categories.

mitosis nuclear division involving chromosomal duplication and the production of two daughter nuclei with the same chromosomal composition as the parent nucleus; usually ends in cell division and the production of two daughter cells from a single parental cell.

molecule the smallest part of a chemical compound or element having the distinctive properties of any larger unit of the same material.

molt to shed a body covering.

monophylletic pertaining to a group of species in a single larger taxon that is believed to include only descendants from a common ancestor.

moraine an accumulation of glacial debris, mostly by deposition from a glacier.

mucous pertaining to mucus.

mucus a sticky, slimy, and/or slippery substance secreted by a cell, tissue, membrane, or organ.

multicellular many celled.

mutation an abrupt but stable change in a gene or chromosome that causes hereditary modification in an individual.

mutualism symbiosis in which both participating organisms benefit and require the relationship.

mycelium a mass of hyphae.

natural group an assemblage of different species recognized by being the only descendants from a common ancestor; a monophylletic group.

natural history the study of all aspects of the universe except those pertaining directly only to man; particularly, a study of things as they exist in nature.

natural selection the tendency in evolution for most organisms possessing certain characters in a given environment to produce many more offspring than do those lacking such characters; roughly, the process tending toward survival of the fittest.

nekton aquatic, swimming organisms that actively direct their movements and are free of the bottom.

nephridium a tubular excretory organ of invertebrates, especially annelids, arthropods, and mollusks.

nerve a bundle of nerve cell fibers occurring outside the brain and spinal cord.

nerve cord a group of nerve cells and often ganglia; with the brain they form the central nervous system.

neuston aquatic organisms that float against or are closely associated with the surface film of water.

neutralism hypothetical symbiosis in which the organisms involved neither benefit nor harm one another.

niche (1) ecological or functional, the status or role of an organism in its environment; its activity and relationships in its environment; (2) habitat or place, the microhabitat or specific area occupied by an organism.

nocturnal pertaining to night or hours of darkness; neither diurnal nor crepuscular.

node the point on a plant stem from which one or more leaves arise; buds often arise here at the angle between the stem and upper surface of a leaf.

nomad an animal that wanders from one locale to another without having a fixed dwelling place.

nomenclature the process and procedure for applying scientific names to organisms.

notochord a longitudinal, internal, elastic, skeletal rod of cells below the nerve cord and found in all embryos and some adult chordates; in most vertebrates it is completely replaced by the backbone or vertebral column.

nucellus a plant tissue in a young ovule; probably represents the female sporangium wall, is located within the integument, and encloses the site of embryo sac development.

nucleic acid an organic acid composed of repeated units of nucleotides (each composed of a sugar phosphate joined to a nitrogenous base); two main types, DNA the carrier of the genetic information and RNA (which is controlled by DNA) the director of metabolic activities.

nucleus a structure within all cells and cell-like organisms except the Monera; designated by an outer membrane, internal sap, and chromosomes.

nutrition the total processes in an organism that involve taking in and using food for maintenance, growth, repair, and energy production.

nymph an immature stage of any insect displaying simple metamorphosis; resembles the adult, but differs mostly in body proportions (e.g., the wings are abbreviated or absent) and perhaps the addition of structures in aquatic forms.

oceanography the study of the geography of the sea; sometimes extended to the study of all aspects of the sea.

oligotrophic pertaining to substrates, especially water, poor in nutrients, especially organic nutrients or sources of nutrients for plants.

omnivore an organism, generally a bulk feeder, that does not feed upon a single type of food or host; generally, a combination carnivore and herbivore.

operculum a lid; in mosses, the lid covering the capsule; in some snails, the lid covering the shell opening; in bony fishes and chimaeras, the lid covering the gills.

opposite leaves or buds those occurring in pairs at a node.

oral pertaining to or near the mouth.

order a taxon between class and family; a large category of soils that includes one or more families.

organ a group of tissues and perhaps some cells that act as a unit to perform one or more functions.

organ system a group of organs acting as a unit to perform a definite function or set of associated functions (e.g., the digestive system, which accomplishes digestion and related functions); the only organ system in plants are flowers and related structures like certain cones.

organelle any specialized protozoan structure that, in performing a specific function, resembles an organ's function.

organic pertaining to, coming from, or having unique features of living organisms.

organic horizon or layer the layer of recognizable organism remains and of underlying humus that occurs above soil.

organism a single living creature, generally restricted to individuals within the Monera, Protista, Plantae, and Animalia, but excluding viruses and nonliving things.

orthogenesis "straight line" evolution; the trend in some evolution for organisms to follow a particular direction for some time; now often called orthoselection (q.v.).

orthoselection orthogenesis explained in terms of mutation and natural selection during a long period of a somewhat continuous amount of change in environment, the "straight line" evolution being due to natural selection gradually changing with environmental change.

osmosis the diffusion of a solvent (generally water) through a semipermeable membrane from the side containing a higher concentration of the solvent to the side containing a lesser concentration.

outwash plain a plain usually found beyond the site of a glacier's terminal moraine, formed from glacial debris, and created mostly by deposition from glacial streams.

ovary (1) in animals, a female sex organ in which eggs are formed and nourished; (2) in flowering plants, the enlarged, basal portion of a pistil that contains ovules or seeds; (3) in any organism, a female sex organ.

ovipositor an organ in female insects functioning in depositing eggs.

ovule an immature seed in a flower ovary; a structure composed of embryo sac, nucellus, and integuments; when fertilized, it develops into a seed.

ovum a nonmotile female gamete, an egg.

ox-bow a flat to nearly closed, arc-shaped remnant of a former stream bend, formed when the stream cuts between two of its closely approaching bends.

oxidation a chemical change involving the loss of charged particles in molecules, typically by removing hydrogen or adding oxygen; in biology, a process releasing energy.

paleogeography the study of past distribution of the hydrosphere, lithosphere, and biosphere or any segment of them.

paleontology the study of fossils.

palp an appendage or projecting part of the head, often near the mouth, generally sensory in function.

papilla any nipplelike structure.

parallelism evolution of adaptations in a similar direction in different organisms.

parapodium a flattened, movable appendage occurring in opposite pairs on the body segments of many polychaetes (Annelida).

parasite a symbiote living partly or entirely upon or within an organism (host) and securing part to all of its food from the organism without killing it immediately (or, perhaps, at all).

parasitism exploitation involving a host and a parasite.

parenchyma a plant tissue composed of simple or unspecialized cells.

parthenogenesis natural or induced development of an unfertilized egg; "virgin birth."

pectoral pertaining to the breast or upper part of the thorax.

pedipalp one of the second pair of appendages in the Chelicerata; often sensory, sometimes serving in locomotion (king crabs), predation (scorpions), or fertilization (male spiders).

pedology the study of soils.

pellicle a thin, protective, surface layer of certain organisms, especially ciliates.

pelvic pertaining to the posterior limb girdle of vertebrates; the part of the skeleton that supports the hind limbs or fins.

peneplain an extensive land form of low relief representing the ultimate stage, old age in a cycle of erosion.

pentactula the hypothetical adult ancestor of the echinoderm–chordate line of evolution.

percolation (of water) the movement, mostly downward and laterally, through the fine spaces between rock or soil particles.

perennial any organism taking more than two years, generally three or more, to complete its life cycle.

perihelion the point on the orbit of a body in the solar system that is closest to the sun; also applies to any body orbiting about another.

Period the fundamental and most distinctive unit of geological time, the time during which a rock system was formed.

periodicity the repeated occurrence of each of the events in the life cycle of an organism or species at frequent and regular intervals.

periphyton aquatic organisms attached to submerged objects other than the bottom of the body of water.

permeable penetrable, as a membrane allowing the passage of liquids or gases.

petiole (1) any stalk; (2) the twiglike part of a leaf.

petrology the study of rocks.

pH a symbol denoting the relative concentration of hydrogen ions in a solution; values range from 0 to 14: 7, neutrality; numbers less than 7, increasing acidity; and numbers greater than 7, increasing alkalinity.

pharynx roughly, "throat"; the often muscular portion of the digestive tract between the mouth and esophagus; in invertebrates, may contain teeth; in many aquatic vertebrates, the region containing gills.

phasic cycle a sequence of organisms in a community, starting with the death of an individual and ending with a member of the same species as the first individual.

phenology the study of periodic phenomena of life and their relations to their environment, mostly weather and climate.

phloem the plant tissue that functions in food conduction; part of a vein, except in brown algae.

photoperiodism the response of plants to duration of darkness; the basis of long- and short-day plants.

photosynthesis the autotrophic nutrition process of carbohydrate manufacture from carbon dioxide and water that uses light energy and chlorophyll and releases oxygen.

phylogeny the evolutionary history of a species or larger taxon.

phylum a major taxon forming a unit of a kingdom and including one or more classes.

physical in contrast to biological, pertaining to nonliving things.

physiology the study of life functions.

pinna (1) in plants, a leaflet; (2) in animals, the appendage of the external ear.

pinnate featherlike, composed of parts arranged on two sides of a central axis.

pistil the central organ of a flower, usually consisting of apical stigma, central style, and basal ovary.

placenta (1) in higher mammals, the organ attaching the later stages of the embryo (fetus) to the uterus of the mother and serving in nourishment, excretion, and respiration; (2) often applied to any parental structure that nourishes an egg or developmental stage.

plain (1) any relatively flat, level, and smooth land without noticeable elevations or depressions; (2) one meaning of "prairie."

planet a heavenly body of size much smaller than a star, which follows a definite elliptical path (orbit) about a star; generally confined to the sun's planets, Mercury, Venus, Earth, Mars, Jupiter, Saturn, Uranus, Neptune, and Pluto, but includes asteroids and planets about any other star.

plankton passively floating, drifting, and weakly swimming aquatic organisms; often microscopic.

plasma (1) the fluid part of blood; (2) protoplasm.

plasmodium a slimy, naked, protoplasmic mass, containing many nuclei, that displays amoebid movement; the vegetative body of a slime mold.

plastid a prominent, often pigmented body (in the cytoplasm of many cells) that is associated with definite functions; probably a special center of chemical activity.

plastron a shell or other external, protective structure, usually skeletal, on the ventral surface of an animal (e.g., a turtle).

plateau a flat-topped, fairly large area that on one to all sides lies above the surrounding land; a tableland.

pollen a mass of pollen grains; each pollen grain is a developing male gametophyte enclosed within a spore wall and was shed from the sporangium of a spermatophyte.

pollen sac the male spore-forming sporangium of a spermatophyte.

pollen tube the structure, formed by a pollen grain upon contacting a pistil stigma, that grows down to the female gametophyte.

polyp (1) the sedentary, vaguely plantlike adult stage in the life cycle of most coelenterates; a sea anemone; (2) sometimes applied to any vaguely plantlike individual within a colony of a single animal species; (3) a swollen and projecting mass of tissue.

polyphylletic pertaining to a single taxon in which all species did not evolve from a common ancestor; two or more natural groups.

population a species or any localized species subunit that may be recognized by preferential reproduction within the group.

porphyry any igneous rock containing scattered larger crystals within its basic materials; often restricted to such rocks with a considerable proportion (approximately 25 per cent or more) of scattered larger crystals.

posterior at or near the hind or rear part of an organism, usually the part facing backward when an organism is moving or the part opposite the head.

prairie loosely, any grassland area; specifically, an area of tall (5 or more feet) grasses, in contrast to other grasses.

Preactualistic Phase the portion of earth history having an environment, especially an atmosphere, unlike the present one; all time prior to about two billion years ago.

preadaptation those behavioral, functional, and structural attributes that enable an organism to survive in previously uninhabited conditions, e.g., habitats created by geological change.

predation symbiosis involving the killing of prey for food by a predator.

predator an organism that kills another (prey), usually for food; generally a bulk-feeding flesh eater, a carnivore.

pressure area any localized irregularity in air particles number, hence air density or weight; a cyclone or anticyclone.

prey an animal killed by a predator; also any living animal having high potential for being killed by a predator.

primary pertaining to a natural history feature which originated, formed, evolved, changed, or otherwise is believed to have come first; often refers to a common or primitive ancestor; not secondary.

primitive pertaining to an early type or stage of an organism; generally implies simple rather than complex and generalized rather than specialized; assumed to denote features developed early in the evolution of life, primitive features; not advanced.

proboscis snout; any tubular prolongation of an animal's head, generally nose, lips, or pharynx; many are eversible or capable of being turned outward or inside out, as in the finger of a glove.

producer an organism capable of using solar (radiant) energy to synthesize organic compounds from inorganic materials; generally a photosynthetic organism.

profundal any mass of deep water below the depth of effective light penetration.

proglottid a body segment, not a true segment or somite, of a tapeworm.

protonema a hairlike, often branching stage, resembling certain algae, in the early development of bryophytes, particularly mosses; often with a gametophore considered two gametophyte stages, but the protonema buds one or more gametophores.

protoplasm (1) collective term for living substance regardless of its organization; (2) here also used to imply Monera organization, which lacks at least complete structural organization of a nucleus.

pseudocoel an animal body cavity called a "false body cavity" because it lacks a complete membranous lining derived from mesoderm; the basis for defining Pseudocoelomata, the Acanthocephala, Aschelminthes, and Entoprocta.

pseudopodium a flowing protoplasmic extension of a cell or protistan that functions in locomotion (amoeboid movement) and feeding.

pteridophyte a collective term, meaning fern plant, for vascular plants that do not produce true seeds; sometimes considered a major taxon, usually a phylum or class, of plants; most likely not a natural group.

Pteridospermae fossil order (Early Mississippian, perhaps upper Devonian, to Jurassic) of fernlike herbs, trees, or vines that produce true seeds; the seed ferns.

pupa an immature stage between larva and adult in insects displaying complete metamorphosis; a "resting" stage featuring great developmental changes and minor body movements but neither feeding nor locomotion.

quarrying the erosion process whereby water or ice removes and transports large masses of rock.

radial symmetry the arrangement of structure, particularly an animal body, so its parts can be divided into two approximate images by an infinite number of vertical cuts, so long as each cut is through the center.

Radiata the mostly radially or biradially symmetrical animals of tissue organization, the Coelenterata and Ctenophora.

radioactivity the spontaneous emission of charged particles by decay or disintegration of certain, usually heavy, elements.

radula the horny, rasping organ, generally used in food getting, in the anterior part of the digestive tract of many mollusks.

rain forest a forest of tall, mostly broadleaved trees, often of different heights and in more than one layer as determined by size; generally restricted to equatorial, evergreen trees in areas lacking a dry season, but is also applied to similar temperate forests (e.g., the Olympic Peninsula forests of Washington state) and similar forests in tropical areas having a dry season.

rain shadow an area occurring on the leeward side of a mountain and having little or no rainfall because the mountain traps most of the moisture from the winds.

receptacle in plants, a structure bearing reproductive structures, e.g., the stalk for the sex organs of certain liverworts, for the sori of ferns, or for the flower of angiosperms.

regeneration healing, ranging from the limited extent in man to restoration of half or more of an organism's body.

regression used in the usual sense of a return to earlier stages of development but often, as stated, not to the exact features or conditions of an earlier stage.

relative humidity the percentage of water vapor in any size sample of air in relation to the amount that could be held at the same temperature.

relict a remnant of a species, community, flora, or fauna from a time when it was more numerous in individuals and, (where pertinent) species and was more widespread.

reproduction the processes involved in the perpetuation of species.

respiration the processes involved in releasing energy from fuel; often restricted to processes within cells, but may include other functions such as those in obtaining oxygen from the environment and releasing carbon dioxide; may or may not involve oxygen.

rhizome a rootstock, or underground (usually horizontal) stem.

rock refer to pp. 68–69.

Rock Group two types are recognized, major and minor; a major rock group is less frequently recognized but consists of rocks formed during an era; a minor rock group is a local unit composed of two or more formations sharing some local peculiarity, in which upper and lower limits vary in age geographically, thus have no corresponding time unit.

Rock Series a geographically localized unit within a rock system that represents a single geological time unit, an epoch.

Rock Stage a geographically localized unit within a rock series that represents the smallest geological time unit, the Age.

Rock System the natural rock unit formed during a geological time period and is separated from overlying and underlying rocks by general differences in rocks or a major structural change in rocks and by a distinct change in fossils; separations imply a marked change in environment.

root a vascular plant organ having neither leaves nor modified leaves; functions in water absorption, as a food reservoir, and as a means of support.

rootstock a rhizome.

salt a compound formed by the replacement of one or more hydrogen atoms of an acid by metal atoms or certain other groups of atoms.

saprophytic pertaining to any organism, generally called a saprophyte, that feeds upon dead organisms or decaying organic materials.

satellite a heavenly body revolving about another; generally restricted to a body revolving about a planet.

savanna an area that is predominantly continuous grassland but has scattered shrubs and/or trees.

scavenger an animal that feeds upon animal wastes and dead organisms that are not killed but are found dead.

schizocoel a coelom originating from a split in the mesoderm; diagnostic of the Schizocoela, Mollusca, Sipunculoidea, Echiuroidea, Annelida, and Arthropoda, but also found in the Lophophorata.

scolex the "head," or anterior attachment organ of a tapeworm.

scrub an area or dense growth of low, perhaps stunted, shrubs and/or trees, e.g., chaparral.

seaweed any of the large marine algae.

secondary that which follows any primary natural history feature.

secretion a useful, generally liquid, product of a cell or gland, or the process of forming the product.

sediments all deposits, usually by water, of the products of erosion; either particles or cemented particles are sedimentary rocks.

seed a plant reproductive structure composed of a ripened ovule.

segmentation when restricted, metamerism.

seif a half-crescent-shaped structure resembling half of a barchane and formed by two prevailing directions of the wind.

selection unless otherwise designated, natural selection.

seral pertaining to developmental and unstable, rather than climax, communities.

sere a single cycle of community changes from initial invasion of life to the climax; a unit of succession.

sessile a sedentary and attached organism in contrast to a free-living one; any part of an organism continuous with another part and usually due to the absence of a connecting (often stemlike) part.

seta a bristle, especially as in annelids.

sex cell a gamete.

sexual pertaining to reproduction involving the fusion of nuclei (fertilization) of two unlike, parental gametes.

shoot a stem or young stem; generally a stem with leaves.

sill a flat body of igneous rock formed by the solidification of magma injected between layers of older rock.

simple pertaining to an organism or a part that is uncomplicated by special structure, function, or behavior and most resembling attributes of ancient life.

social dominance an established group behavior pattern in which one or more individuals by previous combat or threat control or subject others in the group.

social group any aggregation of two or more members of the same species; often mentioned as a colony.

society a social group displaying cooperation within itself.

soil a mixture of organic material and inorganic particles (rocks and minerals) existing in a relatively thin layer over much of the earth; a soil horizon is a layer within a soil; a soil profile is a vertical sample, including soil but extending from the surface to parent material.

solid the state of matter in which movement of component parts is restricted to vibration about fixed average positions; in contrast to a gas or liquid, it has fixed shape and offers resistance to an applied force.

solitary organism any member of a species that normally is not found in groups of its species; a species not forming social groups.

solstice either of the two points in the earth's orbit when the sun's rays become perpendicular to the northernmost (June 21) or southernmost (December 21) possible points from the equator.

solute a substance broken up into fine particles (dissolved) by a solvent, e.g., salt in water.

solution any intimate, homogeneous mixture of two or more substances, one usually being a liquid, that can be separated by simple processes.

solvent the component of a solution that is in excess, provides the characteristic state of the solution, and causes dissolution of the solute.

somite a body unit in metamerism.

sorus a cluster of sporangia in ferns; sometimes applied to any mass of spores.

specialization an adaptation that is primarily due to heredity and is hardly modified by the environment.

specialized pertaining to an organism or any part of an organism that is complex in structure, function, or behavior; generally applied to presumably late developments in the evolution of life and/or complex features whose use is restricted to one or a few environments.

speciation the process of species formation.

species a taxon below the genus; a kind of organism; generally defined in terms of lacking or very limited gene exchange with other such groups; also, a category applied to various nonliving things.

sperm a male gamete; a mature and functional male sex cell; the male fluid containing male gametes.

spermatophyte any plant forming true seeds; sometimes considered a major taxon of plants in contrast to pteridophyte; most likely not a natural group.

spicule a needlelike body.

spiracle an external respiratory aperture; in insects, the external opening of the tracheae system; in cartilaginous fishes, a modified gill slit or opening.

sporangium a spore case; a structure in which spores are formed.

spore (1) the true spore often is limited to a plant bud; often designated bisexual, male, or female in reference to the sexuality of the gametophyte it produces; (2) a resting cell or life-cycle stage generally within a protective covering, e.g., a cyst; (3) asexual spore, a reproductive cell produced by mitosis; (4) sexual spore, a reproductive cell produced by meiosis, includes a true spore.

sporocarp a multicellular, spore-forming body, often nutlike.

sporophyte specifically, the spore-forming adult stage in a diplobiontic life cycle; loosely, any spore-forming plant.

sporulation asexual reproduction in plants, generally by meiosis in which a single cell (a true bud called a spore) is the reproductive body formed.

stamen a flower organ distinctive in containing male spore-forming organs; consisting of anther and filament.

stand a recognizable unit of plant species, somewhat uniform in composition, appearance, and habitat conditions.

statoblast an internal (generally multicellular) bud formed by ectoprocts.

stele a vein of vascular plants.

stem (1) the axis of a plant consisting of nodes and internodes; (2) a stalk in various, mostly sessile, animals; (3) pertaining to the ancestor of a very large group of organisms.

steppe a dry grassland in which plant aerial parts often die back and underground parts enter dormancy during part of the year; also, the climate or soil of such an area.

sterile pertaining to an organism or part of an organism without functional reproductive structures; pertaining to an area devoid of life, particularly microorganisms.

stigma the apical portion of a pistil, which receives pollen and upon which pollen germinates.

stimulus an external or internal change in an organism's environment capable of inducing a reaction by the organism.

stipe a stalk, generally short and supporting in function.

stipule a small, leaflike appendage that may occur on either side of the base of a leaf.

stock in geology, an irregular igneous rock mass of roughly conical or cylindrical shape up to 40 square miles in surface area; formed by subsurface intrusion and solidification of magma; *see* batholith.

stolon a plant stem or animal stemlike structure that periodically by budding gives rise to new individuals; generally, a structure growing horizontally to and upon a substrate.

stoma a minute space between two specialized cells (guard cells) in the epidermis of plants.

strand the ocean shore above the highest tide level but subject to sea wind, sand blasts, and salt spray.

stratum any layer or bed of air, water, rock, organisms, and so on.

strike in geology, the compass direction of an imaginary line formed by intersection of a layer of rocks with the horizontal plane at the surface of the earth; by definition, strike is measured perpendicular to the dip; approximately the direction of an observed surface outcrop of a rock layer; see Figure 4.23, p. 62.

style the part of a flower's pistil between stigma and ovary.

subdominant species any species in a community other than a dominant; a subordinate species.

subordinate species a subdominant.

subsidence sinking, generally of a large part, of the earth's crust.

subsoil the part of a soil profile below the true soil and above weathered bedrock that is occupied by little or no roots or organic material.

subspecies a subunit of a species of variable status, but generally recognized by at least one unique feature or a unique combination of features; often it is the only occupant of a particular area by a species; it may or may not be isolated from like species subunits.

substrate the foundation, substance, or base upon which any object spreads, lies, grows, attaches, or moves; in organisms also includes such things as their nutrients.

succession the development of equilibrium conditions in living or nonliving things by means of a sequence of recognized stages that terminate—theoretically, and often actually—in equilibrium conditions; generally restricted to organism, especially plant succession.

superorganism a community in the sense of its collecting organisms and functioning much like an organism or something greater than an organism.

swamp a semiaquatic habitat having woody plants, trees, and/or shrubs.

sweepstake route an accidental highway in that organisms (probably by chance) are transported from one area to another; e.g., often an ocean region in reference to land organisms.

symbiosis the living together of organisms, usually two or more species; degree of permanence generally is not implied, but temporary symbiosis usually must involve a significant relationship.

syncline a downward arcing or folding of rock layers.

synergism the total activity of various parts, producing an effect greater than the sum of the activities of individual parts.

tactile pertaining to the sense of touch.

tadpole a frog or ascidian larva of general fishlike form.

taiga the northern area of open and stunted, mostly coniferous, trees adjacent to the tundra; sometimes includes the adjacent northern coniferous forest.

taxon any taxonomic category; plural, taxa.

taxonomic category any unit of organism classification based as much as possible on natural relationships through evolution; generally, anything above a species is called a higher category.

taxonomy the study of classification, usually as limited to organisms.

tendril loosely, a slender, branched or unbranched structure in an organism; generally restricted to a plant stem, leaf, or leaf part modified into a hairlike structure that coils about an object and thus supports the plant.

tentacle a slender, flexible, often sensory and anterior, animal organ of various functions (e.g., locomotion, grasping, holding, and/or food-getting).

territory the portion of a home range actively defended by an animal against intruders.

testis in animals, a male sex organ; plural, testes.

thallophyte once a taxon of "plants," including bacteria, fungi, and algae; now usually used to indicate such organisms.

thallus a relatively simple plant body lacking roots, stems, or leaves; generally any algae or bryophyte body; also any thallophyte body.

theory a group of interrelated and much-tested hypotheses that are consistent with one another and observed phenomena.

thermocline a layer or zone of rapid temperature decrease with depth (generally more than 1 degree centrigrade per meter) found in temperature-layered lakes.

thorax the major part of an animal's body behind the head (or neck) and in front of the abdomen; in birds and mammals, the part enclosed by ribs.

till unsorted, unlayered, and generally unconsolidated materials deposited by ice; glacial drift or erratics.

tissue a group of similar cells performing similar functions.

tolerance the ability and capacity of an organism to live under a range of conditions of one or more environmental factors.

topsoil the uppermost layer of soil that is lighter in color but richer in humus than the underlying subsoil.

tracheae a system of small air-conducting tubes present and involved in the respiration of many land arthropods.

transformer often not distinguished from a decomposer; an organism that uses and alters the products of decomposers to molecules, generally even smaller ones, that can be used by plants.

transpiration the loss of water, generally as vapor, from the aerial parts of plants; may be a type of evaporation.

trichocyst a protistan organelle, particularly in ciliate protozoans, that occurs near the body surface and produces hairlike fibers that function in predation, protection, and attachment.

triploid the presence of three complete sets of chromosomes in a nucleus.

trochophore a ciliated and free-swimming, marine larva typical of the Schizocoela.

tuber a short, thick, and fleshy, underground stem containing buds, e.g., a potato.

tundra ranging from bare areas to those consisting of various lichens, mosses, herbs, and dwarf shrubs (but not trees) in arctic or alpine regions.

unconformity the surface occurring between two distinctly different rock layers and representing a time of erosion and/or no deposition.

unicellular pertaining to a single cell.

univalved pertaining to a shell of one solid part as in snails.

vacuole a cavity within protoplasm bounded by a membrane and containing liquids and/or solids.

valve (1) in anatomy, a structure closing an opening or directing movement in one direction; (2) in botany, a covering or lidlike part of a larger structure; any of the units formed from normal separation of parts of a single plant structure, usually a reproductive one; (3) in zoology, any separate piece of a shell as found in mollusks, branchiopods, and barnacles.

vascular bundle a plant vein.

vascular plant any plant containing veins.

vegetative reproduction any asexual reproduction by means of reproductive bodies other than true buds.

vegetative structure any part of an organism without reproductive structures.

vein (1) in plants, a strand of conducting tissue, xylem and phloem; a vascular bundle, stele, or central cylinder; (2) in animals, a tube or vessel carrying blood to the heart; (3) in geology, a crack filled with a mineral or rock deposit.

vellum a washer-like ring attaching by its outer margin to to the undersurface of the medusa stage of the Hydrozoa, especially prominent in hydromedusans.

ventral pertaining to the belly or away from the back.

vernal pertaining to the spring season.

vestigeal degenerate; pertaining to an incompletely formed structure that was fully formed during development or in ancestors of the organism bearing the structure.

viscera the internal organs of an organism.

weather the atmospheric conditions (precipitation, temperature, humidity, cloudiness, wind, pressure, and so on) at a given time.

weathering erosion by atmospheric agents causing physical and chemical disintegration of rocks.

weed any undesirable or troublesome, usually exotic, plant growing without cultivation by man.

whorled generally pertaining to three or more leaves at a single node.

woodland a somewhat open growth of trees or shrubs, not as densely spaced as in a forest or as loosely spaced as in a savanna.

xerarch pertaining to a sere beginning on a dry substrate, especially on bare rock.

xerophyte a plant adapted to dry environmental conditions.

xylem a woody tissue in vascular plant veins that conducts water and water solutions.

zoology the study of animals.

zygote a fertilized egg; a cell resulting from the fusion of two parental gametes.

Index

Boldface numbers indicate the major discussion of the topic.